W9-CKJ-978

PRINCIPLES OF PHYSICS

PRINCIPLES OF PHYSICS · By EARNEST S. GREENE

Library of Congress Catalog Card Number 62-8576

Printed in the United States of America

70980C

PREFACE

This text is intended for physics courses at the liberal arts and premedical level. Many students whose objectives are other than professional physics or engineering have had no previous course in physics. Many of those who have had such a course have not discovered or realized that the heart of physics consists of principles and logical reasoning, rather than specific facts, memorization, and recall. Many have a history of difficulty with mathematics and a fear of it.

In recognition of these common sources of difficulty, the first two chapters attempt to give the student a feeling for what the science of physics really is, to point out potential pitfalls and other sources of possible trouble, and to slay a few of the imaginary dragons so many students feel breathing down their backs when they sign up for a physics course. Many teachers may wish to get into the solid material of the course, which begins with Chapter 3, as promptly as possible, but every student should at least browse through the first two chapters, and some questions or difficulties which arise later in the course may be resolved by returning to these chapters.

Throughout the book, an attempt has been made to warn the student of common sources of trouble and to help him learn to avoid them, though naturally he is expected to become more self-sufficient as the course progresses.

Perhaps all this may seem to imply that this text approaches the level of a survey book, but such is by no means the case. In fact, the Self-Quizzes demand considerably more analytical and logical thought than is typical of review questions, and the text provides ample solid material for the customary one-year course.

The book is founded on the philosophy that basic principles and intelligent reasoning are more important than isolated facts or applications. The student will encounter many facts; he will be expected to remember most of them, and a number of applications do appear. Wherever possible, however, the facts will be supported by logical reasoning and will be offered on the basis of understanding rather than as exercises in rote memorization; and, in general, the applications will be presented as illustrations of principles rather than as an end in themselves.

The choice of topics is always a problem, and so is their order; and no author can expect to please all teachers of physics. The content is "standard," for the most part, and the order of topics conventional. The implications and concepts of "modern physics" have been interwoven in the text wherever appropriate, but only in a very limited manner. The principal treatment of this topic is reserved for nine chapters, comprising almost 18% of the text, near the end of the book. Thus, for example, in the study of mechanics the student is not left with the idea that the classical equation for kinetic energy is valid without limitation or reservation, but neither is he forced to deal with the relativistic equation before he has an opportunity to get some feeling for relativistic concepts in general. In addition to these nine chapters on modern physics, there is a chapter on uses of radioactive substances and a final chapter on health physics—a badly neglected topic in this nuclear age, both in its peacetime aspects and with regard to the possibility of nuclear attack.

Acknowledgments cannot be recorded without the certainty that the list will be incomplete. Nevertheless, an attempt must be made. First must come my family, which has put up with me while I have been struggling with authorship and have been less than an ideal husband and father—though that can't be all blamed on the book, I fear! Special thanks must go to my wife, who read nearly all of the draft and made many contributions to lucidity and grammatical rectitude, and to my oldest daughter, who typed some of a preliminary draft. Great appreciation is gladly given to Mrs. A. J. Menard, who somehow metamorphosed my messy draft into the final neat manuscript. Three colleagues, Mrs. Jean McDill, Dr. Leroy R. Posey, Jr., and Dr. Ronald R. Easter, read portions of the draft and offered helpful comments. A considerable portion of the chapter which includes the discussion of the eye was corrected and rewritten on the basis of help generously offered by Dr. Benjamin Nerenberg, and Mr. A. B. Givens checked the chapter on generators and motors. Another colleague, Mr. Loren Cockrell, made photographs for figures taken (with permission!) from other publications. A number of organizations made contributions for which credit is given in the text. Other organizations which contributed information or assistance include the Polaroid Corporation, the Revere Camera Company, Eastman Kodak Company, Bell and Howell, the Atomic Energy Commission, the Office of Civil and Defense Mobilization, and the Radiological Health Training Section of the Robert A. Taft Sanitary Engineering Center, U.S. Department of Health, Education, and Welfare.

EARNEST S. GREENE

CONTENTS

22

SIMPLE ELECTRIC CIRCUITS

23

INTERCONVERSION OF CHEMICAL AND ELECTRICAL ENERGY

24

MAGNETISM AND ELECTROMAGNETISM

1

YOUR APPROACH TO THE STUDY OF PHYSICS

1-1 Preview

*The way you approach your study
of physics may actually be more important
than your diligence in studying the
subject matter—more important both for the
course itself and for its usefulness in your later life.
Thus, it is worth spending some time at
the very start in order to be sure of starting right.
Your ideas about physics as a field
of study are important factors
in your whole approach to it. It is very easy
to be mistaken in these ideas; even persons
who have taken a course in physics
may be mistaken about the nature of the subject.
A little time spent now on your concept
of this study may enable you to get a far
better comprehension of the field, to avoid hours of
fruitless work, and to grasp more surely
the essential points.*

1-2 What Is Physics, and (Perhaps More Important) What Is It Not?

A great suspension bridge is a marvelous thing, very highly utilitarian and yet a thing of beauty. Certain of its manifold parts are standard, the fruit of much experience; others were specially designed, tested, and perhaps redesigned and retested. The structure was designed by engineers and its parts were properly assembled by skilled workers. Although the finished bridge is a single entity, its unity was derived from the careful and intelligent integration of its many diverse parts.

In many ways, any physical science is like a suspension bridge. Its utilitarian aspects comprise the foundation of our modern industrial civilization. And though one can find viewpoints from which neither the bridge nor the structure of physical science has interest or beauty, from more favorable viewpoints the soaring grace of the bridge is matched by the sheer esthetic beauty of physical science.

The science of physics is constructed of definitions, principles, and laws. Although each of these has meaning and value in itself, in themselves they do not constitute physics any more than its unassembled parts constitute the bridge. Their interrelationships are much more important than themselves, and far more fruitful—both from the utilitarian standpoint and the esthetic—and also vastly more interesting.

Much as bridge engineers develop, test, and if necessary improve the parts of the bridge before they are incorporated into the bridge, scientists have developed, tested, and improved their definitions and their statements of principles and laws; only after rigorous tests are they accepted as part of the structure of physics. Yet even after testing, improvement, and retesting, any one of these parts of physics is by itself almost as useless as one single part of the bridge. To obtain a useful and beautiful structure instead of having just a junkyard of unassembled parts, we must relate each part to the others, whether we are building a bridge or studying physics.

No matter how well a bridge worker can name and describe the components of a bridge, he has no chance of building a structure which is useful, safe, and beautiful if he doesn't understand the *function* of each part so that he can use it in proper relation to the others. And no matter how well you may learn individual laws, definitions, equations, etc., your study of physics will be frustrating and, in some degree, unsuccessful unless you learn how one item of knowledge may be related to another, thereby multiplying the usefulness of each.

Once built, the suspension bridge is complete, ready to perform its function of carrying traffic until it outlives its usefulness and is destroyed to make way for a new structure. On the other hand, the structure of physical science is never complete. Additions are being made constantly; also, people are forever at work modifying and improving existing parts, or finding new or broader relationships between a particular part and others. No end is in sight. We are constantly asking new questions of nature and constantly finding some answers. But, as someone remarked, it is common for each new answer to reveal two or three new questions, with the result that although our knowledge is continually expanding, our ignorance is increasing even more rapidly!

1-3 "Parroting"

It is a common idea that the best way to pass a course is to memorize certain combinations of words and "parrot" them back on quizzes and exams. If this were what your physics instructor wanted, even a parrot might be dangerous competition. Your instructor could teach a parrot to say "velocity is distance divided by time" and "acceleration is change of velocity per unit time." But the parrot could not use either statement; more important, he would be quite unable to deduce from them a relationship among distance, acceleration, and time. His ability to produce these particular sounds in proper sequence is entirely devoid of value to him or to anyone else. Facile and errorless regurgitation of various isolated oddments of scientific information can be done even better by a tape recorder. But when it comes to *making use* of that information, and integrating the individual facts into a coherent structure, the tape recorder is quite powerless, whereas your instructor hopes that you will not be!

Your scientific efforts, therefore, are doomed to be relatively fruitless if you plan to "learn" physics so that you can "parrot" it, and stop there. It is *essential* that you get behind the *words* of a statement and *assimilate* the real meaning. Only then will you be able to build your bridge instead of having just a junkyard of unassembled parts.

1-4 Principles of Physics, and Applications of Physics

Physics is far too broad a field to be encompassed in any book designed for a one-year course. Even after some less essential topics have been eliminated, it is necessary to minimize the discussion of principles or of applications; it is impossible to treat both fully.

This book accepts the point of view that the thing of fundamental importance is an understanding of basic principles. Understanding principles will enable you to understand most of the less esoteric applications, whereas studying applications is of very limited help in understanding principles. Hence, although there will be a sampling of applications, they are not the primary goal; they are offered to clarify principles or to tie seemingly novel physical principles to ordinary experience.

1-5 What Does "Explain" Mean?

The uninitiated often suppose that a science gives a complete and thorough explanation of everything within its proper field. How far this idea is valid depends on what one understands the words "explain" and "explanation" to mean, and it must be admitted that in one sense of these words no science can explain anything at all.

For example, consider the effect of gravity. You would be quite amazed if, after you gave a stone a gentle horizontal toss, it continued out of sight without dropping; and so would I. The stone *must* drop, and does, because there exists between any two bodies—such as the earth and the stone—a force of attraction. We call this force the "gravitational attraction."

But *why* is there such a force? *How* do the two bodies generate it? *By what mechanism* does the force act on the stone, since nothing connects the stone to the earth? Frankly, I can't answer these questions for you. I *can* say that if you had a broad enough background of physics and mathematics you might be able to comprehend fully Einstein's theory of general relativity. But I'd have to say that this theory hasn't been fully substantiated as yet, that it isn't the only theory, and that it doesn't consider that there really is any force, in the usual sense of the word, acting on the stone. The rock simply moves along a "world line" described in terms of non-Euclidian geometry, through space which has been curved or warped by the effects of the mass of the earth and that of the stone; and since we are unaware of this warpage of space, we jump to the erroneous conclusion that the rock is falling because of the action of a force.

——Well, I don't understand it, either! Nor an equally esoteric theory proposed by Eddington.

In spite of these mysteries and complications, gravitational phenomena are so familiar that we accept them without question. Gravitational forces are much more "real" to us than world lines. A long history of observation and analysis has provided mathematical relationships which accurately predict the magnitude of the gravitational force, in a specific case, and the effect of that force. So, though we may be a bit wistful about being unable to follow Einstein and Eddington, we say that we understand gravitation.

As with gravitation, the ultimate basis of our understanding of any phenomenon is familiarity. Commonly, we can relate a comparatively unfamiliar phenomenon to another more general, or simpler, one and this, in turn, to one still more basic. But sooner or later we reach a solid wall beyond which we cannot penetrate, and in the end we are forced to accept something simply because "it is so." Here the scientist does something of which most people would not think him guilty; he emulates a muckraking politician and resorts to name calling.

This is hard to believe? But recall our discussion of the fact that the stone must fall. Unable to understand the esoteric theories of the cause of its fall, and knowing full well that, after all, it *does* fall, we substituted a name, "gravitational attraction," for a fundamental explanation. Even those who can follow Einstein end up by calling names; in this case, "world lines."

Other phenomena share with gravitational attraction this characteristic of "action at a distance," for example, forces of magnetic or electrical origin. Again any fundamental explanation eludes us, so we "understand" these phenomena by analogy with the more familiar phenomenon of gravitation.

Thus the process of "explaining" an unfamiliar phenomenon consists of comparing it, and correlating it, with some more familiar phenomenon. We may or may not be able to correlate this more familiar phenomenon with one still better known, but ultimately we reach the end of the road. Then we must be content to accept this most basic phenomenon on the basis of its familiarity, its experimentally proven validity, or some comparable basis. This most basic phenomenon we must adopt as one of the foundation stones of science.

Obviously we would be more comfortable with an ultimate and "real" explanation. But such an ideal is beyond our grasp. Any breakthrough which explains what has been a "most basic" phenomenon would be in terms of one still more fundamental, and we would have no explanation for this new phenomenon.

Thus, as a working definition, we must consider that "to explain" means "to correlate the unknown or unfamiliar with things better understood or more familiar."

1-6 The Laws of Science and the Laws of Man

Man-made laws are subject to amendment and repeal. Though most of us are law-abiding, it is necessary to have various institutions to deal with those who break the law.

Nature's laws are quite different from man's. Faced with a long flight of stairs to climb, we might relish the idea of writing a subsection to the law of gravitation, providing that our weight be halved whenever we wish to climb. Nature is indifferent to our wishes, however; natural laws are not subject to modification by us. Natural laws are of nature's making, not of ours.

Following clues given in nature, we have been able to discover something of its laws. But our knowledge of a natural law may be incomplete, without our being aware of its incompleteness. We may believe that we have won a thorough understanding of each of two laws; later we may find additional information which reveals these two laws to be but special cases of a single, more general law of which we have had no inkling; nature, however, is not a considerate instructor, who lets us know whether we have deduced all the details and ramifications of a law or hints how many laws still lie completely outside our knowledge.

Thus, we often find it necessary to modify our statement of a law or to develop a statement of a new law, but this does not resemble the continuing modification and expansion of man-made laws. Nature's laws are complete and exact, and absolutely immutable.* Only our knowledge of those laws is changing, requiring us to modify our statements of them.

Not only are nature's laws immutable; they are inviolable. In nature, there are no lawbreakers. Whenever we find an apparent violation, we know it arises solely from some error or inadequacy in our statement of the law. Then we must revise our statement so that the apparent violation is annihilated, but the law itself remains immutable and inviolable as it has been since the beginning of time.

1-7 Pure Science and Applied Science

In this country, we consider material things to be important. This sometimes leads to misunderstanding of the function of pure science and hence to lack of appreciation for it. Applied science and technology seem more important.

The pure scientist is interested solely in asking questions of nature and trying to get answers. What is the real cause of gravitational (or magnetic, or electric) forces? What are the size and mass of an individual atom? Does a galaxy exist that is made of antimatter instead of a familiar variety of matter? Such "impractical" questions fascinate the pure scientist, and to him unlocking the secrets of nature is an end in itself. He may or may not be interested in possible practical applications, but usually he stays with his research rather than participate in making such applications.

For most of us, the applications—from jet planes to automatic electronic cookers for hot dogs, from juke boxes to artificial satellites—are the obvious and the important things. We fail to see that very often these applications stem from the "useless" work of the pure scientist who spends his time asking questions of nature primarily, and often solely, to satisfy

---

* This does not mean that, even if we knew all nature's laws perfectly, we could predict in detail the future history of every physical particle, for—as we shall see in Chapter 35—in the atomic and subatomic domain laws are statistical in nature and cannot be applied to individual particles with certainty.

his curiosity. Without the fundamental physical principles discovered by him, current practical applications achieved by others would have been impossible. In a sense, the most practical of all the various types of scientific activity is that which has as its sole object the investigation of nature.

For example, we shall see later that there exists a possibility of producing almost unlimited quantities of energy from ordinary sea water. With the world's supplies of coal and petroleum dwindling so rapidly, the development of an alternate source of energy is immensely practical. We shall see also that this possibility—or rather, our awareness of the possibility—is the outcome of such investigations as whether there is an all-pervading ether throughout the universe and, if so, how rapidly the earth is moving through it, the internal structure of an atom and the exact masses of individual atoms, and similar matters which most obviously were wholly impractical. Had curious and able men and women not investigated these and similar matters, solely out of curiosity, we would not even be aware of this potential source of a tremendous supply of energy.

We shall meet other examples of investigations pursued solely because of a yearning to *know*, which unexpectedly bore practical fruit.

1-8 "Secrets" of Pure Science

Here again we find ourselves in need of a definition.

Concealing information about the gifts you buy before Christmas, say, illustrates one type of secret. Barring carelessness of tongue or in hiding the presents, the secrets must necessarily remain such until you disclose them at Christmas.

The secrets of the unknown are of a different sort. Persevering archaeologists, for example, may discover an ancient city or tomb and learn a great deal about an unknown people and their manner of life from artifacts and other remains. Modern techniques based on radiocarbon analyses make it possible to place the civilization in its proper historical period. Thus, a great deal that once was completely unknown does not remain so; it yields to the diligence, skill, and intelligence of investigators. The "secrets" no longer are secret.

The secrets of pure science are related to the secrets of concealed Christmas presents only in that they are, for a time, unknown. They resemble archaeological secrets far more closely, since they can be revealed by diligent and intelligent research. They have no nationality; they recognize no political systems, ideologies, or ethical criteria. They are for the taking by any person, group, or nation capable of ferreting them out.

The secrets of pure science are *open* secrets.

1-9 The Vocabulary of Physics

It would seem that a vocabulary is something more appropriate to a course in a foreign language than to physics. However, any field of information, any activity, has associated with it a certain terminology, and a knowledge of that terminology is necessary for clear understanding.

One unaccustomed to baseball terminology, for example, must serve a considerable apprenticeship at games or in front of a radio or TV set before he can understand the significance of terms such as "fly," "liner," "hit," "strike," "bunt," "change-up," "slider," and many others. Some are new words with which he must become acquainted; these give him the least trouble because, at least, he need not *un*learn anything in order to understand them. Others are familiar terms with new meanings, perhaps quite different from their usual significance. An example is "fly." The baseball variety of fly exists only after you swat it, whereas when you swat a specimen of *Musca domestica* it ceases to exist! Other baseball terms are still more baffling. For instance, one must become inured to the facts that only an *un*successful attempt to *strike* a pitched ball with the bat is a "strike" and that *hit*ting the ball with the bat constitutes a "hit" less often than it does *not* constitute a "hit"!

Almost endless examples other than these few taken from baseball could be adduced, but I think perhaps the point has been made. It is an extremely important point.

Try to forget that you are using English to study physics. Try to approach the subject as you would a foreign language, carefully noting each new term as it appears and becoming thoroughly familiar with the significance of each. Try especially hard to close your mind to the non-technical meaning of a word which is used in a technical sense.

If you know Spanish and read of a man drinking *café*, you don't visualize him putting a restaurant through a homogenizer and imbibing it; you know that he is enjoying coffee. A student of German, on reading of a picture on a *Wand*, realizes that the picture is on a wall; he doesn't think of it as being supported by a fairy's magic baton. Nor does one who reads French become indignant if he reads that a man uses a *bride* to control an unruly horse, for he knows that a *bride* is not a new wife, but a bridle.

In such cases, the fact that *all* the words are in a foreign language warns one to interpret *bride*, or *Wand*, or *café*, in terms of its meaning in that language rather than to assign the word its significance in English. But you don't have this warning when you are studying physics, for you are reading English, and if you are not extremely careful, you will tend—especially at first—to give *all* the words their usual interpretations. This, however, may distort the meaning as seriously as would using the English meanings of the words *café*, *Wand*, and *bride* in the examples above.

Many of the terms of physics, such as "dyne," "resultant," "imped-

ance," etc., will be new to you if this is your first course in physics. These you must become thoroughly acquainted with as you meet them. Please note that I did *not* say that you must *memorize* their *definitions*. You must *study* their definitions and *think* about them, *discuss* them, *ask questions* about them if necessary, and *use* them until you have *assimilated* the essential *meaning* behind the words of the definition. You will find then that you *know* the significance of the term without depending solely on blind memory.

Other terms may be common words with essentially the usual meanings. Far more common, however, are new concepts, or severely limited concepts, disguised behind familiar words. Here lies the greatest danger, insofar as vocabulary is concerned. You know, for example, what the word "work" means; but if you try to employ this foreknowledge in physics, you'll get into trouble. In its technical sense, its significance is drastically restricted; no matter how great a weight you may support, for example, or how far you may carry it horizontally, if you only *support* or *carry* it without *lifting* it you are doing no work whatever! In the technical sense, the amount of work done bears no necessary relation to the amount of perspiration produced, or to the amount of fatigue which results.

As this discussion implies, a considerable portion of the study of physics must be devoted to the vocabulary of physics. To help you with your technical vocabulary, each important technical term is presented in italicized boldface type, usually the first time it is met. Usually its technical definition is given at that point, although in a few instances the meanings of terms are implied in the context in which the term appears instead of being formally defined.

1-10 The Place of Mathematics in Physics

Physics is a quantitative science.

When students of biology encounter a physics course, they sometimes ask why physics can't be presented on an essentially non-mathematical basis, as much of biology is. The answer is that it can, if one is to be content with that. But biology is becoming more mathematical, and in the process is becoming more useful. Consider, for example, the science of genetics with its applications to plant breeding and animal husbandry, etc., and compare this with pre-Mendelian genetics. The difference is essentially the quantitative, that is, mathematical, basis on which Mendel placed the science.

Much of biology is so complex that it has not yet been possible to place it on a quantitative basis to the extent that has occurred in physics. The objects and phenomena studied in physics are vastly simpler than the very complex organisms and phenomena which constitute the subject matter of biology. Because of this great difference in complexity, in general, biologists have not yet been able to achieve a quantitative description of their subject comparable with that accomplished by physicists; biology is still confined largely to qualitative considerations of the sort physicists had to be content with a few centuries ago. But as in the case of genetics, biology is becoming more quantitative, and as it does it becomes more interesting and more serviceable.

Returning to physics, consider the matter of an artificial satellite of the earth; what physical relationships apply and how? One might have an intuitive feeling that the weight of the satellite should become less, the higher it is above the earth's surface. He may also be aware that if he twirls an object on the end of a string the tension of the string increases as the object moves faster, and he may have an idea that the tension would be different if the length of the string were different. By combining these ideas, he might possibly get a hazy concept of how an artificial satellite can be made to circle the earth. But if no one's understanding had gone beyond these *qualitative* relationships, there would still be no such satellites. It is necessary to know the exact *quantitative* relationships.

Similarly, it is not enough to know that the more bricks you have the more they will weigh, or that bricks and stones will weigh more than the bricks alone. We must know that (if the bricks are identical) the weight of the bricks is directly proportional to their number and that the combined weight of the bricks and the stones is the sum of their separate weights. Do not be scornful of relationships as obvious as these. Overlooking the obvious is one of the biggest sources of trouble. Yet, on the other hand, we must be careful to avoid pushing the obvious too far and putting too much faith in it. For example, the "obvious" weight relationships among bricks and stones are *not* valid if we try to apply them in the subatomic domain.

We find, then, that mathematics is a principal tool of physics. Throughout physics, we find our understanding sharply limited, and we encounter great difficulty in making useful application of what understanding we do have, if we are content with qualitative considerations. With mathematics, physics is understandable and fruitful; without it, it is mysterious and relatively sterile.

And not only is mathematics an important *tool* of physics; it is an essential part of the *language* of physics. We shall consider this aspect of the value of mathematics in Sec. 2-13 and 2-14.

This does not imply that your course in physics will be a math course. There will be mathematics, but there will be no manipulations of abstract symbols devoid of physical meaning. Mathematics will be used as a tool to aid you in understanding and using the knowledge you acquire.

Trigonometry will be used only incidentally, and you will be at no serious disadvantage if you have not studied trigonometry before.

Although mathematics is essential for any real study of physics and although, in advanced courses, the mathematics may get rather involved, ordinary arithmetic and algebra plus a little plane geometry will suffice for this course. (Appendix G contains the few trigonometric definitions and relationships which might be helpful, with a few examples for practice.)

1-11 Problems

Contrary to popular belief, the purpose of physics problems is not to make life miserable for the student!

Problems have two essential functions: to enable you to test your understanding of a topic and to enable you to solidify that understanding by making use of it. You may conscientiously believe that your study of an assignment has mastered it, and yet find difficulty in applying it. Thus, problems point up weak spots in your understanding and remove them.

Problems will be of various types and of varying degrees of difficulty. A few will be fairly direct applications of a definition or a law. These *can* be solved by "plugging in" data and "turning the crank," but you should require yourself to avoid this approach. Try to see the problem as an application of the definition or law; when you have the problem "set up," stop and ask yourself whether it expresses exactly the interrelationships among the physical quantities that the definition or law specifies.

Another very different sort of problem can't be solved on the basis of any single definition, or law, or equation. To solve such a problem you must think your way along, and commonly two or perhaps more definitions or laws must be brought to bear on it. You would learn very little physics if I offered you only problems you could solve by finding an appropriate equation or a "type problem" to go by.

1-12 Definitions, Principles, and Laws

Consider for a moment an apprentice machinist. He might learn to identify the various hand tools, lathes, milling machines, etc., before he has much idea of their use. Certainly he will have gained an idea of the function of each tool before he acquires skill in its use. But if he stops there, content to know the names and functions of the tools, he will never be a journeyman machinist. He must develop skill in *using* them, and the only way he can acquire this skill is by actually working with the tools.

The definitions, principles, and laws of physics constitute, together with mathematics, the *tools* of physics. True, they are not tools you can use with your hands, but they are still literally tools. Success in the course depends on your understanding these tools and on your skill in using them.

So let me plead with you again to avoid both rote memorization of definitions, principles, and laws, and plugging data into a memorized formula and blindly turning the crank. That approach to physics almost guarantees difficulty. Take the time and trouble to digest and assimilate the essential *meanings* of the definitions and principles and laws. Use mathematical procedures intelligently and thoughtfully rather than merely prayerfully, and always examine the results of your computations to see whether they are reasonable.

And don't worry about your memory atrophying with all this. There'll still be plenty to keep your memory in shape.

1-13 Methods of Study

To an unfortunate degree, our educational system tends to give students the habit of memorizing facts and giving them back in examinations. Many students try to "learn" physics on this basis, but this almost invariably leads to trouble. True, it is essential that you remember certain things, but far more important are *understanding* and *applying* that understanding in specific situations. Physics is by no means a collection of separate facts. There are facts, and they are important, but it is the interrelationships of the facts that is of greatest importance—both from the standpoint of really learning physics and from the standpoint of applying that learning. Thus, memory, though necessary, is less important than intelligence and willingness to think.

Physics is not a subject which can be mastered by attendance at lectures and a single reading of text assignments. Most assignments should be read through first; then they should be gone through a second time much more thoroughly, with as much rereading of difficult portions as necessary. Perhaps two readings will not suffice for a clear understanding. If after a thorough and honest try you still find that some of the material isn't clear, get help.

You will find a Summary at the end of each chapter. This should serve as a review of the chapter and also as a framework on which to base your later reviewing as the course goes on. It may also seem to provide a time-saving method of learning the material in the chapter; but if you can get a thorough understanding of physics from the chapter summaries you are a rare genius.

You will find also a Self-Quiz at the end of each chapter. This consists of some questions which are factual and others which can be answered only by careful analysis and thought. In many cases, the text will provide no direct answer to a question, but if you understand the material in the text thoroughly you should be able to work out an answer. It is highly advisable to make consistent use of these self-quizzes.

There is often a tendency, on turning in an examination paper, to say "That's that" and assume that the material covered can safely be forgotten. But since physics is a logical structure, things you learn in the earlier parts of the course will be applied in much later portions. Hence a regular program of reviewing is very helpful. The more you emphasize understanding and the less you depend on rote memory, the less will be the time necessary for review.

If you can arrange a certain amount of group study, you will find such study—done properly—to be very helpful. No matter how careful and conscientious you are about studying, individual study (except in problem solving) is almost entirely passive; you listen to lectures and you study a text. But if a group of students, no more than four or five, meets occasionally, there is an opportunity for each member to participate actively. He may ask a question, or answer one, or criticize someone's answer, or think up questions to ask. And in any one of these roles, the student is forced to organize his thinking in a way that he would miss without the group study.

Obviously, group study must be preceded by careful individual study by each participant. On the basis of this study, one student may ask another for a definition, a statement of a law, an explanation of a phenomenon, etc. Everyone should be very critical of each answer, refusing to accept something memorized out of the text or an inaccurate or sloppy reply. The student who offered the answer should be required to restate it until no reasonable objection to it can be made. The roles of questioner, answerer, and critic should be changed so that each individual participates in each capacity.

I think it's obvious that this sort of study requires good nature on the part of every participant. A person who refuses to accept criticism could get very little benefit. If carried out in the right spirit, however, such group study forces careful thinking and critical analysis; and I know of no other study technique of comparable potential value.

Since the major value of group study is the clarification of one's own thoughts, it is beneficial for a group of numbskulls or for a group of "brains." It is also helpful for a group of widely different abilities, provided that everyone participates; but it is of relatively little value if it degenerates into a situation in which the majority of the group sits at the feet of one or two wise men. Remember that the source of the benefit is *active* participation by *each* student.

It is not at all uncommon for a student beginning the study of physics to have some difficulty in "getting his feet on the ground." Often such a student feels, quite correctly, that after a while things will begin to make better sense. But, too often, by the time this has occurred he is so far behind that he has no adequate foundation for the new topics and he lacks the time for the double job of catching up and keeping up.

Don't let yourself get behind. Make a good honest effort to understand the material; but if, after you have made a real effort, things still are unclear, *get help right away.* Don't let things pile up. It will take much less of your time, and of your instructor's, to get you straightened out *before* you get seriously behind. And, having cleared up your difficulties, you have a far better chance of understanding the next assignment or topic.

1-14 Your Attitude

If you selected this course as an elective, there may be little in this section for you; skip it if you wish.

There is, however, a fairly strong possibility that you are one of the probable majority whose registration in a physics course is due, at least in part, to a requirement incorporated in the program you are following. There is also a possibility that you feel a bit sorry for yourself. Why, after all, should you be required to take *physics?*

If this is your situation I hope that you will discover, perhaps to your surprise, that physics is really extremely interesting. Strange as it may seem at the moment to some of those who read this, thousands of initially disgruntled students make that discovery every year. To ease the way to such a discovery on your part, may I make a few suggestions?

First, course requirements for a particular objective or major are set by persons experienced in that field. If in the light of their experience and mature judgment they feel that a knowledge of physics is helpful in that field, isn't it possible that such is actually the case?

Second, I want to ask you to approach the course with an open mind and without prejudice. By the time we reach college, most of us have matured sufficiently to begin outgrowing irrational prejudices about our mental as well as about our physical fare. So I ask that you do not decide you dislike this subject until you have had an opportunity to savor the course thoroughly.

But we have seen that we must be careful about the meanings of words, and this is important right here. A mind open in the sense of a tube or a tunnel is no help. Neither should your mind be open in the sense that the door to a warehouse may be open. It should be open in the sense that the receiving door of a factory is open; open to accept raw materials *for use* in fabricating various products which may be far more useful, beautiful, and valuable than the materials from which they were made—but which require quite a bit of intelligence, skill, determination, and sweat to make.

Finally, another observation with regard to foods, mental and otherwise. Your education may have involved quite a bit of "spoon feeding," and this may have generated a subconscious attitude which could lead to trouble. It is the function of the author and the lecturer to provide you with solid mental fare in digestible and reasonably palatable form, but this is all they can do without help from you. In this, their jobs are similar to those of a restaurant staff: to prepare and serve the food. But the diner must pick up his fork, and the student must accept the responsibility for the ingestion and assimilation of his mental fare. Your instructor will be quite willing to help you from this point on; but his assistance does not correspond to the labor of a mother stuffing spinach into the mouth of a reluctant child.

1-15 Self-Quiz on Basic Mathematics

If you can work out the exercises in the list below, you need have no concern whatever about difficulty with the mathematical features of the course. If you have trouble with any of them, it would be wise to review your arithmetic or algebra; and if this is not sufficient, you should get help. If you can work the problems but require an undue amount of time, practice similar problems to develop facility.

Here, as always, the point is *not* to get an answer by means of mysterious rules and procedures. The point is to *understand* what must be done, and *why,* in order to solve the problem. Whether you get correct answers or not, if you don't *understand* the method, get help.

1. With each pair of values below, perform each of the following operations: (1) add; (2) subtract the second from the first; (3) subtract the first from the second; (4) multiply; (5) divide the first by the second; (6) divide the second by the first:

(a) $\frac{2}{3}, \frac{1}{2}$ (b) $\frac{3}{8}, 2\frac{2}{5}$ (c) $\frac{1}{18.7}, \frac{1}{11.2}$

2. If 1.00 in. = 2.54 cm, how many centimeters are there in 43.6 in.? How many in. in 12.5 cm? How many cm in 1 yd?

3. What is the square of 2.5? 25? 0.25? What is the square root of each of these numbers?

4. Measurements are made of each of two related quantities, a and b, yielding four pairs of values as follows:

a	1	2	3	4
b	360	90	40	22.5

That is, when the value of a is 1, the value of b is 360, etc. Does a vary according to the first power of b or according to the square root of b? Is the type of proportionality between a and b direct or inverse? Summarize your two answers to obtain a single concise statement which tells exactly how the value of a depends on that of b. Now interchange a and b in each of these questions, and answer the modified questions.

5. If when $a = 10.0$, $b = 100$, and if b is inversely proportional to the square of a, what is the value of b when $a = 1.00$? 0.100? 100? What is the value of a if $b = 400$? 6.25?

6. If $N = \dfrac{\sqrt{T/m}}{2L}$, in which N = frequency, T = tension, m = mass per unit length, and L = length of loop, make an accurate verbal statement of the relationship defined by the equation—that is, translate this quantitatively accurate algebraic statement into an equally accurate verbal statement.

7. The gravitational force F between any two bodies is directly proportional to the mass, m_1, of one and the mass, m_2, of the other body and is inversely proportional to the square of the distance d between them. This statement of proportionality may be converted to a statement of equality by including a constant G in such a way that F is directly proportional to G. Express all these facts in the form of an algebraic equation.

8. Solve each of the following for x:

(a) $x + 2 = 5$ (b) $3x - 7 = 4x + 6$ (c) $2/x = 5$

(d) $\dfrac{4}{3x} - 2 = 0$ (e) $3x^2 - 8 = 67$ (f) $\sqrt{2x} = 3$

(g) $\sqrt{2/5x} = 3$

9. (a) $x^2 + 6x + 9 = 0$ (b) $x^2 + x - 20 = 0$

(c) $6x^2 - 3x - 10 = 4x + 10$ (d) $x + 5 = \sqrt{20x}$

10. If $v^2 - u^2 = 2as$, solve the equation for v, for u, for a, and for s.

11. If $2\pi fL = \dfrac{1}{2\pi fC}$, solve for f.

12. Derive the equation $N = \dfrac{\sqrt{T/m}}{2L}$ from the equations $V = N\lambda$, $V = \sqrt{T/m}$, and $\lambda = 2L$.

Answers will be found at the back of the book. Here and in every other similar situation, however, you will *interfere* with your efforts to learn if you use the answers improperly. Looking up an answer and using it to work backwards toward a solution should be done only as a last resort, if at all. Always try to get an answer *and* examine it to see whether it seems reasonable *before* you look up the answer given.

1-16 Help with Mathematics

If mathematics troubles you, you may find some help in Appendix F, Review of Mathematics, and Appendix E, The Solution of Equations. You may also want to consult Appendix G, Elements of Trigonometry.

Remember, too, that you should ask for help if you need it.

In over three decades of college teaching, I have had very, very few students flunk *because of difficulty with math,* although I always have a considerable percentage with a history of difficulty with math. Many have flunked, either because they didn't come for help when they should have or because they gave up without a sincere, all-out effort. Those who have come for help *when* they *first needed* it and who have been willing to make a *real* effort have found that mathematics, as used in physics, does "make sense." They have seen that there is a great difference between juggling abstract symbols according to memorized rules and dealing with an equation which represents a reasonable relationship among meaningful physical quantities.

Summary

Physics is not a collection of separate facts; it is an *integrated structure.* Since the facts themselves are usually less useful than their interrelationships, understanding is more important than rote memorization.

No "explanation" in physics can be an "ultimate" explanation. Explanations consist of correlations and interrelationships between the less familiar and the more familiar.

Scientific "secrets" are open secrets which cannot be kept hidden.

Physical laws are immutable and inviolable, although as our knowledge increases, we sometimes must revise our *statements* of the laws.

"Impractical" pure science often gives birth to very important practical applications.

Physics has a language of its own. It includes new terms, but it also includes familiar terms with unfamiliar meanings. It is *essential* that you become familiar with all new terms and that you avoid the usual meaning of a term used in a technical sense.

Mathematics is a very important tool of physics.

It is never sufficient to be able to state a definition, law, etc.; you must *understand* the *meaning* of the statement and you must know how to use it. It is often necessary to combine one definition or law or principle with another.

Problems are very important in testing your understanding and in deepening that understanding.

Study methods are very important, and the best methods of studying physics may differ from what you are used to. Group study can be very helpful. Systematic review is essential.

Self-Quiz

1. An excellent memory may actually be a handicap in the study of physics, if improperly used. Why?

2. Why is it insufficient to be able to state the definitions, principles, and laws and to apply them to problems?

3. In what sense does physics "explain" physical phenomena?

4. In what sense are the "secrets" of science secret? What percentage of the general population would you estimate to be aware of the true nature of scientific secrets? What percentage of lawmakers and administrators?

5. Are there ever any exceptions to, or violations of, the laws of nature? Can they be amended? Are there ever exceptions to, violations of, or amendments to, our statements of the laws of nature? Explain clearly.

6. Why is vocabulary important in studying physics? Insofar as vocabulary is concerned, what is the most dangerous single pitfall?

7. Why is a quantitative understanding of physics both more thorough and more useful than a purely qualitative knowledge? And, by the way, what do the terms "quantitative" and "qualitative" mean?

8. Can you expect to "get" a new topic in physics the first time you read a discussion of it? Will the ability to give a good verbal presentation of the topic be conclusive evidence that you understand it? By what additional means can you test that understanding?

9. What are the merits of group study? Why should individual study precede group study? What is the basic source of the benefit to be found in group study?

10. Do you expect to "get by" by studying chapter summaries? (If so, right now is the best time to drop the course.)

11. When, and why, should you get professional help?

2

MEASUREMENTS AND PROBLEMS

2-1 Preview

We must achieve some degree
of acquaintance with the more important systems
of units. Conversion of a value from
one system of units to another is a common
source of error, but difficulty of this sort
can be minimized by either of
two methods which we shall meet.
It will develop that in many cases a more meaningful
result is obtained if we
"round off" an item of data than if we do not
and that 2.00 cm may mean something very different from 2 cm.
The solution of problems is a bugbear for many students,
but need not be if a proper approach
is used. Several suggestions
are given to help you toward the most effective
approach. There are also
suggestions for simplifying computations
and for checking answers.

2-2 Units of Mass and Force

It is extremely unfortunate that we commonly use the same unit to express either of the two very different physical quantities, mass and force. We may evaluate both force and mass in pounds, or we may measure both in kilograms, even though one pound mass and one pound force are as different from each other as either is from a cubic foot of volume or a mile per hour of speed. Obviously this is a potential source of much confusion.

To minimize the danger of such confusion, wherever you might misinterpret the meaning I shall cue you by specifically writing pounds mass, grams mass, etc. (abbreviated lbm, gm, etc.) or pounds force, grams force, etc. (lbf, gf, etc.). In Chapter 5 we shall gain an understanding of the nature of mass and the nature of force. You will then be able to tell from the context whether the quantity under discussion is a force or a mass; so the use of these cues will be discontinued.

2-3 The Irrationality and Inconvenience of the English System of Units

Familiar things and habitual actions are, to a considerable degree, blessings; but they are not necessarily *unmixed* blessings. Since we have grown up with the English system of units, we tend to consider it superior to other systems; our familiarity with it often blinds us to its disadvantages. We may feel that it is a familiar, sensible system, and one that's easy to use. But although I'll agree with the first adjective, I deny the validity of the others.

Which weighs more, a pound of feathers or a pound of gold? In a *sensible* system of units, they would weigh the same; but our "sensible" (?) English system uses troy weight for gold and avoirdupois weight for nearly everything else, with the result that the pound of feathers weighs about 21.5% more than the pound of gold. Part of this discrepancy arises from the fact that there are twelve troy ounces in one pound troy, whereas in the avoirdupois system there are sixteen ounces in a pound. This would seem to make the avoirdupois pound 33.3% larger than the troy pound instead of only 21.5%; but a troy ounce exceeds an avoirdupois ounce by about 9.7%. Then our "sensible" English system also has the fluid ounce, which bears no particular relationship to the troy ounce or the avoirdupois ounce. I should have said fluid ounce*s*, since the British version is about 4% smaller than the U.S. fluid ounce. On the other hand, the gas mileage of your car should be about a fifth higher in Canada than in this country, because the British Imperial gallon is about 20% larger than its less impressively named American cousin. In this dependence of the size of the unit on the dignity of its name, perhaps we at last find something sensible in our common system of units!

Now, how about ease of use? Suppose that a uranium ore contains 0.020% of the kind of uranium called U^{235}. How many ounces of U^{235} would there be in 400 tons of ore? We must convert tons to pounds, and pounds to ounces. A ton may be 2240 pounds (long ton) or 2000 pounds (short ton), but the latter is used somewhat more commonly so we cross our fingers and use this value. Again, most things are weighed in terms of the avoirdupois system rather than the troy system, so we will consider there to be 16 (rather than 12) ounces to the pound. But we still must multiply three factors together to change from tons to ounces. When more awkward conversion factors, such as 231 cubic inches to 1 gallon, are involved, the conversion becomes still more of a chore.

2-4 The Metric System of Units

The United States and Great Britain are the only major nations backward enough to continue to use the English system of units, and even in these countries the metric system, used by all other major nations, is employed in almost all scientific work.

The metric system has two great advantages over the English system. First, it is a decimal system, like our monetary system. All conversions from one size of metric unit to another are made much as we change a sum in cents to the equivalent number of dollars (or vice versa); it is only necessary to move the decimal point. This eliminates the need to remember conversion factors such as 5280 feet = 1 mile and removes the necessity of doing an arithmetic problem each time we make any conversion.

Secondly, in the metric system the *names* of the units tell us how each one is related to larger or smaller units of the same quantity; thus we can use the names of the units to tell us in which direction, and how far, the decimal point should be moved.

For example, the basic unit of length is the ***meter***. All other units of length are related to the meter by a factor such as 10 or 100 or 1000, etc. Multiples of the basic unit are named by prefixing the Greek names of the conversion factors; submultiples, by prefixing the Latin names of the conversion factors. Thus we have

Multiples	*Submultiples*
1 decameter = 10 meters	1 decimeter = $\frac{1}{10}$ meter
1 hectometer = 100 meters	1 centimeter = $\frac{1}{100}$ meter
1 kilometer = 1000 meters	1 millimeter = $\frac{1}{1000}$ meter

You can learn, and recall, the prefixes of the submultiples without any rote memorization, even if you know no Latin whatever; for they are all familiar in other applications. The *dec-* of decimeter is present in *dec*ade, which means *ten* years; the *cent-* of centimeter appears in *cent*ury and also is the name of the coin which is the *hundred*th part of a dollar; a *milli*pede is a "*thousand*-legged worm," and a *thousand* years is a *mill*ennium. Of the multiples, only the *kilo-*, corresponding to a factor of 1000, is used commonly; this is fortunate, since we don't have common English words in which these Greek prefixes appear.

Suppose, then, that we wish to convert a distance in kilometers to centimeters. We reflect that the *kilo-* means a factor of a thousand: 1 kilometer = 1000 meters. This part of the conversion can be accomplished by moving the decimal point three places to the right.* Next, a centimeter is $\frac{1}{100}$ meter, so there are 100 centimeters for each meter; this part of the conversion is performed by moving the decimal point two places to the right. Hence to convert kilometers to centimeters we merely have to move the decimal $3 + 2 = 5$ places to the right. Compare this with the process of converting miles to inches.

These same prefixes are used for the multiples and submultiples of other basic metric units. The basic unit of mass is the ***gram;*** so 1000 grams is a kilogram, etc. For volume, the primary unit is the ***liter;*** so a milliliter is $\frac{1}{1000}$ liter, etc.

One must be careful in some conversions, however. For example, a surface 1 meter square will have an area of 1 square meter; but its dimensions will be 100 cm by 100 cm, giving an area of 10,000 square centimeters. Thus the linear factor (100) must be squared to get the areal factor (10,000). Similarly a millimeter = $\frac{1}{10}$ cm, but a cu mm is $(\frac{1}{10})^3$ or $\frac{1}{1000}$ cu cm.

Avoid a habit of mentally converting metric measurements into the more familiar English units; it is important to develop a "feeling" for the metric system so that such conversions will not be necessary. However, sometimes conversions *do* have to be made. The factors below are only approximate but are accurate enough for most of our purposes.

Length: 1 meter = 39.4 in.; 1 in. = 2.54 cm
Mass: 1 kilogram = 2.20 lb, 1 lb = 454 g
Volume: 1 liter = 1.06 qt; 1 qt = 946 ml

Because of the irrationality of English units, conversions between metric and English units are as messy as those within the English system.

2-5 The Foot-Pound-Second, Centimeter-Gram-Second, and Meter-Kilogram-Second Systems

In the English system, we commonly think of the basic unit of length as the foot, the pound as the standard unit of mass, and the second as the

* We are concerned here with the principle on which such changes are made. A more convenient method of *making* the changes will be introduced in Sec. 2-12.

basic time unit. Thus this system is sometimes called the foot-pound-second, or fps, system. In a similar manner, we may speak of the centimeter-gram-second, or cgs, system, which has long been the framework of the metric system. More recently, the meter-kilogram-second, or mks, system has come into wide use. It would seem that there is little distinction between these two, since both are within the metric system. In the field of electricity, however, it is customary, in the mks system, to found certain fundamental definitions on a particular physical phenomenon but to base them on a quite different phenomenon if cgs units are used. There can be no question that the approach followed in the mks system is more fundamental and more elegant than the other, so it is almost mandatory for electrical engineers and professional physicists. However, it is also much more abstruse and intangible, so we shall employ the cgs point of view.

Nevertheless we shall have occasion at times to employ mks units instead of cgs; and of course we can't get completely away from the English system.

2-6 Fundamental Quantities and Derived Quantities

Mass, length, and time are usually considered to be the three ***fundamental quantities.*** Each is assigned units which are single terms: grams, pounds, feet, kilometers, seconds, hours, etc. More complex quantities are derived from these fundamental quantities, and in general their units are combinations of those of the fundamental quantities.

Thus we have area and volume, each of which involves only one fundamental dimension but involves it more than once; area is length $\times$ length or $(\text{length})^2$ and its value is expressed in cm^2, ft^2, etc. More commonly, two of the fundamental dimensions are involved, or even all three. Density is mass per unit volume, expressed in g/cm^3, lb/ft^3, etc. Speed is distance traveled per unit time, and it is evaluated in terms of length/time, such as ft/sec, etc. Momentum involves mass, length, and time, and the same is true of energy and force and many other quantities, but in general, the fundamental units are involved in different ways. For example, in Chapter 6 we shall find that momentum is mass $\times$ length $\div$ time, whereas energy is mass $\times$ $(\text{length})^2 \div (\text{time})^2$.

Another type of derived quantity is completely independent of all three fundamental quantities. An example is specific gravity, which is the ratio of the density of a substance to the density of some reference substance. The density of mercury is about 13.6 g per cu cm, and that of water is about 1.00 g per cu cm. Hence the specific gravity of mercury with respect to water is

$$\frac{13.6\ \text{g/cm}^3}{1.00\ \text{g/cm}^3} = 13.6$$

Since the units in the numerator are identical with those in the denominator, they cancel out, and the value of the specific gravity is a pure number without units. There are other quantities which, like specific gravity, are defined as a ratio of two like quantities. Obviously the values of all such quantities are pure (dimensionless) numbers.

But students often get into trouble unless they are extremely careful both about their thinking *and* about accurate expression of their thoughts. The example of mercury in the preceding paragraph shows that the density and the specific gravity (with respect to water) seem to have identical numerical values. But this is true only if the density is expressed in metric units; the density of mercury is about 849 lb per cu ft, which is a far cry from 13.6! Even if we stick to the metric system, we can *not* say "The density in grams per cubic centimeter is equal to the specific gravity." True, the *numerical* values are the same; but one value must have units specified before it has meaning, whereas the other is a pure number. We *can* say, without danger of confusion, "The density in grams per cubic centimeter is *numerically* equal to the specific gravity." Also, of course, we can *not* say that the density of steel is about 7.7. It is about 7.7 *g per cu cm—or* 7700 *kg per cu m, or* 449 *lb per cu ft.*

To many who read this, it will seem that I am quibbling. So be it, if you wish, though I disagree. But if you will be careful to "quibble" about distinctions of this sort, which may seem minor to you, you will avoid much confusion; whereas if you refuse to quibble, you will be in danger of encountering unnecessary difficulties which arise from habits of thought which are less careful than they should be.

Probably no one ever achieves perfectly logical thought or manages to avoid ambiguity in all his statements; this book will undoubtedly provide evidence that I haven't reached that goal. Too many students give up and quit trying when they fall short of perfection in this regard; whereas the same students would not be stopped in the development of their tennis game, for example. As in other aspects of our lives, the impossibility of attaining perfection in logical thought and impeccably precise statement should rather spur us to effort than discourage us from trying.

2-7 Techniques for the Conversion of Units

Conversions, such as 31.2 cm = ? in. or 316 lb = ? g, seem to be a prolific source of error; the student often multiplies when he should divide, or vice versa. Mistakes of this sort may be avoided by either of two methods.

First is inspection of the result to see whether it is reasonable. Ask yourself whether your height in inches is a larger or a smaller number than your height in feet, or whether your weight is a greater number of pounds or a larger number of ounces; then compare the less familiar situation with these obvious ones. Had the students made this test when I was unwise enough to give the weight and length of a very new daughter and asked them to express these quantities in metric units, they would not have reported her to be either submicroscopic or of a tonnage in excess of the world's combined navies.

A second means of avoiding errors is more formal and hence, in a sense, less desirable, but it is safer when a series of conversions must be made or when one is dealing with less familiar or less tangible quantities. It consists of treating units (cm, in., lb, etc.) as algebraic quantities and planning the method of conversion so that unwanted units cancel out and desired ones are introduced. For example, 1.00 in. represents the same length as does 2.54 cm, and since whenever we divide any quantity by itself the quotient is one, we may write

$$1.00 \text{ in.}/2.54 \text{ cm} = 1, \quad \text{or} \quad 2.54 \text{ cm}/1.00 \text{ in.} = 1$$

Multiplication or division of any quantity by one does not alter its value, so we may multiply or divide any length by either of these ratios.

To change 31.2 cm to inches, we note that we must cancel out the cm unit and introduce the in. unit instead; so we set up the conversion:

$$31.2 \text{ cm} \cdot \frac{1.00 \text{ in.}}{2.54 \text{ cm}} = \frac{31.2}{2.54} \text{ in.}$$

If we err *and if* we watch our units, we may perceive the error immediately. For example, if we multiply by the 2.54 cm/1.00 in. ratio we shall have (disregarding numerical values) $\text{cm} \cdot \text{cm/in.} = \text{cm}^2\text{/in.}$, which most certainly is not what we want. However, we may make the conversion by using this ratio as a divisor, since then we have

$$\text{cm} \div \text{cm/in.} = \text{cm} \cdot \text{in./cm} = \text{in.}$$

No matter how many conversion factors you have to use, or how unfamiliar they may be, if each is numerically correct (e.g., 12 in. = 1 ft rather than 1 in. = 12 ft) and if you use this technique of canceling out unwanted units and introducing desired units, you should have no trouble in making correct conversions.

2-8 Dimensional Analysis

Though the term ***dimensional analysis*** may look and sound forbidding, as we shall use dimensional analysis it is quite uncomplicated. It is a very useful extension of the technique of cancellation of units. Basically, it has two facets: homogeneity of equations and the reduction of quantities to what are called "fundamental dimensions."

An equation is ***homogeneous*** if each term represents the same *kind* of quantity. Thus,

2 heads of lettuce + 3 heads of lettuce = 5 heads of lettuce

is a homogeneous equation, whereas the equation

2 heads of lettuce + 3 carrots = ? (carrot salad?)

is not. The equation

6 pencils · 10¢/pencil + 2 erasers · 5¢/eraser = $0.70

does not appear at first glance to be homogeneous, but actually it is, since each term represents a quantity of money. Similarly, an equation would be homogeneous if each of its several terms represented an area, and another would be homogeneous if each term represented a volume; each equation might be meaningful and useful. But an equation in which some terms stand for areas and others represent volumes would be inhomogeneous and meaningless.

In Sec. 2-6 we met the three fundamental quantities, mass, length, and time. Each of these quantities has a corresponding ***fundamental dimension.*** Thus the fundamental dimensions, and their respective symbols, are mass, m; length, l; and time, t.

Numbers, such as the 2, 3, and 5 in the first equation on this page are dimensionless constants and hence may be ignored, insofar as dimensional analysis is concerned. Since each term in the equation

heads of lettuce + heads of lettuce = heads of lettuce

represents the same *kind* of quantity the equation is *dimensionally* valid, whereas

heads of lettuce + heads of cabbage = bunches of celery

is dimensionally *in*valid since the terms stand for different kinds of quantities. Insertion of suitable numerical constants will make the first of these equations numerically valid also; but the second cannot be made to make sense, however we try, because it is inhomogeneous and dimensionally invalid.

This point is very important. For example, dimensional analysis of an equation may yield something like

$$l = l + l$$

and it is easy to make the mistake of thinking this is invalid since algebraically $l + l = 2l$ rather than just one l. But *dimensionally,* the equation *is* valid, since each term represents the same *kind* of quantity, a length. A corollary of this is the fact that dimensional analysis can tell us nothing whatever about the presence or absence of numerical constants in an equation, or about their numerical values if present.

To illustrate the usefulness and simplicity of dimensional analysis, consider the too common student who has forgotten which of the expressions $2\pi r$ and πr^2 represents the circumference of a circle and which is proper for the area. In all probability, he feels that he must ask, or consult a reference, to distinguish with certainty between the two equations; but such is *not* the case.

The circumference is the distance around the circle, that is, a length. Hence, if C is the circumference, dimensionally

$$C = l.$$

To get an area we multiply one linear dimension by another (or by itself) so if the area is A, dimensionally

$$A = l^2$$

and this obviously is in agreement with the fact that we measure area in *square* feet, *square* centimeters, etc.

Now let us try πr^2 as the circumference of a circle:

$$C \stackrel{?}{=} \pi r^2$$

π has no dimensions, and r has the dimension l, so the corresponding dimensional equation is

$$l \stackrel{?}{=} l^2$$

which is inhomogeneous and hence can't possibly be correct. If we try the same expression for area, we have

$$A \stackrel{?}{=} \pi r^2, \quad \text{and} \quad l^2 = l^2$$

which is valid dimensionally.

It is easy to prove, in the same way, that $2\pi r$ cannot possibly yield an area but is dimensionally correct for a circumference.

2-9 Further Considerations of Equations

As noted in the preceding section, dimensional analysis is limited to checking (or developing) the *form* of an equation, the *kind* of quantity each term must represent. It offers no help whatever with numerical constants. But very often confusion about constants can be eliminated by a bit of intelligent inspection.

For example, suppose the confused student of the previous section is uncertain whether the factor 2 belongs in the equation for circumference or in that for area. Here also, he can decide with certainty, without help.

The two possible (?) expressions for circumference are πr and $2\pi r$. Presumably he knows that the value of π is a little greater than 3. If he draws a circle, as in Fig. 2-1, and draws a straight line from A to O and on to B, he will have a distance of $2r$ between A and B. Retracing the line to O will add a distance r, or $3r$ from A to B and back to O. To complete the round trip back to A would make the distance $4r$, which is greater than πr. But the circumference makes this round trip from A through B and back to A the *long* way around; so certainly the circumference must be $2\pi r$ rather than πr.

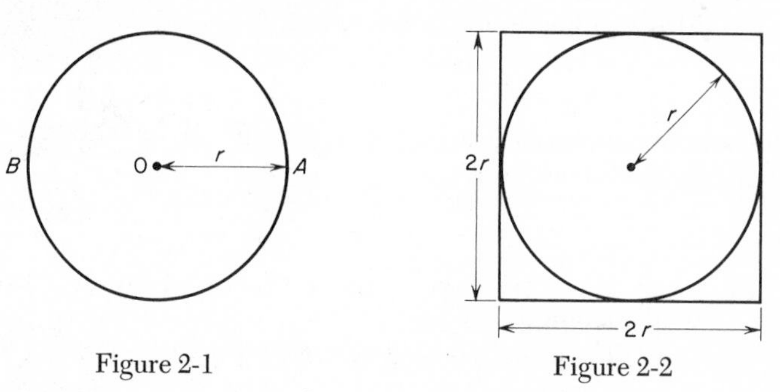

Figure 2-1

Figure 2-2

But perhaps there should be a 2 in the formula for area, also. The student can find out very easily by drawing a circle inscribed in a square. The length of one side of the square is the diameter of the circle, or $2r$, so its area is $(2r)^2$ or $4r^2$. Since the area of the circle obviously is less than that of the square, and since $2\pi r^2$ would be over $6r^2$, the area of the circle *has* to be just πr^2 rather than $2\pi r^2$.

2-10 Illusions of Accuracy: "Places" Past the Decimal Point

It is highly commendable to be careful and accurate in making measurements and in carrying out computations which employ the values measured. But if we aren't careful, it is quite possible to make ourselves needless work and actually to confuse ourselves as to the accuracy of our results. And the kind of "care" required may, at first, seem to be carelessness; so you may have to watch yourself closely until you get the idea.

This matter has three aspects: measurements, computations involving addition or subtraction, and calculations involving multiplication or division. We shall investigate measurements, additions, and subtractions in this section and consider multiplication and division in the next.

Measuring devices have widely different degrees of refinement and hence of accuracy. A meter stick may be used to measure a length to the nearest *tenth* of a centimeter, a vernier caliper will give a measurement of length correct to the nearest *hundredth* of a centimeter, and the values of length read with a micrometer caliper are accurate to the nearest *thousandth* of a centimeter. A generally similar situation exists with all other measuring devices: balances, voltmeters, etc.

"No chain is stronger than its weakest link," and we have an analogous situation with regard to measurements and their use in calculations. How to detect the weakest link, and to judge just how weak it is, is the subject of the rest of this section and of the one following.

Suppose that you want to know the value of the barometric pressure, corrected to 0°C. If you read a mercury barometer which has a vernier scale, you might get a reading of 758.3 mm, the actual value depending somewhat on the weather and greatly on the elevation. If the temperature is 20.0°C, the correction is 2.47 mm, and this must be subtracted from the reading. (We shall ignore the reason for this correction until we reach the topic of heat.) So you write down

Barometric reading	758.3 mm
Correction	2.47 mm
Corrected reading	755.83 mm

But the corrected reading is *not* 755.83 mm. To get this, you had to add a zero in the *hundredths* place of the barometric reading. You got this reading with the aid of a vernier scale, which can be read only to the nearest *tenth* of a centimeter. When you read 758.3 you know that the true value is nearer 758.3 than 758.2 or 758.4, but you do not know that it is 758.3*0*. And since you don't *know* that the value of the hundredths digit is zero, it is *not* permissible to assume that it is. Hence we must round off the corrected reading to 755.8 mm; or we may round off the correction to 2.5 mm before subtracting.

Here the weakest link is the barometric reading, which is correct only to a tenth of a centimeter. Hence any and all values derived by adding to or subtracting from this reading will be limited in accuracy to the accuracy of this weakest link; no such value can be accurate beyond a tenth of a centimeter.

In general, the accuracy of a sum or a difference is limited to the accuracy of the least accurate item in the addition or subtraction; hence time can be saved by rounding off excess digits in individual values before adding or subtracting. Until the final result is obtained, this rounding off should leave *one* more "place" than in the item which has the fewest places. For example, in the left-hand column below we have a value of 29.4 cm and others rounded off to the nearest tenth; in the right-hand column is the same addition, with the others rounded off to the nearest hundredth:

29.4 cm	29.4 cm	
143.2 cm	143.17 cm	
2.9 cm	2.89 cm	
70.8 cm	70.76 cm	
246.3 cm	246.22 cm	or 246.2 cm

Note carefully an implication of all this which is commonly overlooked. Suppose that each of the measurements above was made with a device *capable* of measuring to the nearest hundredth of a centimeter. If equal care was used for all the measurements, the first one must have been "on the nose" at 29.4 cm; otherwise it would have been recorded as 29.42 or 29.39 or a similar value. But since the observer *did not* record this as 29.4*0* he *limited the accuracy of the final result* to *a tenth* of a centimeter; whereas it would have had an accuracy of a *hundredth* of a centimeter if he had recorded that final zero. Thus a zero must be recorded whenever it reveals the *accuracy* of a measurement.

This discussion has been in terms of "places" to the right of the decimal point, but the principles and the criteria are the same for digits to the left of the decimal point. If the values in the examples of addition above were kilograms instead of centimeters, expressing them in terms of grams would change 29.4 kg to 29,400 g. Changing the size of unit used can't affect the accuracy of the measurement, so 29,400 g is only accurate to the nearest hundred grams. Other quantities should be rounded off to the nearest 10 g, and the final sum rounded off to the nearest 100 g.

2-11 Illusions of Accuracy: Significant Figures

The criterion for the "weakest link" in multiplication or division is quite different from that we developed for addition and subtraction. Here the location of the decimal point, or the number of places beyond the decimal point, has no bearing whatever. The important thing is the *number of digits we know* in a value. We saw something of this in the last paragraph of the preceding section. If a measurement of a weight yields a value of 29.4 kg, correct to a tenth of a kilogram, we know the values of three—and only three—digits: 2, 9, and 4. Changing to 29,400 g or to 29,400,000 mg cannot alter the accuracy of the original observation; hence we still know the values of only three digits in each of these cases. Similarly, a value of 71 mg provides information on two, and only two, digits; we may express it as 0.071 g or as 0.000071 kg, and we still know the values of just the same two digits. In all these cases, the zeroes are just "place holders" to put the known digits in the proper location with respect to the decimal point. To return to a previous example, if a value is specified as 29.4 cm we only know that it is somewhere between 29.35 and 29.45 cm; we do not know that the fourth digit is zero. But if it is specified as 29.40 cm, the measurement has been made to the nearest *hundredth* of a centimeter so we know the values of four digits.

Any figure in a measurement, including zero, is a ***significant figure*** if it contributes to the accuracy with which that measurement is expressed. But a zero which is only a "place holder" is *not* a significant figure. In the example above, 29.4 kg has three significant figures whether we express it in that way or as 29,400 g or as 29,400,000 mg; and 71 mg,

0.071 g, and 0.000071 kg have two significant figures each. But 29.40 cm has four significant figures even though 29.4 cm has only three, for the zero shows that the value has been *measured* to the nearest hundredth of a centimeter.

Zeroes before the decimal point, with nothing after the decimal point, present a dilemma. In the examples above they are not significant, but sometimes they are. If, for example, you count a number of objects carefully, you may get a value of 200. Since the value is neither 199 nor 201, but exactly 200, both zeroes are significant. We shall follow this matter a bit further in the following section.

Why bother with significant figures? To find the answer, suppose that we measure the diameter of a wire with a micrometer caliper and find the value to be 0.042 cm. What is the cross-sectional area of the wire? $A = \pi r^2$, r is 0.042/2 or 0.021 cm, and π is 3.1416. Using these data, the area is found to be 0.0013854456 cm^2. Isn't that a fine, accurate value, though? Just look at all those digits.

But we did *not* specify that the diameter was 0.042*0* cm. Perhaps it was, but the calipers can give us the value *only* to the nearest *thousandth* of a centimeter. Any actual diameter from about 0.0416 to 0.0424 cm would have been read as 0.042 cm. But recomputation with these two possible actual diameters gives values of 0.001359181824 cm^2 and 0.001411960704 cm^2, respectively. One of these agrees with our original value *only* in the *first* significant figure, and the other agrees only to two significant figures. If we round all three values off they will agree to two significant figures but no further.

Reviewing this, we see that though we had five significant figures in the value of π, we had only two in the value of the diameter; and we had only two in the final result. Thus our criterion for the "weakest link" in multiplication is the number of significant figures; and the same criterion is valid for division. The result of one or more multiplications or divisions, or any combination of multiplications and divisions, will in general have the same number of significant figures as that factor which had the *least* number.

This means that, having found which value entering into the computation has the smallest number of significant figures, all others may be rounded off to correspond. However, as was the case with addition and subtraction, one extra digit should be carried through the computations. In the example of the cross section of the wire, 3.1416 could have been used as 3.14; but it should *not* be used as 3.1. Also, as was the case with addition and subtraction, it is important to record all significant figures even if the final one may be a zero; for omission of this zero may reduce the number of significant figures which may be carried and limit the precision of the final value.

Up to the final value, one uncertain digit is carried in each value (that is, one more than the least number of significant figures). The final value may be rounded off, or the uncertain digit may be retained if it is identified as being uncertain. Thus, our original value of the cross-sectional area, optimistically recorded as 0.001384456 cm², must be expressed either as 0.0014 cm² or as $0.0013\bar{8}$ cm², the bar above the 8 identifying this digit as uncertain rather than significant.

It should be noted that in the discussion above we ignored a factor which apparently has but one significant figure; this was the 2 which we divided into the diameter to obtain the radius. But by definition the diameter is *exactly* twice the radius; so we are privileged to consider *in this case* that 2 has an infinite number of significant figures. Other examples of values which have an unlimited number of significant figures by definition are 12 inches in a foot, 16 ounces in a pound, etc.

In general, problems in this book will have data which contain three significant figures, and answers will be given to three significant figures only. There will, however, be exceptions to this general situation. In a few instances either more or fewer significant figures may be used. The principal exception to this general rule, however, has to do with the figure 1. *In all definitions in the text* "1" is to be interpreted as *exactly* one, and the figure 1 has the same significance when it appears in the statement of a problem.

A 10 in. slide rule gives values accurate to three significant figures (four, near the left end of the scale), and it will automatically round off any additional digits. It is handy for these reasons, in addition to its virtue as a time saver.

In these two sections the theory of propagation of errors has barely been touched on. Unless your instructor wishes to offer you a more complete coverage, however, the criteria developed will suffice for this course.

2-12 The Use of Powers of Ten

Some numbers are very inconvenient to write and almost impossible to name, if we use the usual means of expressing them. For example, the electric charge on an electron is

0.00000000000000000016 coulomb

and the number of atoms in one gram atomic weight is about

602486000000000000000000

We have seen, too, that there is ambiguity with regard to the number of significant figures in a value which has zeroes before the decimal point (and no digits to the right of the decimal). Finally, computations involving such numbers are very awkward.

We can circumvent all these difficulties by writing such quantities as the product of two numbers, of which the first commonly is between 1 and 10, and the second is some power of 10. The awkward numbers above become, in this system, $1.6 \cdot 10^{-19}$ and $6.02486 \cdot 10^{23}$, respectively. The first of the two factors (such as 1.6 in $1.6 \cdot 10^{-19}$) is the ***number sequence*** and the second (such as 10^{-19}) is the ***order of magnitude.*** This method of expressing values is sometimes called ***scientific notation.***

How is this done? Consider first the *second* example. We begin by writing 6.02486. To achieve the equivalent of the original number we must multiply this number sequence by a very large number. Recall that multiplying by 10 shifts the decimal point one place to the right, multiplying twice by 10 shifts it two places to the right, etc. If we multiply n times by 10, the decimal point will be shifted n places to the right. $10 \cdot 10$ is 10^2, and n factors of 10 multiplied together equal 10^n. Thus, multiplying by 10 moves the decimal one place to the right; by 10^2, two places to the right; or by 10^n, n places. Going back to the original number, start after the first 6 (where we put the decimal point in the number sequence) and count the number of digits; it is 23. Thus we may regenerate the original number by multiplying 6.02486 by 10^{23}; that is, the original number *is* $6.02486 \cdot 10^{23}$.

Changing the other number to the form $1.6 \cdot 10^{-19}$ is done in a similar manner. Dividing by 10 moves the decimal point one place to the *left*, so dividing by 10^n will move it n places to the left. Also, we may think of division by 10^n as identical with multiplication by $1/10^n$, and we may write $1/10^n$ as 10^{-n}. Thus we may start by writing the number sequence as 1.6. Counting from the right of the 1 back to the decimal point in the original number, we count up 19 places; so we need a factor of 10^{-19}. Thus we arrive at the expression $1.6 \cdot 10^{-19}$.

Now what about significant figures? In the order of magnitude, both the 10 and the exponent of 10 are exact, so the number of significant figures depends solely on the number sequence. In $1.6 \cdot 10^{-19}$ there are two significant figures but in $6.02486 \cdot 10^{23}$ there are six. Note that the ambiguity in the number of significant figures, which we had been worried about in the number

$$602486000000000000000000$$

has disappeared.

Addition and subtraction of quantities expressed in this manner is done in somewhat the same way fractions are added or subtracted. With fractions, a common denominator is essential, and this denominator is common to the answer as well as to the original values. Similarly, all quantities added or subtracted must be expressed to the same power of 10. Their number sequences are then added or subtracted, and the same power of 10 appended to the result. Thus, we change

$$4.31 \cdot 10^6 - 3.37 \cdot 10^5$$

to

$$43.1 \cdot 10^5 - 3.4 \cdot 10^5$$

and the difference is $39.7 \cdot 10^5$ or $3.97 \cdot 10^6$.

Algebraically,

$$(A \cdot 10^a) \cdot (B \cdot 10^b) = AB \cdot 10^{a+b}$$

and

$$(A \cdot 10^a) \div (B \cdot 10^b) = \frac{A}{B} \cdot 10^{a-b}$$

Thus,

$$3 \cdot 10^2 \cdot 2 \cdot 10^{-5} = 6 \cdot 10^{-3}$$

and

$$(3 \cdot 10^2) \div (2 \cdot 10^{-5}) = 1.5 \cdot 10^7.$$

Also,

$$(A \cdot 10^a)^n = A^n \cdot 10^{an}$$

and

$$\sqrt[n]{A \cdot 10^a} = \sqrt[n]{A} \cdot 10^{a/n}.$$

It is important to include *all* significant figures in the number sequence, even if this makes the number sequence end with a zero. For example, according to a recent reference the speed of light in a vacuum is known to seven significant figures, its value being $2.997930 \cdot 10^{10}$ cm/sec. But if we were to write this as $2.99793 \cdot 10^{10}$ there would be only *six* significant figures instead of seven.

2-13 Translation: Algebra to English

The neatest and most concise expression of any quantitative relationship is an algebraic equation, so this mode of expression is widely used in this and all other publications in physics. However, many students have difficulty because they lack the ability to look at an equation and see what it means in words. This is essentially a matter of translating algebra into English. Once a student fully realizes this, much of the hazard is eliminated.

Consider the equation $P = F/A$, in which P is pressure, F is force, and A is area. This is the ***defining equation*** for pressure, since its English translation is the verbal definition. But what does the equation mean to you, really *mean?*

Here are some things it will mean to a person experienced at this sort of thing. First, of course, it says that the magnitude of the pressure is obtained by dividing the magnitude of the force by the area on which the force acts. Second, it says that if the area is unchanged the pressure is directly proportional to the force, since if the magnitude of the force is increased by any factor the pressure must be increased by the same factor or the "equation" will become an expression of *in*equality instead; and for the same reason, the force is directly proportional to the pressure. Third, if a given force is applied over a doubled area, the equation requires that the pressure be halved; so pressure is inversely proportional to area and area is inversely proportional to pressure. Fourth, we can see that multiplication of both sides of the equation by A would yield $PA = F$, so the equation tells us that the product of pressure and area is force. Similarly, it says that area (for example, the area of a ski or of the track on a tractor) is the quotient of the force and the pressure.

A slightly more complex equation is

$$N = \frac{\sqrt{T/m}}{2L}$$

in which N is the lowest frequency of vibration of a string, T is the tension of the string, m is its mass per unit length, and L is its length. We shall consider only an aspect of algebra-to-English translation—and a pitfall—not present in the previous example.

It is obvious that an increase in the value of T will cause N to become larger, but doubling T will *not* double N. Since T is under the radical, T would have to be quadrupled to cause a doubling of N. Thus the frequency is directly proportional to the *square root* of the tension. We can *not* reverse this to read "the tension is directly proportional to the square root of the frequency"; instead, the tension is directly proportional to the *square* of the tension, as we can see readily if we square both sides of the original equation:

$$N^2 = \frac{T/m}{4L^2}$$

Note that in this sort of situation (relating frequency to tension and then relating tension to frequency) reversal of the order changes "square root" to "square" or vice versa, but does *not* change the *kind* of proportion from direct to inverse. Similarly, the frequency is *inversely* proportional to the *square root* of the mass per unit length, but the mass per unit length is *inversely* proportional to the *square* of the frequency.

2-14 Translation: English to Algebra

This type of translation also frequently causes trouble. It is extremely important, since it is an essential part of the solution of any "word" problem. Very many students have more trouble with this aspect of the problem than with the physical principles involved or the mathematics of the computations.

We may define average speed by saying, "Average speed is the distance traveled per unit time." How could you translate this to produce the defining equation?

First, "per" or "per unit" always means that the quantity which precedes the "per" is divided by that which follows. Second, "is" may be thought of as "is equal to" and replaced by =. Thus,

$$\text{average speed} = \frac{\text{distance traveled}}{\text{time}}$$

We may make this more concise by using s to indicate the distance traveled, v_a to represent the average speed, and t to stand for the time required. This gives

$$v_a = s/t$$

which is our defining equation for average speed.

If the verbal statement specifies a proportionality rather than an equality, in general our algebraic translation must contain an unevaluated constant. Thus, if I say that my height in inches is directly proportional to my height in feet, you could write

$$\text{height in inches} = k \cdot \text{height in feet}$$

In this familiar case, you would know the value of the constant k; but in a less common situation you might not. Thus, if I say that the width of a rectangle of a given area is inversely proportional to its height, you could write

$$\text{width} = k \cdot \frac{1}{\text{height}}$$

but unless I told you the value of the area you could not evaluate k.

How would you translate this into algebra: The period of a pendulum is directly proportional to the square root of its length and inversely proportional to the square root of the acceleration due to gravity. If the period is T, the length L, and the value of gravitational acceleration g, you could write

$$T = k \cdot \sqrt{L} \cdot \sqrt{1/g}$$

and this could be simplified to

$$T = k \cdot \sqrt{L/g}$$

but you would have no way of knowing that the value of k in this case is 2π.

2-15 The Solution of Problems

The fruits of a neophyte violinist's efforts bear little resemblance to the music he will be able to make after long practice augmented with much professional instruction and help. A future Olympic swimmer doesn't swim the length of the pool the first time he gets into a body of water larger than a bathtub. We except ineptness and initial lack of success in such endeavors because we are well aware of the special skills required.

Too many beginning physics students fail to realize the parallelism between these things and solving problems; but problem solving most definitely requires skill, and that skill can be acquired only by diligent practice supplemented by professional help. Do not be discouraged if you encounter some difficulty at first; this is usual rather than exceptional.

As a start on the professional help, here are some suggestions. Though they are numbered, and although it is obvious that certain steps must precede others, considerable shifting of the order is possible and in some cases desirable.

First: Read the problem. Very often a major source of difficulty is a misunderstanding or misinterpretation of the data, oversight of a key word, or uncertainty of what is asked for. *Be sure* that you *understand* the *statement* of the *problem before* you make any other start toward its solution.

Second: Make a *complete* list of *all* data given *and* of the quantity or quantities asked for. This must be written, and it must include the name of each quantity (or the conventional symbol for it), the unit in which each quantity is expressed and the unit expected for the answer, and all specified or known numerical values.

Third: If at all possible, make a reasonably careful diagram (an accurately constructed figure is not necessary). If different kinds of quantities are represented on the diagram (such as distances and forces) use different colors or use pencil for one and ink for another. Add all pertinent data to the diagram. Often arrows to indicate direction should be included.

Fourth: Examine the data carefully in the light of the statement of the problem. Perhaps one or more useless items of data were tossed in. Careful inspection *coupled with understanding* of the *nature* of the *problem* and of the *physical principles involved* will enable you to ferret out and discard irrelevant data.

Fifth: The number of different physical principles involved in problems is limited, though the statements of the problem may seem to have an almost infinite variety. Try to strip from the problem the camouflage of its verbiage and discover the real heart of the problem—the basic physical principle or principles involved. Fairly commonly a combination of two principles is involved; less commonly, more than two must be brought to bear on the problem. (In the sense used here, "principle" includes also "law" and "definition.")

Sixth: Having in effect reduced the problem to one or a very few basic principles, translate each of these from English to algebra and record it. This step and the preceding one eliminate the need to riffle feverishly—and sometimes futilely—through the pages for an equation into which you can plug the data blindly (and without understanding).

Seventh: In each equation check each symbol for which the statement of the problem provides the value. Circle the symbol of each quantity to be determined. Check also any symbol of an unknown quantity in one equation which can be evaluated from another equation. If there remains a symbol which is not checked or circled, review the statement of the problem, reconsider your analysis of the problem, or see whether you can use an additional relationship to determine the value of the orphan symbol and thus make the solution of the problem possible.

Eighth: Making any necessary conversions of units, substitute the data into the equations and solve the problem.

Ninth: A *very* important step remains. Look at the numerical value to see if it appears *reasonable.* See that you have recorded the *proper* unit (if the quantity solved for has a unit). Unless the problem is quite simple and you are sure that the numerical value is correct, make a rough check of the value by the method outlined in the next section.

You may have been somewhat surprised in these suggestions at the degree of emphasis placed on the analysis of the problem. I have found that if a student is "stuck" on a problem, the most common trouble is that he has been unable to find how to attack it. Once this is clarified by an intelligent analysis of the problem, there usually is very little difficulty. Hence the suggestions above are intended to help you work out the method of attack. If there remains trouble with the mechanics of simple algebraic manipulations, you may find the brief discussion in Appendix E or the review in Appendix F helpful.

2-16 Checking Problems

Arithmetical errors in problems are almost as common as ants at a picnic. A student commonly is aware of this, but feels that a check of the numerical value will be as laborious as the original computation. However, anything but a minor error can usually be revealed very easily if you make use of approximations and of scientific notation. Here is a computation which appears rather messy to check, but isn't:

$$Y = \frac{30.0 \cdot 89.5}{\pi \cdot 0.810^2 \cdot 0.00456} = 286{,}000$$

Let us express 30.0 as $3 \cdot 10$; round off 89.5 to 100 and express it as 10^2; write 0.810 as $8 \cdot 10^{-1}$, which squared would be $64 \cdot 10^{-2}$, or roughly $6 \cdot 10^{-1}$; use 3 as the value of π, and represent 0.00456 as $5 \cdot 10^{-3}$. We then have

$$Y \approx \frac{(3 \cdot 10) \cdot 10^2}{3 \cdot (6 \cdot 10^{-1}) \cdot (5 \cdot 10^{-3})}$$

in which the sign $\approx$ indicates an approximate rather than a precise equality. We may cancel the two 3's. In the denominator the product of 6 and 5 is 30, so the denominator becomes $30 \cdot 10^{-4}$ or $3 \cdot 10^{-3}$. With these changes, the expression becomes

$$Y \approx \frac{10 \cdot 10^2}{3 \cdot 10^{-3}} \approx 3 \cdot 10^{+5}$$

We know, therefore, that the value of Y must have a number sequence which begins with a number not far from 3 and has an order of magnitude of 10^5 or 100,000. This is in reasonable agreement with the computed value of 286,000 or $2.86 \cdot 10^5$.

Actually, with a little use, this method of checking will become less laborious than this example makes it seem.

Care must be taken to avoid misinterpretation if the number sequence is fairly close to 1 (or 10). A rough check value of $1.2 \cdot 10^5$ would not necessarily invalidate a computed value of $9.17 \cdot 10^4$, for $1.2 \cdot 10^5$ may be written as $12 \cdot 10^4$. Thus the orders of magnitude agree and the discrepancy between 12 and 9.17 may or may not be a cause for concern.

How large a discrepancy between the number sequences is acceptable? There is no simple answer. It depends on how ruthlessly the actual values were rounded off, the number of different factors involved, and the additional approximations made in canceling, multiplying, and dividing.

Summary

The English system of weights and measures has many defects, most of which are not present in the metric system. All conversions of units within the metric system may be accomplished merely by shifting the decimal point, and the names of the units furnish clues as to how far the decimal point should be moved. We shall use the centimeter-gram-second system principally, though we shall make some use of the meter-kilogram-second system.

Whatever system we use, confusion may result from the use of the same term for a unit of mass and a unit of force. Until we are in a position to make a distinction between a mass and a force from the context, an m will be appended to the abbreviation of units of mass and an f to those signifying force. Of course this is unnecessary, and will not be done, if the context leaves no reasonable doubt about the meaning.

The three fundamental physical quantities are mass, length, and time. Other physical quantities are derived from these. Such derived quantities may be related to one, two, or three of the fundamental quantities, but a few are pure numbers unrelated directly to mass, length, or time.

Conversion of a given quantity from one unit to another often results in error. Inspection of the result of the conversion, and comparison with some more familiar conversion, will usually reveal such an error. An alternate method of checking, or of avoiding error in the first place, is to set up the original quantity and the conversion factor or factors in such a way that the units involved may be canceled.

Extension of the method of cancellation of units leads to *dimensional analysis*. This makes use of the three fundamental dimensions, mass, length, and time, corresponding to these three fundamental quantities. Although dimensional analysis is extremely useful, it offers no information with respect to the presence of any numerical constant, or the value of such a constant. However, in some cases one can deduce the value of the constant by a little intelligent thought.

Any experimental measurement necessarily has a limited accuracy. It is not permissible to add or to assume zeroes to such a value, or to assume them to be present, in order to find a sum or a difference in which it is involved.

For multiplication or division, rounding off may also be advisable. The number of significant figures in that item of data which has the fewest significant figures limits the accuracy of the computation.

So-called scientific notation makes use of integral powers of 10 to aid in the recording, understanding, and use of numerical values. The value is expressed as the product of two factors: number sequence and the order of magnitude. Addition or subtraction of values expressed in this way requires that all quantities be expressed with the same order of magnitude, and this same order of magnitude is appropriate for the sum or difference. In multiplication, the exponents of 10 are added algebraically; in division, the exponent of 10 in the divisor is subtracted algebraically from that of the dividend. Similar simple operations are involved in raising a numerical value to a power or in extracting a root.

A highly important factor in the successful study of physics is essentially a matter of translation; conversion of a verbal statement into an algebraic equivalent, or deducing verbally expressed interrelationships from an algebraic equation.

Many a physics student digs his academic grave by failing to check the results of his computations. One should always check both the numerical value and the unit in which it is expressed. The former is most easily done by a simplified computation using rough approximations. The latter may be checked by inspection or by dimensional analysis.

Self-Quiz

1. For the time being, how shall we distinguish between (for example) kilograms of mass and kilograms of force? When will this convention be abandoned? Why will it not be continued indefinitely?

2. How do you feel about the English system of units? If you still feel that it would be easier to work with than the metric system, try finding the interest at 6% on a given amount of money in pounds, shillings, and pence; then find the interest on an equivalent sum in dollars and cents.

3. Why isn't the conversion factor between cubic feet and cubic inches simply 12?

4. Did you give one answer, or two, to the preceding question? There *are* two independent (partial) answers, one having to do with the numerical value, and one with units (or *lack* of units).

5. What prefixes are used to indicate submultiples of a basic metric unit? What numerical value is appropriate for each? Must these prefixes be blindly memorized? Why *not?* What prefixes are used for multiples, and what multiple of the basic unit does each imply? Which two of these multiples shall we use very little, if at all?

6. Prepare a table showing the interrelationships of the gram, its multiples and its submultiples, similar to that given in Sec. 2-4 for the meter.

7. In each space in the table below, fill in the number of the unit in the *horizontal row* which equals *one* of the units in the *vertical column:*

	kiloliter	liter	deciliter	centiliter	milliliter
kiloliter					
liter					
deciliter					
centiliter					
milliliter					

8. What is the fps system? The mks system? The cgs system? Which of these shall we use most extensively? Which, if any, will not be used at all?

9. What is meant by a "fundamental" quantity? How many are there, and what are they?

10. What are "derived quantities"? Do all derived quantities have the same combination of fundamental quantities? Do any have only one? Do any have none?

11. Compare the meaning of "is equal to" with that of "is numerically equal to." To what extent are the two expressions similar, if at all? To what extent do they differ, if at all? Had you been aware of the pitfall hidden here before you read Sec. 2-6? If not, you'll have to be "on your toes" to avoid misunderstanding and confusion.

12. What is the simplest and most direct way of testing the "reasonableness" of the answer obtained when you make a conversion from one unit to another? In any given quantity, will the numerical value be larger when a large unit is employed or when a smaller unit is used?

13. In what sense can we say that $12/1 = 1$, or is this never true? In what sense can we say that 12 in./1 ft $= 1$, or is this never true?

14. Discuss the method of making conversions between units by cancellation of units. Using this method, show how to convert tons into ounces. Show how to convert feet per second into miles per hour.

15. Briefly summarize what is meant by "dimensional analysis," and discuss its advantages and limitations.

16. Taking the dimension of s as l, the dimensions of v as l/t, and those of a as l/t^2, determine which of the two equations below may be a valid equation and which cannot be.

$$S = ut^2 + at/2, \qquad S = ut + at^2/2$$

17. Without reference to the text, go through the dimensional proof which distinguishes between the equation for the circumference of a circle and that for the area of the circle.

18. Again without reference to the text, demonstrate that the area of a circle is πr^2 rather than $2\pi r^2$, and that the circumference of a circle is $2\pi r$ rather than πr.

19. For what types of mathematical processes is the number of "places" to the right of the decimal point the most pertinent factor in determining the accuracy of the final result? In what types of mathematical processes is the number of "places" to the right of the decimal utterly meaningless with respect to the accuracy of the final result? Discuss the *reasons* in each case.

20. What is meant by the term "significant figures"? How does one determine how many significant figures a given value has? What source of ambiguity may arise in this determination?

21. Assume that the numbers 31.7, 31.70, and 31.700 are proper records of experimental observations. To what extent are these three values equivalent? In what sense, and to what degree, does each differ from the others?

22. In computations which involve multiplication or division, or both, how does one determine the proper number of significant figures to be retained in the original data and carried through the intermediate steps of the calculations?

23. A student measures the diameter of a wire with a micrometer caliper and obtains a value of 0.82 mm. This is to be used to find the cross-sectional area of the wire, which will then be divided into the length of the wire. The student measures the length of the wire as 212 cm, making no attempt to read tenths of a centimeter, but his lab partner scolds him for being so careless. Which student is in error, and why?

24. What is the so-called scientific notation? Of what value is it? What does the term "order of magnitude" mean? The term "number sequence"? How does one go about expressing a number in this kind of notation? How is the proper exponent of ten determined? What is the significance of a negative exponent?

25. Not from memory or by reference to the text, but on the basis of simple logic develop the procedures used for addition, subtraction, multiplication, division, raising to a power, and taking a root, when scientific notation is used. Refer to the text if absolutely necessary, but go as far as you possibly can on your own.

26. In a later chapter we shall meet the equation

$$F = G\frac{mm'}{d^2}$$

In this equation, F = gravitational force, G is a constant, m and m' represent the masses between which the force F exists, and d is the distance between them. Make an accurate verbal statement of this equation; then express exactly how each of the quantities F, m, and d is related to each of the others.

27. In another chapter we shall find that if a force F acts on a body of mass m it will produce an acceleration a, a being directly proportional to F and inversely proportional to m. Combine these facts to form a valid algebraic equation. (Include a constant, k)

28. Outline the method of checking the numerical value obtained in a problem, by approximation. What advantages does this method have? What disadvantages?

Problems

1. Express 342.8 g in terms of milligrams and in terms of kilograms.

2. How many cubic centimeters are there in 2.91 liters? How many milliliters are there?

3. Express your height in centimeters and in terms of meters, and your weight in grams and in kilograms. Your volume in cubic centimeters will be very nearly equal, numerically, to your weight in grams. Express your volume in liters and in gallons.

4. If in Problem 3 the conversions from the English system to the metric or vice versa were not made by the method of cancellation of units, repeat these three conversions by this method.

5. In the equation $a = F/m$, the dimensions of a are l/t^2. Determine the dimensions of F.

6. Using the dimensions of F found in Problem 5 (check the answer first) determine the dimensions of n in the equation

$$n = \frac{1}{2\pi}\sqrt{\frac{F/l}{m}}$$

7. Of the four expressions,

$$4\pi r^2, \quad \frac{4\pi r^2}{3}, \quad 4\pi r^3, \quad \text{and} \quad \frac{4\pi r^3}{3}$$

two have no significance, one represents the volume of a sphere of radius r, and one yields the area of the surface of the sphere. By dimensional analysis and by logical reasoning with respect to the values of the constants, identify each of the valid equations and prove the other two to be invalid.

8. Express in terms of "scientific notation": 0.000244; 791,300; 0.393.

9. Express in usual form:

$$2.85 \cdot 10^7, \qquad 7.71 \cdot 10^{-11}, \qquad 1.003 \cdot 10^2$$

10. Find the sum, the difference, the product, and the two possible quotients of these two numbers:

$$6.69 \cdot 10^{-4} \quad \text{and} \quad 7.06 \cdot 10^{-5}$$

11. Find the square, the cube, and the square root of $3.6 \cdot 10^5$.

12. Find the square, the cube, and the cube root of $2.7 \cdot 10^{-2}$.

13. Which of these values—412, 41.2, 87.0, 8.70—is the only possible answer to

$$0.0312 \cdot 591{,}000 \div 2127$$

Do *not* carry out the calculation; use the method of approximation.

14. Similarly, determine the only reasonable answer among 0.000223, 0.0223, 0.00434, and 4340 for this quantity:

$$83{,}200 \cdot (0.00513)^2 \div 9{,}710$$

3

FORCES AND OTHER VECTOR QUANTITIES

3-1 Preview

The directions of some physical quantities are just as important as their magnitudes. For such quantities, the usual arithmetical methods of addition and subtraction will not, in general, yield correct results. In this chapter we shall consider the appropriate methods for combining quantities of this nature. We shall find that it is possible, and often very useful, to substitute for a single such quantity an equivalent pair of quantities, and we shall learn how to make the substitution. The concept of equilibrium, and the criterion for the translational equilibrium of a set of forces, will be met.

3-2 Scalar Quantities and Vector Quantities

A ***scalar quantity*** is any quantity of such a nature that it is completely known if its magnitude (including units, if any) is known. If I say that there are 341 pages in a certain book, or that the density of mercury is 13.59 g per cubic centimeter, or that the volume of a vessel is 262 ml, each of these values is complete without further elaboration; therefore they are scalar quantities.

But quantities of another type remain ambiguous even when the magnitude is fully known. A person planning a 3000 mile trip from San Francisco might need a car or a boat, depending on the direction in which he intends to go. He might end the trip on the Atlantic seaboard or in the vicinity of the Midway Islands. A pilot flying from Schenectady to Philadelphia would need quite a bit of time for the trip if he flies *north* from Schenectady. Evidently quantities such as this remain ambiguous until the direction, as well as the magnitude, has been specified. Quantities of this sort are known as ***vector quantities.***

It is important to realize that the distinction between a vector quantity and a scalar quantity is not merely that the direction is specified with one, whereas, with the other, it is not. The concept of direction is utterly *meaningless* with respect to a scalar quantity, but *essential* to the meaning of a vector quantity.

Since a vector quantity has magnitude as well as direction, its magnitude is sometimes called the ***scalar component*** of the vector quantity. Thus, if a car is traveling north at 40 miles an hour its ***velocity*** is 40 mph north, a vector quantity; but we may speak of its ***speed*** as merely 40 mph. But although this is a scalar *aspect* of a vector quantity, it is *not* a scalar quantity; for we can't divorce the *significance* of direction from the concept of speed by failing to *mention* the direction.

3-3 The Addition of Two Vector Quantities

The principle of homogeneity of equations, which we met in Chapter 2, applies to vector quantities as it does to others. We can add cabbages and cabbages but we can't add cabbages and umbrellas; similarly we can add forces and forces but we can't add forces and velocities. But this similarity is accompanied by an equally important dissimilarity; whereas ordinary arithmetical processes are adequate for the addition of scalar quantities, in general they will not yield the correct result if we use them for vector quantities.

Consider the four passengers on the ship in Fig. 3-1. The ship is just getting under way; its velocity is 12 ft per second due east. Passenger A is a track coach standing motionless on the deck; obviously his velocity is also 12 ft/sec due east. The other three are his charges, whom he has

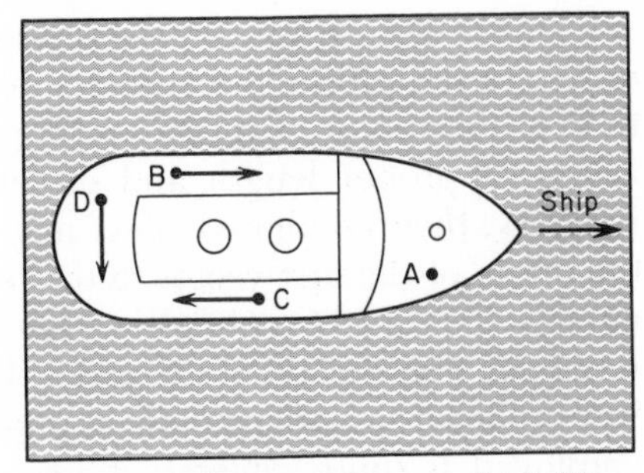

Fig. 3-1. The situation on which Figs. 3-2–3-5 inclusive are based.

ordered to run about the deck. Each is moving at 16 ft/sec with respect to the ship, but Passenger B is headed east, C is headed west, and D is headed south.

We can easily see that B's velocity with respect to the water is 28 ft/sec east, since while the ship carries him forward at 12 ft/sec his own efforts are carrying him forward at 16 ft/sec. On the other hand, C is moving westward along the deck faster than the ship is carrying him forward. During 1 sec the ship moves 12 ft east but he moves 16 ft westward on the deck, so his velocity is 16 minus 12 or 4 ft/sec westward.

Before considering D, let's represent the situations of B and C graphically. We may represent any vector quantity by a properly directed arrow of appropriate length, called a ***vector.*** Let us use a length of 1 cm to represent a velocity of 4 ft/sec. Thus in Fig. 3-2(a) we have vectors 3.0 cm and 4.0 cm long for the velocities of the ship and of B with

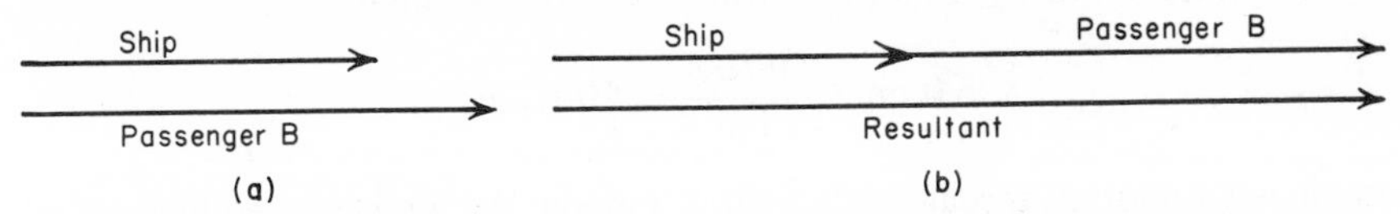

Fig. 3-2. The addition of two vector quantities which have the same direction.

respect to the ship. If we redraw these vectors in Fig. 3-2(b) with the tail of one at the tip of the other we have a total length of 7.0 cm which, according to our scale, represents 28 ft/sec. Trying the same process in Fig. 3-3(a) for Passenger C, the two vectors are oppositely directed because of the opposite directions of the ship's velocity and that of C with respect to the ship. We can't draw one vector from the tip of the other as in Fig. 3-2(b) because they would lie on top of one another; so in Fig. 3-3(b) one is drawn a little below the other. A vector drawn from the tail of the first vector to the tip of the second is only 1.0 cm long and is headed west. Interpreting this in terms of our scale, we see that this gives C's actual velocity as 4 ft/sec west, in agreement with what we got before.

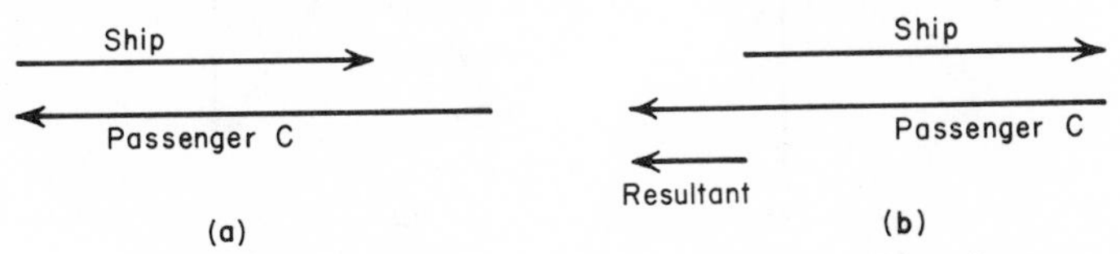

Fig. 3-3. The addition of two vector quantities of opposite directions.

Thus it appears that if we represent one vector quantity by an arrow drawn in the proper direction and of a length proportional to the magnitude of the vector quantity, and from the tip of this arrow draw a second arrow of proper length and direction to represent the second vector quantity, their combined effect may be found by drawing an arrow from the origin of the first vector to the terminus of the second. This will show directly the direction of the over-all result, and the magnitude may be determined with the aid of the scale. Although the two vectors we combined were colinear in both of these examples, it turns out that the procedure we employed is quite general; it may be employed whatever the relative directions of the vectors may be.

This will enable us to deduce the velocity of Passenger D. Casual consideration reveals that his velocity must be less than B's 28 ft/sec but more than C's 4.0 ft/sec, and that it must be generally southeast. A vector diagram will give us the actual speed and direction. Thus, Fig. 3-4(a) shows a vector which represents the velocity of the ship and one which portrays D's velocity relative to the ship. In Fig. 3-4(b) the latter vector is constructed from the tip of the former, each in its proper direction and of proper length. The vector drawn from the tail of the first vector to the tip of the second represents the actual velocity of D. It is 5.0 cm long; so, using a method from Sec. 2-7, we have

$$5.0\text{ cm} \cdot \frac{4\text{ ft/sec}}{1\text{ cm}} = 20\text{ ft/sec}$$

since we adopted a scale in which 1 cm on the graph is equivalent to 4 ft/sec. With the aid of a protractor, we find the direction to be just over 52° from that of the vector for the ship's velocity; thus D's velocity is 20 ft/sec, a bit more than 52° south of east.

In this particular case, D's *speed* could have been determined by the

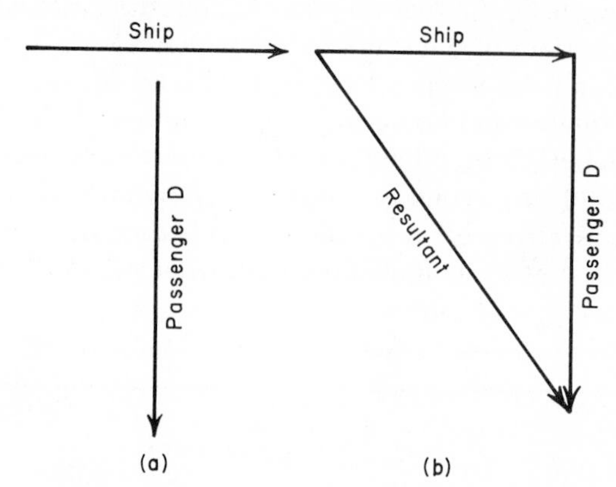

Fig. 3-4. The addition of two non-parallel vector quantities.

Pythagorean theorem (the square of the hypotenuse of a right triangle is equal to the sum of the squares of the sides), but this approach can be used only in the special situation in which the two vector quantities are mutually perpendicular. And in any case, the Pythagorean theorem can't give the direction. The graphical method will yield the magnitude *and* the direction, whatever the relative directions of the original vector quantities.

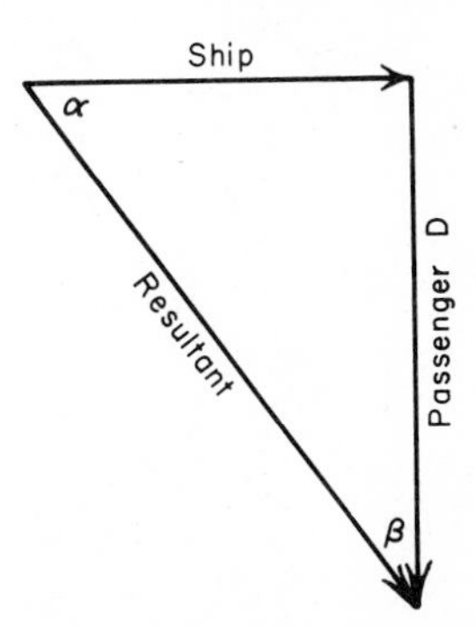

Fig. 3-5. This is Fig. 3-4(b), with the angles identified for the trigonometric method of adding vector quantities.

Thus we see that, in general, a graphical method must be employed to find the combined effect of two vector quantities. This combined effect is known as the ***vector sum*** (to distinguish it from the arithmetical sum), or as the ***resultant.*** Here is a term you should have no trouble with; you can extract its essential meaning simply, by dropping the final syllable.

Trig

(On occasion, as here, trigonometry will be invoked. Such excursions will be signaled by the italicized abbreviation *Trig* as above, and will be in smaller type. Your instructor may or may not require you to make use of these.)

Figure 3-5 is a repetition of Fig. 3-4(b), with the angles α and β identified. From this figure $\tan \alpha = D/S$ or $\tan \beta = S/D$, where D = velocity of passenger D and S = that of the ship. Then $R = D/\sin \alpha$, or other equations, may be used to evaluate the resultant R.

3-4 The Polygon Method of Vector Addition

The graphical method of adding vectors, worked out in the preceding section, is the ***polygon method.*** In Sec. 3-8 we shall consider very briefly another method called the "parallelogram method."

Our examples so far have involved only two vector quantities and their resultant; so the diagrams may not seem to suggest the term *poly*gon. However, we may extend the method to the addition of three or more—any number—of vector quantities, and the diagrams will look much more like your idea of a polygon.

With two original vector quantities, we drew a vector to represent one, and from the terminus of this we drew a vector to represent the other; and we found that if we then drew an arrow from the origin of the first vector to the terminus of the second, this third vector would represent the resultant of the original pair. To extend this method to the addition of three or more vector quantities we need only construct a third vector from the tip of the second, then (if we have four vector quantities to add) construct

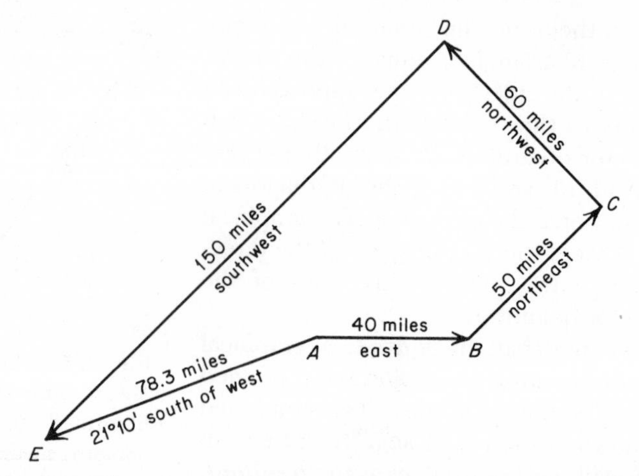

Fig. 3-6. The polygon method of adding several vector quantities.

a fourth vector from the terminus of the third one, etc. When we have incorporated into the diagram a vector for each of the vector quantities we wish to add, we may construct the resultant vector by drawing an arrow from the origin of the initial vector to the terminus of the final vector.

In doing this, of course we must lay off the length of each vector to scale, and each must be drawn in its proper direction.

Sample Problem 1

A flier starts at A and flies 40 miles due east to B, then northeast 50 miles to C, 60 miles northwest to D, and thence 150 miles southwest to E. These successive displacements are represented in Fig. 3-6 by vectors to a scale of 1 cm = 20 miles. The resultant vector AE represents a distance of 78.3 miles in a direction 21° 10′ S of W. Thus when the flier reached E he was 78.3 miles from where he started, in a direction 21° 10′S of W.

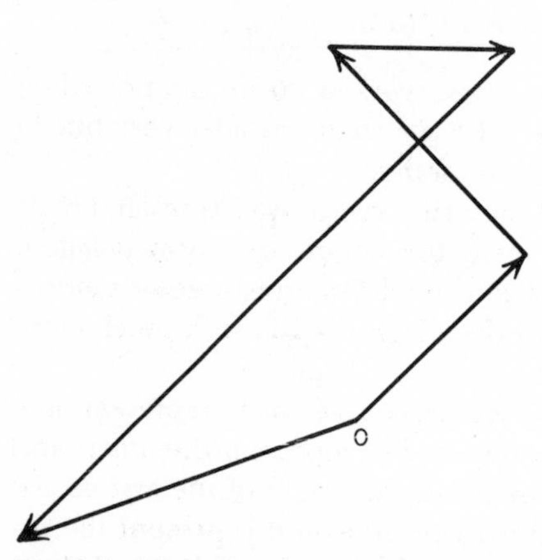

Fig. 3-7. The polygon method of vector addition may not result in an *open* polygon; Fig. 3-7 is exactly equivalent to Fig. 3-6.

Figure 3-7 looks quite different, but an examination of it shows that though the vectors are taken in a different order, each is present and is of the proper length and in the proper direction; and the resultant is identical with that in Fig. 3-6. Thus, if each vector is shown properly, they may be taken in any order whatever; the resultant must be the same. As you see, the "polygon" may be an open figure of the sort you expect, or it may be twisted on itself like a pretzel.

3-5 Some Details of the Polygon Method

It is customary in mathematics and physics to take a direction horizontally to the right as the 0° direction and to measure all angles counterclockwise from this 0° direction, as shown in Fig. 3-8(a). Unfortunately, a quite different convention, shown in Fig. 3-8(b), is used in navigation. If you are accustomed to this latter convention, you must be careful to avoid confusion; it is *not* used in physics.

In the preceding section, we saw that in adding vector quantities graphically it is possible to represent the various quantities in any order we choose and that the resultant is always the same even though the polygon is rather different. Since the same result is obtained, it would appear that the choice of order is entirely arbitrary. However, if the orientations of the various quantities are specified in terms of degrees, in accordance with the convention in the preceding paragraph, there is one particular choice of order which is most convenient.

In terms of degrees, the directions of the successive vectors in Fig. 3-6 are, commencing with vector *AB*, 0°, 45°, 135°, and 225°. On this basis, there would be no problem in constructing the vectors *AB* and *BC*. But when we wish to construct the 135° vector from the point *C* there is no horizontal line from which we may measure the 135°. We may, however, lay the base of the protractor along the direction of the vector *BC*. Since this means that the base of the protractor lies at a 45° angle counterclockwise from the 0° direction, to find the 135° direction we must mark off *not* 135° but (135° − 45°) or 90°. In like manner, to find the direction of any vector after the first (for which we have the 0° line to work from) we may lay the protractor along the last vector constructed and mark off an

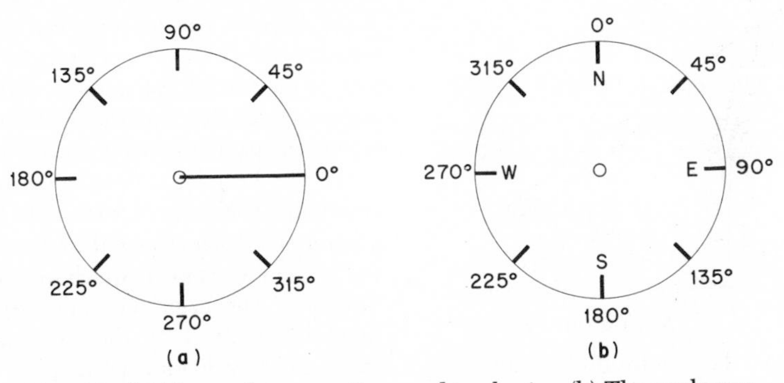

Fig. 3-8. (a) The angle convention used in physics; (b) The angle convention used in navigation—*NOT* used in physics.

angle counterclockwise which is the *difference* between the angle of the vector we wish to construct and that of the vector on which the protractor lies.

In Fig. 3-7 the second vector (the first vector starts at point 0) is at 135° and the third is at 0°. Thus, to find the direction of the third vector, we would have to lay the protractor along the second vector and lay off an angle of $0° - 135° = -135°$ counterclockwise; that is, 135° *clockwise.* This can be a source of confusion. Thus it is usually best to take the various vectors *in the order of increasing angle,* regardless of the order of listing. If you do this, it is highly advisable to check off each quantity as the corresponding vector is drawn in order to avoid oversight or duplication.

Sample Problem 2

Find the resultant of a force of 8.00 lb at 145°, 6.00 lb at 20°, and 3.00 lb at 285°.

If we choose to use the order of increasing size of angle, and a scale of 1 cm = 2 lbf, the diagram will be like Fig. 3-9. The method of laying off the directions of the vectors is detailed in the figure. The resultant is 3.75 lbf at 92.1°.

Trig

If only two vector quantities are to be added, the graphical solution is a triangle; so the law of cosines may be used to determine the magnitude of the resultant and the law of sines to find the angle between it and one of the original quantities. If directions are specified in degrees, according to the convention in Fig. 3-8(a), the angle of the appropriate vector must be added algebraically to the computed angle of the resultant. (For example, if the angle computed by the law of sines is 15° measured clockwise from a vector which has a direction of 62°, the direction of the resultant is $-15° + 62° = 47°$.)

When three or more vector quantities are to be added, usually the simplest procedure is to resolve each into a vertical component and a horizontal component. If the quantity has a magnitude M and a direction θ, these components are $M \sin \theta$ and $M \cos \theta$, respectively. The vertical component of the resultant is the algebraic sum of the vertical components of the individual quantities, and algebraic summation of the various horizontal components yields the horizontal component of the resultant. The quotient of the vertical and horizontal components of the resultants is the tangent of the angle which specifies its direction. The magnitude of the resultant may be obtained by the Pythagorean theorem or by dividing either of its components by the appropriate trig function

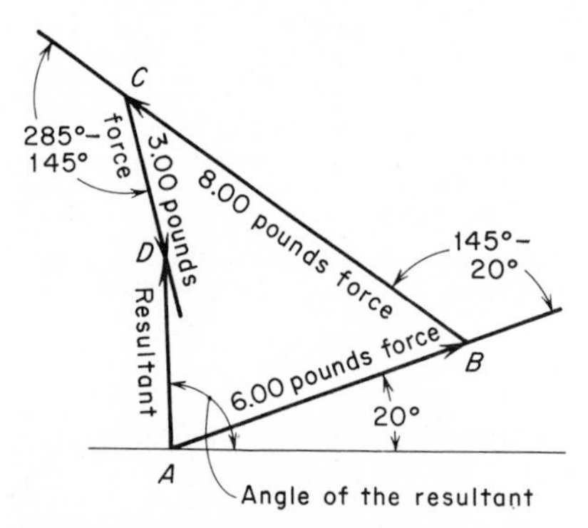

Fig. 3-9. The method of establishing the proper directions of vectors.

of the angle—$V/\sin \phi$ or $H/\cos \phi$, where V is the vertical component and H the horizontal component of the resultant and ϕ is its angle.

3-6 Subtraction of Vector Quantities

If a light plane is headed due west at 100 mph while a wind from the northeast is blowing at 30 mph, the velocity of the plane with respect to the ground may be found as in Fig. 3-10(a). It will be about 123 mph roughly 10° south of west.

Suppose now that the pilot can determine from landmarks and timing that his ground velocity—the resultant speed of the plane with respect to the ground—is 123 mph 10° S of W. Knowing also the plane's air velocity—which is the *plane's* velocity relative to the air—how could he determine the wind velocity? Since the ground velocity is the vector *sum* of the plane's air velocity and the wind velocity, the wind velocity must be the vector *difference* between the ground velocity and the air velocity of the plane.

In algebra, we often carry out a process which has the effect of subtraction, by *add*ing a *negative* quantity. And in Sec. 3-3 and Fig. 3-3(b) we saw that in the case of Passenger C the magnitude of the vector *sum* of two *oppositely* directed vectors was their numerical *difference.* In effect, C's velocity of 12 ft/sec westward along the deck was exactly the same as a velocity of *minus* 12 ft/sec *east*ward. Thus multiplying a vector quantity by -1 has the effect of reversing its direction.

This being the case, to subtract (for example) vector B from vector A we need only reverse the direction of vector B and *add* vectorially. Thus, the wind velocity may be found by drawing the vector for the ground velocity and constructing from the tip of this vector the *reversed* vector of the air velocity of the plane, as in Fig. 3-10(b). The resultant—the wind velocity—is then found as usual by drawing a vector from the origin of the initial vector to the terminus of the final vector. Similarly, if the ground velocity and the wind velocity are known, the velocity of the plane relative to the air may be found by subtracting the latter vectorially from the former as in Fig. 3-10(c).

Though we may think of the -1 in vector subtraction as being exactly equivalent to the -1 of algebra, we may also think of it as an *operator* which has the effect of rotating a vector quantity through 180°.

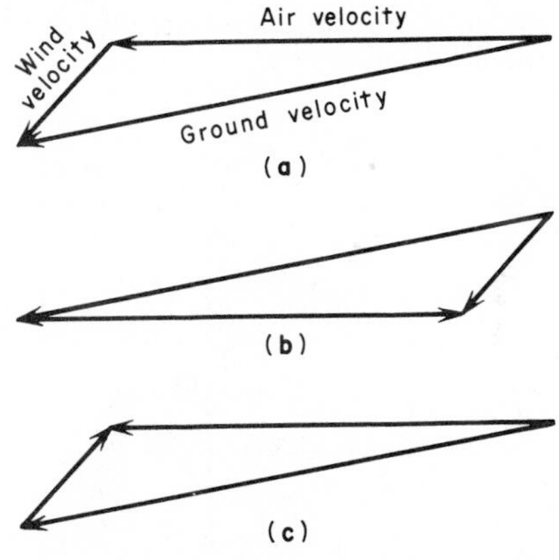

Fig. 3-10. The development of the method of subtracting vector quantities.

3-7 Components of a Vector Quantity

Why can't you park a car on a hill without setting the brakes, as it's possible (though not advisable) to do on level pavement? Probably this seems a very silly question, since it is obvious that the car's weight causes it to roll down the hill unless we prevent this from happening by applying the brakes. But the weight of the car is a *vertical* force and the motion of the car, even though it's on a hill, is much more nearly horizontal than vertical.

Imagine for a moment that we have discovered a way to eliminate weight, and that we use this to eliminate the weight of the car. But we want to keep our discovery a secret. A car normally tends to roll downhill, and its tires are slightly flattened where they contact the pavement, so we must simulate these effects of the non-existent weight by applying appropriate forces. One such force is a force D downhill, parallel to the surface of the hill; and the other is a force N normal to the roadway, as in Fig. 3-11. If we adjust the values of these two forces correctly, their resultant will correspond exactly both in magnitude and direction to the non-existent weight of the car. The actual situation will be exactly *as if* the forces D and N were non-existent and the weight were actually present.

No scientific—or other—magic is available to accomplish these results. But a situation exactly similar, and quite *non*-magical, *does* exist. Instead of replacing a non-existent weight with actual forces D and N we may *think of* replacing the actual weight W with an equivalent pair of *imaginary* forces which have the *actual* weight as their resultant. Such imaginary vector quantities, which have as their resultant a single actual vector quantity, are the ***components*** of that quantity, and the process of breaking a vector quantity up into its components is known as ***resolving*** a vector, or as ***vector resolution.*** Though this example has been in terms of forces, vector resolution is applicable to vector quantities of all kinds, just as vector addition is.

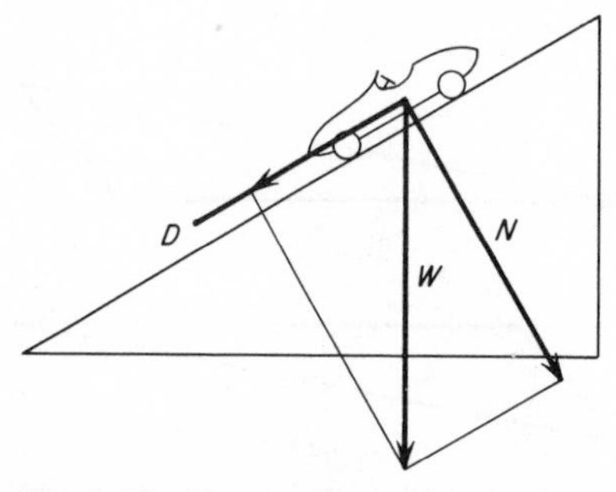

Fig. 3-11. The resolution of a vector quantity: parallelogram method.

3-8 The Parallelogram Method

In the polygon method of vector addition, each new vector is constructed from the tip of the preceding vector; no two of the original vectors originate from the same point, though of course the initial vector and the resultant have the same origin. But in Fig. 3-11 the original vectors D and N are drawn from the same point. This figure employs the

parallelogram method of vector addition—actually a rectangle method in this particular case. The two initial vectors are drawn to scale and in the proper directions from the *same* point. These vectors are then considered to represent two adjacent sides of a parallelogram and the parallelogram is completed by drawing the remaining sides, each parallel to an original vector and (necessarily) of the same length. The diagonal of the parallelogram, from the origin of the initial vectors to the opposite vertex, represents the resultant. You can see that this gives the same results as the polygon method would by laying a card over Fig. 3-11 with one edge parallel to the vector W but not quite covering it; whether you put the card to the right or the left of the W vector the uncovered portion of the figure constitutes (except for one arrowhead) a vector addition by the polygon method.

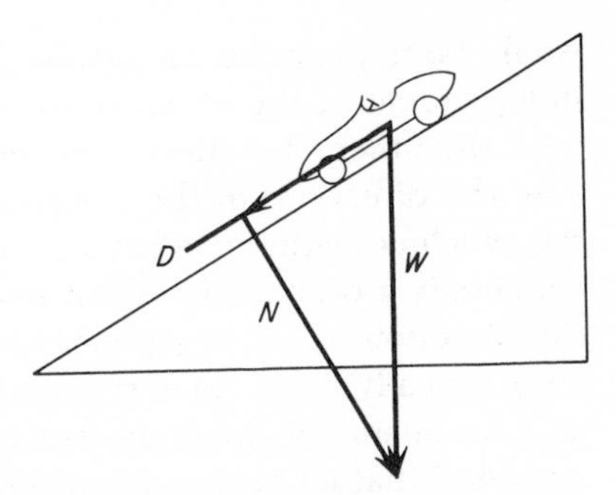

Fig. 3-12. The resolution of a vector quantity: polygon method.

The parallelogram method can be extended to the addition of more than two vectors, but only by using it in successive steps; hence the polygon method usually is much more convenient for vector addition. However, it may be more confusing for vector *resolution* than the parallelogram method. Figure 3-12 represents the resolution of W into D and N by the polygon method, and it necessarily shows the vector N appearing to act at a point far ahead of the car. Figure 3-11, on the other hand, shows both components applied *on* the car; so it seems more sensible. However, we have seen that Fig. 3-11 is exactly equivalent to Fig. 3-12 plus another polygon vector diagram in which the N vector is drawn first and the D vector next. Thus, you may find it a bit easier to understand at first if you use the parallelogram method for resolving vectors, but as soon as you "get the hang of it" you can save a little time by changing to the polygon method.

Trig

If the magnitude of a vector quantity is M and the angle between it and one of its components is α, the magnitude of that component is $M \cos \alpha$ and the magnitude of the other component, normal to the first, is $M \sin \alpha$.

3-9 Further Considerations of the Resolution of Vectors

In Sec. 3-8 we chose the component D parallel to the inclined roadway, since its sole function was to accelerate the car down the hill, and the component N at right angles to the pavement, so that its only effect would be to press the car against the roadway. Thus each component was independent of the other, in the sense that neither aided nor interfered with the other's function. This mutual independence must result whenever the directions of the components are mutually perpendicular, since this precludes either one having a component parallel with the other. Very commonly a problem in vector resolution will be like that example, and if the direction of one component is specified, the direction of the other is automatically fixed, since it must be normal to the first component. This also automatically limits the number of components to two in such cases, provided that all vector quantities and their components lie in the same plane, since any third component could not be independent of the other two. (We shall not extend our considerations into three dimensions, which would call for three mutually perpendicular components—for example, east, north, and up.)

But there are also problems of a nature such that the directions of the components are fixed. Consider, for example, Fig. 3-13(a). A 100 lb body is supported by wires attached to a beam, one of the wires having a direction 40° and the other 20° from the horizontal. The tensions in these two wires may be thought of as components of the vertical upward force of 100 lb required to support the body. Obviously these components are *not* mutually perpendicular; there is an angle of 120° between them.

In solving a problem of this sort, it is best to mark on a semipictorial diagram, like Fig. 3-13(a), the directions of the various forces. In the figure, this is done with dashed lines to distinguish these vectors from the geometrical aspects of the diagram; I strongly advise you to "code" such lines by using a different color or in some other obvious way. Next, these vectors are "pulled" off the original diagram and redrawn—still "coded"

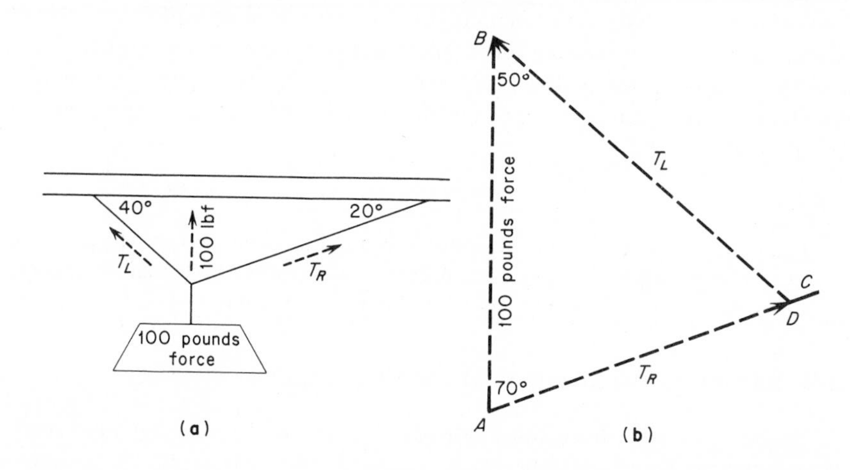

Fig. 3-13. The resolution of a vector into specified nonperpendicular directions.

—in their proper relative directions. Of the three, we know only the total supporting force in *both* magnitude *and* direction; so this should be drawn first. Since this represents the resultant of the two components, one of them must start at the tail of this vector and the other must end at its terminus. We may draw either the vector for the tension T_L in the left wire, or that for the tension T_R in the right wire, from the tail of the 100 lbf vector. If we choose the latter, we know that its direction is 20° from the horizontal, and this is 70° from the vertical; so we may draw it at this angle, to the right and upward toward *C*. Since we don't know its magnitude, we don't know from what point on it we should construct the vector for T_L. But we *do* know that the latter must terminate at the upper end of the 100 lbf vector, and that since its direction is 40° from the horizontal it must approach the vertical 100 lbf vector at an angle of 50°. Hence, from *A* in Fig. 3-13(b) we may construct a line of indefinite length in the known *direction* of T_R and we may construct another in the direction along which T_L must lie, ending at *B*. If we extend both lines far enough, they must intersect at some point *D*, and this fixes the magnitudes of *both* components. By applying the scale used in laying off the 100 lbf vector we find that $T_R = 109$ lbf and $T_L = 88.5$ lbf, approximately.

Trig

In the discussion above it was developed that in Fig. 3-13(b) the interior angles at *A* and *B* are 70° and 50°, respectively. This being the case, the only possible value for the other interior angle is 60°. Knowing only the magnitude of the side *AB*, we wish to find the magnitudes of the other two sides, T_R and T_L. The simplest method of finding them is furnished by the law of sines, which enables us to write

$$\frac{T_R}{\sin 50°} = \frac{T_L}{\sin 70°} = \frac{100}{\sin 60°}$$

Hence,

$$T_R = 100 \frac{\sin 50°}{\sin 60°}, \quad \text{and} \quad T_L = 100 \frac{\sin 70°}{\sin 60°}$$

3-10 Equilibrium of Concurrent Forces

The *con-* of concurrent is common in such words as *con*vention, *con*fluence, and *con*federation, in which it means "with" or "together." The *-current* is familiar as a complete word meaning a running or flowing of something. Thus ***concurrent forces*** are forces which "run together"; that is, their lines of action all pass through a common point. The three forces represented in Fig. 3-14(a) are concurrent, whereas the three in Fig. 3-14(b) are not. (Any *pair* in the latter figure are concurrent but the *system* is non-concurrent since there is no *common* intersection.)

It will be no surprise that the term ***equilibrium*** means a state of balance. This may seem quite definite, but actually it is ambiguous; a

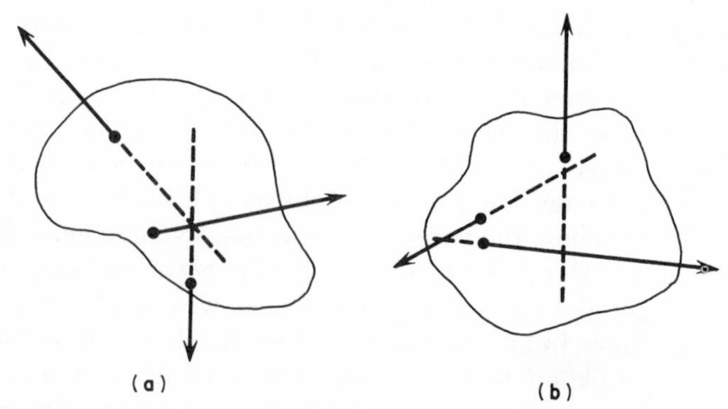

Fig. 3-14. (a) A system of concurrent forces; (b) A system of non-concurrent forces.

body or a system may be in equilibrium in one respect yet be unbalanced in a different sense. This means that the criterion for equilibrium for one type of motion is not the same as that for the other type. So long as we are dealing with forces as we have in this chapter, the effect of the force is a tendency to cause the body on which it acts to move from one location to another. Commonly this is motion in a straight line, but not necessarily; the essential thing is that there be no rotation at all. This type of motion is ***translation*** (literally, from the Latin roots, a *carrying across*). In Chapter 4 we shall meet a different situation, in which the body remains in one location while each point in the body (except those on the axis) describes a circular path about an axis. This type of motion is ***rotation.*** A body may experience either translational motion or rotational motion separately, or it may be subjected to both types simultaneously.

In Fig. 3-9 we found that a given set of forces has a resultant of about 3.75 lbf at 92°. This means that we could dispense with the original set of forces and use this resultant in their stead. To balance the resultant we would require an equal and opposite force, 3.75 lbf at 272°. But a set of forces must be balanced by that force which would balance their resultant.

Thus, any set of concurrent forces may be balanced with respect to translation by a single force; and this force must be equal in magnitude to their resultant, but opposite in direction. This balance force is the ***equilibrant.*** (Much to my displeasure, Webster requires that we accent the *-quil-* in e*quil*ibrant.)

In a vector diagram, evidently only the position of the arrowhead will tell us whether a given vector is a resultant or an equilibrant; *AD* in Fig. 3-9 is the resultant of the given set of forces but *DA* in Fig. 3-15 is the equilibrant of the same set. All that has been done is to reverse the final vector.

In general, when we have shown in a diagram each of the vectors involved, we draw the resultant from the origin of the initial vector to the terminus of the final vector; but in Fig. 3-15 there is no place to draw such a resultant, for the figure is already a closed polygon. Of course, we expected this, for if a system is in equilibrium—and Fig. 3-15 includes the equilibrant—the resultant of the forces in the system must be zero. Otherwise there would be a resultant force and this contraverts the concept of equilibrium.

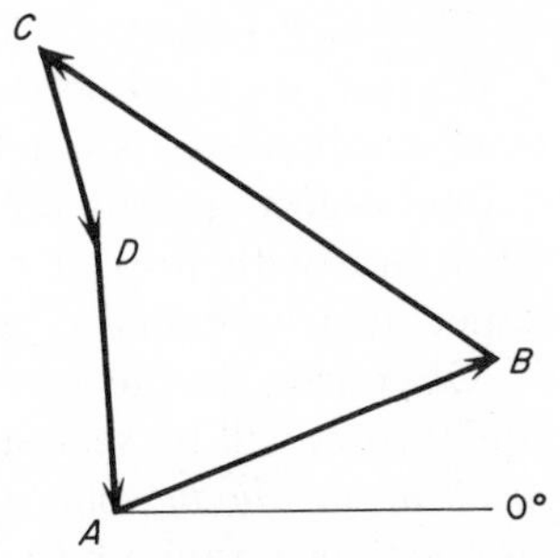

Fig. 3-15. The polygon method of finding the equilibrant of a system of forces. Compare with Fig. 3-9, in which the resultant of the same system of forces is determined.

Thus we may say that equilibrium with respect to translation exists when the vector sum of a set of forces is zero. In different words, such equilibrium must exist if the vector diagram of the set of forces is a closed figure. *If* in addition the system of forces is concurrent, it will also be in equilibrium with respect to rotation.

Before passing to the next topic, let's look again at Fig. 3-15 and recall that if we make a vector diagram of a set of forces, the single vector which will transform the diagram into a closed polygon represents the equilibrant of the system of forces. In our original consideration of Fig. 3-15, we had *AB*, *BC*, and *CD* given, and the equilibrant was *DA*, but note that *any* one of these four vectors could be considered to close the figure composed of the other three. Thus, in a system of forces in translational equilibrium, any one of the forces may be thought of as the equilibrant of a system composed of all the others.

3-11 Further Considerations of Equilibrium; Relativity of Motion

Our concept of translational equilibrium of a body on which a system of forces is acting boils down to this fact: insofar as its translation is concerned, the body acts exactly as if no force whatever were present. But we must not let inexperience in these matters trap us into thinking that this correlates equilibrium with lack of motion, or motion with lack of equilibrium. It is not motion, or the lack of it, which characterizes a body in translational equilibrium; rather, it is *constancy* of motion. This will be much more obvious after we have studied Chapter 5, but meantime let us examine the seemingly opposite expressions "motionless" and "moving with uniform velocity."

As you sit reading this book, are you motionless, in the sense of not moving bodily from one place to another? If your answer is "Yes," my reply is, "Well, *au revoir*. We'll see you again in about 365.25 days after the earth has completed another circuit around the sun at something like 11,000 mph. I hope you won't be lonesome there in space, in the meantime."

"But," you retort, "I mean that I'm motionless with respect to the earth."

To which I answer, "Yours is a very provincial point of view!"

In fact, we need not consider the earth's orbital motion to see that the term "motionless" is much less definite than we usually consider it to be. A "motionless" person on the Equator in Colombia has a speed of almost 1050 mph with respect to the earth's center, or almost 2100 mph with respect to a "motionless" person on the Equator in Borneo.

Of course, this necessarily means that a body which is in translational equilibrium will be seen as motionless by someone who is at rest *with respect to the body,* but it will be seen as being in uniform motion by another person who has a uniform velocity *with respect to the body.* In fact, one of the basic features of the theory of relativity is that it is quite meaningless to try to assign the adjective "motionless," in an absolute sense, to any point.

But people who may never have heard of Einstein are familiar with this *relative* nature of motion. A man in a jet airliner boring through the skies at several hundred miles per hour cannot sense the motion of the plane without looking out of the window. Sitting in a train or bus at a station, with another train or bus alongside, we immediately perceive relative motion when one of the conveyances begins to move, but we often misjudge *which* one has begun to move. Riding a train which passes another on a parallel track, we may be able to determine that our train is moving at, for example, 40 ft/sec with respect to the other. But, if we confine our observations to the other train, excluding all glimpses of the ground or the landscape, there's no way we can tell the velocity of either train with respect to the ground. Speeds of 70 and 30 mph, or 45 and 5, or 40 and 0, or 25 and -15, or any of an infinite number of combinations would make the relative speed 40 ft/sec.

Since all velocities are relative, their values are ambiguous unless the frame of reference is specified. But ordinarily we omit such specification without causing any confusion; for example, 30 mph north means something definite. But it is definite *only* because we automatically interpret this as the velocity relative to the surface of the earth at that point; hence there is no disagreement with the general situation that the value of a velocity has meaning *only* with respect to some stated or tacitly assumed frame of reference.

We shall meet this matter of the relative character of all motion many times. Since it may be an unfamiliar and a somewhat strange idea to you, you should be "on your toes" to avoid confusion.

Summary

A *scalar quantity* is completely determined by its *magnitude alone.* A *vector quantity* has *direction;* so its direction as well as its magnitude must be specified.

In general, *vector* quantities *cannot* be added or subtracted by *arithmetical* procedures. Either *graphical* or *trigonometric* methods must be employed. In the *polygon* method of vector addition, each quantity to be added is represented by an arrow of appropriate length and direction, each one being constructed from the tip of the one preceding. When all the vector quantities to be added have been so represented in the diagram, an arrow drawn from the origin of the first vector to the terminus of the last one will represent the *resultant.* If this final arrow is drawn between the same two points but in the opposite direction it will represent the *equilibrant.*

The resultant, or *vector sum,* of a system of forces is the single force which could replace the entire set and have the same effect (with respect to translation). The equilibrant would balance the entire set. The concept of resultant is applicable to vector quantities other than forces.

In physics, the 0° direction is horizontally to the right, and all angles are measured counterclockwise from this 0° direction.

Vector subtraction is carried out in the same way as vector addition, except that the direction is reversed for that vector which is being subtracted.

Resolution of vectors is the *opposite* of *vector addition;* a vector quantity is broken into components which have the original quantity as their resultant. Usually there are only two components, and commonly (though not always) the components are mutually perpendicular.

A system of forces is in equilibrium with respect to translation if its vector sum is zero. In this case a vector diagram of the system of forces will be a closed polygon.

All motion is relative.

Self-Quiz

1. Criticize this statement: A vector quantity is one in which both the magnitude and the direction are specified, and a scalar quantity is one in which the magnitude is specified but the direction is not.

2. To what extent are the two terms, "speed" and "velocity," similar, and to what extent are they dissimilar?

3. *Why* are arithmetical methods unsuitable for adding or subtracting vector quantities? May arithmetical methods *ever* be used for such purposes? Explain your answer.

4. Would it be possible for a system of three forces to be in equilibrium if their magnitudes were 22, 8, and 13 lb? Why?

5. Distinguish clearly between the term "vector" and the term "vector quantity."

6. Is the Pythagorean theorem generally applicable to the solution of vector problems, or does it apply only to special cases? Explain your answer.

7. Outline in some detail the polygon method of vector addition. Will this method always produce an open polygon?

8. Jim, Joe, and Jack work out the same problem in vector addition by the polygon method, but they use different scales. On Jim's scale, the various vectors range from 2 cm to 6 cm; Joe's scale makes them 5 cm to 15 cm long; in Jack's diagram, their lengths range from 8 cm to 24 cm. Each student uses a metric rule 15 cm long. Which diagram is likely to be most accurate, and why?

9. What convention is used in physics with regard to the interpretation of directions expressed in terms of degrees?

10. What is usually the most convenient order in which to construct the various vectors? Why? Is this the only order which will yield correct results? Why?

11. Vector A is at an angle of 15°. Vector B has an angle of 80° and is constructed from the tip of vector A. To determine its direction a protractor is placed with its base along vector A, the center of the protractor being at the tip of A. What angle should be laid off? If vector C, at 145°, is constructed at the end of vector B, should the angle laid off on the protractor be 145°, or 145° − 80°, or 145° − 80° − 15°? Why?

12. Using the polygon method, a student constructs a diagram to represent the forces acting on a body. He finds that when he constructs the last vector its terminus is at the origin of the initial vector. How is this situation to be interpreted, and why?

13. What modification of the graphical method of vector addition must be made for the subtraction of vectors?

14. What is meant by a "component" of a vector quantity? Is there any limit to the number of components, or the directions of the components, into which a vector quantity may be resolved?

15. In a practical situation, into how many components is a vector quantity resolved? In many cases the two components are taken in mutually perpendicular directions. Why? Are the two components *always* taken at right angles to each other? Explain fully.

16. In Fig. 3-12, a gravitational force is resolved into a component parallel with the slope of a roadway and a component perpendicular to the roadway. Such components can be made use of in computing the acceleration of the car down the hill or the frictional force along the pavement, etc. Does all this mean that these components represent actual forces? That is, does the weight of the car actually act in these directions? If these components aren't "real" forces, how can we get useful results by using them in computations?

17. What is the resultant of the components of any vector quantity?

18. State the condition necessary for equilibrium with respect to translation. For a system to be in equilibrium, need it be motionless?

19. Jones states that to keep a car moving along a level highway at a constant speed the driving force must slightly exceed the total of the resisting forces, but

Johns claims it is only necessary that the driving force equal the total resisting force. Which is correct? Check your answer with your response to Question 18. Was your initial response correct, or did you have to change it to agree with what you answered to the preceding question?

20. Except in a relative sense, does the term "motionless" have any real meaning?

21. It is much easier to back up and pull a loaded wheelbarrow over a low curb than to push it over the curb. Why?

Problems

1. A boy walks 3 blocks east, 5 blocks south, 2 blocks east, 2 blocks north, and 1 block west. How far is he from his starting point? (Assume that the blocks are all the same length.) What is his direction from the starting point?

2. A plane is headed due west, its airspeed being 120 mph. If there is a wind blowing at 30 mph in a direction 30° south of west, what is the velocity of the plane with respect to the ground?

3. Three puppies get their teeth into the same rug. If at a particular instant one is pulling at 0° with a force of 3.8 lb, another at 220° with a force of 3.0 lb, and the third at 130° with a force of 2.5 lb, determine the resultant force.

4. Each of two pith balls has a weight of 2.0 g. They are suspended by light threads of equal length from a common point, but because of electric charges on them they do not hang vertically below the support; instead the two threads form an inverted V with an angle of 40° between them. What is the magnitude of the force between the two charged balls?

5. A 150 lb man carelessly steps with a wet, soapy foot onto a place in a bathtub where the surface is inclined 10° from the horizontal. With how great a force does his foot tend to slip? (Assume that all his weight is on that foot, and disregard any forces not due to his weight.)

6. A car gets stalled in mud. In an attempt to pull it out, the driver takes a rope and ties one end to the car and the other to a tree 100 ft ahead of the car. He then grasps the rope at a point midway of its length and pulls it 3.0 ft sideways with a force of 80 lb. How great a force will this exert on the car?

7. A loaded wheelbarrow with a total weight of 250 lb is being pushed up a ramp which rises exactly 1 ft for each 5 ft of distance along the ramp. Disregarding frictional effects, how much force must be applied parallel with the incline to keep the wheelbarrow from rolling back or to move it at a uniform rate?

8. A rope is 40 ft long and has a breaking strength of 250 lb. It is fastened at its ends to rigid supports which are at the same elevation, and a weight is hung from its midpoint. If the center point of the rope is exactly 8 ft below its ends, what is the maximum magnitude the weight can have without breaking the rope? (Disregard any effects due to stretching.)

9. A man rows directly across a stream 500 ft wide. He rows 250 ft/min so if there were no current he could row directly across the stream in 2.00 min. Because of the current, however, he actually crosses in 2.50 min. (a) On the (unrealistic) assumption that the speed of the current is the same throughout the width of the stream, determine its speed. (b) At what angle to the bank must he head the boat?

10. A ferry travels directly across a river 3600 ft wide in exactly 4 min. If the average speed of the current is 9.0 ft/sec, what is the velocity of the ferryboat with respect to the water?

4

MOMENTS

4-1 Preview

In Chapter 3, among other things we considered forces and the equilibrium of forces with respect to translation. In this chapter, we shall turn our attention to the tendency of a force to produce rotation. This will lead to the concept of equilibrium with respect to rotation and the criterion for rotational equilibrium. Many common applications of these ideas, strangely, do not involve any actual rotation whatever; in fact, these are among the most interesting and useful applications of rotational equilibrium.

4-2 Moment of a Force

Long before you ever heard of the science of physics, you participated in a physics experiment and learned a principle you still know well. The experimental equipment was a "teeter-totter." An older person placed you on one end of the teeter-totter, warned you to hold on, and went to the other end to push down and elevate you delightfully. But he probably didn't use his whole weight, or if he did, he applied it relatively close to the pivot or fulcrum. After further pleasant experimentation you came to realize that persons of greatly different weights could balance each other *if* the lighter person sat relatively near the end of the teeter-totter while the heavier person sat comparatively close to the fulcrum.

Thus you learned that the effectiveness of a force in causing a tilt of the teeter-totter is *not* determined *solely* by the magnitude of the force; it depends also on how far the force is applied from the fulcrum. An increase in either of these factors produces an increase in the turning effect.

These qualitative considerations underlie the quantitative concept of moment or torque. The ***moment*** of a force, also called the ***torque,*** is the measure of the tendency of a force to cause rotation about some axis. For the present, we may consider its value to be determined by the magnitude of the force times the distance of the force from the axis or fulcrum, though toward the end of this section we shall add some essential restrictions.

In Fig. 4-1(a) we have a very artistic representation of a mother initiating her child into the delights of the teeter-totter. Figure 4-1(b) ignores the esthetic features of Fig. 4-1(a) and emphasizes the physically significant factors. The child's weight F_c is applied at a distance d_c from the fulcrum while the mother applies a force F_m at a distance d_m. Using the symbol M to represent moment and employing the same subscripts to distinguish between child and mother, we have

$$M_c = F_c \cdot d_c, \quad \text{and} \quad M_m = F_m \cdot d_m$$

Thus far I have deliberately avoided cluttering the discussion with restrictions, or with a definition of the term "fulcrum." A ***fulcrum*** is a support or pivot about which tilting or rotation may occur. In Fig. 4-1,

Fig. 4-1. A "teeter-totter," and the conventional representation of pertinent physical factors.

the fulcrum is at the center of the teeter-totter, but teeter-totters are often made so that the plank can be shifted, thus causing it to tilt about a point which is *not* at its center. Thus the expression "tendency of a force to cause rotation about some axis" is indefinite until we specifically state the particular axis about which the rotation is to occur. Obviously the moments of all the forces acting on a given body must be considered about the *same* "particular axis."

Now consider Fig. 4-2(a). This differs from Fig. 4-1(b) in that although the forces are still vertical the plank is now tilted, and because of this tilt, the moments of the force are reduced. If this is not obvious, imagine the plank tilted to the vertical; then a vertical force on it would have *no* tendency to cause rotation of the plank, though it would tend to produce translation. A force has a maximum tendency to produce rotation when it is at right angles to the plank.

Since the moment M_c is less than before, we cannot multiply F_c by a distance OA measured along the plank, as before; instead we must use the *component* of OA which is *at right angles* to the line of action of the force F_c. Thus the moment M_c is the product of F_c and the distance OB, and the moment M_m is the product of F_m and the distance OD.

Suppose that the mother, lacking a Ph.D. in physics, applies an oblique force to the horizontal plank of the teeter-totter as in Fig. 4-2(b); again the effectiveness of the force in producing rotation is curtailed. The torque is the product of the force F_m and the component OB of the distance OA. Thus we must modify our initial definition and state that ***moment*** or ***torque*** about any axis or point is the measure of the tendency of a force to produce rotation *about that axis or point.* Its value is the product of the magnitude of the force and the *perpendicular* distance between the center of rotation and the line of action of the force. This distance factor is the ***moment arm*** of the force.

The requirement that the directions of the force and the moment arm must be mutually perpendicular may be included in an algebraic equation by adding arrows to the symbols:

$$M = \overrightarrow{F} \cdot d\downarrow \tag{4-1}$$

However, there is no necessary significance in the particular direction of

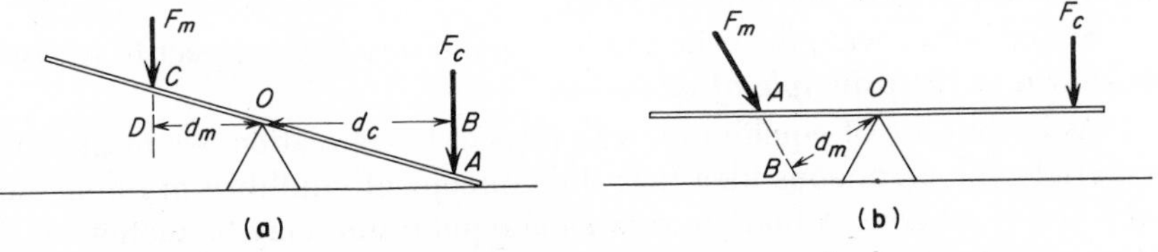

Fig. 4-2. When the direction of a force is not perpendicular to a lever the moment arm can not be measured along the lever.

either arrow *alone;* the essential thing is that the two arrows be mutually at right angles.

We shall meet in Chapter 6 another and entirely different physical concept which is a product of a force and a distance, but in that case the directions must be *parallel* rather than perpendicular. A habit of including arrows in your equations for torque or for this other quantity will circumvent confusion which might otherwise arise.

If you refer again to Fig. 4-2(a) and Fig. 4-2(b), and to the discussion of them, you will realize that it is quite possible and proper to resolve the force rather than the moment arm and multiply the full distance by the component of the force perpendicular to the distance. However, the procedure given (using the full value of the force and the appropriate component of the distance) is often more convenient.

Trig

If the magnitude of the force is F, and if a line from the center of moments to the point of application of the force has a length d and makes an angle θ with the direction of the force, the value of the torque is $Fd \sin \theta$.

4-3 Equilibrium with Respect to Rotation

Obviously, a body cannot be in rotational equilibrium if there exists any *net* or *resultant* tendency for it to rotate. Since a moment is the measure of the tendency to cause rotation, rotational equilibrium will exist if, and only if, the total moment or torque tending to produce rotation in one direction about a given axis is compensated by an equal moment or torque tending to cause rotation in the opposite sense about that same axis.

A torque which tends to cause rotation in the direction followed by the hands of a clock is described as ***clockwise,*** and a ***counterclockwise*** moment tends to cause the opposite direction of rotation. Thus the criterion for rotational equilibrium is that the total clockwise moment about a particular axis must equal the total counterclockwise moment about the same axis. Alternatively, we may assign positive values to counterclockwise torques and negative values to those which are clockwise; then equilibrium with respect to rotation must exist if the algebraic sum of all the torques about a given axis is zero. These two criteria may sound different, but they are fully equivalent and equally valid.

Stated either way, the criterion for equilibrium with respect to rotation is known as the ***principle of moments.***

As in the case of equilibrium with respect to translation, we must avoid carefully the erroneous idea that the concept of equilibrium implies an *absence* of motion. A body in rotational equilibrium may be motionless *or* it may be rotating at a constant rate. It is the *constancy* of motion, rather than *absence* of motion, that characterizes a condition of equilibrium.

4-4 Center of Moments

Thus far, our discussion has been in terms of bodies which have an actual physical fulcrum. Though our definitions and our criteria for equilibrium may have *implied* the existence of a physical fulcrum, they are *not* in fact restricted to such a situation. The principle of moments is as valid with respect to any arbitrarily chosen hypothetical center of rotation as it is with respect to an actual physical fulcrum. This makes it extremely useful in some situations which offer no possibility of rotation.

Any point about which we consider the torques to act, and from which we choose to measure the moment arms of the forces, is a ***center of moments.*** This *may* be an actual physical fulcrum, but it *need* not be; it may be chosen quite arbitrarily, even quite outside the physical boundaries of the body, and there may be no possibility of actual rotation.

This doesn't seem reasonable, but I'll try to convince you. In Fig. 4-3(a) three boys are riding on a rail suspended at its midpoint by a rope. We shall assume that the rail would be balanced without the boys on it; this will enable us to ignore its weight, for reasons which will appear in Sec. 4-5. The boy at the left weighs 100 lb and is 6.00 ft from the rope.* On the

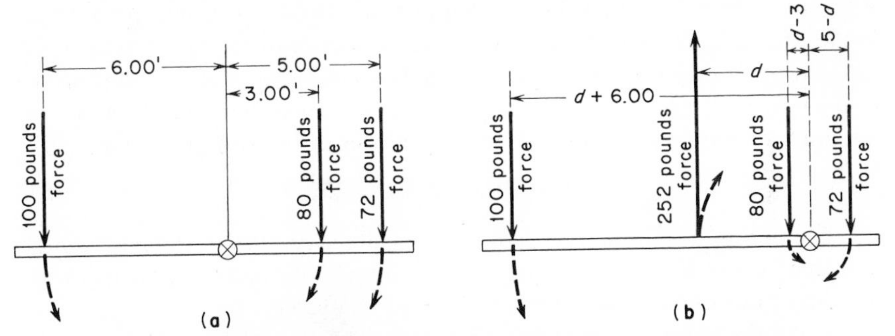

Fig. 4-3. (a) The conventional representation of forces, of the directions of their moments, and of the center of moments; (b) The same system of forces as in part (a) but with the center of moments near the right end of the lever.

---

* An expression such as "100 lb" may seem to violate a promise made earlier, and to be inadequate in another respect. You were promised in Sec. 2-2 that any possible ambiguity in the meaning of such an expression would be prevented by specifying either "pounds force" or "pounds mass." And in Sec. 3-2 you learned that some quantities are ambiguous unless the direction as well as the magnitude is specified. However, the weight of a body is the *force* of the gravitational attraction between the body and the earth; hence an expression such as "a weight of 100 lb force" would be redundant. Also, the weight of any body acts vertically downward, so there can be no uncertainty about the direction of the force even though the direction is not explicitly stated. Explicit specification that a unit refers to force or to mass, or explicit specification of direction, or both, will be omitted in all cases such as this, where the context removes all possible ambiguity.

right are an 80.0 lb boy at 3.00 ft from the rope and a 72.0 lb lad 5.00 ft from the rope. Obviously the point of attachment of the rope is equivalent to a fulcrum, so it may be taken as the center of moments. Then the weight of the boy on the left will cause a counterclockwise moment, and clockwise torques will be produced by the weights of the two on the right:

Counterclockwise	*Clockwise*
$100 \cdot 6.00 = 600$	$80.0 \cdot 3.00 = 240$
	$72.0 \cdot 5.00 = 360$
600	600

Thus the total clockwise moment about the fulcrum is equal to the total counterclockwise moment about the same point, so the system is in equilibrium with respect to rotation.

Now let us choose a different center of moments and see what happens. To make the situation as general as we conveniently can, we shall choose a center of moments at an unspecified point between the two boys on the right, and call the distance between the rope and this center of moments d. This center of moments is indicated in Fig. 4-3(b) by the conventional symbol $\otimes$. We find that we now have four torques instead of the three we had before. Previously the supporting force of the rope had no moment, since its moment arm was zero, but its moment arm is now d. To find the magnitude of this force we may invoke the criterion for translational equilibrium: all forces are vertical, so the total downward force must be equal to the upward force, and the tension in the rope must be

$$(100 + 80 + 72) \text{ lb} = 252 \text{ lb}$$

The moment of the force in the rope is clockwise about the new center, and that of the 80.0 lb boy is now counterclockwise rather than clockwise; the directions of the other two torques are unaltered.

All of the moment arms are changed. The boy at the left is at a distance of $(d + 6.00)$ ft from the new center of moments. The 80.0 lb boy has a moment arm of $(d - 3.00)$ ft, and the 72.0 lb boy's moment arm is $(5.00 - d)$ ft. The moment arm of the rope is d ft. Thus the torques of the various forces about the new center of moments are:

Counterclockwise	*Clockwise*
$100 \cdot (d + 6.00) = 100d + 600$	$252 \cdot d = 252d$
$80.0 \cdot (d - 3.00) = 80d - 240$	$72.0 \cdot (5.00 - d) = 360 - 72d$
$180d + 360$	$360 + 180d$

So again the total clockwise moment equals the total counterclockwise moment, even though the moments were computed about a purely hypothetical center of rotation. If you are not "comfortable" with an algebraic demonstration of this sort, go back and assign a definite value (such as 4.00 ft) to d, find the new value of each moment arm, and carry the computations through.

I do not present this as a mathematical exercise, but as proof that we may choose a center of moments quite arbitrarily at whatever point is most convenient, for this provides a very powerful tool to use in the solution of many problems which would be far more difficult on any other basis.

4-5 Center of Gravity

Every physical body has weight, unless located where there is no gravitational field. We may think of the body as being composed of a large number of small parts, each of which has its own weight, the weight of the body being the sum of the weights of all its parts.

If we take any rigid body we can discover by any of several means a point at which it will balance perfectly, or a point at which it would balance if a supporting force could be applied precisely there. Undoubtedly you have often found such a point by balancing some relatively long and slender body, such as a broom or a yardstick, across your finger.

Suppose we consider such a body to be balanced on a finger as in Fig. 4-4. Imagine the body to be divided into very thin sections as shown, the various individual sections having weights of w_1, w_2, w_3, etc., commencing at the left. A center of moments is chosen (arbitrarily) at the right end of the body, and the distances of the separate sections from this center are d_1, d_2, d_3, etc., respectively. Thus their moments about this center are m_1d_1, m_2d_2, m_3d_3, etc. By making the sections thin enough (with the methods of the calculus we could make them infinitesimally thin), we can eliminate the error which would creep in if the various portions of a single section were at appreciably different distances from the center of moments.

Since the body is in rotational equilibrium, the total counterclockwise moment of all these sections is equal to the clockwise moment of the supporting force F acting at a moment arm d_F; that is,

$$\begin{aligned} &\textit{Counterclockwise} &&= \textit{Clockwise} \\ &w_1d_1 + w_2d_2 + w_3d_3 + \cdots &&= F \cdot d_F \end{aligned}$$

But the body is also in translational equilibrium. Since all the forces are vertical, the total upward force must equal the total downward force:

$$\begin{aligned} &\textit{Upward} = &&\textit{Downward} \\ &F &&= w_1 + w_2 + w_3 + \cdots \end{aligned}$$

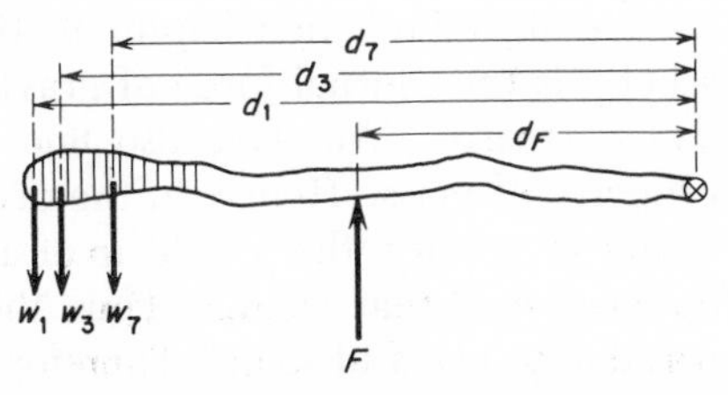

Fig. 4-4. The development of the concept of center of gravity.

For the moment imagine that we can "turn off" all the weights of the individual sections and replace them

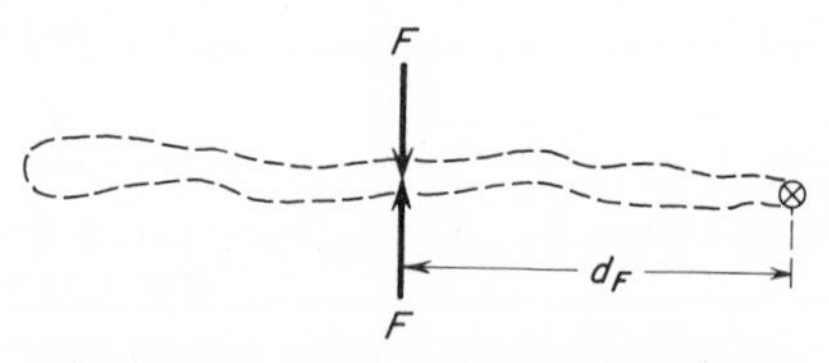

Fig. 4-5. The weight of a body *acts as if* it were all concentrated at the center of gravity.

with a single downward force equal to F; translational equilibrium will still exist, since the only forces are a force F upward and an *equal* force F downward. Rotational equilibrium will also be preserved *if* the moments of the two forces are equal. Since the forces themselves are equal, this requires that their moment arms be equal. Thus removal of all the weights of the separate parts of the body will not disturb the equilibrium of the body *if* a single force equal to the body's weight is applied downward at the balance point. Figure 4-5 represents the body of the previous figure "phantomized," with its entire weight acting at a single point and the supporting force acting at the same point. The two forces are equal and opposite and have identical moment arms; hence equilibrium exists.

Thus, *for some purposes* we may *consider* the entire weight of a body to be concentrated at one particular point. This point is called the ***center of gravity*** of the body. We can't *actually* annihilate the weights of the parts of the body, as we imagined in the preceding paragraph, and replace them with a single force; but *for some purposes*, the effect is exactly as if we could. The solution of certain problems is greatly simplified by the assumption that the entire weight of a body acts at its center of gravity, even though the weight never *is* concentrated at a point.

If you toss a body into the air with a spin, it will rotate about its center of gravity. Where, then, is the center of gravity of a tennis ball? It is at the geometric center of the *hollow* ball. The only weight *actually* there is due to a few molecules of gas, yet the ball acts *as if* its entire weight were concentrated there. What about the center of gravity of an ordinary dining chair, or that of a laboratory stool? In each case the center of gravity is in thin air, completely outside the boundaries of the material of which the chair or stool is made. If these strange things surprise you, they shouldn't; for I have emphasized that the center of gravity is an entirely *artificial* (though very useful) concept and that the weight is not *actually* concentrated at the center of gravity.

We shall find, in Chapter 9, that what we know as the weight of a body is the mutual force of gravitational attraction between the body and the earth. We shall also find that this gravitational attraction is a property of mass. Hence, in the discussion which led to the concept of a center of gravity, the weight w of any small section (Fig. 4-4) was due to the mass m of that section. Thus, the weight w_1 was due to a mass m_1, w_2 was due to m_2, and so on. Therefore, we could apply to the masses of the individual sections the same logic we applied to their weights when we were developing the concept of the center of gravity; in this case the concept of a center of mass emerges. Thus, the ***center of mass*** of a body is that point at which, *for some purposes,* we may *consider* the entire mass of the body to be concentrated. Like the idea of center of gravity, this concept of center of mass is wholly hypothetical, but still very useful.

This convenient trick of thinking of the mass and weight of a body as if they were concentrated at a single point may turn around and trick you, if you let yourself interpret the concept of center of gravity too literally. We shall see in Chapter 9 that the mass of every body in the universe attracts and is attracted by the mass of every other body. The law governing such forces includes an inverse proportionality between the size of the force and the square of the distance between the two masses, and in many instances the effective distance is that between the centers of gravity of the bodies.

Consider, then, the force of attraction between two horseshoes. The center of gravity of a horseshoe is out in the space between its two arms. Thus it is quite possible to arrange two horseshoes somewhat as in Fig. 4-6, so that their centers of gravity coincide. This makes the distance zero, and since the force is *inversely* proportional to the square of the distance, the force must be infinite; it would be quite impossible to separate the horseshoes by any means. Yet this isn't true; even a baby could easily pull them apart. Somewhere our argument went "off the beam." Where?

I hope you spotted the fallacy. True, the distance between the *centers of gravity* is zero, but *no* bit of *mass* in either horseshoe is at zero distance from any bit of *mass* in the other. The center of gravity is a useful concept, but there is *no* mass there. Thus in the case of irregularly shaped objects like this, the effective distance can *not* be measured between the centers of gravity.

4-6 Choice of the Center of Moments, and Application to Problems

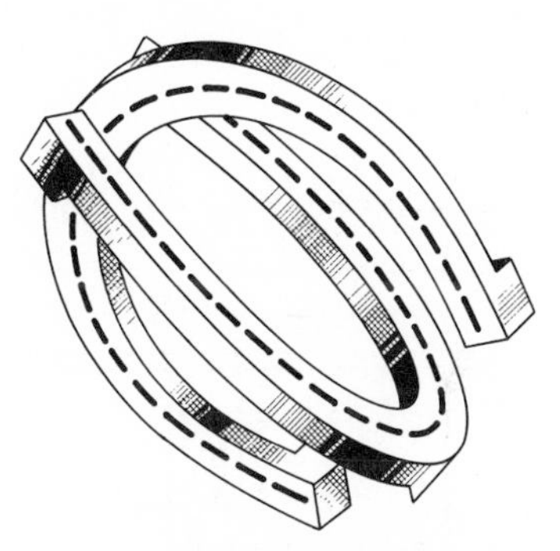

Fig. 4-6. The center of gravity of a body may be outside the physical boundaries of the body; it is even possible for the centers of gravity of two bodies to coincide.

There are tricks in all trades and there is a very useful trick in the use of the principle of moments to solve problems. Often it is necessary to find the magnitudes of *two* unknown forces. This can be done by setting up two independent equations and solving them simultaneously, but there is a much more convenient way. Since we are dealing with moments, we need only recall that if the moment *arm* of a force is zero, the *moment* is also zero (since the moment is the force times the moment arm). Thus we may choose the point of application of one of the unknown forces as the center of moments; this eliminates that force from the equation, leaving only one unknown. We then have a choice of two methods of finding the value of the other force: we may use the principle of moments, taking the center of moments anywhere *except* at the point of application of the unknown force, or we may invoke the criterion for *translational* equilibrium. Use of *both* methods will provide a check on the entire problem.

One must be very careful to avoid misinterpretation of this business of tossing out an unknown force by taking the center of moments at its point of application. *The force is still there.* Its *moment* has been set equal to zero by the choice of the center of moments, but the *force* is not removed or nullified. It must still be considered in any moments equation about any other center, and it must be taken into account in applying the criterion for translational equilibrium.

Sample Problem 1

Mike and Ike are carrying a 100 lb deer on a pole. The deer's center of gravity is 6.00 ft back of Mike's shoulder and 4.00 ft in front of Ike's. The pole weighs 20.0 lb, and its center of gravity is 4.50 ft from Mike's shoulder. How large a supporting force must each man provide?

A diagram will have the twofold virtue of suggesting a method of solution and minimizing the chance of confusion or error. Figure 4-7(a) shows the general setup, F_M and F_I being the forces which must be provided by Mike and by Ike, respectively. Though we may take a center of moments anywhere, taking it at the shoulder of one of the men—either one—will make the moment of one unknown force zero. Arbitrarily choosing Mike's shoulder, we mark the symbol for the center of moments on the diagram as in Figure 4-7(b). Especially on the first few problems, it is *very* important to show the center of moments clearly on the diagram. The next and very important step is to show on the diagram the direc-

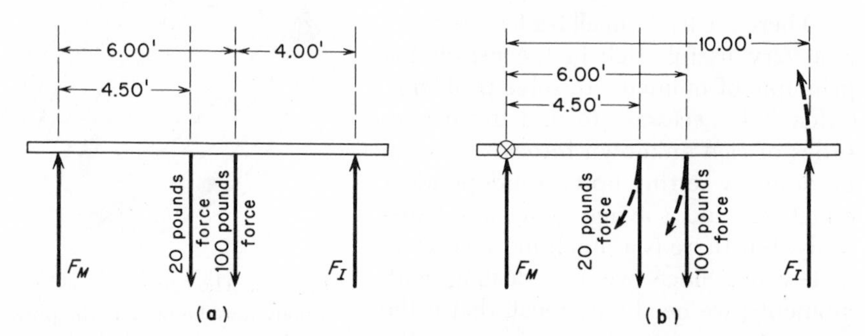

Fig. 4-7. (a) The forces acting on the pole in Sample Problem 1; (b) The torques of the forces about the point where the force F_M is applied.

tion of rotation each force would tend to cause *about the chosen center,* by arcs with arrowheads. In your diagrams, it will be helpful to "code" the lines by using one color for geometrical lines, another color for forces, and a third for the arcs.

Since the force F_M acts at the center of moments, its moment is zero. If the loaded pole is to remain in rotational equilibrium, the total clockwise torque about the center of moments must equal the total counter-clockwise moment about the same center. Thus,

$$\begin{aligned} \textit{Clockwise} &= \textit{Counterclockwise} \\ 20.0 \cdot 4.50 + 100 \cdot 6.00 &= F_I \cdot 10.0 \\ 90.0 + 600 &= 10.0\,F_I = 690 \\ F_I = 690/10.0 &= 69.0 \text{ lb} \end{aligned}$$

so Ike's share of the load is 69.0 lb force.

There is an infinite number of methods by which we can find the other unknown force, but the easiest by far is to note that the loaded pole is in translational equilibrium—it isn't being projected into the upper air nor is it dropping to the ground. Hence,

$$\begin{aligned} \textit{Total Upward Force} &= \textit{Total Downward Force} \\ F_M + 69.0 &= 20.0 + 100 \\ F_M &= 120 - 69 = 51 \text{ lbf} \end{aligned}$$

The next best method of solving for F_M is to set up another moments equation, taking the center of moments at Ike's shoulder. Figure 4-8 illustrates this situation and enables us to write

$$\begin{aligned} \textit{Clockwise} &= \textit{Counterclockwise} \\ F_M \cdot 10.0 &= 20.0 \cdot 5.50 + 100 \cdot 4.00 \\ 10.0F_M &= 110 + 400 \\ F_M &= 510/10.0 = 51.0 \text{ lbf} \end{aligned}$$

which checks with the value obtained by the other method.

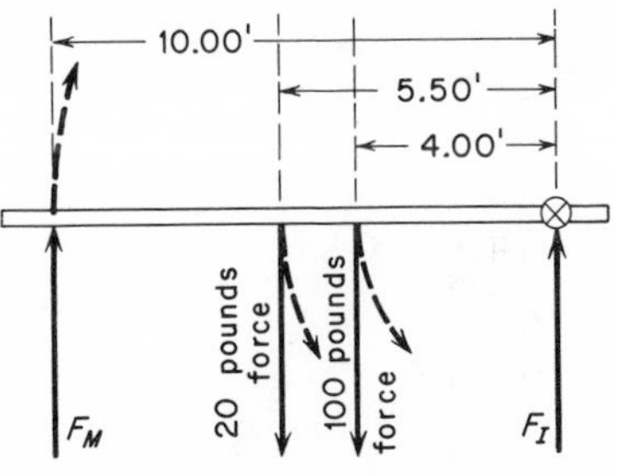

Fig. 4-8. The same system as in Fig. 4-7, but with the center of moments at the point at which the force F_I acts.

Sample Problem 2

A uniform ladder weighs 80.0 lb and is 26.0 ft long. The foot of the ladder is on level ground 10.0 ft from the side of a tall building, its upper end resting against the smooth vertical wall. A man who weighs 150 lb stands on the ladder 20.0 ft from its foot. With how great a force does the ladder press against the wall?

First we must observe conventional interpretations of two key words in the statement of the problem. "Uniform" in this sense means that we may consider the center of gravity of the ladder to be at its midpoint. "Smooth" means frictionless; forces acting against a smooth surface can only have a direction normal to the surface.

Again a diagram is the place to start. Next we must choose a center of moments. There is little choice here, for the force of the ground on the foot of the ladder is unknown *both* in magnitude and in direction. Thus we may construct a diagram like Fig. 4-9(a) showing the various forces and the directions of the resulting torques. Note, however, that the diagram does *not* include the force we must find, the force W of the ladder against the wall. It shows instead the force of the wall against the ladder. Why?

We can solve a problem which deals with the rotational equilibrium of a body by considering the moments of all forces *acting on* a body, or by taking into account the moments of all forces *exerted by* the body; but we'll get nowhere (except into a morass of confusion and frustration) if we *mix* moments of forces acting *on* the body with those of forces exerted *by* the body. Note that if the figure showed the force of the ladder against the wall *all* moments would be counterclockwise.

Recall that the value of a torque is the product of the magnitude of a force and its *perpendicular* distance from the center of moments. We can't use any of the distances specified as moment arms. The moment arms of the vertical forces are found with the aid of Fig. 4-9(b), in which the *direction lines* of these forces are projected downward to the ground level so that the moment arms may be measured at right angles to the direction lines. There are three similar right

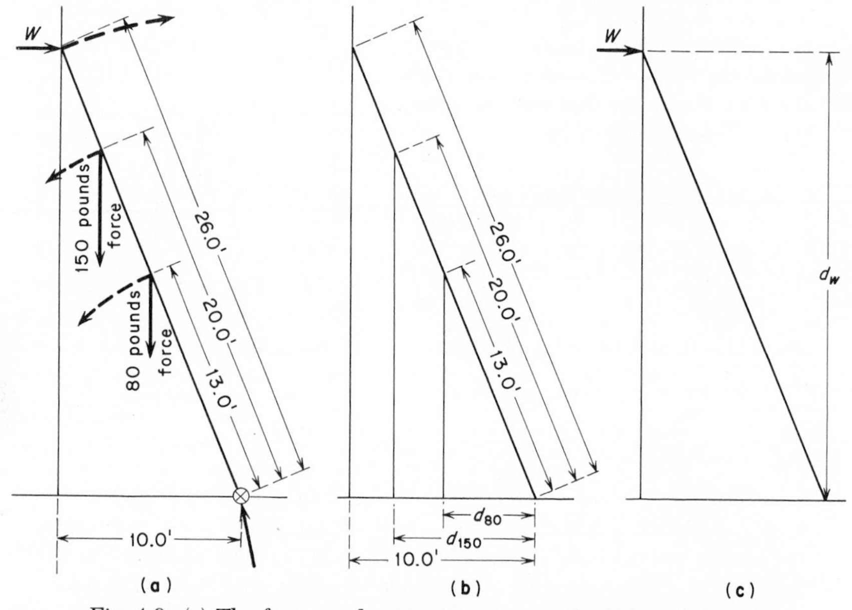

Fig. 4-9. (a) The forces and moments acting on the ladder in Sample Problem 2, with the center of moments at the foot of the ladder; (b) The means of determining the moment arms of the vertical forces; (c) The means of determining the moment arms of the horizontal force.

triangles in this figure so we may use the fact that corresponding sides of similar triangles stand in the same ratio to each other to compute the moment arms:

$$\frac{d_{80}}{10.0} = \frac{13.0}{26.0}, \quad \text{and} \quad \frac{d_{150}}{10.0} = \frac{20.0}{26.0}$$

From these equations we compute that

$$d_{80} = 5.00 \text{ ft}, \quad \text{and} \quad d_{150} = 7.69\bar{2} \text{ ft}$$

Since the wall is smooth, its force against the ladder must be horizontal and hence its moment arm must be vertical. As shown in Fig. 4-9(c), this makes the moment arm of this force equal to the height of the wall to the point where the ladder touches. Since the ground, the wall, and the ladder form a right triangle, we can call on Pythagoras:

$$d_W{}^2 + 10.0^2 = 26.0^2$$

A solution of this equation gives 24.0 ft as the value of the moment arm. We are now ready (finally) to set up the equation for equilibrium with respect to rotation:

$$\begin{aligned} \textit{Clockwise} &= \textit{Counterclockwise} \\ W \cdot 24.0 &= 80.0 \cdot 5.00 + 150 \cdot 7.69\bar{2} \\ 24.0W &= 400 + 115\bar{4} = 155\bar{4} \\ W &= 155\bar{4}/24.0 = 64.7 \end{aligned}$$

Thus we know that the wall pushes against the ladder with a force of 64.7 lb, and if there is to be translational equilibrium, the ladder must push back with an equal force. So the final answer is a force of 64.7 lb acting horizontally to the left in Fig. 4-9.

Trig

If the angle θ between the ground and the ladder is given, the moment of a vertical force F which is applied to the ladder a distance d from its foot is $Fd \cos \theta$. If the length of the ladder is L the moment of the force F' exerted against it by a smooth wall is $F'L \sin \theta$. In the sample problem above the value of θ is not given but it can be deduced from the fact that $\cos \theta = 10.0/26.0$.

4-7 Conditions for the Complete Equilibrium of a Body

There is nothing new in this section; it is included to summarize and *emphasize* some essential facts in this chapter and the one preceding. Each of these chapters contributed a criterion for one kind of equilibrium—translational equilibrium in Chapter 3 and rotational equilibrium in this chapter.

The complete equiiibrium of a body requires that both criteria be met. The vector sum of all the forces acting on the body must be zero, *and* the total of the clockwise moments about any center must be equal to the sum of the counterclockwise torques about the same center.

Not infrequently a student is "stuck" on a moments problem because there just do not seem to be sufficient data—and there may *not* be enough to complete the solution on the basis of moments—but application of the criterion for translational equilibrium often will provide the missing link and enable the student to finish the solution without trouble.

Summary

The *measure* of the *tendency* of a *force* to *produce rotation* about any *particular point* is known as the *moment* of the force about that point. Its value depends on the moment arm as well as on the magnitude of the force, being in fact the product of these two quantities. The *moment arm* is the perpendicular distance from the center of moments to the line of action of the force.

If a system of two or more moments acts on a body, equilibrium with respect to rotation will exist if the sum of all the clockwise moments about any given point is equal to the sum of all the counterclockwise moments about the same point. This criterion for rotational equilibrium is the principle of moments.

The concept of moments, and the principle of moments, are not limited to situations in which rotational motion does, or may, occur; it is very useful in many cases which involve no possibility of rotation.

A center of moments may be chosen arbitrarily at any convenient location. The center of moments may be an actual fulcrum or axis of rotation, but very commonly it is not; there need be no rotation, and the center of moments need not be within the geometrical boundaries of the body on which the forces act.

In any situation such that two unknown forces or their moments are involved, it is convenient to choose as the center of moments the point of application of one of these unknown forces.

The *center of gravity* of a body is that point at which one may consider that the entire weight of the body could be concentrated without causing any error in any moments problem or in some other types of problems.

Many problems, of which "ladder problems" are typical, require care to avoid using incorrect moment arms; *all* moment arms *must* be measured *at right angles to* the lines of action of the corresponding forces. The effective moment arms can be calculated by making use of the fact that corresponding parts of similar triangles are directly proportional.

An excellent way to "foul up" a moments problem is to mix moments of forces exerted *by* the body with those of forces acting *on* the body.

The complete equilibrium of a body requires that the conditions requisite to translational equilibrium *and* those necessary for rotational equilibrium be met.

Self-Quiz

1. In what sense may a force of 1 lb balance a force of 100 lb? Describe a simple physical setup with which this could be accomplished. What can you say about any dimensions in this setup?

2. The physical effect of a force acting on a body is (insofar as motion is concerned) to tend to produce linear motion of the body. What is the analogous physical effect of a moment acting on a body?

3. State the principle of moments. (The principle of moments is *not* the *method* of *computing* a moment.)

4. Show that the principle of moments is an obvious and necessary consequence of your answer to Question 2.

5. Define the terms "fulcrum" and "center of moments." Point out clearly any similarities and any differences.

6. Consider the statement: "For equilibrium with respect to rotation, the total clockwise moment must be equal to the total counterclockwise moment." This statement may appear at first glance to be correct, but it is not. What is wrong with it? Why is it incorrect as stated?

7. What effect, if any, does the direction of a force have on its ability to produce rotation?

8. If you were to grasp the end of the plank of a teeter-totter and pull directly away from the fulcrum, would the force you apply produce a moment? Explain.

9. If a body is in equilibrium when only two forces other than that at the fulcrum act on it, how do the values of the two moment arms compare with the magnitude of the two forces? Why?

10. If you don't mind juggling algebraic symbols, assume a center of moments at a distance d beyond the left end of the bar in Fig. 4-3(a), and show that the total clockwise moment about this point equals the total counterclockwise moment about the same point. If you are uncomfortable with algebraic symbols, take a center of moments 4.00 ft to the left of the end of the bar in Fig. 4-3(a) and prove that rotational equilibrium exists about that center.

11. Return to Question 8. In this question, what would the value of the moment arm of the force be? What would be the numerical value of the moment? Do your answers agree with your previous conclusion and explanation? Did you answer in essentially this way before, or was your answer less definite and precise and more difficult?

12. How can you plan the solution of a moments problem which involves two unknown forces so that one of the two unknowns will be eliminated from the original moments equation? May this force also be omitted in any other equation based on the principle of moments? From any equation based on the conditions necessary for equilibrium with respect to translation? Explain all three answers fully.

13. How can you check answers in moments problems such as Sample Problem 1?

14. Outline the procedure for finding the moment arms of forces in a ladder problem.

15. In any situation such as those in Fig. 4-2(a), 4-2(b), or 4-9, the usual method of finding the moment of a force is to multiply the magnitude of the force by that component of the distance which is perpendicular to the line of action of the force. Alternatively, we may multiply the magnitude of that component of the force which is at right angles to the distance by the full value of the distance. If in the solution of a single problem one were to find the moment of one or more forces by the first method and one or more moments by the second process, should the correct answer be found, or will error result? Why?

16. In a moments problem one can consider the forces acting *on* a body, or if he prefers he can solve the problem by considering the moments of forces exerted *by* the body. If these two points of view are combined in a single problem, will the correct answer be found, or will error result? Why?

17. Were your answers to the two questions immediately preceding the same or opposite? They should have been opposite. Why? If you slipped up, you had better go back and think them through again.

18. Suppose that L represents the length of a ladder, h the height at which it touches a vertical wall, and d the horizontal distance of the foot of the ladder from the foot of the wall. If any two of these three quantities are known, the third can be calculated with the aid of the Pythagorean theorem. Record the three equations.

19. To what extent, if any, does the concept of center of gravity represent physical actuality? What dangers may result from considering this concept to be valid in a concrete sense?

20. Where is the center of gravity of a finger ring? a link in a chain? a paper clip? an empty pan or basket? How concrete do these examples make the center of gravity seem?

21. Make a complete and detailed statement of the criterion for equilibrium with respect to translation and an equally careful statement of the criterion for rotational equilibrium; then make an accurate statement of the conditions requisite to the complete equilibrium of a body.

22. Did the word "motionless" or any such implication creep into any of your three statements in answer to the preceding question? If so, you must warn yourself to be more careful. It is seemingly unimportant details like this that cause the downfall of many a not too careful student of physics.

23. Problem 7 of this chapter gives three items of data to two places beyond the decimal point, one with a single place past the decimal, and two with no digit to the right of the decimal. You may have noticed similar situations in other problems. Is this chance, carelessness on my part, or is there a reason? Assuming that the answer to Problem 7 is 15.278293 . . . ft (which it isn't), should this be expressed as 15 ft, 15.3 ft, 15.28 ft, or how? And why?

Problems

1. The fulcrum of a uniform teeter-totter is at its midpoint. A child who weighs 50.0 lb sits 6.00 ft from the fulcrum and a 90.0 lb youngster sits on the other side. How far should the heavier child be from the fulcrum, if the teeter-totter is to balance?

2. The children in Problem 1 are dissatisfied with the arrangement; they want to shift the fulcrum so that each can sit at one end. If the plank is 12.0 ft long and if the weight of the plank were negligible, how far from the 50.0 lb youngster should the fulcrum be?

3. If in the preceding problem the plank is uniform and weighs 40.0 lb, where should the fulcrum be if there is to be equilibrium when each child is at an end?

4. The plank in the preceding problems is moved again so that the fulcrum is at its center. Each of the original two youngsters sits at an end but a third child also sits on the teeter-totter at a point 2.00 ft from the fulcrum, thereby putting the system in equilibrium. On which side does he sit, and how much does he weigh?

5. The distance of one's incisors from the hinge of the jaw is 2.5 or 3 times the distance from the hinge to the point of attachment of the muscles which close the jaw; assume this value to be 2.7. If to bite a piece of hard candy the incisors must exert a force of 20 lb on it, how great a force must be developed by the muscles?

6. A man's forearm is horizontal and a box weighing 40 lb rests on his hand, its center of gravity being 40 cm from his elbow. To maintain his forearm in this position how great a force must be exerted by the muscles of his upper arm, if the effective moment arm of the muscular force is 5.0 cm?

7. A plank which weighs 120 lb lies loosely on a level platform with one end projecting 5.50 ft over the edge. A 100 lb boy stands on the plank 2.50 ft back from the edge of the platform while his buddy, who weighs 80.0 lb, edges out onto the projecting end. The plank begins to show signs of tipping when the smaller boy is 5.00 ft from the edge of the platform. If the plank is uniform, how long is it?

8. A uniform beam is 10.0 ft long and weighs 90.0 lb. It is hinged at one end so that it hangs vertically but can be raised to a horizontal position. A man raises it (inefficiently) by means of a rope attached to the free end and always pulled in a direction 45° from the vertical. How much force is required (a) when the beam is vertical, (b) when it is 45° from the vertical, and (c) when it is horizontal?

9. A uniform plank 14.0 ft long and weighing 120 lb spans an irrigation canal. A 160 lb man is 5.00 ft from the right end of the plank and his 30.0 lb dog is 4.00 ft from the left end. Find the supporting force at each end of the plank. Assume that the supporting forces act at the ends of the plank.

10. A bridge 30.0 ft long is supported by abutments at its ends. The bridge is uniform and weighs 25.0 tons. A truck is crossing the bridge, the front wheels being 18.0 ft from the left end and the rear wheels being 6.00 ft from the same end. The force exerted vertically on the bridge by the front wheels is 3.00 tons and that exerted by the rear wheels is 12.0 tons. Compute the supporting force on each abutment.

11. A man borrows his neighbor's lawn roller, and to get it onto his lot he has to pull it over a curb 4.00 in. high. The diameter of the roller is 20.0 in., and its weight is 84.0 lb (he will fill it with water to make it more effective, *after* he gets it over the curb). He tries to pull the roller over the curb with a horizontal force. How great a force is necessary? Disregard the weight of the handle.

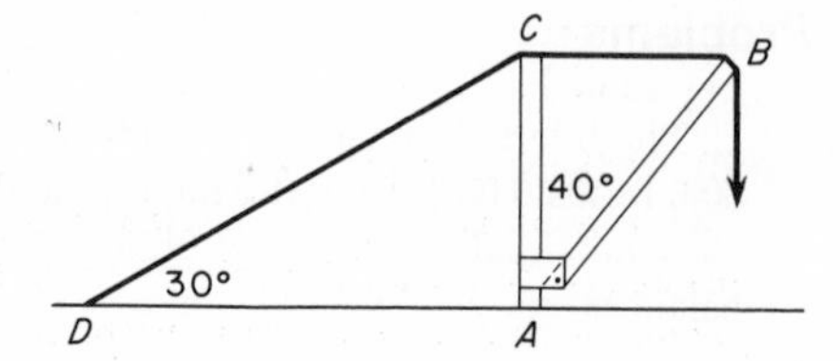

Fig. 4-10. Figure for Problem 13.

12. Make a scale diagram of the roller in the preceding problem, the roller being against the curb and being viewed from the end. By considering the diagram and what you know (I hope) about moments, deduce the most effective direction for the man to pull. What is the angle between this most effective direction and the horizontal? How much force must be exerted at this angle?

13. A derrick is set up as in Fig. 4-10. The cable from the ground to the top of the upright (from D to C) makes an angle of 30° with the horizontal, and the cable from the top of the upright to the end of the boom (from C to B) is horizontal. The upright AC is vertical and the boom AB is 40° from the vertical. A load of 3000 lb is suspended from the end of the boom. Find the tensile force in the cable between B and C, and the compressional force in the boom. Disregard the weight of the boom.

14. Using the data and diagram of the preceding problem, plus the value of the tension in the cable CB from your computations (or from the answer list), find the tensile force in the cable from C to D by considering moments about point A. Then find the compressional force in the upper part of the upright AC by considering translational equilibrium at point C.

15. A uniform ladder is 15.0 ft long and weighs 60.0 lb. The foot of the ladder is on a horizontal surface 9.00 ft from the foot of a smooth vertical wall, and the top of the ladder leans against the wall. A man who weighs 140 lb stands on the ladder at a point 12.0 ft from its foot and a bucket of paint weighing 12.0 lb is at a point 14.0 ft from the foot of the ladder. Compute the magnitude of the force with which the ladder presses against the wall.

16. In the preceding problem, how great a horizontal force tends to make the foot of the ladder slip away from the wall? What is the magnitude of the force of the ground against the ladder, and what is the direction of this force?

17. A uniform ladder which weighs 30.0 lb and is 14.0 ft long leans against a fence. The fence is 8.00 ft high and the foot of the ladder is 6.00 ft from the fence and on level ground, so that the top of the ladder projects beyond the fence. A boy who weighs 45.0 lb stands at a point 4.00 ft above the foot of the ladder. If the top of the fence is smooth, what are the direction and the magnitude of the force it exerts on the ladder?

18. The boy in the preceding problem dares himself to climb slowly up the ladder beyond the point where it rests against the fence. If the ground exerted no horizontal force on the foot of the ladder, how far up the ladder would the lad get before he had reason to regret his venturesomeness?

19. In the solution of Sample Problem 2, I computed the moments of the various forces by using the appropriate components of the distances rather than the full distances. Rework this problem using the full distances along the ladder, but resolving each force into appropriate components.

20. Rework the preceding problem using only algebraic symbols (no numerical values), and leave the final result—the algebraic equation based on the principle of moments—in terms of symbols. Then rework the original solution of Sample Problem 2 in a similar manner. Show that these two methods give identical results.

5

LINEAR MOTION, AND NEWTON'S LAWS OF MOTION

5-1 Preview

After acquiring an acquaintance with the terminology pertinent to motion, we shall work out quantitative relationships. We shall then study the laws of motion which, though stated almost three centuries ago, are still valid except in those relatively rare applications in which speeds occur which are comparable with the speed of light. One of these laws of motion will introduce to us some new units of force.

5-2 Terminology

In Chapters 3 and 4 we have met the concepts of translational motion and rotational motion. This chapter deals with ***linear motion,*** which is translational motion in a straight line. The term, however, is broader than this definition may seem to imply. First, a body may experience a complex motion compounded of linear and rotational *components.* Thus we may consider, for example, the linear motion of an airplane propeller independently of its rotation. Second, *at any particular instant* the motion of any body which is experiencing translational motion is linear, even though the path of the body is curved. For example, as the earth swings around the sun in its nearly circular orbit its speed is approximately constant but its direction is constantly changing. Yet at any particular instant its velocity has a definite direction. If in Fig. 5-1, E represents the earth, its *path* curves along the arc EA but the instantaneous value of its velocity is along the straight line EB, tangent to the path. Thus, though a body may be following a curved path, at any particular moment its ***instantaneous velocity*** will be along a tangent to the path, and hence linear. When we wish to emphasize the element of direction rather than time, we speak of the ***tangential velocity*** rather than the instantaneous velocity, but otherwise these two terms are essentially synonymous.

The ***displacement*** of a body is its change in position. When you go from one classroom to another, your displacement is the straight geometric line drawn through walls and perhaps floors from your initial position to your new location. It is a vector quantity. The term "***distance***" is sometimes used in the same way, but commonly the distance is considered to be the scalar component—the numerical value without any specification of direction—of the displacement. It may also refer to the actual length of an indirect path rather than to the length of a straight line between the initial and final locations.

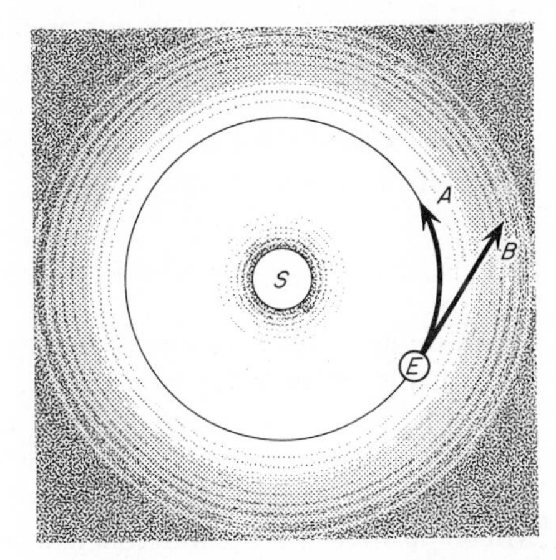

Fig. 5-1. Vector A is the speed of the earth in its orbit, and vector B is the earth's tangential velocity.

Time is required for any displacement, and the rate at which the displacement occurs, or displacement per unit time, is ***velocity.*** Similarly, distance per unit time is ***speed.*** Thus speed is the scalar component of the vector quantity *velocity.* If the actual road distance of a trip is 200 miles and if you make the trip in just 5 hr, the average *speed* is 200 miles/5.00 hr or 40.0 mph. If the destination is 160 miles "as the crow flies" due east of your starting point, the average *velocity* is 160 miles/5.00 hr or 32.0 mph due east.

Speed may be ***uniform,*** which means that its value is constant, though very commonly it is not; in general, the quotient of distance and time is the *average* speed. In the example above, the speed undoubtedly was below 40 mph at some times and higher at others, but the average was 40 mph. Likewise, a velocity may be uniform or not. However, speed may be uniform when velocity is not. For example, the tip of the second hand of an electric clock moves around the clock face at an *un*changing *rate* but in a *continually* changing *direction.*

Imagine a sports car driven by a "gasoline cowboy" and a heavily loaded truck to be moving at 30 mph on a straight highway when they reach the end of a restricted speed zone. The sports car may reach a velocity of 50 mph in seconds, whereas the truck requires a much longer time. Though both undergo the same change in velocity, the time factor is very different. The rate at which the velocity is changed, or change of velocity per unit time, is the ***acceleration.*** If you increase your velocity along a straight roadway from 20 to 50 mph in 15 sec, the acceleration is (50 − 20) mph divided by 15 sec or 2.0 mph per sec.

Note carefully this *double* time unit. Since time is involved in velocity, and because acceleration is change of velocity per unit time, the units for acceleration must contain time *twice.* Different time units may be used as in this example, or the same unit may be used twice: for example, feet per second per second, which may also be written feet per second squared, or abbreviated ft/sec^2.

Acceleration, like displacement and velocity, is a vector quantity. Also like velocity, it may or may not be uniform. Problems dealing with acceleration are relatively simple if the acceleration is uniform or if its effective average value is specified (or can be deduced). Problems such that no effective average value of the acceleration is available are beyond the scope of this book.

5-3 Further Consideration of Acceleration

In defining acceleration as change of velocity per unit time we did not restrict this "change" to an increase. As used in physics, the term acceleration includes *de*celeration as well as what we ordinarily think of as acceleration. The change in velocity is a difference between a final velocity and an initial velocity. If the speed of the body is increasing this difference will be positive, but the difference necessarily will be negative whenever the speed is decreasing. Hence, when we divide the change of velocity by the time, the resulting value of the acceleration will be positive if the velocity is increasing but negative if it is decreasing. In short, a *de*celeration is a *negative ac*celeration. This is in agreement with our convention that a change of the sign of a vector quantity signals a reversal of direction (Sec. 3-6); for if a body has an initial velocity to the right, an acceleration toward the *left* must *de*celerate the body.

The vector nature of both velocity and acceleration gives rise to the seeming paradox that a body may experience a continual acceleration of appreciable magnitude without its speed being affected at all. *This occurs whenever the direction of the acceleration is at right angles to that of the velocity.* In such a case, no component of the acceleration is parallel with the velocity; hence no effect on the magnitude of the velocity is possible, but there *is* a continuing effect on the *direction* as long as the acceleration is present. And there is no paradox at all; for the speed is only the scalar component of the velocity, and it is the directional component which undergoes change. This sort of thing is a univeral feature of all uniform circular motion.

5-4 Relative Nature of Numerical Values

We have met previously the idea that any numerical value of a velocity is ambiguous unless it is stated—or understood—that the velocity is relative to some particular point or body. Two cars on a freeway may have zero velocity with respect to each other but a speed of 60 mph with respect to the pavement, or 120 mph relative to a car headed in the opposite direction—in another lane, we hope!

Similarly, the values of all other quantities pertinent to linear motion are indefinite except with reference to some standard of comparison. To say that the distance of Chicago is approximately 850 miles, or 2210 miles, or 960 miles, is meaningless; but these values do have significance if we say that they represent the respective distances of Chicago from New York, from San Francisco, or from New Orleans. Thus, displacements, like speeds, are relative.

The same is true of accelerations. If you roll a marble down a smooth incline you will be tempted to say that it undergoes acceleration, and it does, *with respect to you.* The same is true if you roll a second marble. But if you roll the two marbles at once, although both will undergo acceleration with respect to you, neither will have any acceleration with respect to the other.

These are very important facts and must not be forgotten. In ordinary circumstances, however, the most convenient and practical basis of reference is the earth's surface at that location. It is customary to interpret all values on this basis unless some other basis of reference is specifically stated.

5-5 Restatement of Verbal Definitions in Algebraic Form

In Sec. 2-14 we met the idea of translating a verbal definition into an equivalent algebraic equation, and we transformed the verbal definition of speed into a defining equation. Exactly the same reasoning will suffice to translate our verbal definition of velocity (Sec. 5-2) into a defining equation. Using v_a, s, and t to represent average velocity, displacement, and time, respectively, the equation is

$$v_a = \frac{s}{t} \tag{5-1}$$

If the velocity is uniform we may use an unadorned v to represent the constant value of the velocity, so

$$v = \frac{s}{t} \tag{5-2}$$

when there is no acceleration.

Equation (5-1) is identical with that developed in Sec. 2-14 for average speed; and Eq. (5-2) might be used for constant speed, though it was developed for constant velocity. The reason, of course, is that the only difference between the concepts of speed and velocity is the directional factor of the latter, and the algebraic equations reveal nothing of the direction.

Now let's try translating our verbal definition of acceleration into a defining equation. If during a time interval t the velocity of a body changes from an initial value v_i to a final value v_f the change of velocity must be $v_f - v_i$. Since the acceleration a is change of velocity per unit time,

$$a = \frac{v_f - v_i}{t} \tag{5-3}$$

We shall frequently meet a change in some quantity, such as $v_f - v_i$ in Eq. (5-3). It is less cumbersome to represent such changes with the aid of the Greek letter delta; thus, instead of $v_f - v_i$ we may write Δv, and Eq. (5-3) becomes

$$a = \frac{\Delta v}{t} \tag{5-4}$$

You may find the original form more convenient, however, if (for example) you are given the values of a and t and the value of *one* of the velocities, and required to find the other.

Unless you are *very* thoroughly "at home" with algebraic symbols, in reading an expression such as Δv you should not think of it as "delta v" or "delta velocity"; you should think of it as "*change* of velocity."

As noted in the last paragraph of Sec. 5-2, acceleration may or may not be uniform. If uniform, its value is given by Eq. (5-3) and Eq. (5-4), but if it is non-uniform these equations will yield only the effective average value of the acceleration.

5-6 Rearrangements of the Defining Equations

The defining equation for average velocity, $v_a = s/t$, will suffice to enable you to compute the value of any one of the three quantities if the values of the other two are known, but it is most convenient for calculating velocity. Though *unnecessary,* it is *convenient* to rearrange it if the unknown is s or t. Multiplication of both sides by t yields

$$s = v_a \cdot t \tag{5-5}$$

and division of this equation by v_a produces

$$t = \frac{s}{v_a} \tag{5-6}$$

Too often a student feels that Eq. (5-5) and Eq. (5-6) are *different* equations from Eq. (5-1). He concludes that he must memorize all three equations. But Eq. (5-1) is merely a sort of shorthand statement of the definition of average velocity; so if you *understand* the verbal definition (rather than having merely memorized a string of words) you can write the defining equation *without* having memorized it. Equations (5-5) and (5-6) needn't be memorized either, since they are not different equations but simply rearrangements of the defining equation for velocity.

Equation 5-3 may also be rearranged in different ways, each most convenient for the evaluation of a particular unknown:

$$v_f = v_i + at \tag{5-7}$$

$$v_i = v_f - at \tag{5-8}$$

$$t = \frac{v_f - v_i}{a} \tag{5-9}$$

But here again we do not have three new equations; we have three alternate *forms* of the original equation.

Consider Eq. (5-7). Although it is not a defining equation, we can see that it is a valid equation by considering the meaning of each term. It says that the final velocity of a body is its original velocity augmented by the change of velocity, since a is the change of velocity per unit time and t is the number of units of time. It is often possible to "see through" an equation merely by inspecting its terms in this way. We can also check the form of an equation by dimensional analysis, of course, as outlined in Sec. 2-8.

Sample Problem 1

How long will it take a truck, starting from rest, to acquire a speed of 30.0 mph if there is a uniform acceleration of 2.00 ft/sec²?

First, we must make the units consistent by changing mph to ft/sec. By the methods of Sec. 2-7 or otherwise you can show that 60 mph is 88 ft/sec (exactly). This "bridge" between miles an hour and feet per second is very convenient; memorizing it will save many tedious conversions. Then 30.0 mph will be half of 60.0 mph and hence half of 88.0, or 44.0 ft/sec.

The defining equation for acceleration is

$$a = \frac{v_f - v_i}{t} \tag{5-3}$$

and we know that $a = 2.00$ ft/sec², $v_f = 44.0$ ft/sec, and $v_i = 0$ (since the truck starts from rest); so

$$2.00 = \frac{44.0 - 0}{t}$$

Multiplication of both sides by t and division by 2.00 produces

$$t = \frac{44.0}{2.00} = 22.0$$

so the time is 22.0 sec.

Alternatively, we could have used a rearrangement of Eq. (5-3). Equation (5-9) states that

$$t = \frac{v_f - v_i}{a}$$

Substitution of the data into this equation yields

$$t = \frac{44.0 - 0}{2.00} = 22.0$$

This avoids the juggling necessary in the preceding method of solution, since that juggling had already been done in deriving Eq. (5-9) from Eq. (5-3).

5-7 Combinations of Basic Equations

Before we develop any new equations by combining some of those previously met, we must pause and recall the warning (in the last paragraph of Sec. 5-2) that many problems in which acceleration appears are beyond the scope of this text. We can deal with such problems *only* if the acceleration is uniform, or if we know (or can deduce) an effective average value of the acceleration. This limitation must be borne in mind, in all interpretations you make of the equations developed in this section.

To Eq. (5-1) through Eq. (5-9) we may add an equation which relates average velocity to the initial and final values of the velocity (*if* the acceleration is constant)

$$v_a = \frac{v_f + v_i}{2} \tag{5-10}$$

in which each symbol has the same significance as in the preceding equations. With some one of these ten equations, or some combination of them, it is possible to solve any problem which concerns uniformly accelerated linear motion. The solution of certain problems, however, requires two or more steps.

Suppose, for example, that we are given the values of the initial velocity, the acceleration, and the time and are required to determine the displacement. We could use Eq. (5-3) or (5-7) to determine the final velocity, combine this with the initial velocity in Eq. (5-10) to get the average velocity, and finally use Eq. (5-1) or (5-5) to solve for the distance. But, if there are many such problems, it would be more convenient to develop an equation which would give the answer by a one-step solution.

This can be done if we note that every one of the quantities we have worked with in this chapter *except* final velocity is given or asked for. This is a cue to eliminate the final velocity from two of the equations we had to use in the stepwise solution. Equation (5-10) is

$$v_a = \frac{v_f + v_i}{2}$$

but according to Eq. (5-7) $\quad v_f = v_i + at$

Putting this value of v_f into the preceding equation yields

$$v_a = \frac{v_i + at + v_i}{2} = \frac{2v_i + at}{2}$$

and so $\quad v_a = v_i + \frac{1}{2}at$

But according to Eq. (5-5) $s = v_a \cdot t$, so

$$s = (v_i + \tfrac{1}{2}at) \cdot t$$

and therefore

$$s = v_i \cdot t + \tfrac{1}{2}at^2 \tag{5-11}$$

Another common type of problem involves all the quantities pertinent to accelerated linear motion except time, so it is convenient to have an equation in which all of them except time appear. Evidently we must combine equations in such a way that t is eliminated. We may begin with Eq. (5-5)

$$s = v_a \cdot t$$

According to Eq. (5-10) $\quad v_a = \dfrac{v_f + v_i}{2}$

and Eq. (5-9) states that $\quad t = \dfrac{v_f - v_i}{a}$

Insertion of these values of v_a and t into Eq. (5-5) yields

$$s = \frac{v_f + v_i}{2} \cdot \frac{v_f - v_i}{a}$$

which simplifies to

$$s = \frac{v_f^2 - v_i^2}{2a} \tag{5-12}$$

Equation (5-11) is almost always used in that form, though of course it may be rearranged in various ways. Equation (5-12) is used "as is" and also in modified forms, such as

$$a = \frac{v_f^2 - v_i^2}{2s} \tag{5-13}$$

and

$$v_f^2 = v_i^2 + 2as \tag{5-14}$$

Note again that, since Eq. (5-3) and Eq. (5-9) assume *constant* acceleration, the derived equations, (5-11)–(5-14), are applicable only to situations in which the acceleration is constant.

You may or may not have noted that there is another restriction on the validity of the equations in this chapter: displacements, velocities, and accelerations are all vector quantities, but the equations have taken no account of relative directions. This means that the equations are valid if, and *only* if, all the vector quantities in a given equation have the *same* direction. Situations in which the directions are colinear but opposite may be handled by reversing the sign (+ to −, or − to +) of any term which represents an oppositely directed quantity. In the case of some equations, like (5-1), values of *components* of quantities parallel to any chosen direction may be used instead of the full values of the quantities. Other equations, such as (5-7) and (5-11), are valid regardless of the relative directions of the various quantities *if* the terms are added *vectorially* rather than arithmetically.

You will be happy to learn that we shall not consider these more complicated situations except for two important special—and relatively simple—cases, one in Sec. 5-9 and the other in Sec. 8-8.

5-8 Gravitational Acceleration

If you hold this book motionless in your hand it will have zero velocity (relative to the floor) but its velocity will not *remain* zero if you drop it. We are all familiar—often painfully so!—with ***gravitational acceleration,*** the downward acceleration experienced by any and every unsupported body near the surface of the earth. Though the value of gravitational acceleration differs somewhat from one place to another, its variation over the surface of the earth is of the order of only 0.5%. Hence we may consider its value to be essentially constant. The value commonly used is 980 cm/sec^2 or 9.80 m/sec^2. This corresponds to about 32.15 ft/sec^2, but this is usually rounded off to 32.0 ft/sec^2. Unless your instructor wishes to give you—or have you look up—the actual values at your location and use them, the values given above may be used in problems. (Answers to problems are based on these values.) Bear in mind, however, that these values *are* approximations.

Since the acceleration due to gravity *is* an acceleration, like any other, all the equations we have developed for accelerated motion are applicable without change to situations which involve gravitational acceleration near the earth's surface.* However, we know that if a body is falling freely, the acceleration is vertically downward. Hence all aspects of the motion must be vertical; either the initial velocity (if any) and the displacement must be vertical, or we must consider only their vertical components. Thus the symbol h, for height, may be used, rather than the more general symbol s, to remind us of the vertical character of the motion. Similarly, instead of employing the general symbol a for acceleration, we may substitute the symbol g to remind us that the acceleration is due to gravity. For example, in the general case Eq. (5-11) is

$$s = v_i \cdot t + \tfrac{1}{2}at^2$$

but for a freely falling body we may rewrite it in the form

$$h = v_i \cdot t + \tfrac{1}{2}gt^2 \qquad (5\text{-}15)$$

We cannot solve any problem with Eq. (5-15) which could not be solved in the identical manner by the other equation, but the symbols in this special form of the equation remind us that the value of the acceleration is known (or should be) and that its direction is downward.

The initial velocity v_i (or its vertical component) may also be downward, or it may have an upward direction; and the same is true of the displacement or height h. Here again we make use of the convention that opposition in the direction of vector quantities is indicated by a reversal of sign. We may choose arbitrarily to take the positive direction as downward, in which case g and any other downwardly directed quantities will be positive and any upwardly directed quantity will be negative; or we may choose exactly the opposite convention. Unless your instructor has a definite preference for one convention or the other, you may find it convenient to consider the downward direction positive in one problem and as negative in another. The only essential thing is that you be consistent throughout any one problem. On the other hand, if this sort of thing tends

* This restriction to locations near the earth's surface arises from two facts. First, we have met two warnings against trying to use our equations unless we know that the acceleration either is constant or has an effective average value which can be found. Second, we shall find in Chapter 9 that the value of gravitational acceleration varies with altitude above the earth's surface, and the type of variation makes the computation of an effective average less simple than we might like. At an altitude of 10 miles, however, gravitational acceleration has a value only about 0.5% less than at the earth's surface; hence very little error will result if we restrict our considerations to elevations of a few thousands of feet, and even a few miles of elevation will not involve a very serious error.

to confuse you, it would be well to adopt one convention and employ it exclusively.

Sample Problem 2

A rock is thrown vertically upward with a speed of 50.0 ft/sec. How high will it be 2.00 sec later?

It may seem that we have insufficient data, but we have enough *if* we realize that the rock will be subject to gravitational acceleration and remember that the value of g is 32.0 ft/sec^2. We must be careful, however, for the direction of the initial velocity is upward, whereas the direction of g is downward. Following the usual convention, we take account of this opposition of direction by appropriate signs (+ or −). We are quite free to choose either the upward or the downward direction as positive, provided only that we are consistent throughout the problem. Arbitrarily taking the upward direction as positive, we have

$$v_i = +50.0 \text{ ft/sec}, \quad g = -32.0 \text{ ft/sec}^2, \quad \text{and} \quad t = 2.00 \text{ sec}$$

and we need the value of the height h. The interrelationship of these particular quantities is defined by Eq. (5-15) or (5-11). Equation (5-15) is

$$h = v_i \cdot t + \tfrac{1}{2}gt^2$$

and putting the data into this equation we have

$$\begin{aligned} h &= +50.0 \cdot 2.00 + \tfrac{1}{2}(-32.0) \cdot 2.00^2 \\ &= +100 - 16 \cdot 4.00 = +100 - 64 \\ &= +36 \end{aligned}$$

Since the positive direction was taken as upward, the rock will be 36 ft above the ground at the end of 2.00 sec.

Note that this result is simply the difference between the height to which the rock would have risen in the absence of gravitational acceleration and the distance through which it would have fallen because of that acceleration. Note, too, that we could have used Eq. (5-7) or (5-3) to determine the velocity at the end of 2.00 sec (−14.0 ft/sec), combined this with the initial velocity to get the average velocity (+18.0 ft/sec), and finally used Eq. (5-5) or (5-1) to compute the distance (+36.0 ft).

5-9 Independence of Components of Motion; Trajectories

We have just observed that the result of Sample Problem 2 may be thought of as the difference between two components of the motion—one component due to the initial velocity and the other due to the acceleration. It would have been quite possible to ignore either component while computing the other. Though both components must be considered, they may be considered independently.

Similarly, if a rock is thrown horizontally from the top of a cliff into the sea, we may consider the horizontal component of its motion quite independently of the vertical component. As in Sample Problem 2, however, the time factor is the same for both components; the rock moves horizontally only while dropping and it continues to drop only while it is moving horizontally. This identity of the time factor in the two components of the motion furnishes us a method of solving an otherwise impossible problem.

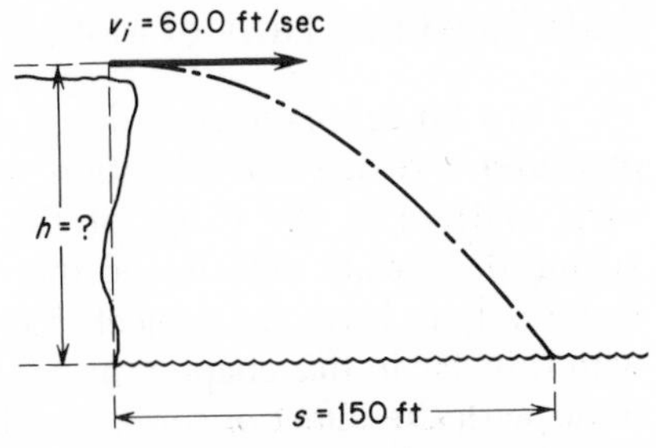

Fig. 5-2. Diagram for Sample Problem 3.

Sample Problem 3

A rock strikes the sea 150 ft from the foot of a vertical cliff after having been thrown horizontally from the top of the cliff with a speed of 60.0 ft/sec. What is the elevation of the point from which it was thrown? Figure 5-2 is a diagram of this situation.

In any problem dealing with a trajectory, such as this, one must be careful to avoid confusing the quantities pertinent to the horizontal component of the motion with those appropriate for the vertical component. It is an excellent idea to make two columns, one headed "horizontal" and the other "vertical" with a big black line between the two columns; this will minimize confusion and error. Only one item will bridge between the two categories. This is the time, which can always be computed from one component of the motion and used in the other.

The first step is to list all items of data given or needed *under the proper headings.*

Horizontal

$s = 150$ ft

$v_i = 60.0$ ft/sec

$a = 0$ (The only acceleration is *gravitational.*)

$v_i = v_a = v_f$ (Velocity is constant *in horizontal direction,* since $a = 0$.)

$t = ?$

Since $v_a = \frac{s}{t}$, $t = \frac{s}{v_a}$, so

$$t = \frac{150}{60.0} = 2.50 \text{ sec}$$

Vertical

$h = ?$

$v_i = 0$ (The initial velocity is *horizontal.*)

$g = 32.0$ ft/sec^2

$t = ?$

$t = 2.50$ sec

Then

$$h = v_i t + \frac{gt^2}{2}$$

$$= \frac{gt^2}{2} \text{ (since } v_i = 0)$$

$$h = \frac{32.0 \cdot 2.50^2}{2}$$

$$= 100 \text{ ft}$$

5-10 Newton's Laws of Motion

Thus far we have considered only the interrelationships among displacement, velocity, acceleration, and time. We have paid no attention to such matters as the cause of the displacement, how the velocity was acquired, or what determined the magnitude of the acceleration. We are now ready to leave the subject of ***kinematics,*** which we have been dealing with thus far in this chapter, and take up the matter of ***kinetics,*** which has to do with the effect of forces on the motion of material bodies. This is a very important portion of our study; in fact, many authorities feel that kinetics constitutes the real heart of classical physics.

Newton's three laws of motion provide a major portion of the foundation of classical mechanics. They also are contained in the more sophisticated laws of motion which are necessary when relativistic speeds—speeds comparable with the speed of light—are encountered. Since the name of Newton is associated with these laws, the implication is that he originated them. Actually, although he was the first to give accurate expression to all three, he owed much to previous investigators.

Newton's first law states that a body tends to continue its existing state of motion unless acted on by some unbalanced outside force.

Newton's second law states that if an unbalanced outside force acts on a body, the resulting acceleration is directly proportional to the magnitude of the force, is in the direction of the force, and is inversely proportional to the mass of the body.

Newton's third law states that whenever, during any kind of interaction between two bodies, one of them exerts a force on the other, the second body exerts an equal but oppositely directed force on the first body. This is often summarized by saying that for every action there is an equal and opposite reaction.

We shall investigate each of these laws, but not in the listed order. Since the second law will require more time than the other two combined, it will be treated last.

5-11 Newton's First Law of Motion

You would suspect a trick if you were to see a marble suddenly speed up, or slow down, or make a sharp turn while rolling along a smooth horizontal surface; such things *can't* happen. And this is exactly what Newton's first law says. A body which is moving must continue to move, in the same straight line at the same speed, unless something alters the situation; and the only thing that can alter it is the application of a force (which is not nullified by another force or forces) to the body. We are accustomed to a body coming to a stop sooner or later, but that is only because we can't eliminate friction, which is an unbalanced force opposing the motion.

Note that "existing state of motion" in the statement of the law includes *absence* of motion as well as motion at a constant velocity. Even if it didn't, we have seen previously that the term "motionless" is without meaning except in a relative sense.

5-12 Newton's Third Law of Motion

This law might be exemplified by saying that if you hit an Irishman in the nose you'd better duck.

The essence of this law is that all forces come in equal and opposite pairs; in other words, they are double ended. Note a particular spot on the unobstructed floor nearby. At the moment, the floor is not exerting any upward force at that point. But now get up and stand on the spot. If the floor isn't exerting an upward force at this spot now, you are due for a trip to the hospital after you've been extricated from the wreckage. Your foot *doesn't* go through the floor, and neither does the floor project you upward toward the ceiling; you are in translational equilibrium. This means that the downward force of your weight must be balanced by an exactly equal upward force supplied by the floor. To the action—the force your foot exerts on the floor—there is an equal and opposite reaction—the supporting force supplied by the floor. Which is just as Newton's third law requires.

In this example, your weight actually compresses, or bends, the floor sufficiently to generate internal forces which tend to eliminate the compression or bending, and these constitute the force which supports you. Another means by which a body subjected to a force generates an opposing force will appear in the latter portion of Sec. 5-14.

5-13 The Concepts of Force and Mass

Before we can investigate Newton's second law of motion we must try to gain some understanding of the terms "force" and "mass."

Though the concept of force is a familiar one, it is surprisingly hard to "tie down." We may think of a force, somewhat ambiguously, as a push or a pull, but this doesn't tell the whole story. For our present purposes, we shall consider a ***force*** to be a physical entity which tends to accelerate any physical body to which it is applied. However, we must not conclude that this is a satisfactory definition; the capable author of a 264 page book on the subject* is unable to produce a clear and concise definition.

Mass is also a very elusive concept. We may think of the ***mass*** of a

---

* Max Jammer, *Concepts of Force* (Cambridge, Mass.: Harvard University Press, 1957).

body as the measure of its resistance to acceleration. Under any ordinary circumstances, and most extraordinary ones, the mass of the body is unchanged. The mass is not *solely* characteristic of the body, however, since if the body is accelerated to a speed comparable with that of light its mass increases; we shall consider this in Chapter 32. But barring this one exception the mass of any body is independent of the location or condition or motion of the body. Hence it is considered to be an intrinsic property of the body.

Most unfortunately, the *mass* of a body is evaluated in terms of the *weight* of the body at a standard location. Thus, if the weight of a body at sea level and 45° latitude is one pound, *by definition* the mass of the body is one pound. But this merely specifies the numerical relationship between weight and mass at that location. It does *not* imply that weight and mass are the same *kind* of quantity. The weight of a body is the gravitational force acting on it and hence tending to *accelerate* it, whereas its mass is the measure of its *resistance* to that *acceleration.*

Furthermore, I have stated that the mass of a body is an intrinsic property of the body. Its resistance to acceleration would be the same at the surface of the earth, at the surface of Mars, or at the surface of Jupiter. But because of the unequal masses and various diameters of these different planets the *weight* of the body on Mars would be less than half its weight on earth, and it would weigh over two and a half times as much on Jupiter as on earth.

Since the mass of a body is an intrinsic property of the body, whereas the force acting on it obviously is not, and since it is a function of mass to resist acceleration, whereas a force tends to cause acceleration, there *should* be no confusion between mass and force. The unfortunate use of the same units for both will trip you up, however, unless you are very careful.

5-14 Newton's Second Law

In the latter portion of Sec. 2-14 we found that the verbal statement of a mathematical proportion can be expressed by an algebraic equation if a proportionality factor is included. Thus, if we use the symbol a to represent acceleration, F for force, m to indicate mass, and k as the proportionality factor, we may translate "acceleration is directly proportional to force and inversely proportional to mass" into algebra by writing

$$a = k \cdot \frac{F}{m} \tag{5-16}$$

The validity of this equation is easily tested. If the values of k and m are left unaltered and F is multiplied by 3, the value of a must be increased threefold; or if F is decreased by any factor, a must be reduced by the term "poundal." In fact, though the expression "one poundal force" might be used for emphasis and certainly would be correct, it would be redundant, for we defined the poundal as a unit of *force*. It can *never* be used to express mass, as the pound may. For the same reasons, the terms "dyne" and "newton" are devoid of any ambiguity about the kind of quantity under consideration. Also, use of these special units of force in the dynamic system automatically removes any ambiguity from the units of mass.

According to the second paragraph above, if a force has a magnitude F when expressed in gravitational units, in the dynamic system its magnitude would be Fg units. In particular, if a body has a mass m, its weight in gravitational units is also m; hence the weight of the body in dynamic units is mg.

It is very important to realize that, since we defined our dynamic units of force in terms of Eq. (5-17), that equation is valid *only* in the dynamic system of units. We can *not* use it, without modification, if we express force in gravitational units.

However, if a force is given as having a magnitude of F gravitational units, its value is Fg dynamic units. Thus Eq. (5-17) becomes

$$a = \frac{Fg}{m}$$

when F is in gravitational units. We can rearrange this to the form

$$a = g \cdot \frac{F}{m} \tag{5-18}$$

which is the algebraic statement of Newton's second law in a form appropriate to the gravitational system. Note that this is merely a modification of Eq. (5-17), not a new equation; it will do nothing that cannot be handled by Eq. (5-17), and the inclusion of the factor g makes it more awkward.

In defining the dynamic units of force we put no restrictions on the nature of the force—it may be gravitational, or it may be elastic, electric, magnetic, or of any other nature. Also, Eq. (5-17) does not contain g or any other factor which may vary in value depending on local influence of any sort. Because of the complete irrelevance of all such factors when dynamic units are employed, the dynamic system is known also as the ***absolute system.***

Frequently one is concerned with the magnitude of the force required to impart a specified acceleration to a given mass. Obviously Eq. (5-17) may be employed for this without modification, but it may be more convenient to rearrange it to the form

$$F = ma \tag{5-19}$$

Suppose, for example, that you place an essentially frictionless toy wagon on a table, tie a string to it, and accelerate the wagon by pulling on the string; if the values of the mass and the acceleration are known, Eq. (5-19) will give the magnitude of the force. But if you are applying a force ma to one end of the string, Newton's third law requires that the string pull back against your hand with a force of the same magnitude ma. What is the origin of this force? Review of the discussion of mass in Sec. 5-13 reveals that the force arises from the tendency of any mass to resist acceleration. This property of mass is called ***inertia;*** in fact, the mass of the body is simply the quantitative measure of its inertia.

Physics instructors sometimes give a very striking—if it works—demonstration of this. The breaking strength of a cord is found by increasing the load hung from a piece of the cord until the cord snaps. A slightly smaller total weight is then suspended by means of another piece of the cord, and a piece of the *same* string is fastened *below* the load. *If* this lower string is given a sufficiently sharp downward jerk, the inertia of the weights will prevent the force of the jerk from acting on the upper string before the lower cord breaks; so the lower cord is broken but the weights remain suspended.

Sample Problem 4

An unbalanced force of 25.0 newtons gives a body an acceleration of 4.00 m/sec². Compute the mass of the body.

Putting the given values into Eq. (5-17), we obtain

$$4.00 = 25.0/m$$

from which

$$4.00\ m = 25.0$$

and

$$m = 25.0/4.00 = 6.25\ \text{kg}$$

Obviously we could have used Eq. (5-19) instead of Eq. (5-17). This would have eliminated one step and would have yielded the same result.

Sample Problem 5

What force, in grams, is required to give a 50.0 g body an acceleration of 80.0 cm/sec²?

Here again either Eq. (5-17) or (5-19) may be employed. Choosing the latter to save one step, and inserting the given data, we find

$$F = 50.0 \cdot 80.0 = 4.00 \cdot 10^3$$

but, since both of the equations (5-17) and (5-19) are valid for dynamic units only, this final value is not $4.00 \cdot 10^3$ g force; it is $4.00 \cdot 10^3$ *dynes*. To obtain the value of the force in grams, we must divide by 980:

$$F = 4.00 \cdot 10^3 \div 980 = 4.08\ \text{g}$$

Alternatively, we could have employed Eq. (5-18) and obtained the result in grams force directly, but the mechanics of the solution would have been essentially the same.

Sample Problem 6

A car is on a hill, with its brakes released, and the slope of the hill is such that the component of the car's weight parallel with the roadway is exactly one-fifth of the weight of the car. If there were no friction, what acceleration would result?

Not sufficient data? But we do have ample data. Our biggest problem is to choose among the methods available for solving the problem.

The simplest method of solution employs that part of Newton's second law which deals with the direct proportionality between force and acceleration. For a given mass, this portion of the law may be expressed by writing

$$\frac{a_2}{a_1} = \frac{F_2}{F_1}$$

Under conditions of free fall the force would be the full weight W and the acceleration would be g; let us put these quantities into the equation for F_1 and a_1 respectively. Then F_2 will be one-fifth of the weight and a_2 will be the unknown acceleration.

Thus

$$\frac{a_2}{g} = \frac{W/5}{W} = \frac{1}{5}$$

so that

$$a_2 = \frac{g}{5}$$

Thus, in the English system, a will have a value of $32/5 = 6.4$ ft/sec^2.

Another approach to the solution would be to use the equation $a = F/m$. If the mass of the car is m, its weight is m gravitational units of force, which is mg dynamic units. Then the effective component of the weight is $mg/5$. So

$$a = \frac{mg/5}{m} = \frac{g}{5}$$

as before.

Finally, in the gravitational system the appropriate equation is $a = g \cdot F/m$. If the mass is m, the weight has the same numerical value m, so the effective component of the weight is $m/5$. Using this approach, we have

$$a = g \cdot \frac{m/5}{m} = \frac{g}{5}$$

exactly as in the other two cases.

5-15 Further Discussion of Newton's Second Law of Motion

A number of items should be discussed before we end our consideration of this law.

Most important is the fact that Newton's second law, in the form in which we have studied it, really is a special case of a more complex law. Although this special case is valid for all accelerations and velocities we ordinarily observe, so that the form of the law we have studied is highly accurate in all such situations, it fails when velocities comparable with the speed of light are met. If a body has a velocity comparable with the speed of light, continued application of the accelerating force does not produce so great an acceleration as Newton's law would require, but—quite remarkably—it produces an increase in the *mass* of the body. This strange situation has necessitated the development of a more sophisticated acceleration law than Newton's. *As is always the case in such a situation,* however, this more complex law reduces to Newton's second law for all cases in which no speed comparable with that of light is encountered.

We shall consider this matter and other unexpected effects which occur at extremely high speeds, in Chapter 32.

Two other items have to do primarily with the solution of problems.

First, the symbol g is used in two rather different ways. The value of gravitational acceleration varies slightly from place to place on the earth's surface, and it varies greatly from planet to planet. Hence, when dealing with a location well above the earth's surface, out in space, or near any other astronomical body, the appropriate local value of g must be employed instead of its value at the earth's surface; and this is true, in principle at least, for different locations at the earth's surface. Thus, in an equation such as $h = v_i t + gt^2/2$ the value of g will depend on the location. On the other hand, in any relation such as $F = mg$ the value of g will always be 980 cm/sec^2 or an equivalent value in the mks or fps system; for the unit of mass was defined in terms of the gravitational force *at a specified* location, and at this location g has a definite value.

Finally, because (for example) a force given in grams must be multiplied by 980 to obtain dynes before using the force in the form of the equation of Newton's second law appropriate to the dynamic system, students often make the error of also multiplying grams *mass* by 980, and students using the equation appropriate for the gravitational system commonly fall into the same trap. Such an error can be eliminated if one realizes that the dyne, the newton, and the poundal are units of *force* and *only* of force; a mass can *not* be expressed in these units. Also, one need only glance at any of the equations (5-17)–(5-19) inclusive to see that if m is multiplied by g this cancels the effect of multiplying F (in gravitational units) by g, with the result that, in effect, Eq. (5-17)—which is valid *only* in the *dynamic* system—is being used with *gravitational* units of force.

Summary

Linear motion is motion in a straight line. However, it is commonly possible to treat motion in a curved path by considering the tangential velocity or by resolving the motion into two linear components.

Displacement is change of location, or distance in a specified direction.

Velocity is displacement per unit time, and the scalar component of velocity is speed. *Acceleration* is the change of velocity per unit time. All of these quantities are vector quantities.

Rather than using the terms "acceleration" and "deceleration," the equivalent terms "positive acceleration" and "negative acceleration" are employed.

Since both velocity and acceleration are vector quantities, the directions of the two may not be the same. In general, algebraic equations deal only with those situations in which the directions of these two quantities are the same or opposite.

Defining equations of velocity and acceleration may be written by substituting algebraic symbols and signs for words. These defining equations may be rearranged to more convenient form. They may also be combined to form other equations which, under some circumstances, are more useful.

The value of g changes slightly at different locations on the earth's surface and greatly for elevations comparable with the earth's diameter or for locations in space or on other astronomical bodies; but for problems restricted to the earth's surface an average value of 980 cm/sec^2 or 32 ft/sec^2 is used.

Newton's first law of motion states that an object tends to retain its existing state of motion unless subjected to an unbalanced outside force. His second law states that if an unbalanced force acts on a body it will produce an acceleration which is directly proportional to the force, inversely proportional to the mass of the body, and in the direction of the force. The third law states that to every action there is an equal and opposite reaction.

Numerical treatment of Newton's second law of motion may be in terms of the common units of force and mass, in which the factor g appears in the computations. Alternatively, the *dynamic system* of units may be used, in which the unit of force is so defined that the g factor is unnecessary. The *new force units* are the dyne, the newton, and the poundal, in the cgs, mks, and fps systems, respectively. In every case, the gravitational unit of force is g times as large as the dynamic unit (the value of g being fixed here also).

Newton's second law of motion is valid for all usual applications but fails if relativistic velocities are encountered. For such velocities a more complex law must be used, but this reduces, for ordinary speeds, to Newton's second law.

Self-Quiz

1. Define the term "linear motion." Are the concept of linear motion and the equations of linear motion applicable only when the motion is in a straight line? Explain.

2. Distinguish between velocity and speed.

3. Which of the following are possible units for acceleration: centimeters per second per second, meters per minute squared, feet per second, inches per hour per year?

4. Using the algebraic definition of acceleration and the appropriate fundamental units (symbolized by m, l, and t; see Sec. 2-8), determine the dimensions of acceleration. Show that these dimensions are appropriate for the concept of acceleration as revealed by the verbal definition; and check your answers to Question 3 against the dimensions of acceleration.

5. An arrow is shot vertically upward and shortly returns to earth. Describe its motion, using the terms "acceleration" and "deceleration." Now restate your description of its motion using only the term "acceleration" but considering the sign of the acceleration.

6. Under what circumstances can a body undergo acceleration without any change in its speed? *Why* doesn't the speed change under these circumstances, and what *does* change?

7. Cite examples of the relativity of displacement, velocity, and acceleration.

8. Record the verbal definition of average velocity; check the definition in Sec. 5-2 if necessary. Now, *without* reference to the text, translate this verbal definition into an equivalent definition in algebraic terms. Repeat for the definitions (verbal and algebraic) of acceleration.

9. For each of the quantities in Eq. (5-7) substitute the correct dimensions (in terms of m, l, and t), and prove that this equation is homogeneous. Repeat for Eq. (5-8) and Eq. (5-9).

10. A student gets rattled in a quiz and writes down $v_f = v_i t + a$; he suspects that this may be incorrect but cannot recall the equation. Show how he can prove by dimensional analysis that his equation is meaningless.

11. Derive Eq. (5-11) from the appropriate equations. Also derive Eq. (5-12).

12. Check the validity of Eqs. (5-11)–(5-14), inclusive, by dimensional analysis.

13. Why is it possible to employ equations developed for motion in a straight line when dealing with the curved flight of a projectile? What is the only quantity which is pertinent to both components of the motion? How does this quantity provide the key to the solution of such problems?

14. State Newton's three laws of motion. Are they precisely valid in all cases, without modification? Explain.

15. A heavily loaded truck is rolling along a straight level highway at 50 mph. Must the driving force be equal to the total resisting force, or must it be slightly greater in order to maintain the motion? Check your answer against Newton's first law of motion. Check it against the concept of equilibrium with respect to translation (Sec. 3-10). Do you want to change your original answer? Or was your original answer correct?

16. Newton's first law may be applied to a single body, or it may be applied to the center of gravity of a system composed of two or more bodies. When the final two stages of an artificial satellite or other rocket separate, how will the motion of their common center of gravity compare with their motion previous to separation? If we arbitrarily consider a space ship at a particular point in space as motionless, and if at any later time (while the spaceship still is in "empty" space) we could find the combined center of gravity of the ship and all the exhaust products ejected in the interim, where would this center of gravity be?

17. Half Dome in Yosemite is a tremendous granite monolith. Joe says that when a single snowflake falls on Half Dome the granite beneath the snowflake must be distorted by the weight of the flake. Jack thinks that Joe is crazy. Jim says that Joe may be correct but if so, the distortion would be undetectably small. To quell the riot, you are called in as arbiter. So what do you say?

18. Why is a constant required in the equation for Newton's second law of motion when gravitational units are employed? What value (or values) does this constant have, and why?

19. What is the basis for evaluation of the magnitude of the mass of a body? Which is more fundamental, the mass of a body or its weight? Why?

20. Using the algebraic statement of Newton's second law in terms of dynamic units, determine the dimensions (in terms of m, l, and t) of force.

21. How is the size of a dyne force related to that of a gram force, and why?

22. The factor g, for gravitational acceleration, is involved in the preceding question, and in general the value of gravitational acceleration varies from place to place. Does this mean that the conversion factor between gravitational and dynamic units of force varies? Explain.

23. A careless or badly confused student is asked to find the acceleration imparted to a 2000 g mass by a 500 g force, using dynamic units. He not only multiplies grams *force* by 980 but also multiplies grams *mass* by 980. Carry out the solution (?) on this basis and show that by erroneously applying the factor 980 to the mass he has, in effect, used *gravitational* units *without* the g factor, and so have gotten an incorrect answer.

24. When an automobile, or bus, or train, comes to an emergency stop, the passengers' heads are seen to jerk *backwards* at the instant the vehicle stops. Why backwards?

Problems

(Ignore effects due to friction, air resistance, etc., in all these problems)

1. A tourist drives 475 miles in 12.5 hr. What is the average speed?

2. A traveling salesman has an appointment for 11:30 A.M. in a city 122 miles away. He leaves at 8:55 A.M. and averages 44.8 mph. Will he be on time?

3. A car starts from rest and reaches a speed of 45.0 mph after exactly 6 sec. What is its average acceleration?

4. How long will it take a truck to accelerate from 15.0 mph to 45.0 mph (60.0 mph = 88.0 ft/sec) if the acceleration is 2.50 ft/sec^2?

5. Using the average speed of the truck in the preceding problem, determine how far the truck will go while accelerating to 45.0 mph.

6. In Problems 4 and 5 you made a two-step solution. Using the same data, solve directly for distance without computing time or average speed.

7. Again solve for the distance traveled by the same truck, using the time but not making use of final (or average) speed.

8. A rock is dropped from a height of 36.0 ft. With what velocity will it strike the ground?

9. A rock is thrown vertically upward with a velocity of 48.0 ft/sec. How high will it rise?

10. With what initial velocity must a body be projected upward to enable it to rise 2500 ft?

11. A cake of ice is sliding with a speed of 24.0 ft/sec up an incline which rises 2.00 ft for every 5.00 ft measured along the slope. How far will the ice slide before it comes to a stop?

12. How long will it take the ice cake in Problem 11 to slow to a stop, reverse its motion, and get back to its original position on the incline?

13. A cake of ice starts from rest and slides 40.0 ft down a ramp in exactly 5 sec. What is the vertical component of its displacement?

14. A body is projected vertically upward at 128 ft/sec. Compute its elevation (a) after 1.00 sec and (b) after 7.00 sec. Compare the results and explain.

15. Determine the velocity of the body in Problem 14 at each of the two instants specified.

16. A 25.0 g body undergoes an acceleration of 48.0 cm/sec^2. Compute the value of the accelerating force in dynes and in grams.

17. A body undergoes an acceleration of 20.0 ft/sec^2 when a force of 15.0 poundals acts on it. Calculate the mass of the body.

18. Repeat Problem 17, using a force of 15.0 lb and compare the answers.

19. In a certain electrical field, the force on an electron is $5.00 \cdot 10^{-10}$ dyne. The mass of an electron is $9.11 \cdot 10^{-28}$ g. Compute the acceleration of the electron.

20. How long would it take the electron in the preceding problem to attain a speed of 10^9 cm/sec?

21. If the acceleration of the electron in Problem 19 were constant, how long would it require for the electron to travel 1 m?

22. An automobile is slowed from 60.0 mph to 18.0 mph in a distance of 200 ft. If the car weighs 4000 lb and if the deceleration is constant, calculate the value of the braking force, in pounds.

23. On a slick pavement the maximum force which can be used to decelerate a 2500 lb sports car without causing a skid is 500 lb. If the speed of the car is 60.0 mph how far will it travel before it comes to a stop?

24. How far from a building 81.0 ft high will a stone strike the level ground if it is thrown from the top of the building with a horizontal velocity of 50.0 ft/sec?

25. With what horizontal velocity must a rock be thrown from an elevation of 100 ft in order that it may strike the level ground after traveling a horizontal distance of 90.0 ft?

26. A rock is tossed upward and outward from the edge of a vertical sea cliff. It is launched at a point 44.0 ft above the water, the horizontal component of its initial velocity being 50.0 ft/sec, and it strikes the sea 100 ft from the base of the cliff. Compute the vertical component of its initial velocity.

27. Determine the magnitude and direction of the initial velocity in Problem 26.

6

WORK, ENERGY, AND MOMENTUM

6-1 Preview

In this chapter we shall meet first the concepts of work and energy, and find that the technical meaning of "work" is much more limited than in ordinary usage. We shall learn how to compute work. The distinction between potential energy and kinetic energy will be considered, and the means of computing the value of each of these quantities will be developed. In this connection we shall meet the intraconvertibility of the various kinds of energy and the principle of conservation of energy. We shall meet the concept of momentum, and the principle of conservation of momentum. The chapter will close with the concept of impulse and the relationship between impulse and momentum.

6-2 Work

No one reaches college without knowing what work is, but the technical significance of the term is so much more limited and precise that our common notion of its meaning is a hindrance rather than a help. In the technical sense, the mythical Atlas did no work whatever while supporting the world on his shoulder. While carrying a heavy load along a horizontal path you may raise a heavy sweat and become quite fatigued, but you are doing no work.

Work is done when a force is exerted, or overcome, over a distance; and the quantity of work is the product of the magnitude of the force and the component of the distance *parallel with the force.* (Alternatively, we may multiply the whole distance by the component of the force parallel with the displacement.) Though Atlas exerted a force, he merely *supported* the earth rather than *lifted* it; hence the distance was zero, and no matter how great a force may be, multiplying it by zero gives zero as the work done. In carrying something over a horizontal distance, neither the force nor the distance is zero, but since the force is vertical whereas the displacement is horizontal, neither has any *component parallel with the other;* thus if we multiply either the force or the displacement by the parallel component of the other factor, the result must be zero; no work is done. Evidently we must exorcise from our minds any idea that the amount of perspiration or fatigue is any index of the quantity of work done.

If a force F acts over a distance s, and if the directions of these two quantities are mutually parallel, the work W is given by the equation

$$W = F\uparrow \cdot s\uparrow \tag{6-1}$$

This equation is similar to Eq. (4-1) in that each involves the product of a force and a distance, but this apparent likeness is illusory. Long before you heard of physics, you knew that a force applied at the end of a crank would tend to turn the crank *if* it were perpendicular to the axis of the crank, and that it had *no* such tendency if applied parallel with the axis of the crank. Thus Eq. (4-1), in which the arrows associated with the two factors are mutually at right angles, represents the measure of a tendency to cause rotation, whereas the parallelism of the arrows in Eq. (6-1) precludes the possibility of any torque. Conversely, the former equation cannot represent work, since the distance factor is not a displacement *parallel to the direction of the force.*

As was the case in Eq. (4-1), only the *relative* directions are of significance in Eq. (6-1). The direction of F happens to be vertically upward, and the same is true of s; thus, this might represent the work you do against the force of gravity in lifting an object from the floor to a shelf. Since the two factors have the same direction, their product is positive. But if, instead of lifting the object, you took it off the shelf and lowered it to the floor, the body (or the force of gravity on the body) would do work on you! For now the direction of the displacement is downward, though you are still exerting an upward force (you're *lowering* the body, not throwing it to the floor!); hence, the signs of the two factors are opposite and their product must be negative. And if the quantity of work you do is negative, you're doing less than *no* work, but work is being done *on* you.

In general, the force may have any direction whatever, and the displacement may have any direction not perpendicular to that of the force. If the two are not parallel, one must be resolved into components perpendicular and parallel with the other, and only the parallel component used in Eq. (6-1). If the force applied to the body and the displacement (or the appropriate component) are in the same direction, work is being done *on* the body; but if they are opposite, the body is *doing* work. For example, the plank of a seesaw exerts upward forces on the youngsters at both ends of the plank. At one end, the displacement is downward, so the work done by the seesaw on the descending child is negative; but the displacement is upward at the other end, so the work done on the ascending youngster by the seesaw is positive.

We meet in the computation of work a situation we have not encountered before: although both force and displacement are vector quantities, their product—work—is a scalar quantity.

The units in which work is measured are commonly composed of the units of the force and the distance: foot pounds, gram centimeters, etc. In the cgs and mks dynamic systems, however, special units are employed. If a force of 1 dyne acts over a distance of 1 cm, the work is 1 dyne centimeter; but the term ***erg*** is employed rather than dyne centimeter. Similarly, one newton meter is one ***joule.***

Sample Problem 1

A 200 lb keg is rolled up a ramp. The ramp is 15.0 ft long and its upper end is 4.00 ft above its lower end. How much work is done?

The essence of the problem is that a 200 lb body was raised 4.00 ft; the rest of the statement of the problem is irrelevant. Hence the work is

$$200 \text{ lb} \cdot 4.00 \text{ ft} = 800 \text{ ft-lb}$$

Sample Problem 2

A uniform iron bar of negligible thickness lies on the floor. Its weight is 72.5 lb. A workman lifts one end of the bar, tilting it up until it stands vertically on one end, and in doing so he does 290 ft-lb of work. How long is the bar?

This may appear to be a pretty tough problem, and indeed it *can* be. But it *need not* be; it's very simple if we strip away the camouflage.

The heart of the problem is that the center of gravity of the bar had been raised, and that this required a known quantity of work. If h is the vertical distance the center of gravity was raised,

$$W = F \cdot h, \quad \text{so} \quad 290 = 72.5 \cdot h, \quad \text{and} \quad h = \frac{290}{72.5} = 4.00$$

So the center of gravity was raised 4.00 ft. Since the bar is uniform, its center of gravity is at its midpoint. One end of the bar is still on the floor and the midpoint of the bar is 4.00 ft above the floor, so the bar must be $2 \cdot 4.00$ ft or 8.00 ft long.

Sample Problem 3

A hand truck, together with the load on it, weighs 500 lb. How much work (disregarding friction) is done when the truck is pushed up a ramp 80.0 ft long if the slope of the ramp is 20.0° from the horizontal?

The first step toward a solution is to determine the vertical distance over which the loaded truck is raised, since weight is a vertical force. The best way to do this (without trigonometry) is to make a carefully scaled diagram and measure the vertical height; it proves to be about 27.4 ft. Then the solution proceeds exactly as in Sample Problem 1, and the result is $1.370 \cdot 10^4$ ft-lb.

Alternatively, once we have the scaled diagram, we could find the component of the weight parallel to the ramp (Sec. 3-7, 3-8, Figs. 3-11, 3-12). We would find this component to be about 171 lb, and multiplication of this component by the distance along the ramp gives a value of $1.368 \cdot 10^4$ ft-lb.

Trig

If F and s are the full magnitudes of the force and the displacement, respectively, and if the angle between them is θ, $W = Fs \cos \theta$.

Thus, in Sample Problem 3, since the weight is vertical and the displacement along the ramp is 20.0° from the horizontal, the value of θ is $90.0° - 20.0°$, or 70.0°. The cosine of 70.0° is 0.3420, so

$$W = 500 \cdot (80.0) \cdot (0.3420) = 1.368 \cdot 10^4 \text{ ft-lb}.$$

Note that an interpretation of $Fs \cos \theta$ as $F \cdot s \cos \theta$ corresponds to the first approach in the non-trigonometric solution of the problem above, whereas its interpretation as $F \cos \theta \cdot s$ corresponds to the second method.

6-3 Energy

The concept of energy, like that of force, is very difficult to define satisfactorily and simply. Though it is an oversimplification, for most of our purposes we may think of ***energy*** as the capacity to do work. We shall find, however, that there are situations in which no work can be done even though there may be energy present (Sec. 16-12).

Evidently the units used to measure work are appropriate for energy. In fact, one of the units of energy cited in Sec. 6-2, the erg, comes directly from the word en*erg*y. Energy, like work, is a scalar quantity.

6-4 Potential Energy and Kinetic Energy

The term *potential* comes from a Latin root which means "to be able," and as an English word in general use "potential" means much the same as "possible." The term ***potential energy*** is applied to what we may think of as *stored-up* energy possessed by a body. Thus the potential energy of a body endows it with the possibility of doing work. In this chapter, we shall confine our attention to those examples of potential energy which are also mechanical energy, though in its broadest sense potential energy includes also chemical energy, the energy available in a radioactive or fissionable element, etc.

When the hammer of a pile driver is poised above the top of a pile, it is *potentially* able to drop, strike the pile, and do work on it by pushing it a bit farther down into the earth. A spring which is distorted—compressed, stretched, bent, or twisted—has a tendency to return to its normal configuration, and in doing so it could exert a force over a distance; that is, it has the potentiality of doing work. Thus a body may possess potential energy by virtue of its position or by virtue of elastic distortion.

Kinetic energy is energy a body has by virtue of its motion; in fact, the term *kinetic* comes from the Greek word for motion. Any physical body which is moving necessarily has kinetic energy as the result of that motion. This must be true since an opposing force is required to stop any moving body, and because the body can't be stopped in zero distance. Thus the moving body is capable of overcoming a force over a distance; that is, it can do work, and to do work it must possess energy.

6-5 Conservation of Energy

The pile driver hammer of the preceding section had potential energy when it was suspended above the pile, but at the instant of impact it had no remaining distance to fall; so it no longer had potential energy. It was moving, however, though initially it was motionless. Thus as it fell it lost potential energy but gained kinetic energy. This sort of intraconversion happens continually in all vibratory motion; the energy of a clock pendulum is all potential at the extremities of its swing but all kinetic as it passes the midpoint of the swing, and at intermediate positions it is partly potential and partly kinetic. In general, any kind of energy can be converted into any other kind, though sometimes indirectly or incompletely. The potential energy of the water in a hydroelectric reservoir becomes kinetic energy as it enters the turbines, where it is converted indirectly into electrical energy. This electrical energy is converted by motors into mechanical energy, by stoves into heat energy, by lamps to light energy, by radios to sound energy, etc.

All such changes are governed by the ***principle of conservation of***

energy which says, in effect, that energy can neither be created nor destroyed. Thus when, for example, potential energy disappears and kinetic energy appears, the quantity of kinetic energy produced must be exactly equivalent to the quantity of potential energy required to produce it, and a similar equivalence must obtain in any and all such conversions.

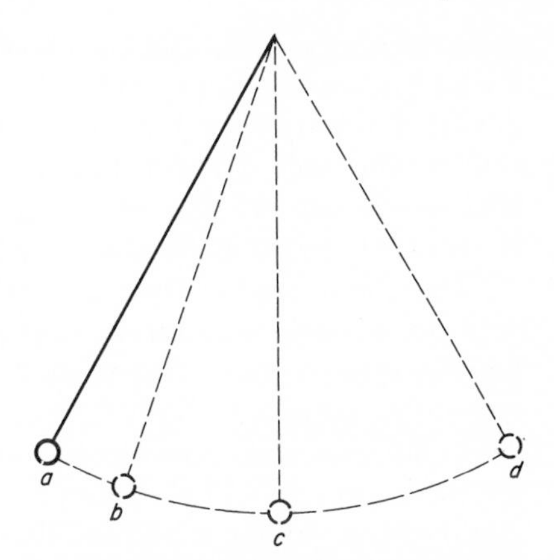

Fig. 6-1. The energy of a vibrating pendulum is all potential at the positions of maximum displacement such as *a* and *d*, and all kinetic at the rest position *c*. At other points such as *b* the energy is part potential and part kinetic; and the total energy at any one point is equal to that at any other point.

This principle became a foundation stone of physical science over a century ago, but for more than half a century we have known that the principle of conservation of energy really is a special case of a more general law. Einstein's restricted theory of relativity says that it is the totality of mass and energy which is constant, and that it is possible to change mass into energy and vice versa (Sec. 32-5–Sec. 32-7 inclusive). But the fact that no production or loss of energy due to such changes had been observed before Einstein proclaimed the possibility, and the fact that experimental verification was a long time in coming, suffice to assure us that any creation or annihilation of energy must occur only under relatively unusual circumstances. The entire field of nuclear energy (Chapters 37, 39, 40, 41), however, exists solely because of this intraconvertibility of mass and energy.

Actually, this intraconversion of mass and energy is extremely common, but in such a conversion the change of mass is far below the ability of any ordinary laboratory device to detect. This is, of course, the reason such intraconversions *were* not detected. It is also why we may still use the principle of conservation of energy, and also the principle of conservation of mass, in all ordinary circumstances. We may consider the law of conservation of energy and the law of conservation of mass to be special cases of the more general single law of conservation of energy *and* mass.

6-6 Evaluation of Potential Energy

The principle of conservation of energy furnishes us with a very simple basis for computing the quantity of potential energy possessed by a body. To endow a body with potential energy we must do work on it—lift a body, compress a spring, etc.—and this is a way of saying that we must expend energy on it. But this energy must still exist, and it exists in the form of potential energy. Thus if we lift a 5.00 lb body 2.00 ft, the work done is force times distance, or 5.00 lb · 2.00 ft = 10.0 ft-lb. This work can be done only if 10.0 ft-lb of energy is exerted on the body, and if the principle of conservation of energy is not to be violated, this energy must be stored up in the body as potential energy.

Thus, to compute the potential energy a body has by virtue of its position, it is only necessary to calculate the useful work done in putting the body in that position. Any work done against friction must be ignored in computing potential energy.

In the case of a body which has potential energy because of distortion, the basic principle of the computation is the same, but there is a slight modification. When a body is lifted against a gravitational force, a constant force is involved (unless the body is lifted a matter of miles so that there is an appreciable decrease of gravitational attraction due to increased elevation). But when a spring is distorted, very little force is required to distort it a very small amount, and as the magnitude of the distortion increases the force required also increases; we shall see in Chapter 11 that the force is directly proportional to the distortion. In such cases, the *average* force is only one-half of the maximum force; so the potential energy is one-half the product of the maximum force and the distortion.

Sample Problem 4

A 16.0 lb hammer is held 3.00 ft above an anvil. What is its potential energy?

Its energy is simply the work which had to be done to lift it from the anvil to its present position;

$$\begin{aligned} \text{PE} &= W = Fh \\ &= 16.0 \text{ lb} \cdot 3.00 \text{ ft} = 48.0 \text{ ft-lb.} \end{aligned}$$

Sample Problem 5

It is found that a force of 500 dynes will stretch a spring exactly 1 cm. What is the potential energy of the spring when it is stretched 12.0 cm?

Since the force is directly proportional to the distortion, it will take 12.0 times as much force to stretch the spring 12.0 cm as to stretch it 1.00 cm.

$$F_{\text{max}} = 12.0 \cdot 500 \text{ dynes} = 6{,}000 \text{ dynes}$$

$$F_{\text{av}} = \frac{F_{\text{max}}}{2} = \frac{6{,}000}{2} = 3{,}000 \text{ dynes,}$$

and

$$W = F_{\text{av}} \cdot s = 3{,}000 \text{ dynes} \cdot 12.0 \text{ cm} = 36{,}000 \text{ ergs}$$

6-7 Evaluation of Kinetic Energy

The principle of conservation of energy also leads directly to a method of computing the kinetic energy of a moving body. An initially motionless body can acquire a velocity only if a force acts on it, and the work done by the force in causing the body to move determines the kinetic energy of the moving body; that is,

$$\text{KE} = W = Fs$$

Newton's second law may be written

$$F = ma$$

if dynamic units are used; and according to Eq. (5-12),

$$s = \frac{v_f^2 - v_i^2}{2a}$$

but since the body was initially motionless v_i = zero, so that

$$s = \frac{v^2}{2a}$$

in which the subscript has been dropped from v_f since it is no longer necessary to distinguish between two different speeds. If we put these values of F and s into the original equation, the result is

$$\text{KE} = ma \cdot \frac{v^2}{2a}, \quad \text{or} \quad \text{KE} = \frac{mv^2}{2} \qquad (6\text{-}2)$$

Had we used the gravitational system of units, our final equation would have been

$$\text{KE} = \frac{mv^2}{2g} \qquad (6\text{-}3)$$

(See Self-Quiz, Question 10.)

It is instructive to try a somewhat different method of derivation. This derivation will be left to you, with just a push now and then. The gravitational force on a body of mass m is numerically equal to m in gravitational units, but in dynamic units it is equal to m . Thus,

$$F =$$

If a body of mass m is raised a distance h, the work done on it, and hence its increase in potential energy, is

$$\text{PE} = Fh =$$

If the body falls from the height h to its initial position, its potential energy will be changed to an equal amount of kinetic energy, so we can write

$$\text{KE} = \text{PE} =$$

Equation (5-13) defines the interrelationship of initial velocity, final velocity, acceleration, and distance. For an initial velocity of zero, v_i drops out, and we may then write simply v in place of v_f. For gravitational acceleration we may write g in place of a, and h instead of s. As thus modified, Eq. (5-13) is

$$=$$

and this may be solved for h, giving

$$h =$$

Putting this value of h into the equation for KE yields

$$\text{KE} =$$

which simplifies to KE $= mv^2/2$ when the two g's are canceled.

6-8 Criteria for Correlating Units and Equations

Students often are uncertain about which of Eq. (6-2) and (6-3) "comes out" in dynamic units and which in gravitational units. Such confusion can be avoided quite easily.

One can go back to the derivation, of course, but many students would not consider this an *easy* method. The simplest way is to reason it out, somewhat as follows:

If the direction of the velocity is horizontal, no work will be done against gravity in accelerating a body of mass m to a speed v; the only force which must be overcome is due to the inertia, that is, the mass, of the body. But the mass of any body is an intrinsic property of that body, completely independent of such matters as the value of gravitational acceleration at any particular location; so the work done in giving a body of mass m a horizontal velocity v would be the same here as on any other planet. This means that the value of the resulting kinetic energy must be independent of gravitational acceleration. That is, the kinetic energy must be expressed in units which are independent of gravity—in absolute or dynamic units. The equation KE $= mv^2/2g$ contains the gravitational acceleration g, so substitution of the correct local value of g would affect the numerical result. On the other hand, the factor g does *not* appear in the equation $mv^2/2$, so it will yield the same numerical value for the kinetic energy (for given values of m and v), here or on some other planet where the value of g is very different. Obviously, then, $mv^2/2$ "comes out" in dynamic units of energy whereas $mv^2/2g$ must be evaluated in gravitational units.

Sample Problem 6

A bullet has a speed of 500 m/sec, and its kinetic energy is $6.25 \cdot 10^9$ ergs. Calculate its mass.

Since the energy is given in ergs, the appropriate equation is (6-2):

$$\begin{aligned} \text{KE} &= mv^2/2 \\ 500\ \text{m/sec} &= 5.00 \cdot 10^4\ \text{cm/sec}, \quad \text{so} \\ 6.25 \cdot 10^9 &= \text{m} \cdot (5.00 \cdot 10^4)^2 \div 2 = 1.25 \cdot 10^9 m \\ m &= (6.25 \cdot 10^9) \div (1.25 \cdot 10^9) = 5.00 \end{aligned}$$

so the mass of the bullet is 5.00 grams.

6-9 Relativity, Again

In Sec. 6-6 and 6-7 we developed methods of evaluating potential energy and kinetic energy, and there may have been some implication that in either case the quantity of energy is quite definite. Such is not the case, however.

Sitting in your chair, you possess no potential energy relative to the chair; but if a chair leg should suddenly collapse, it would become painfully evident that you *had* possessed potential energy with respect to the floor! You must expend more energy to climb to the third floor of a building if you start from the first floor than would be necessary if you had been on the second floor initially, and this is a way of saying that when you are on the third floor you have more potential energy with respect to the first floor than with respect to the second. And while you are on the third floor your potential energy is *negative* with respect to any higher floor.

Situations involving forces which are not gravitational are not always so clear-cut as these examples, but in general it is true that values of potential energy are always relative rather than absolute.

The same is true of kinetic energy. A "motionless" pebble on the ground has no kinetic energy relative to the ground. However, it *does* have kinetic energy due to the earth's rotation, due to the orbital motion of the earth, and probably due to other astronomical motions. A passenger in a moving automobile has no kinetic energy relative to the car, but he certainly *does* have kinetic energy with respect to roadside hazards such as bridge abutments.

Thus the numerical value of either the potential energy or the kinetic energy of a body is only relative. However, relativity also comes into the picture in a much more sophisticated way. The kinetic energy equations we have derived are valid only so long as the velocities are in, or near, the range of speeds we ordinarily observe. If relativistic velocities—velocities comparable with the speed of light—are involved, a quite different equation must be employed (Sec. 32-6). Nevertheless, this more complex relativistic equation for kinetic energy reduces to Eq. (6-2) for nonrelativistic speeds; so here again we have a relationship which is fully adequate for ordinary conditions, although actually it is a special case of a more general relationship.

6-10 Use of the Principle of Conservation of Energy to Solve Problems of Motion

Suppose that I tell you that a circus performer, starting from rest, slides down a sloping wire which descends 15 ft in a distance of 40 ft, and ask you to compute the speed he would have when he reaches the lower end of the wire, if there were no friction. If you assume that the wire is perfectly straight (no "sag") you can find the component of the performer's weight parallel to the wire by resolving the weight. Knowing the value of the component parallel to the wire you can compute the acceleration. Finally, from the acceleration and the distance you can calculate the final velocity.

Now let's take a quite different point of view. The performer starts from an elevated position, which means that he is endowed with potential energy. Since it is specified that we are to neglect any frictional effects, and since energy is conserved, he can't lose any of his initial store of energy. But he *can* lose potential energy, *provided* that he acquires an *equal* quantity of kinetic energy. Thus we may simply equate the initial potential energy to the final kinetic energy, evaluate the potential energy according to Sec. 6-6 and the kinetic energy by the method of Sec. 6-7, put in the known values, and solve directly for the final velocity!

Note that this approach to the solution not only saves considerable work as compared with the method available to us before this chapter; it eliminates the need to know the length of the wire, and the unrealistic assumption that there is no sag.

Sample Problem 7

A weight is attached to a rigid support by a string exactly 1.75 ft long. The weight is moved to the side and up, keeping the string taut, until the cord is horizontal. The weight is held motionless in this position and then released so that it swings pendulumwise. What maximum speed will it attain, assuming no stretch of the string?

A solution appears impossible; we have but a single datum! If it proves that the value of g is pertinent, we have two bits of data. But let's try.

Obviously the weight will fall and hence will lose potential energy; hence it must gain kinetic energy. Equally obviously, it will have its maximum kinetic energy when *all* of its potential energy has been changed to kinetic; and the only location at which it will have no potential energy will be at the bottom of its swing. Since the string is 1.75 ft long, the weight will lose 1.75 ft of elevation and a corresponding quantity of potential energy; but it will gain the same quantity of kinetic energy:

$$\text{PE} = \text{KE}$$

$$mgh = \frac{mv^2}{2} \quad \text{(in terms of absolute units)}$$

Since the unknown mass very conveniently appears on *both* sides of the equation, we may cancel it out, obtaining

$$gh = \frac{v^2}{2}, \quad \text{or} \quad v^2 = 2gh,$$

and
$$v = \sqrt{2gh} = \sqrt{2 \cdot 32 \cdot 1.75} = 10.6$$

Hence the maximum speed of the body will be 10.6 ft/sec.

6-11 Power

In ordinary usage, "power" has many meanings, but as is so often the case, its technical significance is much narrower. If we see a large machine doing a job that would require a number of smaller machines, or doing it a great deal faster than a smaller machine, we marvel at the power of the big machine. This common usage of the term is the meaning it has in technical applications; ***power*** is the *rate* at which work is done, or the *rate* at which energy is produced or expended. We may *not* use the term to mean force or energy; it is work per unit time, or energy per unit time.

Evidently we can use such units as foot pounds per minute, gram centimeters per second, ergs per second, etc., as units of power. Three other units are commonly employed also: the ***watt,*** which is one joule per second (or 10^7 ergs/sec); the ***kilowatt,*** obviously 1000 watts; and the ***horsepower***, which is $5.50 \cdot 10^2$ ft-lb/sec or $3.30 \cdot 10^4$ ft-lb/min.

We may define power algebraically by the equation

$$P = \frac{W}{t} \tag{6-4}$$

If we express the work as the product of force and distance, the equation becomes

$$P = \frac{F \cdot s}{t} \tag{6-5}$$

and by definition s/t is the (average) velocity. Thus,

$$P = Fv \tag{6-6}$$

which often is very convenient, but is *not* a *defining* equation for power.

Sample Problem 8

A force of 85.0 kg acts over a distance of 300 m in 15.0 sec. Compute the power in kw (kilowatts).

Equation (6-5) will be most convenient, but since kilowatts is a dynamic unit we must change 85.0 kg to $85.0 \cdot 9.80$ newtons. Then

$$P = \frac{85.0 \cdot 9.80 \cdot 300}{15.0}$$

$$P = 16.7 \text{ kw}$$

Sample Problem 9

The motor of a certain car must deliver 40.0 hp to maintain a speed of 30.0 mph. What is the effective magnitude of the resisting forces?

We have met the fact that 60 mph is 88.0 ft/sec, so 30 mph = 44.0 ft/sec. One hp = 550 ft-lb/sec, so, using Eq. (6-6),

$$40.0 \cdot 550 = F \cdot 44.0$$

$$F = \frac{40.0 \cdot 550}{44.0}$$

$$F = 500 \text{ lb}$$

6-12 Momentum

We have found that the concept of the kinetic energy of a body, determined by its mass and its speed, is very useful. If you drop even a very "live" tennis ball onto the court it will not bounce *quite* to the height from which it was dropped; that is, in colliding with the court it loses some kinetic energy. The sum of the kinetic energies of two billiard balls after collision is always a bit less than their total kinetic energy before the collision. (This doesn't mean that some energy is destroyed; the kinetic energy "lost" is converted into heat energy.) Some collisions on the submicroscopic scale do not involve any diminution of kinetic energy, but all other collisions of any kind do. This means that the concept of kinetic energy alone will not enable us to predict the motion of two bodies after collision even if we know the motions of both of them before impact and the motion of one after impact.

Another quantity which is determined by the mass and velocity of a body is its ***momentum;*** it is defined as the product of mass and velocity:

$$p = mv \tag{6-7}$$

in which p represents momentum. The chief virtue of the concept of momentum is that, unlike kinetic energy, momentum *is* conserved in any collision. If two bodies collide, their total momentum after the impact is identical with their total momentum before they collided; the momentum may be redistributed, one body gaining momentum lost by the other, but the total is unchanged. Furthermore, momentum, unlike kinetic energy, is a vector quantity. Thus, if we know the velocity of each of two bodies before impact and the velocity of either one after the collision, we can determine the speed of the other *and* the direction in which it is moving. The situation is much more complicated if instead of two bodies we have a larger number, but no matter how complex the system, the total momentum is unaffected by collisions within the system.

The ***principle of conservation of momentum,*** which we met in the preceding paragraph, is really a corollary of Newton's second and third laws of motion. Algebraically, the second law is $a = F/m$—Eq. (5-17)—which may be rewritten

$$F = ma$$

The third law states that if a body exerts a force F_1 on another body, the second body exerts an opposite force F_2 on the first one. Thus,

$$F_1 = -F_2, \quad \text{and therefore,} \quad m_1a_1 = -m_2a_2$$

The "reaction" force F_2 can exist only while the "action" force F_1 acts, so the one symbol t may be used for the time each force acts, and we may multiply both sides of the equation by t

$$m_1a_1t = m_2a_2t$$

But since acceleration is change of velocity per unit time, it follows that

$$a_1t = \Delta v_1, \quad \text{and} \quad a_2t = \Delta v_2$$

and so

$$m_1 \Delta v_1 = -m_2 \Delta v_2 \tag{6-8}$$

which says that the change of momentum of the first body is equal in magnitude to that of the second body but opposite in direction. And this is precisely what the law of conservation of momentum states.

In this discussion of the principle of conservation of momentum we have dealt with the interaction of two bodies. The principle is far more general, however; it applies to *any* system of bodies, no matter how complex, *provided* that no external forces act on the system.

6-13 Impulse

Suppose that you want to compute the force exerted by a bullet on a target. In deriving the principle of conservation of momentum we used Newton's second law in the form $F = -ma$. The negative sign in the equation shows that the force exerted by the bullet is in the same direction as the bullet's velocity and that the acceleration (really *de*celeration) of the bullet is opposite its velocity. This equation would enable us to calculate the magnitude of the force if we knew the values of the mass and the acceleration. It may be very difficult to make a direct measurement of the acceleration of the bullet during impact, however. It would be easier to measure the duration of the impact. If t symbolizes the time during which the bullet undergoes a deceleration $-a$, we may multiply both sides of $F = -ma$ by t. The result is

$$Ft = -mat, \quad \text{or} \quad Ft = -m \Delta v \tag{6-9}$$

This product of force and time, Ft, constitutes a quantity called ***impulse,*** and Eq. (6-9) states that the impulse is equal to the change of momentum.

Obviously this derivation of the impulse-momentum equation is open to criticism, since it was based on a tacit assumption that the acceleration, and hence the force, were constant throughout, and this assumption is generally invalid. If the more sophisticated mathematical tools of the calculus were available to us, however, we could carry out a rigorous derivation which would result in the identical final equation.

Summary

Work is done whenever a *force* is exerted *over* a *distance.* The quantity of work is the product of the force and the distance, provided their directions are colinear; otherwise it is the product of one and the appropriate component of the other.

Energy may be thought of as *capability* to perform *work,* though in many situations there is no practical way in which the energy can be converted into work. The units of energy are the same as those for work.

Mechanical energy may be *potential* or *kinetic.* A body possesses potential energy by virtue of its position or distortion, or kinetic energy by virtue of its motion. These two kinds of energy may be interchanged, provided that a loss of one is accompanied by a precisely equal increase in the quantity of the other. The principle of conservation of energy states that energy can neither be created nor destroyed. Though this principle is applicable with high precision to "ordinary" interchanges of energy, it actually is a special case of a more general law which must be used when relativistic speeds are encountered.

The principle of conservation of energy enables us to evaluate the energy possessed by a body by computing the work which must be done to give the body that energy. This leads to a means of evaluating potential energy in terms of force and displacement and kinetic energy in terms of mass and speed.

Since position is relative and the same is true of velocity, the quantity of energy possessed by a body—potential energy, or kinetic, or both—is also relative. And if the speed of a body is comparable with that of light, a very different means of computing its kinetic energy must be employed.

Some types of problems which deal with the motion of a body may be solved on the basis of energy conservation more easily than on any other basis.

Power is the *rate* of *doing work* or the rate at which energy is expended.

Momentum is the *product* of *mass* and *velocity.* It is an important quantity because in any interaction which involves two or more bodies momentum is conserved, whereas kinetic energy ordinarily is not. The principle of conservation of momentum is a necessary consequence of Newton's laws of motion.

Impulse is the product of the *magnitude* of a force and the *time* during which the force acts.

Self-Quiz

1. Contrast the usual significance of the term "work" with the meaning it has in physics. Are the two concepts completely dissimilar?

2. How much work would you do on an 80 lb trunk in carrying it up a short flight of porch steps 3.0 ft high? In carrying the trunk 20 ft along a hallway? How much work does the *earth's gravitational field* do *on* the trunk when you carry the trunk down to a basement 8.0 ft below the ground floor?

3. Since both moment and work are computed by multiplying a force by a distance, why do the products represent different physical quantities?

4. Define the erg and the joule. Prove that 1 joule = 10^7 ergs.

5. What does the principle of conservation of energy say about the conversion of one kind of energy to another kind? Does this imply that it is always possible to convert all of one kind of energy to any other kind? Explain your answer.

6. A couple of decades ago someone, a non-physicist, wrote an article in which he advocated a gliding bent-knee walk which would save energy by keeping the center of gravity of the body a constant height above the ground and thus eliminating the continuing necessity to raise it at each step. Where did the author of this article "miss the boat"?

7. What determines the quantity of potential energy a body has? Is this an absolute quantity, or is it relative? Why? What determines the magnitude of the body's kinetic energy? Is this quantity absolute? Why?

8. What is our present view of the validity of the principle of conservation of energy, and why do we take this particular view?

9. Since quantity of energy is computed in terms of work done, and since work is calculated by multiplying force by displacement, it would seem that the potential energy of a compressed spring would be the product of the shortening of the spring and the force required to cause that shortening; but the potential energy actually is only half that product. Where does the $\frac{1}{2}$ factor come from, and why?

10. Following the general method of Sec. 6-7, derive the equation for kinetic energy in the gravitational system of units.

11. Since energy is evaluated in terms of work, we may replace KE in Eq. (6-2) by Fs. Make this substitution and then replace each quantity in the equation *except* F by the fundamental dimensions (in terms of m, l, and t) of that quantity; and solve for the dimensions of F. Repeat for Eq. (6-3). What do the results tell you about which system of units is appropriate to each equation? Do the results agree with the other approaches suggested in Sec. 6-8?

12. Compare and contrast the technical significance of the term "power" with its usual meaning(s).

13. Compare and contrast the concepts of kinetic energy and momentum. What important property does momentum have which kinetic energy lacks? Why is this property so important?

14. Derive the principle of conservation of momentum from Newton's laws. (I did *not* ask you to *look it up;* I asked you to *derive* it. Refer to the text only if you are really "stuck," and then only to clear up the immediate difficulty.)

15. Discuss the concept "impulse." Suppose that you know the number of gallons of water delivered per minute by the nozzle of a fire hose and the velocity with which the water issues from the nozzle. How could you compute the force of the stream against a wall? What other datum would you need?

Problems

(Ignore the effects due to friction, air resistance, etc., on all these problems.)

1. A hiker who weighs 160 lb climbs the Ledge Trail from the floor of Yosemite Valley up to Glacier Point. The elevation of the valley floor is about 4000 ft above sea level and that of Glacier Point is about 7200 ft. How much work does the hiker do, in ft-lb and in ft-pdl?

2. A car is driven from sea level to a mountain pass at 2700 ft elevation. The distance as measured on a map, with the aid of the map scale, is 15.0 miles but the road is far from straight and the car's odometer shows a distance of 23.1 miles. If the car and passengers weigh a total of 4500 lb, how much work was done?

3. What is the potential energy of the hiker in Problem 1 when he is at Glacier Point (a) with respect to the valley floor and (b) with respect to sea level? (c) Before he leaves the valley floor, what is his potential energy with respect to Glacier Point?

4. What is the potential energy of the same hiker with respect to sea level, before he leaves the valley floor? Compare this value with the difference between your answers to Problem 3(b) and 3(a), and explain.

5. If the hiker in Problem 1 took exactly $1\frac{1}{2}$ hr to reach Glacier Point, compute his average horsepower during the hike.

6. Compute (a) the kinetic energy and (b) the momentum of a 4000 lb car traveling at 60.0 mph.

7. A particle has a velocity of 20,000 cm/sec and a kinetic energy of 70.0 ergs. Compute the mass of the particle.

8. (a) If the speed of the body in Problem 7 were doubled, how would its kinetic energy be affected? (b) If another body had twice the mass of that in Problem 7 but the same kinetic energy, how would its speed compare with that in Problem 7?

For Problems 9–14 inclusive, rework the following problems from Chapter 5 on the basis of the conservation of energy: 8, 9, 10, 11, 22, and 23.

15. A body with a mass of 65.0 g is moving due eastward at 3.00 cm/sec when it encounters a 5.00 g body which had an initial velocity of 4.00 cm/sec due west. After the impact the less massive body rebounds with a velocity of 9.00 cm/sec due east. Determine the final velocity of the more massive body. Also determine whether kinetic energy was conserved in the collision.

16. A 5.00 g bullet with a speed of 500 m/sec hits a 100 g wooden block (which is free to move) and remains embedded in the block. Determine the speed of the block containing the bullet. Was kinetic energy conserved?

17. Calculate the force exerted on a wall by a stream of water if the stream carries 500 g/sec at a speed of 80.0 m/sec.

7

BASIC MACHINES

7-1 Preview

There are only a few different types of simple mechanical elements, though there are various forms of each, and most of the complex devices we think of as machines are made up of combinations of these simpler devices. It is these mechanical elements which we shall study in this chapter. We may consider either the forces involved, or the energy, in evaluating the usefulness of a machine. We shall see that a machine may multiply (or reduce) the force applied to it, but that it can never deliver quite as much energy as is expended on the machine. As you might expect from the fact that physics is a logical structure, the present chapter will depend heavily on what you have learned previously, especially in Chapter 6. The chapter will close with a brief consideration of the topic of friction.

7-2 Machines in General and Basic Machines

From the standpoint of physics, a ***machine*** is *any* device which is capable of receiving mechanical energy and delivering it in a more useful manner. It may be a tremendously complicated mechanism in an automated factory, or it may be as simple as a crowbar. The term ***basic machine,*** or ***simple machine,*** is reserved for uncomplicated mechanical elements such as the crowbar.

The number of basic machines is very limited. We shall consider six; but half of these are really special forms of the other three. We have met the lever already, in Chapter 4 (see Figs. 4-1–4-3 inclusive). The other types are depicted schematically, and identified, in Fig. 7-1. We shall consider each of these types later.

7-3 Mechanical Advantage

You may have noted an implication of our study of moments in Chapter 4. There we found that a relatively small effort force can balance a larger force, if the former has a correspondingly longer moment arm. This means that, in effect, *the lever multiplies the effort applied to it.* A load of 500 lb applied $\frac{1}{2}$ ft from the fulcrum can be balanced, for example, by a 62.5 lb force acting at a point 4.00 ft from the fulcrum. In this example, the lever increases the effectiveness of the 62.5 lb force by a factor of 8.

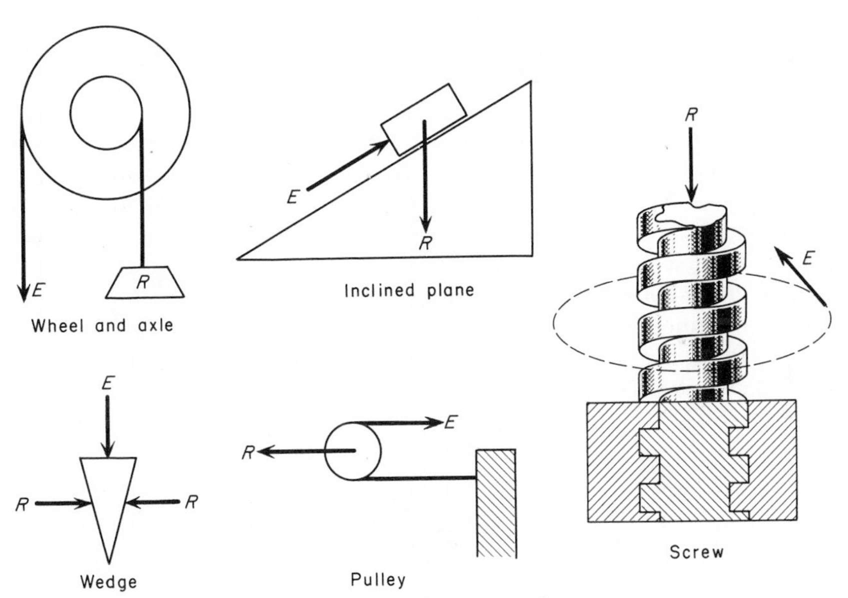

Fig. 7-1. Types of basic machines.

The factor by which any machine multiplies the effective magnitude of a force is the ***mechanical advantage*** of the machine. It is evaluated by dividing the load, or resistance, R by the effort E:

$$\text{MA} = \frac{R}{E} \tag{7-1}$$

Note that we are dealing here with *forces, not* with work or energy. Note also that, since the mechanical advantage is a quotient of two forces, the unit in which the forces are expressed cancels out; hence mechanical advantage is a dimensionless number.

Commonly the value of the mechanical advantage is greater than one, as in the example in the first paragraph of this section. Some machines, however, are designed to increase the displacement or the velocity rather than the force. For such machines the resistance force is necessarily smaller than the effort (for reasons which will appear in Sec. 7-10), thus the mechanical "advantage" is *less* than one.

We must be careful to avoid letting considerations of *convenience*, such as a change in the direction of a force or an increase in the displacement or the speed, becloud our understanding of the term "mechanical advantage." We must limit its significance strictly to the multiplication or reduction of the effort force.

7-4 Practical Mechanical Advantage and Ideal Mechanical Advantage

The discussion in the preceding section was based, tacitly, on a static condition of balance. In any *working* machine there must be motion, and motion of any mechanical device unavoidably involves friction. Instead of applying only a ***balancing effort*** as before, a ***working effort*** must be exerted on the machine; and this must exceed the balancing effort by whatever is necessary to overcome the opposing frictional forces. It may also include effort necessary to lift part of the machine itself, like the lower pulley in Fig. 7-7 (p. 135).

The ***actual mechanical advantage,*** or ***practical mechanical advantage,*** is obtained by dividing the resistance R by the *working* effort E_w, and the ***ideal mechanical advantage,*** or ***theoretical mechanical advantage*** is the quotient of the resistance and the *balancing* effort E_b:

$$\text{AMA} = \frac{R}{E_w} \tag{7-2}$$

and

$$\text{IMA} = \frac{R}{E_b} \tag{7-3}$$

Obviously the value of the actual mechanical advantage must always be smaller than that of the ideal mechanical advantage.

The only way to determine the practical mechanical advantage of a machine is to measure the actual forces when the machine is being used, for the influence of friction cannot be computed accurately. But since ideal mechanical advantage is in terms of the balancing effort, it ignores frictional losses; and for any type of basic machine there is a fairly simple way of determining the value of the ideal mechanical advantage without applying any forces—or even before the machine is constructed. We shall investigate such means of determining the ideal mechanical advantage, in the several sections following.

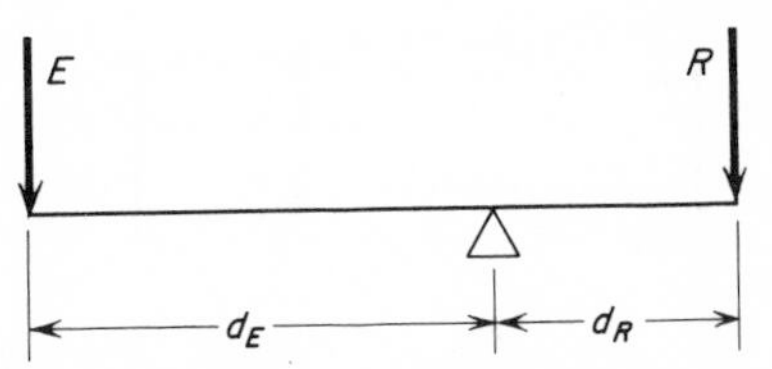

Fig. 7-2. Forces on a lever, and corresponding moment arms.

7-5 The Lever

In Fig. 7-2 is a ***lever*** on which an effort E and a resistance R are acting, in addition to the supporting force at the fulcrum. The lever is in equilibrium, that is, the clockwise and counterclockwise moments are equal, if

$$E \cdot d_E = R \cdot d_R$$

in which d_E and d_R are the moment arms of the effort and the resistance, respectively. Dividing both sides of the equation by E and by d_R, we obtain

$$\frac{d_E}{d_R} = \frac{R}{E}$$

Since by definition R/E is mechanical advantage, d_E/d_R must also represent mechanical advantage. We assumed a condition of balance; hence E is the balancing effort rather than the working effort and the equation relates to ideal rather than to actual mechanical advantage. Therefore, *for a lever*

$$\text{IMA} = \frac{d_E}{d_R} \tag{7-4}$$

but this equation is *not* valid in general for other machines.

A lever may be one of three types, depending on the relative locations of the two forces and the fulcrum. In a ***first class*** lever the fulcrum is between the effort force and the resistance. The resistance is between the effort and the fulcrum in a lever of the ***second class.*** If the effort is between the resistance and the fulcrum the lever belongs to the ***third class.*** An example of each class appears in Fig. 7-3.

If we bear Eq. (7-4) in mind, a glance at Fig. 7-3 reveals that the ideal mechanical advantage is invariably greater than unity for a second class lever and always less than one for a third class lever, but no such restric-

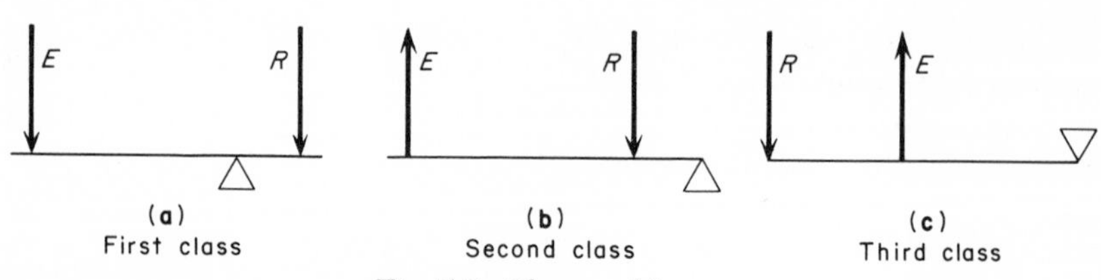

Fig. 7-3. Classes of levers.

tions limit the possible values of the ideal mechanical advantage of a lever of the first class.

It may appear that a third class lever would be rather impractical and therefore uncommon, since the resistance overcome must always be *smaller* than the effort. Such levers, however, do have the advantage of multiplying displacement and speed. They also find application where other arrangements would be impractical, as in your body. The commonest type of lever in your mechanical structure is the third class; your forearm, with the fulcrum at the elbow, is a classical example.

7-6 The Wheel and Axle

The basic machine called the ***wheel and axle*** may take any of various forms, one of which is depicted in Fig. 7-1 and 7-4. In these diagrams, the larger drum is the "wheel" and the smaller one is the "axle." In another common form, the "wheel" is replaced by a crank. A gear wheel may replace either drum. In any case, the "wheel" and the "axle" are connected rigidly so that they must rotate together.

The principle of any form of the wheel and axle is the same as that of the type in Fig. 7-4. Evidently we can apply the principle of moments, the moment arm of either force being the radius of the drum to which that force is applied. Thus, at equilibrium,

$$E \cdot r_E = R \cdot r_R$$

which may be rearranged to

$$\frac{r_E}{r_R} = \frac{R}{E}$$

Fig. 7-4. Wheel and axle.

In general, R/E is mechanical advantage, so r_E/r_R must also be mechanical advantage; but this must be the ideal rather than the actual, since measurements of the radii can't reflect the influence of friction. So

$$\text{IMA} = \frac{r_E}{r_R} \tag{7-5}$$

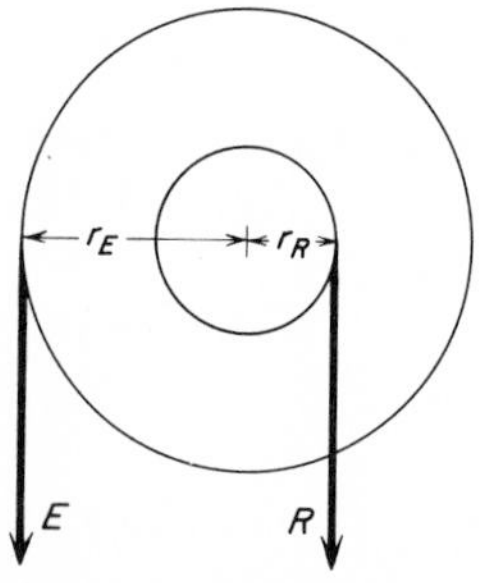

Usually the diameter is easier to measure than the radius. In terms of the diameters d_E and d_R

$$\text{IMA} = \frac{d_E}{d_R} \tag{7-6}$$

This equation is identical with that for the lever, Eq. (7-4). This fact and a review of the discussion in this section indicate that the wheel and axle is simply an adaptation of the lever.

7-7 The Inclined Plane

Perhaps the inclined plane is the commonest type of machine, but in many of its applications we don't think of it as a machine. An ***inclined plane*** is any arrangement which causes the motion to have a direction at an angle to the direction of the resisting force. Thus, the effort need overcome only a *component* of the resistance rather than the full resisting force. An effort force equal to the weight of a car and passengers would be required to lift them vertically from the elevation of a valley to that of a mountain pass, but a far smaller force will move the car along the highway from the valley to the same pass; therefore this portion of the highway is a machine—an inclined plane.

Figure 7-5 represents an inclined plane, or ramp, which has a ***vertical height*** h and a ***slant height*** L. An object is moved up the slope by an effort E applied parallel with the surface of the ramp. If the weight of the object is R, the work necessary to lift it a vertical distance h is Rh. Actually the object is raised a distance h by applying the effort E over the distance L, so the work done is EL. In the absence of friction (a condition which the concept of ideal mechanical advantage assumes),

$$R \cdot h = E \cdot L, \quad \text{so} \quad \frac{R}{E} = \frac{L}{h}$$

and since R/E is mechanical advantage and friction is ignored,

$$\text{IMA} = \frac{L}{h} \tag{7-7}$$

Trig

If a plane is inclined at an angle θ to the horizontal, IMA $= 1/\sin\theta = \csc\theta$.

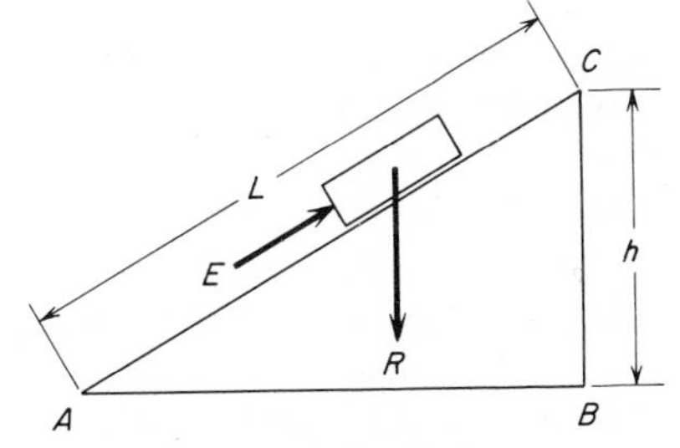

Fig. 7-5. Inclined plane.

7-8 The Wedge and the Screw

If in Fig. 7-1 you draw a line from the apex of the wedge so that the wedge is bisected, you will see

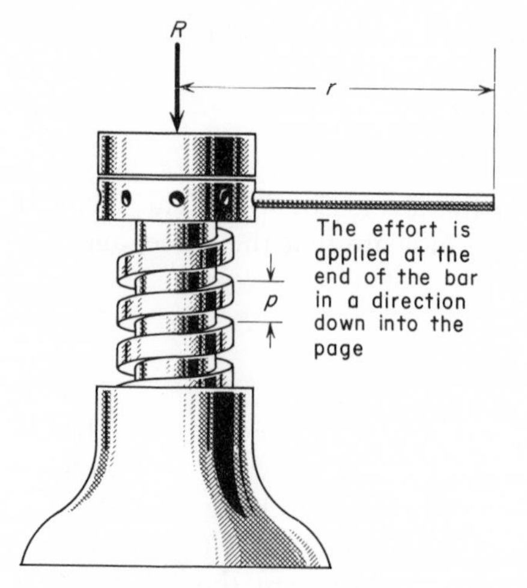

Fig. 7-6. A screw.

that the wedge is really a pair of inclined planes. The resistance would be perpendicular to the common base of the inclined planes rather than to the slope, which would modify the derivation of the ideal mechanical advantage slightly. However, frictional forces on a wedge are typically so large that the concept of *ideal* mechanical advantage is useless; therefore, we shall not consider it.

A ***screw,*** such as that in Fig. 7-6, is another adaptation of the inclined plane, the "inclined plane" being wrapped spirally about the axis of the screw. This figure represents a jackscrew of the sort used by house movers. A bar inserted into one of the holes in the flat head of the screw is used to turn the screw. On the diagram p is the distance the screw will advance in one complete turn of the screw; this is the ***pitch*** of the screw. Thus in order to raise the load R a distance p, an effort E applied at the end of the bar must move through a distance $2\pi r$. That is, the work done *by* the machine is $p \cdot R$ and that done *on* the machine is $2\pi r \cdot E$. If there were no friction, these two quantities would be identical:

$$p \cdot R = 2\pi r \cdot E, \quad \text{and} \quad \frac{R}{E} = \frac{2\pi r}{p}, \quad \text{so} \quad \text{IMA} = \frac{2\pi r}{p} \tag{7-8}$$

7-9 Pulley Systems

Consider the ***pulley system*** in Fig. 7-7. Here we have a system composed of a rope, a double ***pulley*** fastened to a rigid support, and a movable single pulley. The load R is supported indirectly by the effort E.

The rope is one continuous piece; the portion marked *4* passes over the uppermost pulley and becomes the portion marked *3*. We may think of this pulley as a sort of continuous lever with equal lever arms. This means that, in the absence of friction, the tension in the segment *4* must equal that in segment *3*. Similarly, the tensions in segments *3* and *2* must be identical, and the same is true of those in segments *2* and *1*. Newton's third law requires that if there is a tension T upward or downward at any point in the rope, there must be an equal tension in the opposite direction; thus we are privileged to consider any of these tensions upward or downward. So far as the lower pulley is concerned, segments *1*, *2*, and *3* all apply upward forces. Since these are all equal, translational equilibrium requires that the tension in each be equal to one-third of R. But the tension in segment *4* is equal to that in any other segment of the rope, so E must be one-third of R, or R/E must have a value of 3; that is, IMA = 3. But this is simply the number of strands of rope which act directly against the resistance.

It would be unsafe to jump to conclusions on the basis of a single example, but investigation of others will confirm that in any pulley system which makes use of a single continuous rope the ideal mechanical advantage is equal to the number of ***supporting strands.*** A supporting strand is one which acts *directly* on the resistance (or on the pulley attached to the resistance). In Fig. 7-7 strand *4* acts only after passing over a fixed pulley, so its effect is applied *in*directly through strand *3*. Also, the effort is applied *down*ward on strand *4*, so it can't aid *directly* in moving the load *up*ward. From either point of view, strand *4* doesn't qualify as a supporting strand.

The pulley system in Fig. 7-8 may appear identical with that in Fig. 7-7, but instead of being anchored at the top and used to lift an object up, it is anchored at the *bottom* and used to pull a lever *down*. Thus strand number *4* now acts *directly* against the resistance and therefore is a supporting strand. Hence the ideal mechanical advantage is 4, rather than 3 as it was before. Evidently you must be "on your toes" to avoid error due to confusion over whether the strand to which the effort is applied is, or is not, a supporting strand.

There are various pulley systems which make use of two or more separate pieces of rope; and since in general the tensions in the different pieces will *not* be equal, this method of finding the ideal mechanical advantage

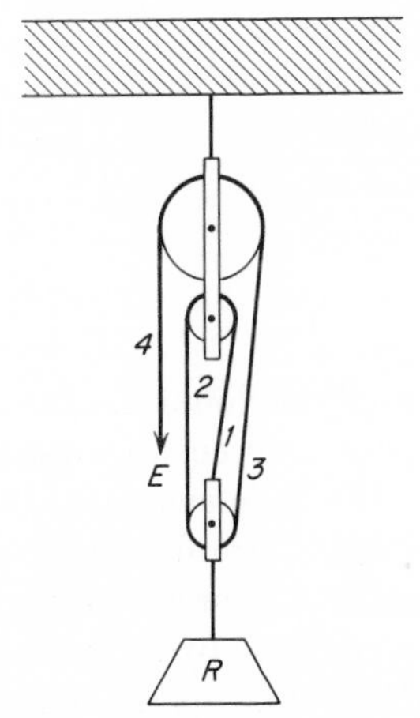

Fig. 7-7. Pulley system: IMA = 3.

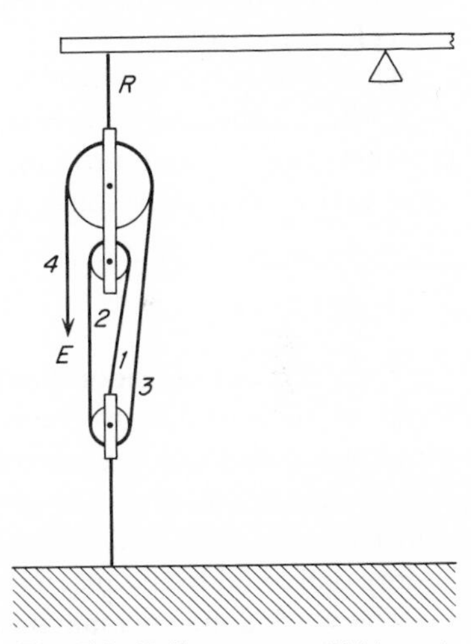

Fig. 7-8. Pulley system: IMA = 4.

is restricted to those pulley systems which employ a single continuous length of rope. Did you note this restriction, in the third paragraph of this section?

7-10 Distance Ratio and Velocity Ratio

Though we have used various approaches in working out the ideal mechanical advantage of the various types of basic machines, a single general principle would have sufficed: the law of conservation of energy. If a resistance R is overcome over a displacement s_R by an effort E acting through a displacement s_E, this law requires that in the absence of friction

$$R \cdot s_R = E \cdot s_E$$

and on rearrangement this equation becomes

$$\frac{s_R}{s_E} = \frac{E}{R} \tag{7-9}$$

The quantity s_R/s_E is called the ***distance ratio,*** and the equation states that, although a smaller force may overcome a larger one (with the aid of a machine), it must be exerted over a relatively great distance. The distances are inversely proportional to the respective forces.

A resisting force can be overcome only during the time that an effort is being applied, so we may divide both distances by this common time, obtaining

$$\frac{v_R}{v_E} = \frac{E}{R} \tag{7-10}$$

in which v_R and v_E are the respective velocities of the forces and v_R/v_E is the ***velocity ratio.***

The right-hand member of Eq. (7-9) and Eq. (7-10) is the reciprocal of R/E, the mechanical advantage. Thus there is an inverse proportionality between the distance ratio and the ideal mechanical advantage, and the same is true of velocity ratio and ideal mechanical advantage.

7-11 Efficiency

Thus far, our considerations of the usefulness of machines has been in terms of their ability to modify the magnitude of a force, the distance through which the force moves, and the speed. We have evaluated these characteristics in terms of mechanical advantage, distance ratio, and velocity ratio. We shall now turn our attention to a comparison of the energy delivered to the machine with the useful work done by the machine.

The work done *on* a machine is the ***input*** and that done *by* the machine is the ***output.*** Because of friction and other factors, the output of a machine is never quite as large as the input. If we divide the useful work done by a machine by the quantity of energy delivered to the machine, the quotient is an index of the ***efficiency*** of the machine.

$$\text{Efficiency} = \frac{\text{output}}{\text{input}} \tag{7-11}$$

It is customary to express efficiency in percentage.

In the symbolism of the preceding section, the output is $R \cdot s_R$ and the input is $E \cdot s_E$, so

$$\text{efficiency} = \frac{R \cdot s_R}{E \cdot s_E}$$

and this may be rewritten in the form

$$\text{efficiency} = \frac{R}{E} \div \frac{s_E}{s_R}$$

But R/E is the actual mechanical advantage (actual, because we are *not* ignoring frictional effects), and according to the last paragraph of the preceding section, s_E/s_R is the ideal mechanical advantage. Thus the last equation may be restated:

$$\text{efficiency} = \frac{\text{AMA}}{\text{IMA}} \tag{7-12}$$

where AMA represents the actual mechanical advantage and IMA the ideal mechanical advantage. This equation is sometimes more convenient, than Eq. (7-11); but Eq. (7-12) is *not* to be considered a defining equation.

One must be very careful to note that mechanical advantage and efficiency are totally different concepts. Though both are indices of the merit of a machine, the former is in terms of forces, whereas the latter is in terms of work or energy. Mechanical advantage may have any value from a small fraction to a very large number, and its value most commonly is greater than unity, but on the other hand, no machine has an efficiency as high as unity (100%).

7-12 Combinations of Machines

As previously noted, a complex machine is an assemblage of simple machines. Direct measurement of forces and distances will enable one to compute the actual mechanical advantage and the efficiency, and if both of these have been evaluated, the ideal mechanical advantage may be computed. But how may we obtain the ideal mechanical advantage of the machine without actually measuring the forces?

Since each component of the complex machine will be one of the basic machines considered in Sec. 7-5–7-9, inclusive, the ideal mechanical advantage of each component can be found. A very common error of students is to *add* the mechanical advantages of the separate components, but mechanical advantage is a *factor* by which a force is *multiplied.* Thus if a machine with a mechanical advantage of 5 is combined with one which has a mechanical advantage of 8, the first machine increases the effort fivefold and delivers this augmented force to the second machine, which causes an eightfold increase; the combined effect is an increase by a factor of $5 \cdot 8$ or 40. Thus mechanical advantages must be *multiplied* rather than added.

Similar considerations will show that the actual mechanical advantages or the efficiencies of the separate units must be multiplied, but the direct approach of measuring actual working forces and distances is usually preferable.

7-13 Sample Problems

These problems have been postponed until various factors could be brought to bear on each example.

Sample Problem 1

A load of 100 lb is suspended from a rope which is wrapped around the "axle" of a wheel and axle. The diameter of the "axle" is 4.00 in., and that of the "wheel" is 20.0 in. An effort of 25.0 lb is required, and it is applied to a rope which is wrapped around the "wheel" (see Fig. 7-4). Find (a) the ideal mechanical advantage, (b) the practical mechanical advantage, (c) the velocity ratio, and (d) the efficiency.

(a) From Eq. (7-6), IMA $= d_E/d_R$, so

$$\text{IMA} = \frac{20.0}{4.00} = 5.00$$

(b) By definition, AMA $= R/E$; thus

$$\text{AMA} = \frac{100}{25.0} = 4.00$$

(c) We have no data directly applicable to the computation of the velocity ratio, though we could use the known diameters and assume any convenient number of revolutions in any convenient time. However, the easiest solution lies in the fact that the velocity ratio and the ideal mechanical advantage are reciprocally related, so that if IMA $= 5.00$, the velocity ratio is $1/5.00 = 0.200$.

(d) We also lack data for the direct computation of efficiency; though here again we could make reasonable assumptions and work it out. But the relationship stated in Eq. (7-12) offers the easiest approach:

$$\text{eff.} = \text{AMA}/\text{IMA} = 4.00/5.00 = 80.0\%$$

Sample Problem 2

An inclined plane rises 6.00 ft in a horizontal distance of 8.00 ft, and its efficiency is 75.0%. Determine (a) its ideal mechanical advantage, (b) its practical mechanical advantage, and (c) the effort (parallel to the incline) necessary to move an 800 lb load up the incline.

(a) For an inclined plane, IMA $= L/h$. The value of L is not specified, but it is the hypotenuse of a right triangle which has legs of 6.00 ft and 8.00 ft; so, according to our friend Pythagoras,

$$L^2 = 6.00^2 + 8.00^2 = 36.0 + 64.0 = 100$$
$$L = \sqrt{100} = 10.0$$

Then
$$\text{IMA} = \frac{10.0}{6.00} = \frac{5}{3} \approx 1.67.$$

(b) Since efficiency $=$ AMA/IMA it follows that

$$\text{AMA} = \text{eff.} \cdot (\text{IMA}) = 75.0\% \cdot \frac{5}{3} = \frac{3}{4} \cdot \frac{5}{3} = \frac{5}{4} = 1.25$$

Note that the computations were slightly simplified, and accuracy retained, by using the exact value of IMA in the form of the fraction 5/3 instead of the approximate and more awkward form 1.67.

(c) As is so common, we have a choice of methods for finding the value of the effort. The easiest way is to use the defining equation for actual mechanical advantage: AMA $= R/E$. This may be rearranged to

$$E = \frac{R}{\text{AMA}} = \frac{800}{1.25} = 640 \text{ lb}$$

7-14 Friction

Friction, like fire and nuclear energy, is a sort of Dr. Jekyll and Mr. Hyde affair, extremely useful and important in some situations but highly undesirable in others.

Friction is responsible for a tremendous economic loss. It causes machines, tires, shoes, clothing, etc., to wear out. It wastes energy by reducing the efficiency of machines. But if a Congressman with no understanding of physics were to have a law passed outlawing friction, and if it happened that the physicists were wrong about the immutability of natural law, what a mess would ensue! Buildings would collapse because, with no friction, all the nails would pull out, and people could not escape the wreckage because of lack of friction between their shoes and the floor. If by a miracle a car held together and its machinery still operated, it would stand in one place (if the street was level) with the wheels merrily spinning. The strings of a violin would always be slack because nothing would prevent a tuning peg from spinning in its hole until the last trace of tension in the string had disappeared. Even if the violinist could somehow circumvent this, the violin would be quite voiceless, for the frictionless bow would slide over the strings without disturbing them. And we would find a great many other things drastically changed.

From the examples above it is evident that ***friction*** must be some kind of force which interferes with the relative motion between two surfaces. It may hinder, but not prevent, the motion; this is ***sliding,*** or ***kinetic,*** friction. On the other hand, it may prevent any motion from occurring; this sort is ***starting,*** or ***static,*** friction.

Sliding friction occurs whenever there is relative motion between two bodies which are in contact, or between portions of the same body. It exists whether the bodies are solid, liquid, or gaseous, though with fluids the term ***viscosity*** is used more commonly than friction. The direction of the frictional force invariably is parallel to the surfaces which are sliding over each other and opposite that of the motion.

No matter how smooth a surface may seem, on a microscopic or submicroscopic scale it is not perfectly smooth; thus the humps on one surface tend to drop into the hollows of the other. How much this impedes the motion depends on such factors as the contour of the humps and hollows, the hardness of the material, the presence or absence of lubrication, etc. The cause of the friction which acts on a rolling body is considered to be similar to what one observes when a car moves slowly over a soft asphalt pavement on a hot day; the wheel is always in a slight depression, with a small "hill" ahead of it.

Starting friction arises from the same influences that generate sliding friction.

7-15 The "Laws" of Friction

Experiments have given rise to certain very crude relationships which are sometimes flattered by being termed "laws." We must remember that their accuracy is limited. We must note that in no case does a law compare one set of sliding surfaces with a different set; it relates to the *same* surfaces under different circumstances. The relationships are:

> The frictional force is directly proportional to the force pressing the surfaces together.
> The frictional force is independent of the area of contact.
> The frictional force is independent of the velocity of the sliding motion.

The first of these rules may be stated algebraically by writing

$$F_f \approx \mu F_n \tag{7-13}$$

in which the frictional force is F_f, the normal force pressing the surfaces together is F_n, and μ is a proportionality constant called the ***coefficient of*** *friction.* The equation may be rearranged to form a defining equation for the coefficient of friction:

$$\mu \approx \frac{F_f}{F_n} \tag{7-14}$$

Though the factor μ is termed a constant, its value is not the same for different surfaces; it may be less than 0.10 for lubricated smooth surfaces, or much larger, for example, 0.7 for two dry bricks. For a given pair of surfaces the value of μ is affected greatly by lubrication, and it may depend in much smaller degree on other factors.

The apparent lack of influence of the area of contact on the size of the frictional force is both inexact and illusory. Very rarely are two surfaces in actual contact over their entire common area; only the "high spots" touch. If a block which was flat on a table is set up on edge, there appears to be a considerable reduction in the area of contact, but since there are now fewer "high spots" in contact with the table and since they must support the same force as before, each must "squash out" to an increased area; and the total area of *actual* contact is much as it was before.

7-16 Starting Friction and Sliding Friction

An item of very considerable practical importance is the fact that a larger force is required to start a sliding motion between two surfaces than to maintain the motion once it is initiated. Stated otherwise, if sufficient force is exerted to cause sliding, that force must be reduced appreciably and perhaps considerably—more than 50% in some cases—before the sliding will stop. This means, in effect, that even for a given pair of surfaces under specified conditions as to lubrication, etc., there isn't *a* coefficient of friction; instead, there are two: a larger one for starting, or static, friction and a smaller one for sliding, or kinetic, friction.

This difference between starting friction and sliding friction is the basis for one of the rules laid down by experts for safe driving: avoid using the brakes so strongly that the wheels slide. A larger frictional force can be maintained, and hence the car can be stopped in a shorter distance, if the wheels retain their grip on the pavement, and this requires that they continue to turn rather than slide. A similar situation exists with respect to the tendency to skid on a turn. Many an accident has occurred because the driver did not know, or realize, that the frictional force available to hold the car in the turn is reduced the instant the car commences to skid.

Summary

A machine is any device which is capable of *altering* the *magnitude* or *direction* of a *force*. The *basic machines* are the lever, the wheel and axle, the inclined plane, the wedge, the screw, and the pulley. Of these, the wheel and axle may be thought of as a modification of a lever, and the wedge and the screw as adaptations of the inclined plane. All more complex machines are assemblages of some combination of basic machines.

The *merit* of a particular machine may be evaluated in three different ways: One is the *ideal mechanical advantage,* which is the factor by which the machine would multiply the force impressed on it if there were no friction. *Practical mechanical advantage* is similar, but it takes into consideration the effects of friction. *Efficiency* is the ratio of the work done by the machine to the work done on the machine.

The *ideal mechanical advantage* of a machine may be deduced from pertinent *dimensions.* For a *lever,* it is the ratio of the effort arm to the resistance arm; for a *wheel and axle,* the quotient of the radius (or diameter) of the drum to which the effort is applied and that to which the load is applied; for an *inclined plane* it is the ratio of the slant height to the vertical height; for a *screw* it is 2π times the effort arm, divided by the pitch of the screw; and for a *pulley system* (which employs a single continuous length of rope) it is the number of strands of rope which support the load.

The distance ratio is the ratio of the distance moved by the resistance to that covered by the effort, and the velocity ratio is the corresponding ratio of speeds. The distance ratio and the velocity ratio are necessarily identical in value, and this value is the reciprocal of the ideal mechanical advantage.

Self-Quiz

1. Why do we use three different ways of expressing the usefulness or effectiveness of a machine?

2. Compare and contrast ideal mechanical advantage, practical mechanical advantage, and efficiency.

3. Under what circumstances might the concept of practical mechanical advantage be more useful than ideal mechanical advantage? Under what circumstances might the reverse be true?

4. Name the "basic machines." Which of these may be considered to be special forms of another of the basic machines and (in each case) why?

5. In general, what limit, if any, is there for values of mechanical advantage? Modify your answer, if necessary, for each of the three classes of levers.

6. What general relationship exists between the value of the ideal mechanical advantage of a particular machine and the value of its practical mechanical advantage? Why?

7. What is the significance of a mechanical advantage which has a value less than 1? Is the mechanical advantage of a machine ever negative? Why?

8. What limit, if any, is there for values of efficiency? Why?

9. State the principle of conservation of energy. What pertinence has it with respect to this chapter? What pertinence has it with respect to Questions 6 and 8, above?

10. Carry out a detailed algebraic proof that the efficiency of an inclined plane is equal to the practical mechanical advantage divided by the ideal mechanical advantage.

11. In Sec. 7-7 the principle of work (conservation of energy) is used to obtain the ideal mechanical advantage of the inclined plane. Determine the ideal mechanical advantage instead, by resolving the load into a component parallel with the incline and one normal to the incline and then making use of similar triangles.

12. If an object is sliding down an inclined plane at a uniform speed, how must the magnitude of the frictional force compare with the component of the object's weight parallel to the incline? This being the case, how would the effort required to slide the same body up the incline compare with the effort which would be required if there were no friction? And with this relationship between the magnitude of the practical effort and that of the ideal effort (no friction), what is the efficiency of the inclined plane? Make a general statement of the maximum value of the efficiency of an inclined plane which can be employed if there is to be no chance of the load slipping back down when the effort is removed. (This maximum efficiency is applicable generally; it is of no importance in many cases, but is very important in the case of the house mover's screw jacks and some types of automobile jacks.)

13. In a pulley system which employs a movable block, what factor other than friction has the effect of reducing the efficiency? (Remember that efficiency has to do with work done by the machine; that is, useful work done on the load, not work done on a part of the machine itself.)

14. Make a diagram of a pulley system which has an ideal mechanical advantage of 5. Make a second diagram to show how the *same* pulley system could be used so that its ideal mechanical advantage is *not* 5. What is its value in the second diagram, and why are the two values different?

15. Student drivers are instructed that if a car starts to skid on a turn, the steering wheel should be "turned into the skid"; that is, the sharpness of the turn should be decreased momentarily until the skid stops. Discuss the physics of this trick for checking a skid.

Problems

1. Using the data from Problem 5, Chapter 4, determine (a) the mechanical advantage and (b) the velocity ratio of the human jaw.

2. Using the data from Problem 6, Chapter 4, determine (a) the mechanical advantage and (b) the velocity ratio of the human forearm.

3. A lever is 50.0 cm long. (a) What is its maximum mechanical advantage if the resistance is at one end and the fulcrum is 4.00 cm from that end? (b) What is its mechanical advantage if the positions of the effort and the resistance are interchanged?

4. The lever in Problem 3 is used as a second class lever, the fulcrum being at one end, and the resistance acting 4.00 cm from that end. (a) What is its maximum mechanical advantage? (b) Recompute the mechanical advantage if the positions of the effort and the fulcrum are interchanged.

5. Compare the mechanical advantages of the two levers in Problems 3 and 4 (before interchange of positions). Which is larger and by what percentage?

6. A lever is 5.00 ft long and the fulcrum is 15.0 in. from one end. A force of 90.0 lb is applied at the longer end, forcing the shorter extremity up under the end of a second lever. This second lever is 40.0 in. long and has a fulcrum at the far end. If friction is ignored, how large a resistance could be overcome by this combination of levers if the resistance is applied 5.00 in. from the fulcrum of the second lever?

7. (a) If in the preceding problem the efficiency of the first lever is 90.0% and that of the second lever is 95.0%, what resistance would be overcome by an effort force of 90.0 lb? (b) What effort force would be required to overcome the resistance computed as the answer to Problem 6?

8. The small drum or "axle" of a wheel and axle has a diameter of 20.0 cm and the large drum or "wheel" has a diameter of 50.0 cm. (a) What is the ideal mechanical advantage? (b) If the efficiency is 85.0%, what is the practical mechanical advantage? (c) What effort would be required to raise a load of 40.0 lb?

9. A winch has a velocity ratio of 0.125, and the efficiency is 80.0%. If the load is 100 kg, calculate the magnitude of the effort.

10. A winch is to be built for the purpose of raising loads of 250 lb. It is desired to keep the effort force down to 50.0 lb. Because of lack of space, the crank arm cannot be longer than 30.0 in. It is assumed that the efficiency will be 75.0%. What should the diameter of the drum be?

11. A steep pitch on a mountain road has a grade of 20.0%, which means that in any horizontal distance it rises 20.0% of that distance (1 ft rise for each 5 ft of horizontal distance, etc.). (a) Make a diagram of a 20.0% grade to scale and from the diagram deduce the theoretical mechanical advantage of such a grade. (b) What driving force parallel to the road is necessary to move a 4000 lb car up the grade? (Assume 100% efficiency)

12. A platform is 5.00 ft above the ground, and a plank 16.0 ft long forms a ramp from the ground to the platform. An object which weighs 200 lb is slid up the plank from the ground to the platform. If there were no friction, what effort force parallel with the plank would be required?

13. The effort actually required in Problem 12 is 90.0 lb. Compute the efficiency.

14. A 240 lb barrel is rolled up the plank in Problem 12 with negligible friction. Compute the effort required if (a) the effort is applied parallel to the plank and on a line which passes through the center of the barrel, (b) if the effort is applied parallel with the plank but on a line tangent to the upper surface of the barrel. (c) Compare the two values and explain.

15. Compute the effort force which would be required in Problem 12 if the effort were applied in a horizontal direction and if there were no friction.

16. A jackscrew for house moving has a pitch of exactly $\frac{1}{2}$ in., and its efficiency is 40.0%. If it is used to lift 5.00 tons and if the effort is applied at the end of a bar 30.0 in. long, compute the effort.

17. A wooden block is being slid over a level wooden table, the coefficient of friction being 0.35. A horizontal force of 200 g is just sufficient to maintain a constant speed of the block. What is the weight of the block?

18. (a) If the table in Problem 17 is tipped so that its surface is 30.0° from the horizontal, compute the force of friction between the table and the block. (b) What force parallel with the table top would be required to push the block up the incline?

19. If the block in Problem 18 were sliding down the incline, what would be the value of its acceleration?

20. If a car traveling 20.0 mph cannot be brought to a stop in less than 20.0 ft, compute the effective value of the coefficient of friction between the tires and the pavement.

21. Using the coefficient of friction from Problem 20 (or from the list of answers) calculate the stopping distance if the initial speed of the car is 60.0 mph.

22. (a) Using the coefficient of friction obtained from Problem 20 (or from the list of answers) compute the minimum stopping distance for a car moving at 45.0 mph up a hill which rises 20.0 ft in each 100 ft of distance along the road. (b) Recompute for the car moving at the same initial speed down the hill.

8
ROTARY MOTION

8-1 Preview

Rather commonly, students find the material in this chapter very difficult and confusing, but this unfortunate situation usually arises from the student's approach; he tries to "learn" the material as something new rather than to base it on what he already knows. In Chapter 5 we met a number of concepts pertinent to linear motion, some definitions, defining equations, and derived equations. We shall meet a few *new concepts here, with their defining equations. But for the most part we shall be able to write the necessary equations by analogy with those we met in Chapter 5 rather than having to derive them or blindly memorize them. The latter part of the chapter will include a brief consideration of gyroscopic action and of the radially directed accelerations and forces present in rotational motion.*

8-2 Periodic Motion

We commonly use the term "period" in the sense of a lapse of time: a period in history, a geological period, etc. Similarly, the ***period*** of any repetitive motion is the length of time in which one complete cycle of motion is completed—one vibration of a pendulum, one rotation of a wheel, etc. If the motion has a constant period it is said to be ***uniform,*** and it is spoken of as ***periodic motion.*** The motion of an automobile wheel in "stop and go" traffic is non-uniform; it lacks a definite period and thus is ***aperiodic.***

8-3 Radian Measure

Whereas linear displacements are measured in terms of centimeters, miles, etc., we usually measure a rotational displacement in terms of the number of revolutions. Since one revolution is 360°, rotational displacements may be expressed in terms of angles; so the term ***angular motion*** is synonymous with ***rotary motion.*** However, often it is most convenient to use a new unit of rotational displacement called the "radian."

Imagine the circle in Fig. 8-1 to be a solid disk of sufficient thickness so that you could stretch a string along *OA*, grip it at *A* with one hand and at *O* with the other, and then stretch this segment of string counterclockwise around the circumference of the disk, starting at *A*. It would reach to *B*. The arc *AB* would then be one radian. Thus, one ***radian of arc*** is a segment of a circle such that its length equals the radius of the circle. Also, the angle subtended by one radian of arc—angle *AOB* in Fig. 8-1—is one ***radian of angle;*** so we see that the term "radian" may be used as a measure of arc or as a measure of angle. In some applications, it makes no difference which of the two meanings we employ; in situations such that a particular interpretation must be used, the context will furnish a clue to the proper one.

Just as you convert a distance from inches to feet by dividing by the number of inches in a foot, we convert the value of an arc measured in linear units into radians by dividing by the number of linear units in the radius. If an arc is 25.0 cm long and the radius is 10.0 cm, the length of the arc in radians is 25.0 cm ÷ 10.0 cm = 2.50 radians (rad); or, in general

$$\theta = \frac{s}{r}, \quad \text{and} \quad s = r\theta \qquad (8\text{-}1)$$

in which θ is the value of the arc in radians, s is its length in linear units, and r is the value

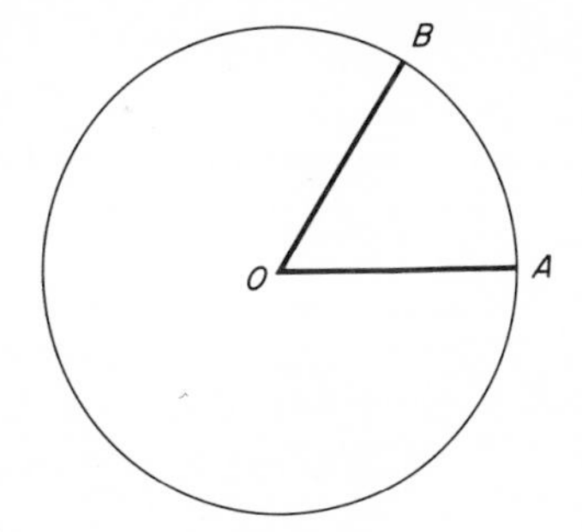

Figure 8-1

of the radius. The values of s and r must be in the same units. Note that these units cancel out, so that θ is a pure number.

If θ_{rad} is the value of an angular displacement in radians and θ_{rev} is the corresponding displacement in terms of revolutions, the definition of a radian obviously requires that

$$\theta_{rad} = 2\pi\theta_{rev}, \quad \text{and} \quad \theta_{rev} = \frac{\theta_{rad}}{2\pi} \tag{8-2}$$

8-4 Velocity and Acceleration in Rotary Motion

According to Sec. 5-2 and Eq. (5-1), $v_a = s/t$, in which v_a is the average speed (average velocity if the directions are specified), and s is the distance moved in the time, t. Similarly, we define the average ***angular velocity*** as the angular distance per unit time:

$$\omega_a = \frac{\theta}{t} \tag{8-3}$$

in which ω_a is the average angular velocity (or speed).

Also in Sec. 5-2, linear acceleration is defined, and the defining equation (5-3) states that $a = (v_f - v_i)/t$. In an exactly similar manner we may define the ***angular acceleration*** as the change of angular velocity per unit time:

$$\alpha = \frac{\omega_f - \omega_i}{t} \tag{8-4}$$

Though any units of angular displacement could be used in Eq. (8-3), it is most convenient to express the value of θ in radians. Thus the unit of angular velocity will be radians per second, radians per minute, etc. As with linear acceleration, there is a double time unit for angular acceleration; so it is expressed as radians per minute per second, radians per second squared, etc. Since we have seen that θ is dimensionless, the fundamental dimension of ω is $1/t$ and that of α is $1/t^2$.

Comparison of Eq. (5-1), (8-1), and (8-3) reveals that

$$\omega = \frac{v}{r}, \quad \text{or} \quad v = r\omega \tag{8-5}$$

and similar comparison of Eq. (5-3), (8-4), and (8-5) shows that

$$\alpha = \frac{a}{r}, \quad \text{or} \quad a = r\alpha \tag{8-6}$$

8-5 Moment of Inertia, and Newton's Second Law as Applied to Rotation

We may think of the mass of a body as the measure of its resistance to linear acceleration, or ***inertia,*** since Newton's second law says that the greater the mass of a body the *less* its acceleration will be, other things being equal. Similarly, the measure of the resistance of a body to *angular* acceleration is called its ***moment of inertia.*** As in the linear case, this depends on the mass, but—*un*like the linear case—it depends also on the *distribution* of the mass about the axis of rotation. This is obvious if you roll a pencil back and forth between your thumb and finger, the rotation being about the long axis of the pencil. You are hardly aware of any resistance to the angular acceleration you impose on the pencil as you start and stop the rolling. But if you take the end of the pencil between the thumb and finger and move it rapidly back and forth pendulumwise you will be unable to cause as great an angular acceleration as before, and you will be definitely aware of the resistance of the pencil. Evidently mass is only *part* of the quantity we call the moment of inertia.

We may find how to compute the moment of inertia with the aid of Fig. 8-2 and Newton's second law of motion. This law states that the linear acceleration imposed on a body is related to its mass and to the accelerating force by Eq. (5-17), which says $a = F/m$, provided that the dynamic unit of force is used. We found in Chapter 4 that torque rather than force alone is responsible for any tendency toward rotation, and we have just seen that the moment of inertia resists angular acceleration as mass resists linear acceleration. Thus the same logic which leads to $a = F/m$ for the linear case will produce

$$\alpha = \frac{M}{I} \tag{8-7}$$

in which the moment is M, and the moment of inertia is I. Dimensional analysis will confirm the validity of the form of this equation, and the absence of any numerical constants—provided dynamic units are employed—can be verified by experiment.

In Fig. 8-2 an arm of length r is attached at right angles to a vertical shaft AB, and there is a mass m at the end of the arm. Assume that the shaft and arm have no appreciable mass and that the dimension of the mass m in the direction of r is small enough so that the entire mass may be considered to be at a distance r from the axis of rotation. If a horizontal force F is applied to the mass in the direction of the arrow, and if its direction is always at right angles to the arm, the mass will be accelerated around the circular path indicated by the dotted line, the value of the acceleration being F/m.

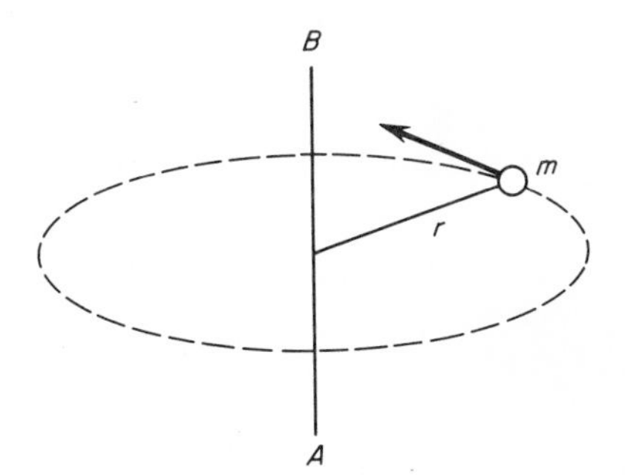

Figure 8-2

In terms of rotary motion, we are concerned with the moment M rather than the force F. In general,

$M = F \cdot d$, according to Eq. (4-1), so in this case $M = Fr$ and $F = M/r$. Also, $a = r\alpha$, according to Eq. (8-6). Thus the equation $a = F/m$ becomes

$$r\alpha = \frac{M/r}{m}$$

which rearranges to

$$\alpha = \frac{M}{mr^2}$$

and comparison of this with Eq. (8-7) shows that

$$I = mr^2 \tag{8-8}$$

Thus the moment of inertia of a mass m, all of which is located at a distance r from the axis of rotation, is mr^2. This expression is valid for a thin ring or a thin hollow cylinder of mass m and radius r rotating about its axis; but for objects like solid cylinders, balls, rectangular bodies, etc., the moment of inertia is less than mr^2 because most of the mass is at a distance less than r from the axis. In general,

$$I = kmr^2 \tag{8-9}$$

in which k is a dimensionless constant. By means of the calculus it is possible to evaluate k for a particular body rotating about a particular axis—and also to derive Eq. (8-8) without the unrealistic assumptions we were forced to make. The expressions for the moment of inertia of a few bodies are given in Table 8-1.

It is sometimes convenient to think of the ***radius of gyration*** of a body, which is the value of a radius such that the moment of inertia would be unchanged if the entire mass of the body were at that distance from

Table 8-1

VALUES OF THE MOMENTS OF INERTIA OF VARIOUS UNIFORM BODIES

Description of body	Axis of rotation	Moment of inertia
Circular disk	Through center of disk, perpendicular to plane of disk	$mr^2/2$
Solid sphere	Through center of sphere	$2mr^2/5$
Very thin hollow cylindrical shell	Axis of cylinder	mr^2
Very thin hollow spherical shell	Through center of sphere	$2mr^2/3$
Long thin rod, length r	Through center of rod, perpendicular to length of rod	$mr^2/12$
Long thin rod, length r	Through one end, perpendicular to length of rod	$mr^2/3$

the center of rotation. If the radius of gyration is a, this definition means that

$$I = ma^2 \tag{8-10}$$

but since in general $I = kmr^2$, according to Eq. (8-9), it follows that

$$a^2 = kr^2, \quad \text{or} \quad a = r\sqrt{k} \tag{8-11}$$

For example, the radius of gyration of a uniform solid sphere would be $r \cdot \sqrt{2/5}$, or about 0.632 times its radius. This means that if all the mass of the sphere could be rearranged into a very thin spherical shell without altering the value of the moment of inertia, the radius of the cylindrical shell would have to be approximately 0.632 times that of the original sphere.

8-6 Equations Pertinent to Angular Motion

As noted in the preview, equations for rotational motion will be developed from those appropriate for linear motion, by analogy, rather than being derived rigorously. On either basis, we must be familiar with the equivalences summarized in Table 8-2.

Now let us make a table of equations for linear motion and the equivalent equations for angular motion. Equations for linear motion appear in the left side of Table 8-3, and a *few* of those for angular motion are given. But the blanks on the right side show that "us" in the second sentence above was meant literally.

A dimensional check may reassure you that the equations you write are valid, at least in form. Let us check one of those provided, $W = M\theta$, Eq. (8-15). First we must find the dimensions of the quantity work, W.

Table 8-2

ANALOGOUS QUANTITIES, WITH SYMBOLS

Linear motion		Angular motion	
Quantity	Symbol	Quantity	Symbol
Displacement	S	Angular displacement	ϕ
Velocity	v	Angular velocity	ω
Average velocity	v_a	Average angular velocity	ω_a
Initial velocity	v_i	Initial angular velocity	ω_i
Final velocity	v_f	Final angular velocity	ω_f
Acceleration	a	Angular acceleration	α
Force	F	Torque	M
Mass	m	Moment of inertia	I

Table 8-3

Equations for linear motion		Equivalent equations for angular motion	
$v_a = s/t$	(5-1)	$\omega_a = \theta/t$	(8-3)
$a = (v_f - v_i)/t$	(5-3)	$\alpha = (\omega_f - \omega_i)/t$	(8-4)
$v_f = v_i + at$	(5-7)	$\omega_f = \omega_i + \alpha t$	(8-12)
$s = v_i t + at^2/2$	(5-11)	$\theta = \omega_i t + \frac{1}{2}\alpha t^2$	(8-13)
$v_f{}^2 = v_i{}^2 + 2as$	(5-14)	$\omega_f{}^2 = \omega_i{}^2 + 2\alpha\theta$	(8-14)
$a = F/m$	(5-18)	$\alpha = M/I$	(8-7)
$W = Fs$	(6-1)	$W = M\theta$	(8-15)
$P = W/t$	(6-4)	$P =$	(8-16)
$P = Fv$	(6-6)	$P = M\omega$	(8-17)
$\text{KE} = mv^2/2$	(6-2)	$\text{KE} = \frac{1}{2} I\omega^2$	(8-18)
$p = mv$	(6-7)	$p = I\omega$	(8-19)
$\text{Ft} = m\,\Delta v$	(6-9)	$Mt = \Delta I\omega$	(8-20)

In the linear case $W = Fs$, and according to Newton's second law, $F = ma$, so $W = mas$. Dimensionally, $a = l/t^2$ and $s = l$; so in terms of dimensions

$$W = m \cdot \frac{l}{t^2} \cdot l = \frac{ml^2}{t^2}$$

In the rotational case, we have $W = M\theta$ and $M = Fr$, so $M = mar$. Dimensionally this is identical with mas, since r, like s, is a length; so the dimensions of M are ml^2/t^2, exactly as for W. This looks bad, since we must multiply M by θ; but it's OK because $\theta = s/r$, according to Eq. (8-1) and hence has dimensions of l/l; that is, it is dimensionless.

Sample Problem 1

The rotor of a small electric motor has a mass of 80.0 g and a radius of gyration of 1.50 cm. What torque is necessary to give it an angular acceleration of 20.0 radians per second per second?

The moment of inertia is given by Eq. (8-10):

$$I = ma^2 = 80.0 \cdot 1.50^2 = 80.0 \cdot 2.25 = 180 \text{ g cm}^2$$

Newton's second law says

$$\alpha = \frac{M}{I}$$

so

$$M = I\alpha = 180 \cdot 20.0 = 3600 \text{ cm dynes}$$

Sample Problem 2

If the initial angular velocity of the rotor in Sample Problem 1 is 50.0 rad/sec, how many revolutions will it make before attaining an angular velocity of 500 rad/sec?

From Eq. (8-14) in Table 8-3,

$$\omega_f^2 = \omega_i^2 + 2\alpha\theta$$

$$500^2 = 50.0^2 + 2 \cdot 20.0\,\theta$$

$$250{,}000 - 2500 = 40.0\,\theta = 247{,}500$$

$$\theta = \frac{247{,}500}{40.0} = 6.19 \cdot 10^3 \text{ rad,}$$

or

$$\theta = \frac{(6.19) \cdot 10^3}{2\pi} = 985 \text{ rev}$$

Let me emphasize again that if you know the equations for linear motion, you can write any equivalent equation for angular motion by analogy. You do *not* have to memorize a whole new set of equations.

8-7 Application of Newton's First Law to Angular Motion; the Gyroscope

If there were such a thing as a *completely* frictionless level surface, and if you were stranded motionless in the middle of it, it might seem that you would have to stay until a rescuer threw you one end of a rope; for there would be no apparent way in which you could bring an accelerating force to bear. Actually, however, you could rescue yourself easily by simply removing a shoe and throwing it.

As applied to linear motion, Newton's first law says that there can be no acceleration without an unbalanced outside force, and this is equivalent to stating that only if such a force acts on a body can the momentum of the body be altered. But momentum is a *vector* quantity, and if a body or system has zero momentum initially it is only necessary that the *net* momentum remain zero. A *part* of a system may acquire a momentum *if* the *remainder* of the system simultaneously acquires an *equal and opposite* momentum. (The *vector* sum of two equal and opposite momenta is zero, just as the resultant of two equal and opposite forces is zero.) So by throwing your shoe you would cause yourself to slide slowly in the opposite direction—slowly, since equality of the magnitudes of the two momenta requires that the velocities be inversely proportional to the respective masses.

Now consider Newton's first law as applied to angular motion. With logic similar to that in Sec. 6-12, where the principle of conservation of linear momentum was developed, we could show that whatever the value

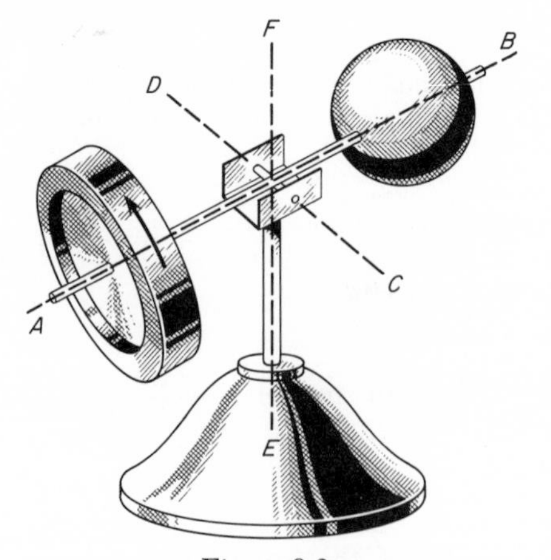

Figure 8-3

of the angular momentum of a body about a particular axis may be (including zero), that value must remain constant unless there is an outside unbalanced torque *about that axis* (or one parallel to it). A torque about a *horizontal* axis, for example, cannot affect the angular momentum about a *vertical* axis.

In Fig. 8-3 we have a gyroscope with the wheel spinning counterclockwise (as seen from the left) about a horizontal axis *AB*. There can be tilting about the horizontal axis *CD*, but before the wheel was set rotating the counter-weight near the right end of the axis *AB* was adjusted so that there was no tendency to tilt. The whole system (except the stand) can rotate about the vertical axis *EF*.

Suppose that with the wheel rotating as shown you push down on the counterweight. You might be surprised at the result, but if we analyse the situation first we see that the result is inevitable. Instead of the counterweight tipping down, the axis *AB* remains practically horizontal while the whole system commences to rotate clockwise (as seen from above) about the axis *EF*. Why?

Initially there was no angular momentum about the vertical axis *EF* and there has been no torque about this axis, so Newton's first law requires that the *net* angular momentum about this axis remain zero. The downward force on the counterweight causes a *slight* tilt about the axis *CD*, so the wheel is tilted up slightly. *If* such a tilt were to continue until the axis *AB* had become vertical, *A* at the top, the angular momentum of the wheel would be counterclockwise as seen from above. Thus *any* tilt in that direction, no matter how small, introduces a small *component* of the wheel's angular momentum to the vertical axis, in a counterclockwise sense as seen from above. But the *net* angular momentum about the vertical axis *must* remain zero (just as the net linear momentum of you-plus-shoe had to), and this can be achieved only if an equal angular momentum in a *clock*wise direction appears about the vertical axis. And this is precisely what occurs. The rotation of the gyroscope about a vertical axis as the result of a torque about a horizontal axis is ***precession.***

A similar analysis of the effect of a torque about the vertical axis *EF* will show that the axis *AB* will tilt up or down.

8-8 Centripetal Acceleration

Uniform circular motion seems to present a paradox. There must be a force acting constantly on any body which is moving around a circular path, since the direction of the motion is changing continuously and Newton's first law says that the "state of motion can *not* change unless a force acts." Yet, since the circular motion is *uniform*, the speed of the body is constant in spite of the continued application of the force.

Realization that forces, velocities, and accelerations are all *vector* quantities removes any inconsistency, leaving only a requirement that the force be always perpendicular to the velocity. Under these circumstances, the acceleration can never have any component parallel with the velocity; so it will be *only* the *direction* of the velocity which is affected, leaving the *speed* uniform. Since at any instant the direction of the velocity is tangential to the circular path, the direction of the acceleration must be along a radius; hence it is termed ***centripetal acceleration.***

The relationship of the centripetal acceleration to other quantities may be deduced with the aid of Fig. 8-4. At some particular instant the body may be at the position marked *1* in Fig. 8-4(a), and it will have a velocity v_1. After a time interval t has elapsed it will be at position 2 and its velocity will be v_2. This new velocity must be the vector sum of the initial velocity and the change of velocity; in symbols, $v_2 = v_1 + \Delta v$ *if* we interpret the "+" as implying *vector* addition. This vector addition is represented in Fig. 8-4(b), in which v_1 and v_2 are constructed in the proper directions and of the correct length, and the vector responsible for the change of direction is Δv. According to Eq. (5-4), $a = \Delta v/t$ so $\Delta v = at$. Since at any instant the acceleration must be perpendicular to the velocity and since the direction of the velocity changes uniformly from that of v_1 to that of v_2, the vector Δv, or at, must be an arc rather than a straight line.

The magnitude of the velocity is not changing, so the vectors v_1 and

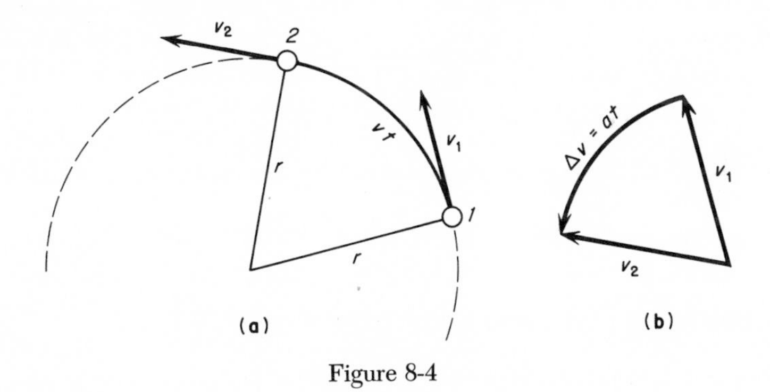

Figure 8-4

v_2 have the same length. The angle between these vectors in Fig. 8-4(b) is equal to that between the two radii in Fig. 8-4(a), because the velocities and the radii are mutually perpendicular. And obviously the two radii are of equal length. Thus the circular sector formed by the two radii and the arc vt in Fig. 8-4(a) is similar to the circular sector in Fig. 8-4(b). As with similar triangles, corresponding parts must be directly proportional. Thus,

$$\frac{a_c t}{v} = \frac{vt}{r}$$

In this equation, the subscript c has been added to the symbol a to emphasize that the equation deals with *centripetal* acceleration rather than with acceleration in general. Also, the subscripts have been dropped from v_1 and v_2 because the velocities are equal in magnitude. Division of both sides of the equation by t and multiplication by v produces

$$a_c = \frac{v^2}{r} \tag{8-21}$$

Since $v = r\omega$, according to Eq. (8-5) we may replace v^2 by $r^2\omega^2$ in Eq. (8-21). The r in the numerator will cancel one of those in the denominator, so

$$a_c = r\omega^2 \tag{8-22}$$

Sample Problem 3

A boy swings a small pail of water in a vertical circle of 70.0 cm radius. What is the minimum number of revolutions per second required to prevent him from getting an impromptu bath?

Gravitational force is always acting on the water, so it is subject to a constant downward acceleration g. If, when the pail is directly overhead, the value of g is less than the centripetal acceleration required to keep the water in its curvilinear path, the boy's arm must supply the additional downward acceleration, and the water will remain in the bucket. If g exceeds the necessary centripetal acceleration, the water will leave the bucket and douse the lad. At the "break-even" point the centripetal acceleration is just equal to the gravitational acceleration; that is,

$$a_c = g, \quad \text{but also} \quad a_c = r\omega^2$$

so

$$r\omega^2 = g$$

or

$$\omega = \sqrt{g/r} = \sqrt{980/70.0} = \sqrt{14.0} = 3.74 \text{ rad/sec}$$

From Eq. (8-2) the number of revolutions is the number of radians divided by 2π, so

$$\text{rps} = \frac{\omega}{2\pi} = 3.74 \div 2\pi = 0.596$$

8-9 Centripetal Force and Centrifugal Force

No acceleration is possible without a force, and according to Newton's second law the force in dynamic units is related to the mass and the acceleration by Eq. (5-17), $F = ma$. In Eq. (8-21) and (8-22), we found the centripetal acceleration to be v^2/r or $r\omega^2$, so there must be a ***centripetal force*** such that

$$F_c = \frac{mv^2}{r} \tag{8-23}$$

or

$$F_c = mr\omega^2 \tag{8-24}$$

in which F_c represents the centripetal force.

Newton's third law of motion states that for every action there is an equal and opposite reaction. When you apply a horizontal accelerating force to a loaded grocery cart in a supermarket, the cart exerts an equal force back against you because the mass of the loaded cart resists acceleration. Similarly, if you swing a bunch of keys on a chain around in a circle, you must apply a centripetal force to constrain the keys to a circular path. Their inertia tends to carry them along a *straight* path rather than a curved one, so they pull outward against your hand; that is, they exert a ***centrifugal force*** equal in magnitude to the centripetal force, but outwardly rather than inwardly directed.

Note carefully that the centrifugal force does *not* act on the bunch of keys. It acts on the key chain and, through the agency of the chain, on your hand. There is *no* force acting radially outward *on the keys*. If there were such a force acting on the keys, when you release the chain the bunch of keys should fly radially outward, but they don't; they fly *tangentially* away.

Students often confuse the terms "centripetal" and "centrifugal," but this can be avoided easily. A *fugitive* is one who flees, so a centri*fug*al force is a center-*fleeing* force; that is, an *out*wardly directed one.

Sample Problem 4

A car which has a mass of 3600 lb is "taking" a turn which has a radius of 200 ft at a speed of 30.0 mph. Compute the centripetal force in pounds required to hold the car in the turn.

Since 60.0 mph is 88.0 ft/sec, 30.0 mph will be 44.0 ft/sec. The centripetal force is equal to mv^2/r, according to Eq. (8-23), so

$$F_c = \frac{3600 \cdot 44.0^2}{200}\text{ pdl} = \frac{3600 \cdot 44.0^2}{200 \cdot 32.0}\text{ lb} = 108\bar{9} \text{ or } 1090 \text{ lb}$$

Sample Problem 5

If in Sample Problem 4 the road surface is horizontal (the turn is not banked), what is the minimum value of the coefficient of friction between the tires and the road which will make the turn possible without skidding?

According to Eq. (7-14), $\mu = F_f/F_n$. The force of friction must supply the centripetal force, so F_f must be at least as large as F_c. Having solved Sample Problem 4, we need only divide the centripetal force of 1090 lb by the weight of 3600 lb.

But let us consider this as an entirely new problem. $\mu = F_f/F_n$, and for the minimum value of μ, $F_f = F_c$. Algebraically,

$$F_c = mv^2/r, \quad \text{and} \quad F_n = mg$$

Hence,
$$\mu = \frac{mv^2}{r} \div mg = \frac{v^2}{rg} = \frac{44.0^2}{200 \cdot 32.0} = 0.302$$

Note that the fact that m canceled out means that we can handle a problem of this sort in terms of accelerations rather than forces.

Sample Problem 6

A 100 g weight is tied at the end of a string and whirled in a horizontal circle of 15.0 cm radius at a rate of 3.00 revolutions per second. What breaking strength must the cord have?

3.00 rps is $3.00 \cdot 2\pi$ rad/sec.

$$F = mr\omega^2$$

so
$$F = 100 \cdot 15.0 \cdot (6.00\pi)^2 = 5.33 \cdot 10^6 \text{ dynes}$$

We could have used the equation $F = mv^2/r$ instead, in which $v = 2\pi r \cdot \text{rps}$; this would have yielded the same result.

Summary

Any type of *motion* which *repeats* itself is *periodic motion;* it is *uniform* periodic motion if the *period,* the time required for one complete cycle, is *constant.*

One *radian* is an *arc* such that the *length* of the arc is equal to the *radius.* It is also the *angle subtended* by that arc.

Angular velocity and *angular acceleration* are defined in a manner exactly parallel with the definitions of the *corresponding linear quantities.* The equations for these two quantities in rotational motion may be written by taking the corresponding equations for linear motion and substituting symbols appropriate for rotary motion for those pertinent to linear motion. All other equations dealing with rotary motion may be obtained in a similar manner from the corresponding equations for linear motion.

In *rotational motion, torque* has the function which *force* has in linear motion, and *moment of inertia* has the function which *mass* has in linear motion. The moment of inertia is dependent on the distribution of the mass about the axis of rotation, as well as on the mass itself.

As applied to rotary motion, Newton's first law states that the angular momentum of a body about a particular axis must remain unchanged unless an unbalanced torque acts about that axis. Analysis of this statement furnishes an explanation for the precession of a gyroscope.

Any body in *uniform circular motion* is subject to a *constant centripetal acceleration.* The centripetal acceleration is due to a *centripetal force.* The *reaction* of the *body* to the *centripetal force* is the *centrifugal force.*

Self-Quiz

1. Explain clearly how the speed of a body may remain constant even though it is constantly being accelerated. In what type of motion is this situation the normal thing?

2. What is radian measure? What is a radian? How can you convert from revolutions to radians? How can you determine the number of degrees in a radian (without just looking it up)? Did you give one definition, or two, to answer the question, "What is a radian?"

3. Why isn't the concept of mass used in dealing with rotational motion instead of the much messier concept of moment of inertia? Why can't the same equation be used for computing the moment of inertia of a solid sphere (for example) as for calculating that of a disk?

4. Derive the form of the equation for the moment of inertia. Go as far as you can without referring to Sec. 8-5.

5. In what ways must Newton's first law of motion be modified in order to make it conveniently applicable to rotary motion? Explain the necessity of each such modification.

6. If in a certain system there is initially no linear momentum and if no unbalanced force from outside the system acts on it, does this mean that there can never be any linear momentum whatever in the system? Explain.

7. In Sec. 8-6 we found that the dimensions of work and energy are ml^2/t^2. In view of this, what are the dimensions of power? Make a dimensional analysis of the equation $P = M\omega$; does this equation yield the correct dimensions?

8. Show that the equation $\theta = \omega_i t + \alpha t^2/2$ is dimensionally homogeneous. Also show that the equation $\mathrm{KE} = I\omega^2/2$ yields the proper dimensions for energy.

9. Construct a table similar to Table 8-2, preferably without referring to that table.

10. List as many equations pertinent to linear motion as you can, somewhat as in the left-hand side of Table 8-3, and opposite each write in the corresponding equation for rotary motion. If you "get stuck" don't refer to Table 8-3; refer instead to the table of equivalents you have made in answer to Question 9.

11. Explain the precession of the gyroscope in Fig. 8-3, referring as little as possible to Sec. 8-7. Now analyze the effect of applying a horizontal force to the counterweight in such a direction that the resulting torque tends to rotate the system in a clockwise sense about the vertical axis *EF*.

12. On the basis of Newton's first law of motion as applied to rotational motion, show how a bicyclist can turn a corner "hands off" by leaning in the direction he wishes to turn.

13. Distinguish between the terms "centripetal" and "centrifugal." How can you easily avoid confusing them, without resorting to rote memorization?

14. Why is a centripetal force necessary in rotational motion?

15. A passenger in a car driven by a gasoline cowboy may be thrown toward the right side of the car when a sharp turn is made to the left, or vice versa. If he isn't a physics student, he may incorrectly believe that centrifugal force is responsible. In the absence of any such force acting on him, why is he thrown toward the outside of the turn?

16. Explain how a ballet dancer or figure skater can increase or decrease her rate of spinning by folding her arms across her chest or extending them. What basic principle is involved? What means does a fancy diver or tumbler use to control his rate of turning?

17. If you take a key chain with keys and whirl the bunch of keys in a circle, allowing the chain to wind around your finger, the value of r decreases, causing that of I to be reduced. Since momentum must be conserved and $p = I\omega$, the value of ω must be inversely proportional to that of I, so ω increases. But KE $= I\omega^2/2$, and since $I\omega$ is constant, $I\omega^2/2$ must increase; that is, the kinetic energy is *in*creased. Where does the extra energy come from?

Problems

1. From the number of degrees in a circle and the number of radians in a circle calculate the number of degrees in a radian.

2. If the tire on a car has a diameter of 30.0 in. and if the wheel has an angular velocity of 10.0 rad/sec, what is the speed of the car in ft/sec and in mph?

3. A wheel has a diameter of 18.0 cm and the diameter of the hub is 5.00 cm. (a) What is the linear acceleration of a point on the rim of the wheel if the angular acceleration is 50.0 rad/sec²? (b) What is the linear acceleration of a point on the hub?

4. Compute the centripetal acceleration of each of the two points in Problem 3 at an instant when the angular velocity is 30.0 rad/sec.

5. A uniform disk has a radius of 6.00 cm and a mass of 400 g. A second such disk has a radius of 20.0 cm and a mass of 1500 g. (a) Compute the moment of inertia of each individual disk, if the axis of rotation coincides with the axis of the disk. (b) If the two disks were rigidly connected on a common axis what would their combined moment of inertia about that axis be?

6. A constant tension of 20.0 lb is maintained on the free end of a cord which is wrapped around a uniform drum of 15.0 in. radius. If the mass of the drum is 16.0 lb, compute its angular acceleration.

7. With the aid of the conversion $r\omega = v$, prove that the kinetic energy of a uniform sphere which is rolling with a linear velocity v is $0.700\ mv^2$.

8. A solid sphere, a solid disk, and a thin hollow cylinder roll down the same inclined plane, and a block slides down the plane. The vertical height of the plane is 45.0 cm and each object starts at the top. Each of the bodies is uniform and (we shall assume) moves with no loss of energy due to friction. Calculate for each object the linear speed with which it reaches the bottom of the incline.

9. If in the previous problem the time of descent for the disk is 5.00 sec, compute the time of descent for each of the other bodies.

10. A yo-yo has a mass of 50.0 g and a moment of inertia of 100 g cm^2, and at a certain instant it is rising on the string with a linear velocity of 7.50 cm/sec and an angular velocity of 200 rad/sec. If there were no friction how much higher would the yo-yo rise? What would this value be if the efficiency were 85.0%?

11. The rotor of an electric motor is "coasting" (turning after the electric power has been cut off). The angular acceleration is -62.5 rad/sec^2 and after the rotor has turned through 5200 rad the angular velocity is 700 rad/sec. Calculate the initial angular velocity.

12. If in the preceding problem the torque is 50,000 cm dynes and the moment of inertia 800 g cm^2, how long did it require for the rotor to reach the final angular velocity? (This problem can be solved with no data except that in the preceding problem; try both methods of solution.)

13. (a) What centripetal acceleration is necessary to enable a jet plane flying at 600 mph to make a turn (in a horizontal plane) with a radius of 5000 ft? (b) For a turn of the same radius, what velocity would require a centripetal acceleration exactly four times as great as gravitational acceleration?

14. A stunt flyer puts his plane through a loop (in a vertical plane) which is "tight" enough so that at the top of the loop he is pressing against his seat with the same force as if he were in normal flight. Prove that the speed of the plane at the top of the loop is related to the radius of the loop by the equation $v = \sqrt{2rg}$.

15. A car which weighs (with passengers) 4000 lb negotiates a turn which has a radius of 800 ft. (a) If the speed of the car is 60.0 mph, compute the centripetal force required to hold the car in the turn. (b) Either graphically or by trigonometry determine the angle of "bank" of the roadway in the turn which would eliminate any tendency to skid at this speed.

16. A body with a mass of 10.0 kg is fastened to a cord and swung in a vertical circle with a radius of 20.0 cm. The angular velocity is 8.00 rad/sec and we shall assume that this velocity is constant. Compute the tension in the cord (a) when the body is at the highest point of the circle, and (b) also when it is at the lowest point.

17. Assume that an experimental plane has been climbing, cuts off power and coasts along a circular arc in a vertical plane, and continues to descend. Assume also that while the plane follows the arc its speed is 2400 mph and that at that altitude the acceleration due to gravity is 31.0 ft/sec^2. If as the plane moves through the arc the pilot is "weightless," determine the radius of the arc.

18. Compute the radius of gyration of each of the disks in Problem 5, and also the radius of gyration of the combination of the two disks.

9
UNIVERSAL GRAVITATION

9-1 Preview

In this chapter we shall meet Newton's law of universal gravitation. This law, with the aid of the equation for centripetal force, accounts for the manner in which the planets move in their orbits about the sun—hardly surprising, since previous astronomical observations of planetary motions were the basis from which Newton developed the law. What is *surprising is the ingenuity with which Newton's law of gravitation was used as the basis of a laboratory method for "weighing" the earth. This law also furnishes much of the foundation which enabled such things as artificial satellites to escape from the pages of science fiction to the world of reality.*

9-2 The Paradox of "Action at a Distance"

We know from Newton's first law of motion, which we met in Chapter 5, that neither the magnitude nor the direction of the motion of a body can change unless an unbalanced force acts on the body. If the terms "motionless" and "moving" had any real significance, this would mean that a motionless body must remain so and a moving body must continue to move in the same direction at an unchanging speed, unless some accelerating force acts on it.

Yet our lives are full of experiences which seem to contradict this. At an age when a rattle was as important to you as a convertible may be now, you found that if you relaxed your grip on the rattle it underwent a downward acceleration; and this sort of thing has been so common since that you probably take it for granted. But the problem remains: *without any physical contact* between the earth and a body, the earth seems to exert a force on the body. At least, the body is accelerated downward unless an upward force is applied to it to prevent such acceleration.

What is the source of such forces, and by what means are they applied? As you were warned in Chapter 1, we find ourselves up against a brick wall. If we had sufficient background in mathematics and physics, and a robust imagination, we could use these as a pole to vault to the top of the wall, where we could see over and understand the nature of such forces, and how they act. We are limited to a glimpse through a chink in the wall, however, and when we peep through it we shall be inclined to disbelieve our eyes. There are no such forces, mysteriously applied, at all; they are illusions. Instead, in the neighborhood of any mass, space is warped or curved; and so masses move serenely along "world lines" in this warped space, giving the *illusion* that they are undergoing acceleration and hence *seeming* to be subjected to non-existent accelerating forces.

Another glance through our peephole reveals that there is another kind of warpage of space caused by magnetic poles, and still another due to electric charges, and that, in general, each of these causes of warpage is unaffected by any warpage due to a different cause.

Obviously, at our level, these ideas give us no real basis for even a qualitative understanding, and the mathematics requisite to a quantitative understanding are equally beyond most of us.

Hence we shall label all such phenomena as examples of "action at a distance." We shall assume that there is no warpage of space, that the apparent accelerations are real, and that they are due to actual forces. These assumptions will enable us to "understand" much better than the more esoteric point of view could, and they will enable us to work out quantitative relationships which are experimentally valid. In speaking of action-at-a-distance forces as "real," however, and using them in computations, we must not forget that we probably are using an oversimplification rather than dealing with reality.

The situation is somewhat like that we met in the last paragraph of Sec. 6-9. There we found, after deriving an equation for kinetic energy, that it is valid only for nonrelativistic speeds. When the value of v is small compared with the speed of light, however, the equation which is applicable regardless of the speeds—relativistic or nonrelativistic—reduces to $KE = mv^2/2$. Somewhat similarly, we may consider our treatment of action-at-a-distance forces to be a simplified special case of a more esoteric treatment.

9-3 Newton's Law of Universal Gravitation

Legend has it that Newton conceived the idea of the law of gravitation when, as he was sitting under an apple tree, an apple fell and "conked" him on the noggin. If I had unlimited faith in that legend, I would be tempted to have my physics class in an apple orchard while lecturing! (Or maybe in a cocoanut grove!)

The real situation seems to have been that Newton was interested in the basis of the stability of the solar system. Why do planets remain in their orbits around the sun, when it is "natural" for bodies to move in a straight line? Astronomers had accumulated much data with regard to the motions of the planets and the moon, and one of them, Kepler, had stated three laws of planetary motion. These data, and Kepler's laws, furnished a starting point for Newton. Since Newton's law of gravitation is more fundamental, however, we shall consider it first; and later we shall derive one of Kepler's laws as a logical consequence of the law of gravitation.

Newton's law of universal gravitation states that there is a force of *mutual* attraction between *any* two bodies anywhere in the universe, the magnitude of the force being directly proportional to the mass of each body (and hence to the product of the two masses) and inversely proportional to the square of the distance between them. We found in Chapter 5, when trying to translate Newton's second law of motion into algebra, that it was necessary to include a proportionality constant to make the resulting equation numerically valid, and a similar situation exists here. If the gravitational force is F_g, the mass of one body m_1 and that of the other m_2, and if the distance between them is d,

$$F_g = G \cdot \frac{m_1 m_2}{d^2} \tag{9-1}$$

The constant G is necessary to make the equation dimensionally valid, as well as for numerical validity. It is called the ***universal gravitational constant;*** and its value is

$$6.67 \cdot 10^{-8} \text{ dyne cm}^2/\text{g}^2$$

or

$$6.67 \cdot 10^{-11} \text{ newton m}^2/\text{kg}^2$$

or

$$1.07 \cdot 10^{-19} \text{ pdl ft}^2/\text{lb}^2$$

Note that this law not only says that the earth attracts you with a force equal to your weight; it also says that *you* attract the *earth* with an equal force. We should have expected this, of course, since Newton's third law of motion certainly requires it. More striking and novel are these facts: you attract the book you are reading and it attracts you; there is a force between you and the materials of the ceiling and roof, and this *gravitational* force acts *upward* on you; each of your shoes experiences a gravitational attraction for the other—and for every other shoe anywhere; etc.

It is instructive to note what the law of gravitation does *not* say. No physical factors other than the magnitudes of the masses and the distance between them are involved, and there is no minimum limit on the masses and no maximum limit on the distances. There is no factor to reflect the influence of any medium which may exist between the two masses, so gravitational forces are the same whether they act through a vacuum or through very dense matter; it is impossible to "insulate" a body against the gravitational attraction of another by interposing something between them as we insulate one electric charge from another by interposing a sheet of glass or other nonconductor.

Before proceeding, we must consider more carefully the "distance between" the two masses. For astronomical bodies, this distance is so tremendous that the diameter of either body is negligible by comparison. This is not true, however, if we are concerned with the attraction between two metal spheres which are close together, or in any similar situation. In the case of the spheres, if they are uniform the pertinent distance is that between their centers. We may be tempted to generalize this and use in every situation the distance between the centers of mass of the two bodies; but as we found in the last three paragraphs in Sec. 4-5, this may lead to invalid results. Except where an effective distance is specified, our considerations must be limited to uniform spheres, unless the distance between the bodies is very large compared with their dimensions.

9-4 The Evaluation of "G"; How to "Weigh" the Earth

After Newton stated his law of gravitation, more than a century passed before the value of the constant G was determined. This measurement was made by Cavendish, who used an apparatus represented (in much simplified form) in Fig. 9-1, which assumes that the point of view is directly above the apparatus. At O is a vertical wire (seen end-on, so that it is just a dot) which supports a very light but strong horizontal arm. At

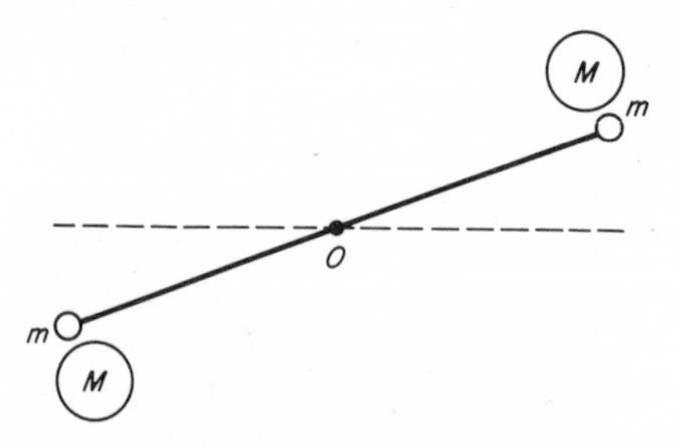

Fig. 9-1. The Cavendish experiment.

each end of the arm is a lead ball of mass m. Initially the arm assumes the position shown by the dashed line, but if large lead spheres each of mass M are placed as shown by the larger circles, the gravitational forces between each mass m and the adjacent mass M cause a torque which moves the arm to the position shown in solid lines. This causes a slight twist in the supporting wire, thus generating an opposing torque in the wire.

To obtain a value of G from this experiment, the relationship between the torque applied to the wire and the resulting twist must be found. Suppose that the masses M were to be removed and the arm (still carrying the masses m) were to be displaced through a small angle. When released, it would twist back to the rest position but its momentum would carry it beyond, so it would oscillate for a time. Obviously the less resistance the wire offers to being twisted, the longer the period of oscillation, and vice versa, since according to Eq. (8-7), angular acceleration is directly proportional to torque. In fact, we shall see in Chapter 12 that if we know the mass of a body which is suspended from a spring, and the period of vibration, we can compute the relationship between the force applied to the spring and the resulting distortion; and in a similar manner the relationship between torque and angular displacement of the wire in the Cavendish experiment may be computed from the period of vibration and the moment of inertia. Once the torque has been determined in this way, force may be calculated by dividing the moment arm into the torque. Since there are *two* pairs of balls, half of this computed force is the force of gravitational attraction between *one* mass m and the adjacent mass M. (As a first approximation, we may ignore the gravitational force between a mass m at one end of the arm and the mass M near the *other* end. The inverse square law and the fact that the moment arm of such a force would be very small combine to make the effect of these forces extremely small.) There is no difficulty in determining the mass of each lead ball and the distance between their centers of gravity; so everything in Eq. (9-1) is known except the value of G. By this method, Cavendish's data give a value of G about 2% higher than the values in the preceding section.

Since the weight mg (in dynamic units) of a body at the earth's surface is the gravitational attraction between the body and the earth, it follows that for a body of mass m

$$F_g = \text{weight}, \quad \text{or} \quad \frac{GmM}{r^2} = mg$$

in which M is the mass of the earth and r is its radius. Canceling out m and rearranging, we obtain

$$M = \frac{gr^2}{G}$$

Since the value of gravitational acceleration and that of the earth's radius were known, Cavendish's evaluation of G made it possible to compute the mass of the earth and its density. In fact, it was in terms of the earth's density rather than of the gravitational constant G that Cavendish reported his experiments.

Sample Problem 1

Compute the gravitational attraction between the earth and the moon.

The mass of the earth is $5.98 \cdot 10^{24}$ kg and that of the moon is 0.0123 times the earth's mass. The distance between the earth and the moon is $3.84 \cdot 10^5$ km or $3.84 \cdot 10^8$ m. Substitution of these data into Eq. (9-1) yields

$$F = (6.67 \cdot 10^{-11}) \cdot \frac{5.98 \cdot 10^{24} \cdot (0.0123 \cdot 5.98 \cdot 10^{24})}{(3.84 \cdot 10^8)^2}$$

$$= 1.97 \cdot 10^{20}$$

which is the force in newtons. This would be very near to $2.00 \cdot 10^{19}$ kg or $2.00 \cdot 10^{16}$ metric tons, or roughly $2.2 \cdot 10^{16}$ tons.

9-5 Kepler's Laws of Planetary Motion

Consider a planet of mass m moving in an orbit of radius r around the sun, and let M represent the mass of the sun. According to Newton's law of gravitation, if we symbolize the gravitational force by F_g,

$$F_g = G \cdot \frac{mM}{r^2} \qquad (9\text{-}2)$$

For any body to move in a circular path a centripetal force is required, and in Sec. 8-9 we found that the magnitude of this force is

$$F_c = m \cdot \frac{v^2}{r} \qquad (8\text{-}23)$$

in which m is the mass of the planet and F_c is the centripetal force. According to Newton, it is the mutual gravitational attraction between the sun and the planet which supplies the centripetal force required to constrain the planet to its orbit; that is, for this situation F_g in Eq. (9-2) and F_c in Eq. (8-23) are one and the same force. Hence it follows that

$$G \cdot \frac{mM}{r^2} = m \cdot \frac{v^2}{r}$$

The mass of the planet cancels out, and so does one of the r's, leaving

$$\frac{GM}{r} = v^2 \tag{9-3}$$

What does this imply concerning the radius of a planetary orbit and the period (the time required for one complete trip around the orbit) of the planet? The velocity of the planet is distance per unit time; and in this case the distance is the circumference of the orbit, $2\pi r$, and the time is the period t. So

$$v = \frac{2\pi r}{t}$$

and we may put the right-hand side of this equation into the preceding equation in place of v. This yields

$$\frac{GM}{r} = \left(\frac{2\pi r}{t}\right)^2 = \frac{4\pi^2 r^2}{t^2}$$

Collecting the r's on one side and the t's on the other, we have

$$GMt^2 = 4\pi^2 r^3$$

G, 4, and π are all constants, and M has a fixed value so long as we use the equation only for planets of the sun; so all these may be lumped into a single constant k:

$$t^2 = kr^3 \tag{9-4}$$

This final equation says that the squares of the periods of the various planets are directly proportional to the cubes of the radii of their respective orbits. This relationship is known as ***Kepler's Third Law.***

This derivation is not precise since two tacit assumptions have been made, neither of which is valid. Fortunately, however, neither of these invalid assumptions produces any serious error. The use of Eq. (8-23) for the centripetal force implies that the orbit is circular, whereas planetary orbits actually are slightly elliptical. Also, the cancellation of the r in the centripetal force expression and one of those in the gravitational force expression is not quite correct, since these two r's are not identical. They would be identical if the sun remained fixed as the planet revolves around it, but actually the sun-planet system revolves about a common center of mass.

Kepler's other two laws will not be developed, since they are more geometrical in nature and the underlying physical principles are not so obvious as is the case with Kepler's third law. They will merely be stated and explained briefly.

Kepler's first law says that the orbit of a planet is an ellipse and the sun is at one focus of the ellipse. In Fig. 9-2 the ellipse is the orbit of the planet P, and the sun S is at one focus of the ellipse. The actual orbits of the planets are much more nearly circular than this diagram would imply.

(If you are unfamiliar with the focus of an ellipse, proceed as follows: Stick two pins firmly into paper, two or three inches apart. Make a loop of string long enough so that when the loop is placed over one pin it will reach an inch or so past the other pin. Next put the loop over *both* pins, put the point of a pencil inside the loop, and move the pencil outward over the paper until the string is taut. Now move the pencil point around the loop, keeping the loop over both pins and keeping it taut. You have drawn an ellipse, and each pin is at one of the two foci of the ellipse.)

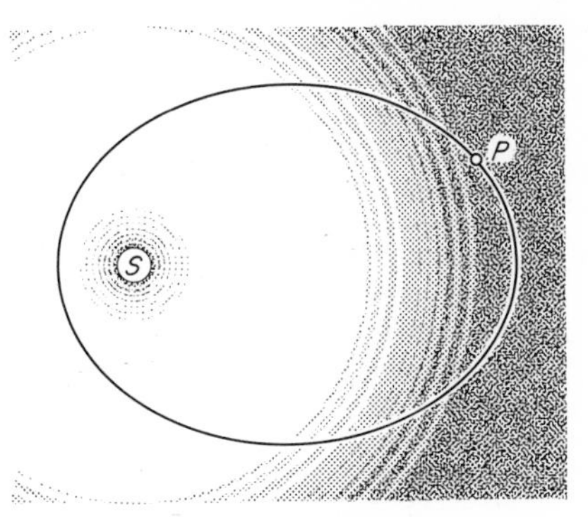

Fig. 9-2. The orbit of a planet is an ellipse (much exaggerated here) with the sun at one focus of the ellipse.

Kepler's second law states that the radius vector sweeps out equal areas in equal times. The radius vector is the line drawn from the sun to the planet, such as SP_1 in Fig. 9-3, and the area "swept out" is any area such as SP_1P_2 or SP_3P_4. Obviously this law means that when the planet is relatively near the sun it must move more rapidly than when the radius vector is longer. We should expect this, for as the planet moves around its orbit from A to B its distance from the sun is increasing, in spite of the gravitational force between it and the sun. This means that it is doing work against the sun's gravitational field, and the energy to do this work must come from its store of kinetic energy. So in this part of its orbit the planet trades kinetic energy for potential energy, and hence its speed decreases. But from B back to A the radius vector is decreasing, so the sun's gravitational field is doing work on the planet; thus it loses potential energy but gains kinetic energy.

9-6 The Universal Gravitational Constant and the Acceleration Due to Gravity

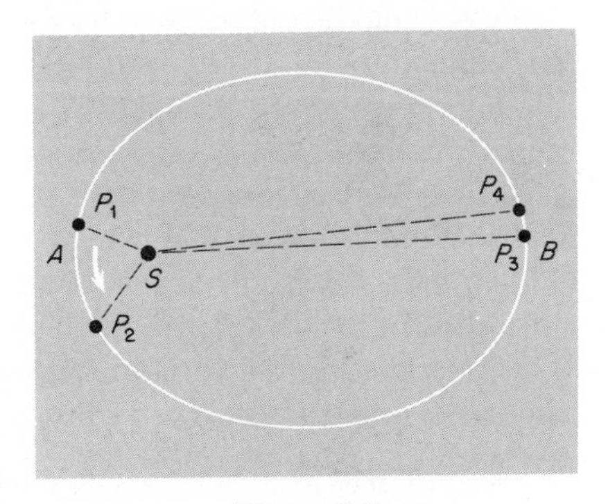

Figure 9-3

Let us consider again a body of mass m at the earth's surface. If the earth's mass is M and its radius r, the gravitational force between the body and the earth is

$$F_g = \frac{GmM}{r^2},$$

according to Eq. (9-2). Division of both sides of this equation by m produces

$$\frac{F_g}{m} = \frac{GM}{r^2}$$

Newton's second law says that if an unbalanced force F acts on a mass m, there will be an acceleration a; or, algebraically, $F/m = a$ (if dynamic units are used). We have been using g to symbolize the acceleration caused by gravity, so $F_g/m = g$. Thus our equation becomes

$$g = \frac{GM}{r^2} \tag{9-5}$$

Here we can really see for the first time why the acceleration of a freely falling body is independent of its mass. We also see what factors determine the value of gravitational acceleration, which has been a purely experimental value heretofore.

It is worth while to note in passing that it is highly ambiguous to speak of "gee" unless the context furnishes a definite clue as to whether "gee" is g or G. Unfortunately, since the same letter is used to symbolize both of these very different quantities, confusion is possible. Unfortunately, too, students are prone to speak of "gee" as representing "gravity" which generates copious additional confusion. *Gravity* is a phenomenon to which both g and G are pertinent, but which is *represented* by *neither:* g represents the *acceleration* caused by a gravitational force, whereas G represents the universal gravitational *constant.* By being careful, rather than sloppy, in your terminology, you can save yourself much difficulty and confusion.

9-7 Escape Velocity

Because the force of gravitational attraction obeys an inverse square law, the weight of a rocket or other body 4000 miles above the earth's surface would be only 25% of its weight at the surface; and this factor would be reduced to 1% at an altitude of 36,000 miles. Thus, as the rocket rises, the energy required to attain any specified additional elevation becomes much smaller; if the energy required for the first thousand feet above the surface is W, that necessary for the first thousand feet beyond 4000 miles is $0.25W$, and only $0.01W$ would be needed for the thousand feet beyond 36,000 miles. A result of this is that a finite quantity of energy would enable a rocket to escape the earth's gravitational field—as some have done. This energy is equal to GmM/r,* where m is the mass of the rocket, M the earth's mass, and r the radius of the earth.

* The derivation of this is beyond the scope of this book, but if you have any acquaintance with integral calculus you can derive it easily, commencing with Eq. (9-2).

To enable a body to escape the earth, we need only give it sufficient kinetic energy. If we disregard the relatively minor quantity of energy lost because of atmospheric friction, a body will just be able to escape if

$$\frac{mv^2}{2} = \frac{GmM}{r}$$

When this is solved for velocity, the result is

$$v = \sqrt{2GM/r} \tag{9-6}$$

Note that the mass of the body, m, cancels out; thus the minimum velocity a body must have to enable it to escape is the same for all bodies regardless of mass. This minimum velocity is the ***escape velocity,*** or the ***velocity of escape.*** Its value is just under 7 miles per second, or approximately 25,000 mph.

Since the gravitational force on the rocket is always directed toward the earth's center, these values of the escape velocity are relative to the center of the earth. A "motionless" rocket at the earth's surface before firing has zero velocity relative to the surface at that point, but the rotation of the earth gives it a velocity relative to the center of the earth. At the equator this velocity is a bit over 1000 mph. If a rocket at the equator were fired horizontally eastward, it would have to be given a speed of about 24,000 mph (relative to the surface) to escape; but one fired westward horizontally would require a speed in excess of 26,000 mph.

9-8 Artificial Satellites and "Space Stations"

The discussion of Kepler's laws led us to Eq. (9-3): $GM/r = v^2$, in which G is the universal gravitational constant, M is the mass of the sun, and r is the radius of the orbit of a planet which has an orbital velocity v. But the equation is not restricted to a sun-planet system. Properly interpreted, it is equally applicable to any system composed of a massive body about which a far less massive body is moving in an orbit. Thus Eq. (9-3) is valid for the earth-moon system, if we interpret M as the mass of the earth. And it may be applied, for exactly the same reasons, to the motion of any "artificial satellite"—rocket case, instrument package, nose cone, radio or TV reflector, etc.—moving in an orbit around the earth. These differ from "natural" satellites in that they may move at small enough elevations so that there is appreciable energy loss due to friction, and in such cases the gradual loss of energy causes them to spiral down to destruction in the denser layers of the atmosphere.

These considerations suggest the possibility of a "space station" in an orbit well above the earth's atmosphere. As we have seen in the preceding section, once a rocket is several earth-diameters above the earth little energy is required to move it much farther away. Thus, any interplanetary vehicles "taking off" from the earth's surface would require a great deal of energy for the very start of their journey, and very little once they were well away from the earth. Hence, it might prove more economical to reserve powerful space craft for a shuttle service between the surface and space stations, leaving the major part of the journey to be accomplished by far less powerful interplanetary craft.

Summary

At our level of scientific and mathematical sophistication, we cannot perceive the ultimate cause of what we call "gravitational attraction"; so we consider such phenomena to be caused by the action of actual forces. Newton's law of universal gravitation states that these forces exist *between any two bodies,* the magnitudes of the forces being *directly proportional* to the *product* of the *masses* and *inversely proportional* to the *square of the distance* between them.

Measurement of the force of gravitational attraction between two bodies (neither of which is the earth) makes possible a computation of the mass of the earth.

The value of gravitational acceleration can be computed with the aid of the law of gravitation.

The law of gravitation leads to many facts and relationships which are basic to rocketry and space travel.

Self-Quiz

1. In Sec. 9-2 there is a very strong implication—which we have met before—that the terms "motionless" and "moving" are meaningless. Why are they? How can they be given definite meaning?

2. Newton's law of gravitation states that *any* body exerts a gravitational force on *every* other body. If this is true, why don't we notice such forces? Why, for example, won't two billiard balls or bowling balls on a hard smooth surface move toward each other because of this force?

3. We are accustomed to consider that an apple falls all the way to the earth. Is this correct, or does the earth fall part of the way toward the apple? Explain your answer.

4. Two particles of different masses are in empty space and are initially motionless with respect to each other. As they accelerate toward each other under the influence of their mutual gravitational attraction, does the center of gravity of the two change its position, or does it remain where it was? Why?

5. It was emphasized that G is the *universal* gravitational constant. This being the case, why were *three* different values given for it?

6. If the distance between two masses is increased by a factor of 5, by what factor would the mass of *one* of them have to be altered to maintain the same gravitational force? Would this be an increase or a decrease in the mass?

7. Suppose that there were a planet which had twice the radius of the earth and three times as large a mass. How would the value of g on that planet compare with its value on earth? How would the values of G compare on the two planets?

8. An artificial satellite is decreasing in altitude as it nears the end of its "life." What does Eq. (9-3) say about the way its velocity will change? How is this result possible, since the satellite is "dying" because of a *loss* of energy?

9. Determine the dimensions of G by dimensional analysis of Eq. (9-1). Show that these dimensions are in agreement with the units used to express the value of G.

10. Compare and contrast G and g; the significance of the terms, their numerical values, their dimensions, and the mathematical relationship between them.

Problems

1. Jolly performed an experiment similar to Cavendish's, though with a different experimental setup. He used a spherical flask of mercury with a mass of 5.00 kg and a lead sphere which had a mass of 5775 kg. The distance between the two centers of gravity was 0.570 m. Compute the gravitational attraction between the two masses.

2. A 180 lb halfback and a 120 lb co-ed are classmates, and the seats are so spaced that the distance between their effective centers of mass is 30.0 in. Compute, *not* the "physical," but the *physical* attraction between them.

3. If the gravitational force between a 5.00 g body and a 2.00 kg body is exactly 10^{-6} dyne, compute the distance between their centers of mass.

4. (a) The radius of Jupiter's orbit is between 13 and 14 times that of the orbit of Mercury. To a first approximation what is the ratio of the period of Jupiter to that of Mercury? (b) The period of Pluto is a little more than 1000 times that of Mercury. What is the approximate ratio of the radius of Pluto's orbit to that of Mercury?

5. If there were a planet which had a mass exactly 5 times that of earth and if its radius were exactly 2/3 as great as the earth's, the value of the gravitational acceleration would be how many cm/sec^2? This would be what per cent of the value of g on the earth?

6. Calculate the value of g at the earth's equator with the aid of Eq. (9-5), taking the mass of the earth as $5.98 \cdot 10^{24}$ kg and its radius as $6.38 \cdot 10^6$ m.

7. The mass of Mars is 0.1065 of that of the earth, and the diameter of Mars is 6860 km, whereas that of the earth is 12,800 km. Compute the value of g on Mars.

8. If a body of mass m is at a distance r_1 from the center of the earth (r_1 being

equal to or greater than the earth's radius), the energy required to move it to a greater distance r_2 is $GMm(1/r_1 - 1/r_2)$. Since G and M are constant, this may be written $km(1/r_1 - 1/r_2)$. If m is in tons and values of r are in thousands of miles, the energy will come out in ft-lb if the numerical value of k is $1.67 \cdot 10^{11}$. Compute the energy necessary to raise a 5.00 ton spaceship (a) from the earth's surface to an altitude of 2000 miles, and (b) from 10,000 miles above the earth to 12,000 miles. (c) The second quantity of energy is what per cent of the first?

9. Prove that the energy required to lift a rocket 4000 miles above the earth's surface is half the energy required for it to escape.

10. Assume that rockets are designed to shuttle between the earth's surface and a space station and that interplanetary craft are designed to take off from the space station. If the two types of craft have the same mass, and if nine-tenths of the energy required for escape is to be supplied by the shuttle craft, compute the altitude of the space station above the earth.

10

MECHANICS OF FLUIDS

10-1 Preview

*In this chapter we shall take
our first peek at the internal structure
of matter on a submicroscopic scale.
This will enable us to understand
the dynamic nature of the
pressure of a gas and the manner in which the
pressure of a sample of a gas depends on its volume.
We shall consider also the pressure
within a liquid, the transmission of pressure
from one point within a liquid to other
points, and some of the consequences of this.
Turning once again to the principle
of conservation of energy,
we shall find that its application in
fluid mechanics underlies such
diverse phenomena as the operation
of a spray gun, the flight of a plane,
and the unroofing of a house in a hurricane.
We shall close this topic with a brief
consideration of the surface tension of fluids.*

10-2 What is a Fluid?

It is common to consider "fluid" as synonymous with "liquid," but the former includes *any* substance which can flow. The Latin verb which means "to flow" is the origin of the term "fluid." Since only solids are *in*capable of flow, gases as well as liquids are included within the term ***fluid.*** If you have not considered a gas to be a fluid, you must be careful to avoid confusion.

10-3 The Internal Structure of Matter

By the time we get to Chapter 33 we shall be in a position to go much more deeply into the internal structure of matter than we can—or have time to do—now. For the present, we shall consider only a few items essential to our understanding of the mechanics of fluids.

If a sufficiently powerful supermicroscope existed, it would reveal to our eyes that any matter we might examine is made up of a fantastically large number of unimaginably tiny particles called "molecules."* For example, in a single drop of water the number of molecules is *several thousands* of times as great as the number of *seconds* since the universe was created!

In a liquid, the molecules are crowded about as close together as possible, and they are kept so by the forces of mutual attraction acting between one molecule and any other. Unlike the situation in a solid, however, they are free to move around, relative to one another; and it is because of this freedom that a liquid has no definite shape and can accommodate itself to the shape of any vessel into which it may be poured. A given mass of liquid does have a definite volume, however (except for relatively slight changes if the temperature is not constant), so it has a free surface.

On the other hand, the molecules of a gas are separated much more widely, as is evident in the small densities of gases compared to the liquid forms of the same substances. Water increases its volume about seventeen hundredfold when it vaporizes at its normal boiling point, and the volume of air at ordinary temperatures is approximately seven hundred times that of the same mass of liquid air. Since the mutual attraction between any

---

* The chemist makes a sharp distinction between atoms and molecules; he considers any *molecule* to be made up of two or more *atoms,* and for most purposes the physicist adopts the same point of view. However, a particle consisting of a single atom of helium contributes to the physical properties of a sample of helium gas in the same way that a *molecule* of carbon dioxide—a single particle composed of an atom of carbon and two atoms of oxygen—contributes to the physical properties of a sample of carbon dioxide gas. Therefore, *when dealing with the mechanical properties* of a fluid, and especially of a gas, the physicist calls the smallest particles *molecules,* whether they consist of a single atom or of several atoms.

two molecules decreases rapidly with increasing distance, as we found to be the case with gravitational forces, these forces among molecules are much smaller in a gas than in a liquid. In fact, in a gas they may be ignored entirely unless unusual accuracy is required. Because of the extreme weakness of these attractive forces, the molecules can wander apart and occupy any available volume; a given mass of gas does not have a definite volume, as a specified mass of liquid does.

10-4 The Kinetic Theory of Gases

Whether a substance is a solid, a liquid, or a gas, its molecules are never without motion (except at the absolute zero of temperature), and the degree of this motion increases as the temperature is raised. (In a solid the particles vibrate rather than move from place to place.) In fact, we shall see in Chapter 16 that the average kinetic energy of the molecules of a gas is an index of the temperature of the gas. In the air about you, the molecules have an effective average speed of the order of 500 meters/sec—over 1100 mph! On the average, a molecule travels only about 10^{-5} cm between collisions with other molecules; so it is taking part in something like $5 \cdot 10^9$—five billion—collisions each second!

When we investigate the pressure of a gas and the relationship of pressure to volume (Sec. 10-6, 10-7), we shall find that the heart of the matter is this feverish motion of the molecules of a gas; and the relationship between the temperature of a gas and its pressure or volume (Sec. 16-11, 17-2) rests on the same foundation.

10-5 Pressure

Commonly, "pressure" and "force" are used more or less synonymously, but in physics ***pressure*** is force per unit area:

$$P = \frac{F}{A} \tag{10-1}$$

Thus force, instead of being synonymous with pressure, is the product of pressure and area:

$$F = P \cdot A \tag{10-2}$$

The sharp edge of a knife is more effective in cutting a tough steak than is the back of the knife, and the spiked heel of a 100 lb girl hurts your toe more than the broad heel of a 200 lb man does. In each case, the pressure rather than the force is the pertinent quantity. The supporting force, in pounds, provided by the air in an automobile tire may be something like thirty times the pressure, in pounds *per square inch*, of that air.

10-6 The Mechanism of Gas Pressure

We have seen that the molecules of a gas are rushing around banging into each other. Obviously there will be also a barrage of collisions against any surface contiguous with the gas. In such collisions, the molecules are undamaged and no energy is lost in the collisions.

But any collision necessarily involves a change in velocity, and hence an acceleration; and we found in Sec. 5-10 that any acceleration must be the result of an accelerating force. According to Eq. (6-9), $Ft = -m\Delta v$; so if in a collision with a wall a molecule suffers a change of momentum $m\Delta v$, the wall must have delivered an impulse Ft to the molecule, equivalent to a force F acting for a time t. By courtesy of Newton and his third law, which says that for every action there is an equal and opposite reaction, we may drop the negative sign in Eq. (6-9) and say that if, on colliding with a wall, a molecule suffers a change of momentum $m\Delta v$, it will deliver to the wall an impulse Ft. Thus each of the myriad of impacts exerts a momentary force, and even though each is extremely small, the continuous application of momentary forces results in a relatively great and steady force. This is analogous to the individually negligible impacts of the drops of water from a fire hoze nozzle combining to produce a force great enough to knock a man down. And since pressure is force per unit area, if the impacts of the gas molecules against a surface constitute a force, they also generate a pressure against the surface.

Thus we see that the pressure exerted by a gas is not due to the "dead weight" of the gas. The origin of pressure is dynamic, not static. An ordinary automobile tire will contain less than one-half *pound* of air, despite the fact that a tire gauge will read 25 or 30 pounds *per square inch.* It may startle you, the next time you see a large and heavily loaded truck barreling down the highway, to realize that its *only* support is provided by the collisions of the molecules of air in its tires.

10-7 The Relationship between the Volume of a Gas and Its Pressure; Boyle's Law

Suppose that we have a sample of a gas in a cylinder, the cylinder being closed by a piston as in Fig. 10-1(a). While we are exercising our imaginations, let's do a good job and suppose that the piston fits the cylinder so that it is both frictionless and leakproof. The piston and a weight placed on it exert a downward pressure which is the quotient of their combined weight and the area of the piston. This pressure is balanced by the pressure P_1 of the gas in the cylinder. Remember that this gas pressure is dynamic, resulting from the impacts of the gas molecules against the underside of the piston. The gas in the cylinder has a volume V_1.

Now let us imagine an additional force F to be applied to the top of the piston, as in Fig. 10-1(b), so that the volume of the gas is reduced to one-third of its initial value: $V_2 = V_1/3$. How will the pressure of the gas be affected?

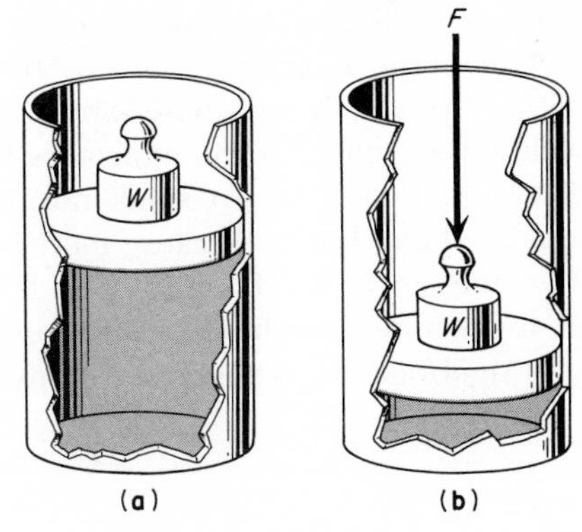

Figure 10-1

Since the piston was leakproof, we still have in the cylinder all the molecules we had originally, but they are crowded into only one-third of the initial volume. Hence we have three times as many molecules per unit volume. This means that there will be three times as many collisions with the piston, per unit time, as previously. And since it is these impacts which give rise to the pressure of the gas, the pressure will be tripled.

Evidently reducing the volume to one-third of its former value triples the pressure; so there seems to be an inverse proportionality between volume and pressure. There are, however, several restrictions which must be included in any statement of such a relationship.

First, we must not forget that we have been considering a *gas*. Any relationship we deduce will *not* apply to liquids or solids. Second, in specifying that the cylinder must be leakproof, we limited our considerations to a *definite mass* of gas. Third, we tacitly assumed that, on the average, the force of each impact against the piston was the same after the reduction of volume as before. This is equivalent to saying that the molecules of gas must have the same effective average speed in both cases and this situation will exist only if there has been no change in temperature (Sec. 16-5).

We are now in a position to state that, for a definite mass of a gas at a constant temperature, the pressure of the gas is inversely proportional to its volume. Of course we may reverse this: within the same restrictions, the volume is inversely proportional to the pressure. In either form, this relationship is known as ***Boyle's law,*** being named for Robert Boyle, who performed experiments which enabled him to state the law.

Even with the restrictions we have imposed, Boyle's law is not exact, for two reasons. First, we have assumed that the volume within the cylinder is identical with the volume available for the molecules to move around in. This is equivalent to assuming that the molecules themselves are dimensionless points which occupy no space. Actually, if we reduce the *total* space by a factor of 3 we shall have reduced the *empty* or *free* space by a slightly larger factor, since the relatively small volume occupied by the molecules does not change. Secondly, we have considered that the only influence tending to crowd the molecules together was the pressure applied by the piston; but there are very small forces of mutual attraction between the molecules, and as the average distance between adjacent molecules is reduced, these forces will increase. Both of these factors (the volume occupied by the molecules themselves and the forces of attraction between them) are so small normally that for most purposes we may ignore them, but both cause more serious errors as the volume of the gas becomes smaller. Hence Boyle's law may be seriously in error if applied to a gas under conditions near those at which the gas will liquefy.

Algebraically, we may state Boyle's law thus:

$$\frac{P_1}{P_2} = \frac{V_2}{V_1} \tag{10-3}$$

in which P_1 and V_1 are the initial values of the pressure and the volume, respectively, and P_2 and V_2 represent the values of the same quantities under a different set of conditions. This equation may be rearranged to

$$P_1V_1 = P_2V_2$$

So long as the temperature remains constant an infinite number of different pairs of values of P and V will satisfy Boyle's law:

$$P_1V_1 = P_2V_2 = P_3V_3 = P_4V_4 = \cdots$$

and this can be summarized by writing

$$PV = k \tag{10-4}$$

where k is the common value of all the products of different pairs of pressures and volumes.

Here is an example of the fairly common situation which can cause trouble if one fails to recognize the danger: the algebraic statement of the law gives no hint of the restrictions on its applicability or of the limitations on its accuracy.

Sample Problem 1

The air in a cylinder such as that in Fig. 10-1 has a volume of 15.0 ft^3 and its pressure is 20.0 lb/in.^{2}. The diameter of the piston which closes the cylinder is 8.00 in. If a force of 1000 lb is exerted against the outside of the piston, and if the temperature remains unchanged, compute the new volume of the air in the cylinder.

Though it wasn't specifically stated that the system was in equilibrium initially, we must assume that it was; otherwise the piston would have been subjected to an acceleration and no solution would have been possible. Hence we shall take the initial pressure of the piston against the gas as 20.0 lb/in.^{2}.

When the force is applied, this pressure is increased. The additional pressure is the force divided by the area, and the latter is πr^2 or $\pi \cdot 4.00^2$. Thus,

$$\Delta P = \frac{1000}{\pi r^2} = \frac{1000}{\pi \cdot 4.00^2} = 19.9 \text{ lb/in.}^2$$

where ΔP is the *increase* in pressure. Thus the total pressure now exerted against the gas must be 20.0 + 19.9 or 39.9 lb/in.².

Then
$$P_1V_1 = P_2V_2$$

and so
$$V_2 = V_1 \cdot \frac{P_1}{P_2} = 15.0 \cdot \frac{20.0}{39.9} = 7.52 \text{ cu ft}$$

Note that this method of solution may be thought of as a multiplication of the original volume by a ratio of pressures. Similarly, an unknown pressure could be found by multiplying the initial pressure by a volume ratio. Furthermore, in either case the ratio may be set up on a common-sense basis rather than by slavish application of a formula; here, for instance, we know that a larger pressure will result in a decreased volume, so we may multiply the original volume by a pressure ratio set up with the smaller value on top, without worrying whether the proper ratio is P_1/P_2 or P_2/P_1.

10-8 Pressure of a Liquid

Suppose that we have a rectangular tank like that in Fig. 10-2. If the bottom of the tank has an area A and if it is filled with liquid to a depth h, the volume of liquid contained will be Ah. As defined in Sec. 2-6, the ***density*** of any substance is its mass per unit volume:

$$\rho = \frac{m}{V} \qquad (10\text{-}5)$$

in which ρ is the density of a substance which has a mass m and a volume V. This equation, which defines density, may be rearranged to $m = \rho V$, and thus the mass of liquid in the tank in Fig. 10-2 will be ρAh. The weight of any mass m, in dynamic units, is mg; so if the weight is F_g,

$$F_g = \rho Ahg$$

By definition, pressure is force per unit area—Sec. 10-5, Eq. (10-1)—so

$$P = F_g \div A = \rho Ahg \div A$$

or
$$P = \rho hg \qquad (10\text{-}6)$$

Division of the right side of Eq. (10-6) by g will modify the equation so that the pressures will be in gravitational rather than dynamic units. Obviously the same result would have been achieved if we had expressed the weight of the liquid in gravitational units, in the eleventh line above.

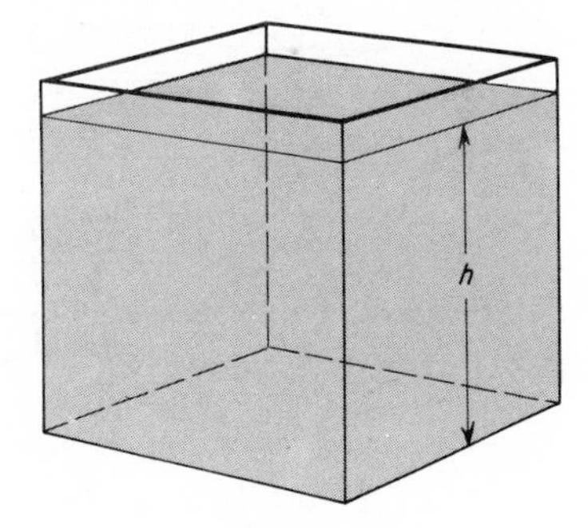

Figure 10-2

Suppose that in the derivation above we substitute the value *one* for A. *Numerically* (though *not* dimensionally) the final step, division by A, would have been unnecessary. Thus, the pressure due to a liquid is *numerically* equal to the weight of the column of liquid above unit area.

Note that in computing the pressure due to a liquid we have used the density ρ. Liquids are virtually incompressible, so even if the liquid is very deep the value of ρ is essentially constant. But in the atmosphere the pressure of the air changes with elevation, and this causes a similar change in density; so the value of ρ which might be applicable at one elevation would be incorrect at another. Hence the discussion in this section, and the equations, are *not* applicable to gases, unless the effective average density of the gas is known.

10-9 Considerations of Direction

Force is a vector quantity, but area is a scalar quantity. To which class does force per unit area, or pressure, belong?

If you place a piece of aluminum foil in a horizontal position at a depth h beneath the surface of a liquid, as in Fig. 10-3, the liquid above it will exert a pressure ρhg; and if the area of the foil is A, there will be a force $F = PA = \rho ghA$ acting on the upper surface of the foil. Yet you will observe no downward acceleration commensurate with this force. Here again Newton's third law of motion comes in; the downward force due to the pressure of the liquid above the foil is matched by an equal upward force on the lower surface of the foil. The motion of the foil will be dictated solely by its weight and the effects of the viscosity of the liquid. Thus we must conclude that though the pressure of the liquid is due to its weight, the pressure at any given depth is exerted upward as well as downward.

If the container of the liquid had a small hole in the side, at the same depth at which you place the foil, liquid would issue from the hole; so the pressure must also act horizontally. Further and more rigorous investigation would show that pressure at a given depth within a liquid acts equally in all directions. Since its effectiveness is independent of direction, pressure appears to be a scalar quantity.

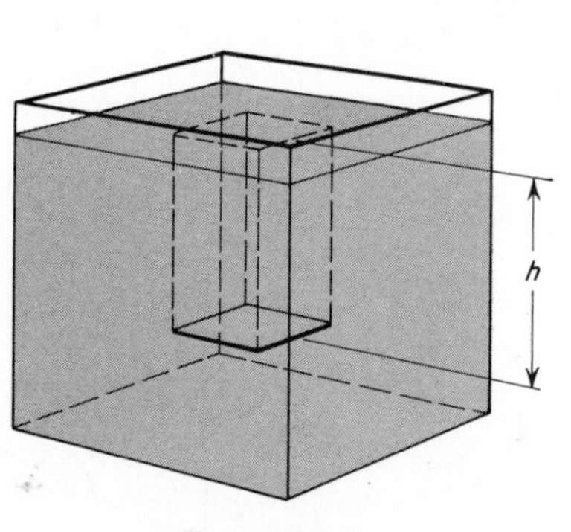

Figure 10-3

However, consider the dam in Fig. 10-4. At any given point on the upstream face of the dam, the water will exert a pressure. If there is to be no automatic and continuous circulation set up along the face of the dam, the pressure can have no net component parallel to the face of the dam. This means that the pressure, or at least the *resultant* pressure, must act

Figure 10-4

at right angles to the face of the dam. Here pressure seems to be a vector quantity.

Because of considerations such as these, it is usual to consider that pressure *within the body* of a liquid is a scalar quantity but that it becomes a vector quantity when applied to any surface.

Although, for concreteness, the discussion in this section has been in terms of a liquid, the conclusions are applicable to fluids in general.

10-10 The Transmission of Pressure within a Fluid; Pascal's Law

Figure 10-5 represents three containers filled to the same depth with water. Each container is open at the lower end, but the opening is blocked by a pad on the pan of a balance, and a weight applied to the other arm of the balance holds the pad against the opening of the vessel with just sufficient force to support the water in the vessel and, in effect, close the vessel. The area of the opening is the same for all vessels. It may surprise you that the weight on the other arm of the balance is also the same in all cases.

But if we had taken time to think, we should have been startled if *different* weights had been required. All vessels are filled to the same depth with the same liquid, so each must have the same water pressure at its lower extremity. Since pressure is force per unit area and the areas are the same, the water must exert equal forces against the pads in the three cases, the different shapes of the vessels and the different weights of water they contain notwithstanding.

But it still doesn't seem reasonable, the first time you meet a situation of this sort. How can we make it appear more reasonable?

The straight-sided vessel offers nothing at variance with our intuitive feeling as to what "makes sense"; since its sides are vertical, the force on the bottom should be simply the weight of the water, and this is the actual situation. In the case of the vessel with flaring sides, the force of the water against the side is at right angles to the side. At any point, this may be resolved into a vertical component and a horizontal component. The latter can contribute nothing to the *vertical* force against the pad, and the former acts not against the pad but against the flaring side. Thus in

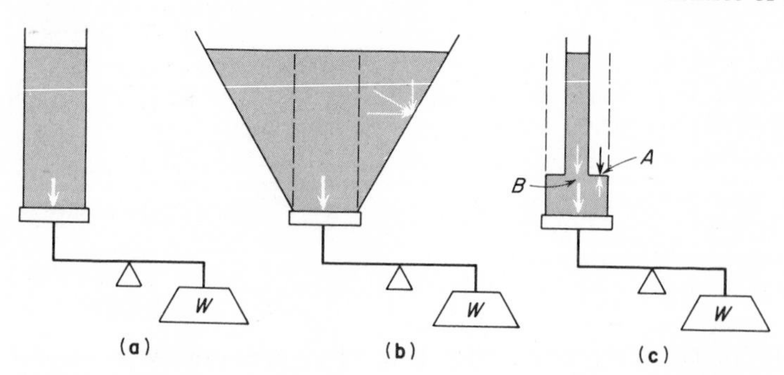

Fig. 10-5. The force exerted against the pads is the same in all three cases.

effect, we can consider that only the column of water within the dotted lines in Fig. 10-5(b) is supported by the pad, and the rest is supported by the sides.

But what about the vessel in Fig. 10-5(c)? Here the force of the water against the pad is much *greater* than the weight of the water. In this case, as in the previous one, the effect is as if the weight of a column of water contained within the dotted lines were acting on the pad, even though most of this space is outside the vessel and contains thin air instead of water. To achieve this effect, the horizontal surfaces of the vessel (such as at point *A*, for instance) must be exerting the same downward pressure on the water in contact with them as the water above this level would exert if the vessel were straightsided like that in Fig. 10-5(a). That is, the downward pressure at point *A* must be the same as that at point *B*. According to Newton's third law of motion, this means that the water at *A* is pressing upward against the surface of the vessel with a pressure equal to that of the water at *B*. Since there is no water *above* point *A* to generate this pressure, it must be due to the pressure of the water in the tube. This means that the pressure of the water at point *B* is transmitted to point *A*, and that the magnitude of the pressure is the same at the two points. The same is true, of course, for all other points at the same level, with the result that at any point at a lower level the pressure is the same as it would have been if the vessel had had straight sides instead of having a sharply constricted upper portion—provided, of course, that the depth of the water in the vessel was the same in both cases.

Thus we see that in a confined liquid a pressure which acts on the liquid at any point is transmitted with no decrease in its magnitude to all portions of the liquid. And here again our conclusion is applicable to gases as well as to liquids. This relationship is known either as ***Pascal's law*** or ***Pascal's principle.***

Sample Problem 2

A vessel contains a layer of mercury 4.00 cm deep with a layer of oil 25.0 cm deep above the mercury. The density of mercury is 13.6 g/cm³ and that of the oil is 0.850 g/cm³. The vessel is open to the air, and the atmospheric pressure is 1020 g/cm². What is the pressure at the bottom of the tank?

The pressure of any liquid due to its own weight is the product of its depth and its density; and Pascal's law says that pressure exerted on a fluid is transmitted undiminished to all portions of the fluid; thus, the pressure at the bottom of the vessel will be the sum of the three separate pressures. So, in terms of gravitational units,

$$\begin{aligned} P &= 4.00 \cdot 13.6 + 25.0 \cdot 0.850 + 1020 \text{ g/cm}^2 \\ &= 54.4 + 21.2 + 1020 \text{ g/cm}^2 \\ &= 1096 \text{ g/cm}^2 \end{aligned}$$

(Note that since we don't know that the air pressure is 1020.*0* g/cm² we must "round off" the tenths digit in the sum.)

10-11 Atmospheric Pressure and the Barometer

The gases of the earth's atmosphere exert a pressure which has a value, at sea level, of about 14.7 lb/in.². *If* the density at all elevations were the same as at sea level, this would be a blanket of air about 5 miles thick, but both pressure and density decrease with increasing elevation, so there is no "top" to the atmosphere (other than a purely arbitrary one, such as that elevation above which there is only some specified small percentage of the atmosphere).

These considerations make it necessary to evaluate the pressure of the air on some basis other than the average density and depth. Instead, use is made of Pascal's law to measure atmospheric pressure by balancing it against the pressure of a column of mercury. A device for doing this is a mercury ***barometer.*** A simple barometer is diagramed in Fig. 10-6. Such a barometer is prepared by filling a glass tube more than 76 cm long with mercury, closing the open end with a finger, inverting the tube and submerging its open end beneath the surface of mercury in a dish, and then removing the finger. All this must be accomplished without any air getting into the tube. The pressure of the air acts on the free surface of the mercury in the dish, and according to Pascal's law

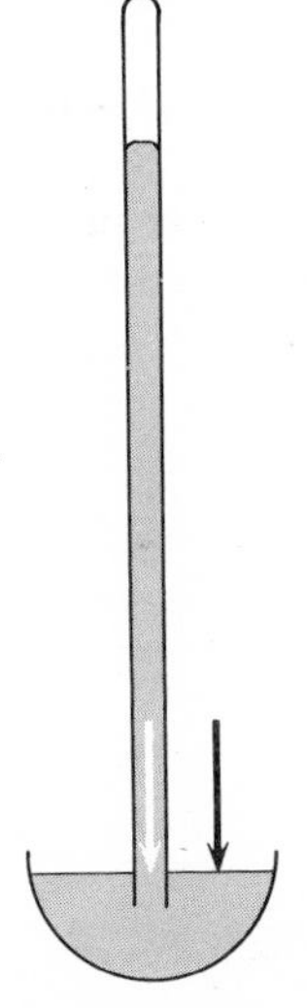

Fig. 10-6. Mercury barometer.

this pressure is transmitted throughout the mercury. Within the tube, at the level of the mercury in the dish, this pressure tends to force mercury up into the tube, while the pressure due to the column of mercury tends to force it out. If the tube extends 76 cm or more above the mercury level in the dish, the mercury column will drop until its height is about 76 cm (depending considerably on elevation and somewhat on weather conditions). The space above the column will contain only mercury vapor, which will have so small a pressure that we may ignore it.

If the mercury column stands 76.0 cm above the level of the mercury in the dish, its pressure is

$$76.0 \text{ cm} \cdot 13.59 \text{ g/cm}^3 \cdot 980 \text{ dynes/g} = 1.012 \cdot 10^6 \text{ dynes/cm}^2$$

the second factor being the density of mercury. Since this is balanced by the pressure of the atmosphere, the latter is also $1.012 \cdot 10^6$ dynes/cm^2. This is equivalent to about 14.7 lb/in.^{2} or, as an approximation, 15 lb/in.^{2}.

In this computation of pressure from the height of the mercury column, the last two factors are constants; so the pressure of the air will always be a constant $(13.59 \cdot 980)$ times the height of the mercury column; thus a given column height will always correspond to the same unique pressure. Hence it has become customary to say that the atmospheric pressure is "758.0 mm," or "29.85 in.," etc. Such a value is obviously meaningless; a pressure is a force per unit area; it is *not* any linear measurement. We *should* say that the pressure is *equivalent to that of a mercury column* 758.0 mm or 29.85 in. *high.* But unfortunately we imperfect humans usually use the former and incorrect mode of expression, so you must be prepared to interpret it as it is *meant* rather than as it is *stated.*

10-12 The Hydraulic Press

We have seen that the mercury barometer is an application of Pascal's law. Another, and very useful, application is the ***hydraulic press.*** Although this book is concerned primarily with principles rather than applications, this application will make Pascal's law more tangible and also will furnish a bit of review.

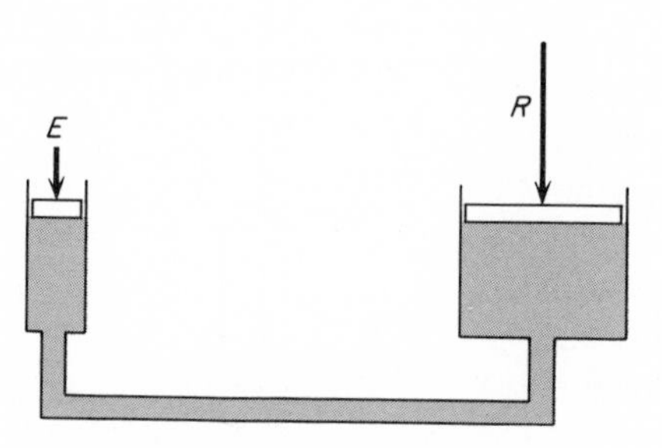

Fig. 10-7. Hydraulic press.

A simplified hydraulic press appears in Fig. 10-7. It consists of two cylinders of different diameters, each fitted with a piston. The two cylinders are connected by a pipe, and the whole system is filled with a liquid. If an effort force E is applied to the small piston, and if the area of that piston is a, the resulting pressure is E/a. By courtesy of Pascal, this pressure is transmitted undiminished throughout the liquid, including the lower face of the large piston. If the area of this piston is A, a resisting force R acting on it would generate a pressure R/A. Under equilibrium conditions, this pressure will be just balanced by that due to the effort force on the smaller piston; that is, $R/A = E/a$. This may be rearranged to the form $R/E = A/a$. But by definition, R/E is mechanical advantage—Sec. 7-3, Eq. (7-1); and it is ideal mechanical advantage, since we assumed equilibrium conditions. Therefore,

$$\text{IMA} = \frac{A}{a} \tag{10-7}$$

If the radius of the large piston is R and that of the small one r, the respective areas are πR^2 and πr^2, so $A/a = \pi R^2/\pi r^2 = (R/r)^2$. But the ratio of the radii is the same as the ratio of the diameters, so we may write

$$\text{IMA} = \left(\frac{D}{d}\right)^2 \tag{10-8}$$

wherein D and d are the diameters of the large and small pistons, respectively. As is always the case, Eq. (10-7), (10-8) apply only to the type of machine for which they were designed, the hydraulic press.

Even for a hydraulic press, these equations are valid only if the two pistons are at the same elevation. If the smaller piston is a height h above the other, the pressure on the larger piston is the sum of that due to the effort on the small piston and that due to the pressure of a column of the liquid of height h.

Sample Problem 3

A hydraulic jack for a truck is a form of the hydraulic press. The diameter of the large piston is 2.00 in. and that of the small piston is 0.500 in. Force is applied to the small piston with the aid of a second class lever, the moment arm of the piston being 1.00 in. and that of the effort being 15.0 in. What is the ideal mechanical advantage of this jack? If its efficiency is 90.0% and it must raise a load of 4.00 tons, calculate the magnitude of the effort.

So far as the hydraulic press part of the jack is concerned, the ideal mechanical advantage is the square of the ratio of the diameters. This is $(2.00/0.500)^2 = 4.00^2 = 16.0$. The lever has an ideal mechanical advantage equal to the ratio of the moment arms, which is 15.00/1.00 or 15.0. The over-all ideal mechanical advantage is the product of the separate values, so

$$\text{IMA} = 16.0 \cdot 15.0 = 240.$$

However, since the efficiency is 90.0%, the practical mechanical advantage is $240 \cdot 0.900 = 216$. If the load is 4.00 tons or 8000 lb, the actual effort required will be $8000/216 = 37.0$ lb.

10-13 Specific Gravity

Specific gravity is a term which is often confused with density, though the two words represent very different concepts. The confusion arises partly from the fact that both concepts have to do with the "heaviness" of substances and partly from the fact that there is a coincidence of some of the numerical values of specific gravity and density. Unfortunately, it also arises in part from careless usage by some of us who know better.

We may define the ***specific gravity*** of a substance in either of two ways which sound rather different but are fully equivalent. According to one definition, specific gravity is the ratio of the weight of a body to the weight of an equal volume of a reference substance:

$$\text{specific gravity} = \frac{\text{weight of the body}}{\text{weight of an equal volume of the reference substance}}$$

Students very commonly misstate this definition, and confuse themselves as a result, by saying that specific gravity is the weight of the sample divided by an equal volume of the reference substance. But it is *not* a weight divided by a *volume;* it is one weight divided by another *weight* —the weight of the sample divided by *the weight of* an equal volume of the reference substance.

The other definition is obtained from the first by dividing both the numerator and the denominator by the volume. This volume is the same for both, so the value of the quotient will be unchanged. But in each case, division of the weight by the volume gives us the corresponding density. Hence we may define the specific gravity of a substance as the ratio of its density to the density of a reference substance:

$$\text{specific gravity} = \frac{\text{density of the body}}{\text{density of the reference substance}}$$

For the specific gravity of a solid or a liquid, the reference substance virtually always is water; it may be assumed that this is the situation unless there is explicit notice to the contrary. For gases, the reference substance most commonly is air, but it may be hydrogen or some other substance.

A large majority of texts give only the second of the definitions above, but the first one has an advantage which will be apparent in the next section.

Note that either of our definitions shows that the specific gravity is a pure number. The *density* of quartz is 2.65 *grams per cubic centimeter* or $2.65 \cdot 10^3$ *kilograms per cubic meter* or 165 *pounds per cubic foot,* but its *specific gravity* is 2.65, "*period.*"

The previous paragraph reveals that, because of this difference with respect to units, density and specific gravity cannot be the same kind of

Table 10-1

SPECIFIC GRAVITIES OF SOME SOLIDS AND LIQUIDS

Solids		Liquids		
Substance	Specific gravity	Substance	Specific gravity	Temperature, °C
Aluminum	2.699	Chloroform	1.489	20
Brass	8.4–8.75	Ethyl alcohol	0.791	20
Concrete	2.7	Gasoline	0.66–0.69	
Copper	8.89–8.93	Glycerin	1.260	20
Gold	19.26–19.30	Mercury	13.596	0
Lead	11.00–11.35	Sea water	1.03	
Magnesium	1.75			
Platinum	21.37			
Steel	7.7–7.8			
Uranium	18.7			
Zinc	7.04–7.19			

quantity—which is also evident in their definitions—but that paragraph also includes a *numerical* value of 2.65 for density as well as for specific gravity. If you try hard enough, you can become confused by this. (Many students don't even have to try!) But there is also a numerical value of $(2.65) \cdot 10^3$ and a numerical value of 165 for the density, neither of which is within shouting distance of the value of the specific gravity. *If* density is expressed in terms of grams per cubic centimeter, the *numerical* value of the density of a substance is the same as the *numerical* value of the specific gravity. But this is true *only* for the density in grams per cubic centimeter; it is manifestly untrue for density in kilograms per cubic meter or pounds per cubic foot. Even when the density is in grams per cubic centimeter the *values* aren't the same, only the *numbers* are; the *values* include units in one case but not in the other and thus are *not* the same.

Table 10-2

SPECIFIC GRAVITIES AND DENSITIES OF SOME GASES

Gas	Specific gravity with respect to air	Density at 0°C, in g/cm³
Air	1.0000	$1.2929 \cdot 10^{-3}$
Carbon dioxide	1.5290	$1.977 \cdot 10^{-3}$
Helium	0.13804	$0.1785 \cdot 10^{-3}$
Hydrogen	0.06952	$0.0899 \cdot 10^{-3}$
Nitrogen	0.96724	$1.2505 \cdot 10^{-3}$
Oxygen	1.10527	$1.4290 \cdot 10^{-3}$

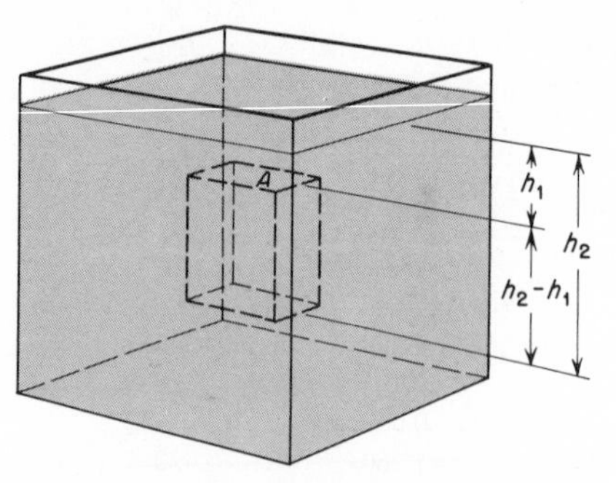

Fig. 10-8. Basis of Archimedes' principle.

10-14 Archimedes' Principle

You are well aware that some objects will float on water, and probably you have noted that you are rather "light on your feet" when standing in a swimming pool with the water up to your armpits. You may have observed that the weight of a large rock or other dense object seems less when the object is submerged. These are all examples of the application of ***Archimedes' principle,*** which states that any floating or submerged body is buoyed up by a force equal to the weight of the fluid it displaces.

In the case of an insoluble rectangular object, it is easy to derive this relationship with the aid of Fig. 10-8. If the upper surface of the body is horizontal, and if it is at a depth h_1 beneath the surface of a liquid of density ρ, the pressure acting downward on it (in dynamic units) is $h_1\rho g$. If this surface has an area A, the force acting downward on it is $Ah_1\rho g$. Similarly, you can show that a force $Ah_2\rho g$ must act upward on the lower surface of the body, if that surface is at a depth h_2. Since h_2 exceeds h_1, there is a net upward force equal to the difference between the two forces:

$$F_{\text{net}} = Ah_2\rho g - Ah_1\rho g = A(h_2 - h_1)\rho g$$

A glance at the diagram reveals that the product $A(h_2 - h_1)$ is the volume of the body. Since the body must displace its own volume of the liquid,

$$F_{\text{net}} = V\rho g \qquad (10\text{-}9)$$

in which V is the volume of liquid displaced. But $\rho = m/V$, so $m = \rho V$; and since a mass m has a weight mg in the dynamic system, $V\rho g$ is simply the weight of the liquid displaced by the body.

Though this derivation is strictly valid only for a liquid and though it assumes a rectangular body, Archimedes' principle is valid for a body of any shape, and it applies to gases as well as to liquids.

Now suppose that we wish to determine the specific gravity of some irregularly shaped insoluble body, such as an ore specimen. The experimental method need involve nothing more than two weighings: the sample is weighed in the normal manner and then is reweighed while it is submerged in water. Our first definition of specific gravity is

$$\text{specific gravity} = \frac{\text{weight of sample}}{\text{weight of an equal volume of water}}$$

The weight of the body when submerged is less than when weighed in air because of the buoyant force of the water, and according to Archimedes, this buoyant force is the weight of the displaced water. Obviously an immersed body will displace its own volume of water—if we permit no air bubbles to stick to it—so the denominator in the equation at the bottom of the preceding page is simply the difference between our two weighings.

10-15 Work and Energy

It may seem that it would be difficult to derive an expression for the work done by a fluid, but all that is needed is a few definitions—which we have had—and a simple diagram.

Suppose that a fluid is being pumped through the pipe in Fig. 10-9, from left to right. Imagine a circle of aluminum foil being carried by the fluid from position 1 to position 2. This will require some force F to be exerted through the distance s, so the work necessary is Fs. But the opposing force is the pressure P in the pipe multiplied by the cross-sectional area A of the pipe: $F = PA$. Thus,

$$W = Fs = PAs$$

The product As is simply the volume V of fluid which has passed the point 1; therefore

$$W = PV \tag{10-10}$$

We may think of the volume V which passes point 1 as a change of volume in the part of the system to the right of this point; thus, following the usual symbolism, we may use ΔV instead of the V in Eq. (10-10). This yields

$$W = P\Delta V \tag{10-11}$$

If the fluid is a gas we may use Eq. (10-11) to compute the work required to compress the gas, ΔV in this case representing the *reduction* of volume. However, any change of volume of the gas (as constant temperature) will affect the pressure; thus values obtained by Eq. (10-11) *when dealing with a gas* will be approximations, and will be seriously in error unless the ratio of ΔV to V is small enough so that the pressure remains essentially unchanged.

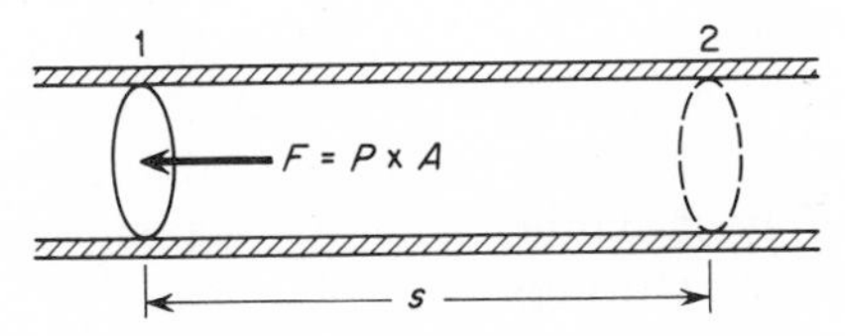

Fig. 10-9. Work done against fluid pressure $= P \times A \times s = PV$.

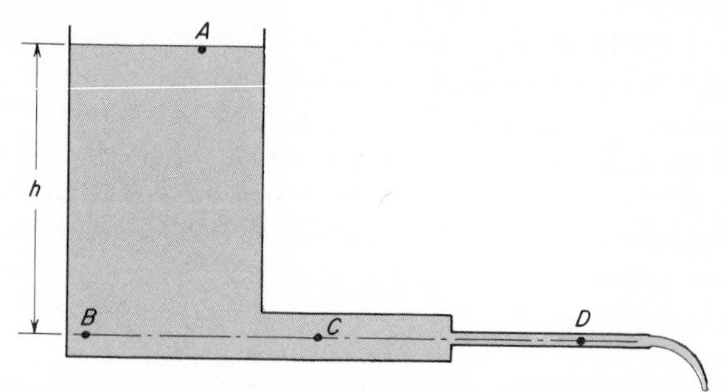

Fig. 10-10. Basis of Bernoulli's principle.

10-16 Further Considerations of Energy: Bernoulli's Principle

Consider a tank of water with a horizontal outlet as in Fig. 10-10. We shall assume that the capacity of the tank is great enough so that the water level doesn't fall appreciably during our investigation. A small quantity of water of mass m and volume V, located at point A on the surface, would have potential energy mgh relative to point B, by virtue of its elevation. Since there is a depth h of liquid above point B, whereas point A is at the surface, there is a greater pressure at point B; let us call this difference of pressure ΔP. According to Eq. (10-10) the product ΔPV must have the dimensions of energy, and we saw in Eq. (10-11) that the work done in forcing a volume of liquid ΔV past a point against a constant pressure P is equal to $P\Delta V$. Similarly, in order to increase the pressure of a volume V of a liquid by an amount ΔP, we must do a quantity of work equal to the product of ΔP and V. Thus a quantity of water of mass m and volume V located at point B will have, with respect to point A, potential energy equal to ΔPV due to the difference of pressure. A similar mass and volume of water at point C will have an appreciable velocity v, so it will possess kinetic energy equal to $mv^2/2$.

The only force which would move this sample of water from A to B is gravitational; so any "pressure energy" ΔPV gained must be obtained at the expense of the gravitational potential energy mgh. Similarly, the only physical influence available to give the water kinetic energy as it moves from B to C is the pressure P; so the gain in the kinetic energy $mv^2/2$ is at the expense of the energy ΔPV. Thus as the sample of water moves from A toward B and on to C there is a continuous change in the kind or kinds of energy it possesses; but since any gain of a new kind of energy comes from the supply of another kind, its total energy remains the same. We may express this by writing

$$W = mgh + \Delta PV + \frac{mv^2}{2} = k \tag{10-12}$$

In view of this constancy of energy, what will happen as the water passes into the constricted portion of the outlet pipe? The volume passing point C in any time must be identical with that passing point D in the same interval; so the velocity of the water at D must be considerably greater than at C. But this means that the kinetic energy of a given mass of water has been increased. Since C and D are at the same elevation, and since the *total* energy is constant, the kinetic energy must increase at the expense of the "pressure energy"; any increase in the quantity $mv^2/2$ must be accompanied by an equal *de*crease in the quantity ΔPV. And it must be the pressure P which is reduced, since, for a given mass of water, V can't be altered. Thus, rather surprisingly, we find that the pressure of the water is *reduced* as it passes through the constricted portion.

This fact that in general an increase in the velocity of a fluid necessarily decreases its pressure is known as ***Bernoulli's principle.***

10-17 Applications of Bernoulli's Principle

Applications of this principle are surprisingly common and diverse. One is shown schematically in Fig. 10-11. If the lower end of an open tube is immersed in a liquid and a stream of air is blown with sufficient velocity over the upper end of the tube, the reduction of pressure above the tube allows the atmospheric pressure to force the liquid up the tube and out into the airstream. Thus droplets of liquid are formed and blown along with the airstream. This is the basis of throat sprays, perfume atomizers, insect sprays, paint gun sprays, etc.

The Bernoulli effect has been responsible for some accidents. If a car zooms past a bicyclist, the "rush" of air involves a lowering of pressure between the car and the bicycle; so air from the other side tends to tilt the bicycle toward the car, and if the driver isn't a physicist he will blame the bicyclist for the accident. (He *isn't* a physicist, or he would have allowed extra clearance!) In a similar manner, passengers standing too close to the edge of a train or subway platform when a train whizzes by have "fallen" onto the tracks—with an assist from Bernoulli.

Other applications range from the curving flight of a spinning baseball, to the tendency of a clammy shower curtain to swing against you when the spray of water from the shower head causes a downrush of air, to the unroofing of a house by hurricane winds forced to detour up over the roof and down the other side.

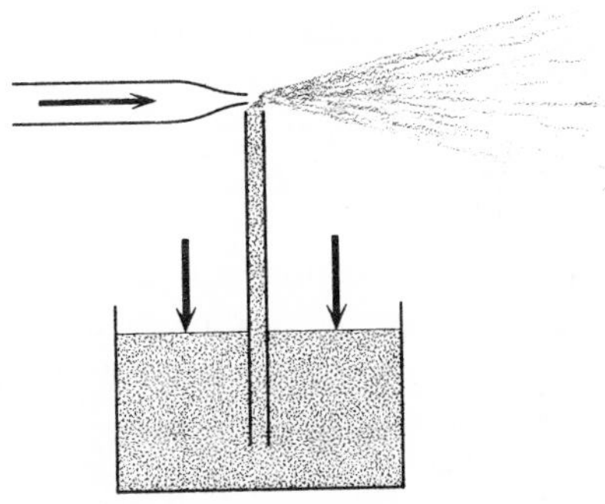
Fig. 10-11. Principle of the "atomizer."

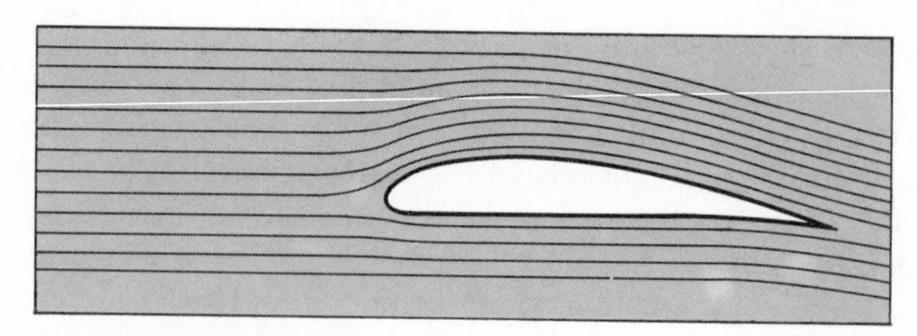

Fig. 10-12. Streamline above airfoil is longer than that below, giving rise to Bernoulli effect.

One application deserves special consideration because of its importance, and because the facts are often misunderstood and still oftener misstated. This is the flight of a plane.

As the wing of a plane advances through the air, the trailing edge of the wing is below the leading edge, so the lower surface strikes molecules of air and deflects them downward. Each molecule thus deflected acquires a downward momentum at the instant of contact with the wing, and so each delivers an upward impulse to the wing. But the force resulting from this process is only a minor part of that required to support the plane.

Figure 10-12 represents an airfoil, such as the wing of a plane, moving through the air. Since all motion is relative, we may consider the airfoil to be stationary, with the air moving past it. Due to the shape of the airfoil, the path of an airstream immediately above it is longer than that of one just beneath the airfoil. To move farther in the same time, the air above the airfoil must have a greater speed than that below. Bernoulli's principle requires that this faster-moving air exert a smaller pressure. Thus there is a smaller pressure above the wing than below, so there is a resultant pressure upward; and this resultant pressure, acting upward on the airfoil, causes an upward force. This force normally is a major fraction of the weight of the aircraft.

The fact that the pressure reduction above the wing is responsible for the major portion of the supporting force on the plane has given rise to the statement that "most of the lift is above the wing." But we have seen that in any gas, whatever its pressure, the molecules are rushing around, colliding into each other and against any surface. It is manifestly impossible for the bombardment of the *upper* surface by the air molecules *above* it to cause an *up*ward force on the surface. Each impact contributes a *down*ward force instead. It is quite true that the Bernoulli effect causes a marked reduction of the *opposition* to the pressure *beneath* the airfoil, but *all up*ward forces on the airfoil act against its *lower* surface. More than three centuries ago, it was found that the pressure of the atmosphere *pushes* water up into the cylinder of a pump, but some people still speak of the water being "pulled" into a "vacuum"; so it may be that until another three centuries have passed, the statement that there is "lift" *above* the wing of a plane will continue to confuse and mislead people.

10-18 Surface Tension

Figure 10-13 represents a microscopic view of the situation near the surface of a liquid. The closely grouped circles are molecules in the liquid phase, at the surface or just below. The scattered circles above the surface indicate the relatively few molecules in the vapor phase. (The one solid black circle isn't the black sheep of the molecule family; it has been blackened so we can fix our attention on one particular molecule at the surface.)

Sections 10-3 and 10-7 mentioned the forces of mutual attraction among molecules. In the horizontal plane, the "black molecule" is surrounded on all sides by other molecules; so their attractive forces are equal in all directions, and there is no resultant force on the "black molecule," in the horizontal plane. But there are many molecules beneath the "black molecule" and few above, and those above are (on the average) farther away. Thus the forces acting downward on the "black molecule" exceed those upwardly directed, and there is a resultant force urging the "black molecule" inward, away from the surface. Every other molecule at the surface is subjected to a similar inward force. These forces are responsible for the phenomenon known as ***surface tension.***

Owing to these inward forces on all molecules at the surface, there is a tendency of any liquid to minimize the area of the surface, though in most situations other and stronger forces may prevent this. For a given mass of liquid, a spherical shape will have the least surface area; so any small mass of liquid tends to form a spherical droplet. Thus the liquid seems to act *as if* it has an elastic skin.

If we take an actual elastic membrane, such as a strip of thin sheet rubber, the force required to stretch the strip a given distance depends on the width of the strip; it will be directly proportional to the width. This means that if we divide the force by the width we shall have a value which is the same for all strips, regardless of width; hence this value will be characteristic of the elastic membrane. For the same reasons, the significant measure of surface tension is not force, but force per unit "width" measured at right angles to the force. Thus the usual unit for surface tension is dynes per centimeter.

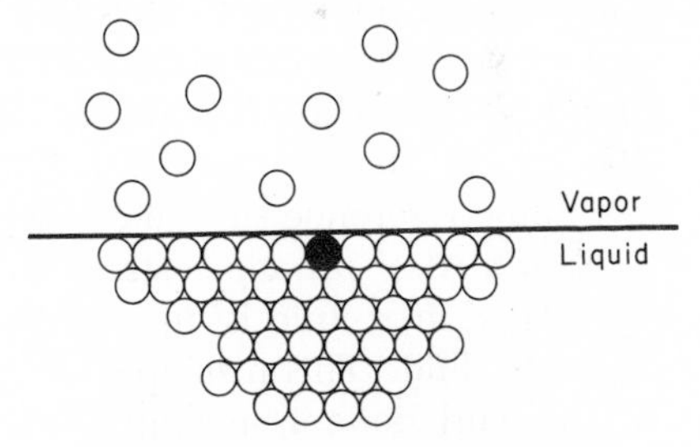

Fig. 10-13. Cause of surface forces.

Values of the surface tensions of different liquids vary over a wide range. That of water is considerably higher than the values for most other liquids. Solutions of certain substances have markedly different surface tensions than does the pure solvent, though other solutes have relatively little effect. It is the ability of soaps and other detergents to lower the surface tension of water that gives them their value as laundering agents. Due to its surface tension, pure water may be unable to penetrate the interstices between the fibers of a fabric; but soapy water, or water containing some other detergent, may be able to penetrate because of its lesser surface tension.

Summary

The term "fluid" includes not only liquids, but also gases. The difference in the internal structure of liquids and gases lies in the distance between the particles (atoms or molecules) of the substance. In liquids, these particles are rather closely packed, whereas in gases, the average distance between them is much greater. In a liquid, they can move about among the other particles but remain in relatively close contact with them. In a gas, they can move rather freely with no limitation—other than that imposed by a containing vessel—on how far apart they are.

Because the molecules of a gas are free to move, they collide with other molecules and they bombard any surface with which the gas is in contact. Any collisions of a molecule with a surface causes an acceleration of the molecule; hence a force is exerted against the surface by the molecule. The summation of such forces gives rise to a force against the surface.

Pressure is *force per unit area.* For a definite sample of a gas at a constant temperature, the pressure is inversely proportional to the volume. This relationship is *Boyle's law.*

The pressure of a liquid due to the weight of the liquid may be computed by multiplying the depth of the liquid by its density. Within the body of a liquid, this pressure acts equally in all directions; at any surface with which the liquid is in contact, the pressure is considered to act at right angles to the surface.

Any pressure applied to an enclosed liquid is transmitted undiminished to all parts of the liquid. This relationship is *Pascal's law.*

The *specific gravity* of a body may be defined as the *weight* of the body *divided* by the *weight of an equal volume* of water, or as the ratio of the density of the body to the density of water. In either case, some reference substance other than water may be used.

Archimedes' principle states that any body which is floating on, or submerged in, a fluid is buoyed up by a force equal to the weight of the displaced fluid. This principle is the direct consequence of Pascal's law.

The work done in moving a volume of fluid against a pressure is simply the product of the volume and the pressure.

Bernoulli's principle says that any increase in the velocity of a fluid must be accompanied by a decrease in the pressure it exerts. This principle has very extensive applications, including the flight of a plane.

The imbalance of the mutual attractive forces on the molecules lying near the surface of a liquid gives rise to a phenomenon known as *surface tension.*

Self-Quiz

1. The term "molecule" has a broader significance with respect to the kinetic theory of gases than in most other applications. In what way is its meaning broader, and why is this more inclusive connotation used in this application of the word?

2. In one cubic centimeter of air there are normally approximately $2.5 \cdot 10^{19}$ molecules. Imagine these to be divided equally among the inhabitants of the world—say $3 \cdot 10^{9}$ people, in round numbers. If you could find a market for your share at 100 molecules for a penny, how rich would you be? Are you convinced that the number of molecules in a small quantity of matter is *really* large?!

3. If in gaseous form a substance occupies one thousand times the volume it would occupy in liquid form, how does the average distance between the centers of the molecules in the gas compare with the corresponding distance in the liquid?

4. Compare and contrast the terms "force" and "pressure." Also determine the fundamental dimensions of each of these quantities and show that the definition of pressure is in accord with these dimensions.

5. If a service station attendant repairs a "flat" and then puts "thirty pounds of air" into the tire, is the weight of the tire increased by thirty pounds? Explain your answer. Criticize the expression "thirty pounds" in this application.

6. On the basis of logic rather than memory or reference to the text, write out a clear summary of the argument used to develop Boyle's law.

7. What restrictions are necessary, and in each case why, in the statement of Boyle's law? What limitations on the accuracy of the law are not included in its statement, and why are these omitted?

8. It was stated that the pressure of a gas is dynamic rather than static. What does this statement mean, and why is it true?

9. A sample of gas is allowed to expand at constant temperature. The original pressure and both volumes are known. The new pressure is to be computed by multiplying the original pressure by the ratio of the volumes. *Without* reference to the text and *without* considering or applying any formula, state whether the greater volume should be in the numerator or in the denominator. Explain the basis of your choice. ("The flip of a coin" is *not* an acceptable explanation even if it happens to give the correct result!)

10. Define the two concepts, "density" and "specific gravity." Compare and contrast them from the standpoints of their significance, their units, their fundamental dimensions, and their numerical values.

11. The very common statement "specific gravity is equal to density" is incorrect, even if the density is expressed in grams per cubic centimeter. Why?

12. Give statements of Pascal's law, Archimedes' principle, and Bernoulli's principle.

13. Does the force exerted on the upstream face of a dam depend on the length of the artificial lake above the dam? Explain.

14. Two rectangular tanks have the same cross-sectional area and are filled to the same depth. One is 5 m long but the "length" of the other is only $\frac{1}{2}$ mm. Compare the force on an end of the short tank with that on an end of the long one, and explain clearly.

15. Make a rough estimate of the area of your hand and multiply this area by the air pressure, which is very roughly 15 lb/sq in. If you hold your hand flat and in a horizontal position, how large a downward force does the air exert on it? Why are you unaware of this force?

16. Each of two identical bowls weighs 250 g and has a capacity of 400 ml. A housewife puts water into one of them until it is perhaps $\frac{1}{4}$ or $\frac{1}{3}$ full, and then puts the second bowl into the first one. Will it float? Explain. It is sometimes said that "an object is buoyed up by the water that isn't there"; does this seem to be true?

17. Check the validity of the equation $W = \Delta PV$ by dimensional analysis.

18. Of what use is the principle of conservation of energy in this chapter?

19. Water is brought into a house through a 1 in. pipe and then the pipe is reduced to $\frac{1}{2}$ in. A youngster with more scientific curiosity than sense drills a hole in the top of each pipe, using the same size drill. Discuss the relative heights of the fountains from the larger and smaller pipes (a) when no water is flowing through the pipes and (b) when there is a rapid flow through them. Explain your answers clearly.

20. Vacuum cleaner salesmen sometimes stage a striking demonstration by arranging the machine so that it blows a stream of air out of the hose, the direction of the stream being not far from vertically upward, and then placing a ball in the stream. The ball remains "floating" above the outlet of the hose, though most observers would expect the airstream to blow it aside and let it fall. Why does the ball remain in the airstream?

21. Under any conditions, what is the reaction of any gas against any surface, and why? Can the air above the wing of a plane exert any lift on the wing? Why is it often said that there is a lift above the wing?

22. Explain the cause of surface tension. Why does the effect of surface tension resemble the effect which would be produced by an elastic skin?

23. Surface tension causes water in a tube of small diameter to rise; in a tube of 0.2 cm diameter water will rise about 15 cm. It has been suggested that water be raised by surface tension through a large number of such tubes from a tank at one level to another at a higher level as in Fig. 10-14. The water could operate a water wheel as it returns to the lower tank, thus providing a free source of energy. But the system *won't* produce energy. Other than because of the principle of conservation of energy, why won't it work?

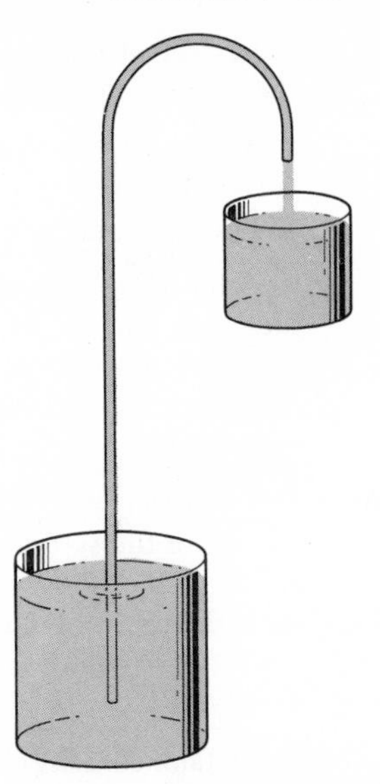

Fig. 10-14. Creation of energy by a pump driven by surface tension (?!).

Problems

1. A table has four legs, and the diameter of the legs at their feet is exactly 3/4 in. The table and the objects on it have a total weight of 120 lb. What is the pressure of the legs against the floor?

2. A camper weighs 180 lb, and when he lies down on an air mattress 900 in.^{2} of his body make contact with the mattress. What is the air pressure in the mattress if the atmospheric pressure is 14.7 lb/in.^{2}? (The pressure inside the mattress is that due to the man's weight *plus* that due to the atmosphere.)

3. A tire gage gives a reading of 28.0 lb/in.^{2} for the pressure in an automobile tire. If this tire must carry a weight of 1050 lb, how large an area of pavement will be in contact with the tire?

4. A service station attendant puts a new tubeless tire on a wheel and inflates it until the gage reads 29.4 lb/in.^{2}, which is exactly two atmospheres. He reports that he has "put 29.4 lb of air" into the tire. The volume of the tire is 80.0 liters, and the density of air at atmospheric pressure may be taken as 1.20 g/liter. (a) What mass of air, in pounds, did the attendant actually put into the tire? (b) What is the total mass of air in the tire? (1 lb = 454 g)

5. The average mass of the individual molecules in air is about $4.83 \cdot 10^{-23}$ g. If the average speed of the molecules is $5.00 \cdot 10^4$ cm/sec, and if the speed is unchanged when a molecule bounces off a wall, compute the change of momentum for a single molecule.

6. (a) The total mass of the molecules in one cm^3 of air at room temperature and normal pressure is $1.205 \cdot 10^{-3}$ g. If their effective average velocity is $5.02 \cdot 10^4$ cm/sec, what is the total kinetic energy of these molecules? (b) Compute the pressure, in dynes per cm^2, of a column of mercury 76.0 cm high, which is the normal atmospheric pressure. (c) The kinetic theory of gases yields an equation which says that the product of the pressure and the volume of a sample of gas is equal to 2/3 of the total kinetic energy of the molecules in the sample of gas. Check your answers to parts (a) and (b) with this relationship.

7. A compressed air tank has a volume of 12.5 ft^3. Initially the pressure gage reads zero, then air is pumped in until the gage reads 88.2 lb/in.^{2}. How many

cubic feet of air, measured at normal pressure, were pumped in? Assume no change of temperature.

8. A toy rubber balloon has a volume of 0.500 ft^3 and an actual internal pressure of 20.0 $lb/in.^2$. If it bursts, and if there is no change of temperature, what volume will the air from the balloon occupy?

9. A bicycle tire has a volume of 670 $in.^3$ and contains air at atmospheric pressure. It is pumped up by a pump which adds 67.0 $in.^3$ of air (measured at normal pressure) on each stroke. After four strokes of the pump, what will the pressure in the tire be? Disregard any temperature change. What pressure would a tire gage show?

10. A piston type pump is being used to establish a vacuum in a system. The volume of the system is 400 cm^3 and each stroke of the pump has the effect of adding 200 cm^3 of volume. (The next stroke again commences with 400 cm^3.) (a) If the pressure in the system is 100 $dynes/cm^2$ initially, what is it after three strokes have been completed? (b) If at some moment the air in the system had a density of $1.20 \cdot 10^{-4}$ g/cm^3, what was the density after three more strokes?

11. A tank consists of a rectangular lower portion 50.0 cm square and 10.0 cm deep. Above the top of this portion a vertical pipe 2.00 cm square extends upward 4.00 m. The tank is filled to the top of the pipe with water. (a) What is the weight, in dynes, of the water in the tank? (b) What is the pressure of the water at the bottom of the tank? (c) What force does the water exert on the bottom of the tank? (d) What force does the water exert upward on the top of the lower rectangular part of the tank? (e) Compare the sum of the answers for parts (a) and (d) with the answer for part (c) and explain.

12. A hydraulic press has a small piston with a diameter of 2.00 in. and a large piston with a diameter of 15.0 in. (a) Compute its ideal mechanical advantage. (b) If the effort is 60.0 lb and the efficiency is 85.0%, calculate the maximum resistance which can be overcome.

13. The small piston of the press in the preceding problem is moved so that instead of being at the same level as the large piston, it is 15.0 ft higher. The liquid in the press has a density of 56.0 lb/ft^3. The effort and the efficiency are unchanged. Compute the ideal mechanical advantage and the maximum resistance under these conditions.

14. A rectangular block of aluminum has a mass of 216 g. It is 2.00 cm thick, 4.00 cm wide, and 10.0 cm long. Determine (a) its density in g/cm^3, (b) its density in kg/m^3, and (c) its specific gravity.

15. A sample of a metal weighs 41.5 g in air, but its apparent weight when immersed in water is 36.1 g. Calculate its specific gravity.

16. A block of wood was found to weigh 57.2 g. A metal sinker was suspended below it and immersed in water, the block still being in the air; under these conditions the reading of the balance was 194.5 g. When both the sinker and the wooden block were dunked, the balance read 123.2 g. Compute the specific gravity of the wood.

17. The "gas bag" of an airship has a volume of $1.50 \cdot 10^6$ liters and is filled with helium. (a) If the density of the helium is 0.167 g/liter and that of air is 1.210 g/liter, and if the airship floats with no tendency to rise or fall, what is the total weight of the airship? (b) What is the weight of the ship, exclusive of the helium?

18. (a) Calculate the pressure of a column of water 80.0 ft high. The density of water is 62.4 lb/ft^3. (b) If a pump raises 500 gal of water from a well 80.0 ft deep, how much work must be done? (1 gallon = 0.133 cu ft) (c) If 500 gal of water are pumped from the well per minute, how many horse power are required?

19. Small platinum wire is used to form a ring which has a circumference of 4.00 cm and the ring is placed in contact with the surface of water. The surface tension of the water, having a value of 72.8 dynes per cm, acts on the ring when the ring is pulled upward, forming a film on each side of the wire. What force is required to pull the ring free from the surface?

20. A soap bubble is 5.00 cm in diameter and is formed from a soap solution with a surface tension of 34.0 dynes per cm. This tension acts on the inside of the soap film, as well as on the outside. By how much does the pressure within the bubble exceed atmospheric pressure?

ELASTICITY

11-1 Preview

In some degree, this chapter will be an extension of ideas and relationships we've met previously, so it will afford a limited review of some topics. We shall be concerned with the distortions which result, and the energy involved, when a distorting influence is brought to bear on an elastic body. The basis of all this is the concept of elasticity. We shall find, as is so often the situation, that our preconceptions of what elasticity *means must be modified drastically. What we learn in this chapter will be an essential part of the foundation needed for an understanding of vibratory motion, in the following chapter. This understanding, in turn, is prerequisite to our study of wave motion, sound, and the physical basis of music, in the ensuing chapters.*

11-2 The Concept of Elasticity

Our ordinary usage of the terms, "elastic" and "elasticity," does not provide a safe foundation for our study of this topic.

We usually consider a body to be elastic if it is capable of being distorted and then returning to its original condition. Thus a rubber band is elastic because it can be stretched, and a strip of spring steel is elastic because it can be bent; and in each case the body is capable of returning to its original dimensions or shape—provided the distortion was not too great. But a strip of sheet lead is not elastic since, though it can be bent, it's quite happy to *remain* bent. Also, we commonly say that a tennis ball is "live" if it will rebound nearly to the elevation from which we dropped it, or "dead" if it rebounds poorly. Less commonly used terms are "highly elastic" for the "live" ball and "relatively inelastic" for the "dead" ball.

But if you take a tennis ball in each hand, you can make a deeper dent with your thumb in the "dead" ball than in the "live" one. This fact carries the startling implication that the more elastic a body is, the more it resists distortion; and this is a valid implication. Your thumb can't make any impression on a steel ball, so the steel ball must be *more* elastic than the tennis ball. Thus if a tennis ball and a steel ball are dropped from equal heights the latter should bounce higher; and it will if you drop them onto a sufficiently hard surface. In fact, if you drop a steel ball and a glass marble from equal heights onto a massive body with a sufficiently hard surface—such as an anvil—the marble will bounce higher than the steel ball, showing that glass is more elastic than steel.

In view of these things, it seems that ***elasticity*** is a property which enables a body to undergo temporary distortion without permanent change resulting and that the quantitative measure of the elasticity of a body is its *resistance* to distortion.

However, if on our first attempt to compare the bounce of a steel ball and a marble we drop them from too great a height, we shall be unable to proceed without getting another marble! If the tensile force applied to a rubber band is too great, the band will break. Thus, in general, a substance has an ***elastic limit*** beyond which it will be permanently distorted or destroyed.

Note that there is no connection between elasticity and fragility or malleability. Glass is fragile but highly elastic, whereas lead is very malleable and has a very low elasticity, but with both of these, the elastic limit is reached with relatively small distortions. Again, steel is highly elastic and can undergo relatively great distortions before its elastic limit is reached, while rubber also has a high elastic limit but a low elasticity.

11-3 Elastic and Inelastic Collisions

In Sec. 6-12 we met the idea that in a collision, such as the impact of a tennis ball against the pavement, some kinetic energy is converted into heat energy. This obviously accounts for the fact that a tennis ball never bounces up quite to the point from which it was dropped. We have said that the higher a ball bounces under these circumstances, the more elastic it is. If there were such a thing as a perfectly elastic ball, and a perfectly elastic surface for it to fall onto, it would rebound *exactly* to its original height; that is, it would retain all its mechanical energy rather than have some of it changed to heat energy. Thus we define a perfectly ***elastic collision*** as one in which kinetic energy is conserved, and an ***inelastic collision*** as one in which some portion of the kinetic energies of the colliding bodies is converted into heat.

In the realm of macroscopic objects, no collision is perfectly elastic, though some may approach it very closely; all collisions are inelastic, but in widely varying degrees. In contrast, the collisions between molecules of a gas normally are perfectly elastic. We shall see later, principally in Chapter 34, that molecular collisions *may* be inelastic, and commonly are at sufficiently elevated temperatures; but under ordinary conditions, almost all of them are perfectly elastic.

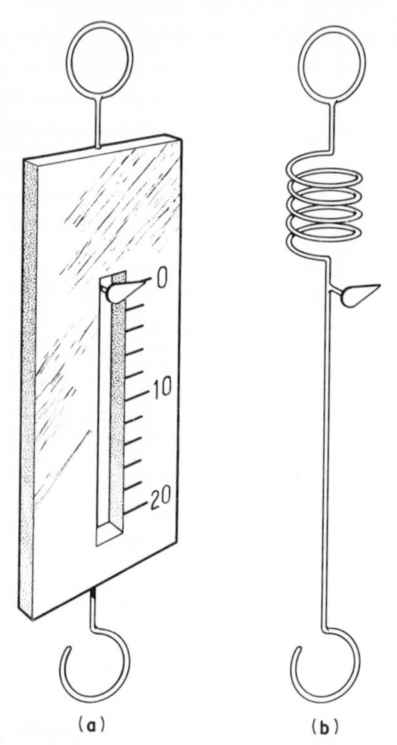

Fig. 11-1. Hooke's law is exemplified by the spacing of the graduations on a spring balance.

11-4 Hooke's Law

Figure 11-1(a) shows a spring balance, and the "innards" of the balance are depicted in Fig. 11-1(b). With no load on the hook, the index is at its highest position, and this is marked 0 on the scale. The addition of a load causes the spring to stretch, so that the index moves to a lower position on the scale. If the balance has a capacity of 20 lb, examination of the graduations will show that the 10 lb mark is just twice as far from the zero as is the 5 lb line. The 20 lb graduation is twice as far down as the 10 lb mark; the 15 lb line is three times as far down as the 5 lb graduation, etc. This orderly arrangement of the marks is an illustration of ***Hooke's law,*** which says that the distortion produced in any elastic body is directly proportional to the magnitude of the distorting influence, provided that the elastic limit is not exceeded.

In the case of an elastic body which undergoes a change of length e as the result of the application of a force F, we may express Hooke's law by writing

$$F = ke \tag{11-1}$$

in which k is a proportionality constant characteristic of that particular body. In this case, k would represent the value of the force required to produce unit change of length.

However, for two steel wires identical except in diameter, the value of k in Eq. (11-1) would be different. Some sort of index characteristic of a particular *substance* would be much more useful than one applicable only to a specific *object.*

In the case of stretching a steel wire, a relatively large force would be required to cause a given elongation in a wire of large cross-sectional area, or a smaller force to stretch a smaller wire the same amount. However, the force per unit area of cross section would be the same in both cases, if the wires were identical otherwise. This quotient of force divided by cross-sectional area is the ***stress.*** Similarly, if a wire is 1 cm long, a very large force would be required to stretch it 0.1 mm, but a much smaller force would cause the same stretch in a wire 1 m long (if they are otherwise identical). The *percentage* elongation is a hundred times as large in the first case as in the second. Thus we see that elongation per unit length, or ***strain,*** is a more useful concept than elongation alone.

If the force is F, the cross-sectional area A, the elongation e, and the length L, we can write

$$\text{stress} = \frac{F}{A} \tag{11-2}$$

and

$$\text{strain} = \frac{e}{L} \tag{11-3}$$

as the defining equations for these quantities. In these terms, Hooke's law becomes

$$\text{stress} = k \cdot \text{strain} \tag{11-4}$$

This may be rearranged to

$$k = \text{stress}/\text{strain}$$

or

$$k = \frac{F/A}{e/L} \tag{11-5}$$

In these equations the value of k is characteristic of the substance rather than the particular object, so they are more general and more useful than Eq. (11-1).

For definiteness, this discussion has been couched in terms of the stretching of a wire, but this is only one of many kinds of elastic distortion. The same general sort of logic applied to any other kind would have led us to the concepts of stress and strain, and to Eq. (11-4). We can use Eq. (11-5) for compression as well as for elongation, if we interpret e as a shortening. For other types of distortion, such as changes of volume, bending, or twisting, we cannot use Eq. (11-5). Instead, appropriate defining equations for stress and strain must replace Eq. (11-2), (11-3), and these will lead to an equation similar in principle to Eq. (11-5) but different in detail.

In a sense, Hooke's law is a statement of the properties of an elastic body, and sometimes an elastic body is defined as one which obeys Hooke's law. If we accept this definition, however, we must be prepared to depart still further from our preconceptions of elasticity. The substance most people would cite as an example of an elastic material, rubber, does *not* obey Hooke's law.

11-5 A Special Form of Hooke's Law: Young's Modulus

When a tensile or compressional stress is applied along the axis of a body which has a constant cross-sectional area throughout its length, Eq. (11-5) is applicable and the value of k is known as ***Young's modulus.*** The symbol Y replaces k, giving

$$Y = \frac{F/A}{e/L} = \frac{FL}{eA} \tag{11-6}$$

Approximate values of Young's modulus for a number of materials appear in Table 11-1. (Heat treatment and mechanical working of metals affect their elastic properties, and the annealing of glass may have a similar effect. Also, the composition of brass, steel, and glass will have an influence. Hence it is not possible to supply universally accurate values in a short table.)

Though Young's modulus is defined in terms of a distortion which involves a change of length, its usefulness is not limited to such applications. It is directly concerned in the bending of any body, and it is one of the factors which determines the speed of a longitudinal wave through a solid.

Table 11-1
YOUNG'S MODULUS

Material	dynes/cm^2	lb/in.^{2}
Aluminum	$6.9 \cdot 10^{11}$	$10.0 \cdot 10^6$
Brass	$11.0 \cdot 10^{11}$	$16.0 \cdot 10^6$
Steel	$20.0 \cdot 10^{11}$	$29.0 \cdot 10^6$
Glass	$5.3 \cdot 10^{11}$	$7.7 \cdot 10^6$

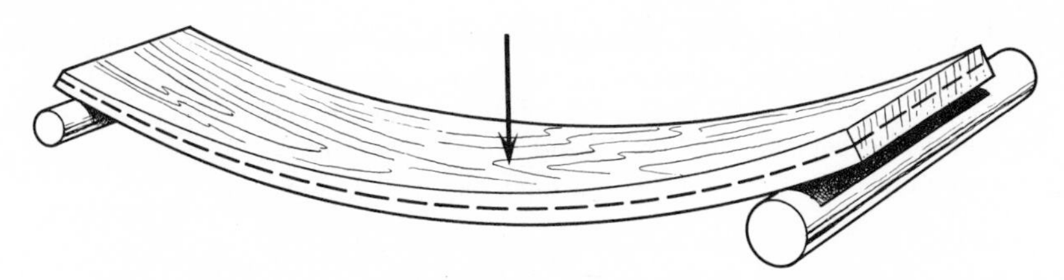

Fig. 11-2. When a beam is bent the upper portion is compressed and the lower portion is elongated.

We can understand its application to bending by considering Fig. 11-2. If a plank is supported in a horizontal position as shown and a heavy load placed on it, it will sag as shown. Before the plank was bent, its length was the same along its upper and lower surfaces, but now it is shorter on the top and longer on the bottom. All parts of the plank above the dashed line have been compressed and all below have been stretched—and Young's modulus applies to distortions of exactly these types.

For a uniform beam supported at its ends and subjected to a perpendicular force applied at its center, the bend is given by the relationship

$$B = \frac{FL^3}{4Ybd^3} \tag{11-7}$$

in which B is the bend occasioned by the force F, the length of the beam being L, its width or breadth b, and its depth d. Y is the value of Young's modulus for the material in the beam.

Sample Problem 1

A steel column has a cross-sectional area of 10.0 sq in., and its length is 15.0 ft. How much will it be shortened if a load of 6.00 tons is applied?

It will be convenient to solve Eq. (11-6) for e:

$$e = \frac{FL}{YA}$$

From Table 11-1, the value of Y is $29.0 \cdot 10^6$ lb/in.^{2}. Units of force must be consistent, so 6.00 tons must be changed to pounds; and e and L must also be in consistent units. Making these changes in units, and inserting the data into the equation above, we have

$$e = \frac{(6.00 \cdot 2 \cdot 10^3) \cdot (15.0 \cdot 12)}{(29.0 \cdot 10^6) \cdot 10.0} = 7.45 \cdot 10^{-3}$$

so the shortening is 0.00745 in.

Sample Problem 2

Two horizontal wooden beams are exactly equivalent except that one is 6.00 in. deep and the other is 10.0 in. deep. They are supported at their ends, and equal loads act at their midpoints. The bend of the shallower beam is how many times that of the deeper one?

If we apply Eq. (11-7) to each of the beams, the two equations would be identical except for the bend B and the depth d, so for our present purposes we can lump F, L, 4, Y, and b into a single constant k, and write

$$B = \frac{k}{d^3}$$

which says that the bend is inversely proportional to the cube of the depth. The same relationship may be expressed by writing

$$\frac{B_1}{B_2} = \left(\frac{d_2}{d_1}\right)^3$$

which could also be derived by writing Eq. (11-7) for each beam, dividing one equation by the other, and canceling out common factors. Assigning the subscript 1 to the beam with the 6.00 in. depth, we have

$$\frac{B_1}{B_2} = \left(\frac{10.0}{6.00}\right)^3 = 4.63$$

so the bend of the 6.00 in. beam is 4.63 times that of the 10.0 in. beam. Looking at the same facts another way, the deeper beam is 4.63 times as stiff as the shallower one.

11-6 Elasticity and Newton's Third Law of Motion

One of our expressions of Hooke's law stated that the distortion produced in any elastic body is directly proportional to the magnitude of the distorting influence. Since the third law of motion says that for every action there is an equal and opposite reaction, to keep Sir Isaac Newton happy the distorting influence must be accompanied by an equal and opposite restoring influence. In more definite but more restricted terms, if a force is causing a distortion there must be an equal force which tends to restore the body to its undistorted configuration. Thus we may express Hooke's law by saying that in an elastic body the restoring influence is directly proportional to the distortion—provided as always, of course, that the elastic limit is not exceeded.

At this stage in your study of physics, this modification of Hooke's law should be fairly obvious. Another point of contact between Hooke's law and Newton's third law is much less obvious—until you see it. This has to do with what are called ***passive forces.*** Barring unusual and unfortunate situations which could put you in the hospital, and a few other momentary situations, wherever your weight is applied a supporting force appears. It wasn't there until your weight was applied, and it disappears the instant your weight is transferred elsewhere. Whenever any force is applied to an object without any acceleration resulting, the object must somehow generate an equal and opposite force. But where do these passive forces come from, why do they disappear, and how is it that they are intelligent enough—and public-spirited enough—to time themselves so accurately and adjust their magnitudes so perfectly?

Mr. Hooke has the answer. Even if you are standing on solid granite—on the solid granitic monolith of Half Dome in Yosemite, almost a mile above the valley below, for example—your weight causes an elastic distortion of the granite beneath your feet, thereby generating a restoring force; and it is this restoring force which—fortunately—supports you.

11-7 Work Done on (or by) an Elastic Body

For a moment, let's forget physics and turn our attention to a bit of geometry. In Figure 11-3(a) we have a triangle *ABC*, and we know that its area is one-half the altitude times the base. If point *D* moves from *A* to *B* along the base of the triangle while point *E* moves along the hypotenuse from *A* to *C* in such a manner that the line *DE* remains parallel to *BC*, we might think of the area of the triangle being "generated" or "swept out" by the line *DE*. The length of *DE* is zero when both *D* and *E* coincide with *A*, and increases until it equals *BC* when *D* reaches *B* and *E* reaches *C*. At any intermediate location, the length of *DE* is directly proportional to the distance *AD*. The average value of *DE* is half of *BC*, so the area of the triangle is the average value of *DE* times the base of the triangle.

Figure 11-3(b) is a graphical representation of the relationship between the force applied to a coil spring and the resulting stretch. Since Hooke's law requires that the stretch be directly proportional to the force, the graph is a straight line. The force is zero when the stretch is zero; when the spring has been stretched a distance d_1, the force is represented by the vertical line segment above d_1; and the line segment above d_2 indicates the force when the elongation is d_2. Comparison with Fig. 11-3(a) reminds us that the area of the triangle is half the altitude times the base, which in this case means half the maximum force times the stretch. But

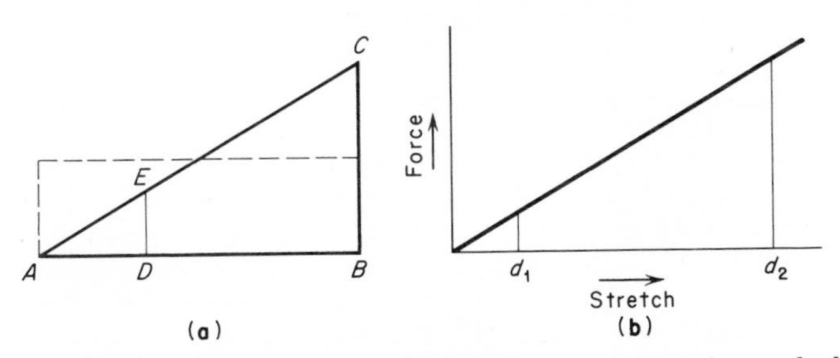

Fig. 11-3. (a) Area of a triangle; (b) Work done against a force which obeys Hooke's law is the area of the triangle.

any product of force and distance (in the same direction as the force) is work or energy. Thus the work done in stretching a spring is *half* the product of the maximum force and the stretch. If F_{max} is the maximum force, e is the corresponding elongation, and W represents the work,

$$W = \frac{F_{max} \cdot e}{2} \tag{11-8}$$

This may also be written

$$W = F_{av} \cdot e \tag{11-9}$$

in which F_{av} is the average force, since the average force is half the maximum.

Students very commonly make the error of using Eq. (6-1), $W = Fs$, for the work done in distorting an elastic body, but that equation is appropriate for a *constant* force F acting over a distance s; so to use Eq. (6-1) instead of (11-8) or (11-9) is to ignore Hooke's law and the properties of elastic bodies.

Though this has been worked out in terms of the stretching of a spring, the situation is similar for any other type of elastic distortion in which Hooke's law is obeyed.

Our initial algebraic statement of Hooke's law was $F = ke$, in which k represents the force required to produce unit elongation, Eq. (11-1). The force reaches its maximum value when the distortion is a maximum; $F_{max} = ke_{max}$. If we put this value of F_{max} into Eq. (11-8), we obtain

$$W = \frac{k(e_{max})^2}{2} \tag{11-10}$$

Sample Problem 3

The end of a diving board is depressed 4.00 in. when a 160 lb man walks out and stands at the end. How much would the tip be depressed by a 200 pounder?

In general, if d is the displacement of the tip of the board, $F = kd$, so for the lighter man 160 lb $= k \cdot 400$ in.; then $k = 160$ lb/4.00 in. or 40.0 lb/in. For a heavier man 200 lb $= 40.0$ lb/in. $\cdot\, d$ in., which yields $d = 5.00$ in.

Obviously we could also have solved this problem by setting up a direct proportion between displacements and forces.

Sample Problem 4

How much work does the force of gravity do on the board in each of the two cases in Sample Problem 3?

We may use either Eq. (11-8) or (11-10). If we use the former for the case of the 160 lb man, the maximum force times the maximum displacement is

$$160 \text{ lb} \cdot \frac{4.00}{12.0} \text{ ft} = 53.3 + \text{ft-lb}$$

and half of this is 26.7 ft-lb.

For the sake of variety let's use Eq. (11-10) for the second case. In Sample Problem 3 we found the value of k to be 40.0 lb/in., and this is $12 \cdot 40.0$ lb/ft. The maximum displacement is 5.00/12.00 ft. So

$$W = (12 \cdot 40.0) \cdot \frac{(5.00/12.00)^2}{2} = 41.7 \text{ ft-lb}$$

It has been tacitly assumed that the equations developed for the work done in distorting an elastic body represent *useful* work; that is, that any energy lost in overcoming friction is not included in the computed values of W. Within this limitation, the equations are also valid for the potential energy possessed by the body in its distorted condition.

Sample Problem 5

A coil spring in a toy is compressed, and when it is released, it shoots a marble out horizontally. If the marble has a mass of 20.0 g and if it takes 490 g to compress the spring 2.50 cm, what velocity will the compressed spring be able to give the marble?

The potential energy of the spring is $Fd/2$ and the kinetic energy of the marble is $mv^2/2$, but the former is in gravitational units (g cm) and the latter is in dynamic units (ergs); so we must change F grams to Fg dynes. Then conservation of energy requires that

$$\frac{mv^2}{2} = \frac{Fgd}{2}$$

Multiplying both sides by 2 and putting in the known values we have

$$20.0v^2 = 490 \cdot 980 \cdot 2.50$$

$$v^2 = \frac{490 \cdot 980 \cdot 2.50}{20.0} = 490 \cdot 49.0 \cdot 2.50$$

$$= 49.0^2 \cdot 25.0$$

$$v = \sqrt{49.0^2 \cdot 25.0} = 49.0 \cdot 5.00$$

$$= 245 \text{ cm/sec}$$

Summary

An *elastic body* is one which is capable of undergoing distortion and returning to its original configuration and volume when the distorting influence is removed. The *measure* of *elasticity* is the *resistance* to distortion, *not* the *ease* of *distortion.*

In a perfectly elastic collision, kinetic energy is conserved. Some kinetic energy is converted into heat in any inelastic collision.

Provided that the distortion of a body does not exceed the elastic limit, the distortion is directly proportional to the magnitude of the distorting influence. This relationship is *Hooke's law.* It may also be stated by saying that the restoring influence is directly proportional to the distortion.

To make possible a comparison of the elastic properties of bodies of the same material and generally similar form, but different dimensions, the concepts of stress and strain are convenient. In terms of these concepts, Hooke's law says that stress is directly proportional to strain.

Young's modulus is the value (for a particular material) of the proportionality factor which relates a tensile stress or a longitudinal compressional stress to the corresponding strain.

Passive supporting forces have their origin in an elastic distortion of the body which furnishes the force.

Since the work done in distorting an elastic body is performed against an increasing resistance rather than against one of constant value, the quantity of work is not the product of the maximum force and the displacement; it is one-half of this quantity. This factor of $\frac{1}{2}$ also applies, of course, to the computation of the potential energy of the distorted body.

Self-Quiz

1. Compare the significance of the term "elasticity" as used in physics with its meaning—or meanings—in ordinary usage. Consider especially carefully the quantitative aspect.

2. If an imperfectly elastic body, such as a tennis ball, is dropped onto a hard surface it may bounce repeatedly, but its height of rise decreases with each successive bounce. This means that it must be losing energy. What becomes of the energy it loses?

3. Why is it incorrect to think of a fragile substance as being inelastic, or to consider that an elastic substance is not fragile?

4. Take a rubber band and slowly stretch it as far as you can without breaking it. Repeat several times, if necessary, until you have a fair idea of how the force required depends on the amount of stretching. Does the rubber band obey Hooke's law?

5. Define the terms "stress" and "strain."

6. It was stated that Eq. (11-4) is more general than Eq. (11-1). Explain clearly why this is true, and why the former may be more useful. Does this mean that though Eq. (11-1) may be of theoretical interest, it has no practical applications? Explain.

7. Why is Young's modulus, which has to do with elongation or longitudinal compression, applicable to the calculation of the bend of a beam?

8. What has Newton's third law of motion to do with elasticity?

9. If you cross a small creek on a plank, what is the source of the force which supports you? What happens, and why, if your weight is too great for the plank—beg pardon—if the plank is too weak for your weight?

10. If you weigh 140 lb and your weight depresses the plank exactly 3 in. ($\frac{1}{4}$ ft), why is the work done on the plank 17.5 ft-lb instead of 35 ft-lb?

11. Derive the relationship involved in the preceding question.

Problems

1. By putting into the right-hand side of Eq. (11-6) the fundamental dimensions of each quantity, determine the dimensions (in terms of m, l, and t) of Young's modulus. Also determine these dimensions from the units specified in the middle column of Table 11-1.

2. A ball is dropped from a height of 250 cm onto a hard surface and rebounds, but 19.0% of its original store of energy is converted into heat. Compute, not necessarily in this order, (a) its velocity at the instant before it strikes, (b) its velocity the instant it leaves the surface, and (c) the height of the rebound.

3. A flat steel spring is bent so that its tip is displaced 3.50 cm by a force of 210 g. (a) How much would it be bent if the force were 120 g? (b) How great a force would be required to bend it 5.00 cm?

4. A steel wire is exactly 2 m long and one mm in diameter. How much will it stretch if a load of 10.0 kg is suspended from it?

5. A hollow aluminum column is exactly 6 in. square (external dimension) and the wall is exactly 1 in. thick. If the column is shortened $2.25 \cdot 10^{-3}$ in. by a load of 1.50 tons, calculate the length of the column.

6. A brass wire and an aluminum wire are of the same diameter, and the brass wire is 175 cm long. When equal weights are suspended from the two wires they undergo equal elongations. What is the length of the aluminum wire?

7. A brass wire and an aluminum wire of the same diameter are fastened 40.0 cm apart to a horizontal support, and their lower ends are fastened to a horizontal bar of negligible mass at points 40.0 cm apart. If the bar is to remain precisely level when a weight is hung from it, how far from the brass wire should the weight be applied to the bar?

8. Compute the energy expended in each of the three cases in Problem 3.

9. A spring is compressed until 93.0 ft-lb of energy have been stored up in it. If a force of 82.7 lb is required to produce a distortion of exactly 1 ft, compute the distortion.

10. If it requires twenty turns of the stem of a watch to wind the mainspring, and if this stores sufficient energy to keep the watch running for 30.0 hr, how long will it run if the stem is given only ten turns?

11. Show that Eq. (11-7) is dimensionally homogeneous.

12

VIBRATORY MOTION

12-1 Preview

We met the concept of periodic motion in Sec. 8-2 as an introduction to uniform circular motion. Vibratory motion is another type of periodic motion, and we shall see that the simplest and smoothest kind of vibratory motion is related very closely to uniform circular motion. On the basis of this interrelationship we shall consider the vibration of a weighted spring and that of a pendulum. It will develop that a study of the vibration of a pendulum will lead to an indirect method of measuring the acceleration due to gravity. Much of Chapters 13, 14, and 15 will depend on what we learn in the present chapter.

12-2 Concepts Pertinent to Vibratory Motion, and Their Definitions

Whereas circular motion is a dizzying motion in an unchanging sense around a circular path, ***vibratory motion*** is an oscillatory motion, back and forth over a limited path which usually is a straight line. Less commonly, the path of the vibrating body may be an arc or the body may vibrate in a rotary sense, twisting one way and then the other. One ***vibration*** consists of one complete round trip of the body, back and forth; it is one complete ***cycle*** of vibratory motion. As defined in Sec. 8-2, the time which elapses during one complete vibration is the ***period.*** The A string of a violin has a period of 1/440 sec, so during any one second it makes 440 vibrations; the number of vibrations per unit time (usually per second) is the ***frequency.*** Obviously the period and the frequency are reciprocally related; if the period is t and the frequency is N (for *n*umber of vibrations per second),

$$t = \frac{1}{N}, \quad \text{and} \quad N = \frac{1}{t} \tag{12-1}$$

(The obvious symbol for frequency would be F, but we have used F to represent force, and we shall have to represent both frequency and force in the same equation.)

The excursions of the vibrating body may cover considerable distance, as in the case of a child in a swing; but they may be almost imperceptible, as in the case of a lightly bowed violin string. This characteristic of a vibratory motion is related to its ***amplitude,*** which is defined as the distance from the rest position to the point of maximum displacement. Note that the amplitude is *not* the full range of the vibration, from the position of maximum displacement in one direction to the point of greatest displacement in the opposite direction; the amplitude is only half this distance. For most vibrations the amplitude is measured in linear units, but in some cases, such as the vibration of a pendulum, the amplitude may be measured in degrees or radians.

12-3 Simple Harmonic Vibration

Vibrations may be very complex, such as those of a piano string or those which occur during an earthquake, or they may be very simple. There is a dearth of examples of the simplest kind of vibrations, however. Perhaps the vertical vibration of a weight suspended from a spiral spring is the best example.

From a purely qualitative (and hence incomplete) point of view we may think of ***simple harmonic vibration,*** or ***simple harmonic motion,*** as the simplest and smoothest possible type of vibratory motion. More accurately and less ambiguously, we may define it either as the type of vibratory motion executed by a body which obeys Hooke's law or as the projection, on a straight line, of uniform circular motion. Disparate as these two quantitative definitions may seem, we shall find that they are closely related and fully equivalent.

Let's examine the second of these accurate definitions; we come back to the first in Sec. 12-6. Imagine yourself on a beach on the Atlantic coast just at sunrise, or on the Pacific coast at sunset. (Don't let your imagination run away with you, now. We still have work to do.) You have a beach bag with a rope handle, and you are swinging this around with uniform circular motion, the plane of the circle being vertical. You notice your shadow, and that of the moving bag, on the vertical cliff face behind you, and you find that by changing your position you can make the shadow of the bag move up and down the cliff in a vertical line. This rectilinear motion of the shadow is the projection on a straight line (on the face of the cliff) of the uniform circular motion of the bag; so the shadow is—by definition—moving with simple harmonic motion.

To learn more of the nature of simple harmonic vibration and its relation to uniform circular motion, consider Fig. 12-1. A point P is moving uniformly in a counterclockwise sense around a circular path of radius r, and this uniform circular motion is being projected onto the straight vertical line AB. As P moves around the circle, another point P' moves along the line AB in such a manner that a line joining P and P' is always horizontal. (If this seems too intangible, think of point P as the beach bag, point P' as its shadow on the cliff, and the dashed horizontal

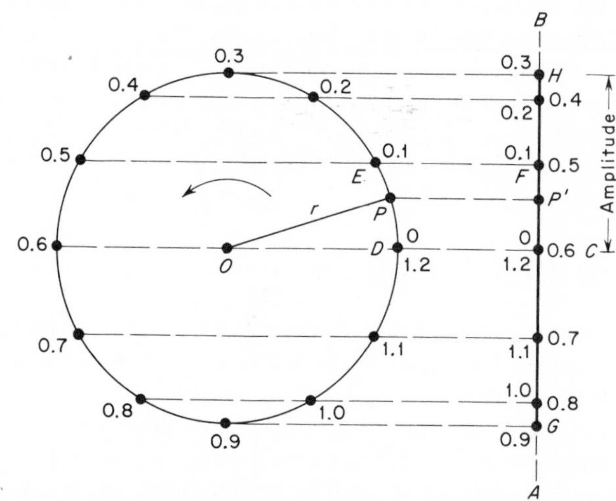

Fig. 12-1. Development of simple harmonic motion from uniform circular motion.

lines as the sun's rays.) Thus the displacement of P' always is the *vertical component* of the displacement of P, and we shall find in the next two sections that the velocity and acceleration of P' are similarly related to those of P.

In Fig. 12-1 it is assumed that the period is 1.2 sec, and the positions of P and P' at intervals of 0.1 sec are marked and labeled. It is assumed that at time zero the point P is horizontally to the right of the center O of the circle. At 0.1 sec, P will have moved to point E and P' to F. At 0.3 sec, P will have reached its highest possible location, and the same must be true of P'. At 0.6 sec, P will be horizontally to the left of O and P' will be at the same position as at zero time. Both P and P' will reach the maximum downward displacement at 0.9 sec, and at 1.2 sec the situation will be exactly as it was at zero time. Thus while P moves once around the circle, P' completes one cycle of vibration over the path between G and H.

Obviously the amplitude CH or CG of the vibratory motion has exactly the same magnitude as the radius OP of the circle; and since one transit of P around the circle corresponds to one complete vibration of P', the period and frequency of the vibration are identical with those of the circular motion.

Some examples of simple harmonic motion are actually generated by uniform circular motion. More commonly, however, no circular motion whatever is involved. Even in such cases, analysis of the vibratory motion is simplified greatly if we consider a *hypothetical* uniform motion around a circle. Whether we *imagine* uniform circular motion of the same period and frequency as those of the vibration to occur in a circle which has a radius equal to the amplitude of the vibration, or whether such circular motion actually exists, the path of the circular motion is called a ***circle of reference.***

12-4 Velocity in Simple Harmonic Motion

In Fig. 12-1 the length of arc covered by point P in any 0.1 sec interval is the same as in any other equal time, since the circular motion is uniform. On the other hand, the distance covered by the vibrating point P' is greater between 0 sec and 0.1 sec than between 0.1 and 0.2 sec, and it is still less between 0.2 and 0.3 sec; so the speed is decreasing throughout this 0.3 sec interval. At point H the direction of motion reverses and during the ensuing 0.3 sec, P' moves with ever-increasing speed. It again slows to a momentary stop at G and then accelerates toward C.

We can understand this variation of speed by considering Fig. 12-2. This is an enlargement of a portion of Fig. 12-1, and represents the situation at 0.1 sec when P is at E and P' is at F. Though the path of P is circular, at any instant its velocity v is tangential as shown in Fig. 12-2.

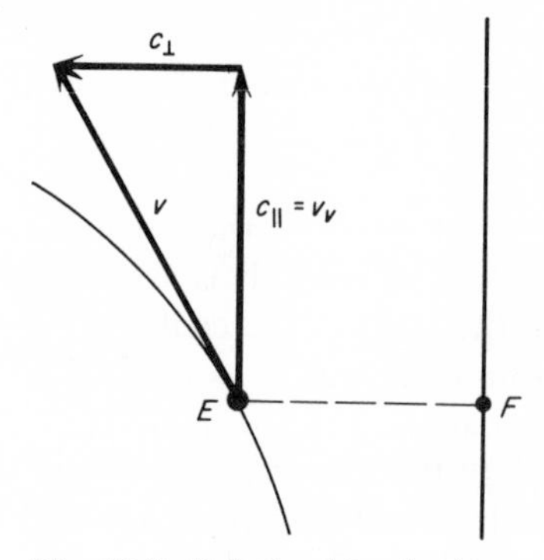

Fig. 12-2. Relationship of velocity in simple harmonic motion to tangential velocity in uniform circular motion.

Since simple harmonic motion is the projection of uniform circular motion on a straight line, and we have chosen to project it onto a vertical line, it is only the vertical *component* of v which is effective in the vibratory motion. More generally, it is the component $c_\parallel$ of the velocity in the circular motion parallel with the path of vibration which is effective; and the component $c_\perp$ normal to the path of vibration is irrelevant.

A glance back at Fig. 12-1 reveals that at the instant the vibrating body passes through its rest position—in either direction—the velocity of the point in the circle of reference is parallel with the path of the vibration; so at these instants the velocity of the vibrating body is identical with that of the point in the circle of reference. On the other hand, when the vibrating body is at either extremity of its range, the velocity of the point in the circle of reference is perpendicular to the path of vibration; thus there is no component parallel to the path of the vibrating particle, so just at that instant the speed of the vibrating body is zero.

12-5 Acceleration in Simple Harmonic Vibration

We have just seen that as the vibrating body moves away from the rest position its speed decreases, and its speed increases as it approaches the rest position. Thus it experiences a negative acceleration during its outward journey and a positive acceleration when moving toward the rest position. Since a negative sign on any vector quantity simply means a reversal of direction, we may summarize this situation by saying that the acceleration of the vibrating body is always toward the rest position. This is strongly reminiscent of the fact that in circular motion the acceleration is always directed toward the center of the circle. In fact, the acceleration of a body which is vibrating with simple harmonic motion is always identical with the appropriate component of the centripetal acceleration in the circle of reference.

Figure 12-3 also represents part of Fig. 12-1, with some added features. The vibratory motion has an amplitude CH equal (of course) to the radius OP of the circle of reference. The vibrating point is at P' when the point in the reference circle is at P. The centripetal acceleration a_c in the circle of reference has been resolved into a component $c_\perp$ normal to the path of the vibration and a component $c_\parallel$ parallel to that path. The latter is also labeled a_v since the acceleration of the vibrating point is identical with this component of the centripetal acceleration. (All three vectors which represent accelerations or components of accelerations are shown in solid lines with arrowheads to differentiate them from the geometrical lines, which are dashed.)

The acceleration a_c lies along the radius OP and the component $c_{\parallel}$ or a_v lies on the line PJ, which is constructed perpendicular to OC. Also, the component $c_{\perp}$ is parallel to OJ. Thus the triangle formed by the centripetal acceleration and its components is similar to triangle OJP, so we can write

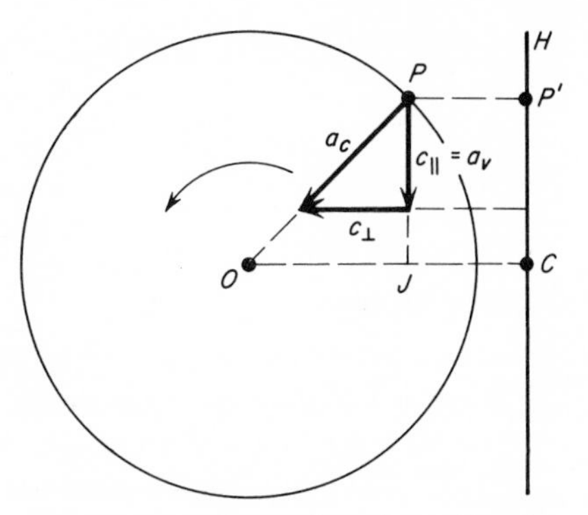

Fig. 12-3. Relationship of acceleration in simple harmonic motion to centripetal acceleration in uniform circular motion.

$$\frac{c_{\parallel}}{a_c} = \frac{PJ}{PO}$$

But $c_{\parallel}$ is identical with the acceleration a_v of the vibrating point, PJ is equal to the displacement CP', which we may call d, and the radius OP is equal to the amplitude CH, which we may represent by d_{max}. Putting these equivalent quantities into the equation yields

$$\frac{a_v}{a_c} = -\frac{d}{d_{\text{max}}}, \quad \text{or} \quad a_v = -a_c \cdot \frac{d}{d_{\text{max}}} \tag{12-2}$$

in which the minus sign signifies the fact that the direction of the acceleration is opposite that of the displacement. According to Eq. (8-21), (8-22), the centripetal acceleration is v^2/r or $r\omega^2$, in which v and ω represent the tangential and angular velocities, respectively, of a point describing uniform circular motion in a path of radius r. In the present application, the point is on the circle of reference and the radius of this circle is equal to the amplitude of the vibration, so we may substitute d_{max} for r. Equation 12-2 then becomes

$$a_v = -\frac{v^2}{d_{\text{max}}} \cdot \frac{d}{d_{\text{max}}}$$

which simplifies to

$$a_v = -(v/d_{\text{max}})^2 \cdot d \tag{12-3}$$

Similarly,

$$a_v = -d_{\text{max}}\omega^2 \cdot \frac{d}{d_{\text{max}}} \quad \text{or} \quad \boxed{a_v = -\omega^2 d} \tag{12-4}$$

If we wish to express the vibrational acceleration in terms of period or frequency rather than in terms of velocity in the reference circle, we may use the fact that $v = 2\pi r/t$ and $\omega = 2\pi/t$, plus the fact that $t = 1/N$, to obtain

$$a_v = -\frac{4\pi^2}{t^2}d \tag{12-5}$$

and

$$a_v = -4\pi^2N^2d \tag{12-6}$$

Sample Problem 1

A tuning fork has a frequency of 256 vps and the amplitude at the tips of the prongs is 1.25 mm. (a) What are the maximum and minimum velocities attained by a tip of a prong, and when does the prong tip have these velocities? (b) What are the maximum and minimum values of the acceleration of a prong tip, and when do these occur?

(a) Without the concept of a circle of reference, this would be a difficult problem, but the maximum velocity of a vibrating body is equal to the speed of a point in the circle of reference. The radius of the circle of reference is the amplitude of vibration, or 0.125 cm. Thus the point in the reference circle goes a distance of $2\pi \cdot 0.125$ cm during one vibration, or $256 \cdot 2\pi \cdot 0.125$ cm/sec, which is 201 cm/sec. As we saw in Sec. 12-4, this maximum velocity will occur as the prong passes through the rest position. We also saw that the velocity must be zero at the points of maximum displacement.

(b) In Sec. 12-5 we found that the acceleration is zero at the rest position and has its maximum value at the points of maximum displacement; furthermore, this maximum acceleration is equal to the centripetal acceleration in the reference circle. Thus we may use Eq. (8-21) or (8-22), or any among Eq. (12-3)–(12-6) inclusive. Choosing Eq. (12-6) and setting the displacement equal to the amplitude,

$$a_v = -4\pi^2 \cdot 256^2 \cdot 0.125 = -3.23 \cdot 10^5 \text{ cm/sec}^2$$

Trig

If we define the angle *COP* in Fig. 12-1 as θ, and if the displacement of the body from the rest position is *d*, for any value of θ the displacement is given by $d = d_{max} \sin \theta$, d_{max} being the amplitude (maximum displacement). If the frequency of the vibration is *N*, at any time *t* (measured from any instant at which $\theta = 0$), $d = d_{max} \sin 2\pi Nt$.

Similar expressions for the velocity *v* of the vibrating body are $v = v_t \cdot \cos \theta$ and $v = v_t \cdot \cos 2\pi Nt$, v_t being the value of the tangential velocity of the point in the reference circle.

The acceleration a_v of the vibrating body is given by $a_v = a_c \cdot \sin \theta$ and $a_v = a_c \cdot \sin 2\pi Nt$, in which a_c is the centripetal acceleration in the reference circle as given by Eq. 8-21 or Eq. 8-22.

12-6 The Relationship of Hooke's Law to Simple Harmonic Motion

Thus far, I have been ignoring the first of the accurate definitions of simple harmonic vibration which I gave you in Sec. 12-3, the one in terms of obedience to Hooke's law. It is high time to consider this definition, and fortunately we are now in a position to do so.

Since, as we have seen, simple harmonic vibration is related to *uniform* circular motion, for any simple harmonic motion of constant amplitude and frequency all of the quantities in Eq. (12-3)–(12-6) are constant except a_v and d; so all these constant quantities may be lumped into a single constant k. This simplifies each of these equations to the single equation

$$a_v = -kd \tag{12-7}$$

But Newton's second law of motion says that any acceleration is related to the magnitude of the accelerating force and the mass of the body undergoing acceleration according to Eq. (5-17): $a = F/m$. Thus, if F_v is the force responsible for the acceleration of a vibrating body of mass m,

$$\frac{F_v}{m} = -kd$$

We may multiply both sides of this equation by m, and since m is constant we may replace the product km by a single constant k'. This yields

$$F_v = -k'd \tag{12-8}$$

in which the minus sign indicates that the direction of the accelerating force is opposite that of the displacement; that is, it is a restoring force. So, translated into English, Eq. (12-8) reads "The restoring force is directly proportional to the displacement but has an opposite direction." If this doesn't sound familiar, it should! It is the situation which must exist in an elastic body if the body is to obey Hooke's law as stated in the first paragraph of Sec. 11-6.

Thus we see that if we take the concept of simple harmonic motion as the projection of uniform circular motion on a straight line, we are led directly to the fact that only if a body obeys Hooke's law can it execute simple harmonic vibration.

Sample Problem 2

What will the acceleration of a prong of the fork in Sample Problem 1 be when the displacement is 0.750 mm?

Again we have a wide choice of methods. We can use any of Eq. (12-3)–(12-6) inclusive, or Eq. (8-21) or (8-22) combined with Eq. (12-7). Or, having solved (b) in Sample Problem 1, we may invoke Eq. (12-7). If the acceleration is $-3.23 \cdot 10^5$ cm/sec^2 when the displacement is 1.25 mm, it will be 0.750/1.250, or $\frac{3}{5}$ of $-3.23 \cdot 10^5$ when the displacement is 0.750 mm, and the result is $-1.94 \cdot 10^5$ cm/sec^2.

12-7 The Period of a Simple Harmonic Vibration

For concreteness, we shall consider the period of vibration of a mass m suspended from a spiral spring, the path of the vibrations being vertical. According to Eq. (12-5) the acceleration of the vibrating body is

$$a_v = -\frac{4\pi^2}{t^2} \cdot d$$

when the body is displaced a distance d from its rest position. As we were reminded in the preceding section, $a = F/m$, when F is expressed in dynamic units, and so

$$\frac{F}{m} = -\frac{4\pi^2}{t^2} \cdot d$$

Solving for the period t, we obtain

$$t = 2\pi\sqrt{-md/F}$$

which may be rearranged to the form

$$t = 2\pi\sqrt{m/-(F/d)} \qquad (12\text{-}9)$$

At first glance, this appears useless since the square root of a negative number is irrational. However, the displacement d and the restoring force F are oppositely directed; so when we put in numerical values, with a minus sign on one of them to indicate this opposition of direction, the minus sign under the radical will disappear.

The expression in the denominator under the radical, $-F/d$, represents the restoring force divided by the displacement; that is, the restoring force per unit displacement. Since Hooke's law requires that the force be directly proportional to the displacement, this restoring force per unit displacement, $-F/d$, has a constant value which is called the ***force constant*** of the spring. If we represent it by K, the equation for the period is

$$t = 2\pi\sqrt{m/K} \qquad (12\text{-}10)$$

Equation 12-10 is applicable to certain types of vibrations other than the one for which we derived it.

A more rigorous derivation would show that instead of using m as the mass of the body suspended from the spring, it should represent that mass plus one-third of the mass of the spring itself; but in many practical cases a fairly accurate value of the period can be obtained without making this correction.

Sample Problem 3

A mass of 500 g is suspended from a spiral spring and set into vibration in a vertical path, its period being 0.450 sec. How much did the spring stretch when the mass was hung from it, before the vibrations were initiated?

According to Eq. (12-10), $t = 2\pi\sqrt{m/K}$, and we have the values of t and m, so we can find the force constant K; and knowledge of its value will lead us to the final answer:

$$0.450 = 2\pi\sqrt{500/K}$$

$$0.450^2 = 4\pi^2 \cdot \frac{500}{K}$$

$$K = \frac{4\pi^2 \cdot 500}{0.450^2} = 9.75 \cdot 10^4$$

Our derivation of Eq. (12-10) was in terms of dynamic units, so K is $9.75 \cdot 10^4$ dynes/cm. K was defined as the restoring force per unit displacement; that is, $K = -F/d$. The minus sign indicates that whereas the displacement was downward, which we may arbitrarily choose as the positive direction, the restoring force was upward. When the mass was hung from it, the spring stretched until a restoring force $F = -mg$ was generated, in accordance with Newton's third law. Since $K = -F/d$,

$$K = \frac{mg}{d}$$

and

$$d = \frac{mg}{K} = 500 \cdot 980 \div (9.75 \cdot 10^4) = 5.03$$

Thus the 500 g mass stretched the spring approximately 5.03 cm.

12-8 The Simple Pendulum

We shall consider only one special case of the equation we developed in the preceding section: that suitable for a simple pendulum.

If a pendulum vibrates with a large amplitude, its motion is not simple harmonic motion; but the smaller the amplitude is, the more nearly it becomes simple harmonic. Thus we may consider that, for a sufficiently small amplitude, the vibrations are simple harmonic.

A so-called ***simple pendulum*** consists of a mass m supported by a wire or cord which is so strong that it can't be stretched yet has zero mass, and there must be no friction or other influence which could affect the vibrations. Obviously such a pendulum does not exist, but it can be approximated rather closely. And we can theorize about such a pendulum, whereas a derivation which allowed for the mass of the wire, its stretching, and frictional effects would make the derivation too complicated.

An idealized pendulum of this sort is represented in Fig. 12-4. A wire of length L is supported at O, and in turn it supports a mass m. If at rest, the mass would be at A, but it has been displaced through the arc AB to point B. When the mass is at B (or any other position except A) its weight will have a radial component c_r colinear with the wire and a tangential component c_t, and the latter will tend to accelerate the mass toward the rest position.

The triangle BCD is similar to triangle OEB, which is formed by extending the *direction* of c_t until this extended line intersects a line drawn

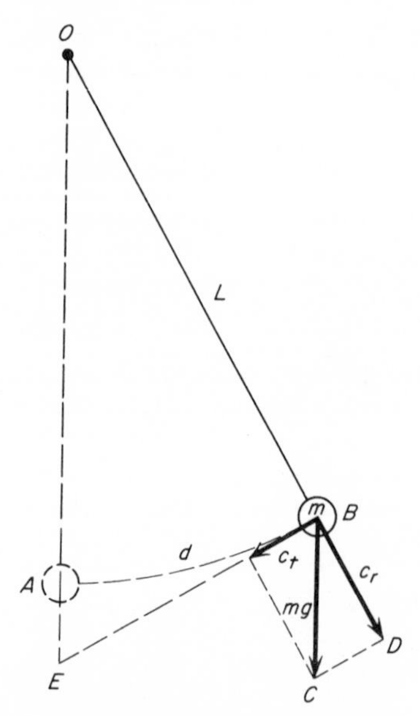

Fig. 12-4. Basis for derivation of the period of a pendulum.

from O downward past A; so corresponding sides in the two triangles are directly proportional. Thus,

$$\frac{DC}{BC} = \frac{BE}{OE}$$

The vector BC represents the weight of the mass m, and in dynamic units this weight is mg. The vector c_t, which indicates the tangential component of the weight, is equal to DC. The vibrations would depart considerably from simple harmonic motion if the amplitude were as great as that in Fig. 12-4; and if we were to redraw the figure with a properly reduced amplitude the point E would be hardly distinguishable from the point A. Thus, as a very good approximation at this small amplitude, we could replace the line BE by the arc BA; and BA is equal to the displacement but oppositely directed, so $BA = -d$. Finally, OE and OA are very nearly equal and OA is the length L of the pendulum.

Use of these equivalences (or near equivalences) modifies the equation above to

$$\frac{c_t}{mg} = -\frac{d}{L}$$

Since it is the component c_t of the weight which accelerates the mass m, we have

$$c_t = F = ma_v$$

in which a_v is the acceleration of the vibrating pendulum bob. Thus our equation becomes

$$\frac{ma_v}{mg} = -\frac{d}{L}$$

Cancellation of the m's and rearrangement produces

$$a_v = -\frac{dg}{L}$$

According to Eq. (12-5)

$$a_v = -\frac{4\pi^2}{t^2} \cdot d$$

so

$$-\frac{dg}{L} = -\frac{4\pi^2}{t^2} \cdot d$$

Division by $(-d)$ and rearrangement yields

$$t^2 = 4\pi^2 \frac{L}{g} \qquad (12\text{-}11)$$

and hence,

$$t = 2\pi\sqrt{L/g} \qquad (12\text{-}12)$$

Sample Problem 4

What would be the length of a simple pendulum (a) on the earth and (b) on the moon, where $g = 167$ cm/sec^2, if the period of the pendulum is 5.00 sec?

Equation (12-11) may be rearranged to the form

$$L = \frac{gt^2}{4\pi^2} = g \cdot \left(\frac{t}{2\pi}\right)^2$$

$$= g \cdot \left(\frac{5.00}{2\pi}\right)^2 = 0.633g$$

(a) At the earth's surface $L = 0.633 \cdot 980 = 620$, so $L = 620$ cm
(b) On the moon $L = 0.633 \cdot 167 = 106$, so $L = 106$ cm

Evidently the equation for the period of a pendulum can be used to determine the value of gravitational acceleration, g, if the length of a pendulum and its period are known. The pendulum must approximate a simple pendulum as nearly as possible, and its amplitude must be kept very small, unless a more complex equation which takes into account the influence of amplitude is used in place of our simplified equations.

12-9 Energy in Simple Harmonic Motion

In Fig. 12-4 the pendulum bob is at a greater elevation when at B than if it were at A. Thus work must have been done when it was moved from A to B, which is to say that it possesses potential energy at B. When the bob at position B is released, it will be accelerated back toward A; that is, it will gain kinetic energy. But its elevation will be decreasing, so it will lose potential energy; and its loss of potential energy will be precisely equal to the kinetic energy it gains, provided there are no frictional losses (the law of conservation of energy is still on the books!). Thus, there is a continual interplay of potential and kinetic energies as a pendulum vibrates. This interplay is indicated in Fig. 12-5. A similar situation obtains in the vibration of any body, such as, for example, a violin string or the air column within a trumpet.

According to Eq. (11-10),

$$W = \frac{k(e_{max})^2}{2}$$

in which W is the energy possessed by an elastic body which has been stretched by distance e_{max} and k is the force required to produce unit

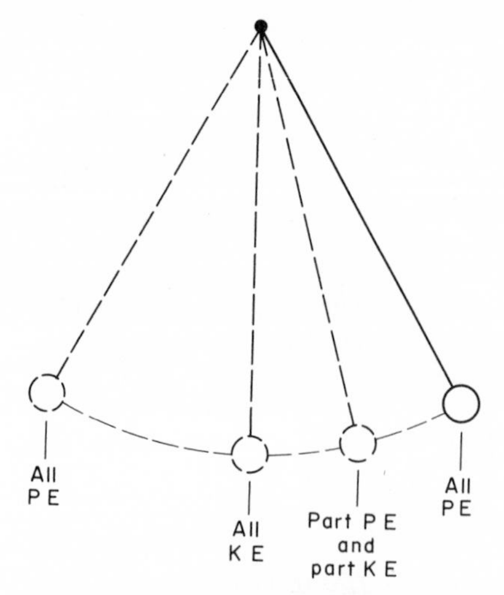

Fig. 12-5. Interplay of potential and kinetic energy in a vibrating pendulum.

elongation. If we replace the elongation e_{max} by the amplitude a and the factor k by the more general equivalent K, we have

$$W = \frac{Ka^2}{2} \qquad (12\text{-}13)$$

as the energy of vibration.

Vibrational energy depends not only on the amplitude but also on the frequency. If a mass m is vibrating with a frequency N and an amplitude a, the energy of vibration is

$$\boxed{W = 2\pi^2 N^2 a^2 m} \qquad (12\text{-}14)$$

Sample Problem 5

A simple pendulum is set into vibration by pulling it aside until the pendulum bob is 10.0 cm above its rest position and then releasing it. With what velocity will it pass through the rest position?

The data seem insufficient. However, the problem is simple, and the data are adequate, *if* we approach the solution from the standpoint of conservation of energy. Before the bob is released, its energy is entirely potential, but it has only kinetic energy as it passes through the rest position. If energy is to be conserved

$$\text{kinetic energy} = \text{potential energy}$$

so $$\frac{mv^2}{2} = mgh$$

$$v^2 = 2gh$$

$$v = \sqrt{2gh} = \sqrt{2 \cdot 980 \cdot 10.0} = \sqrt{1.96 \cdot 10^4} = 1.40 \cdot 10^2$$

Thus the speed is 140 cm/sec.

Note that this result is not restricted to a pendulum of a particular length; it is valid for a pendulum 5.00 cm long or to one of any greater length whatever. (The bob of a shorter pendulum couldn't be raised 10.0 cm.)

Summary

Vibratory motion is a *reciprocating* type of *periodic motion.* The smoothest possible type of vibratory motion is *simple harmonic vibration.* This is the type of vibration exhibited by a body which obeys Hooke's law, and it may also be defined as the *projection* on a *straight line* of *uniform circular motion.*

The number of complete vibrations completed per unit time—usually per second—is the *frequency*. The *amplitude* of a vibration is the *distance*—linear or angular, depending on the type of vibration—from the *rest position* to the point of *maximum displacement*.

Simple harmonic vibration is most easily studied in terms of a circle of reference which has a radius equal to the amplitude of the vibration. If a point moves uniformly around this circle, the appropriate components of its displacement, velocity, and acceleration are equal to the displacement, velocity, and acceleration, respectively, of the vibrating body.

The *force constant* of a *spring* is the magnitude of the force required to cause unit displacement or distortion. For many types of vibration, the period is directly proportional to the square root of the mass of the vibrating body and inversely proportional to the square root of the force constant.

The *period* of a *simple pendulum* is directly proportional to the square root of its length and inversely proportional to the square root of the value of gravitational acceleration.

The *energy* of a *vibrating body* is directly proportional to the square of its amplitude and to the square of its frequency. There is a continual interchange of kinetic and potential energies, the total energy remaining essentially constant.

Self-Quiz

1. Which of the following terms is most general, and which least: vibration, periodic motion, simple harmonic motion. Explain the reasons for your arrangement of the three terms.

2. Demonstrate that the two quantitative definitions of simple harmonic vibration are equivalent.

3. Define period, frequency, amplitude. One of these is often used incorrectly; which one is it, and what is the incorrect interpretation? What numerical relationship exists between the correct and incorrect values of this quantity?

4. Precisely what is meant by "the projection on a straight line of uniform circular motion"? Give a concrete example or analogy other than that in the text.

5. What is a circle of reference, and how is it related to simple harmonic motion? Need there be any actual circular motion when a body is describing simple harmonic motion? Why do we bother with the concept of circle of reference?

6. It is sometimes considered that a reciprocating motion in a mechanical device—for example, the motion of the piston in an automobile engine—is undesirable because of the sudden sharp impulse suffered by the piston at each end of its stroke. Is this point of view valid? Explain.

7. Make diagrams similar to Fig. 12-2 (reasonably accurate freehand drawings will be good enough) for each of the following positions of the point P in Fig.

12-1: *D*, .2, and .3. If you cannot visualize clearly how the velocity of the vibrating body will vary during the remainder of the cycle, choose other points and make diagrams until you have a clear understanding of how the velocity varies *and why*.

8. Similarly, make diagrams like Fig. 12-3 for enough positions of the point *P* so that you clearly understand the variation of the acceleration during a complete cycle of simple harmonic vibration.

9. Make a qualitative statement of the variation of velocity throughout one cycle of simple harmonic motion, and also a similar statement of the variation of the acceleration. Compare the two and point out any similarities and/or differences.

10. Since vibratory motion may be confined to a straight line, students are often confused by the fact that the quantity π appears in equations which have to do with vibration. Show clearly how this quantity comes into such equations.

11. Explain clearly how Eq. (12-9) can be meaningful in spite of the fact that the quantity under the radical carries a negative sign.

12. Why is Eq. (12-12) likely to yield an approximate value rather than a precise value? Does this limitation apply to the equations from which it was derived? What other relationship(s) in this chapter are approximations, if any?

13. How does a "simple" pendulum differ from any practical pendulum? Do these differences make mathematical relationships derived for a simple pendulum useless in practical applications? Explain.

14. (a) Pendulum A has a period nine times as great as that of Pendulum B, both being at the same location. How do their lengths compare? (b) Pendulum C has a length nine times that of Pendulum D at the same location. Compare their periods. (c) Pendulums E and F are identical but, courtesy of Buck Rogers, E is in a location where g is nine times as great as that where F is. Compare their periods.

15. By considering terms such as *iso*celes and *chrono*meter deduce the meaning of the term "isochronous." Is simple harmonic vibration isochronous? Why?

16. Why is the energy of a vibrating body determined by the square, rather than the first power, of its amplitude?

17. A body is vibrating in a horizontal line. Discuss the interplay of potential and kinetic energies, including any quantitative factors. A second body is hung from a spring and set into vertical vibration. Again discuss the interplay of energies. (This is *not* identical with the first case. Here gravitational potential energy is a factor.)

18. Compare the method of solution of Sample Problem 5 in Sec. 12-9 with the example discussed in Sec. 6-10 and with the method of solution of Problem 8 in Chapter 5. Why does a single method of solution apply to the three different physical situations? Explain clearly why the differences in the details of the various physical setups are irrelevant.

Problems

1. (a) The lower and upper limits of audible frequencies are roughly 30 and 15,000 vps, respectively. Determine the corresponding periods. (b) The period of the radio waves sent out by a certain broadcasting station is 1.47 microsec ($1.47 \cdot 10^{-6}$ sec). What is the frequency?

2. The motor of an automobile is "turning over" at a rate of 3600 rpm, so each piston oscillates at a rate of 3600 per minute. The stroke (double amplitude) of the piston is 4.00 in. Assuming the motion to be simple harmonic, compute the maximum speed of the piston, in ft/sec, and in mph.

3. A string on a musical instrument is vibrating with an amplitude of 3.00 mm. If the maximum velocity of the string is 198π cm/sec, calculate (a) the period, (b) the frequency, and (c) the maximum acceleration.

4. A body is vibrating with an amplitude of 5.00 cm. When the displacement is 1.00 cm the acceleration is 200 cm/sec^2. Compute the period of the vibration and the maximum velocity.

5. A violin string is vibrating with a frequency of 880 vps and an amplitude of 2.00 mm. (a) What is the maximum acceleration? (b) What is the acceleration when the displacement is 0.500 mm?

6. Check several of the equations in this chapter for dimensional homogeneity by expressing each quantity in terms of the appropriate fundamental dimensions (m, l, and t).

7. A loose piece of metal is lying on a machine when the operator starts the machine up. The machine vibrates in a vertical direction at a frequency of 12.0 vps. As the amplitude of vibration increases, the operator suddenly begins to hear a click twelve times a second because of the metal striking the machine after "floating" momentarily above it. At what amplitude does this effect first appear?

8. What must be the length of a simple pendulum if the period is exactly 2 sec? Compute the answer in metric units and also in English units, using the usual values for g.

9. A simple pendulum has a period of 2.020 sec and its length is 101.5 cm. What is the value of the acceleration due to gravity at that location?

10. A simple pendulum with a length of 80.0 cm is displaced 60.0° from the vertical and then released. What maximum velocity will the bob of the pendulum attain?

11. The maximum speed of the bob of a vibrating pendulum is 125 cm/sec. Compute the vertical rise of the bob at the position of maximum displacement.

12. A loaded spring is vibrating with an amplitude of 8.50 cm, the energy of vibration being 5.00 joules. Compute the force constant.

13. A simple pendulum consists of a string 120 cm long supporting a bob which

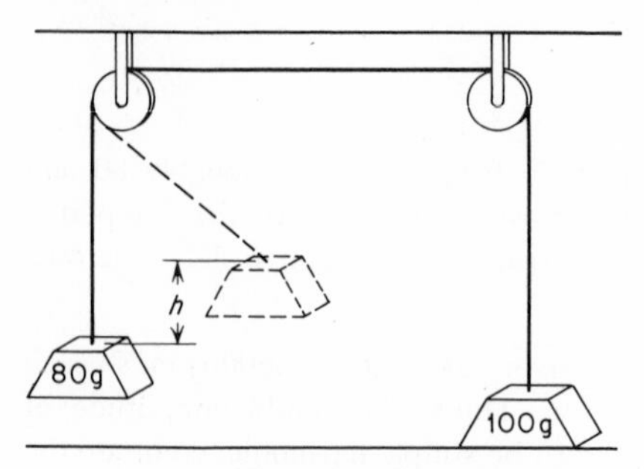

Figure 12-6

has a mass of 250 g. The breaking strength of the string is 400 g. As the pendulum vibrates, what is the maximum height the bob may rise at the point of maximum displacement without probable breakage of the string during the ensuing period?

14. By an arrangement like that in Fig. 12-6, one can cause a relatively small weight to lift a heavier weight—momentarily—by displacing the smaller mass and letting it swing as a pendulum. If the effective length of this pendulum is 50.0 cm and if the masses are as shown, what initial elevation of the smaller mass will enable it just to balance the weight of the larger mass momentarily?

13

WAVE MOTION

13-1 Preview

In this chapter, we shall investigate wave motion in general, and some specific examples of wave motion. It will develop that there are two distinct types of waves and that the physical nature of a medium determines whether either or both kinds of wave can be propagated through it. We shall find that though there are different equations for the velocity of waves of different kinds and in different media, all these are special cases of a very general equation. The "shape" of waves will be investigated, especially a very simple form related to simple harmonic motion. We shall find that more complex forms may be analyzed into a combination of simple forms. Chapter 11, on elasticity, and Chapter 12, on vibration, constitute an essential foundation for this chapter. In turn, the present chapter will furnish concepts and relationships which will be essential to our understanding of sound, in Chapters 14 and 15, and of light, in later chapters.

13-2 Wave Motion, in General

Waves of many sorts, and their effects, are a common part of our experiences—wind-generated waves rippling a flag, invisible waves in the air bringing sound to our ears, light waves which enable us to see, radio waves which carry messages and music around the earth, etc. These and all other examples of ***wave motion*** transmit energy from one location to another by means of a periodic disturbance between the two points. Often, as in the first two examples above, this "periodic disturbance" involves an elastic distortion of the substance, or ***medium**** through (or over) which the waves are being propagated. In other cases, like the last two examples, there is no physical medium; and the "periodic disturbance" involves only the electric and magnetic fields of empty space. If a physical medium is involved, any particle of the medium vibrates as a wave passes, but it remains in approximately its original location; the medium does not move along with the wave. A fortissimo trumpet blast by your ear might damage your eardrum, but it couldn't blow your hat off; and a swimmer at an ocean beach floating lazily outside the breaker line isn't carried bodily toward the beach by the passing waves.

As the definition of wave motion implies, it is usually repetitive, many successive waves of similar wavelength being produced and following each other through the medium. The shock wave caused by a supersonic plane "breaking the sound barrier," or that resulting from an explosion, usually is not repetitive, but instead consists of a single ***pulse*** or a train of relatively few waves. We shall confine our attention to repetitive wave motion; treatment of discontinuous pulses is beyond the scope of this book. We shall also limit our discussion to waves in physical media, leaving light and similar wave phenomena for later chapters.

13-3 Transverse Waves and Longitudinal Waves

We have seen that as waves pass through, or over, a medium, the particles of the medium are not carried along with the wave; rather, they oscillate about a fixed position. There are two distinct types of waves, depending on the relative directions of the wave propagation and the vibratory motion of the particles of the transmitting medium.

The term "transverse" means crosswise, or at right angles to; so in any ***transverse*** wave the particles of the medium vibrate in a direction *perpendicular* to the direction of wave propagation. On the other hand, the particles vibrate back and forth in a direction *parallel* with the direction of propagation if the wave is ***longitudinal.*** Thus, in Fig. 13-1(a), a hand

* The plural of medi*um* is medi*a*, which—because it doesn't end with an *s*—very often is used *erroneously* as if it were the singular form.

is moving the end of the spiral spring rapidly back and forth in a horizontal direction, and this causes waves to be sent up the spring. Since the cause of the disturbance is horizontal displacement, the displacement of any particular loop of the spring will also be in a horizontal direction. Thus the displacement is perpendicular to the direction of wave propagation and the wave is transverse. In Fig. 13-1(b), on the contrary, the hand is moving up and down, so it causes a vertical displacement of the individual turns of wire in the spring, resulting in the turns being crowded together in some places and spread apart in others. Since any particular turn of the coil spring moves in a vertical direction as the wave passes upward along the spring, the direction of displacement is parallel with the direction of propagation. This, then, is a "longitudinal wave." An alternate term for longitudinal waves is ***compressional*** waves.

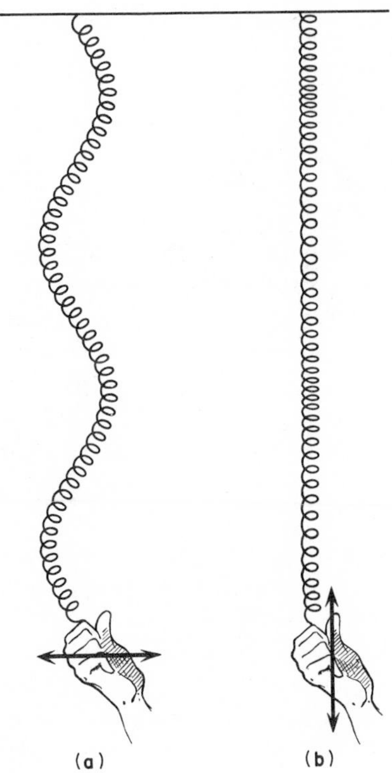

Fig. 13-1. (a) Transverse wave on a spiral spring; (b) Longitudinal wave on a spiral spring.

Why does the motion of the hand in Fig. 13-1(a) send a wave up the spring? When the hand is suddenly jerked to the right, only the lower portion of the spring is displaced initially, because of the flexibility and the inertia of the spring; so the situation will be as in Fig. 13-2(a). The length of the spring obviously has been increased by the displacement of its lower end, so the tension of the spring is increased. Since this tension acts along the axis of the spring, the tensions above and below point a in Fig. 13-2(a) will have a resultant toward the right, so this portion of the spring will be accelerated, and therefore displaced, to the right. This will cause the bend, now at point a, to move farther up the spring. Wherever the bend may be at a particular instant, there will be a resultant force toward the right and a rightward acceleration and displacement of the spring at that point. Thus the pulse of displacement to the right will be propagated up the spring. When the lower extremity of the spring is jerked to the left, a similar sequence will ensue, a displacement to the left being generated and propagated up the spring. Hence a back-and-forth motion—a vibration—of the lower end will send a train of transverse waves up the spring.

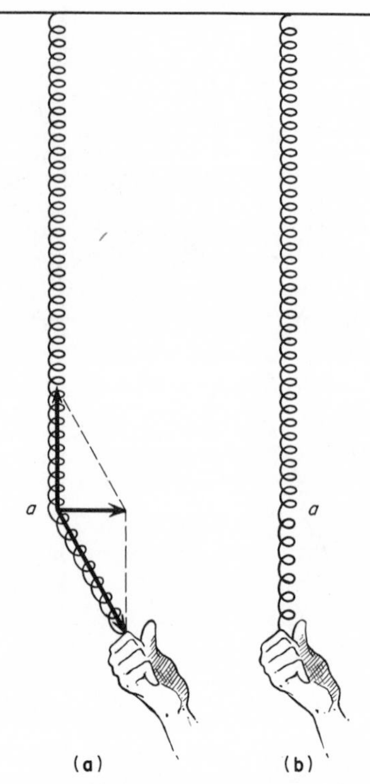

Fig. 13-2. (a) Initiation of a transverse pulse; (b) Initiation of a longitudinal pulse.

In the case of a longitudinal wave, as in Fig. 13-1(b), a downward motion of the hand will spread apart the lower turns of the spring without immediately affecting the upper portion, provided the downward motion is quite sudden. This increases the tension in these few coils—below point *a* in Fig. 13-2(b)—so again we have an imbalance; but this time there is no lateral component and hence no lateral displacement. The resultant will be a downward force along the axis of the spring, and this causes a downward acceleration of the coils immediately above *a*. The tension within these few turns is increased thereby, so that the imbalance of tension moves upward along the spring; and this is a way of saying that the pulse of downward displacement will be propagated up the spring. A later motion of the hand suddenly upward will initiate a similar chain of events, except that the individual turns of the coil tend to move together and the resulting change of tension will be a reduction rather than an increase. Those coils in which the tension is lessened will be accelerated upward by the resulting imbalance of tensions. Thus the upward displacement is propagated up the spring.

By analogy with waves on the surface of water, the "humps" and "hollows" of a transverse wave are called ***crests*** and ***troughs.*** You must guard against a too literal interpretation of these designations, however. For example, in Fig. 13-1(a) the direction of propagation is vertical, so the assignment of the designation "crest" to a rightward displacement would be no more or less logical than calling it a "trough"; the choice is quite arbitrary.

Since a longitudinal wave has no transverse displacements, the terms "crest" and "trough" would be quite meaningless. Instead, a portion of the medium where there is a momentary reduction of volume is called a ***compression*** or, by some authors and lecturers, a ***condensation;*** and the term ***rarefaction*** is applied to a portion of the medium in which there is a transitory increase in volume. (Probably the term "rarefaction" is misspelled—and mispronounced—more often than any other term in physics. The word is rarefac′ tion, *not* rarefica′ tion.)

13-4 Graphical Representation of Waves

Fig. 13-3. Form of a simple transverse wave.

Transverse waves lend themselves readily to graphical representation, since the displacements are normal to the path of propagation. A graph, such as Fig. 13-3, is essentially a stylized picture of the actual wave.

Unfortunately, the situation is quite different for a longitudinal wave. A semipictorial representation of a longitudinal wave in a gas appears in the upper part of Fig. 13-4. The relatively crowded condition of the molecules in a compression is revealed by the denser stippling, and the minimum density of stippling represents the abnormally low density of the particles in a rarefaction. We can't get much closer to a real picture of a longitudinal wave than this. But it isn't nearly so convenient, or so useful, a representation as that used for transverse waves. Instead of trying to *picture* the wave, however, we may show graphically how some *property* of the medium, such as its density, differs in the various portions of the wave train; and this *graph* of a property of the medium through which a longitudinal wave is passing will *look* like the *pictorial* representation of the transverse wave. Thus in the lower part of Fig. 13-4 the straight horizontal line represents the normal density of the medium; all points above this line represent abnormally high density and those below indicate densities less than normal. The wavy line then reveals the variation of the density of the medium in the different portions of the wave. Note that such a diagram is meaningless unless at least one crest or one trough is properly labeled a compression or a rarefaction.

Any other physical property of the medium, such as particle displacement or particle velocity, may be presented graphically and considered to be a representation of a longitudinal wave, *provided* that the graph is correctly labeled. It is conventional to show values greater than normal *above*

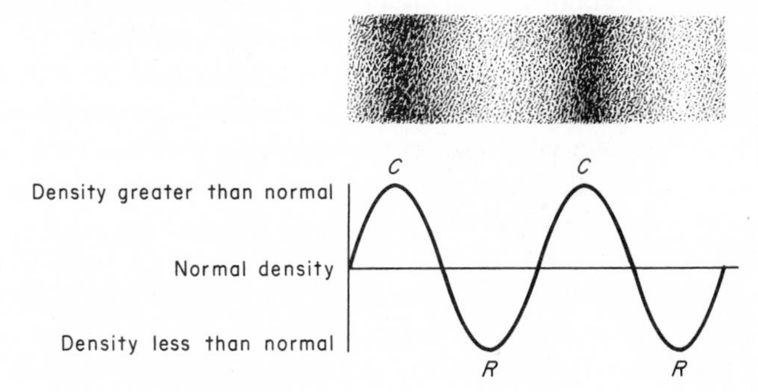

Fig. 13-4. Longitudinal wave. "Pictorial" representation above and graphical presentation below.

the "normal" line, and subnormal values below, as in Fig. 13-4; but this is not essential *provided* that the graph is labeled consistently. The graph may begin on the "normal" line as in this figure, but this also is inessential; if you slide the right edge of a card up to the vertical line in Fig. 13-4 and continue to move it toward the right, the visible remainder of the figure will be a correct representation—if properly labeled—so long as one full wave remains uncovered.

Though this convention of representing a longitudinal wave graphically as in the lower part of Fig. 13-4 is very convenient, it can be very dangerous to your understanding *if* you fail to realize fully that *the graph is not in any sense a picture of the wave.*

13-5 Properties of the Medium Required for the Two Types of Waves

Imagine the two springs in Fig. 13-1 to be enclosed in flexible fabric so that we could see only two slender cylinders. As a transverse wave travels up one cylinder, we would see an obvious change of shape; but only a change of length—and hence of volume—would be apparent as a longitudinal wave moves up the other cylinder. Thus, the passage of a transverse wave involves a change in the shape of the medium, whereas the propagation of a longitudinal wave affects only the volume.

This means that a transverse wave can be propagated only if the medium resists a change of shape, and only if there is a resistance to change in volume can a longitudinal wave be transmitted; the two types of wave require different kinds of elasticity in the medium. If the medium has no elasticity of either sort, no wave of any kind can be transmitted through it.

Solids, liquids, and gases all offer resistance to change of volume, which means that any of these may serve as a medium for the transmission of longitudinal waves. On the other hand, neither liquids nor gases offer any resistance to change of shape, so they are unable to serve as media for the propagation of transverse waves; these can travel only through solids. True, as waves travel horizontally over the surface of a liquid the particles of the liquid rise and fall, but they also move back and forth horizontally; thus such waves are not truly transverse or longitudinal (though they are sometimes classified with true transverse waves). The actual motion of particles of liquid as a wave passes is circular (in a vertical plane) unless the liquid is shallow, in which case the motion is flattened in the vertical direction and becomes elliptical.

13-6 Terminology

Terms necessary for the description of wave motion include "amplitude," "frequency," "period," "wavelength," and "phase." Three of these five we met and defined in the preceding chapter, and in general those definitions are applicable with respect to wave motion. They may, however, be redefined from a different point of view, and in a special case one of them will have to be defined quite differently. We shall consider these three first, and the new terms last.

For a vibration, the "amplitude" is the distance between the rest position and the point of maximum displacement. Similarly, for most types of waves, the amplitude is the maximum displacement from the rest position experienced by the particles of the medium as the wave passes. Most simple waves are symmetrical; if you photograph a train of transverse waves on a vertical rope and make a print in which right and left are reversed, no one could tell the difference. The displacement is the same in a "crest" as in a "trough," and the contour of one is the *exact* reverse of the shape of the other. But in a wave on the surface of a liquid, the height of a crest above the general level is greater than the depth of a trough, and the contour of a crest is rather sharp, whereas that of a trough is relatively flat. Thus there is an assymetry which makes the usual definition of amplitude ambiguous; so for waves on the surface of a liquid, and *only for such waves,* the amplitude is defined as the vertical distance between a trough and a crest (which would be *double* the amplitude for any other type of wave).

Frequency was defined as the number of complete vibrations per unit time. A single wave results from a single vibration; hence we may define the frequency of wave motion as the number of complete waves produced per unit time, or as the number of complete waves passing a given point per unit time. Period, as always, is the reciprocal of frequency; so the period of wave motion is the time within which one complete wave is produced, or the time required for one complete wave to pass a given point.

Now we come to a new term, "wavelength." This is obviously the length of a wave, but between what two points should such a length be measured? The ***wavelength*** is the distance between any two corresponding points on adjacent waves. Thus, in Fig. 13-5 the wavelength may be considered to be the distance between the two successive crests labeled a and b. The distance between b and c would also be a wavelength; but although both a and c mark crests, the distance between them is not a wavelength since they are not crests of *adjacent* waves. The wavelength is also the distance between the successive troughs labeled d and e. And, though it is commonly most convenient to measure between crests or be-

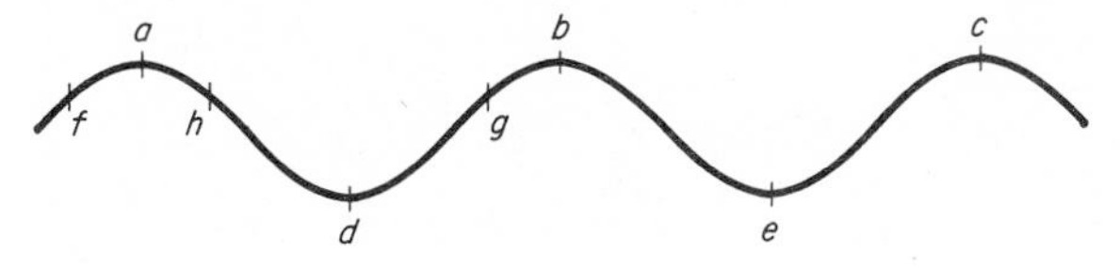

Figure 13-5

tween troughs, the wavelength is the distance between *any* two similar points on successive waves, such as points *f* and *g*. Here, however, we must be careful. It may appear that point *h* is similar to points *f* and *g*, since its displacement is the same as theirs, and that therefore the distance *fh* or *hg* could be taken as a wavelength. But point *h* differs from the others in that it is on the right-hand slope of a crest whereas the other two are on left-hand slopes.

One other concept pertinent to wave motion is ***phase.*** This term has a number of related meanings. As applied to a vibrating point or to a point on a wave, it indicates how much of a whole cycle of vibration has been completed. Unless otherwise specified, the cycle is considered to begin as the point passes through the rest position. Thus, returning to Fig. 12-1, point P has gone about $\frac{1}{20}$ of the way around the circle, so point P' has completed $\frac{1}{20}$ of a vibration; hence we could specify the phase of point P' as $\frac{1}{20}$ of a vibration, or as $\frac{1}{20}$ of a period. A more common, and very convenient, manner of expressing the phase is in terms of the angle DOP in the circle of reference. In this case this angle is about 18°, so we may say that the phase of point P' is 18°. We can see the application of these ideas to a wave more clearly if we look ahead to Fig. 13-7.

Often we are concerned with *relative* phase rather than with phase alone. In Fig. 13-5, for example, points *a*, *b*, and *c* are in the *same* phase, since each is at the crest of a wave, and points *d* and *e* are also in the same phase because each is at a trough; however, points *a* and *d* are of opposite phase, for one is at a crest and the other at a trough. Reference to Fig. 12-1 or to Fig. 13-7 shows that we could express the relative phases of points *a* and *b* in Fig. 13-5 by saying that their phase difference is 0°, and similarly we may say that there is a phase difference of 180° between points *a* and *d* in Fig. 13-5.* The specification of relative phase in terms of degrees is both more flexible and more precise than its description as "same phase" or "opposite phase."

13-7 The Velocity of Propagation of a Wave

For definiteness, consider a steel rod which is struck sharply on one end with a hammer. We may ignore the resulting translational motion of the entire rod, or we may assume that it is clamped so that there is no

* Points *a* and *b* obviously have an actual phase difference of 360°, and the phase of point *c* differs from that of *a* by 720°; similarly, points *a* and *e* have a phase difference of 540°. For most purposes, however, it is customary—and more convenient—to use only angles less than 360° in expressing relative phases. For actual phase angles of 360° or over, this is done by subtracting the appropriate integral multiple of 360° from the actual phase angle. Thus the phase difference between points *a* and *c* in Fig. 13-5 is $720° - 2 \cdot 360° = 0°$, and that between points *a* and *e* is $540° - 360° = 180°$.

displacement of the rod. We are concerned only with displacement of particles *within* the rod with respect to the rod as a whole.

The impact of the hammer will compress the end of the rod very slightly, giving rise to a restoring force due to the elasticity of the rod. All forces are "double ended." (Which of Newton's laws says so?) Hence this force will push back against the hammer and forward against the (as yet) uncompressed particles in the layer adjacent to the initially compressed layer at the end of the rod. Thus particles a little way from the end will be accelerated away from the end, much as if the hammer had struck them directly. This will cause a crowding of the particles still farther along the rod and hence a restoring force in this region; so particles still farther from the end will be accelerated forward, etc. Thus, the pulse initiated by the impact of the hammer travels steadily along the rod. Since the propagation of the pulse is related to the acceleration of the particles of the medium, it seems reasonable that the velocity of propagation should depend on the magnitude of the particle acceleration.

This brings Newton's second law into the picture, but it isn't practical to consider the mass of each individual particle of the medium and the force acting on it. Instead, it is more convenient to consider the acceleration of larger portions of the medium, such as one cubic centimeter. The mass of this volume of the medium will be numerically the same as the density, by definition. Since we are considering the mass of unit volume rather than that of an individual particle, we are not concerned with the force on one particle; it is force per unit area that is pertinent. But according to Eq. (11-2), force per unit area is stress, and this stress is the result of the strain caused by the impact of the hammer—Eq. (11-3). Thus Young's modulus for the medium, Eq. (11-6), is the appropriate measure of the accelerating influence acting on unit volume of the medium. These considerations lead to

$$v = \sqrt{Y/\rho} \tag{13-1}$$

as the equation for the velocity of a longitudinal wave along a rod, v being the velocity of the wave, Y the value of Young's modulus for the medium, and ρ the density of the medium.

Young's modulus is the ratio of the applied stress to the resulting strain; but since whenever a distorting stress is applied to an elastic body an equal and opposite *restoring* stress results (Newton's third law, again), Young's modulus is also a measure of the resistance of the medium to compressional distortion—that is, a measure of its "volume" elasticity. Hence Eq. (13-1) may be generalized to

$$v = \sqrt{E/\rho} \tag{13-2}$$

in which E represents the elasticity of the medium and the other symbols have the same significance as in Eq. (13-1). This new and more general equation, however, is applicable to *any* type of wave motion without restriction, provided that the appropriate measures of elasticity and density are used, whereas our first equation is strictly limited to longitudinal waves in a solid rod (or in any solid if the wavefront encompasses the entire cross-sectional area of the body).

You can find rigorous derivations of Eq. (13-1) and Eq. (13-2) in more advanced or specialized texts, if you wish, but I do not think that the derivations are important enough to give them the necessary space.

An important special case, which we shall use in Chapter 15, is the transverse vibration of a string, such as a violin string. Any such string is under tension, and if it is displaced, this tension increases, since any displacement of the string necessarily stretches it slightly. ("The shortest distance between two points"—the ends of the string—"is a *straight* line.") Obviously, then, the tension of the string tends to keep it straight; that is, the measure of its resistance to displacement—its elasticity, by definition—is its tension. So we may substitute the tension T for the elasticity E in Eq. (13-2). As a transverse wave pulse passes along the string, the tension tends to accelerate the particles which comprise the string toward the rest position. As with our original example of the steel rod, it is not convenient to consider the effect of the inertia of each separate particle. But with a string of such small diameter it doesn't seem reasonable to consider the density—the mass of a cubic centimeter (or of a cubic foot or cubic meter) of the material of the string. The significant index turns out to be the mass per unit length, which is sometimes called the ***linear density.*** If we append the subscript l to the usual symbol ρ to emphasize that we are dealing with *linear* density, we have

$$v = \sqrt{T/\rho_l} \tag{13-3}$$

as the equation for the velocity of transverse waves on a string.

We shall consider no other special cases of the general equation (13-2). There are many others, some rather complex. I shall merely remind you that, if the elasticity and density are properly evaluated, Eq. (13-2) is valid for any wave whatever. In fact, this equation will yield the speed of light in a vacuum if we use the proper measures of the magnetic and electrical properties of empty space for the elasticity E and the mass equivalent (according to Einstein) of the energy per unit volume for the density ρ.

13-8 The Interrelationship of Wavelength, Frequency, and Velocity

Figure 13-6 represents, according to the convention of the latter portion of Sec. 13-4, the sound waves generated by a blast of a factory whistle. At a certain instant, the whistle opened up and sent out the first wave,

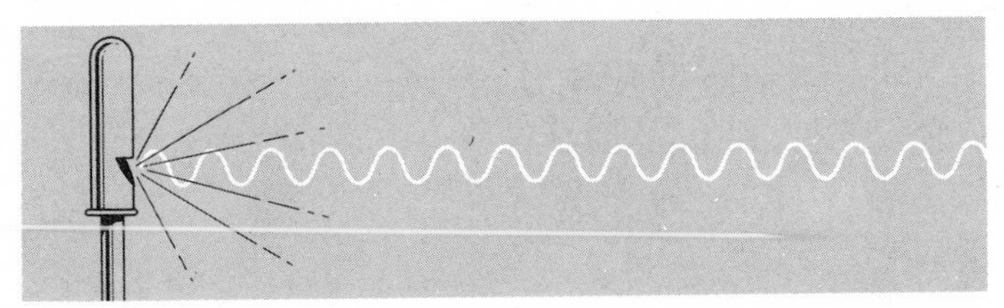

Fig. 13-6. Basis of relationship among frequency, wavelength, and velocity.

which is now some distance away at the end of the wave train. The frequency of the whistle is N and the wavelength is λ.

If the waves shown were sent out during a time interval T, the number of waves emitted must be NT, since N is the number sent out per unit time. We see these NT waves laid out end to end; so since each wave covers a distance λ, the length of the entire train must be $NT\lambda$. But this length is precisely the distance traveled by the front of the initial wave. And since velocity is distance per unit time, s/T, the velocity of the waves must be $NT\lambda/T$ or simply $N\lambda$. Thus we have

$$v = N\lambda \tag{13-4}$$

This relationship is valid for any wave motion whatever.

The interrelationship of these three quantities is analogous to that among the speed at which you walk, the number of steps you take per unit time, and the length of a step. If your step measures 2.5 ft and if you take 40 steps a minute, either the coefficient of friction is remarkably low or you are moving at $2.5 \cdot 40$ or 100 ft per minute. Similarly, if a whistle emits 330 waves each second and if each wave is 3.40 ft long, the wave train must be progressing at $330 \cdot 3.40$ or 1120 ft/sec.

Too often, students fall into asinine errors because of remembering this important relationship, expressed by Eq. (13-4), incorrectly, whereas if they would stop and *think* a moment they could work out the correct relationship on the basis of plain "horse sense."

13-9 The Sine Wave

Waves (or their graphs, if the waves are longitudinal) have various shapes or forms, some very complex and others quite simple. We shall investigate this simplest of waveforms in this section, leaving the more complex shapes to Sec. 13-10 and 15-16.

In Chapter 12 we studied the simplest and smoothest possible type of vibratory motion, which we termed "simple harmonic motion." As might be expected, the simplest and smoothest waveforms are generated by simple harmonic motion. This special form of wave is known as a ***sine wave,*** and any wave of this form is said to be ***sinusoidal.***

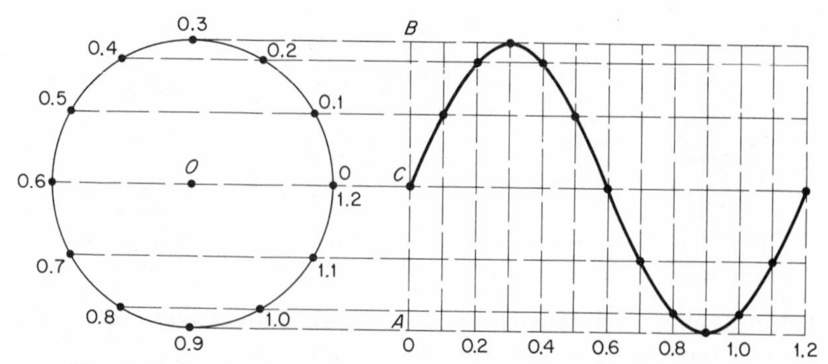

Fig. 13-7. Development of sine wave from simple harmonic motion.

We may develop the form of a sine wave by an extension of the treatment of simple harmonic motion given in Sec. 12-3 and Fig. 12-1. In Fig. 13-7 we have at the left a reference circle divided into twelve equal parts and a projection of this circle onto the straight line *AB*. As a point moves uniformly around the circle in a counterclockwise sense, it generates a simple harmonic motion along *AB*, the rest point being at *C*. So far, this diagram is similar to Fig. 12-1 except for lettering and minor details. Now let us spread this simple harmonic motion out in a direction at right angles to itself. This is done in the remainder of the diagram, in which the uniformly spaced vertical lines represent instants of time. Note that they are numbered to correspond with the numbered instants of time in the reference circle. The sine wave is constructed by locating a point at the intersection of a horizontal line which passes through a numbered position on the reference circle and the vertical line which carries the same number. After all such points of intersection have been located, a smooth curve is drawn through them.

If this somewhat abstract geometrical treatment "leaves you cold," consider (as we did in Sec. 12-3) horizontal rays from the left casting a shadow of an actual body moving uniformly in a circle. In Sec. 12-3, we imagined these rays to fall on a vertical surface so that the shadow moved up and down with simple harmonic motion along the line *AB*. In the present instance, we shall think of the line *AB* as a slit in the paper (or other more concrete surface if you wish) and the part of Fig. 13-7 to the right of *AB* as a sheet of photographic paper. As the body moves uniformly around the circle, the photographic paper is held at right angles to the page and fed downward through the slit *AB* at a uniform velocity. If no extraneous light is present, the motion of the shadow up and down on the photographic paper, superimposed on the steady linear motion of the paper, will cause the shadow to follow a wavy path over the paper; and development of the paper would bring out exactly the sine curve shown in the figure.

It must not be thought that the right-hand side of Fig. 13-7 represents *the* shape of a sine wave. This is *one example,* in which there is a certain ratio between the wavelength and the amplitude. Had I used a different radius in the reference circle in that figure, or had I spaced the vertical lines differently, the shape would have been altered but it would have been sinusoidal. Each of the curves in Fig. 13-8 except the uppermost is a sine wave, but each has a shape somewhat different than the others.

13-10 Analysis of Complex Waveforms

Neither the theory nor the method of analysis of complex waveforms is within the scope of this text; we shall merely note that Fourier developed a method of analysis and pass on to some of its results.

Any wave which repeats itself with a definite period may be analyzed into two or more—in some cases an infinite number—of pure sine waves, no matter how complex the original waveform may be (except for a type of wave never encountered in physics). One of these will have the same wavelength as that of the original complex wave, another will have a wavelength half as great, and the wavelengths of the others will be $\frac{1}{3}$, $\frac{1}{4}$, $\frac{1}{5}$, etc., of the longest wavelength. This means that the various components have frequencies which are integral multiples of the lowest frequency, this lowest frequency being that of the complex wave. This is the ***fundamental frequency.*** If we represent this fundamental frequency by N_f, according to Fourier—and experimental fact—the other components may have frequencies of $2N_f$, $3N_f$, $4N_f$, etc. Some of these frequencies may be absent, even the fundamental; but no frequencies other than integral multiples of the fundamental frequency will result from the analysis.

Figure 13-8(a) shows two complete waves. These are of complex form, but of the *same* form; so they must be repetitive. Thus it is possible to analyze these to a combination of sine waves; and these simple components are shown in parts *b*, *c*, and *d* of the figure. That in part *b* is the fundamental and has the same wavelength and frequency as those of the original waves. That in part *c* is the first overtone; its wavelength is half as great and hence its frequency twice as great as those of the fundamental. The last curve is the second overtone, with one-third the wavelength of the fundamental and three times the frequency.

Since a sinusoidal waveform is associated with simple harmonic vibration, the vibration which produced the wave in Fig. 13-8(a) cannot have been simple harmonic. It was a complex mode of vibration which was *equivalent* to three separate but simultaneous modes of simple harmonic vibration, one with a frequency N_f, another having a frequency $2N_f$, and a third with a frequency $3N_f$. The amplitudes of these modes of vibration were different, as revealed by the unequal amplitudes of the three component waves.

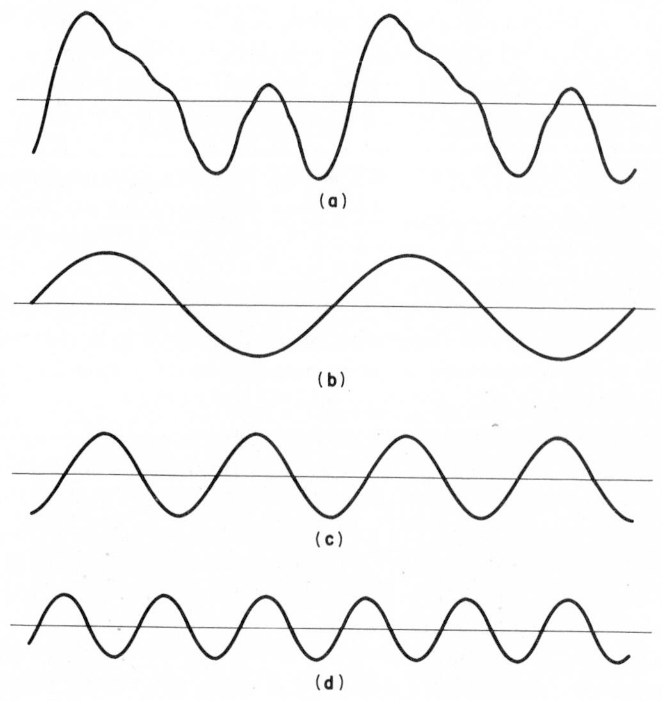

Fig. 13-8. (a) A complex wave form which analyzes (approximately) into the combination of pure sine waves in parts (b), (c), and (d); (b) Fundamental component of complex wave; (c) First overtone of complex wave; (d) Second overtone of complex wave.

Note carefully that Fig. 13-8 and the associated discussion represent only *one* example. There is an infinite number of complex waveforms, and very few of them would have three components; most would have more. In fact, variation of only the relative amplitudes of the three components in Fig. 13-8 would result in an infinite number of different waveforms, and the same is true for a variation of relative phases. Thus, changing the phase of the fundamental by 180° but making no other changes in either phase or amplitude alters the waveform from that in Fig. 13-8(a) to that in Fig. 13-9.

13-11 The Energy of Waves

In the preceding chapter the energy of a vibrating body was stated to be given by Eq. (12-14):

$$W = 2\pi^2 N^2 a^2 m$$

in which W is the energy, N the frequency, a the amplitude of vibration, and m the mass of the vibrating body. It is not convenient to apply this to

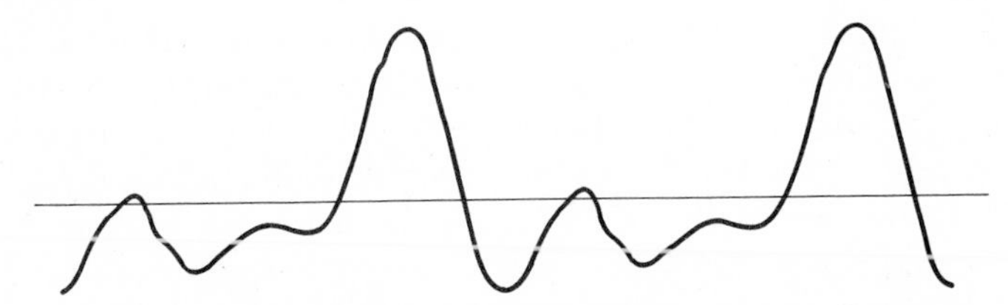

Fig. 13-9. Another complex wave form. This form analyzes into exactly the same components as does the wave in Fig. 13-8(a), except that the phase of the fundamental is reversed.

individual particles of the medium, and if we apply it to the entire medium, the value of a will not be the same, in general, throughout the medium. The most convenient approach is to consider the energy per unit volume. Since mass per unit volume is density, division of Eq. (12-14) by volume yields

$$W = 2\pi^2 N^2 a^2 \rho \tag{13-5}$$

in which W now represents energy *per unit volume*, or ***energy density***, instead of being *total* energy as in Eq. (12-14); and the density of the medium is indicated by ρ.

Summary

Wave motion is a process by which energy is transferred from one point to another through an intervening *medium* by means of an *elastic disturbance* in the medium, and without direct contact between the *source* of the energy and the *body* which receives it. Commonly, but not necessarily, wave motion is repetitive.

In *transverse waves*, the particles of the medium vibrate in a direction at right angles to that of the wave propagation, whereas in a *longitudinal wave* these two directions are mutually parallel. Transverse waves may be described in terms of crests and troughs, longitudinal waves in terms of compressions and rarefactions. The graph of a transverse wave is essentially a picture of the wave itself. For a longitudinal wave, the graph is in no sense a picture; it is a graphical representation of how some physical property of the medium varies in different portions of the wave. Waves on the surface of liquid combine the aspects of transverse waves and longitudinal waves, but are sometimes classified as a special type of transverse wave.

Longitudinal waves can be propagated through a solid, a liquid, or a gas. *Transverse waves* can be propagated only through a solid, or over the surface of a liquid, if the circular waves on the surface of a liquid are classified as transverse.

The terms "frequency" and "period" have essentially the same meanings as when applied to vibrations, though they may be restated in terms more conveniently applicable to wave motion. Amplitude has a significance equivalent to its meaning for vibratory motion, for most kinds of waves; but for waves on the surface of a liquid, which are unsymmetrical, the amplitude is the vertical distance between trough and crest. Wavelength is the distance between corresponding points on adjacent waves.

In general, the velocity of a wave motion is the square root of the quotient of the elasticity and the density of the medium. There are many special cases of this general relationship.

For any type of wave motion the velocity is the product of the frequency and the wavelength.

The simplest and smoothest possible shape of a wave is sinusoidal. Such a waveform results from simple harmonic vibration. Any other waveform, if repetitive, can be analyzed into two or more sine waves which have frequencies equal to integral multiples (including one) of the frequency of the complex wave.

The energy contained in any wave disturbance is directly proportional to the square of the frequency and also to the square of the amplitude.

Self-Quiz

1. What is simple harmonic vibration? What determines the energy of a vibrating body?

2. What form or shape of waves results from simple harmonic vibration?

3. What *is* wave motion? Is all wave motion repetitive? Discuss briefly.

4. What property or properties must a medium have if it is to transmit waves? Are the necessary properties identical for all types of waves? Is a physical medium necessary for all kinds of wave motion?

5. Heat is carried from the bottom of a pot of water on a stove to the top by an upward flow of the water itself. Is this analogous to the transmission of energy through a medium by waves? Explain.

6. What is wrong with this statement? "Any kind of elastic media is capable of transmitting longitudinal waves."

7. Other than by blind memorization, how can you avoid confusion between the terms "transverse" and "longitudinal," as applied to waves?

8. Describe in some detail the mechanism by which a longitudinal wave may be propagated along a coil spring. Repeat for a transverse wave.

9. Define the term "compression" as used in wave motion. What term is the opposite of compression? How is it spelled, and how is it pronounced? Define it.

10. Compare the graphical representation of transverse waves with that of longitudinal waves. In what respects, if any, are they similar? In what very important respect are they quite dissimilar? Why?

11. Review of the mechanism of propagation of longitudinal waves in Sec. 13-3 will show that in a compression the particles of the medium are moving in the direction of propagation and that in a rarefaction they are moving in the opposite direction. Make a diagram similar to the lower part of Fig. 13-4 and label it correctly to show these facts.

12. As a longitudinal wave passes, any small element of the medium will have its volume alternately increased and decreased. Imagine the designations with respect to density in Fig. 13-4 to be replaced with similar designations with respect to volume. Would this part of the diagram be correct without other change or would further relabeling be necessary? Explain.

13. Compare the two new definitions of period with that met in Chapter 12, and show that all three are fully equivalent. Repeat for the two new definitions of frequency. What change is necessary in the definition of amplitude? Why?

14. What is meant by the wavelength? What is the significance of the word "corresponding" (or synonym) in this definition? Why must the word "adjacent" (or synonym) be included?

15. The speed of sound waves in steel is between 14 and 15 times as great as in air. One commonly hears this difference ascribed to the greater density of the steel. Check this explanation against the implications of Eq. (13-2). To what is the greater speed in steel actually due?

16. By dimensional analysis (using only m, l, and t) show that Eq. (13-2) is dimensionally valid.

17. Show that Eq. (13-4) is reasonable, on the basis of the meanings of the quantities and "horse sense." Suggest an analogy other than that given.

18. Develop a sine curve as was done in Sec. 13-9 and Fig. 13-7. Refer to the text only if you "get stuck." Are there any straight lines anywhere in the curve? Why?

19. Can any portion of a sine curve be perpendicular to the midline (in Fig. 13-7, to the horizontal line through 0.6)? For such a situation, how would the velocity of the point in the generating circle have to compare with the velocity at right angles to the simple harmonic motion? In view of this, can a series of semicircles represent a sine wave?

Problems

1. The value of Young's modulus for steel is $20.0 \cdot 10^{11}$ dynes/cm² and its density is 7.70 g/cm³. Compute the speed of a longitudinal wave in steel.

2. The speed of sound in aluminum is 5100 m/sec and the density of aluminum is 2.70 g/cm³. Calculate the value of Young's modulus for aluminum.

3. The diameter of a steel piano string is 1.20 mm. If the velocity of a wave on the string is 50.0 m/sec, compute the tension. Take the density of steel from Problem 1.

4. The lower and upper limits of audible frequencies are sometimes given as 30 vps and 15,000 vps, respectively. If the speed of sound in air is 1130 ft/sec, compute the wavelength for 30 vps and for 15,000 vps.

5. If the wavelength of a sound with a frequency of 440 vps is 78.5 cm, compute the speed of sound.

6. The velocity of electromagnetic waves, including radio waves, is $3.00 \cdot 10^{10}$ cm/sec or $1.86 \cdot 10^5$ miles/sec. If the waves sent out by a radio station have a frequency of 680 kc/sec, compute their wavelength in meters and in feet.

7. A body with a mass of 15.0 g is vibrating with an amplitude of 2.50 mm and a frequency of 500 vps. Compute its energy of vibration.

8. What is the period of a vibrating body if its vibrational energy is 1.20 joules, its amplitude 1.32 cm, and its mass 8.00 g?

9. (a) If a complex wave has a frequency of 440 vps, list the frequencies of several possible sinusoidal components. (b) If the sinusoidal components of a complex wave have frequencies of 100, 200, and 250 vps, what is the frequency of the complex wave? What is somewhat unusual about this complex wave?

10. (a) A soprano is singing a note at the same time as a basso is singing a note with exactly one-eighth the frequency of the soprano note. If the energies of the two sounds are equal, how does the amplitude of the bass note compare with that of the soprano note? (b) How would the amplitudes compare if the bass note produced energy at twice the rate of the soprano note? At half the rate?

14

SOUND

14-1 Preview

We hear because our ears respond to sound waves, and nearly always these waves come to our ears through the air. This chapter considers the response of the ear to the sound waves which impinge on it—the range of audible frequencies, the bases of our judgement of pitch and loudness, etc. We shall find that the ear has a truly amazing sensitivity. The propagation of sound in air will be considered—what physical factors influence the speed of sound and which ones do not; the reflection, refraction, and diffraction of sound waves; the interference of sound waves and the beats which may result. Finally, we shall consider the change of pitch which results when there is relative motion between the source of sound and the observer. Chapters 12 and 13 constitute the principal foundation of this chapter; and these plus the present chapter provide a basis for Chapter 15, which treats the physical basis of music.

14-2 What is Sound and How is it Produced?

You may have heard a question such as this: Is there sound, or is there no sound, when there is an electrical storm over a lifeless desert? This is a perfect start for a quite pointless argument, if you enjoy such, for according to one definition of sound the answer is "Yes," but according to another the answer is "No." We may define ***sound*** as a periodic disturbance in the air or some other elastic medium, or we may define it as the response of the ear to such a disturbance. The first definition is more useful in physics, the second in psychology; but both are quite valid. We shall make use of both points of view in this chapter and the next.

There is no room for differing viewpoints on the mechanism by which sound is produced. Invariably, sound results from the vibration of some ***source*** of sound, these vibrations generating ***waves*** in the air (or other medium).

14-3 Sound Waves in Air

According to the considerations in Sec. 13-5, it is obvious that sound waves in air must be longitudinal. Their velocity must be in agreement with Eq. (13-2) which is

$$v = \sqrt{E/\rho}$$

Longitudinal waves consist of compressions and rarefactions. If we try to compress air or any other gas, the pressure is increased, in accordance with Boyle's law—Sec. 10-7; Eq. (10-3), (10-4). Hence we may think of the pressure of a gas as representing the resistance of the gas to compression. But elasticity is defined as the measure of the resistance to distortion, so it appears that we can replace the general symbol E (for elasticity) in Eq. (13-2) by P (for pressure). However, as sound waves pass rapidly through any medium, alternately compressing and expanding each small element of the medium, the temperature is elevated slightly in the compressions and depressed in the rarefactions. Since Boyle's law is valid only if the temperature is constant, a correction must be made. This is accomplished by including a factor γ (the Greek letter gamma) with the pressure.* For air, which is almost entirely composed of diatomic molecules (two atoms per molecule), the numerical value of γ is 1.40. Thus, for the velocity of sound waves in a gas, we may rewrite Eq. (13-2) as

$$v = \sqrt{\gamma P/\rho} \tag{14-1}$$

* γ is the ratio of the specific heat of air at constant pressure to its specific heat at constant volume. The former is greater because (for example) as the temperature of the air rises at constant pressure, energy is required to increase the internal energy of the gas *and also* to push back the environment as the gas expands; whereas if the volume is constant energy is needed for only the first of these functions.

and for sound waves in air this becomes

$$v = \sqrt{1.40\ P/\rho} \tag{14-2}$$

Examination of these equations will tell us much about the dependence of the speed of sound on various physical factors, or its independence of such factors. But such examination must be careful, for some relationships are implicit rather than explicit.

How will a change of temperature affect the speed of sound? Apparently it should have no effect, since temperature does not appear in the equations. An increase in temperature, however, will cause gas to expand, with a resultant decrease in the density; and since density appears in the denominator, the velocity must be greater at higher temperatures.

What about a change in pressure? Apparently the velocity should be directly proportional to the square root of the pressure; but this overlooks Boyle's law, which requires that the volume be inversely proportional to the pressure. Since density is mass per unit volume, it follows that (at a constant temperature) any change of pressure must be accompanied by a proportional change in density, leaving the quantity under the radical unchanged. Hence the speed of sound in a gas is independent of the pressure.

It might seem that amplitude or frequency might have an influence on the speed. However, neither appears in Eq. (14-1) or (14-2); and neither is hidden in a factor which does appear, as we found the temperature to be. The speed of sound is independent of amplitude and frequency.

We have seen that the speed of sound in air is greater at higher temperatures. Its velocity is 331.7 m/sec or 1088 ft/sec, at 0°C or 32°F (the temperature at which water freezes). When we have studied the topic of heat, we shall be able to derive from Eq. (14-1), (14-2) similar expressions which enable us to compute the speed of sound in a gas at any desired temperature. For the metric system the final result, which for now we must take on faith, is

$$v = 331.7\sqrt{\frac{273.2 + t}{273.2}} \tag{14-3}$$

in which t is the temperature in degrees Celsius (centigrade) and v is the speed, in meters per second, of sound in air at that temperature.

For many purposes and for temperatures not far from room temperature, reasonably accurate values of the velocity may be calculated by the following empirical equations:

$$v = 332 + 0.6t \text{ m/sec} = 33{,}200 + 60t \text{ cm/sec} \tag{14-4}$$

t being the temperature in degrees Celsius; and

$$v = 1053 + 1.1t \text{ ft/sec} \tag{14-5}$$

t now being the temperature in degrees Fahrenheit.

Since these two relationships are not based on any derivation, but only on a "cut and fit" basis, they must not be used for temperatures very far from ordinary room temperatures. For all temperatures normally encountered, errors will be 1% or less.

14-4 Frequency and Pitch

Here for the first time we meet a pair of quantities which are interdependent but which cannot be correlated precisely by any mathematical relationship. Frequency is a physical quantity which was defined in Sec. 12-2 for vibrations and redefined in Sec. 13-6 for waves. In contrast, ***pitch*** is a purely subjective entity; it is one's judgment of how "high" or "low" a sound is. Since it is subjective, it is not susceptible to quantitative measurement. In fact, even the terms "high" and "low," as used to describe pitches, are quite arbitrary; the Greeks used the Greek equivalents of high and low in a sense exactly opposite our usage.

Under such conditions, all we can do is to make the qualitative statement that a sound judged to have a high pitch will have a relatively high frequency, and one with a relatively low frequency will be judged to be low in pitch. But we must *not* be tempted to pervert this relationship by saying that frequency and pitch are directly proportional, since no numerical evaluation of pitch is possible. We can't even say that if two sounds have identical frequencies their pitches will agree. This will be true if they are of equal loudness, or if neither is extremely loud; but if one is extremely loud and the other is not, the extremely loud sound may have a lower pitch even if the two frequencies are identical. Nevertheless, the influence of loudness, however great, is far less than that of frequency; for all sounds of ordinary loudness, including the loudest bands and orchestras, the pitch depends solely on frequency.

14-5 Intensity and Loudness

Here again we have a measurable physical quantity, intensity, and a related subjective entity, loudness. ***Intensity*** refers to the energy of the sound wave, per unit area of wave front. ***Loudness,*** on the other hand, is the purely subjective response of the individual to that intensity. The greater the intensity, other things being equal, the greater the loudness, and vice versa.

Though loudness, like pitch and other psychological responses, is entirely subjective, psychological studies with large groups yield statistical relationships. These relationships are described by the Weber-Fechner law, a general (though approximate) psychophysical law which says that the strength of the response is determined by the logarithm of the strength of the stimulus. This means, for example, that if a sound intensity I produces a subjective loudness L, an intensity $2I$ will not cause a loudness $2L$; instead, the intensity must be I^2 for a loudness of $2L$, I^3 for a loudness of $3L$, etc. Such a relationship between intensity and loudness is only applicable, however, if the frequencies are the same.

A similar relationship exists between frequency and pitch, provided that the intensity is not extreme.

14-6 Ranges of Audibility

Though from the standpoint of the first definition of sound in Sec. 14-2 any periodic disturbance in an elastic medium may be considered to be sound, the term "sound" is commonly applied only to sound audible to human ears. This implies that there are limitations to the ability of the ear to respond to periodic disturbances. Two attributes of sound, frequency and intensity, are the roots of such limitations. It is often said that the human ear is sensitive to frequencies within the range of about 30 to 20,000 vps, but these values are very rough. Even for persons who have no hearing impairment, these limits will vary from one individual to another. Unless you are an exception, your upper limit of audible frequencies is lower by a few thousands of vibrations per second than when you were a child. Thus it is obvious that no precise values of these limits may be stated.

Furthermore, a frequency which is completely inaudible at one intensity may be readily perceived at a higher intensity. Also, the sensitivity of the ear depends very strongly on the frequency. If a tone at 30 vps is just audible and the same is true of another at 3000 vps, the intensity of the former must be about 10 million times as great. Thus, it is apparent that the limits of audible intensities, like those of audible frequencies, are indefinite. An intensity sufficient to make one tone fairly loud may be far too low to make a tone of a different frequency audible.

Figure 14-1 presents much information about normal hearing. The lowest curve is the ***threshold of hearing;*** any tone which has a frequency and an intensity both on this line is just barely audible to the average normal ear. The top curve is the ***threshold of pain;*** tones having a combination of frequency and intensity which lie on or above this curve are not heard as sounds but are perceived as pain. (The threshold of pain is in no way related to the character of the "music," logical as such a relationship might seem!) Examination of the figure reveals that the ear is most sensitive at a frequency of about 3500 vps, the sensitivity dropping somewhat (that is, higher intensities being required for audibility) at higher frequencies and the sensitivity also dropping very sharply at lower frequencies. Each of the other curves defines the combinations of frequency and intensity required for some specific loudness. For example, any combination of frequency and intensity which lies on the curve labeled "Quiet Residence" will produce the same loudness as any other such combination.

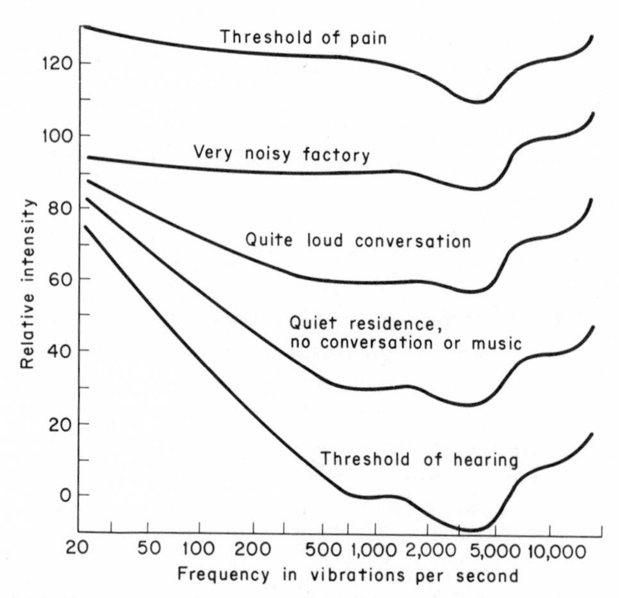

Fig. 14-1. Sensitivity of the ear. Any combination of frequency and intensity which falls on a given line will be just as loud as any other such combination on the same line.

14-7 Minimum Perceptible Increments of Pitch and of Loudness

Most of us think that a person with a well-trained ear can perceive any change of pitch, but this is not true. No matter how good a musician one may be, or how well one's ear is trained, if two tones which initially have identical pitches are sounded alternately and one is raised or lowered slightly and gradually, it is impossible to perceive that the two are not identical until the change reaches a definite minimum called the ***minimum perceptible increment of pitch.*** (If the two are sounded simultaneously there is no minimum perceptible increment, for reasons which we shall meet in Sec. 14-13.) The ear can detect such changes of pitch more readily at relatively high frequencies and relatively high intensities. Near the threshold of hearing and at very low frequencies, the minimum perceptible increment may be equivalent to three half-steps on the piano keyboard.

A similar situation obtains with respect to discrimination between tones of the same intensity. If two such tones are sounded alternately and the intensity of one is varied slightly and gradually, the change of intensity must exceed a certain minimum before it is perceptible. Here again the ear perceives changes more readily at the higher frequencies and higher intensities.

14-8 Sensitivity of the Ear

We talk of the compressions and rarefactions in a train of sound waves and of the amplitude of the particles, but in doing so we are liable to conceive of the energy involved, the deviations from normal pressure, and the displacements of the particles of the medium as being of a much larger order of magnitude than they are.

The usual lamp used to decorate and illuminate Christmas trees is rated at 6 watts; thus it uses 6 joules of energy each second. Suppose that these 6 joules of energy could be used with 100% efficiency to produce a continuous sound at the frequency to which the ear is most sensitive and at an intensity barely audible to a normal ear 1 ft from the source. Over how long a period could this barely audible sound be maintained? The answer is not in terms of seconds or minutes or even hours; it is in terms of thousands of years!

When you listen to an orchestra, your ear is subjected to alternate compressions and rarefactions, but by how much does the pressure in a compression or a rarefaction differ from that of undisturbed air? By less than the change of pressure due to difference of altitude as you stand up or sit down!

And if a normal ear hears a barely audible sound at the frequency at which the ear is most sensitive, what is the amplitude of the sound wave: that is, how far do the molecules of air move from their normal positions as the waves pass? They are displaced by an average distance no greater than their own diameter!

Thus we see that the ear is almost incredibly sensitive; but this is not the whole story. The range of energies handled by the ear is equally astonishing. The energy of a sound with an intensity at the threshold of pain is about 10^{13}—ten millions of millions—times that of a barely audible sound! Any man-made acoustical device which would respond at the lower intensity would be so delicate that the higher intensity would wreck it, and any device which could handle the higher energy would be insensitive to the lower.

14-9 Reflection of Sound Waves

Suppose that a single pulse of compression is traveling through the air toward a wall, as indicated semipictorially in Fig. 14-2(a) and schematically in Fig. 14-2(b). Ahead of the pulse is air at normal pressure. The particles in the compressed region have a momentum in the forward direction, and this, combined with the pressure difference, causes them to move forward. Thus the pulse is propagated forward. But when it reaches the wall, the particles are unable to move forward so there is momentarily a layer of slightly compressed air adjacent to the wall as in parts (c) and (d)

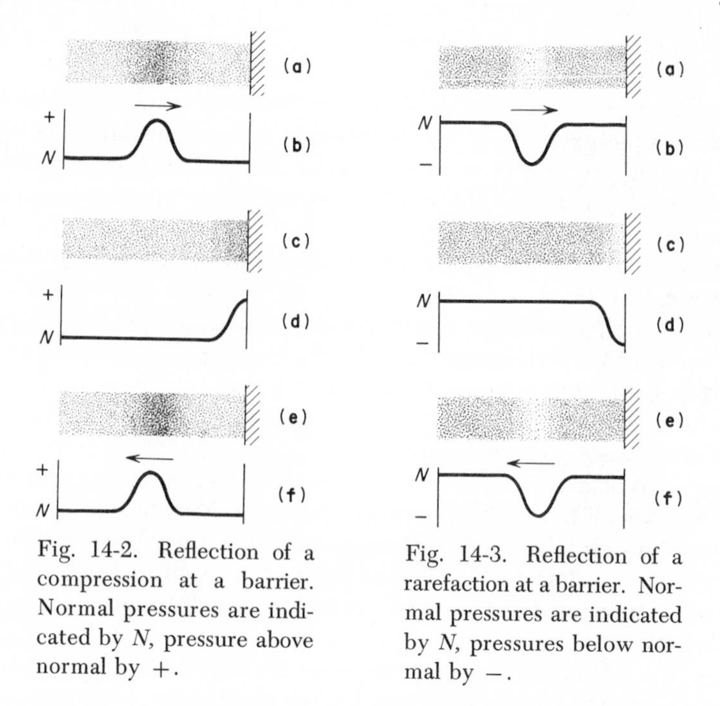

Fig. 14-2. Reflection of a compression at a barrier. Normal pressures are indicated by N, pressure above normal by $+$.

Fig. 14-3. Reflection of a rarefaction at a barrier. Normal pressures are indicated by N, pressures below normal by $-$.

of Fig. 14-2. Heretofore, the particles were unable to move back into the normal pressure region behind the pulse, because of the forward momentum of the particles. But this forward momentum is changed into a rearward momentum by the impact of the particles with the wall (or with other particles which have struck the wall). Hence the particles move back away from the wall toward the normal pressure region farther from the wall, which is a way of saying that the pulse is propagated back in a direction opposite its original direction of propagation, as in parts (e) and (f) of Fig. 14-2.

A single pulse of rarefaction will be reflected in an analogous manner. In the rarefied region, the particles of air have a rearward momentum. This allows particles from farther forward to move back into the rarefied region but interferes with the tendency of particles behind the pulse to migrate into the pulse of rarefaction; so the pulse moves forward as in Fig. 14-3(a) and (b). But when the pulse reaches the wall, as in parts (c) and (d) of the figure, particles cannot move out of the wall into the rarefaction to relieve the pressure deficiency so the pulse of rarefaction is trapped against the wall as in Fig. 14-3(c) and (d). With the pulse unable to move forward, and air at normal pressure behind it, particles will move from the normal pressure region into the rarefied region; that is, the pulse will be propagated backward as in parts (e) and (f) of the figure.

These same processes will occur if instead of single pulses of one kind or the other we have a series of alternate compressions and rarefactions, that is, a train of sound waves. Reversal of the direction of propagation of sound in this way is termed ***reflection*** of sound. It is commonly observed in echoes and reverberations and is also important in the production of sound by many types of musical instruments.

The discussion has been in terms of pulses in air striking a wall, but a similar situation exists whenever a pulse or a train of waves traveling in one medium impinges on a denser medium.

If, on the other hand, a pulse or wave train moving through one medium reaches a different and less dense medium, the situation is quite different. Imagine a pulse of compression propagated upward in water. As it travels upward, the particles in the pulse move upward because of their forward momentum and the difference of pressure within the pulse and ahead of it. But the pulse can move into a new region only by crowding the particles there, increasing the pressure and giving them a forward momentum. It happens that as the pulse passes any given region it leaves that region with just normal pressure. Now, when the pulse reaches the surface it will tend to relieve its excess pressure by compressing the medium ahead and giving its particles a forward momentum. But the air above the surface is far more easily compressed than is the water, and its lower density makes it much easier to impart a momentum to its particles. Thus the abnormal conditions within the pulse are reduced more readily as it is propagated into the air than when traveling within the water; yet under the latter conditions, the region through which a pulse of compression had just passed was restored just to normal. Hence as the pulse reaches the surface, this restoration will overshoot; the pressure in the water actually is reduced *below* normal. But this leaves a pulse of rarefaction sitting at the surface, with water at normal pressure

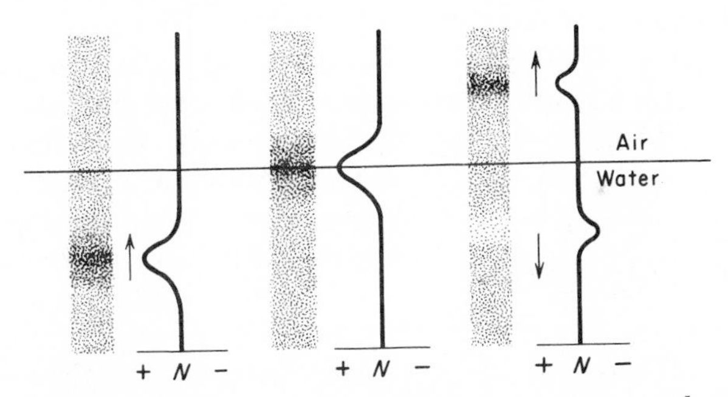

Fig. 14-4. Partial reflection of a compression in water as the pulse reaches the surface. The reflected portion of the pulse is a rarefaction, not a compression.

below, so particles of water move upward into the rarefied region. This constitutes the first step of the propagation of a pulse of *rarefaction* back down from the surface. Thus a pulse of compression is partially reflected as a rarefaction. ("Partially" because part of the pulse is propagated into the air, still as a compression.) Figure 14-4 illustrates this process.

A similar analysis will show that a rarefaction would be partially reflected as a compression under these circumstances.

Thus we see that when a wave train is reflected at the surface of a more dense medium it is reflected ***in the same phase;*** a compression is reflected as a compression, and a rarefaction is reflected as a rarefaction. But at the surface of a less dense medium a wave train is partially reflected ***with reversal of phase;*** a compression is reflected back as a rarefaction and vice versa. For reasons which are apparent if you go back to the development of the sine curve from the circle of reference, ***zero phase change*** is synonymous with "in the same phase," and "reversal of phase" may be described by the expression ***180° phase change.***

14-10 Refraction

The direction of propagation of a wave or wave train may be altered by two phenomena other than reflection. The first of these is ***refraction,*** which is a change of direction of travel resulting from a change of speed which does not act simultaneously on all parts of a wave front. In Fig. 14-5 a train of waves is moving from the lower part of the figure toward the horizontal boundary between two media. The speed of the waves in the medium above the boundary is $\frac{4}{3}$ of that in the original medium.

Some three hundred years ago, Huygens showed that any point on a wave front may be considered to be the source of a series of circular wavelets emanating from that point. This may not seem intuitively reasonable, but you can demonstrate its validity very easily by putting water in any sort of container and placing a barrier with a narrow gap across the vessel. If you start waves on one side of the barrier they will be stopped except at the opening, and semicircular waves will move out from the opening.

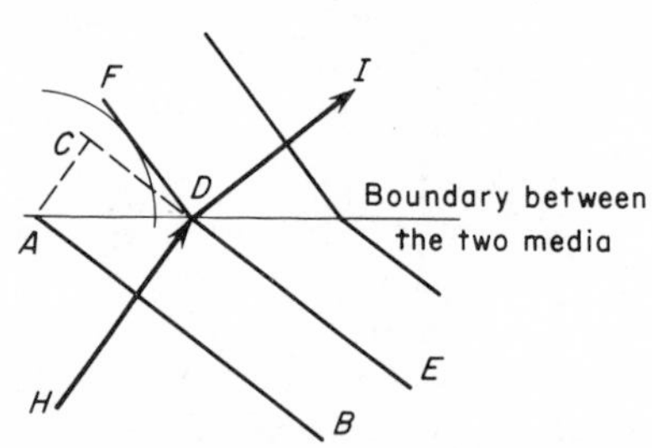

Fig. 14-5. Mechanism of refraction of a wave.

Consider a wave front indicated by the line AB in Fig. 14-5 moving toward the boundary. Exactly one period later, this wave front will have moved forward one wavelength, and part of it will lie along the line DE; but part will have penetrated into the new medium. Where will this part be? The speed of the waves is increased by one-third; thus it will travel $\frac{4}{3}$ as far in the new medium,

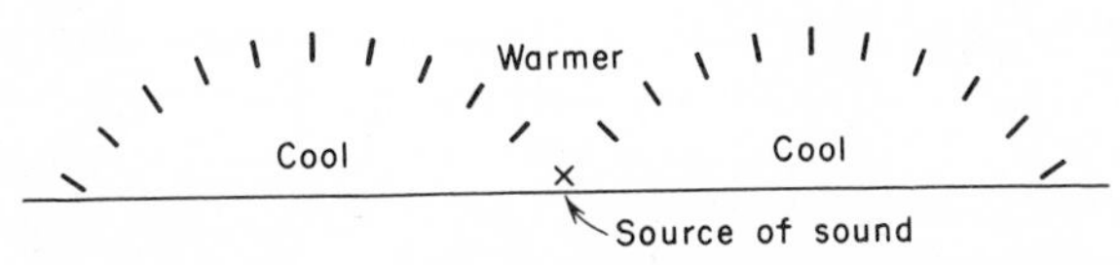

Fig. 14-6. Refraction of sound due to difference in temperature. The upper edges of the wave fronts are always traveling in slightly warmer air, so they get ahead of the lower edges.

during any time interval, as it would have in the old medium. We have imagined it to travel one wavelength in the old medium, so if there had been no change in medium the point *A* would have moved one wavelength to *C*. Because of the increase in speed it must move a distance $\frac{4}{3}$ of *AC* to some point on the arc centered on *A*. A fraction of a period later than the wave reaches *A*, another part of the wave will strike the surface between *A* and *D*, and by similar logic we could construct an arc to show where this portion of the wave front must be at the end of the period. Continuing in this way we may show that when the portion of the wave in the original medium is along *DE* the part which has moved into the new medium lies along *FD*. Obviously the orientation of the wave front has been altered, and since (except in unusual situations which don't concern us here) the direction of propagation is perpendicular to the wave front, the direction of propagation has been altered from *HD* to *DI*.

Perhaps the most familiar example of the refraction of sound is the remarkable "carrying" of sound over large distances under certain atmospheric conditions. This occurs when the air temperature is higher—and hence the speed of sound greater—well above the ground than very near the ground. Thus sound waves which start out on an upward slant are refracted downward, passing over intervening obstructions and returning to the ground level at relatively great distances from their origin, as in Fig. 14-6.

A sort of pseudo refraction is responsible for an even more familiar phenomenon. A soapbox orator can be heard farther downwind than upwind, and the usual explanation is that the sound is "carried" downwind but "blown back" in the upwind direction. When one considers that the speed of sound is well over 700 mph, it is obvious that any wind which could blow the sound back would also blow the soapbox out from under the orator. But because of ground obstructions, the speed of the wind is always less near the ground than above. Therefore those waves headed downwind will have their wave fronts tilted forward as in the right side of Fig. 14-7, and thus the effect is essentially the same as in the preceding paragraph and Fig. 14-6. Upwind, however, the upper edges of the wave fronts are tilted back so that in effect they are refracted upward toward outer space. (Too bad the winds can't blow from *all* sides toward some orators.)

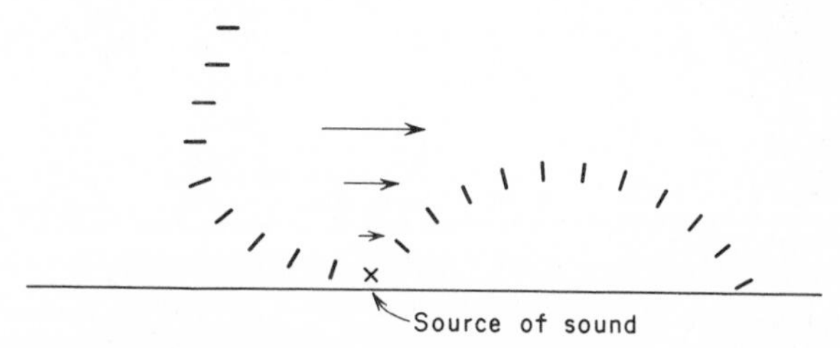

Fig. 14-7. Effect of wind on sound. The wind velocity is greater at increasing elevations, as indicated by the arrows, so the upper edges of the wave fronts are moved downwind with respect to the lower edges.

14-11 Diffraction

The second of the phenomena other than reflection which cause a reorientation of the direction of propagation is ***diffraction.*** This is a sort of sidewise squeezing of a wave, or a train of waves, behind an obstruction. You made much use of diffraction long ago when, playing hide and seek, you heard the youngster who was "it" counting while you were hidden. The sound waves were diffracted around the building or object you were hiding behind.

We can understand this seemingly peculiar property of waves with the aid of Fig. 14-8. When the first compression in the wave train reached the position *AB*, one might expect that it would have gone on without sneaking behind the obstruction. But at the instant this compression, with its excess pressure, passed the corner, it was adjacent to the normal air behind the obstruction, with no barrier between the two. The two unequal pressures cannot exist side by side, and the readjustment increased the pressure behind the obstruction; that is, a compression was generated just at the corner. Huygens' principle applies here again, and this pulse was propagated behind the obstruction in the form of a quarter circle. The same occurred when a rarefaction passed the corner, except that in this case the air from behind the obstruction moved into the rarefaction, causing a rarefaction to be born behind the obstruction. In either case, of course, the wave train continued on in its initial direction as well, slightly weakened by losing some energy to the waves generated behind the obstruction.

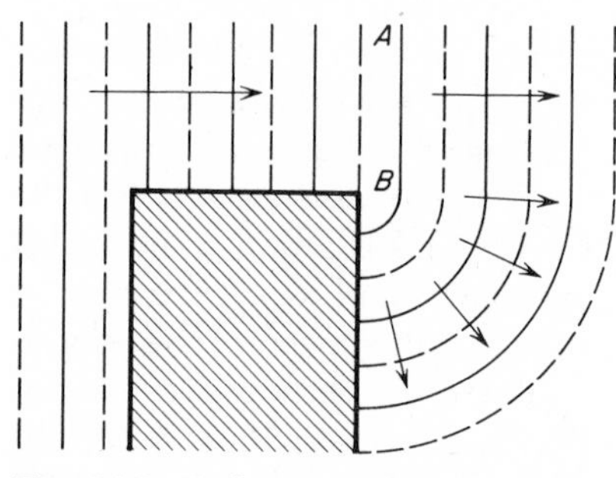

Fig. 14-8. Diffraction of sound waves around an obstruction. Compressions are represented by solid lines, rarefactions by dashed lines. Arrows indicate directions of propagation.

14-12 Interference

So far we have considered only a single wave train. What happens if two or more wave trains are present simultaneously in the same medium? To avoid undue complexity, we shall limit our considerations to just two wave trains.

If two compressions meet, they aid each other to produce a single stronger compression, and two rarefactions combine to a single stronger rarefaction. On the other hand, when a compression and a rarefaction meet, one is trying to increase the pressure of the same part of the medium in which the other is trying to reduce the pressure. If the two are of equal intensity, they nullify each other completely; if one is stronger than the other, it is weakened but not annihilated.

These situations can be visualized most easily in terms of transverse waves on a string, rather than sound waves in air. Suppose that two different generators of the same frequency are delivering waves to the same end of a string, and also imagine that the two wave trains are in phase so that crests of one coincide with crests in the other. If Fig. 14-9(a) represents one of the wave trains and if (b) in the figure represents the other, their combined effect will be as shown in (c). But if they are of opposite phase, as in (a) and (b) of Fig. 14-10, they will annihilate each other as indicated by (c) in that figure. The original waves in Fig. 14-10 have equal amplitudes; the result of two wave trains of identical wavelength, opposite phases, and unequal amplitudes might be as in Fig. 14-11.

The term ***interference*** is applied to the phenomena dealt with in the preceding paragraphs; the interference is ***constructive*** (how's that for con-

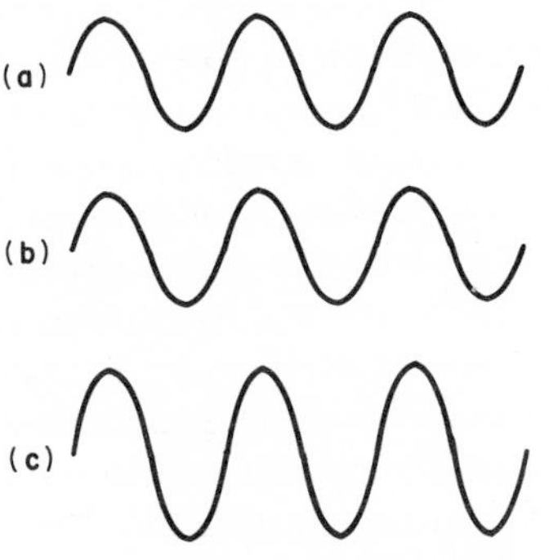

Fig. 14-9. Constructive interference. Two wave trains of identical amplitude and frequency, and exactly in phase, aid each other; their energies (not their amplitudes) are additive.

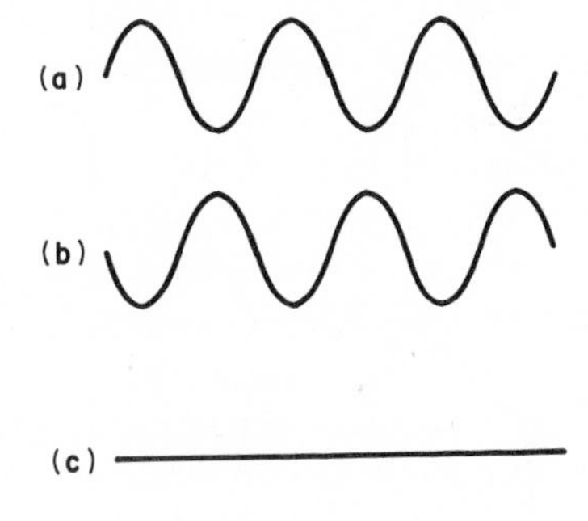

Fig. 14-10. Destructive interference. Two wave trains of identical amplitude and frequency but of opposite phase nullify each other.

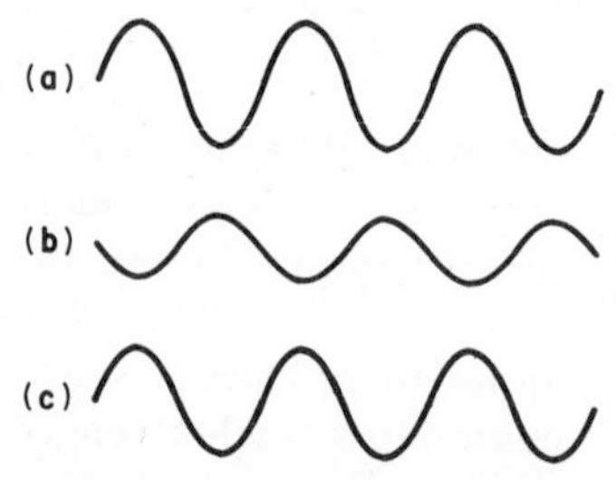

Fig. 14-11. Destructive interference. Two wave trains of identical frequency but of opposite phase and with unequal amplitude partially nullify each other.

tradictory terminology?) when the two pulses are of the same phase and ***destructive*** when the phases are opposite.

Interference is used in military sound ranging. Destructive interference between a direct train of sound waves from a fog horn and one reflected from the water is responsible for the occasional "zones of silence" which are reputed to have caused some shipwrecks. We shall find in the next chapter that interference is also very important in music.

The discussion above deals with wave trains of equal wavelengths traveling in the same direction along a common path, and there may seem to be an implication of such restrictions in other parts of this section. However, interference occurs in any and all situations in which two disturbances arrive simultaneously at the same point in the medium. Either disturbance may be a single pulse or part of an extended wave train; wavelengths may be identical or highly disparate; there is no restriction on the relative phases; directions of propagation may be the same, opposite, or crossing each other at any angle. However, the result of the interference will depend strongly on such factors. We shall meet one important situation in the next section and others in the following chapter.

14-13 Beats

Whenever two sounds which have almost but not quite the same frequency (or pitch) reach the ear together, we observe a special sort of interference. Even though each sound individually has a constant intensity, we hear a periodic pulsation of loudness. The sound gets stronger, then dies away to a minimum—which may or may not be complete inaudibility—then increases to a maximum again, and repeats this variation as long as both sounds continue. The waxing and waning observed under such circumstances constitutes a phenomenon known as ***beats.*** Any one complete cycle of variation of loudness is a single beat. This periodic variation of intensity is due to a progressive change of relative phase, the type of interference changing from constructive to destructive and back again.

Suppose that one string has a frequency of 200.0 vps and another has a frequency of 202.0 vps, and suppose that both are sounding and are perfectly in phase at a certain instant. If one is producing a compression, the other is doing likewise; they are interfering constructively. After $\frac{1}{4}$ sec one will have completed $200.0/4 = 50.0$ vibrations, but the other will have made $202.0/4 = 50.5$ vibrations. Thus, at that instant one will be generating a compression while the other is sending out a rarefaction, and their interference will be destructive. After $\frac{1}{2}$ sec, they will have produced 100.0 and 101.0 vibrations respectively, so they will be back in phase and the interference will be constructive. At $\frac{3}{4}$ sec, they will be interfering destructively again since one will have made 150.0 vibrations and the other 151.5. Constructive interference will exist at the end of the second, when one will have completed 200.0 vibrations and the other 202.0. Hence the combined sound will be at a maximum at the start of the second, a minimum at $\frac{1}{4}$ sec, maximum at $\frac{1}{2}$ sec, minimum after $\frac{3}{4}$ sec, and again maximum at the end of the interval. That is to say, there will be exactly two beats during the second. Analysis of any other combination of frequencies will confirm what seems to be implied by this example; the ***beat frequency***, or number of beats per second, is simply the difference between the two frequencies.

The same thing is represented graphically in Fig. 14-12, in which (a) and (b) represent two wave trains of slightly different frequencies—and hence unequal wavelengths—and (c) indicates the net effect.

Although in a physical sense, beats occur between any two frequencies, the ear may not perceive the beats as such. If, for example, a frequency of 200 vps and one of 300 vps are sounded simultaneously, there will be a beat frequency of 100 vps. The ear responds to this beat frequency exactly as it would if there were no beats but instead a third source producing a sound with a frequency of 100 vps. Thus beats are perceived as

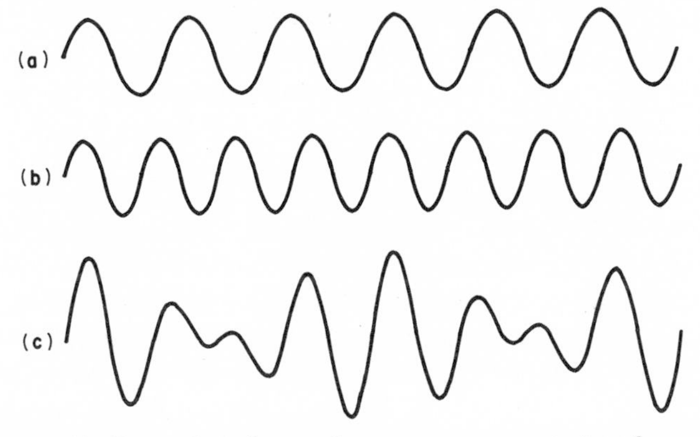

Fig. 14-12. Beats. Interference between two wave trains of unequal frequencies alternates between constructive and destructive. *Note:* Crests in this figure indicate energy due to compression and troughs represent energy due to rarefaction. The graph is presented on this basis rather than in terms of amplitudes, to make more obvious the effects of the progressively changing type of interference.

such only if the beat frequency is below the minimum audible frequency (Sec. 14-6); for beat frequencies above this minimum frequency, the beats are heard as a tone of definite pitch. We shall find in the next chapter that this is of considerable importance.

14-14 The Doppler Effect

It is a very common experience to hear a jet plane pass overhead, and curious persons with little knowledge of physics may be mystified by the strange fact that all aspects of the noise which have definite pitches drop in pitch as the plane passes over. This implies a decrease in the frequency of the sound waves. But this frequency decrease must have something to do with the motion of the plane, since it invariably occurs while the plane is passing over; there is no reason to suppose that the frequencies actually emitted by the plane should change, and every reason to believe that they do not.

Figure 14-13 provides a basis for understanding this effect. The numbered dots represent positions of any source of sound at different times, the source moving from any point to the adjacent one in exactly the period of the sound it emits. Each of the numbered circles (or arcs) represents the sound wave sent out when the source was at the corresponding position. Thus when the source was at point 1 it sent out the wave identified by the numeral 1. One period later, the source was at point 2 and sent out the wave so numbered. Each wave is centered on its point of origin, but since the points of origin are moving to the right, the waves are not con-

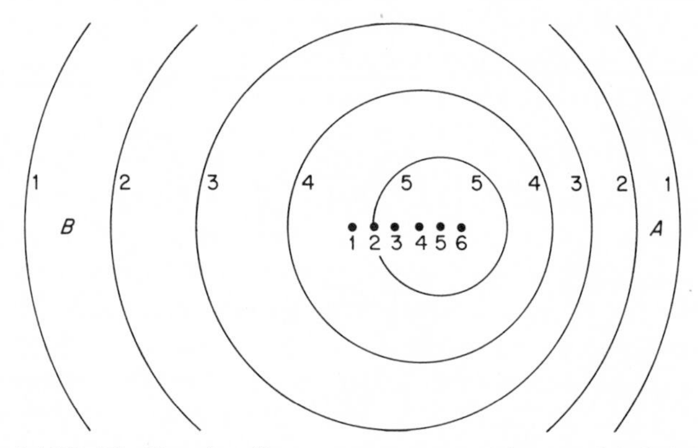

Fig. 14-13. The Doppler effect: moving source. The wave labeled 1 was produced when the source was at the position marked 1. During one period the source moved to position 2 and as it passed through that position it generated wave 2; etc. The smallest wave was sent out as the source passed position 5 and the source is just about to generate a wave at position 6.

centric. They are spread out on the left and crowded together on the right. Hence for a person at A, the wavelength is less than it would have been had the source not moved, but to a person at B, the wavelength is increased. As always, $v = N\lambda$—Eq. (13-4)—and the fact that the source is moving has no effect whatever on the speed with which the sound waves pass through the air. Therefore, since v is fixed, any decrease of wavelength occasioned by the approach of the source will cause a proportional increase in the frequency; and the increase in wavelength resulting from the recession of the source will be accompanied by a corresponding decrease of frequency.

A similar effect is observed if the source is stationary but the observer is moving toward or away from the source; the pitch of a crossing bell is unchanging for a motorist waiting for a train to pass, but to a passenger on a fast train there is a definite drop in pitch as he whizzes past the signal. In this case there is no change of wavelength as when the source is moving. A stationary observer will receive N waves per second from the source. If during 1 sec he moves from point P in Fig. 14-14 to another point Q closer to the source, however, he will receive the full quota of N waves he would have received had he stayed at P, but additional waves will have passed Q without as yet reaching P. Thus N waves have impinged on his ear due to the motion of the sound waves and ΔN additional waves have impinged on it due to his motion; so though the emitted frequency is N, the effective frequency for the moving observer is $N + \Delta N$, and he hears a pitch above the true pitch. On the other hand if during 1 sec an observer moves from R to S, he fails to receive the full N waves which arrived at R during that second, so the effective frequency is lowered below N, and he hears a pitch lower than the true pitch of the source.

What of a passenger on a train listening to the whistle of the locomotive? Here both source and observer are moving; how will the apparent pitch be affected? In each of the cases discussed before, there was relative motion between the source and the observer, but in this case though both are moving there is no relative motion. It turns out that the lowering of pitch due to the motion of the source is precisely canceled by the raising of the pitch due to the observer's motion. The whistle is heard at its true pitch. Of course, we should have anticipated this result, since only *relative* velocities have any real meaning.

We have tacitly assumed that there is no wind. What happens during

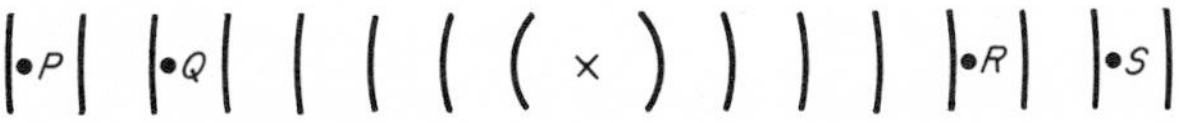

P Q × R S

Fig. 14-14. The Doppler effect: source stationary, observer moving. If during one second the observer moves from P to Q he will receive more than one second's quota of waves. He will receive less than one second's quota of waves if during that second he moves from R to S.

an outdoor concert if there is a wind? Does a stationary listener hear the music in true pitch or does the wind affect the pitch? We have seen previously that only *relative* motion has any real meaning, so it makes no difference whether the source and observer are moving at the same rate through still air (locomotive whistle and train passenger) or the air is moving past a stationary source and a motionless observer (wind at an outdoor concert). In neither case is there relative motion, and without *relative* motion between the source and the observer there can be no Doppler effect. The frequency observed and pitch heard differ from those of the source *only* when there is *relative* motion between the source and the observer.

14-15 Generalizations

This chapter has to do with sound and the discussion has been almost entirely in terms of sound and sound waves, though other types of waves were used at times to make the discussion more concrete. Nevertheless, much of what we have found in this chapter applies to wave phenomena in general rather than to sound alone. Waves of all kinds exhibit (under proper circumstances) the phenomena of reflection, refraction, and diffraction, though in some cases we would have to reword our explanations. Interference is a characteristic property of all wave phenomena; we shall see in Chapter 27 that the interference of light waves is one reason we must consider light to be a wave phenomenon in spite of much contradictory evidence. Interference of radio frequency waves in electrical circuits is the basis of certain circuits used in radio receivers. Beats are observed with waves of many kinds. The Doppler effect in light enables us to measure the radial velocity of a star and make other seemingly impossible astronomical determinations.

Summary

Sound is always the result of *vibration.* Sound waves are *longitudinal.* The speed of sound in air is independent of pressure, frequency, and amplitude, but it is greater at higher temperatures.

The *pitch* of a sound is determined almost entirely by its frequency, high frequencies producing higher pitches; but at extremely high intensities, an increase of intensity may cause a relatively slight change of pitch. Pitch is purely subjective, whereas frequency is a quantitative physical entity. Similarly, loudness is the subjective counterpart of the physical quantity intensity.

The *limits of audible frequencies* vary considerably from one individual to another and they change with age. These limits also depend on intensity. The ear is far more sensitive to frequencies of a few thousand vibrations per second than to those nearer the lower limit of audible frequencies; the sensitivity of the ear also drops off somewhat as the upper limit of frequencies is approached. Contrary to the general impression, the ear cannot perceive either very small changes of pitch or very small changes of loudness. Nevertheless, the ear is astonishingly sensitive.

Sound waves are reflected without change of phase when they strike the boundary of a medium more dense than the one they are in; they are reflected with reversal of phase when they strike the boundary of a less dense medium.

Sound waves are *refracted* when they pass obliquely from one medium to another in which their speed is different. They are *diffracted* when they pass an obstruction, enabling them to pass behind or around the obstruction.

Two sound pulses meeting in phase *interfere constructively;* they interfere *destructively* if their phases are opposite. Two simultaneous sounds of slightly differing frequencies undergo a progressive and continuing change of phase, the result being alternation between constructive and destructive interference and hence a periodic variation in loudness. This is the phenomenon of *beats*. The beat frequency is the difference between the two parent frequencies. Beats are heard as tones rather than as beats if the beat frequency is in the audible range.

Relative motion between a source of sound and an observer will result in the observer's hearing a pitch differing from the actual pitch of the source. Relative approach raises the observed pitch and relative recession lowers it.

Many of the phenomena considered in terms of sound waves are also present, and important, in other kinds of waves.

Self-Quiz

1. Give two quite different definitions of sound. Why are there *two*? Is either more valid than the other?

2. Why is it "obvious that sound waves must be longitudinal"?

3. Equations (14-1) and (14-2) show that the speed of sound in a gas is inversely proportional to the square root of the density. What do these equations imply concerning the speed of sound in air at different densities if the difference in density is due to a difference in pressure? What is their implication about the relative velocities of sound in gases which are at the same temperature and pressure but differ in density due to different chemical composition? Are your two answers the same? Explain.

4. If you were concerned with the speed of sound at 500°C, would Eq. (14-3) or (14-4) give the more reliable result? Why?

5. Compare the concepts of frequency and pitch. Is it permissable to say "Pitch is directly proportional to frequency"? Why *not?*

6. Similarly compare and contrast the concepts of intensity and loudness.

7. Why were precise values of the lower and upper limits of audible frequencies not given, instead of the rather ambiguous discussion in Sec. 14-6?

8. Can a violinist tune a string exactly to the pitch of a piano string if the two are never sounded simultaneously? If they *are* sounded simultaneously? Give a full explanation of the reason, in each case.

9. Outline in some detail the mechanism by which a compression is reflected when it meets the boundary of a medium of greater density than the one in which it has been traveling. Repeat for a rarefaction.

10. Similarly outline the reflection of each type of pulse at a boundary where the pulse meets a decrease of density of medium.

11. Make a pair of rough diagrams similar to Fig. 13-7, one above the other, with the generating point at the same position in the reference circle and with the same wavelength. Now draw a third diagram beneath the other two with the generating point on the other side of the circle and compare this wave train with the others. Why is "in phase" described as "0° phase difference" and "opposite phase" called "180° out of phase"? Finally draw a fourth diagram which, with one of the others, will show a 90° phase difference. How do the two wave trains compare?

12. Reconsider your first three diagrams, from the standpoint of type of interference between the wave trains, and discuss constructive and destructive interference in terms of phase difference.

13. On Fig. 14-5 (or a rough copy) draw a perpendicular to the surface at point *D*, the perpendicular extending into both media. Note that the direction of propagation, shown by the broken line *HDI*, crosses this perpendicular at the boundary between the two media. Is this necessarily the case, or might the direction in the new medium lie to the left of the perpendicular? Explain clearly.

14. State in some detail the mechanism by which a rarefaction diffracts into the space behind an obstruction.

15. Whatever the individual frequencies of two tones may be, if one frequency is exactly twice the other no beats are detectable. Why? But if both tones are in the audible range and one has a frequency almost but not exactly twice that of the other there will be very obvious beats. Why?

16. When you see a rainbow, the red is due to light waves of relatively long wavelength and the blue to those which are comparatively short. Assume that two stars emit the same color of light but we observe one as redder than it is and the other as bluer than its true color. What conclusion can we draw? (Actually, the unaided eye cannot perceive any color differences so slight; observable differences have other causes. But these slight differences are detected, and measured, by suitable optical instruments.)

Problems

1. (a) At 0°C and normal pressure the density of dry air is 0.001293 (g/cm^3). Compute the speed of sound in air at this temperature.
   (b) Repeat for 20°C, at which temperature the density is 0.001205 g/cm^3.

2. Calculate the speed of sound in air at 20°C by (a) Eq. (14-3) and (b) Eq. (14-4). Compare the two answers, and also compare the second answer with the answer to problem 1(b).

3. The velocity of sound in air is often said to be 1120 ft/sec. At what Fahrenheit temperature would this value be valid?

4. A wave front striking an obstruction at any angle is reflected from the surface at the same angle. Prove this graphically with the aid of Huygens' principle.

5. If a wind is blowing steadily with a velocity of 30.0 mph and if the temperature is 70°F, determine the effective speed of the sound (a) upwind, (b) downwind, and (c) at right angles to the wind direction.

6. Two wave trains have amplitudes of 4.00 mm and 5.00 mm respectively. When these two wave trains cross each other, what will the resulting amplitude be (a) where the phase difference is 0° and (b) where it is 180°?

7. There are three beats per second between two strings, one of which has a frequency of 440 vps. (a) What are the possible frequencies of the other string? (b) What is the only possible frequency of the second string if the beat frequency is reduced when its tension is decreased?

8. A string has a frequency of 264 vps. There is a high frequency of beats between this string and a second one, but as the tension of the latter is increased the beat frequency drops to 4 per sec. A third string then is sounded with each of the others in turn; there are 5 beats per sec between the second and third strings and 1 beat per sec between the first and third strings. What is the frequency of the third string?

9. When two strings are sounded together, the beats produce a third tone which has $\frac{5}{4}$ of the frequency of the lower of the two strings. If that string has a frequency of 384 vps, find the frequency (a) of the beats and (b) of the higher string.

15
THE PHYSICAL BASIS OF MUSIC

15-1 Preview

Although music is classified as an art, and properly so, it is by no means solely *an art. A very solid foundation of physical principles underlies the art; and though it is a rather rare musician who is fully aware of the physical basis of his art, no musician could create music if this physical basis did not exist. Some consideration of things musical, therefore, is properly a part of such a course as this. Little knowledge of music is assumed or required; in only a few instances will those with a background of music have any considerable advantage over others who know little of music. The material in this chapter is based on the chapters on vibratory motion, wave motion, and the first chapter on sound: Chapters 12, 13, and 14.*

15-2 Musical Intervals

Thus far, when discussing frequency or pitch we have fixed our attention on a single tone, except in the case of beats. We shall now consider the relationship of one tone to another. Whether we sound them simultaneously or successively, we can tell whether the tones are of the same pitch; and if they aren't, we can detect which is the higher and which the lower, and how much higher one is than the other. All of this is incorporated in the significance of the term ***interval.*** We call an interval "small" if it is produced, for example, by adjacent keys of a piano; we call it "large" if one note has a pitch quite a bit higher than that of the other. The most familiar interval, at least to non-musicians, is the octave, such as that between one C on a piano and the next C above.

We have seen in the preceding chapter that the pitch of a tone is determined by its frequency, and since there is a difference between the pitches of the two tones which comprise an interval we may be tempted to jump to the conclusion that the size of a musical interval is determined by the difference between the two frequencies. It turns out that this is incorrect; it is the quotient, or ratio, of the two frequencies which characterizes a particular interval. Thus, the frequency of the higher note in an interval of an octave is always twice that of the lower note; and this is true whether the tones which comprise the octave are in the deep bass, the high treble, or anywhere else in the audible spectrum. Each other musical interval is characterized by its own frequency ratio, the values for the common intervals being given in Table 15-1. The table will be more meaningful to non-musicians if it is studied in connection with Fig. 15-1, which represents part of a piano keyboard including an octave from middle C to the next C above. Each white key within this octave is identified by the usual letter and also by the name of the note of the scale starting on middle C; and the frequency of each note in this octave is recorded. You can check the frequency ratios in the table by taking the appropriate frequencies from the figure and canceling common factors.*

It must not be thought that, for example, the only major third is that listed in Table 15-1. There are two other major thirds within the octave, fa–la and sol–ti, as you can prove by working out the corresponding frequency ratios. *Any* interval, anywhere in the audible range, is a major third, if the ratio of the two frequencies involved is 5/4; and a similar statement applies for each of the other intervals.

---

* Instructors differ widely about the importance of the material in Table 15-1, especially for non-musicians; your instructor may or may not wish you to have more than a general idea of this material.

Table 15-1
MUSICAL INTERVALS AND THEIR FREQUENCY RATIOS

Name(s) of interval	Example of interval, in terms of C, D, E, etc.	Example of interval, in terms of do, re, mi, etc.	Frequency ratio of interval
Half tone, minor second	E–F	mi–fa	16/15
Whole tone,* major second,* minor tone	D–E	re–mi	10/9
Whole tone,† major second,† major tone	C–D	do–re	9/8
Minor third	E–G	mi–sol	6/5
Major third	C–E	do–mi	5/4
Perfect fourth	C–F	do–fa	4/3
Perfect fifth	C–G	do–sol	3/2
Minor sixth	E–c‡	mi–do′‡	8/5
Major sixth	C–A	do–la	5/3
Minor seventh	C–d	mi–re′	9/5
Major seventh	C–B	do–ti	15/8
Octave	C–c	do–do′	2/1

* Small. See Sec. 15-3 and Fig. 15-1 for explanation.
† Large. See Sec. 15-3 and Fig. 15-1 for explanation.
‡ Lower-case letters, and note names with a prime (′), refer to notes in the next higher octave.

15-3 The Natural Scale

The sequence of frequencies which appears in Fig. 15-1 constitutes what is known as the ***natural scale*** or the ***just scale.*** The reason for the former adjective will appear in later sections. The pattern of this scale may be described by either of two different, but equivalent, sets of frequency ratios. One such set is developed by comparing the frequency of each tone with that of the preceding tone, the other by comparing each frequency with the frequency of the lowest note (do) in the scale. These patterns are given in Fig. 15-2, which you can develop from the information in Fig. 15-1.

You will note that three frequency ratios suffice for all the successive intervals. Intervals having a frequency ratio of 9/8 or 10/9 are called ***whole tones*** and those characterized by the 16/15 ratio are ***half tones.*** Obviously, then, there are two different sizes of "whole tones" rather than one, but they differ so slightly that they are hard to tell apart.

Any sequence of tones with the pattern of frequency ratios in Fig. 15-2 is an octave of the natural scale, regardless of the pitch or frequency of any individual note.

15-4 Addition of Intervals

From Table 15-1 we see that the interval from C to E is a major third and that its frequency ratio is 5/4. We also see that from E to G is a minor

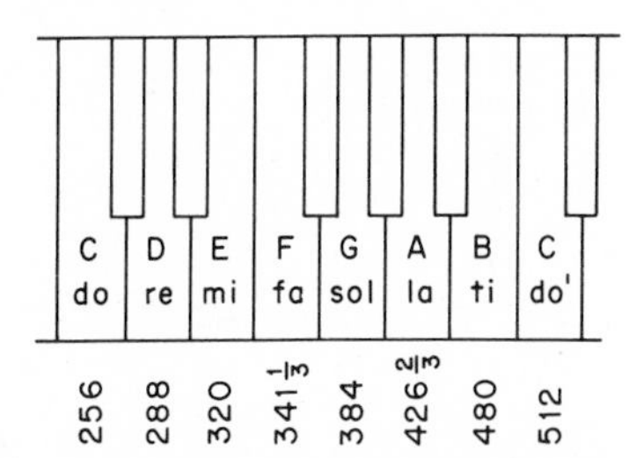

Fig. 15-1. One octave of a piano keyboard. The frequencies given are on the basis of the so-called physical pitch.

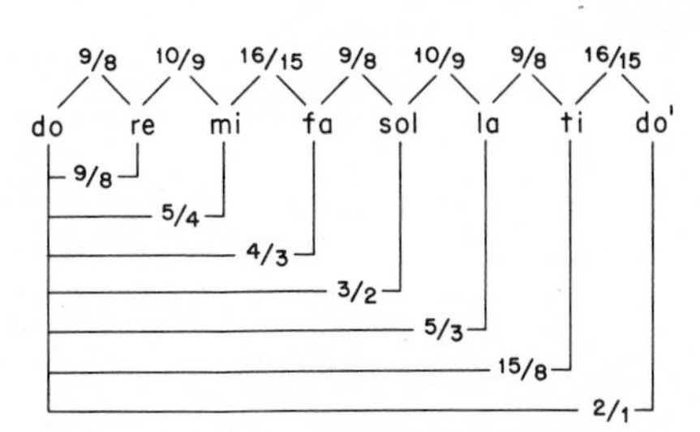

Fig. 15-2. An octave of the just scale. Frequency ratios of intervals between successive notes appear at the top of the figure. Frequency ratios in the lower part show the interval between the lowest note (do) and the other notes.

third, which is characterized by a frequency ratio of 6/5. Thus, the frequency of E is 5/4 as great as that of C, and the frequency of G is 6/5 that of E. Combining the two statements in the last sentence, we find that the frequency of G is 6/5 of 5/4 of the frequency of C. If this is the case, the interval between C and G should have a frequency ratio of $6/5 \cdot 5/4$, which comes out to 3/2. Checking Table 15-1, we see that this is correct for this interval. You can test this method of combining intervals for generality by choosing other pairs, if you wish.

Thus, if we wish to find the frequency ratio of the interval formed by adding two (or more) musical intervals, we multiply the frequency ratios of the intervals. Conversely, to subtract intervals, we divide the frequency ratio of the larger interval by that of the smaller.*

15-5 Difficulties with the Natural Scale

Though the natural scale has many advantages, it is used only rarely. Composers write music in many different keys or signatures, but an instrument such as the piano would have to be retuned for each different key (signature) if the natural scale were used. There are two reasons for this.

One obvious reason is the fact that there are two different sizes of "whole" tones. If a piano is tuned to the key of C, for example, these whole tones get mixed if we try to play a composition written in any key other than C. This is apparent in Fig. 15-3. The whole tones between c and d and between d and c are not correct for the key of F, though they are proper for the key of C. (To maintain the proper pattern of the just

* If you are familiar with logarithms, you will see that this means that the size of an interval is determined by the logarithm of its frequency ratio. Since the "size" of the interval is subjective and we may consider the frequency ratio to be the stimulus which causes this subjective response, you see that all this is in accordance with the Weber-Fechner law (Sec. 14-5).

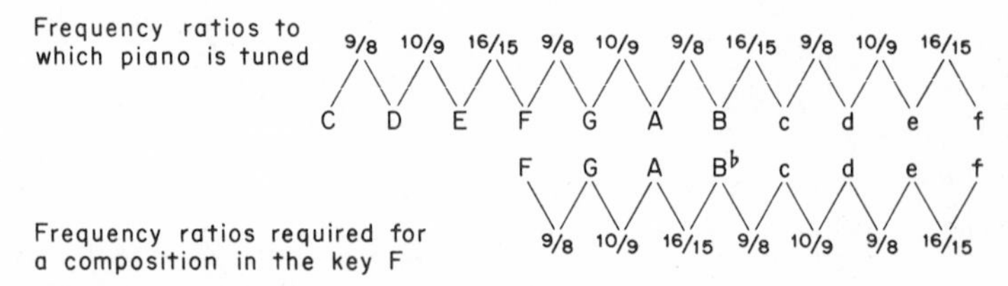

Fig. 15-3. A piano tuned to the just scale in the key of C is out of tune for the key of F, even though B♭ is used instead of B.

scale we must use the black key B♭ instead of the white key B, in the key of F; but we may assume that the B♭ is tuned so that the frequency ratios are as shown.) A similar inversion of the order of the "whole" tones occurs if we attempt to play in any other key than the one to which the instrument is tuned.

The second major disadvantage arises from the fact that the sum of two "half" tones is larger than either of the two "whole" tones. This means, for example, that B♭, a half tone below *B*, must have a lower pitch than A♯, a half tone above A; a single black key between A and B won't serve for both A♯ and B♭.

Thus, if we wish to play compositions written in different keys on the same piano (without retuning the entire piano for each change of key) we must do one of two things: we must make the keyboard far more complex by adding enough extra keys to compensate for all possible discrepancies of the sorts noted in the two paragraphs above, or we must use something other than the natural or just scale. We have no choice; it would be impossible to play on so complicated a keyboard. So the pattern of the scale must be modified to eliminate the disadvantages of the just scale.

15-6 The Equally Tempered Scale

Once upon a time each of two young men was wooing the object of his heart's delight. One whispered, "When I look into your face time seems to stand still." The other said, "Your face would stop a clock." From an objective, dispassionate point of view, the two statements were essentially equivalent in meaning, but it cannot be said that the same was true of their effects on the young ladies!

Similarly, we feel quite differently if we say that we are going to *temper* a scale than if we say that we intend to *mistune* the scale. The meaning is the same, but the euphemistic term ***temper*** gets that meaning across without raising the hair on our backs. The ***equally tempered scale*** results from the type of ***temperament*** now used almost universally.

Equal temperament makes each of the five "whole tones" in an octave exactly equal, and makes any single whole tone exactly equivalent to two half tones. Thus the five whole tones and two half tones in an octave, taken together, are equivalent to twelve half tones. We found in Sec. 15-4 that intervals are added by multiplying their frequency ratios, and we know that the frequency ratio for an octave is 2/1, so if v is the value of an equally tempered half tone it must be true that

$$v^{12} = 2, \quad \text{or} \quad v = \sqrt[12]{2} \tag{15-1}$$

Since the twelfth root of 2 is an irrational number, to speak of the frequency *ratio* of a half tone would be a contradiction of terms; that is why the term "value" was used rather than "frequency ratio." However, in all other respects this "value" is equivalent to the other term.

The equally tempered scale is described in Table 15-2, both in the form of roots and in decimal values correct to 4 places. Decimal values on the just scale are also given for comparison.

15-7 Vibrations of Strings; Standing Waves

Let us turn now from the nature of the musical scale to the means by which musical notes are produced, and the factors which determine their frequencies. We shall consider first the vibration of a string, and later the production of tones by each of two types of organ pipe.

If you tie one end of a rope to a post and shake the other up and down, you can easily find a combination of tension and frequency which will cause the rope to form a pattern similar to that in Fig. 15-4. The rope breaks up into a series of loops separated by spots where there is relatively little motion or displacement.

The term ***standing waves*** refers to such a pattern. It is characterized by positions at which the displacement of the rope is always small (zero in the ideal situation), termed ***nodes,*** separated by regions in which the rope is displaced alternately in one direction and then in the other, called ***loops.***

Table 15-2

COMPARISON OF INTERVALS ON THE EQUALLY TEMPERED SCALE WITH THOSE ON THE JUST SCALE

Name of interval	Value on the equally tempered scale: as a root	Value on the equally tempered scale: in decimal form	Frequency ratio on the just scale
Minor second	$\sqrt[12]{2}$	1.0595	1.0667
Major second	$(\sqrt[12]{2})^2 = \sqrt[6]{2}$	1.1225	1.1111 or 1.1250
Minor third	$(\sqrt[12]{2})^3 = \sqrt[4]{2}$	1.1892	1.2000
Major third	$(\sqrt[12]{2})^4 = \sqrt[3]{2}$	1.2599	1.2500
Perfect fourth	$(\sqrt[12]{2})^5$	1.3348	1.3333
Perfect fifth	$(\sqrt[12]{2})^7$	1.4983	1.5000
Minor sixth	$(\sqrt[12]{2})^8 = (\sqrt[3]{2})^2$	1.5874	1.6000
Major sixth	$(\sqrt[12]{2})^9 = (\sqrt[4]{2})^3$	1.6818	1.6667
Minor seventh	$(\sqrt[12]{2})^{10} = (\sqrt[6]{2})^5$	1.7818	1.8000
Major seventh	$(\sqrt[12]{2})^{11}$	1.8877	1.8750
Octave	$(\sqrt[12]{2})^{12} = 2$	2.0000	2.0000

Fig. 15-4. Standing waves on a rope.

The point of maximum displacement within the loop (usually at the center of the loop) is an ***antinode.*** The terms ***stationary waves*** or ***stationary vibrations*** are sometimes used instead of standing waves.

Though Fig. 15-4 shows transverse waves and the discussion is largely in terms of such waves on a rope, under proper conditions standing waves occur with longitudinal waves just as they do with transverse waves.

Standing waves result from interference between two or more wave trains of the same frequency and hence of equal wavelength. In the most important applications, a wave train passes over or through a medium while a reflection of this same train simultaneously moves over or through the same medium in the opposite direction. Thus two wave trains of identical frequency and wavelength and of practically the same amplitude move in opposite directions on, or in, the same medium. As they pass through each other, the wave trains interfere with each other.

We can understand the development of standing waves by studying Fig. 15-5. Because it is easier to visualize transverse than longitudinal waves, the discussion will be in terms of transverse wave trains on a string; however, if we think of the curves in the figures as graphs of some physical property in a longitudinal wave (such as deviation from normal pressure) and modify the terminology of the discussion accordingly, both the diagrams and the discussion will be valid for longitudinal waves.

The series of nine diagrams in Fig. 15-5 represents an original train of transverse waves moving to the right, and a reflected wave train traveling toward the left. There is a time lapse of one-eighth of a period between successive diagrams, so that each wave train moves a full wavelength. This regular travel of the train of original waves may not be apparent at first glance, but becomes quite evident if we note that the dotted line slanting downward to the right of vertical connects successive positions of a trough marked *T*, which is part of the original wave train. Similarly, a crest *C* in the reflected wave train moves progressively to the left as revealed by the leftward slanted dashed line.

At the ends of the string, we see that whenever the original wave train is tending to displace the string upward, the reflected train has an equal tendency to displace it downward, and vice versa, with the result that there is never any displacement at these points. This is to be expected,

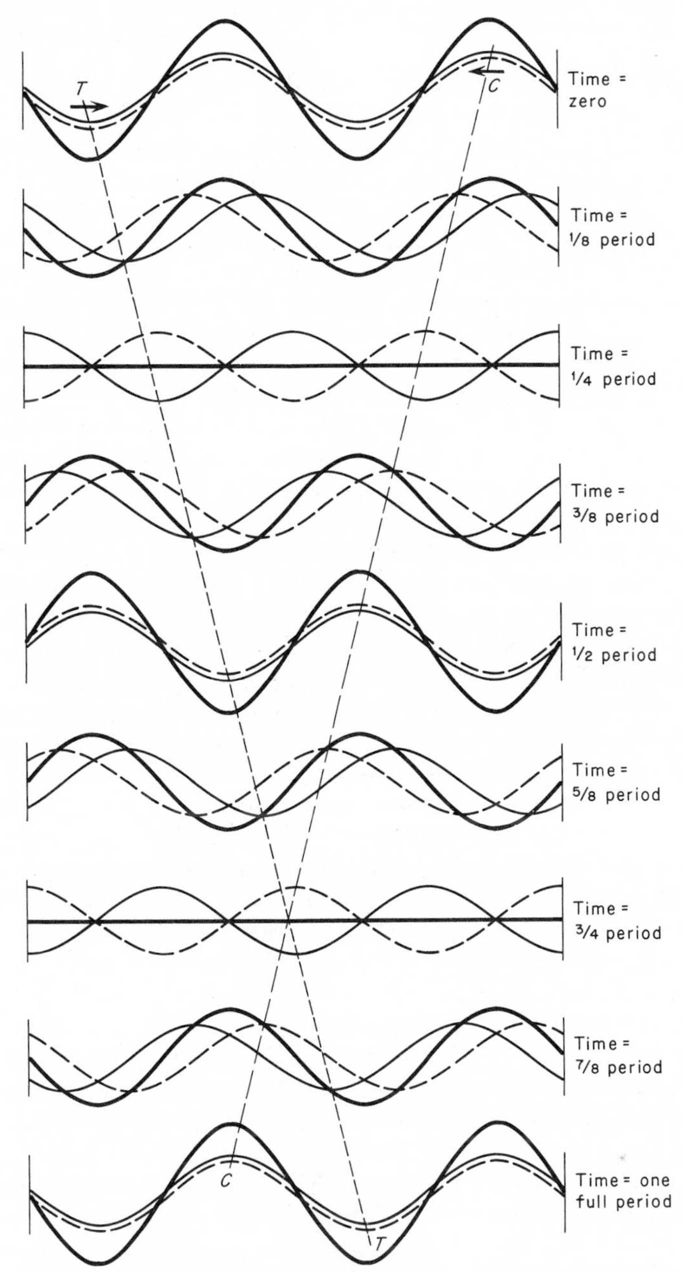

Fig. 15-5. Development of standing waves on a string. An original wave train — is moving to the right and its reflection –– is moving to the left. Each diagram represents the situation one-eighth of a period later than that in the diagram next above. The symbol *T* represents a particular trough in the original wave train, and *C* identifies a specific crest in the reflected train. Neither the original nor the reflected wave train is visible on the string. Only the standing wave pattern —, which is their net result, is apparent.

naturally; the ends of the string are fixed. But the same situation is found at other points on the string; if you note any point where the resultant displacement is zero on the first diagram (or on any other except those in which *no* part of the string is displaced) and follow this point downward through the series of diagrams, you will find that the displacement is *always* zero at that point. Such points are the nodes, and they exist because the two wave trains always interfere destructively at these locations.

Between any two adjacent nodes, the situation is quite different. The relative phases of the two wave trains change continuously. In the first diagram, both the original and the reflected train have troughs at the point marked *T*. For the remainder of this paragraph, let us confine our attention to this portion of the string. At this instant, the two troughs interfere constructively to produce a maximum downward displacement. One-eighth of a period later, the original wave train has moved one-eighth of a wavelength to the right, and the reflected train one-eighth of a wavelength to the left. The two troughs which were at *T* are now a quarter of a wavelength apart, but still close enough to cooperate in producing a trough somewhat shallower than it was. In the third diagram, one-fourth of a period has elapsed, so each wave train has progressed a quarter of a wavelength, and since they are moving in opposite directions, this brings each crest of one into coincidence with a trough of the other; hence there is destructive interference, and the string is not displaced at all. As the two wave trains continue to move, we find two crests approaching each other where the two troughs had been at the start of the period; and at the end of half a period, these two troughs coincide exactly, producing a maximum upward displacement. During the ensuing quarter of a period this crest weakens and collapses, and a trough of maximum depth is formed during the final quarter of the period. This is exactly the situation we had at the start, so during the period this section of the string has made one complete cycle of transverse vibration.

Meantime, the same sort of thing is happening in each of the other portions of the string between adjacent nodes, the phases of the vibrations being opposite on opposite sides of a node; that is, a whole series of antinodes appears, the displacements in adjacent antinodes being opposite at any given instant.

Thus the end effect of two similar trains of waves passing through each other in opposite directions is a pattern of loops and nodes in which there is no obvious evidence of the wave trains themselves. Though motion occurs in the loops, it is a purely vibratory motion which is devoid of any suggestion of the motion of the wave trains.

15-8 Reflection of a Wave at the Fixed End of a String

If a pulse, such as the crest in Fig. 15-6, is moving to the right on a string which is rigidly fastened at both ends, obviously the tension will

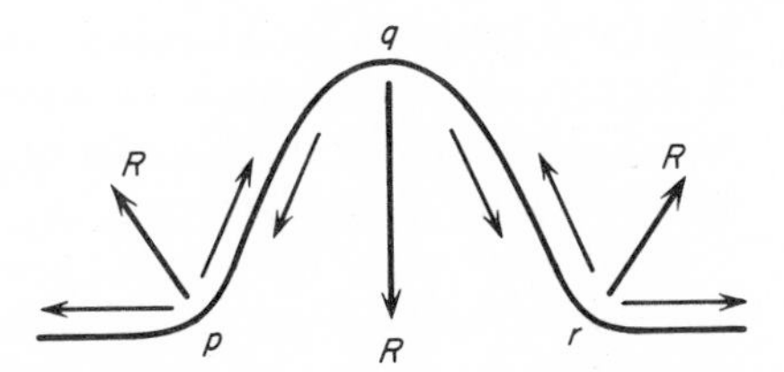

Fig. 15-6. Forces acting on a crest on a string. Unlabeled arrows indicate tensions in the segments of the string adjacent to the arrows. The resultant forces are marked R.

tend to erase this abnormal situation. The tensions on the two sides of point p have a resultant which is generally upward, so it appears that the string would tend to move upward at this point. The pulse is moving to the right, however, so just an instant ago point p was in a crest and it has just moved down to its normal position. In doing so, it acquired a downward momentum, and this opposes the tendency of the resultant force to accelerate point p upward. At point q, the tension on each side has a downward component, whereas this was true of only one tension at p. Thus the resultant force at q exceeds that at p, so it is able to overcome the upward momentum of the string at this point and accelerate it downward. This situation at r is similar to that at p except that the pulse is just arriving and so the string has no momentum; thus the resultant force is able to accelerate point r upward. The combination of these processes causes the pulse to move to the right along the string.

When the pulse reaches the fixed end of the string, it exerts an upward force on the post or clamp which holds it, just as it did on the point r in the discussion above. Obviously, however, the post won't be accelerated upward as was a point on the string. But this is a way of saying that the post offers a greater force to oppose the upward force on it, and thus the portion of string in the crest is accelerated downward more sharply than it was before it reached the end of the string. Hence instead of returning to a position of zero displacement, it overshoots and forms a trough. This trough is then propagated back down the string. Thus we see that a crest reaching the end of a cord is reflected as a trough; that is, it is reflected with reversal of phase.

Similar analysis would show that a trough must be reflected as a crest; and since a wave train is but a series of alternate crests and troughs, the entire train will be reflected with reversal of phase.

15-9 The Frequency of a String

The frequency of a string is determined by three factors: the tension on the string, its length, and its mass per unit length. But exactly how does the frequency depend on each?

If one sets a string on any musical instrument into vibration, the string moves back and forth in a pattern of standing waves, but there is no evidence of waves traveling along it. It might appear that the obvious way to approach the problem of finding an equation for the frequency of the string is to consider the vibrations, but it turns out that this is by no means so simple as it might appear. It is much easier to "go around Robin Hood's barn" and approach the matter from the standpoint of the waves traveling back and forth along the string.

In the preceding section, we saw that if a crest moves along a string it will be reflected as a trough. Thus, as the pulse and its reflection make one round trip along the string and back, the string will be displaced in one direction and then in the other. That is, one round trip of the wave constitutes one complete vibration of the string.

This being the case, the frequency of the string—the number of vibrations per second—is simply the number of round trips a wave can make in 1 sec. This is equal to the velocity of the wave divided by the distance of one round trip. If the length of the string is L, the distance traveled in one round trip is $2L$. Using N as the frequency and v to represent the velocity, we have

$$N = \frac{v}{2L}$$

But according to Eq. (13-3)

$$v = \sqrt{T/\rho_l}$$

in which T is the tension of the string and ρ_l represents its linear density (mass per unit length). Putting this expression for v into the preceding equation, we have

$$N = \frac{\sqrt{T/\rho_l}}{2L} \qquad (15\text{-}2)$$

15-10 Laws of Strings

From Eq. (15-2) we can derive the three laws of strings (if you are a string player you may know them as Mersenne's laws).

Since the length L appears in the denominator, if other factors remain unchanged any increase in L will cause the frequency to be less, and vice versa; thus the frequency is inversely proportional to the length of the string. This is the ***first law of strings.***

The second law of strings relates the frequency to the tension. The tension is in the numerator, so N and T are directly proportional; but since the T is under the radical, the square root of the tension is involved rather than the tension itself. Hence the ***second law of strings*** states that the frequency is directly proportional to the square root of the tension.

The third factor, the linear density, is also under the radical, and an examination shows that any change in the value of the linear density would generate an opposite change in the value of the frequency. Thus, the frequency is inversely proportional to the square root of the linear density. This is the ***third law.***

A special case of the third law may be applied to strings made of the same material. Under these conditions, the frequency is inversely proportional to the diameter of the string. (See Question 10 in the Self-Quiz.)

15-11 Overtones of a String

In developing Eq. (15-2), we considered that a single crest moved along the string, was reflected as a single trough, and that this was repeated in subsequent round trips of the pulse. The string was vibrating as a whole. There was but a single antinode, or loop, on the string. Such a situation is represented schematically in Fig. 15-7(a). But a string need not, and commonly does not, vibrate in this manner; there may be two loops of the standing wave pattern as in Fig. 15-7(b), three loops as in part (c) of the same figure, etc.

Each of these different modes of vibration has its own frequency, the lowest frequency being produced by the mode of vibration in which there is a single loop on the string, and the frequency becoming greater as the number of loops increases. The lowest frequency is the ***fundamental frequency*** as given by Eq. (15-2). This is the frequency of the ***fundamental tone,*** or simply the ***fundamental,*** of the string. All other modes of vibration produce ***overtones;*** the ***first overtone*** is produced when there are two loops, the ***second overtone*** results if the string vibrates in three loops, etc.

In developing the concept of overtones, it is simplest to consider each individually as if under any given set of circumstances only one overtone, or only the fundamental, would be produced. Actually, any string vibrates simultaneously in many different modes, producing the fundamental and many different overtones. It is the combination of overtones and fundamental which makes the note "full" and "rounded." A naked fundamental without overtones would be unacceptable to a musician.

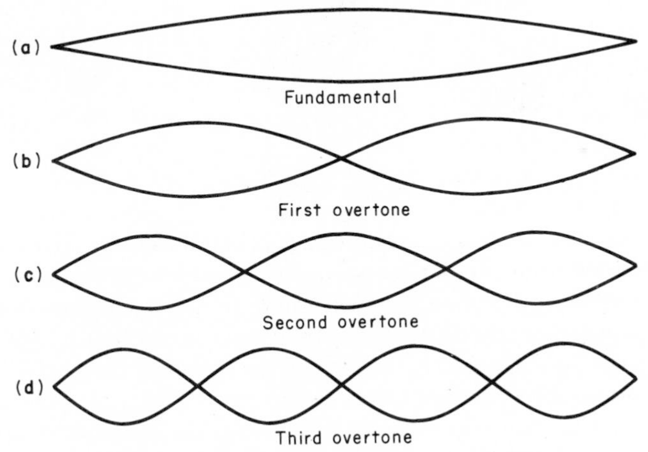

Fig. 15-7. Fundamental and overtones of a string.

15-12 Frequencies of the Overtones of a String

In Eq. (15-2), L represents the length of the string, which is also the length of one loop when the string is producing its fundamental tone. If there are two loops on the string, so that the first overtone is sounding, each loop is just half the length of the string. Suppose now that we had a string just half the length of our original string but otherwise the same, and imagine it to be sounding its fundamental. According to the first law of strings, its frequency should be exactly twice that of the longer string. Hence the first overtone of a string has a frequency twice that of the fundamental. This means that it is an octave higher than the fundamental.

Hence we may restate the first law of strings in terms of length of loop instead of length of string and thus make it applicable to the overtones of a string. (In its original form it is applicable to the fundamental frequencies of different strings.) This leads to a very simple conclusion: the frequency of any overtone is the product of the frequency of the fundamental and the number of loops on the string. Examination of Fig. 15-7 reveals that in general the number of loops is one greater than the number of the overtone (since the tone produced by a single loop is not the first overtone but rather the fundamental). Thus the frequency of the nth overtone is $(n + 1)$ times that of the fundamental. In symbols, if N_f and N_n are respectively the fundamental frequency and that of the nth overtone, and if n is the number of that overtone,

$$N_n = (n + 1) \cdot N_f \quad (15\text{-}3)$$

By applying this equation to each of a pair of overtones and finding the ratio of the resulting frequencies, we may determine the interval between any two overtones. Thus we can show that the first overtone is an octave above the fundamental, the second a perfect fifth above the first, etc. It may be that it was the presence of these musical intervals, occurring naturally between the overtones of a string, which determined the sizes of the intervals used in the just scale. One may easily find intervals between overtones which are not included in this scale, but one cannot discover any interval in the scale which does not occur between some pair of overtones.

15-13 The Frequency of an Open Pipe

One type of organ pipe has an opening or mouth near the lower end and the upper end of the pipe is open; such a pipe is called an ***open pipe.*** Another type also has the mouth, but the pipe is sealed at the upper end; this is termed a ***closed pipe*** even though it is open at the mouth. We shall consider open pipes in this section and closed pipes in the next. Although the discussion will be in terms of organ pipes, the principles are applicable to other wind instruments: a flute or a trumpet, for instance, acts as an open pipe; a clarinet acts as a closed pipe.

We have seen in Sec. 14-9 that if a train of sound waves passes into a less dense medium it will be (partially) reflected with reversal of phase, this reflection and phase reversal being due to the increased "ease" with which the disturbance travels in the less dense medium. A similar situation exists when a pulse which has been traveling within the confines of a tube or pipe reaches the open end of the pipe. Whereas so long as the pulse is in the pipe it can react only against the air ahead, when it emerges from the pipe it can also react against the air on all sides. Thus, when a pulse of compression reaches the open end of the pipe some particles will move forward as before, but also others will move sidewise. Thus a compression, on emerging from a pipe, will "overshoot" in its return to normal, and a rarefaction is generated just outside the end of the tube. This then reacts on the air within the tube, and so a rarefaction is propagated back down the pipe.

A similar effect is observed when a rarefaction emerges from the open end of the pipe. Here the "overshoot" of the adjustment toward normal results in the production of a compression just outside the end of the pipe, and this compression is then propagated back down the tube. The mouth acts as an open end also, so at both ends of the pipe sound pulses are reflected with reversal of phase.

When an organ pipe is sounding, instead of separate pulses there is a continuous train of sound waves sent up the pipe and hence a continuous train of reflected waves moving back down the pipe; and standing waves are set up.

As with the string, a fundamental tone and several overtones will be produced. By definition, the fundamental will have the lowest frequency and hence the greatest wavelength. Since at the ends compressions are reflected as rarefactions and vice versa, conventional representation of the original wave train (shown by a solid line) and the reflected train (dashed line) will result in an antinode at an open end as in Fig. 15-8. From another point of view, the air can move in and out here so there must be an antinode; at a node there would be no displacement.

To represent the longest possible wavelength and still have an antinode at both ends of the pipe, we must have only a single node in the pipe; thus Fig. 15-8(a) represents the standing wave configuration for the fundamental.

The first overtone must have a higher frequency and thus a shorter wavelength than the fundamental, but it must also have an antinode at each end. In

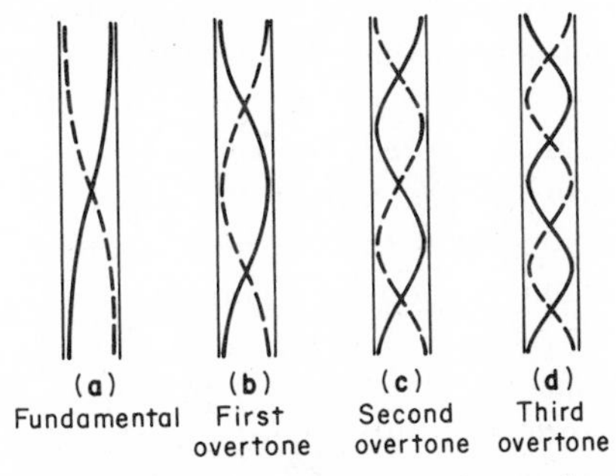

Fig. 15-8. Configuration of standing waves for the fundamental and the first three overtones of an open pipe.

addition, the wavelength must be as great as possible without duplicating that of the fundamental; otherwise it would not be the *first* overtone but a higher one. These considerations dictate a standing wave pattern with two nodes in the air column as in Fig. 15-8(b). In a similar manner, we can construct the other parts of the figure to represent some of the higher overtones.

We might think of Fig. 15-8(a) as a "snapshot" of the standing waves for the fundamental mode of vibration at a particular instant. The solid line shows a crest, which we may consider to represent a compression, just starting from the mouth (that is, from the lower end of the pipe). If we had a series of diagrams like frames of a slow motion movie film, we would see the compression moving steadily up the tube to the top. There it would be reflected as a rarefaction, and this rarefaction would migrate back down the tube. At the mouth, it would again be reflected with reversal of phase and start back up as a compression. Thus, in one round trip of the pulse, the air in the tube has been subjected to a compression and a rarefaction, and this constitutes one complete vibration of the air column. So we find that the frequency of the vibration is simply the number of round trips a sound pulse makes up the air column and back in 1 sec. Note the similarity between this situation and that of a vibrating string.

The number of round trips per second will be equal to the velocity divided by the length of a round trip; so if N is the frequency, v the speed of sound in air, and L the effective length of the tube,

$$N = \frac{v}{2L} \qquad (15\text{-}4)$$

We may arrive at this same result in another way. In Fig. 15-8(a), the curved solid line represents half a wavelength and it occupies the full length of the pipe, so a complete wavelength must be twice the effective length of the pipe: $\lambda = 2L$. But as always $v = N\lambda$ and $N = v/\lambda$; and when we put $2L$ into this last equation in place of λ the result is Eq. (15-4).

Note that the reflection of a sound pulse at the open end of a pipe actually occurs *beyond* the end of the pipe, since it is the result of the sidewise reaction of the pulse. Hence the ***effective length*** of the air column exceeds the actual length of the pipe; we must add an ***end correction*** for the top of the pipe and another for the mouth. The former is roughly 0.3 times the diameter; the latter is approximately 1.4 times the diameter, depending on the area and shape of the mouth.

As with a string, it is the rule rather than the exception that more than one frequency is produced. What we have discussed so far is the fundamental frequency of the pipe. However, only part (a) of Fig. 15-8 represents the configuration of standing waves for the fundamental; the others represent the corresponding configurations for the successive overtones. We see in Fig. 15-8(b) that for the first overtone the wavelength is identical with the effective length of the pipe; and when we combine this with the universal relationship $N = v/\lambda$ we find $N_1 = v/L$, in which N_1 symbolizes the frequency of the first overtone. Similarly, Fig. 15-8(c) shows a wave and a half to be equivalent to the length of the pipe, which leads to the eventual result that $N_2 = 3v/2L$, N_2 being the frequency of the second overtone. Continuation of this line of reasoning will yield an equation for the frequency of any particular overtone.

If we now compare the equations for the fundamental frequency and the frequencies of the first two overtones, we find that $N_1 = 2N_f$ and $N_2 = 3N_f$. This is exactly the pattern we discovered in the case of a vibrating string; so we may apply Eq. (15-3) to the overtones of an open pipe as well as to those of a string.

15-14 The Frequency of a Closed Pipe

As noted at the beginning of the preceding section, a "closed" pipe is closed only at the upper end; the mouth is open. Thus what we have learned of the reflection of a sound pulse at the mouth of a pipe applies here just as it did for the mouth of an open pipe. But the closed end of a pipe is a barrier against which the pulses impinge. A compression "piles up" against it momentarily and then expands back along the air column, still as a compression; and a similar process reverses the direction of travel of a rarefaction but leaves it a rarefaction. There is no phase change when reflection takes place at the closed end.

The air in the pipe can surge out of the mouth and back in, just as with the open pipe, so there must be an antinode at the mouth. But at the closed end the air "has no place to go," so this surging is impossible; there must be a node at the closed end.

Thus, the effective length of a closed pipe is equal to the physical length plus approximately 1.4 times the diameter.

In view of these facts, and remembering also that for the fundamental tone the frequency must be as low, and hence the wavelength as long, as possible, we are able to construct Fig. 15-9(a) to represent the standing waves in a closed pipe sounding its fundamental pitch.

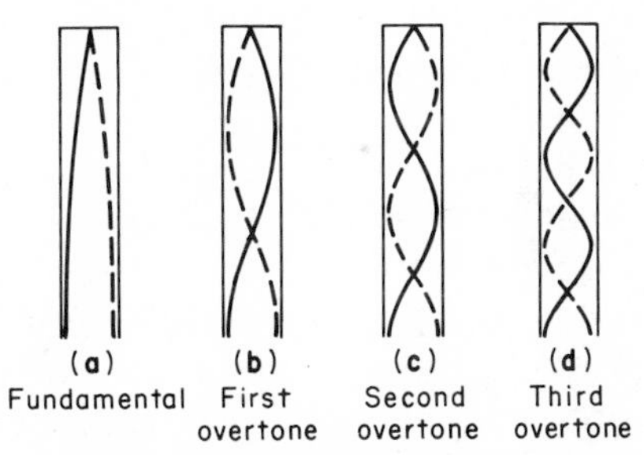

Fig. 15-9. Configuration of standing waves for the fundamental and the first three overtones of a closed pipe.

The curved solid line does not extend from crest to trough as it did in Fig. 15-8(a); here it represents only a fourth of a wave instead of a half. Hence the wavelength is four times the effective length of the pipe: $\lambda = 4L$. Again combining this result with the general relationship $N = v/\lambda$, we have

$$N_f = \frac{v}{4L} \tag{15-5}$$

Figure 15-9(b) is constructed much as the (a) part of the figure was. There must be a node at the closed end and an antinode at the mouth. Also, for the first overtone, the wavelength must be as long as possible without duplicating the wave configuration in Fig. 15-9(a). This requires one node in the body of the pipe.

Following the solid line up from the mouth to the closed end we see that there is three-fourths of a wave in the pipe, so the wavelength is four-thirds of the effective length of the pipe. Again combining this result with the equation $N = v/\lambda$ we have for the first overtone $N_1 = 3v/4L$. Continuation of the same process yields the wave configurations for the other overtones, and the equations

$$N_2 = \frac{5v}{4L}, \qquad N_3 = \frac{7v}{4L}, \qquad \text{etc.}$$

Evidently we have a different pattern of overtones than we had for the string and the open pipe. For those, every overtone had a frequency which was an integral multiple of the fundamental frequency, and for every integral multiple of the frequency of the fundamental there was an overtone. All this was summarized in Eq. (15-3), $N_n = (n + 1) \cdot N_f$. But for a closed pipe, all of the frequencies which are even multiples of the fundamental frequency are absent; only odd multiples are present. If we wish to generalize this situation, Eq. (15-3) won't do, since it will give us the even multiples as well as the odd; instead we must use

$$N_n = (2n + 1) \cdot N_f \tag{15-6}$$

to describe the frequencies of the overtones of a closed pipe.

We shall see shortly that this difference in the overtone structure of notes from these different sources results in a different quality of the musical notes.

Before leaving the topic of closed pipes, we should note that, as a comparison of Eq. (15-4) and Eq. (15-5) reveals, if an open pipe and a closed pipe have the same effective length the frequency of the former will be exactly twice that of the latter. Thus the open pipe would have a pitch exactly an octave above that of the closed pipe. Because of this difference, in nearly all pipe organs the deep tones are produced by closed pipes; often there just isn't room to use an open pipe long enough to give these very low notes.

15-15 The Reinforcement of Sound

For a musical sound to be of satisfactory loudness, sound waves of adequate amplitude must be generated in the air. But although a vibrating string on a piano or a violin will produce the desired frequencies, such strings present a very small area to the air as they vibrate; so in themselves they are quite incapable of setting up a sufficiently strong disturbance. Similarly, a trumpet player's unaided lips could produce the desired pitch but hardly the desired fortissimo for a fanfare. The actual source of the sound must be aided by some reinforcing agency.

In the case of the trumpet player, the vibrations of the lips are not presented directly to the open air, but instead they are impressed on the end of the air column contained within the trumpet. This air column acts like that in an open organ pipe, so it has a definite frequency—or, rather, a whole gamut of frequencies as described by Eq. (15-4), (15-3). The trumpeter further increases the available frequencies by using the valves of his trumpet to lengthen or shorten the length of the air column. Thus he is able to make one of the ***natural frequencies*** of the air column coincide with the frequency of his vibrating lips. Hence when his lips produce a compression, it travels along the air column and is reflected at the open end (the bell) as a rarefaction. This rarefaction travels back toward the mouthpiece and there it is again reflected, this time as a compression. Since the musician has adjusted the natural frequency of the air column to agree with the frequency of his lips, his lips generate a new compression at the precise moment when a compression produced an instant earlier is starting a second round trip through the air column in the trumpet. Thus the two reinforce each other, producing a strengthened compression. This continues, the energy of the pulses building up as new pulses are added to the reflections of earlier ones. This sort of build-up, and the resulting reinforcement of the original sound, are both called ***sympathetic vibration*** or ***resonance.*** It occurs whenever a ***source***—in this instance the player's lips—and the ***reinforcing agency***—here the air column of the trumpet—have the same *natural* frequency.

The situation is rather different with the piano or the violin. Again we have a source—the string—and a reinforcing agency—the body of the violin or the sound board of the piano. But if you plunk either of these reinforcing agencies with your finger you don't hear a musical tone; they do not have a natural frequency within the audible range, as did the air column in our trumpet. Instead of vibrating freely and naturally in sympathy with the strings, they are shaken mechanically by the vibrating strings and thus *forced* to vibrate at the frequency (actually frequencies) of the string. Therefore this type of reinforcement is known as ***forced vibration.***

Note carefully the restricted significance of the term "resonance." It is synonymous with sympathetic vibration; its meaning does *not* include forced vibration.

15-16 The Quality of a Musical Sound

When listening to an orchestra, you need not see the instruments to know when, for example, a theme which was being played by a saxophone is taken over by a violin. Even if the two instruments produce tones of identical pitch and loudness, one instrument "sounds" different from the other. This would be true even if there were no difference such as that between the sustained tone of a flute and the initially loud but rapidly dying note of a piano. Characteristics of a musical sound, other than those in the preceding sentence, which enable us to perceive a difference between instruments are summed up in the term ***quality.*** The expressions ***timbre*** and ***tone color*** are also used.

Roughly a century ago, Helmholtz stated that the quality of a musical note depends on what overtones are present with the fundamental, on their relative frequencies and their relative intensities. Only a ***pure tone*** consists of a naked fundamental, and such a tone is quite unacceptable in music. (Note that what a physicist calls a "pure" tone is very different from what the same expression means to a musician.)

A pure tone is produced by a simple harmonic vibration, and the resulting sound waves are sinusoidal in form. Any good musical tone is the result of a complex vibration, so the shape of the sound waves is also complex. The mathematician Fourier showed that (with a few exceptions never encountered in the sound waves of musical tones) any waveform, no matter how complex, may be resolved into a series of sinusoidal waves whose frequencies are integral multiples of the frequency with which the wave repeats itself. This is equivalent, though it sounds rather different, to Helmholtz' statement of the basis of sound quality. An example of a fairly complex wave and the sinusoidal components which comprise it appears in Fig. 15-10. We met a less complex example in Fig. 13-8.

It is now known that there is a quite different factor of tone quality which was undiscovered by investigators until a few decades ago. This is the presence of what is termed a ***formant.*** This is a broad and continuous band of frequencies characteristic of a particular instrument. Whereas the overtones are discrete frequencies, are limited in number, and vary in pitch as the tone sounded by the instrument is changed, the formant has essentially all the frequencies in a fairly wide band and these frequencies do *not* change as the pitch of the musical note is changed. One class of instruments, such as the violin family, has a different formant than that of a different class, such as the woodwinds. Within one such class, different members have somewhat different formants but these formants resemble each other more than they resemble the formant of another family of instruments; for example, the formant of a violin and that of a cello will differ yet bear a strong family resemblance. Finally, there are still more minor differences between the formants of different examples of the same instrument; a Stradivarius violin will not have the same formant as that of a mail order violin, but the two formants will resemble each other more closely than either resembles the formant of a cello.

Since the discovery of the formant and its contribution to tone quality

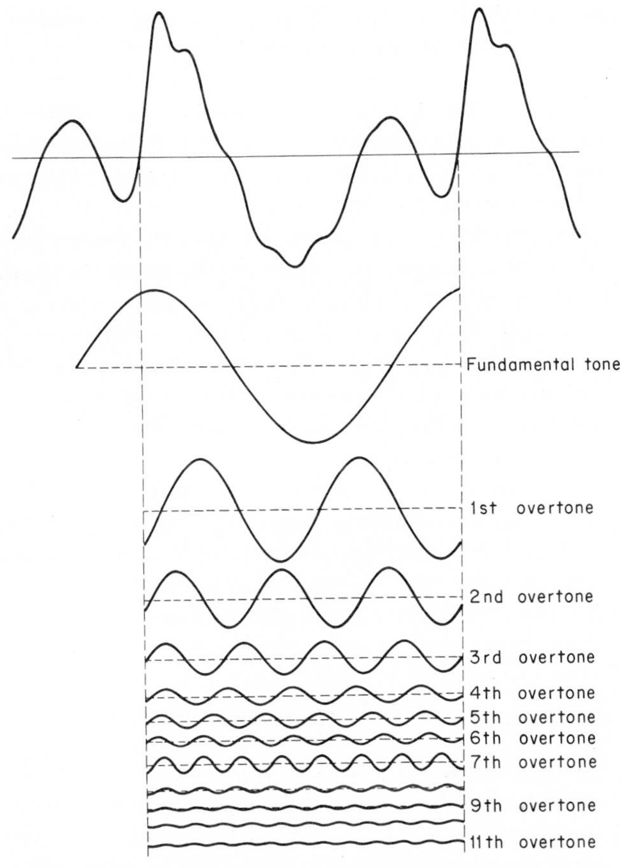

Fig. 15-10. The curve at the top of the diagram is the wave form of an open organ pipe. Below this complex wave are the sinusoidal waves of the various components which comprise the tone of the organ pipe. Note that, in general, these components differ in amplitude and in phase. Note also that the wavelength of the fundamental is twice that of the first overtone, three times that of the second overtone, etc. (This figure is a modification of a diagram first published by D. C. Miller in *Science of Musical Sounds,* MacMillan.)

is relatively recent, it is evident that its effect is less obvious than the contributions of the overtones.

15-17 Combination Tones

We have seen in Sec. 14-13 that beats may occur between two sounds which have slightly different frequencies and that the frequency of the beats is the difference between the two parent frequencies. In the latter part of that section, we found that if the beat frequency is above the minimum audible frequency the beats are not apparent as such, but that instead one hears a tone of definite pitch, the pitch corresponding to the beat frequency.

Since the frequency of such a tone is the difference between the two original frequencies, a tone of this kind is called a ***difference tone.**** If two frequencies are sounded simultaneously, and strongly, one can often hear a tone which has a frequency equal to the sum, rather than the difference, of the parent frequencies; such tones are known as ***summation tones.*** Even if but a single frequency is sounded, with no overtones, overtones may be heard because of the addition of the original frequency to itself. It may also add to its own summation tones, giving frequencies twice that of the tone actually sounded, or three times, or other integral multiples of the parent frequency. Since summation tones of this special sort have the same pattern of relative frequencies as do the overtones of a string or open pipe, they are called ***aural harmonics.***

Difference tones and summation tones (including aural harmonics) together are known as ***combination tones.*** Of these, only difference tones are physically present as sound waves of appropriate frequency. The others are called ***subjective tones*** since they have no physical existence. The ear creates these subjective tones†; this is the basis of the term *aural* harmonics. (The Latin word for ear is auris.)

15-18 Practical Significance of Combination Tones

Were it not for difference tones, Edison probably would have been disgusted with his phonograph and would have given up. The same is true of the radio and even of the telephone. Why?

In their earlier forms, these devices could not produce the low

---

* If you are a violinist you probably know these as Tartini tones.

† The production of these subjective tones results from the fact that the ear does not respond in either a linear or a symmetrical manner to variations of pressure at the ear drum. Thus, if a pure sinusoidal wave impinges on the ear drum the stimulus presented to the auditory nerve is *not* sinusoidal.

frequency notes. Even today, relatively inexpensive radios, phonographs, and TV sets do not sound the lower bass tones. A standard telephone may reproduce frequencies around 250 vps poorly (this is about middle C on a piano keyboard) and it may generate no sounds at all below about 200 vps (roughly, G below middle C). Yet we usually hear a man's deep bass voice at its true pitch, over a telephone; and this "true pitch" may correspond to a frequency below 200 vps. But in general the voice will have overtones, and if the frequency of the fundamental (which determines the pitch of the voice) is N, these overtones will have frequencies of $2N$, $3N$, $4N$, etc. Hence though the frequency N may not be transmitted at all, the frequencies $2N$, $3N$, $4N$, etc., will be; and any two successive overtones (such as $3N$ and $4N$, for example) will produce a difference tone whose frequency is N. Thus, even when the fundamental pitch is not transmitted at all, we can still hear it, because of these difference tones.

Many radios and phonographs cannot reproduce the bass notes properly, but difference tones are generated just as with the telephone, enabling us to hear these low notes. It should be obvious, however, that the intensity of notes due to difference tones is less than it would be if the tones were actually reproduced by the phonograph or radio. This lack of intensity of the lower pitches is the primary cause of the "tinny" sound of many such instruments.

Summary

The size of a *musical interval* is determined by the *ratio,* rather than the *difference,* of the frequencies of the two tones which comprise the interval. This being the case, intervals are added by multiplying their frequency ratios; to subtract intervals, the frequency ratio of the larger interval is divided by that of the smaller interval.

The *natural,* or *just, scale* is made up of two slightly different sizes of "whole" tones and a "half" tone which actually is larger than half of a "whole" tone. Because of this an instrument such as a piano can be played only in a single key (signature) if it is tuned to the just scale. Hence the scale is tempered. In the equally tempered scale, two half tones make one whole tone, exactly, and all whole tones are equal.

When a wave train and its reflection travel over, or through, the same medium they *interfere* in such a way that they produce *standing waves.* These standing waves consist of nodes alternating with loops or antinodes.

Reflection of a transverse wave on a string occurs at the fixed end of a string with *reversal of phase.* Reversal of phase also occurs when a sound pulse is reflected at the open end of a tube, but reflection at the closed end of a tube occurs with no reversal of phase.

The frequency of the *fundamental* of a string is most easily determined by studying the travel of transverse waves along the string; this leads to the equation

$$N = \frac{\sqrt{T/\rho_l}}{2L}$$

From this equation the laws of strings may be derived.

A string or an air column does not vibrate at a single frequency; there are several modes of vibration occurring simultaneously, and these produce the fundamental pitch and the various overtones. For strings and air columns, *overtones* have frequencies which are *integral multiples* of the *fundamental* frequency; all such multiples may be present in the case of a string or an open pipe but only the odd multiples are present in the overtone series of a closed pipe.

In general, a *source of sound* in a musical instrument requires a *reinforcing agent* of some kind. Reinforcement may be by *resonance*, in which the reinforcing agency has the same natural period as the source; or it may be by *forced vibration*, in which the reinforcing agency is forced to vibrate at the frequency of the source, this frequency not being a natural frequency of the reinforcing agent. Resonance is also called sympathetic vibration.

The *tone quality* of a musical sound is determined primarily by the *pattern of overtones* which accompanies the fundamental, and by the *relative intensities* of all the partials. Another factor is the *formant*.

We may hear tones which are not produced by the source to which we are listening; these are combination tones. Difference tones, like beats, have frequencies which are the difference between two of the frequencies produced by the source; they are physically present. A difference tone may enable us to hear a low pitch over a telephone, radio, or other acoustic instrument even though the instrument fails to reproduce that pitch. Subjective tones have no physical existence in the sound waves which reach the ear. Their frequencies are the sum of frequencies which are physically present.

Self-Quiz

1. Is a particular musical interval characterized by the difference, or by the ratio, of the frequencies of the tones which comprise the interval? Check by considering the examples of a major third between do and mi, fa and la, and sol and ti. Take the frequencies from Table 15-1 or Fig. 15-1.

2. What is the mathematical method of adding two musical intervals? *Why* does this method "work"? How are intervals subtracted, and why is this the correct method?

3. Could a pipe organ be used for music in any key (signature) if it were tuned to the just scale? Could a trombone? Explain, in each case.

4. What is meant by the expression, "tempering" the scale? Would "tampering" be a suitable word? Why?

5. What is the value of a half tone on the equally tempered scale? Exactly why is this particular value chosen? And why don't we call it a ratio, as we did for intervals on the just scale, instead of a value?

6. What are standing waves, and under what conditions are they produced? Do they occur only with transverse waves, only with longitudinal waves, or may they occur with either type? What other name is applied to them?

7. What condition, or conditions, exist at a node on a string? At an antinode?

8. By considering the propagation of transverse waves back and forth along a string, work out an equation for the period of a string which is vibrating at its fundamental frequency. Compare this with Eq. (15-2) and show that the two equations are consistent.

9. State the three laws of strings and illustrate each with a simple numerical example.

10. Remembering that density is mass per unit volume and that unit length of a string would be a small cylinder, show that for two strings of the same material—that is, the same density—the frequencies are inversely proportional to the diameters. (This relationship is a special case of the third law of strings.)

11. Discuss in some detail the propagation of a sound pulse in an open pipe, its reflection at the ends of the pipe, and the production of standing waves. Is there a node, or an antinode, at the end of the pipe? Why?

12. Discuss what happens in the air column in a closed pipe much as you did for an open pipe in the preceding question. Add any details which are applicable to the closed pipe but not to the open pipe.

13. Compare the overtone series of a closed pipe with that of an open pipe, and explain.

14. Why is an end correction necessary? Is the end correction for an open pipe the same as that for a closed pipe? Why?

15. Why is reinforcement necessary in musical instruments? What are the two kinds of reinforcement? In what respects are the two types alike? In what respects do they differ?

16. Compare the significance in physics of the term "resonance" with its nontechnical meaning.

17. Discuss in detail the basis of tone quality. How does your discussion differ from what one of your parents might have given when a student?

18. What are combination tones? Why are they so called? What kinds of combination tones are there, and how are they related to the frequencies in the sound waves?

19. In what way is the complex waveform of the sound from, say, a violin related to sinusoidal waves of the sort we met in Sec. 13-9?

20. Discuss in some detail the mystery of the missing but nevertheless audible low tones one may hear over a telephone, phonograph, etc.

21. In general, the overtones of bars, bells, etc., do not have frequencies which are integral multiples of the fundamental frequency. Show that this underlies the fact that one usually hears only a melody (a single note at a time) rather than harmony (two or more notes sounded simultaneously) on a carillon.

22. A train whistle heard at a great distance is heard in its true pitch, but under similar circumstances the pitch of a church bell is much higher than it is if one is relatively close to the bell. Why the difference in the effect of distance on the bell and the whistle? Explain in some detail.

Problems

1. Musical instruments are tuned on the basis of A = 440 vps rather than on the physical scale recorded in Fig. 15-1. With the aid of pertinent data from Fig. 15-2 compute the frequency of middle C.

2. If the frequency of the E above middle C is 330 vps, compute the frequency of the E an octave higher.

3. What is the interval between two tones if their frequencies are 495 vps and 660 vps?

4. Add a perfect fourth and a perfect fifth (see Table 15-1 for data) and identify the resulting interval.

5. A perfect fifth on the equally tempered scale is the sum of seven half tones. Compute the value of an equally tempered perfect fifth. (This problem is beyond your power if you do not know how to use logarithms.)

6. A string is 50.0 cm long and is under a tension of exactly 2 kg. The string has a linear density of 0.00125 g/cm. (a) Compute the frequency of the fundamental of the string. (b) Compute the frequencies of the first three overtones.

7. Two strings are identical except for the tension; on one the tension is 3.00 lb and on the other it is 6.75 lb. If the frequency of the higher-pitched wire is 495 vps, what is the frequency of the other?

8. Two strings have frequencies of 132 vps and 396 vps, and they are identical except for their linear densities. If the higher-pitched string has a linear density of $1.50 \cdot 10^{-3}$ g/cm, calculate the linear density of the other string.

9. The A string of a violin has a frequency of 440 vps. If a violinist shortens the string by one-fifth, by fingering it, what will its frequency be?

10. If the fundamental of a string has a frequency of 220 vps, what are the frequencies of the fifth and seventh overtones?

11. (a) What is the effective length of a closed pipe which has a frequency of 55.0 vps? Assume the speed of sound to be 1130 ft/sec. (b) What is the effective length of an open pipe of the same frequency?

12. (a) Calculate the frequency of an open pipe which has an effective length of 2.14 ft, if the speed of sound is 1130 ft/sec. (b) Compute the frequencies of the first three overtones.

13. If the effective length of a closed pipe is 2.88 ft and if the speed of sound is 1140 ft/sec, compute (a) the frequency of the fundamental and (b) the frequencies of the first three overtones.

14. If the frequencies of two tones are 264 vps and 396 vps, compute the frequency of (a) a summation tone, (b) a difference tone, and (c) four different aural harmonics.

The following problems are intended for musicians only.

15. If a violin string is 32.0 cm long, how far from the nut should the string be fingered to produce a tone a minor third above the open tone of the string?

16. By computation, rather than from your musical knowledge, determine the interval between (a) the second and fourth overtones, (b) the third and fifth overtones, (c) the ninth and eleventh overtones of a string.

17. Between what two overtones of a string may (a) a major third, (b) a minor sixth, and (c) a half tone be found?

18. The strings of a violin are said to be tuned a perfect fifth apart. The E string is also supposed to be one 8va + *M*6 above the G string. Check by adding three *P*5's, then adding 8va + *M*6, and compare. The cause of the discrepancy may be found by referring to Fig. 15-1 and finding the frequency ratio of the interval between D and A.

19. Assume that an open pipe and a closed pipe have the same effective length. In each of the following cases, determine the interval between the tones of the two pipes, and state which is higher: (a) the fundamentals, (b) the first overtones, (c) the second overtones, (d) the fourth overtones, and (e) the seventh overtones.

16
TEMPERATURE AND HEAT

16-1 Preview

We shall begin with the concept of temperature and temperature scales and find how to convert a temperature from one scale to another. It will develop that all scales of temperature are arbitrary. We shall meet the concept of heat as a form of energy. The interrelationship of heat, temperature, and other pertinent quantities will be investigated. The concept of an absolute zero of temperature will appear, and it will provide the basis for a relationship between the temperature of a gas and its pressure.

16-2 Temperature and Temperature Difference

Both the concept of temperature and that of temperature difference are familiar, but we have found that this sort of familiarity may be a pitfall. For example, you can pick a hot biscuit out of the pan as soon as it is out of the oven without much discomfort—far less than you will experience if you pick up the metal pan! Although the temperatures are the same, the metal pan *seems* much hotter.

Thus our senses are unreliable and we must turn to a more reliable criterion for defining relative temperatures. We base our concept on a hypothetical experiment in which two bodies, A and B, are brought into contact. If there is no flow of heat energy between the bodies, their temperatures are the same. If heat flows from A to B, the two temperatures are unequal and that of A is the higher, or if there is a heat flow in the other direction, A is at a lower temperature than B.

When we come to a quantitative evaluation of a temperature difference, we find it to depend on our choice of a temperature scale, since different temperature scales employ different sizes of degrees. This is similar to the obvious situation that the height difference, in feet, between two floors of a building has a different numerical value than it does in meters.

The "actual" height of either of the two floors could be measured from the ground level, or it could be referred to some other basis, such as sea level; but if the heights of the floors are referred to the *same* reference level, the *difference* between the two heights will necessarily be the same as would be obtained by measuring directly from one floor up to the other. Similarly, any specification of a temperature—not a temperature *difference*, but a *temperature*—necessarily involves some basis of reference. This basis of reference may be quite arbitrary, like the ground level around the building, or it may be more fundamental, like sea level, in the example of the building. But whatever basis is chosen, any *difference* of temperature is independent of that choice, just as the choice of a reference level for measuring the height of each floor has no effect on the *difference* in height.

The units in which temperatures and temperature differences are measured are ***degrees;*** like units of length or mass, they come in different sizes, depending on the choice of the ***scale*** of temperature. The "basis of reference" is the ***zero*** of the temperature scale. Thus 70° on the Fahrenheit scale (conveniently recorded as 70°F) is a temperature 70 Fahrenheit degrees above the zero of the Fahrenheit scale, and 85°F is a temperature 85 Fahrenheit degrees above that zero. The difference between these two temperatures is 15 Fahrenheit degrees.

There is a unique relationship between a specific temperature and 70°F, and similarly only one temperature can be expressed as 85°F. On the other hand the *difference* of 15 Fahrenheit degrees might be between 70°F and 85°F, or between 721°F and 736°F, or −11°F and +4°F, etc.—just as a difference of 15 ft in height might occur between the second and third or nineteenth and twentieth floors of a building, or between two levels in a deep mine.

Since we are familiar with heights and differences of height, the use of the same unit (such as feet) to express both doesn't cause any confusion; clues are provided by the context which enable us to interpret (for example) 20 ft as a height or as a *difference* of height. Similar clues enable one to distinguish between a temperature and a temperature difference. To most of us this is a less familiar situation, however, and students are prone to overlook the clues.

To minimize the chance of error from misinterpretation, many authors use different terms and symbols for temperature than they do for temperature differences. You will note that in introducing scales and degrees of temperature the expression "degrees Fahrenheit" was used for a specific temperature, and "Fahrenheit degrees" for a *difference* of temperature. Similarly, a *temperature* of 70° on the Fahrenheit scale will be presented as 70°F; but if between some two temperatures there is a difference of 70 Fahrenheit degrees, this *difference* will be recorded as 70F°. This same convention will be applied to other scales of temperature. I feel that this is very helpful, so I shall make this distinction consistently. Many authors and lecturers prefer to leave such distinctions to the context, however, as is generally done for heights and differences of height.

16-3 The Fahrenheit and Celsius Scales of Temperature

We are all so familiar with the Fahrenheit scale of temperature that some knowledge of it was assumed in the discussion above. It is the basis of weather reports of temperature, recipes for cooking, fever thermometers and most other thermometers met outside a laboratory, etc. Most laboratory and scientific work is done on the basis of what is commonly known as the "centigrade scale." The latter was renamed the Celsius scale fairly recently.

Either of these scales is entirely arbitrary, both in the size of the degree and in the choice of the zero temperature.

Any scale of temperature is based on two ***fixed points*** based on the thermal properties of some substance. Each fixed point is assigned a numerical value of temperature, and the temperature interval between them is divided up into a number of equal degrees. For both the Fahrenheit scale and the Celsius scale, the fixed points are the temperature at which pure water freezes (or ice melts) and that at which pure water boils (or steam condenses), normal atmospheric pressure being specified in both cases.*

* Many students feel that water must freeze at a temperature *lower* than that at which ice melts and that there is a similar disparity of temperature between boiling water and condensing steam; but this impression is incorrect for reasons we shall meet in Chap. 18.

The ***Fahrenheit*** scale of temperature assigns a value of 32 to the temperature at which water freezes, and a temperature of 212 to boiling water. Thus there are 180 degrees between these two fixed points. On the ***Celsius*** scale these same fixed points have values of 0 and 100, respectively. Hence there are 100 degrees between the fixed points, and this is the obvious basis of the older name ***Centigrade*** (hundred graduations).* Figure 16-1 is a representation of both scales. We shall meet other scales of temperature in Sec. 16-10.

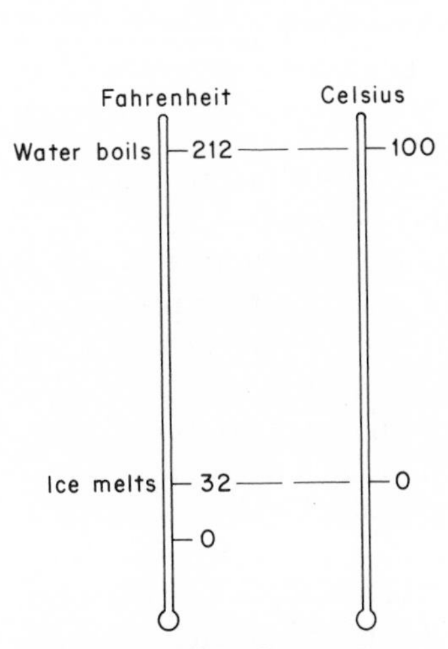

Fig. 16-1. Fahrenheit and Celsius scales of temperature.

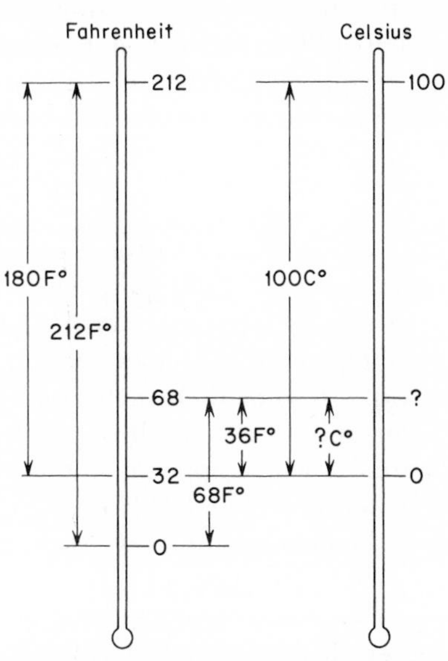

Fig. 16-2. Conversion of a temperature of 68° on the Fahrenheit scale to the equivalent temperature on the Celsius scale.

16-4 Conversion of a Temperature from One Scale to the Other

Suppose that a Fahrenheit thermometer gives a reading of 68° and that it is necessary to know the temperature in terms of the Celsius scale. The almost standard procedure is to plug data into a blindly memorized formula, turn the crank, and record the result without considering whether it is sensible or not. A formula is the most *convenient* means of making a conversion, if you have many to make, but it is *never* a *necessary* means. The information in Fig. 16-1 provides all that is necessary.

For example, by "68°F" is meant a temperature 68F° above 0°F, as shown in Fig. 16-2. But this is only (68 − 32) or 36F° above the freezing point of water. Between the freezing and boiling points of water there are

* Though Celsius is the officially correct designation for this scale, your instructor may—or may not—prefer to have you aid your memory and understanding of it by thinking of it as centigrade instead.

180F° but only 100C°; thus there are 5C° for every 9F°. Therefore, a range of 36F° would be 5/9 of 36 or 20C°. So we now know that the temperature is 20C° above the freezing point of water; and since on this scale the freezing point is 0°C, the temperature is 20°C.

Similarly, 95°C is 95C° above 0°C, and hence 95C° above the freezing point of water. This would be 9/5 of 95 or 171F° above the freezing point, which is at 32°F. So the temperature is (171 + 32) or 203°F.

If you review these examples, thinking of C as the Celsius temperature and F as the Fahrenheit temperature in place of the numerical values used, you will find that they can be generalized to the following expressions:

$$C = \tfrac{5}{9}(F - 32) \tag{16-1}$$

and

$$F = \tfrac{9}{5}C + 32 \tag{16-2}$$

But you should *not* let these equations blind you to the fact that *any* conversion can be made quite easily *without* either equation.

Students often make errors when converting a temperature by one of these equations, the commonest one being the omission of the parentheses in Eq. (16-1) or their inclusion in Eq. (16-2). Such errors, however, can occur only as the result of carelessness or deep mental anesthesia. The figure 32, which appears on the right side in both equations, is in *Fahrenheit* degrees. The left side of Eq. (16-1) is in Celsius degrees, so the 32 must be changed to the Celsius scale by being multiplied by $\tfrac{5}{9}$; and inclusion within the parentheses assures this. In Eq. (16-2) the left side of the equation is in Fahrenheit degrees. Since the 32 already is in Fahrenheit degrees it must be left undisturbed; the $\tfrac{9}{5}$ factor must operate *only* on C.

16-5 The Nature of Heat

One sometimes hears a statement such as "There's more heat in a cup of coffee than in a tub of cold water," but this is an entirely erroneous use of the term "heat." The *temperature* of the coffee is higher, but because of its relatively small mass, it contains much *less* heat than does the cold water. For example, 10 gal of water at 40°F could melt about 4 lb of ice whereas a large cupful of water at the boiling point could melt only about half a pound.

Before continuing, we should make the acquaintance of two adjectives used to indicate the relative scale of size, either of particles or processes. The ***macroscopic*** domain includes everything of "ordinary" size, with no upper limit. It also includes things or processes which are very small by ordinary standards; it may even include particles of a size visible only through a microscope. The molecular, atomic, and subatomic world is referred to as ***microscopic;*** this is an order of magnitude often termed *sub*microscopic.

A brief glimpse of the internal structure of matter was afforded us in Sec. 10-3, 10-4. Whether a substance is a gas, a liquid, or a solid, the particles of which it is composed are in restless motion. This motion is, in general, random. For example, while a car is parked, the air in its tires has no directly observable translational motion. Nevertheless, the individual molecules are moving, and in their motions are found all possible directions and a wide range of speeds. But these motions are completely disorganized except in two respects: they are confined within a definite space, and the vector sum of the velocities of all the individual molecules is zero. When the car is in motion, the vector sum of the molecular velocities within the tire must be identical with the velocity of the car, and this organized translational motion is superimposed on the continuing random motion of the molecules. In considering the topic of heat, we are concerned only with the random microscopic translational motion of particles of matter; any organized motion of the particles—that is, any macroscopic motion of the mass as a whole—is irrelevant.*

In a non-metallic solid, the microscopic motions of the particles are almost entirely vibrational, and in a monatomic gas, they are essentially limited to translation. In substances of other kinds, either or both of these kinds of motion may be present, and there may also be internal vibrational or rotational motion of the individual molecules. Whatever the type of the microscopic random motion of the particles, the summation of all their energies constitutes the ***internal energy,*** or the ***thermal energy,*** of the substance comprised by the particles.

For a given mass of a specific substance, the quantity of internal energy determines the temperature, and vice versa. Thus, if the temperature of the substance rises, it does so because of an increase in the thermal energy, and any decrease in the internal energy causes the temperature to fall.†

In a non-technical sense, we assign the term "heat" to the internal energy of a body, but the technical significance of the term is somewhat different and more restricted. As a background for a definition of heat, recall from our study of mechanics the two terms "energy" and "work." They represent essentially the same concept, the quantity of energy is evaluated on the basis of the quantity of work, and the same units are used to express work and energy quantitatively; yet the two terms are by no means synonymous. Energy is possessed by a body, but work is not; work is done only when, during some interaction between two (or more) bodies, energy is transferred from one body to another. In a similar manner, a

---

* Note that this irrelevancy of any macroscopic motion follows from the fact that all such motion is relative (Sec. 3-11, 5-4).

† It is assumed here that there is no change of state (melting, evaporation, or their opposites). Thermal effects involved in change of state will be considered in Chapter 18.

body possesses internal energy or thermal energy, rather than heat; but the term ***heat*** is applied to this thermal energy while it is being transferred from one body to another, or from one part of a body to another part of the same body. It must be admitted, however, that few authors and lecturers confine their use of the word to this limited technical significance. For example, in the opening paragraph of this section "heat" appears where "internal energy" would have been technically preferable—but only technically!

Heat may exist as thermal energy both before and after transfer, simply flowing from a warmer body to a cooler one. However, the energy may exist initially as microscopic internal energy and after transfer it may be in the form of macroscopic mechanical energy, and the reverse may also occur. The conversion of the thermal energy of exploding gasoline to mechanical motion of an automobile is one of many familiar examples of the former process. We have ample evidence of the latter process also: primitive peoples and Boy Scouts start fire by friction, a basketball player may get a "floor burn" (literally) as he slides along the floor, a firmly embedded nail is hot immediately after being pulled, etc.

Since the phenomena in which mechanical energy is converted into thermal energy are so common, it is remarkable that until late in the eighteenth century the accepted concept of heat was of a weightless fluid called "caloric," which was present in greater amount in a hot body than in a cold one.* In the closing years of that century, Count Rumford reported the observation that when a dull tool was used for boring cannon much heat appeared, even though both the tool and the cannon blank were originally cold. The concept of heat as a weightless fluid eventually was abandoned, though its name remains with us in such terms as calorie, calorimeter, etc.

We shall consider the interconversion of heat and mechanical energy further in Sec. 16-12.

16-6 Units of Heat Measurement

There are three different units of heat quantity, but there is an unfortunate and confusing inconsistency in the use of one of them.

One ***calorie*** (cal) is the quantity of heat energy necessary to raise by 1 Celsius degree the temperature of 1 g of water. Unfortunately, to warm a gram of water from 10°C to 11°C (for example) does not require exactly the same quantity of heat as does a 1 degree rise starting from a different temperature, though the maximum difference is less than 1%. For precise work, the ***15° calorie*** is used, which is the quantity of heat energy required

* At that time the steam engine was in its infancy and the gasoline engine had not been invented, so conversions of thermal energy to mechanical energy were far less familiar than they are now.

to heat 1 g of water from 14.5°C to 15.5°C (both temperatures being exact).

One ***kilogram calorie,*** or ***kilocalorie*** is defined as the calorie is, with the exception that the mass of water is 1 kg instead of 1 g. Thus 1 kilocalorie = 1000 calories. A kilocalorie is also called a ***large calorie.***

One ***British thermal unit*** (Btu) is that quantity of heat required to raise by 1 Fahrenheit degree the temperature of 1 lb of water or, more precisely, to heat 1 lb of water from 58.5°F to 59.5°F. By comparing the sizes of the pound and the gram, and the Fahrenheit and Celsius degrees, you can show that 1 Btu = 252 cal.

If, however, a woman goes on a 1200 or 1500 calorie diet to lose weight, and if she uses our definition of a calorie, she most certainly would lose weight! If she tried to keep on the diet, she'd die of starvation. A physiologist or dietician or doctor applies the term *calorie* to what more commonly is defined as a *kilogram calorie.* It is important that we be aware of this unfortunate discrepancy in terminology.

16-7 Specific Heat and Thermal Capacity

If you take equal masses of various substances and deliver the same quantity of heat to each, in general they will experience *un*equal temperature rises; or if each is heated through the same temperature interval, a different quantity of heat may be required in each case. It is because of this characteristic that the definitions of heat quantities in the preceding section specified water (though any other one substance could have been used instead of water, when the units were *first* defined). Thus, in general we must know not only the mass of a body and its temperature rise to determine the quantity of heat; there must also be a factor characteristic of the substance. This factor is called the ***specific heat*** of the substance, and is defined as the quantity of heat required to raise the temperature of unit mass of the substance 1 degree. Values for the specific heats of a number of substances appear in Table 16-1. Thus the specific heat of aluminum at 20°C is 0.214 cal per g per C°, which means that 0.214 calories of heat will raise the temperature of 1 g of aluminum one Celsius degree (if the

Table 16-1

SPECIFIC HEATS OF A FEW SUBSTANCES

$\left(\text{Values are in } \frac{\text{calories}}{\text{gram Celsius degree}}{}^{*}\right)$

Aluminum	Brass	Copper	Lead	Mercury	Silver	Steel	Wood
0.214	0.0917	0.0921	0.0306	0.0335	0.0558	0.107	0.42

* These values are for 20°C, but may be used as good *approximations* over a range of several hundred degrees.

temperature is near 20°C). Here again, the value varies somewhat at different temperatures, so reference books give specific heats at a number of different temperatures.

It should be obvious that the specific heat of water is 1 cal per g per C° and also 1 Btu per lb per F°.

Unfortunately, terminology is not entirely consistent. Some authors define specific heat somewhat differently than was done above. Often the term "heat capacity" or "thermal capacity" is used instead of, or as a synonym for, specific heat. In this book, however, "thermal capacity" will be used in a different sense. And to reduce confusion, the term heat capacity will be avoided.

Instead of considering the heat necessary to warm unit mass of a body 1 degree—the specific heat—it often is more convenient to use the ***thermal capacity*** of the body, which is the quantity of heat energy required to increase the temperature of the entire body by 1 degree. If both the mass of a body and its specific heat are known, their product is the thermal capacity of the body; but the concept of thermal capacity is most useful when the mass or the specific heat is unknown and not easily determined.

16-8 Calorimetry

Consideration of the definitions of specific heat and thermal capacity, and the units required by those definitions, reveals that if Q is quantity of heat, m is mass, s the specific heat, and Δt the temperature change

$$Q = ms\,\Delta t \tag{16-3}$$

Also, if we use c to symbolize thermal capacity,

$$Q = c\,\Delta t \tag{16-4}$$

If two or more substances at different temperatures are brought together, they will come to ***thermal equilibrium;*** that is, heat will flow from the warmer to the cooler substance until a common temperature is achieved. If there is no gain of energy from the environment, and no such energy loss, the heat lost by part of the system must be exactly equal to that gained by the rest of the system; for heat is a form of energy and the law of conservation of energy has not been repealed. Each quantity of heat gained or lost by a portion of the system may be evaluated in terms of Eq. (16-3) or (16-4), and an equation set up with the quantities which represent heat gain on one side and those which stand for heat loss on the other.*

---

* This statement is valid only if there is no change of state. We shall modify it in Sec. 18-8 to take care of changes of state.

Sample Problem 1

A calorimeter cup which has a thermal capacity of 22.0 cal/C° contains 50.0 g of water at 5.0°C. An 80.0 g mass of aluminum at 300.0°C is dumped into the water and stirred until the temperature has become steady. What is that temperature?

For the water, Δt will be $(t - 5.0)$ C°, where t is the final temperature. Since the water is contained in the cup, we may assume that it also is at 5.0° initially, and so will have the same Δt as the water. For the aluminum, Δt will be $(300.0 - t)$. The specific heat of aluminum is found, in Table 16-1, to be 0.214 cal/(g C°). As a starting point, we invoke the law of conservation of energy, and go on from there. Subscripts c, w, and a identify symbols pertinent to the cup, the water, and the aluminum, respectively.

$$\text{HEAT GAIN} = \text{HEAT LOSS}$$

$$c_c\,\Delta t_c + m_w s_w\,\Delta t_w = m_a s_a\,\Delta t_a$$

$$22.0\frac{\text{cal}}{\text{C}^\circ}\cdot(t-5.0)\text{C}^\circ + 50.0\text{g}\cdot 1\frac{\text{cal}}{\text{g}\cdot\text{C}^\circ}\cdot(t-5.0)\text{C}^\circ = 80.0\text{g}\cdot 0.214\frac{\text{cal}}{\text{g}\cdot\text{C}^\circ}\cdot(300.0-t)\text{C}^\circ$$

$$(22.0t - 110)\text{ cal} + (50.0t - 250)\text{ cal} = (5136 - 17.12t)\text{ cal}$$

$$89.12t\text{ cal} = 5496\text{ cal}$$

$$t = 61.7^\circ\text{C}$$

Note that although the inclusion of the specific heat of water has no effect on the *numerical* value of the result, the equation would be inhomogeneous with respect to units if this factor were omitted. Since checking for homogeneity is a very useful way of testing the validity of any equation, it is desirable to include the specific heat of water.

The sudden appearance of "°C" from "cal" calls for comment. The terms summed up to yield $89.12t$ were either $c\,\Delta t$ or $ms\,\Delta t$ (which simplifies to $c\,\Delta t$); thus division of both sides by 89.12 also divides Q cal by c cal/C°, and this yields C°. But since all other temperatures were measured from 0°C, we must interpret the answer as 61.7C° above 0°C, which is 61.7°C.

16-9 The Concept of an Absolute Zero of Temperature

Recall again the example of the height of the floors of a building in Sec. 16-2. It was said that they might be measured from the general ground level or referred to some other basis, such as sea level. If ground level were used, the basis of reference would be different for each building in a hilly town. Sea level provides a common basis applicable to every building; hence it is much more fundamental.

Our two scales of temperature employ different bases of reference: the zero of the Celsius scale is the freezing temperature of water, but the Fahrenheit zero is 32F° below that temperature. Is there a common and more fundamental basis of reference? And, if so, how can we determine it?

Consider an enclosed sample of gas as we did when we were developing Boyle's law in Sec. 10-7. As we found in Sec. 10-6, the pressure of this gas is dynamic in origin. The restless molecules impinge on the walls of the container, and each impact generates a momentary force according to the equation $Ft = -m\,\Delta v$—Eq. (6-9). It is the summation of the myriad of such impulses which constitutes the force against the walls of the container, and hence the pressure on them. Section 10-7 mentioned briefly that (for a given gas) a certain average velocity of the molecules corresponds to a definite temperature. And we have just seen in Sec. 16-5 that if we increase the thermal energy content of a substance we increase the microscopic energy of its particles. For a gas, this means an increase in the average kinetic energy and hence in the average speed. If the molecules move faster, the impacts against the walls will be more frequent, and according to Eq. (6-9), the average force resulting from each collision will be augmented.

Thus we see that a rise in the temperature of an enclosed sample of gas will increase its pressure, and vice versa. If we keep the volume of the gas constant and measure the pressure at each of many different temperatures over a wide range, a graphical representation of the results would look like Fig. 16-3, which shows the results of a hypothetical but typical experiment. The solid straight* line represents the data over the temperature range investigated experimentally, individual items of data being indicated by small circles. Because any gas will condense if the temperature is sufficiently low, and since as the gas approaches condensation, its behavior departs noticeably from its behavior at higher temperatures (as indicated by one circle off the lower end of the line), experimental data cannot be obtained to carry the solid line as far as the temperature axis.

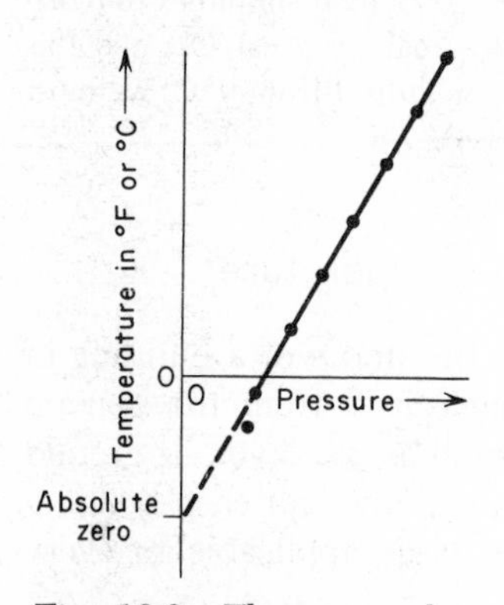

Fig. 16-3. The means by which absolute zero is located.

The dashed line in the figure is an ***extrapolation*** of the experimental data and represents what *would* be observed experimentally *if* the temperature-pressure relationship at higher temperatures were still obeyed at these low temperatures.

It is no surprise that this extrapolated line meets the temperature axis. But recall that we have imposed only a single restriction other than that we are dealing with a definite mass of a gas: the volume must remain constant. Nothing was said of the volume of gas used, or of its chemical constitution. Thus, with a proper readjustment of the values along the pressure axis, Fig. 16-3 could be

* The fact that the solid line is straight is presented only on the basis of experimental fact. However, a rigorous derivation of the pressure-temperature relationship would establish the essential straightness of the line.

made to represent the temperature-pressure relationship of *any quantity* of *any gas*, and *in all cases the extrapolated line would intersect the temperature axis at the same point.*

Thus there exists an ***absolute zero*** of temperature such that the pressure of any and all gases *would* become zero at that temperature *if* the temperature-pressure relationship they exhibit at higher temperatures were obeyed down to absolute zero. Absolute zero is at a temperature of −273.16°C. For our purposes, we may think of it as −273°C or −459°F.

Absolute zero has not been reached experimentally and probably never will be, though it has been approached within a few thousandths of a degree. Many strange things happen at temperatures close to absolute zero. One of the most striking is the phenomenon of superconductivity; some metals lose essentially all resistance to the flow of electric currents at such extremely low temperatures. This has applications which may become common in the near future.

16-10 Absolute Scales of Temperature

You will recall that the Celsius and Fahrenheit temperature scales are arbitrary, both in the choice of the fixed points and in the size of the degree. A scale would be less arbitrary if based on absolute zero, but the size of degree would still be arbitrary.

There are at least two temperature scales based on absolute zero and therefore known as ***absolute*** scales. One is the ***Kelvin*** scale, which uses the same size of degree as the Celsius scale,* and the other is the ***Rankine*** scale, in which the Fahrenheit size of degree is employed. The Kelvin scale is far more common, so we shall ignore the Rankine scale henceforth. The Kelvin scale, and its relationship to the Celsius and Fahrenheit scales, are depicted in Fig. 16-4. Obviously, temperature conversions between the Kelvin and Celsius scales are the essence of simplicity:

$$K = C + 273, \quad \text{and} \quad C = K - 273$$

where K represents any temperature in °K and C symbolizes the same temperature in °C.

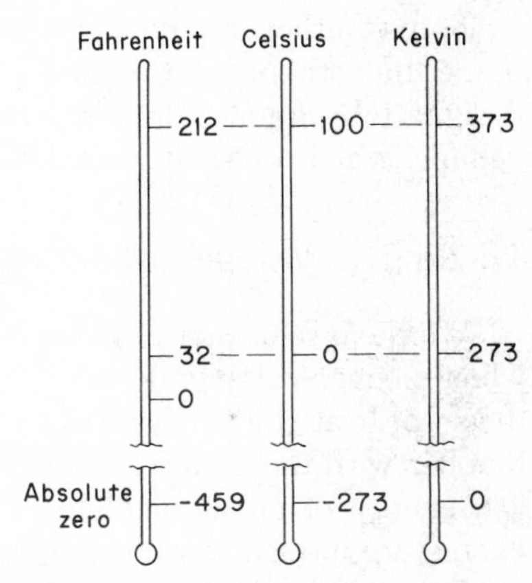

Fig. 16-4. Comparison of the Fahrenheit, Celsius, and Kelvin scales of temperature.

* The Kelvin scale is commonly called the "absolute scale," but the term "absolute" applies to the Rankine scale also.

16-11 The Relationship between the Temperature of a Gas and Its Pressure

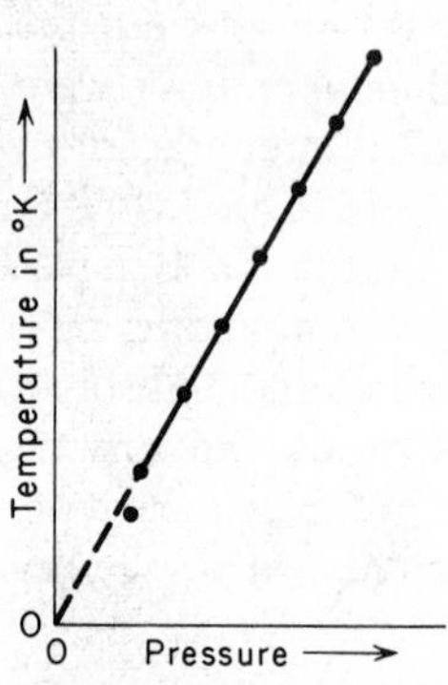

Fig. 16-5. The pressure of a definite mass of gas is directly proportional to its temperature on an absolute scale.

In Fig. 16-3 the horizontal pressure axis is drawn at the zero of a non-absolute scale of temperature—the Fahrenheit or Celsius scale. If we move this pressure axis down to zero on an absolute scale, we obtain Fig. 16-5, which is identical with Fig. 16-3 in other respects, except for the designation of the Kelvin scale of temperature.

A graph of one quantity against another will be a straight line through the origin if—and only if—there is a direct proportionality between the two quantities. Thus we may state that for a definite mass of a gas at constant volume the pressure is directly proportional to the absolute temperature—for our purposes, to the Kelvin temperature, since we shall not employ the Rankine scale at all. In algebraic terms, if P_1 and T_1 are the initial pressure and temperature, respectively, and if P_2 and T_2 are the corresponding values at a later time,

$$\frac{P_2}{P_1} = \frac{T_2}{T_1} \tag{16-5}$$

provided that T_1 and T_2 are in degrees *Kelvin.*

Some authorities do not identify this relationship with any special name, but others call it ***Charles' law*** or the ***Law of Gay-Lussac.*** These designations are also applied to a relationship between temperature and volume, which we shall meet in Sec. 17-2.

16-12 The Mechanical Equivalent of Heat

We have seen that observations of the appearance of thermal energy when mechanical energy was expended caused the downfall of the caloric theory of heat, and we have observed that heat is a form of energy. We are familiar with the conversion of the heat of exploding gasoline to mechanical energy of an automobile. Thus the fact that heat and mechanical energy are intraconvertible hardly needs comment.

It is necessary, however, to correlate the units of heat energy with those of mechanical energy. This was first done by Joule. Much as hanging weights are used to drive a "grandfather clock," they were employed by Joule to turn a paddle wheel in a sort of churn containing water. The thermal energy generated could be evaluated in terms of the mass of water, its specific heat, the thermal capacity of the churn, and the temperature rise. The magnitudes of the weights and their distances of fall yielded the quantity of mechanical energy expended. The results, in terms of later and more accurate determinations, are (to three significant figures)

$$4.18 \text{ joules} = 1 \text{ cal}, \quad \text{or} \quad 778 \text{ ft-lb} = 1 \text{ Btu}$$

Let us pause a moment and summarize some of our findings about energy relationships. In Sec. 16-8, we based our calorimetric procedures on the principle that the total heat gained by part of a system must equal the total heat lost by the remainder, if the system is thermally insulated from the environment. This principle is simply a special case of the law of conservation of energy. In the present section, we have seen that thermal energy may be converted to mechanical energy, and the reverse, which again is a form of the law of energy conservation. If we distinguish between heat (which, as we have seen, technically is thermal energy in the process of transfer from one body to another) and internal energy, we can combine the two special conservation principles we have met in Sec. 16-8 and this section into a statement which includes both: The increase in the internal (thermal) energy of a substance is equal to the heat energy delivered to that substance plus the mechanical work done on the substance. This is one form of the principle known as the ***first law of thermodynamics.***

Returning now to the intraconversion of mechanical energy and thermal energy, we shall soon discover that there's a fly in the ointment. We can take a given quantity of mechanical energy and change it entirely into thermal energy. But though we can change *part* of a quantity of thermal energy into mechanical energy, it is never possible *even in theory* to convert the thermal energy *entirely* into mechanical energy.

A mechanical analogy will indicate the reason for this. Consider a hydroelectric plant in the mountains at an elevation of 5000 ft, with water in a reservoir above the power station. The water has potential energy which can be used to generate electrical energy, but this plant can extract only the potential energy the water has *with respect to the 5000 ft elevation.* It retains all the potential energy it has with respect to any *lower* elevation. If additional power plants were constructed in sufficient number, conceivably all the energy the water originally had with respect to sea level could be used to produce electrical energy. But at sea level the water still has weight, so it still retains potential energy with respect to any level above the center of the earth. We can't *use* this remaining energy, however, since there's no place to put the water which would be discharged at the lower level. Thus the potential energy which can be converted to electrical energy is only a fraction of the potential energy the water originally had with respect to the center of the earth.

Similarly, a steam engine may receive steam at a high temperature and discharge the steam (or water) at a lower temperature, converting the energy taken from the steam into mechanical energy. But the steam (or water) will necessarily be discharged at a temperature at, or above, that of the environment—unless an artificially cold environment is created, which could be done only by *expending* more energy than would be gained. All the thermal energy which the steam (or water) still retains with respect to absolute zero is unavailable to the engine. Thus, as Carnot originally showed, the fraction of the thermal energy which can be converted to mechanical energy is limited, and the thermodynamic efficiency of a heat engine is

$$\text{eff} = \frac{T_r - T_d}{T_r} \tag{16-6}$$

in which T_r is the temperature at which the thermal energy is received and T_d the temperature at which it is discharged, T_r and T_d being in °K.

This equation applies to heat engines of all types. We can immediately see, on the basis of this equation, why an internal combustion engine is more efficient than a steam engine, and why a Diesel engine (which uses the thermal energy generated by compression of the gases in the cylinder, instead of an electric spark, to ignite the fuel) is more efficient than a gasoline engine.

An implication of Eq. (16-6) is that, in *any* process of this sort, "high-grade" energy (in this case internal energy of a substance which has a temperature above that of the environment) is partially converted into unavailable "low-grade" energy. Similar considerations apply to all other spontaneously occurring processes; in *any* spontaneous process there is a conversion of available energy to unavailable energy. If the internal energy of a substance is increased in the amount ΔQ by the absorption of this quantity of heat at a temperature T on the Kelvin scale, the ***entropy*** of the substance is increased by the amount $\Delta Q/T$. As the value of T decreases, that of $\Delta Q/T$ increases. In these terms, the statement in the second sentence above says that any spontaneously occurring process involves an increase of entropy. Comparing the two statements, we see that the entropy of a substance is a measure of the *un*availability of the energy it contains.

The fact that every spontaneous process inevitably changes some high-grade energy to low-grade energy—in other words, involves an increase in entropy—is embodied in the principle called the ***second law of thermodynamics.*** It is a very broad and very general law, and because its applications are so varied it may be stated in a great variety of seemingly quite different ways. For our purposes, we shall think of it only in terms of the degradation of energy, unless your instructor wishes to take you further.

Summary

The concept of a *difference of temperature* between bodies is based on the presence of a *flow of heat energy* between them. All scales of temperature are arbitrary with respect to the size of a degree, and the Fahrenheit and Celsius scales are also arbitrary with respect to the location of the zero. Absolute scales, such as the Kelvin scale, use absolute zero as the basis of the scale.

The conversion of a temperature from Fahrenheit to Celsius or vice versa may be done quite easily merely by considering the values of the fixed points on the two scales.

A very common source of confusion and error may be eliminated if a distinction is made between *temperatures* and *temperature differences.* The symbols °C and C° mean different things.

The *internal energy* of a substance, also called its *thermal energy,* is the *total energy* the particles of the substance *possess* because of their random microscopic motions. The term *heat* is applied to this energy when it is being transferred, but only while it is being transferred. Units of the quantity of heat energy include the calorie, the kilogram calorie, and the British thermal unit. The term "calorie" is used differently in connection with nutrition than in other applications.

The *specific heat* of a substance is the quantity of heat energy required to cause a temperature rise of 1 degree in unit mass of the substance. The thermal capacity of a body is the quantity of heat necessary to raise the temperature of the body 1 degree.

The basic principle used for problems in calorimetry is the law of conservation of energy.

There is a temperature at which the pressure of any gas would become zero if it obeyed the same temperature-pressure relationship at extremely low temperatures as it follows at higher temperatures. This temperature is *absolute zero.*

The pressure of a given mass of gas at constant volume is directly proportional to the absolute temperature.

The impossibility of converting heat energy entirely into mechanical energy limits the efficiency of any heat engine.

Self-Quiz

1. Test your judgment of temperature difference by holding one finger in hot water and another in ice water, then transferring both fingers to the same dish of lukewarm water. How reliable is your judgment?

2. Compare and contrast "20°C" with "20C°."

3. A mother describing her child's recovery from an illness states, "He no longer has any temperature." Is this possible? What did she mean to say?

4. Without reference to the text make a diagram which depicts and compares the Fahrenheit and Celsius scales of temperature. In what respects are they alike? How do they differ?

5. What advantage has the term "centigrade" over Celsius?

6. Using simple logic and your diagram of the two scales of temperature, convert 37.0°C to °F. Check by reconverting the Fahrenheit value—by step-by-step logic—back to °C.

7. Derive Eq. (16-1), (16-2) from your solution for the preceding question.

8. Convert 37.0C° to F°. Is this the same problem as Question 6? Which question is simpler, and why? Why are the answers different?

9. Aside from the fact that they would give erroneous results, why are

$$C = \tfrac{5}{9}F - 32, \quad \text{and} \quad F = \tfrac{9}{5}(C + 32)$$

not correct equations?

10. In what respects is our present understanding of heat in agreement with the old concept of caloric? In what respects does it differ?

11. Compare and contrast the terms "heat" and "internal energy." Why are they not synonymous?

12. Define and compare the terms "macroscopic" and "microscopic."

13. Define and compare the terms "specific heat" and "thermal capacity." What is the relationship between them?

14. From what standpoint, and why, may the specific heat of water be omitted from a computation? From what standpoint, and why, should it be included?

15. Outline in some detail the basis for the concept of absolute zero and how it is evaluated.

16. Why is it improbable that absolute zero will ever be attained?

17. Make a diagram to show and compare the Fahrenheit, Celsius, and Kelvin scales of temperature. Why is the term "Kelvin" rather than "absolute" used to identify the scale on which the freezing point of water is 273°?

18. What restrictions must be included in any statement of Charles' law?

19. The temperature of a definite mass of gas is changed from 20°C to 60°C with no change of volume. Does this triple the pressure of the gas? Explain clearly.

20. Why can't all the thermal energy a substance possesses be transformed into mechanical energy?

Problems

1. Absolute zero is −273.16°C. Find its value on the Fahrenheit scale, correct to 5 significant figures.

2. (a) Compute the temperature at which the Celsius and Fahrenheit readings would be equal. (b) Construct equations, based on this temperature, for changing °C to °F and vice versa.

3. (a) Compute the Fahrenheit temperature which would be twice the Celsius temperature. (b) Calculate at what Celsius temperature the reading would be one-tenth of the Fahrenheit temperature. (c) What Celsius temperature is equal to the Fahrenheit temperature but of opposite sign?

4. (a) What is the thermal capacity of a body which experiences 35.0°C rise of temperature when it absorbs 140 cal of heat? (b) If the mass of the body is 120 g, determine its specific heat.

5. (a) Change 120°C to °F. (b) Change 200°C to °F. (c) Find the difference between the answers to parts *a* and *b*. (d) Convert 80C° directly to F°.

6. A 15.0 g calorimeter cup of aluminum contains 45.0 g of water at 0.0°C. A 500 g mass of hot lead shot is added to the cup. If the final temperature is 40.0°C, what was the temperature of the lead?

7. 220 g of brass pellets at a temperature of 500°C are added to a calorimeter cup which has a thermal capacity of 25.0 cal/C° and contains 120.0 g of water. If the original temperature of the water and cup was 20.0°C and the final temperature is 78.6°C, calculate the specific heat of the brass.

8. What mass of water at 20.0°C would be required to cool 800 g of mercury at 200.0°C to 35.0°C?

9. A sample of gas is heated from 27°C to 477°C at constant volume. If the initial pressure was 15.0 lb/in.^{2}, what will the new pressure be?

10. 90.0 ft^3 of gas at atmospheric pressure is cooled without change of volume from 377°C to −23°C. Determine its pressure in lb/in.^{2}. Atmospheric pressure is 14.7 lb/in.^{2}.

11. A sample of gas which has an initial pressure of 500 g/cm^2 is heated from 20°C to a temperature at which its pressure is 1200 g/cm^2. If the volume was constant, compute the temperature.

12. A 4000 lb car is brought from a speed of 60.0 mph to a complete stop by its brakes. Compute the quantity of thermal energy generated.

13. A 3000 lb car travels from a mountain pass down to the level plain 2500 ft below. If half the energy lost by the car is due to braking, calculate the quantity of thermal energy produced.

14. An aluminum block slides at constant velocity down an inclined plane 20.0 m long. The angle of inclination from the horizontal is 30.0°. If the block absorbs 90.0% of the thermal energy produced, determine its temperature rise.

15. Upper Yosemite Fall is a sheer drop of 1430 ft. Only a fraction of the potential energy the water loses goes to heat energy in the water, but *if* it all were converted to thermal energy in the water what would the temperature rise be?

16. If a heat engine receives thermal energy at 200°F and discharges it at 80°F, compute its thermodynamic efficiency.

17. A steam engine receives in one second an amount of steam which contains $2.00 \cdot 10^4$ Btu. If the steam enters at 400°F and is discharged at 220°F, compute the maximum possible horsepower of the engine.

17
THERMAL EXPANSION

17-1 Preview

This chapter is concerned with the changes of dimensions or volume which occur as the result of temperature changes. We begin with the expansion of gases as the temperature rises and combine this with previously encountered laws of gases to develop a general gas law. This is followed by a consideration of the linear expansion of solids and the volume expansion of liquids and solids. The importance of a peculiarity in the thermal expansion of water will be noted.

17-2 Thermal Expansion of a Gas

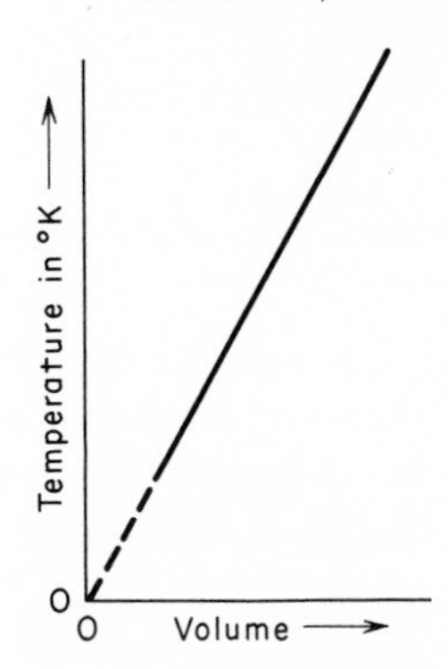

Fig. 17-1. The volume of a definite mass of gas is directly proportional to its temperature on an absolute scale.

In Sec. 16-9 we considered the effect of a temperature rise on a sample of gas which was enclosed so that its volume could not change. We found that a temperature rise was the index of an increase in the average speed of the molecules. This velocity increase resulted in more frequent and more severe impacts of the molecules, and hence in a higher pressure. These considerations led to the concept of absolute zero and the determination of its value, and to the relationship between the temperature and pressure of a gas at constant volume.

If we consider a definite mass of gas, as before, but imagine it to be in a cylinder closed by a leakproof and frictionless piston, the same argument will lead to the conclusion that the increased activity of the molecules which results from a temperature rise will push the piston outward. Since it is free to move there will be no augmentation of pressure, but the volume will be increased. A plot of experimental data would yield a graph similar to Fig. 16-3, the horizontal axis now being labeled "Volume" rather than "Pressure." The extrapolated line would meet the temperature axis at $-273°C$ or $-459°F$. Moving the horizontal axis down to absolute zero, as we did in obtaining Fig. 16-5 from Fig. 16-3, would produce Fig. 17-1. Interpreting this as we did Fig. 16-5, we may state that for a definite mass of gas at constant pressure, the volume is directly proportional to the absolute temperature. Algebraically, if V_1 is the initial volume, V_2 the final volume, and T_1 and T_2 the corresponding temperatures *on an absolute scale,*

$$\frac{V_2}{V_1} = \frac{T_2}{T_1} \tag{17-1}$$

This relationship is known as ***Charles' law*** and also as the ***Law of Gay-Lussac.*** You will recall that these designations may be applied also to the temperature-pressure relationship expressed in Eq. (16-5).

17-3 The General Gas Law

We now have three laws which deal with the volume, pressure, and temperature of a gas; but each considers only *two* of these three factors. In algebraic form, they are

at constant temperature, $$\frac{P_2}{P_1} = \frac{V_1}{V_2} \tag{10-3}$$

at constant volume, $$\frac{P_2}{P_1} = \frac{T_2}{T_1} \tag{16-5}$$

and at constant pressure, $$\frac{V_2}{V_1} = \frac{T_2}{T_1} \tag{17-1}$$

Suppose that we take a definite sample of a gas under a set of conditions we may identify as condition a, and change it to a new condition b by changing the pressure while keeping the temperature constant. As modified to describe this change, Eq. (10-3) is

$$T_b = T_a, \quad \text{and} \quad \frac{P_b}{P_a} = \frac{V_a}{V_b}$$

Now let us change the temperature, keeping the pressure constant, thus arriving at a set of conditions c. For this situation, Eq. (17-1) is

$$P_c = P_b, \quad \text{and} \quad \frac{V_c}{V_b} = \frac{T_c}{T_b}$$

Substituting P_c for P_b and T_a for T_b, we obtain

$$\frac{P_c}{P_a} = \frac{V_a}{V_b}, \quad \text{and} \quad \frac{V_c}{V_b} = \frac{T_c}{T_a}$$

If we multiply these two equations together V_b cancels out and we obtain

$$\frac{P_c V_c}{P_a} = \frac{V_a T_c}{T_a}$$

and this may be rearranged to

$$\frac{P_c V_c}{T_c} = \frac{P_a V_a}{T_a}$$

Since we are dealing with a definite mass of gas, we may consider that for any fixed values of any two of the three quantities P_a, V_a, and T_a the third quantity can only have one possible value; and a similar necessary relationship exists among P_c, V_c, and T_c. This is a way of saying that the properties of the gas under the new set of conditions do not depend on *how* the change of conditions was made. We could have changed the temperature and pressure at constant volume and then changed the volume at constant temperature or at constant pressure; or we could have varied P, V, and T simultaneously in any conceivable way, and the final relationship among P_c, V_c, and T_c would have been exactly the same. Thus we may put our result in more general form:

GENERAL GAS LAW

$$\boxed{\frac{P_2 V_2}{T_2} = \frac{P_1 V_1}{T_1}} \tag{17-2}$$

A moment's consideration will show that if a third set of conditions is achieved we could change the subscripts on either side of the equation to 3 to obtain a valid equation, or to 4 for a fourth set of conditions, etc. Thus the value of PV/T always is the same for any given sample of gas. In symbols,

$$\frac{PV}{T} = k \tag{17-3}$$

in which k is a constant for any given sample of gas.*

Equation (17-2) or (17-3), or an equivalent verbal statement, is known as the ***general gas law.*** It is much more useful than the less general laws from which it was derived (and which are contained within it as special cases). It describes an ideal situation, however, and in any actual cases there will be some slight deviations from its predictions, especially if the gas is near the conditions under which it will condense. (Review Sec. 10-7 if you have forgotten the causes of these errors.)

Errors occur too frequently in students' application of the general gas law, usually because of the too-common habit of using an equation without thinking about it or noticing whether the result makes sense or not.

Sample Problem 1

A 400 ml sample of gas has a pressure of 760 mm at a temperature of 27°C. What will its pressure be at 177°C if the volume is 500 ml?

Before we do anything else, we should change the temperatures to °K

$$27°\text{C} = (27 + 273)°\text{K} = 300°\text{K},$$

and similarly

$$177°\text{C} = 450°\text{K}$$

Though "760 mm" is not a proper expression for pressure (see the last paragraph of Sec. 10-11), it is very common; and we may leave the pressure factor in this form if we want the final pressure in the same form. We may set the problem up according to Eq. (17-2):

$$\frac{P_2 \cdot 500}{450} = \frac{760 \cdot 400}{300}$$

and solution of this equation yields $P_2 = 912$ mm.

But let's look at the problem logically rather than in terms of an equation. The new pressure will equal the original pressure as modified by the changes of temperature and volume. Certainly a temperature rise tends to increase the pressure, so we can simply set up a temperature ratio as a factor to multiply the pressure. The possibilities are 300/450 and 450/300, but only the latter will *increase* the value of the pressure. Similarly, the possible volume ratios are 400/500

---

* For chemists: Eq. (17-3) is most useful in the equivalent form $PV = nRT$, in which n is the number of moles of gas and R is the molar gas constant, the value of R being 8.31 joules/(C° mole) or 82.06 (cm³ atmospheres)/(C° mole).

and 500/400; but since an increase in volume will tend to *de*crease the pressure, the former ratio is the pertinent one. So we may write

$$P_2 = 760 \cdot \frac{400}{500} \cdot \frac{450}{300} = 760 \cdot \frac{4}{5} \cdot \frac{3}{2} = 912 \text{ mm}$$

17-4 Linear Thermal Expansion of a Solid

By ***linear*** expansion is meant the increase of any one dimension, such as length.

A sample of gas has no definite volume because of the relatively large distances between molecules and the consequent weakness of the attractive forces among them. Hence there is little to interfere with the expansion of a gas except the external pressure acting on it. As we have seen, this leads to a very simple relation of volume to temperature (at constant pressure) which is the same (ideally, and nearly so in practice) for all gases.

The internal situation in a solid is quite different. The forces of mutual attraction hold the particles together and give the macroscopic assembly of particles a definite volume and a definite shape. A solid contains thermal energy as energy of the particles, as does a gas, but the energy is vibrational and is unable to separate the particles (so long as the body remains a solid). Thus there is no simple and universal relationship between the temperature of a solid and its dimensions, as there is between temperature and volume for gases.

If a metal rod (for example) has a length L_0 initially and a length L at some other temperature, the new length will be equal to the old plus a change of length ΔL:

$$L = L_0 + \Delta L$$

ΔL may be either positive or negative, depending on the substance and the direction of the temperature change.

Here, as with the elastic distortions studied in Chapter 11, the change in length depends on the original length; the greater the initial length, the greater the change in length, other things being equal. The change in length depends also on how much the temperature rises and on the characteristics of the particular solid. If the thermal expansion properties of the solid are represented by a factor α and if Δt symbolizes the temperature change, these facts may be summarized by the equation

$$\Delta L = L_0 \alpha \, \Delta t \qquad (17\text{-}4)$$

The factor α is the ***linear coefficient of thermal expansion*** of the solid. It is defined as the change in length per unit length and per degree of temperature rise. A rearrangement of Eq. (17-4) yields an algebraic definition:

$$\alpha = \frac{\Delta L}{L_0 \, \Delta t} \qquad (17\text{-}5)$$

Since, normally, a solid expands as the temperature rises, the values of this coefficient are generally positive; but for some substances, and over limited ranges, the coefficient may have a negative value. Note that the value of Δt may be positive (temperature rise) or negative (a drop in the temperature) and that the sign of Δt, together with that of α, will determine the sign of ΔL and thus identify it as an expansion or a contraction.

Values of the linear coefficient of thermal expansion for a few substances are given in Table 17-1. Note that although these values differ markedly, the largest one is only about 15 times the smallest.

In view of Eq. (17-4) we may write

$$L = L_0 + L_0\alpha\,\Delta t \qquad (17\text{-}6)$$

Sometimes this equation is more convenient in the equivalent form

$$L = L_0(1 + \alpha\,\Delta t) \qquad (17\text{-}7)$$

Linear Expansion

Sample Problem 2

At what temperature will the length of a steel wire be 100.100% of its length at 20.0°C?

We lack a value for either L or L_0, but we *do* know that $L/L_0 = 1.00100$. Or we can say that the increase must be 0.100% of the initial length, so $\Delta L/L_0 = 0.00100$. We can divide both sides of Eq. (17-7) by L_0 and set the result equal to 1.00100, or we may divide both sides of Eq. (17-4) and set the result equal to 0.100. The former approach yields

$$1 + \alpha\,\Delta t = 1.00100$$

whereas the latter gives

$$\alpha\,\Delta t = 0.00100$$

Subtraction of 1 from both sides of the first equation reduces it to the second equation, so the two approaches merge at this point. Taking the value of α from Table 17-1 and setting Δt equal to $(t - 20.0)$, we have

$$\begin{aligned} 10.5\cdot 10^{-6}\cdot (t - 20.0) &= 0.00100 \\ t - 20.0 &= 10^{-3} \div (10.5\cdot 10^{-6}) \\ &= 9.52\cdot 10^{+1} \\ t &= 95.2 + 20.0 = 115.2^\circ\text{C} \end{aligned}$$

Table 17-1

LINEAR COEFFICIENTS OF THERMAL EXPANSION, PER C°

Metals		Non-metals	
Aluminum	$25.5\cdot 10^{-6}$	Glass, "Pyrex"	$3.6\cdot 10^{-6}$
Brass	$19.3\cdot 10^{-6}$	Glass, soft	$8.5\cdot 10^{-6}$
Copper	$16.8\cdot 10^{-6}$	Wood, oak—parallel to grain	$4.92\cdot 10^{-6}$
Silver	$18.8\cdot 10^{-6}$	Wood, oak—perpendicular to grain	$54.4\cdot 10^{-6}$
Steel	$10.5\cdot 10^{-6}$		

17-5 The "Expansion" of a Hole

Suppose that you have a steel block with a cylindrical hole drilled through it, and you heat the block. As the steel expands, will it expand into the hole, decreasing the diameter of the hole, or will the hole enlarge instead? Now repeat this imaginary experiment, but before heating the block insert a cylindrical plug of the same steel into the hole, the plug fitting well but not tightly. Now, as you heat the block, the plug also will be heated and it will expand—or tend to. At the higher temperature, will it be "stuck" in the hole because of the inward expansion of the hole? The block and plug constitute, in effect, a solid block with no hole or plug. Thus, if you say that the steel will tend to expand inward and squeeze the plug, you are saying that a similar stress would occur in a solid block. Since this conclusion is untenable, it must be that the steel does *not* tend to expand inward into the hole; instead, it expands outward, enlarging the hole.

If this still seems strange, consider the circumference of the hole; this is a *length,* as truly as if it were an equal distance along a straight line. Hence the equations in the preceding section apply, and the circumference of the circular hole must increase as the temperature rises. But this implies an increase in diameter.

Thus we must conclude that any opening in a solid "expands" and "contracts" with changing temperature exactly as would a portion of the solid itself which had the same shape and volume as the void.

17-6 Volume Expansion

If we were to return to the fourth paragraph of Sec. 17-4, where the quantitative discussion of linear thermal expansion began, and change the word "length" to "volume" throughout, the argument would detail the relationships pertinent to volume expansion. We would have to substitute V for L in the equations, however, and to avoid confusion a different symbol should be used for the coefficient.

Since the basic ideas and logic are no different, I shall proceed immediately to the one new definition and to the modified equations. The ***volume coefficient of thermal expansion*** is the change of volume per unit volume and per degree of temperature change. It is represented by the symbol β. Thus,

$$\beta = \frac{\Delta V}{V_0 \, \Delta t} \qquad (17\text{-}8)$$

$$V = V_0 + V_0 \beta \, \Delta t \qquad (17\text{-}9)$$

and

$$V = V_0(1 + \beta \, \Delta t) \qquad (17\text{-}10)$$

Table 17-2

VOLUME COEFFICIENTS OF THERMAL EXPANSION, PER C°

Benzene	$12.37 \cdot 10^{-4}$
Ether	$16.56 \cdot 10^{-4}$
Glycerin	$5.05 \cdot 10^{-4}$
Mercury	$1.8186 \cdot 10^{-4}$
Water	$2.07 \cdot 10^{-4}$

Table 17-2 contains the volume coefficients of thermal expansion for some liquids. But *none* for gases or solids. We know from Sec. 17-2 that we need none for gases. Neither are they necessary for solids, as we shall see immediately.

Dimensionally, $V = L^3$. According to Eq. (17-7)

$$L = L_0(1 + \alpha \, \Delta t)$$

therefore,

$$L^3 = [L_0(1 + \alpha \, \Delta t)]^3 = L_0^3(1 + 3\alpha \, \Delta t + 3\alpha^2 \, \Delta t^2 + \alpha^3 \, \Delta t^3)$$

A glance at the values of α in Table 17-1 reveals that all are very small. Hence α^2 will be much smaller, and α^3 extremely small. Because of this, the terms containing α^2 and α^3 may be dropped from the equation without introducing as much error as is already present since values of α are given only to three digits and may vary somewhat with temperature. For example, for a sample of aluminum heated from room temperature to its melting point, the error due to dropping the last two terms of the equation is less than 0.08%. Elimination of these terms changes the equation to

$$L^3 = L_0^3(1 + 3\alpha \, \Delta t)$$

and if we substitute V for L^3 and V_0 for L_0^3, we have

$$V = V_0(1 + 3\alpha \, \Delta t) \qquad (17\text{-}11)$$

This equation is identical with Eq. (17-10) except that it contains 3α in place of β. Therefore we conclude that the volume coefficient of thermal expansion is three times the linear coefficient:

$$\beta = 3\alpha \qquad (17\text{-}12)$$

Only rarely will you find in references a table of *volume* coefficients for solids; you look up the value of the *linear* coefficient of thermal expansion and triple it to obtain the volume coefficient.

Sample Problem 3

A copper vessel has a capacity of exactly 1500 ml at 20.0°C. What is its capacity for boiling water?

As the copper vessel expands, the space within it increases in exactly the same amount as a solid copper body of the same shape and volume would; so we may use the value of β for copper. From Table 17-1, α is $16.8 \cdot 10^{-6}/C°$ for copper, so β is

$$3 \cdot 16.8 \cdot 10^{-6}/C° = 50.4 \cdot 10^{-6}/C°$$

The temperature of boiling water is 100.0°C, so Δt is (100.0 − 20.0) or 80.0C°. Using these data in Eq. (17-11), we have

$$\begin{aligned} V &= 1500 \cdot (1 + 50.4 \cdot 10^{-6} \cdot 80.0) \\ &= 1500 \cdot (1 + 4.03\bar{2} \cdot 10^{-3}) \\ &= 1500 \cdot 1.00403\bar{2} = 1506.05 \text{ ml} \end{aligned}$$

17-7 Differential Expansion

One often is concerned with a difference in expansion of two things rather than in the expansion of either alone. If, for example, a container C has a capacity V and if it is filled with a liquid L, what volume of liquid will spill out if the container is heated through some temperature interval Δt? We can solve the new volume of each, and find the difference, but there is an easier way. For the liquid, Eq. (17-9) or (17-10) yields

$$V_L = (V_0)_L \cdot (1 + \beta_L \Delta t) = (V_0)_L + (V_0)_L \beta_L \Delta t$$

and for the container

$$V_C = (V_0)_C \cdot (1 + \beta_C \Delta t) = (V_0)_C + (V_0)_C \beta_C \Delta t$$

Subtracting the second equation from the first, we obtain

$$V_L - V_C = (V_0)_L + (V_0)_L \beta_L \Delta t - (V_0)_C - (V_0)_C \beta_C \Delta t$$

Since the container originally was full, $(V_0)_L$ and $(V_0)_C$ are equal. Thus the first and third terms on the right cancel each other, and we may drop the subscripts associated with V_0 in the other terms. So

$$V_L - V_C = V_0 \beta_L \Delta t - V_0 \beta_C \Delta t = V_0(\beta_L - \beta_C) \Delta t$$

Thus the differential change in volume is the initial volume times the ***differential expansion coefficient*** times the temperature change.

A similar analysis of an example of differential linear expansion would show that the differential linear expansion is the product of the initial length, the difference between the linear expansion coefficients of the two substances, and the temperature change.

Note, however, that in arriving at these results we made use of the fact that the initial dimension (volume or length) of the two substances was the same. For situations in which the original volumes, or lengths, are *not* equal, we must compute the expansion of each substance separately, and subtract to find the differential expansion.

Sample Problem 4

A "Pyrex" glass volumetric flask is filled exactly to the 50 ml graduation with water at 18.0°C. What volume of water will be above the graduation mark at 88.0°C? From Table 17-1, α for hard glass is $3.6 \cdot 10^{-6}/\mathrm{C}°$, so β is $10.8 \cdot 10^{-6}/\mathrm{C}°$. From Table 17-2, β for water is $2.07 \cdot 10^{-4}/\mathrm{C}°$, which is $207 \cdot 10^{-6}/\mathrm{C}°$. Thus the differential coefficient is

$$(207 - 10.8) \cdot 10^{-6}/\mathrm{C}° \quad \text{or} \quad 196 \cdot 10^{-6}/\mathrm{C}°$$

Then

$$\begin{aligned} V &= 50.0 \cdot 196 \cdot 10^{-6} \cdot (88.0 - 18.0) \\ &= 50.0 \cdot 1.96 \cdot 10^{-4} \cdot 70 \\ &= 0.686 \text{ ml} \end{aligned}$$

17-8 The Thermal Expansion of Water

Water has the unusual—though not unique—property of having a *negative* coefficient of thermal expansion between 0°C and 3.98°C. Thus, as warm water cools, it contracts only until the temperature reaches about 4°C; if the temperature continues to *drop*, the water *expands.* This means that it has a minimum volume, and hence a maximum density, at about 4°C. The situation is indicated graphically in Fig. 17-2.

It is interesting to consider some of the implications of this anomalous behavior of water. In climates where lakes and streams freeze, the lowering of the temperature of the water is accompanied by an increase in density—but *only* until the temperature reaches +4°C. Further decrease in the temperature *lowers* the density of the water, with the inevitable result that all water with a temperature below 4°C is at, or near, the surface. Thus freezing commences *at the surface.* And since the ice is a poor conductor of heat, and because of the high specific heat of the liquid water beneath the ice, the layer of ice thickens only slowly even when the air temperature is far below freezing.

Suppose this reversal of the contraction of water did not occur. The coldest water would be at the *bottom* of the lake or stream, so freezing

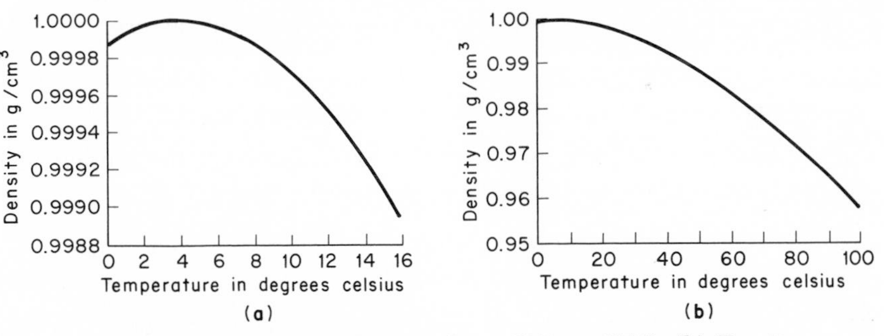

Fig. 17-2. (a) Density of water from 0°C to 16°C; (b) Density of water from 0°C to 100°C.

would begin at the bottom. Convection currents in the water in a lake, or turbulence in a stream, would facilitate the removal of heat from the upper layers of water, so the lake or stream might freeze to a solid block of ice.

In the spring, the ice at the surface would melt, and the upper layers of water would be warmed; but they would tend to stay on top because of their reduced density. But the actual case is that when the ice melts no warm layers of water can collect and remain on top until the entire body is "warmed" to at least 4°C.

Would the course of evolution have been altered if water had no negative values of its thermal expansion coefficient? If so, how, and in what degree? These are questions for a biologist and a text in biology to answer, but their basis lies in physics. And wherever such questions come from, or wherever their answers may be found, they certainly are interesting and thought-provoking.

17-9 Thermal Expansion and Force

We have seen that a gas which is heated but prevented from expanding exerts an augmented pressure (Sec. 16-9, 16-11), and its pressure decreases if it cools at constant volume. What would happen if, for example, a steel bar were heated while adequately strong bulwarks at its ends prevented it from expanding? We would expect a force to be developed; but how great a force, and what determines its magnitude?

Initially, we may so adjust the bulwarks at the ends that they are in contact with the bar but exert no pressure. As the temperature rises and the bar tends to expand, it exerts a force against the bulwarks; so, according to Newton's third law, they will exert an equal force on the bar and thus prevent it from expanding. That is, the tendency of the bar to expand is exactly canceled by an equal tendency of the resulting forces to shorten the bar. Thus you see that Young's modulus comes into the picture.

Equation (11-6) relates Young's modulus to pertinent factors:

$$Y = \frac{FL}{eA}$$

and we may solve it for e, which in this case represents the tendency of the forces exerted by the bulwarks to shorten the bar:

$$e = \frac{FL}{YA}$$

But the temperature rise tends to elongate the bar according to Eq. (17-4):

$$\Delta L = L_0 \, \alpha \, \Delta t$$

Since the bulwarks actually prevent any change of length, the tendency toward elongation, ΔL, must be equal to the tendency toward shortening, e. Therefore

$$\frac{FL}{YA} = L_0 \, \alpha \, \Delta t$$

The two symbols, L and L_0, represent the same length, so they cancel out. On rearranging the remaining quantities, we obtain

$$F = YA\alpha \, \Delta t \qquad (17\text{-}13)$$

Summary

The *volume of a definite sample of gas* at *constant pressure* is *directly proportional* to the *absolute temperature.* This may be combined with other relationships to produce the general gas law which states that, for a given mass of gas, the product of the pressure and the volume is a constant times the absolute temperature. It may be safer to reason out a gas-law problem than to depend blindly on an equation.

No universal expression for thermal expansion can be applied to solids or liquids; a factor characteristic of the substance must be included. This factor is the *thermal coefficient of expansion* (linear or volume). The volume coefficient of thermal expansion is three times the linear coefficient.

A hole or void in a solid will "expand" as the temperature rises exactly as a piece of the solid of the same size and shape would.

Water has a *minimum volume* and hence a *maximum density* at about 4°C. This unusual property has some practical applications.

The compressional (or tensile) force generated in a bar which is heated or cooled but not allowed to change in length may be computed with the aid of Young's modulus.

Self-Quiz

1. Analyze the physical basis for the relationship between the temperature of a definite mass of a gas and its volume, at constant pressure, in some detail—much as the temperature-pressure relationship was analyzed in Sec. 16-9.

2. Derive Eq. (17-2) or (17-3) by considering a definite mass of gas in a condition a, changing to a condition b according to the dictates of Eq. (16-5), then to a condition c according to Eq. (10-3) or (17-1).

3. (a) Express P and V in Eq. (17-3) in terms of the fundamental dimensions m, l, and t, leaving T in terms of K°, and find the dimensions of k. (b) The product of P and V represents energy (Sec. 10-15). From this point of view, what does k stand for? (c) In view of your answers to (a) and (b), what are the fundamental dimensions of energy? Check the result with the first part of Question 11 in the Self Quiz for Chapter 6, page 125.

4. Proceeding as I did in the *latter* part of Sample Problem 1, set up an algebraic equation for the new volume of a sample of gas which undergoes an increase of pressure and a decrease of temperature, and check the result against Eq. (17-2). Deduce a similar equation for the new temperature of a gas which has its volume reduced and its pressure increased.

5. Using only Eq. (17-2) and the fact that it applies only to a definite mass of gas, deduce Boyle's law and the two laws credited to Charles, *with* their restrictions.

6. Equation (17-10) may be used to describe the expansion of a gas, as well as of a liquid or a solid. When used for a gas, the value of β is 1/273 at 0°C, but its value is different at any different temperature. Show that if this value of β is used Eq. (17-10) reduces to Eq. (17-1). What would the appropriate value of β be at 27°C?

7. The values of α in Table 17-1 and β in Table 17-2 are given in terms of "per C°." Show that this is the correct "unit," in terms of Eq. (17-5), (17-8).

8. The value of α for Pyrex glass is $3.6 \cdot 10^{-6}$/C°. What is its value per F°, and why?

9. Discuss in some detail the "expansion of a hole."

10. Prove that if the area of a metal plate is A_0 initially and has a value A after a temperature change Δt,

$$A = A_0(1 + 2\alpha\,\Delta t)$$

If necessary, check Sec. 17-6 to get a start.

11. What limitations are placed on the method of calculating differential expansion developed in Sec. 17-7, and why?

12. What is the significance of a negative thermal expansion coefficient? Is this a property of water only? Of what practical or theoretical importance may it be in the case of water?

13. How does Young's modulus get into a chapter on the topic of heat?

Problems

1. A sample of gas has a volume of 25.0 liters at a temperature of −73°C. If the pressure remains unchanged, what will the volume be at 327°C?

2. As the temperature of a sample of gas is changed, at constant pressure, to 57°C, the volume increases from 40.0 ft^3 to 55.0 ft^3. What was the initial temperature?

3. If a sample of gas has a volume of 36.0 liters at 127°C and one atmosphere of pressure, what will its volume be at 227°C and 2.50 atmospheres pressure?

4. If 90.0 ft^3 of gas has a pressure of 5.00 atmospheres at 327°C, what will its pressure be at 227°C if its volume is 60.0 ft^3?

5. At $-23°C$ and a pressure of 760 mm of mercury, a sample of gas has a volume of 600 ml. At what Celsius temperature will its volume be 1000 ml if the pressure is 1140 mm of mercury?

6. (a) A silver ring has a circumference of exactly 1.5π cm at 27°C. Compute its circumference at 127°C. (b) From the data in part (a) and your answer, calculate the initial and final values of the diameter of the ring. (c) Compute the diameter at 127°C from the original diameter, the expansion coefficient, and the temperature rise.

7. A steel tape has a length of precisely 100 ft at 70.0°F. Determine its length at 97.0°F.

8. What will the percentage error in the tape in Problem 7 be at a temperature of 3.0°F?

9. By what percentage will the volume of a block of oak wood increase if the temperature is changed from 20.0°C to 100.0°C?

10. Because the mercury in a barometer and the brass scale do not expand in an equivalent manner, slightly different readings of the same pressure will result at different temperatures. Making use of the definition of density, and the relationship between the pressure of a liquid and its depth and density, plus pertinent ideas from the present chapter, show that if a barometer reads 760.00 mm at 0.0°C it will read 762.47 mm at 20.0°C.

11. A shelf must remain exactly 30.0 in. above the floor despite wide ranges of temperature. To achieve this, special legs are used, each made of two vertical rods of unequal length, one of which is brass and the other steel. The longer rod rests on the floor and projects above the shelf, and has the shorter rod attached to its top. The shelf is supported at the bottom of the shorter rod. How long is each of the rods?

12. A flask with a capacity of exactly 100 ml is made of soft glass. It is filled just to the point of overflowing with glycerin. If there is a 60.0C° rise in temperature, what volume of glycerin will overflow?

13. In a certain machine, a brass ring must fit snugly on a steel shaft which has a diameter of 3.00 cm when both are at 20.0°C. For assembly, the diameter of the ring must exceed that of the shaft by 0.0500 mm. At what minimum temperature (of both parts) must the assembly be performed?

14. A steel bar 6.00 ft long and 6.00 $in.^2$ in cross-sectional area is prevented from expanding while the temperature rises 135F°. Compute the resulting force.

15. A ring made of aluminum wire with a cross-sectional area of 1.00 mm^2 is heated and slipped over a copper shaft. When the ring has cooled to 40.0°C it is just a snug fit. Calculate the tensile force which develops in the ring as it cools to 20.0°C. Assume that the copper rod is always at 20.0°C.

18
CHANGE OF STATE

18-1 Preview

This chapter deals with the melting or solidification of a substance, and its vaporization or condensation. A review of the internal structure of matter will show that such changes cannot occur without energy being absorbed or evolved. We shall find that both the boiling point of a liquid and the quantity of heat needed to vaporize it depend strongly on the pressure. It will develop that the processes of evaporation and drying are not simple one-way processes.

18-2 Change of State: Definition

We have met the idea that matter may exist in any of three different phases or ***states:*** solid, liquid, and gaseous. A substance undergoes a ***change of state*** whenever it changes from any one of the three states to any other. Because it is very familiar in all three phases, water will be used as the principal example. Thus, the melting of ice is a change of state from solid to liquid; a change of state from liquid to gaseous occurs when water vaporizes; and the formation of frost involves a change of state from gaseous to solid. Many other substances can exist in any of the three states, as water does; but certain substances, due to their physical or chemical nature, may exist in only one or two of these states.

For example, at ordinary pressure solid carbon dioxide exhibits a change of state directly from the solid to the gaseous—which is why it is known as "dry ice." Iodine, when heated, shows the same change of state. The form of sulfur called "flowers of sulfur" is formed by condensation of the vapor directly to the solid state, as frost is. If we heat ordinary baking soda (sodium bicarbonate), it doesn't melt but decomposes to sodium carbonate. The latter can be melted, but it decomposes if we try to vaporize it. These changes in chemical composition are not changes of *state,* in the sense in which we use the term here.

18-3 Differences between the Internal Structure of a Solid and a Liquid

We have had previous glimpses of this topic, and related matters. You may wish to review Sec. 10-3 and 10-18.

In a crystalline solid, the particles which comprise the units of the crystal are restricted to fixed locations in the crystal lattice, but each is free to vibrate within its own limited region. The situation is crudely analogous to a cell block in a prison, with each prisoner able to move about within his cell but unable to escape its confinement. The bonds which maintain the rigid structure of the crystal are forces of mutual attraction among the molecules.

The particles of a liquid are not constrained to definite positions relative to one another. Mutual forces of attraction exist, but they are inadequate to prevent translational motion of the particles. Thus the particles are free to move about, somewhat as individuals can in a fairly dense crowd; hence the particles of a liquid possess translational energy, which the particles of a solid do not have. The forces of mutual attraction are sufficient, however, to keep the particles approximately as close together as they would be in a crystal, thus imposing a definite volume on the liquid.

18-4 Fusion and Solidification

We are accustomed to these facts: water put into the freezing compartment of a refrigerator changes to a mixture of ice and water, and finally entirely to ice; also, a piece of ice changes (at temperatures above freezing) into a mixture of ice and water, and finally entirely to liquid. But if we could prepare a mixture of ice and water at 0°C and prevent any energy whatever from entering or leaving the mixture, it would remain forever a mixture of the solid and liquid phases of water in equilibrium with each other. The ***melting point*** of any substance is that temperature at which equilibrium will exist between the solid and liquid phases of the substance, at normal pressure (760 mm of mercury), and this same temperature may be termed the ***freezing point.*** If heat is added to the mixture, some solid will melt. *If* enough is added, all the solid will disappear, and the temperature of the liquid will rise above the melting point. Conversely, withdrawal of heat will increase the quantity of the solid phase, and continued extraction of heat will produce a solid, with no liquid, at a temperature below the freezing point.

An analogy will help you to understand the change from the solid to the liquid phase, a process called ***fusion.*** You probably recall playing with a ball tethered at the end of a rubber thread. By holding the other end of the rubber string and moving your hand back and forth, you were able to set the ball into vibration in a more or less horizontal path. Moving your hand more energetically, you were able to increase the amplitude of the vibration, and you may have continued to add energy of vibration to the ball until it had enough to break the rubber string and escape.

Something rather similar happens when a crystalline solid such as ice, initially well below its freezing point, is warmed. As heat energy is added, the vibrational energies of the units in the crystal lattice are increased. The most obvious result of this is a rise in temperature, and in general the increased amplitude of vibration will cause some slight increase in volume, as we found in Chapter 17. Continued input of heat augments these vibrational energies to a point such that the individual particles can escape the bonds which have restricted them to their individual places in the crystal lattice. This destroys the lattice; which is to say that the solid has melted or ***fused.*** If we start with a liquid and cool it, the removal of heat causes—in fact, *is*—a reduction in the translational energies of the particles of the liquid. As their migrations slow to a more sedate pace, a point is reached at which one particle can no longer pass another but is trapped by the force of mutual attraction. Thus the orderly arrangement and rigid structure of the crystal lattice appear; the substance has changed to the solid state.

If I may change my analogy, think of a particle of the substance as being related in some respects to a rocket. For a rocket to rise, it must be given sufficient energy to move against the earth's gravitational field; and there is a minimum energy which it must have to escape that field. When it has escaped, much, and perhaps all, of its original store of kinetic energy has been changed into potential energy. If a rocket which has been in outer space returns to the earth, in doing so it loses the potential energy it acquired during its escape. In a crystal, the forces of mutual attraction constitute bonds which maintain the crystal lattice; and particles of a crystal can become particles of a liquid only if they acquire sufficient energy to escape from the bonds of the crystal structure. Having escaped, they possess this energy as potential energy. Since it is potential and remains so (so long as the substance doesn't return to the solid phase), it does not contribute to the motional energy and hence does not cause any change in the temperature. During solidification, the particles lose this potential energy as they reenter the crystalline structure.

To melt unit mass of any substance at normal pressure requires a definite quantity of heat energy, the amount being characteristic of that substance. This quantity of heat is the ***heat of fusion.*** Table 18-1 contains the heats of fusion of a number of substances.

18-5 Differences between the Internal Structure of a Liquid and a Gas

In a gas, the internal structure has reached the maximum of simplicity and freedom. Whereas in a liquid the average distance between particles is, to a first approximation, the same as in the solid state of the substance, in a gas the distance between adjacent particles is (in general) much greater, and there is no maximum imposed on this distance. Thus a gas has no fixed volume. In ordinary circumstances, the forces of mutual attraction are so weakened by the greater separation of the particles that, for most purposes, they may be ignored. Thus while developing Boyle's law, in Sec. 10-7, we were able to consider, as an excellent approximation in most cases, that

Table 18-1

HEATS OF FUSION AND HEATS OF VAPORIZATION

(Values, in calories per gram, at the normal melting and freezing points)

Substance	Heat of fusion	Heat of vaporization
Ammonia	108.1	327.1
Benzene	30.3	94.3
Ethyl alcohol	24.9	204
Mercury	2.82	70.6
Water	79.7*	539.6*

* For most purposes the heat of fusion of water may be taken as 80.0 cal/g, and its heat of vaporization as 540 cal/g.

pressure alone determines the volume of a given mass of gas at a fixed temperature. The molecules of a gas are essentially free to move wherever they will.

18-6 Vaporization and Condensation

Review of Sec. 10-18 and Fig. 10-13 will remind you that, though the forces of mutual attraction on any particle within the body of a liquid are symmetrical and have a resultant of zero, this is not true very near the surface. Here there is a resultant force directed inward from the surface, arising from the relative paucity of molecules of the substance in the gaseous phase above the surface. We saw that this situation gives rise to the phenomenon of surface tension.

The significance of this situation, with respect to vaporization and condensation, lies in the fact that a molecule in the liquid phase cannot escape unless it has at least a certain minimum quantity of energy.

Suppose that we have a vessel provided with a pressure gage and that we partially fill the vessel with water, pump out all the air, and seal the vessel. Whatever the temperature, the space above the liquid will soon be "filled" with water vapor. And this is the reason: though at any specific temperature there is a definite *average* energy of the water molecules in the liquid, the *individual* energies range far above and below the average; thus even at 0°C some molecules can escape through the surface and become molecules of water vapor. But this is not a one-way process. As soon as there are any molecules in the gas phase, their translational motion will cause some of them to strike the water and be trapped. At first, this recondensation is much less rapid than the vaporization, but after a time, the two processes will become equal in rate and equilibrium will exist. Though any molecule may be in the liquid phase one instant and in the vapor phase a moment later, there is no longer any *net* change. Since there will be a definite number of molecules per unit volume in the gas phase and a definite temperature, the pressure gage will give some definite reading (Sec. 10-4, 10-6). Raising the temperature by adding heat energy will increase the average energy of the molecules, so a larger fraction of the molecules in the liquid will have sufficient energy to escape; and when equilibrium is reestablished at the new temperature, the pressure of the vapor will be greater than before. If instead, heat energy is removed, the temperature will be reduced; also a smaller fraction of the molecules in the liquid phase can escape, so the pressure of the gas under equilibrium conditions will be smaller.

Thus we see that at any temperature there will be a pressure of the gaseous phase of a substance such that the liquid and gaseous phases are in equilibrium. This is the ***vapor pressure*** of the liquid at that temperature. The temperature at which the vapor pressure of a liquid is equal to normal atmospheric pressure is the ***boiling point*** of the liquid, which could also be called its ***condensation temperature,*** though it is more common to use the former term for condensation as well as for boiling. Various liquids have different boiling points, since at any particular temperature their vapor pressures will (in general) be unequal.

18-7 Vaporization and Condensation (continued)

To reduce the number of new ideas to be grasped at once, the preceding section did not discuss the reason for the requirement that a molecule must have a certain minimum quantity of energy in order to escape from the liquid phase.

The situation is similar to that of a particle in a crystal, which must have enough energy to overcome the bonds which hold it to the crystal lattice. Here, it is the surface tension forces which oppose the escape of the molecule. Any molecule reaching the surface (from within the liquid) will encounter this unbalanced opposing force, which has its origin in the relative paucity of the molecules above the surface. In addition, any gas above the surface will exert a pressure which tends to force the escaping molecules back into the liquid. Thus, if it has less than the requisite energy to overcome these restraints, the molecule will emulate a jumping fish, and fall back into the liquid. If, however, it does possess the necessary minimum of energy, or more, it will escape the liquid phase, trading kinetic energy for potential energy. If it returns later to the liquid phase, it will lose the potential energy and gain kinetic energy, thus adding to the thermal energy of the liquid. The analogy of the energy changes of a rocket is applicable here also.

The quantity of heat energy required to vaporize unit mass of a substance under normal atmospheric pressure is the ***heat of vaporization*** of the substance. Like heats of fusion, the heats of vaporization vary widely for different substances. Table 18-1 contains a few examples of heat of vaporization.

18-8 Calorimetry, Again

In Sec. 16-8, we learned how to make use of the principle of conservation of energy, and various concepts pertinent to heat, to solve calorimetric problems; but it was stated there that modifications would be necessary when situations involving change of state were met. The modification is simply the inclusion of a term (or terms) which expresses the quantity of heat absorbed or evolved during a change of state. If a mass m of a substance is melting or solidifying, such a term will have the form mq_f, in which q_f represents the heat of fusion of the substance. And if a mass m

of a substance which has a heat of vaporization q_v undergoes vaporization or condensation, the term will have the form mq_v.

Sample Problem 1

A cup which has a thermal capacity of 15.0 cal/C° contains 105.0 g of water at 15.0°C. Steam at 100.0°C is bubbled into the cup until 5.00 g have condensed. What is the final temperature?

As in Chapter 16, we commence with a statement of the conservation of energy, then express each quantity of heat in appropriate terms and enter it on the proper side of the equation. Quantities pertinent to the steam, the cup, and the water may be distinguished by the subscripts *s*, *c*, and *w*, respectively. After the steam has condensed, the resulting water will lose heat; the term which represents this heat loss is enclosed in parentheses with a subscript *s* to distinguish it from the term which indicates the heat gained by the water originally present. For the water from the steam, Δt is $(100.0 - t)$, and for the cup and the water it contains Δt is $(t - 15.0)$.

$$\text{HEAT LOSS} = \text{HEAT GAIN}$$

$$m_s(q_v)_s + (m_w s_w \, \Delta t_w)_s = c_c \, \Delta t_c + m_w s_w \, \Delta t_w$$

$$5.00\text{g} \cdot 540 \frac{\text{cal}}{\text{g}} + 5.00\text{g} \cdot 1.00 \frac{\text{cal}}{\text{gC}^\circ} \cdot (100.0 - t)\,\text{C}^\circ = 15.0 \frac{\text{cal}}{\text{C}^\circ} \cdot (t - 15.00)\,\text{C}^\circ + 105.0\text{g} \cdot 1.00 \frac{\text{cal}}{\text{gC}^\circ} \cdot (t - 15.00)\,\text{C}^\circ$$

$$2700 \text{ cal} + 500 \text{ cal} - 5.00t \text{ cal} = 15.0t \text{ cal} - 225 \text{ cal} + 105.0t \text{ cal} - 1575 \text{ cal}$$

$$5000 \text{ cal} = 125.0t \text{ cal}$$

$$t = 5000/125.0 = 40.0^\circ\text{C}$$

Sample Problem 2

A calorimeter cup has a thermal capacity of 25.0 cal/C°, and it contains 75.0 g of water and 20.0 g of ice. A 50.0 g mass of copper pellets at 250°C is added to the cup and the contents stirred. Determine the final condition of the system.

We can approach this problem much as we did the preceding one, equating the heat lost by the copper to the total heat necessary to melt the ice and warm the cup and contents to the final temperature. The solution will be left to you; it comes out that the final temperature is about −3.6°C.

Quite obviously something is wrong—though a ridiculous answer like this is too common on quiz papers!

How can the addition of the *hot* copper *lower* the temperature *below* the initial temperature of the cup and its contents? This is impossible. What happened was that the heat available in the copper was insufficient to melt all the ice; so the problem of "determining the final condition of the system" is a matter of finding how much ice is left, *not* a matter of solving for a new temperature. Since the cup and the water in it were at 0°C and remained at that temperature, they neither gained nor lost heat, and we may safely ignore them. Thus the problem simplifies to the following:

HEAT LOST BY COPPER = HEAT GAINED BY ICE

$$m_c s_c \, \Delta t_c = m_i q_f$$

$$50.0\text{g} \cdot 0.0921 \frac{\text{cal}}{\text{gC}^\circ} \cdot (250 - 0)\,\text{C}^\circ = m_i \text{ g} \cdot 79.7 \frac{\text{cal}}{\text{g}}$$

$$1151 \text{ cal} = 79.7 m_i \text{ cal}$$

$$m_i = 1151/79.7 = 14.4\text{g}$$

Thus 14.4 g of ice will have melted, leaving 5.6 g.

18-9 Dependence of Freezing Point on Pressure

The temperature at which a substance melts, or solidifies, may show a dependence on pressure. This is in accordance with a very general law of nature which says: If any change is imposed on a system which initially was in equilibrium, an adjustment occurs which tends to compensate for the change.* Consider three cases of solids at their normal melting points. If a substance contracts on solidifying, an augmentation of pressure will enable it to solidify at a higher temperature, since a pressure increase favors a reduction in volume; so its freezing point will rise as the pressure is increased. If, on the other hand, a substance expands as it freezes, a higher pressure will oppose that expansion more strongly, and a lower temperature must be attained before freezing will occur. Only if the density of a substance at its melting point is the same in the liquid and solid phases will its melting point be independent of pressure.

Water is an example of a substance which expands (by about 9%) as it freezes. As a result, its freezing point is lowered by an increase in pressure. Few ice skaters realize that the blades of their skates are not gliding on ice but on a film of water which results from this momentary reduction of melting point due to the extreme pressure of the blade.

18-10 Dependence of Boiling Point on Pressure

There is no variation among different substances in the effect of pressure on the boiling point, as we found there to be for their freezing points. The volume of a given mass of any substance is greater in gaseous form than as a liquid. Thus any increase in pressure must oppose the formation of the vapor phase, and so require that a higher temperature be attained

* For example, a ship floats because there is equilibrium between its weight and the weight of the water it displaces. When the ship receives a cargo, equilibrium is upset momentarily, but the ship sinks a bit lower and displaces just enough more water to compensate for the weight of the cargo. Again, if you have a sample of gas under equilibrium conditions, any reduction in volume causes a pressure increase (unless the temperature is lowered) which tends to oppose any further decrease of volume. If you have studied chemistry, you've met examples in the law of mass action and in Le Chatelier's principle.

before boiling can occur. Conversely, a reduction of pressure must lower the boiling point.

These facts are evident also if we recall the discussion in Sec. 18-6. As the temperature of a liquid rises, so does its vapor pressure. Boiling, or ***ebullition,*** will occur when the vapor pressure becomes equal to the pressure above the surface of the liquid. This equality of pressure will enable bubbles of the vapor phase of the liquid to form within the body of the liquid,* but the production of such bubbles is impossible if the vapor pressure is less than the external pressure. Hence any increase in pressure will prevent boiling until the vapor pressure is equally augmented, and this can occur only at an elevated temperature.

18-11 Variation of the Value of the Heat of Vaporization

As the definition in Sec. 18-7 states, the term "heat of vaporization" refers, in the absence of any specification to the contrary, to the quantity of heat needed to vaporize unit mass of a liquid at its normal boiling point. However, we have just seen that the boiling point may not be "normal"; and if it isn't, the value of the heat of vaporization will be different from the normal value.

To determine its value at a temperature other than the normal boiling point, we again invoke the law of conservation of energy. If a given quantity of energy is required to convert a system from an initial thermal condition to a final thermal condition by any method, precisely the same quantity would be necessary to accomplish the identical over-all change by any other method. Thus if we vaporize a liquid at its normal boiling point and then heat the vapor to some higher temperature, the same quantity of energy will heat the liquid to the new temperature and vaporize it at that temperature. But since the specific heat will not be the same in the gaseous phase as in the liquid, the two heats of vaporization will be different. The sample problem below will clarify this.

Sample Problem 3

At a pressure 10% above normal atmospheric pressure, water boils at about 102.3°C. What is the heat of vaporization at this temperature?

The heat of vaporization at 100.0°C is 539.6 cal/g. The specific heat of liquid water is 1.00 cal/(gC°) but that of steam is about 0.48 cal/(gC°). If the heat of vaporization at 102.3°C is q'_v, the heat required to warm 1 g of liquid water from 100.0°C to 102.3°C and vaporize it at that temperature is $(1.00 \cdot 2.3 + q'_v)$ cal;

---

* Actually, this can occur only at the surface, since the pressure beneath the surface necessarily exceeds that at the surface. Thus, the boiling point of a liquid really is a range of temperatures, increasing at greater depths. In most practical cases we can ignore this, however; for example, the increase for water is less than 0.003C° per cm of depth.

and that necessary to vaporize it at 100.0°C and warm the steam to 102.3°C is (539.6 + 0.48 · 2.3) cal. Therefore,

$$1.00 \cdot 2.3 + q'_v = 539.6 + 0.48 \cdot 2.3$$
$$2.3 + q'_v = 539.6 + 1.10$$
$$q'_v = 539.6 + 1.1 - 2.3 = 538.4$$

So the heat of vaporization of water at 102.3°C is approximately 538.4 cal/g.

18-12 Drying

Evaporation of liquids and drying of wet fabric occur at temperatures far below the boiling points of the liquids, because at any temperature some of the molecules in a liquid have sufficient energy to enable them to escape into the gas phase.

However, we have seen that for a given liquid, such as water, there is one definite vapor pressure for each specific temperature. This seems to imply that if a damp towel is hung on a clothesline, it should dry at a rate—hence, in a time—which depends *solely* on the temperature. But this is contrary to experience; it will dry much more rapidly on a dry, breezy day than on a still, dry day, and the drying will be much slower on a humid day—even though the temperatures are identical.

Actually, there is no contradiction whatever, for the rate of drying is a *differential* rate—the *difference* between the rate at which molecules leave the liquid phase and depart from the towel (to pursue the same example) and the rate at which molecules of water vapor in the air return to the towel. On a dry and windy day, the air contains little water, and that which evaporates from the towel will be carried away from it; so recondensation will have very little effect. If there is no wind, the water vapor resulting from the evaporation will not be removed from the vicinity so readily; so there will be more recondensation, hence slower drying. And if the day is very humid, the condensation rate may nearly equal the evaporation rate; so drying is extremely slow. After a time, nearly all the water molecules initially present will have left, but they will have been replaced, in large part, by other molecules from the damp air.

18-13 Cooling by Evaporation and Warming by Freezing

We found in Sec. 18-7 that vaporization cannot occur unless the heat of vaporization is supplied from some source. This necessarily means that whenever evaporation occurs spontaneously, the remainder of the liquid, or something else in the environment, must be cooled. If the liquid is perspiration on your skin, the most copious source of heat is your body. This is the basis of the system by which our bodies keep the body temperature down when we exercise, or on very hot days. If there is a larger mass of liquid, the liquid itself is cooled; this fact is the basis of applications ranging from industrial cooling towers to camp coolers consisting of wet burlap wrapped around an orange crate. When a liquid evaporates below its boiling point, only the molecules with relatively high energies can escape; the "hot" molecules leave, and the "cold" molecules remain behind.

When a gas condenses to a liquid, its heat of vaporization is evolved. Thus a burn from steam may be worse than from water at the same temperature.

Similarly, heat of fusion is evolved as a liquid freezes. The juices of vegetables and fruits, being solutions, freeze at lower temperatures than does water; so tubs of water have been placed in vegetable cellars to minimize or prevent freezing of the vegetables. As the temperature drops the water freezes, giving off its heat of fusion, and this may keep the temperature of the cellar above the freezing point of the vegetables.

18-14 Sublimation

Sublimation is a phase change directly from the solid state to the gaseous phase. The term "condensation" refers to the reverse of sublimation as well as to the opposite of vaporization, though the latter meaning is far more common. Examples of sublimation were given in the second paragraph of Sec. 18-2. Since sublimation and the reverse are the least common changes of state, I shall not pursue the topic beyond mentioning a few analogies. Sublimation temperature corresponds to boiling point and is sensitive to pressure for the same reason the boiling point is. Heat of sublimation is analogous to heat of vaporization, and its value also depends on the pressure under which the sublimation occurs.

Summary

Any conversion of a substance from a *solid*, a *liquid*, or a *gas* to *either* of the *other two* phases is a *change of state*. *Fusion* of a substance requires energy to *disrupt the bonds of the crystal lattice* and allow the particles to escape. *Vaporization* requires energy to cause *relatively great separation between molecules* and to enable the vapor phase to expand against the external pressure. Energy used to produce fusion is retained by the particles as potential energy, and the same is true of energy employed to cause vaporization.

A liquid has a *vapor pressure* at *any temperature* (except 0°K), its value being greater at higher temperatures. The liquid will *boil* when its vapor pressure becomes equal to the external pressure. Its normal *boiling point* is the temperature at which its vapor pressure equals normal atmospheric pressure. The *freezing point* of a substance is the temperature at which the liquid and crystalline phases will be in equilibrium.

The boiling point of a liquid depends strongly on the *pressure*, rising with increasing pressure. The freezing point may or may not be affected by pressure changes.

The value of the heat of vaporization of a liquid varies as the temperature at which boiling (or evaporation) occurs is altered.

Drying is a differential process.

Self-Quiz

1. Distinguish among the three states of matter on the basis of their internal structure.

2. Define fusion, vaporization, solidification, condensation, sublimation, melting point, freezing point, heat of fusion, heat of vaporization. Point out any pair(s) of synonyms and any pair(s) of antonyms. In some cases, a single term may have two rather different meanings. Which are they, and why doesn't confusion result from the contradictory meanings?

3. What happens when a crystalline solid is melted? Why is energy required? What becomes of this energy? Why doesn't the delivery of this energy raise the temperature of the substance?

4. Discuss vaporization, and the energy involved, as the preceding question asks you to discuss fusion.

5. If ice forms because the temperature of the environment drops, how can the process of freezing *produce* heat energy?

6. In a steam radiator, what is the major source of the heat?

7. Explain clearly the origin of the force which tends to prevent a molecule of a liquid from passing outward through the surface.

8. What fact is the basis of the ability of a liquid to evaporate at a temperature below its boiling point? In what way does this ability vary as the temperature changes, and why?

9. Check the units carefully (if you didn't before) throughout Sample Problems 1 and 2. Are all the equations homogeneous? Assign units in Sample Problem 3 and check for homogeneity.

10. Give at least one other example similar to those in the footnote in Sec. 18-9.

11. If you know that increasing pressure raises the melting point of a substance, what can you conclude regarding the relative densities of the solid and liquid phases at the normal melting point? Explain clearly.

12. Why isn't there an obvious streak of water on the ice after a skate blade has passed over the ice?

13. Present two clear and independent (though equivalent) explanations of the effect of pressure on boiling point.

14. On the basis of a flash judgment, would you expect the heat of vaporization of water to be greater when water evaporates at room temperature than when it boils, or less? Now analyze the situation as in Sec. 18-11 and Sample Problem 3.

15. An electric fan *raises* the temperature by exactly the same amount the same quantity of electric energy delivered to a heating coil would, yet you use an electric fan to *cool* you. Resolve this apparent contradiction.

Problems

1. How many grams of ice at 0.0°C could be melted by the quantity of thermal energy which would vaporize 10.0 g of water at 100.0°C?

2. A calorimeter cup which has a thermal capacity of 16.0 cal/C° contains 64.0 g of water at 90.0°C. Ice is added, and after thermal equilibrium is established the temperature is 5.0°C. What mass of ice was used?

3. A calorimeter contains water at 50.0°C before 40.0 g of ice at 0.0°C are put into the calorimeter. Steam at 100.0°C is then bubbled in until the temperature is again at 50.0°C. Calculate the mass of steam added.

4. Ice at 0.0°C is put into a pan on a stove at 9:00:00. At 9:03:00 the ice has melted completely and the temperature is 0.0°C. If heat continued to be added to the contents of the pan at the same rate, (a) at what time would the water commence to boil and (b) at what time would the last of the water be evaporated?

5. A calorimeter cup has a thermal capacity of 20.0 cal/C° and contains 90.0 g of water at 5.0°C. Steam at 120.0°C is bubbled in until 10.0 g of steam have condensed. Compute the final temperature. Take the specific heat of steam as 0.48 cal/(gC°).

6. A calorimeter cup contains 675 g of water and 175 g of ice. The cup has a thermal capacity of 75.0 cal/(gC°). Determine the final condition of the system after 20.0 g of steam at 100.0°C have been added and thermal equilibrium established.

7. A calorimeter cup has a thermal capacity of 30.0 cal/(gC°) and it contains 120 g of water and 25.0 g of ice. What will the equilibrium condition of the system be after 8.00 g of steam at 100.0°C are added?

8. A calorimeter cup is made of aluminum and has a mass of 100 g. It contains 700 g of water and 25.0 g of ice initially. Steam at 100.0°C is bubbled in until thermal equilibrium exists. Determine the final temperature and mass of the system.

9. Compute the heat of fusion of ice at −12.0°C. Take the specific heat of ice as 0.496 cal/(gC°) and the heat of fusion at 0.0°C as 79.7 cal/g.

10. If the specific heat of water vapor is 0.434 cal/(gC°) and the heat of vaporization of water at 100.0°C is 539.6 cal/g, determine the heat of vaporization at 20.0°C.

11. No hailstone ever strikes the ground with sufficient kinetic energy to melt the ice which composes it. What minimum velocity at impact would be required?

12. Assume that a lead bullet has a temperature of 27° C and a speed of 1,000 ft/sec when it strikes an impenetrable wall. *If* the entire kinetic energy of the bullet were available to heat it to the melting point and melt part of it, what per cent of the mass of the bullet would melt? Take the specific heat over this range of temperatures as 0.0325 cal/(gC°), the melting point as 327° C, and the heat of fusion as 5.86 cal/g.

20

818 x 36000

1760

818

20

16360

19
HEAT TRANSFER

19-1 Preview

This chapter will treat two direct methods and one indirect method by which thermal energy may be transferred from one location to another. In one case, the discussion will lead to a new view of the internal structure of metals, and this will provide a basis for understanding the electrical conductivity of metals (in Chapter 21) as well as their thermal conductivity. In another case, we shall encounter something which classical physics is unable to explain, and which is the seed in which the quantum concept had its genesis.

19-2 Processes of Heat Transfer, Direct and Indirect

There are two quite different processes by which thermal energy may be transferred from one point to another. These are conduction and convection. In addition there is a process which has the over-all effect of transferring thermal energy, but which does not transfer it as such. The situation is analogous to the "transmission of sound" by telephone or radio. No *sound* whatever is transmitted. Sound energy is used to produce fluctuations of electric current or to modulate electromagnetic waves, the currents or waves are transmitted, and then they are used to recreate sounds. In an analogous manner, radiation is a process in which internal energy is transformed to radiant energy, later being changed back to thermal energy.

Conduction will be considered in Sec. 19-3 – 19-6, inclusive; convection in Sec. 19-7, 19-8; and radiation in Sec. 19-9 – 19-12, inclusive.

19-3 Conduction

We have seen that the macroscopic entity we call the thermal energy of a body is the summation of the microscopic energies of its particles (Sec. 16-5). Consider a homogeneous body which has a uniform temperature throughout. There will be statistical fluctuations of the microscopic energies, some particles having (momentarily) more energy and some less than the average value appropriate to the existing temperature. However, in any macroscopic portion of the body (such as a cube 1 mm on a side) the total thermal energy will be the same as in any other equivalent portion.

If, however, heat energy is delivered to one portion of the body, the microscopic energies of the particles there will be augmented. Whether their energy is translational or vibrational, they will jostle their neighbors more severely (on the average) than before, thus increasing the motions and hence the energies of those neighbors. These particles, in turn, will jostle other particles farther from the point at which heat energy is being supplied to the body; and the process continues. To some degree, this mechanism of transmission of heat energy is analogous to the propagation of a pulse of compression in an elastic medium (Sec. 13-3). The transmission of heat energy by this method is known as heat ***conduction.***

Thermal conduction occurs in solids, liquids, and gases. In fluids, however, it usually is unimportant for two reasons. First, in general, fluids are rather poor conductors of heat. Second, heat transfer by convection takes place in fluids, and normally this is far more effective than conduction. There is a wide variation in the effectiveness of different solids as conductors of heat.

19-4 Thermal Conductivity

Even if flexibility were not a problem we would not make clothing of aluminum or copper, and we don't make cooking utensils of asbestos. We are well aware that these metals are good conductors of heat, and we think of asbestos as a heat "insulator." However, nothing whatever is able to block heat flow completely. An "insulator" is merely a substance which is a very poor conductor.

The effectiveness, or ineffectiveness, of a substance as a conductor of heat is indicated by the value of its ***coefficient of thermal conductivity.*** Figure 19-1 will provide a basis for defining this term. A cube 1 cm on a side is represented in Fig. 19-1(a). Heat is applied uniformly over one face of the cube, as symbolized by the incoming arrow, and it flows out of the opposite face, as indicated by the other arrow. There is a temperature drop of 1 Celsius degree between these two faces of the cube. Under these circumstances, the heat flowing through the cube in 1 sec is the measure of the coefficient of thermal conductivity of the substance of which the cube is made. Thus we may define this coefficient as the quantity of heat which will flow between opposite faces of a 1 cm cube in 1 sec, when the difference in temperature between the faces is 1 Celsius degree.

The definition is somewhat different if English units are used in place of metric. Figure 19-1(b) represents a block of material 1 ft square but only 1 in. thick. The coefficient of thermal conductivity of the material is the quantity of heat which would flow from one of the broad faces of the block to the other in 1 sec when there is a temperature difference of 1 Fahrenheit degree between these faces.

Values of thermal conductivity coefficients of some substances are given in Table 19-1.

19-5 Determination of the Quantity of Heat Conducted

Obviously, an increase in the area through which heat can be conducted will increase the rate of heat flow, and the greater the temperature drop

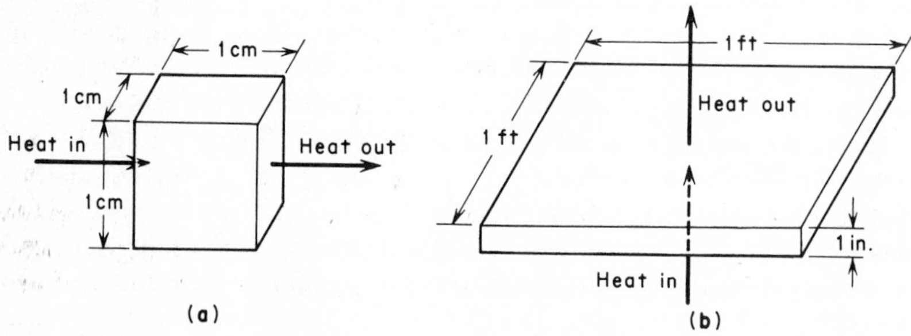

Fig. 19-1. Bases of definitions of coefficient of thermal conductivity.

Table 19-1

COEFFICIENTS OF THERMAL CONDUCTIVITY*

Values in cal/(cm C°sec)†

Metals		Non-metallic solids	
Substance	k	Substance	$k \cdot 10^4$
Aluminum	.49	Asbestos fiber	1.9
Copper	.92	Brick	15
Steel	.11	Concrete	22
Silver	.97	Window glass	25
		Wood (fir, across grain)	0.9

Liquids		Gases	
Substance	$k \cdot 10^4$	Substance	$k \cdot 10^5$
Benzene	3.3	Air	6
Glycerin	6.5	Carbon dioxide	4
Water	14	Helium	35

* Since values vary with temperature, precise values cannot be given. Those stated in the table are approximate values at ordinary temperatures.

† To convert to (Btu in.)/(ft² F°sec) multiply by 0.806.

along the path of the heat flow, the greater the rate of heat flow will be. For a given temperature difference, the heat flow will be more rapid if the length of the path over which it flows is shorter, and vice versa. Also, it is obvious that the quantity of heat flow will be the product of the rate and the time. Finally, the rate and hence the quantity will depend on the effectiveness of the substance as a heat conductor, as indicated by the value of its coefficient of thermal conductivity.

Thus, if Q is the quantity of heat which flows in T seconds through a body which has a cross-sectional area A and a length or thickness l when the temperature difference between the ends of the path is Δt, and if the material has a thermal conductivity coefficient k,

$$Q = \frac{kA\,\Delta tT}{l} \qquad (19\text{-}1)$$

In the metric system, Q is in calories, A in cm^2, Δt in C°, T in sec, and l in cm; thus the units of k must be cal/(cmC°sec). But in the English system, the units of A and l are inconsistent, and a similar analysis shows that k has as its units (Btu in.)/(ft^2 F°sec).

Often the actual temperature difference Δt and the length of the path of heat flow l are less important or less convenient than the ratio of these two quantities, $\Delta t/l$, which is the ***thermal gradient.*** This term, and its significance, can be remembered by analogy with the gradient (slope) of an inclined plane. The greater the gradient of the plane, the greater the acceleration of a sliding or rolling body on the plane; and the greater the thermal gradient, the greater the rate of heat flow. Sometimes Eq. (19-1) is more convenient in the equivalent form

$$Q = kAT \cdot \frac{\Delta t}{l} \tag{19-2}$$

Sample Problem 1

A window pane is 24 in. wide, 30 in. high, and exactly $\frac{1}{8}$ in. thick. If its coefficient of thermal conductivity is

$$2.0 \cdot 10^{-3} \text{ (Btu in.)/(ft}^2\text{ F}^\circ\text{sec)}$$

how much heat will be conducted through the pane in 1 hr, when the temperature is 72°F inside and just freezing outside?

The value of A must be in ft², so

$$(24 \cdot 30) \text{ in.}^2 = (2.0 \cdot 2.5) \text{ ft}^2 = 5.0 \text{ ft}^2$$

Δt is 72°F − 32°F = 40 F°. In 1 hr there are $3.6 \cdot 10^3$ sec. Then, according to Eq. (19-1),

$$Q = \frac{(2.0 \cdot 10^{-3}) \cdot 5.0 \cdot 40 \cdot (3.6 \cdot 10^3)}{1/8}$$

$$= 1.15 \cdot 10^4 \text{ Btu}$$

Sample Problem 2

What thermal gradient would be required to cause 500 cal of heat per minute to flow along an aluminum rod 4.0 cm² in cross-sectional area? The thermal conductivity coefficient for aluminum is 0.49 cal/(cm C° sec).

Equation (19-2) may be rearranged to

$$\frac{\Delta t}{l} = \frac{Q}{kAT}$$

$$= \frac{500}{0.49 \cdot 4.0 \cdot 60} = 4.3 \text{ C}^\circ/\text{cm}$$

19-6 Heat Conduction in Metals

A glance at Table 19-1 reveals that metals have much higher coefficients of thermal conductivity than do non-metals. This is a familiar fact, though you may not have thought of it just this way. It is equally well known that metals are much better conductors of electric currents than non-metals are. There is no coincidence here. The excellence of metals for both types of conductivity rests on a difference between their internal structure and that of other substances.

Commencing in Chapter 21, we shall consider something of the internal structure of an individual atom, and Chapter 33 will be devoted to this topic. For the present, we must content ourselves with a preliminary peek into this fascinating field.

Any and all atoms consist of a central core or nucleus which bears a positive charge of electricity. Surrounding this nucleus somewhat as the planets "surround" the sun are electrons—anywhere from 1 electron per atom of hydrogen to 92 electrons per atom of uranium, and more in the case of the artificially produced "transuranic" elements. Each electron is identical with any other and consists essentially of a charge of negative electricity. The positive charge on the nucleus is equal in magnitude to the total negative charge of the electrons in the atom. Opposite kinds of electric charges (positive and negative) attract each other strongly, so the nucleus of an atom attracts the electrons which surround it.

Somewhat as each planet occupies its own orbit around the sun, groups of electrons may be thought of as occupying definite orbits or shells around the nucleus of the atom. For each such shell of electrons, there is a particular number of electrons which will make the atom most stable, and the electrons in the outermost shell or shells are responsible for the chemical and physical properties of the element to which that atom belongs.

It is known that in general an atom of a metal has relatively few electrons in its outermost shell. Abundant chemical evidence shows that in a chemical reaction atoms tend toward a stable configuration of their outermost shells, but metals do this by losing electrons from that shell and non-metals do it by acquiring extra electrons. Thus it appears that atoms of non-metals hang onto their normal complement of electrons more tenaciously than do atoms of metals, and this is confirmed by direct measurements of the energy required to remove a single electron.

In spite of this difference, so long as a single atom is isolated it will jealously guard its full complement of electrons, whether it is an atom of a metal or a non-metal. But the situation is vastly different in any macroscopic bit of matter containing many atoms. Atoms of a non-metal retain their own electrons as tenaciously as before. In a metal, however, the relatively loosely held outermost electrons may become associated as much with one nucleus as with another; they are not definitely associated with any particular atom. Thus, any one of these "free" electrons may wander from atom to atom as it wishes, much as a molecule of gas may migrate with virtually no restrictions except the walls of the containing vessel.

For these reasons, we may think of the geometrical space within the boundaries of a piece of metal as containing an "electron gas" which moves freely through the space almost as if there were no atoms there. As the temperature rises, the average energy of the electrons in this "electron gas" is augmented, though the relationship is very different than for an actual gas. This increase in energy is propagated through the "electron gas," and this process accounts for the major portion of the thermal conductivity of the metal.

19-7 Convection

We have seen in Chapter 17 that in general a rise in the temperature of a substance causes an expansion and hence a reduction of density. This decrease in density tends to cause a circulation of the fluid, the heated portion rising and being replaced by cooler portions. Thus thermal energy is carried from one location to another by mass motion of the substance itself. This process of heat transfer is known as ***convection.***

Thus, in Fig. 19-2, the pressure of the liquid at the bottom of the container will be the product of the depth and the density—Eq. (10-6). If heat is being applied beneath point A, the liquid there will be heated and its density reduced. Therefore the average density of the column of liquid above point A will be less than that above point B, and the excess of pressure at B will cause liquid to flow from B toward A. Thus the warmed liquid at A is forced upward, carrying its newly acquired thermal energy with it. So long as the source of heat remains beneath A, this inequality of densities and hence of pressures will exist, so an automatic circulation is set up which carries heat to all portions of the vessel.

Viewing the same situation a bit differently, any mass of heated liquid above A will displace more than its own weight of cool fluid. Thus we have Archimedes' principle involved, and the cooler liquid must exert a buoyant force on the warm liquid. This causes the heated liquid to rise; cooler liquid takes its place, is heated and expands, and is buoyed up by the cooler liquid. So, again, we find an automatic and continuing circulatory process carrying the thermal energy away from its source. Since Eq. (10-6) isn't applicable to gases, the argument in the preceding paragraph is not adequate for convection in gases; but Archimedes' principle applies to gases as well as to liquids.

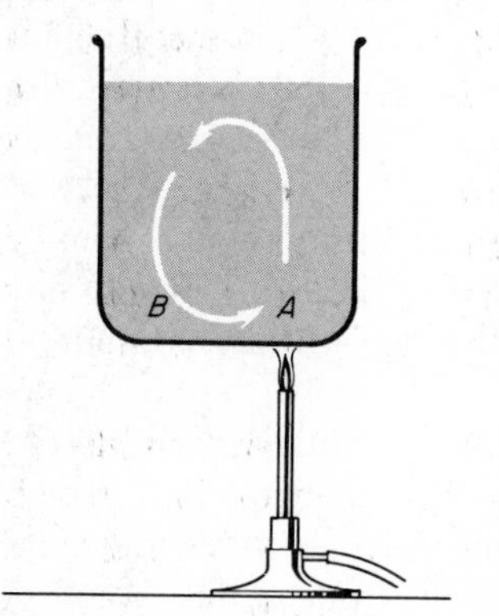

Fig. 19-2. Convection in a liquid.

We shall not be able to set up a quantitative relationship for the rate of heat transfer by convection, but we can consider the matter qualitatively. The greater the coefficient of thermal expansion of a fluid, the greater the reduction in the density of the heated fluid, and hence the more rapid the circulation. The higher the specific heat of the fluid, the more thermal energy will be transferred by any given circulation rate. A higher viscosity will mean a reduction in the rate of heat transfer since the circulatory flow will be slower. And obviously, any mechanical hindrances to the movement of the fluid will reduce the transfer of heat by convection.

19-8 "Warmth" of Wool and Similar Substances

The last sentence of the preceding section is far more important than it may appear, for within it lies the reason for the warmth of woolen fabrics, the heat insulating properties of fiberboards, etc. The coefficient of thermal conductivity of air is only about $6 \cdot 10^{-5}$ cal/(cm C° sec), which is far smaller than most other values in Table 19-1. In a fabric or any other open fibrous material, the solid fibers themselves occupy little space. Most of the space is in the tiny airfilled interstices between fibers. Because of the small dimensions of these interstices, almost no convection can occur, so any heat which passes must be *conducted* through the air spaces. Thus it isn't the wool itself which insulates, it is the air trapped in the fabric. If the air is replaced with water, which has a thermal conductivity three or four times as great as that of air, the fabric isn't nearly so "warm." The fact that the fibers themselves play little part in heat insulation is even more evident if we compare the coefficient of thermal conductivity of glass wool with that of the glass from which it is made; the ratio is approximately 1 to 20.

19-9 Radiation

As noted in Sec. 19-2, radiation is not, strictly speaking, a process of heat transfer. ***Radiation*** is a process in which internal energy in one body generates electromagnetic waves; when these waves are absorbed by another body, they generate thermal energy in that body. This is analogous to using electrical energy at one location to charge a storage battery (which involves changing the electrical energy to chemical energy), carrying the battery to another point, and there using its chemical energy to produce electric current. The electromagnetic waves which carry the energy have longer wavelengths than those of light, and their wavelengths are shorter than those of radio waves; but all these kinds of waves have essentially the same nature.

The rate at which energy is radiated from unit area of the surface of a body is directly proportional to the fourth power of the temperature of the body, the temperature being measured on an *absolute* scale. In general, however, two bodies at the same temperature and with the same surface area will not radiate at equal rates. The term ***emissivity*** applies to an index of the relative effectiveness of a surface as a radiator. The best radiator is a so-called ***black body,*** for which the value of the emissivity is unity. The blacker and duller a surface is, the more nearly its radiations will approximate those of a perfect black body. Lighter colors, and a more polished surface, will radiate less effectively; if (for example) the rate of radiation per unit area is one-third that of a black body under equivalent circumstances, the emissivity of the surface is 1/3.

The algebraic expression of these relationships is

$$Q = e\sigma T^4 \tag{19-3}$$

in which Q is the quantity of energy radiated per second from each square centimeter of surface at a temperature of T°K, if the emissivity of the surface is e; σ is a proportionality constant which has a value of

$$5.67 \cdot 10^{-5} \frac{\text{ergs}}{\text{cm}^2 \text{ sec } (\text{K}^\circ)^4}, \quad \text{or} \quad 5.67 \cdot 10^{-8} \frac{\text{watts}}{\text{m}^2\ (\text{K}^\circ)^4},$$

or

$$1.35 \cdot 10^{-8} \frac{\text{cal}}{\text{m}^2 \text{ sec } (\text{K}^\circ)^4}$$

Sample Problem 3

A body which has a surface area of 5.00 cm² and a temperature of 727°C radiates $3.00 \cdot 10^9$ ergs of energy each minute. What is its emissivity?

Since, in Eq. (19-3), Q is in ergs/(cm² sec), the value of Q is

$$\frac{3.00 \cdot 10^9}{5.00 \cdot 60} \quad \text{or} \quad 1.00 \cdot 10^7 \text{ ergs/(cm}^2 \text{ sec)}$$

T has a value of 727 + 273 or 1000°K. Thus,

$$1.00 \cdot 10^7 = e \cdot 5.67 \cdot 10^{-5} \cdot 1000^4 = 5.67 \cdot 10^7 e$$

$$1 = 5.67e, \quad \text{and} \quad e = \frac{1}{5.67} = 0.176$$

19-10 "Radiation of Cold"

Probably you realize that a literal interpretation of the heading of this section is meaningless. How can *absence* of thermal energy be radiated?! Yet if you hold your hand near a block of ice without touching it your hand "feels" the "cold" of the ice.

The explanation of this seeming paradox lies in Eq. (19-3), which says quite plainly that *everything* is continually radiating energy, since *nothing* has a temperature of 0.0°K. Thus your hand is radiating, and hence, losing energy. The ice is also radiating, and losing energy. But because of the higher temperature of your hand, energy is leaving your hand at a rate in excess of the rate at which it is being received from the ice. Thus the net result is a loss of energy from your hand, and a resultant cooling. But the cooling effect is not nearly so great as it would be if the ice were present but not radiating at all.

This exchange of radiant energy has many applications. For example, you may be chilly in a room even though a thermometer reads 72°F, if the walls are cold; but you may be comfortable in a room with warm walls when the temperature is considerably lower. This is the basis of "radiant heating" systems, which do *not* heat you by radiation but do decrease your net radiation loss.

19-11 Absorption of Radiant Energy

Through mechanisms which we are not in a position to investigate, radiant energy received by a body agitates the particles of which the body is composed, thereby increasing their motional energy; thus energy of radiation is changed back into thermal energy.

We found that the effectiveness of a body as a radiator depends on the character of its surface, so we should expect different surfaces to be unequal in their ability to absorb radiations. Is the ability to absorb radiations related to the ability to emit them? And, if so, just what is the relationship? We may find a definite answer with no experimental equipment other than our reason.

In Fig. 19-3 we have two bodies, *A* and *B*. They are identical in every respect, including temperature, except that the surface of *A* which faces toward *B* is a poor radiator whereas the surface of *B* which faces *A* is a good radiator. The two bodies are isolated in an evacuated space so that we may ignore all outside influences. Let us *assume* that a poor radiator is a good absorber, and vice versa, and see where this assumption will lead us.

Because of the differences in the surfaces facing each other, the thermal energy in *B* will be transformed into radiant energy and sent across to *A* at a rate in excess of the rate at which *A* is delivering radiant energy to *B*. Since *B* is losing energy more rapidly than *A* is, its temperature will tend to drop more rapidly. According to our assumption, the relatively large amount of radiant energy reaching *A* from *B* will be effectively absorbed, while even the small quantity which *B* receives from *A* will be absorbed very poorly. Thus *A* must gain energy more rapidly than *B* does. Since we have outlawed any energy transfer to, or from, the outside, and since the total quantity of energy should remain constant, these processes must result in a net transfer of energy from *B* to *A*. Hence the temperature of *A* must rise and that of *B* must fall. If both *A* and *B* contain coils of pipe, we can heat water in *A* to run a steam engine and cool a refrigerant gas in *B* to operate a freezer. And we started with two bodies at

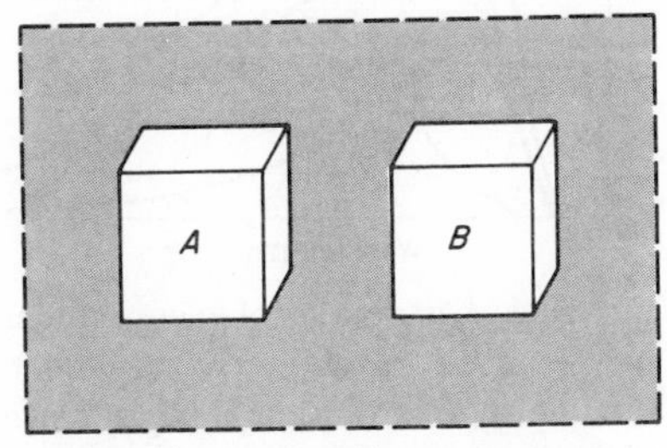

Fig. 19-3. An isolated system of two almost identical bodies at the same temperature.

the same temperature, and we've expended no energy whatever on them! This is even better than perpetual motion!

But the law of conservation of energy has not yet been repealed, and there seems to be no prospect that it will be; so obviously neither our engine nor our refrigerator will operate in this sort of an arrangement. The basic reason is that any spontaneously occurring process involves an increase in the entropy of the system, as we found in Sec. 16-12. But since the entropy change is $\Delta Q/T$, if a quantity of heat energy ΔQ were transferred, as we have imagined, from a lower to a higher temperature, the entropy would be *de*creased. Thus the second law of thermodynamics tells us that our conclusions are impossible of realization, and therefore the assumption on which they were based is untenable. Thus we must conclude that the effectiveness—or ineffectiveness—of a surface as a radiator must be *exactly* matched by its characteristics as an absorber. The slightest mismatch would constitute a violation of the conservation principle.

You may have recognized that the argument in this section is an example of the device logicians call *reductio ad absurdum*—reduction to an absurdity. It is a trick which often is very handy.

19-12 A Fissure in the Ramparts of Classical Physics

Like the energies of individual particles in a body at any specific temperature, the wavelengths emitted by a body at a given temperature range far above and below their effective average. Figure 19-4 shows the distribution of the radiated energy among the various wavelengths, at each of three temperatures. Values on the vertical axis are proportional to the energy radiated per unit time, within a small increment of wavelength, and those on the horizontal axis represent wavelengths. Thus the total area under a curve is proportional to the product of wavelength and energy per unit wavelength, and hence is an index of the total energy radiated at that temperature, per unit time. The greater area under the curves for the higher temperatures is obviously logical.

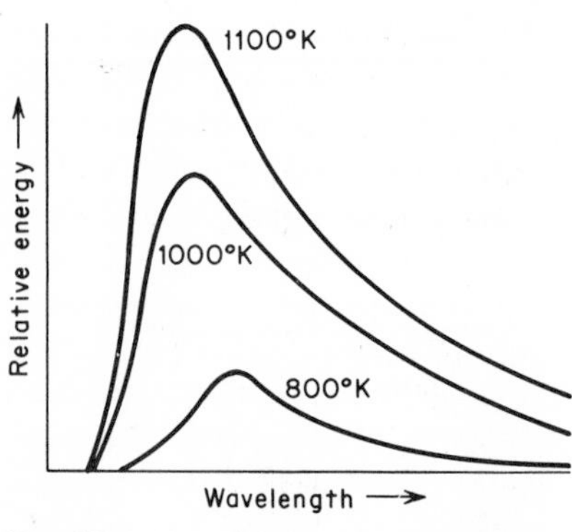

Fig. 19-4. Distribution of energy among wavelengths. Each curve represents the energy distribution at a particular temperature, as labeled. The energy within a narrow band of wavelengths is plotted against the wavelength.

We know that if we heat a piece of metal there is no visible glow at first, then we see a dull red, and as the temperature rises, the glow becomes a brighter red, and the filament of an incandescent lamp is so hot that it appears almost white. In Chapter 27, we shall find that the early radiations from the hot metal were too long in wavelength to affect our eyes, that the red color was due to shorter wavelengths, and that the change toward white was due to an increasing shift toward shorter wavelengths. All this is in accordance with the curves in Fig. 19-4.

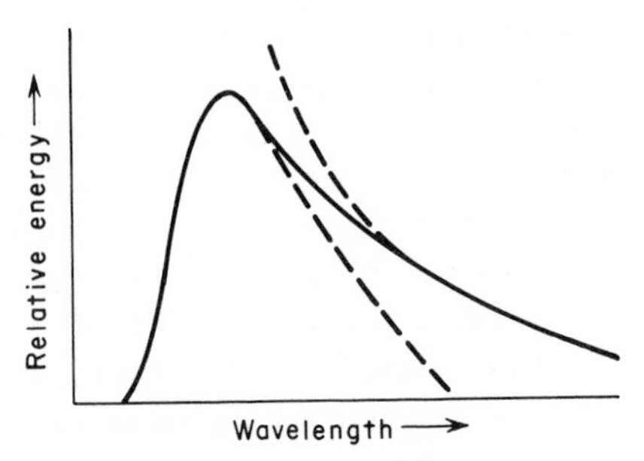

Fig. 19-5. Dashed lines are approximate representations of two different theoretical energy distributions, based on classical physics. One agrees well with experimental data, indicated by solid curve, at low values of wavelength; the other is in agreement for long wavelengths. The theoretical distribution based on the quantum concept agrees with experimental data at all wavelengths.

These curves, however, proved to be very embarrassing to physicists at the end of the last century, for their knowledge was inadequate to account for the shape of the curves. On the basis of classical physics, it was possible to derive a law which fitted the experimental curves well at lower wavelengths but fell too low at longer wavelengths. Another approach fitted well at longer wavelengths but continued upward toward infinity at shorter wavelengths. These are indicated by dashed lines in Fig. 19-5, in which the solid curve represents the troublesome experimental facts. No other attempt founded on classical physics was able to improve the situation; the concepts and laws of the physics then known were inadequate to account for the experimental results.

In 1900, Max Planck took a novel approach, and he managed to derive a law which was in excellent agreement with the experimentally derived curves. He assumed that the radiation was not emitted or absorbed continuously. By this he meant that it was emitted and absorbed in packets or bundles of energy, each of which had an energy $h\nu$, where ν is the frequency of the radiations and h is a constant. Since no packet of energy of frequency ν can contain a smaller or larger quantity of energy than $h\nu$, any quantity of energy radiated at this frequency must be an integral multiple of this basic quantity or *quantum* of energy; there could never be a quantity of energy, such as $h\nu/2$ or $113h\nu/17$, for example, emitted or absorbed.*

This was the birth of the *quantum* concept of energy. Though Planck

* Although packets of each and every specified *single* frequency must have quantities of energy which are integral multiples of the same basic quantity, the *total* radiation from the hot body contains a continuous range of energies because there is a continuous range of frequencies.

himself considered it more as something that gave a correct result than as a correct description of nature, Einstein extended the concept in 1905 to the transmission of the radiant energy as well as its absorption and emission; from that time on, the quantum theory has proliferated and has enjoyed outstanding success. In honor of the originator of the quantum concept, we call h "Planck's constant."

We shall see much more of the quantum concept of nature in later chapters. It will be an indispensable tool in most of the latter portion of the text, beginning with Chapter 33.

Summary

Thermal energy may be transferred from one place to another by *conduction* or, in fluids, by *convection.* It may also be converted into *radiant energy* and changed back to internal energy when another body absorbs the radiant energy.

Metals are the best conductors of heat. This is largely due to the *free electrons* which are present in metals. The *rate* at which heat is conducted through a substance depends on the *material,* the *area* available for the flow, and the *thermal gradient.*

Convection is a process of thermal energy transfer in fluids which involves a mass motion of the fluid. This motion is due to thermal expansion and the application of Archimedes' principle. The low conductivity of air and the inhibition of convection by the fibers of a fabric are responsible for the low heat conductivity of fabrics and other fibrous materials.

The *rate* of *radiation* depends on the fourth power of the absolute temperature. The spectrum of wavelengths includes more of the shorter wavelengths as the temperature rises. Difficulties in accounting for the distribution of radiant energy among the various wavelengths gave rise to the *quantum* concept of radiation.

Self-Quiz

1. What limitations, if any, are there on the types of direct or indirect heat transfer available to solids, liquids, and gases? Justify your answers.

2. Suggest another analogy than telephone, radio, or storage battery, for the indirect transmission of heat by radiation.

3. In a homogeneous solid at a uniform temperature, do all particles have the same energy? Explain. What happens, and why, if additional energy is supplied to some of the body?

4. Of what is the coefficient of thermal conductivity of a medium the measure? The metric and English units of this coefficient differ more than they do for most quantities. Why?

5. Verify the metric units used for the coefficient of thermal conductivity by substituting the appropriate units for each quantity except k in Eq. (19-1). Repeat for English units.

6. Explain clearly why the rate of heat conduction should be directly proportional to the cross-sectional area. Why should it be inversely proportional to the length or thickness?

7. After uniform heat flow has been established between the ends of a uniform rod of constant cross section, the temperature drop along its length will be uniform. Show this graphically by plotting assumed values of temperatures against distance along the rod. The graph should suggest the basis of the term, "thermal gradient."

8. Discuss the reason for the relative excellence of metals as heat conductors.

9. It could be said that the topic of convection belongs in mechanics rather than here. What justification is there for this statement? Any adverse argument?

10. "Warm" fabrics may be made from any of several synthetic fibers. Does this mean that, if such fibers were compressed to a thin sheet, the sheet would have a markedly low coefficient of thermal conductivity? Explain clearly.

11. Wool fibers are more curly and kinky than cotton fibers. What does this difference imply with regard to the relative "warmth" of woolen and cotton fabrics? Explain.

12. In conduction, heat is transmitted through a motionless medium. In convection, heat is carried by the motion of the medium. What, if anything, can be said concerning a medium in the radiation process?

13. Why is the transfer of thermal energy by radiation considered to be an indirect process?

14. What factors determine the rate of radiation from a body?

15. Why can't we use Fahrenheit or Celsius temperatures in computing the rate of radiation?

16. How does the ability of a surface to emit radiations compare with its ability to absorb them, *and why?*

17. Discuss the birth of the quantum concept.

Problems

1. Prove that the conversion factor from metric to English units, for a coefficient of thermal conductivity, has a numerical value of approximately 0.806.

2. A room has an unbroken brick outside wall 7.0 ft high, 18 ft long, and 8.0 in. thick. If the temperature is 40F° lower outside than in the room, how many Btu will be conducted through the wall in 1.0 hr?

3. A metal tube is 25 cm long, has a diameter of 2.0 cm, and its wall thickness is 0.50 mm. Hot water passes through the tube for 30 min, causing a difference of

0.050C° between the temperatures of the inner and outer surfaces of the tube. During this time, $2.0 \cdot 10^4$ cal of heat pass through the tube wall. Compute the value of its thermal conductivity coefficient.

4. An aluminum rod is 60 cm long and has a cross-sectional area of 2.5 cm^2. In 5.0 min, 560 cal of heat are conducted from one end of the rod to the other. Calculate (a) the difference in temperature between the ends of the rod and (b) the thermal gradient.

5. An oven door has a window made of glass 3/8 in. thick (exactly). The window is 8.0 in. long and 5.0 in. high. If the oven is kept at 400°F for 20 min, while the kitchen temperature is 75°F, how many Btu of heat are lost by conduction through the glass?

6. An aluminum pan containing 1500 g of water at 100°C sits on a stove. The bottom of the pan has an area of 320 cm^2 and is 2.0 mm thick. The temperature drop through the bottom of the pan is 6.0C°. If heat entered the water only by conduction through the bottom of the pan, how long would it take to boil the pan dry?

7. A boiler contains 500 ft of steel piping. The piping has an effective area of 72 in.^{2} per foot of length, and it is 3/16 in. thick. The temperature of the firebox is 1440°F and the temperature inside the pipes is 240°F. If the heat of vaporization of water is 950 Btu/lb at 240°F, how many pounds of steam at 240°F can be produced in a day?

8. (a) What temperature gradient would be required to transmit 20 cal/sec along a silver rod which has a uniform cross section of 10 cm^2? (b) What would be the necessary thermal gradient if the rod were of steel?

9. A sheet of steel is laminated with a copper sheet exactly twice as thick as the steel. If the temperature drop within the copper is 80C° when heat is passing through this laminated sheet, what is the temperature drop in the steel?

10. If the area of the laminated sheet in Problem 9 is 500 cm^2 and its thickness is 2.0 mm, how much heat is passing through it each second?

11. A metal sphere has a diameter of 2.0 cm and an emissivity of 0.35. Compute the quantity of thermal energy lost by radiation each second (a) at −73°C and (b) at 527°C.

12. A cube 3.0 cm on a side radiates energy at the rate of $2.0 \cdot 10^9$ ergs/sec when the temperature is 727°C. Determine its emissivity.

13. If, in an experimental determination, perfect black body radiation from an area of 2.50 cm^2 produced $1.20 \cdot 10^{10}$ ergs each minute when the temperature was 827°C, compute the per cent error.

20

FIELDS OF FORCE

20-1 Preview

This chapter introduces our study of electricity and magnetism. Students commonly encounter difficulty with these topics because of the intangibility of some of the concepts; but I shall try to minimize this intangibility and the resultant mystery by relating these new concepts to more familiar ones from the topic of gravitation. Thus, the equation for the force between two electric charges and that for the force between two magnetic poles will be presented by comparing them with the algebraic statement of Newton's law of universal gravitation. The concepts of electric and magnetic fields, field intensity, and potential will also be related to similar concepts pertinent to gravitation. This requires a bit of review of the phenomenon of gravity, part of this review being from a standpoint different from that in Chapter 9. Though some of the basic ideas relative to magnetic forces and fields will be met here, the principal treatment of magnetism will be postponed to Chapter 24. Those portions of the material in this chapter which deal with motionless electric charges are often classified as **static electricity** *and discussed in a separate chapter, but you will get a better understanding of gravitational, electrostatic, and magnetic fields if their parallelism is made obvious at the beginning of your study of electricity and magnetism.*

20-2 Fields of Force

In Chapter 1 and again in Chapter 9, we met the fact that any body in the earth's gravitational field is subject to a force which tends to accelerate the body toward the center of the earth though there is no apparent agency by which the earth can apply a force to the body. We also found that, at our level of sophistication, we have no real explanation of the cause of such forces or of how they are applied. We know also that similar ***action at a distance*** is characteristic of magnetic forces; a tack isn't simply *held* to a magnet, it is attracted toward the magnet before contact occurs. Similarly, a plastic or rubber pen barrel (or similar object) rubbed on wool attracts and picks up small bits of paper or lint. For phenomena of these two sorts, as for gravitation, there is no fundamental explanation available. We must accept the experimental fact that such forces exist, foregoing any real understanding of them, and contenting ourselves with quantitative considerations as we did with gravitation.

While studying gravitation, we met the concept of the gravitational *field*, but there was no formal definition of it. A ***field*** is any region within which an action-at-a-distance force may occur. There are several kinds, each generating a force of a particular sort and hence being independent, in general, of other kinds of fields. Thus a gravitational field is any region within which a mass may experience a force. An electric charge will be subject to a force in an electric field, and a magnetic field will exert a force on a magnetic pole. But a mass will be quite insensitive to electric and magnetic fields, a motionless electric charge will be affected only by an electric field* (though any mass associated with the charge will be influenced by a gravitational field, of course), and only a magnetic field can cause a force on a magnetic pole.

In the case of gravitation, we found that the force is mutual—as Newton's third law requires. Thus, if there is a gravitational force between two bodies, we may consider either one of them to be producing a gravitational field which acts on the other. Any electric charge is surrounded by an electric field, and any magnetic pole by a magnetic field, just as a gravitational field surrounds any mass.

20-3 Factors Which Influence the Magnitudes of the Forces

According to Eq. (9-1), the mutual force of gravitational attraction F_g between a mass m_1 and another mass m_2 is given by the equation

$$F_g = G\frac{m_1 m_2}{d^2}$$

---

* We shall discover in Chapter 24 that there is interaction between an electric charge and a magnetic field if there is relative motion between the two.

where d is the distance between the centers of gravity of the bodies and G is the universal gravitational constant.

The equations for the force between two magnetic poles, and for the force between two electric charges, are very similar to the equation for a gravitational force. They will be presented here, and in the next two sections we shall investigate their similarities and differences.

For a force between two magnetic poles, the equation is

$$F_m = \frac{m_1 m_2}{\mu d^2} \tag{20-1}$$

in which F_m is the force of magnetic origin, m_1 and m_2 represent the strengths of the magnetic poles, rather than masses as before, d is the effective distance between the poles, and μ is a constant called the ***permeability*** of the medium between the poles.

Between two electric charges q_1 and q_2 separated by a distance d, the force F_e is given by the equation

$$F_e = \frac{q_1 q_2}{k d^2} \tag{20-2}$$

k being the ***dielectric constant*** of the medium.

20-4 Comparison of the Force Equations: Similarities

A casual comparison shows that Eqs. (9-1), (20-1), (20-2) are almost identical in form. First, the magnitude of a gravitational force is directly proportional to the magnitude of each of the two masses, and hence to their product. Similarly, the size of a magnetic force is directly proportional to the product of the two pole strengths; and the magnitude of a force of electric origin is directly proportional to the product of the sizes of the two electric charges.

Second, gravitational, magnetic, and electric forces are all ***inverse square forces,*** since the presence of d^2 in the denominator of each equation shows that in all cases the magnitude of force is inversely proportional to the square of the distance between the two entities (masses, magnetic poles, or electric charges) responsible for the force.

Third, in each equation a constant appears, though it is in the denominator in two of the equations and not in the other (Eq. (9-1)). This apparent difference is illusory, however, for we could delete the G from Eq. (9-1) if we put a constant equal to $1/G$ in the denominator.

Thus we have a situation reminiscent of the parallelism between the equations of linear motion in Chapter 5 and those pertinent to rotary motion in Chapter 8; we were able to write the latter by analogy with the equations for linear motion. And if we know the equation for Newton's law of universal gravitation, we should have very little trouble in writing those for magnetic and electric forces.

And here is a final point of similarity: like gravitational forces, all forces of magnetic or electrical origin are mutual. Any other situation would make poor Sir Isaac (Newton) most unhappy!

20-5 Comparison of Force Equations: Differences

Though there is but one kind of mass,* there are two kinds of magnetic poles—north and south—and two kinds of electric charges—positive and negative. Since there is but one kind of mass, there can be but one kind of gravitational force—attraction. But the different kinds of magnetic poles give rise to repulsion as well as attraction; like poles repel each other, and unlike poles attract. Likewise, the force between two electric charges may be attraction or repulsion. Here also like charges repel, and unlike charges attract each other, as revealed by the pairs of suspended charged pith balls in Fig. 20-1. (There are rumors that this law of attraction of unlikes has applications outside the field of physical science.)

The equations in Sec. 20-3 do not forecast this difference between gravitational forces and those of magnetic or electric origin, nor do Eqs. (20-1), (20-2) appear to be able to distinguish between attraction and repulsion. We may interpret "positive" and "negative" in a mathematical sense, however, and assign appropriate signs to the values we substitute for q_1 and q_2 in Eq. (20-2); if so, we should also add a minus sign to the right side of the equation, so that any computation which yields a positive value of F_e will indicate attraction, and a negative value will identify repulsion.

We may put a minus sign on the right side of Eq. (20-1) also, if we wish, and *arbitrarily* agree to give a north pole a positive value and a south pole a negative value. Then, as in the electrical case, the sign of a computed magnetic force will identify it as attraction or as repulsion.†

A second difference among these phenomena and the equations which describe them is related to the significance of the constants, G, μ, and k. The only way you can change the gravitational force between two masses is by altering the distance between them. Interposing some material has no effect. G is called the *universal* gravitational constant because gravitational forces are independent of the presence or absence of a medium between the masses, and of the nature of any medium which may be present. But both magnetic forces and electric forces are influenced by

* We shall find in Chapter 33 that "anti-matter" as well as ordinary matter may exist, but the difference from ordinary matter does not influence gravitational effects.

† I prefer to use the equations for magnetic and electric forces as given and apply the rule of likes-repel–unlikes-attract, but many authors and instructors prefer the formal method.

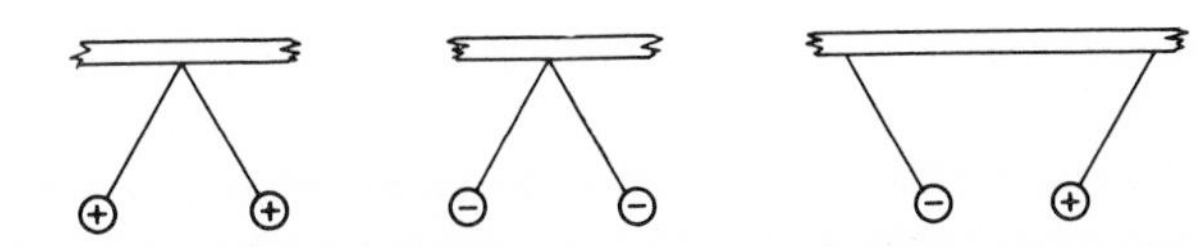

Fig. 20-1. Like electric charges repel, and unlike charges attract.

the presence of a physical medium and by the nature of the medium. Since the only factors in the equations which could reflect the influence of the medium are the permeability μ in the equation for magnetic forces and the dielectric constant k in that for electric forces, μ and k are not constants in the sense that G is.

In devising the dynamic system of units, we defined a new unit of force of such size that we could dispense with any proportionality constant. We couldn't dispense with it in the gravitational system because that system uses units previously established. Similarly, using established units, we must have the constant G in the equation for gravitational attraction to make the equation numerically valid as well as to make it dimensionally homogeneous. But we shall define magnetic pole strengths in terms of Eq. (20-1) and the unit of electric charge in terms of Eq. (20-2); so we are free to choose any basis of evaluating μ and k we wish (*before* we define the units of m and q).

A value of unity is assigned as the value of the dielectric constant when the electric charges are in a vacuum. If any physical material whatever is interposed between the charges, the force between them is reduced. Since k appears in the denominator, this means that it must have a value greater than 1 for any physical medium. For gases the value is only slightly above unity, and it is very roughly of the order of 10 for most solids* and liquids, though a few substances have markedly higher values. Table 20-1 lists a few values.

When we are dealing with a magnetic field instead of an electric field,

Table 20-1

DIELECTRIC CONSTANTS†

Solids	k	Liquids	k	Gases	k
Diamond	16.5	Ethyl alcohol	24.3	Air, 1 atm	1.0006
Glass (various kinds)	3.8–9.5	Benzene	2.28	Carbon dioxide, 1 atm	1.0010
Ice, −5°C	2.85	Chloroform	4.81	Carbon dioxide, 40 atm	1.060
Paraffin	2.0–2.5	Water	80.36	Steam, 140°C	1.008

† Many values are approximate; also values vary with temperature and may vary with pressure.

---

* The concept of dielectric constant is limited to substances which are not "conductors" of electricity.

we are concerned with the permeability μ instead of the dielectric constant k. As in the case of the dielectric constant, and for similar reasons, the value of the permeability of a vacuum is taken as unity. For the great majority of materials the value of the permeability is close to unity, but it may be either greater or less than 1 (though there are no *negative* values). However, a relatively small number of materials have permeabilities measured in the thousands—even hundreds of thousands, in a very few cases. (Table 24-1 gives the values for some substances.)

20-6 Units of Electric Charge

Having established the value of the dielectric constant of a vacuum, we are now in a position to define the unit of electric charge, with the aid of Eq. (20-2). Our procedure is similar to that we used in defining the dynamic units of force (Sec. 5-14). If, in the equation

$$F_e = \frac{q_1 q_2}{kd^2}$$

we set the values of F_e, k, and d equal to unity, and if we specify that q_1 must have the same value as q_2, the only possible value of each charge is 1. Thus 1 ***electrostatic unit of charge,*** also called a ***statcoulomb,*** is an electric charge of such magnitude that if it is placed 1 cm from an equal charge, in a vacuum, the force between the two charges will be 1 dyne. The term, "electrostatic unit of charge," is commonly shortened to esu of charge, or, when the context is such that there will be no ambiguity, just esu.

This quantity of charge is very small, so usually it is more convenient to use the so-called practical unit of charge, the ***coulomb,*** which is $2.998 \cdot 10^9$ statcoulombs (to four significant figures). For most purposes, this factor may be rounded off to $3.00 \cdot 10^9$. We shall meet another, and more fundamental, definition of the coulomb in Sec. 23-8.

The term, "coulomb," like nearly all of the units in electricity and magnetism, is the name of a pioneer in the field.

1 coulomb = 3×10^9 e.s.u.

20-7 Field Intensity

For the most part, our consideration of gravitational forces in Chapter 9 was in terms of forces on objects at, or very near, the earth's surface. All such forces have a direction toward the center of the earth, and the weight of any body is determined solely by its mass. A space traveler, however, would have to take a much less provincial point of view. The magnitude of a weight would depend on the distance from the center of the earth or other astronomical body; and as the space ship leaves the gravitational field of one body and enters that of another, the direction of the weight would change also.

This broader concept of gravitation is the one which will be useful in studying electric and magnetic fields, since in general such fields are not uniform, either in magnitude or in direction. Therefore it will be helpful to look at the phenomenon of gravitation from a different standpoint than that in Chapter 9.

According to the concept of a field, a gravitational field exists in any region if a mass in that region is subject to a gravitational force. The ***intensity*** of the gravitational field is defined as the force it exerts on unit mass:

$$\text{gravitational field intensity} = \frac{F_g}{m} \qquad (20\text{-}3)$$

For a body of mass m at the earth's surface, the gravitational force, in terms of the dynamic system of units, is mg, where g is gravitational acceleration. Thus, at the earth's surface,

$$\text{gravitational field intensity} = \frac{mg}{m} = g$$

Since, in *this* application, g represents force per unit mass, it must be expressed in newtons/kg, dynes/g, pdl/lb, etc., rather than the familiar units of acceleration; but its numerical value is unchanged from that appropriate for gravitational acceleration. Thus the intensity of the gravitational field at the earth's surface is 9.80 newtons/kg, 980 dynes/g, and 32 pdl/lb.

In general, the intensity of any other gravitational field will have a different magnitude than that at the surface of the earth. We may express the gravitational force between any astronomical body of mass M and any other body by writing

$$F_g = \frac{GMm}{d^2}$$

if m is the mass of the body and d is the distance between the centers of gravity of the two bodies; this is a slight modification of Eq. (9-1). At the location of m, the intensity of the gravitational field will be, by definition,

$$\text{gravitational field intensity} = \frac{F_g}{m}$$

and therefore,

$$\text{gravitational field intensity} = \frac{GM}{d^2} \qquad (20\text{-}4)$$

Thus the intensity at any point within a gravitational field is directly proportional to the mass of the body causing the field, and inversely proportional to the square of the distance from the center of gravity of that body. It is completely independent of the masses of bodies introduced into the field, as indicated in Fig. 20-2 on the next page.

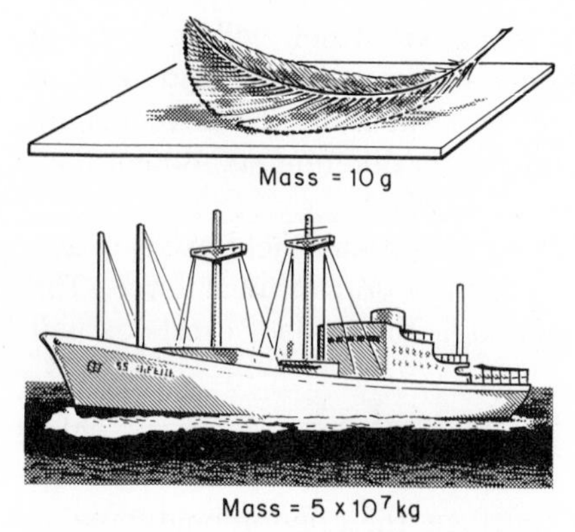

Fig. 20-2. The intensity of the gravitational field is the same (9.80 newtons/kg or 980 dynes/g) for the feather and the ship.

Since gravitational field intensity is *force* per unit mass, it is a vector quantity.

The concept of the intensity of an electric field is almost exactly parallel with that for gravitational field intensity, but—unlike a gravitational force—the magnitude of a force of electric origin is dependent on the nature of the medium. To avoid ambiguity, we specify that the field and the charge are in a vacuum. Under these circumstances, ***electric field intensity*** is force per unit charge. Algebraically,

$$E = \frac{F_e}{q} \tag{20-5}$$

in which E is the intensity of an electric field, in a vacuum, and F_e is the force it exerts on a charge q.* Compare this equation with Eq. (20-3).

According to the defining equation (20-5) electric field intensity may be measured in terms of newtons per coulomb, or in terms of dynes per statcoulomb.

Equation (20-2) is

$$F_e = \frac{q_1 q_2}{kd^2}$$

and if we divide both sides by q_1 we obtain

$$\frac{F_e}{q_1} = \frac{q_2}{kd^2}$$

Comparison of this with Eq. (20-5) shows that the right side is electric field intensity due to a charge q_2. Thus, if a charge q is responsible for an electric field, at a distance d from that charge the field intensity will be given by the equation

$$E = \frac{q}{kd^2} \tag{20-6}$$

* The introduction of any electric charge into an existing electric field will modify that field. Nevertheless, there will be a definite force between a charge q_1 at a point P_1 and a charge q_2 at point P_2, as given by Eq. (20-2). We may think of the force on q_2 as being due to the effect on q_2 of the field generated by q_1; or we may consider the same force to be the reaction to the effect of the field of q_2 on q_1. From either point of view, we need consider the field of only a *single* charge; the resultant field of the two is irrelevant. Hence, we may determine an electric field intensity *before* the introduction of a new charge and use this intensity to find the force on that charge, without worrying about the *resultant* field after its introduction.

This equation is analogous to Eq. (20-4). The intensity of an electric field is directly proportional to the magnitude of the charge which produces that field. As in the gravitational case, the magnitude of the force is inversely proportional to the square of the distance from the source of the field. But there is a major difference between the effect of G in Eq. (20-4) and k in Eq. (20-6); unlike G, k has different values for different media. Thus the electric field intensity is inversely proportional to the dielectric constant of the medium in which the field exists.

In an exactly analogous manner, we may define the ***intensity of a magnetic field*** as the force it can exert on unit magnetic pole. We shall not pursue this topic further until we get to Chapter 24.

20-8 The Direction of an Electric Field

The intensity of any field is a vector quantity, as we saw in the case of a gravitational field. Quite arbitrarily, the ***direction of an electric field*** is defined as the direction of the force it would exert on a *positive* electric charge. Thus the direction of the field due to a positive charge would be away from that charge, but a field caused by a negative charge would have a direction toward the charge (Fig. 20-3). Since like charges repel and unlikes attract, the direction of an electric field is *opposite* the direction of the force it would exert on a *negative* charge.

Inspection of Eq. (20-6), in the light of the definition of field direction, shows that directional factors are automatically taken care of. A positive value of q in the equation will yield a positive value of E, indicating that a positive charge would tend to move away from q, whereas a negative charge would be attracted toward q. Figure 20-3(a) shows that this is consistent with the repulsion of like charges and the attraction of unlike charges. If we replace the charge $+q$ with a negative charge $-q$, Fig. 20-3(b) shows that now a positive charge will be attracted and a negative one repelled, indicating that the field direction has been reversed. According to the sign convention used for vector quantities, E should be negative; and it is, for the value of q in Eq. (20-6) is negative.

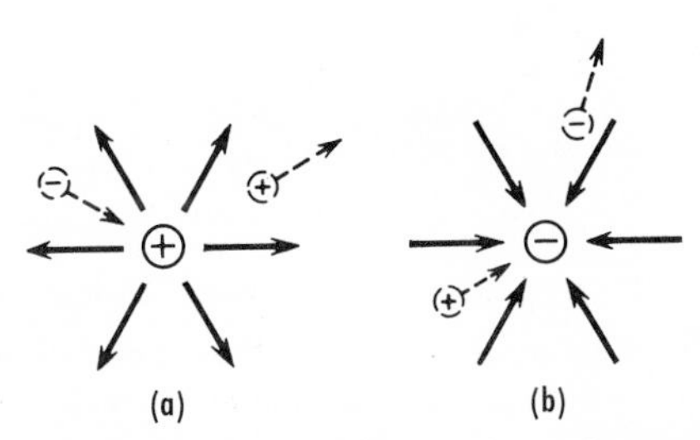

Fig. 20-3. The direction of an electric field is away from a positive charge and toward a negative charge. Positive charges tend to move in the direction of the field and negative charges tend to move opposite the field direction.

Equation (20-5) may be rearranged to

$$F_e = qE \qquad (20\text{-}7)$$

which says that if a charge q is in an electric field of intensity E

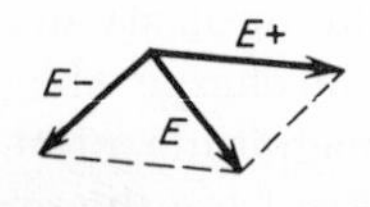

Fig. 20-4. The electric field due to two electric charges is the vector sum of the two separate fields.

it will experience a force F_e. If q is positive, the force will have the same sign as the field and therefore will be in the same direction, but a negative value of q will result in unlike signs for E and F_e, indicating that the direction of the force is opposite that of the field.

Here, as in Sec. 20-5, casual inspection will reveal all relative directions, so it is not essential that you make use of the sign conventions in the equations—unless your instructor prefers to have you consider it in that way.

Commonly an electric field is due not to a single charge but to a combination of charges. The vector property of field intensities enables us to find the effective field; we can add vectorially the fields due to the individual charges as in Fig. 20-4, and thus determine the resultant field intensity.*

Sample Problem 1

What is the magnitude of an electrostatic charge, if the charge is immersed in water and the electric field intensity at a distance of 2.00 cm from the charge is 0.125 dyne per statcoulomb?

According to Eq. (20-6)

$$E = \frac{q}{kd^2}$$

which may be rearranged to

$$q = E \cdot kd^2$$

From Table 20-1 we may obtain a value of 80.36 for the dielectric constant of water. Insertion of this value and the other data gives

$$q = 0.125 \cdot 80.36 \cdot 2.00^2 = 40.18, \quad \text{or} \quad 40.2 \text{ statcoulombs}$$

Sample Problem 2

An electrostatic charge of $+25.0$ statcoulombs and one of -40.0 statcoulombs are situated 7.50 cm apart in a vacuum. Determine the intensity and direction of the electric field at a point P on a line between the charges and 2.50 cm from the positive charge.

Again using Eq. (20-6), and remembering that the dielectric constant in a vacuum is unity, we may compute the field intensity for each charge separately and then determine the resultant field intensity. For the positive charge we have

$$E_1 = \frac{25.0}{2.50^2} = \frac{25.0}{6.25} = 4.00 \text{ dynes per statcoulomb}$$

Point P is $(7.50 - 2.50)$ cm from the negative charge, so the field intensity due to the negative charge is

* Obviously this is practical only for a fairly small number of charges.

$$E_2 = \frac{40.0}{5.00^2} = \frac{40.0}{25.0} = 1.60 \text{ dynes per statcoulomb}$$

Since field direction is defined in terms of its effect on a positive charge, the direction of E_1 at P will be away from the $+25.0$ esu charge, and that of E_2 will be toward the -40.0 esu charge. Hence the resultant field intensity is

$$4.00 + 1.60 = 5.60 \text{ dynes per statcoulomb toward the } -40.0 \text{ esu charge}$$

20-9 Potential

In Sec. 6-4 we met the concept of potential energy, and in Sec. 6-6 we learned how to evaluate the potential energy of a body. We found in Sec. 6-9 that any value of potential energy is relative, so that in Sec. 6-6 we were really working with differences in potential energy.

If a body which has a mass m is near the earth's surface, its weight, in dynamic units, is mg. To lift the body through a small vertical height h we must do mgh units of work; thereby we endow the body with potential energy in the amount mgh. Under the same circumstances, we would have to expend Mgh units of energy on a body of mass M to achieve the same vertical displacement, so the body would acquire Mgh units of potential energy.

In each case we may think of the total potential energy gained by the body as the product of its mass and the energy gain per unit mass:

$$\text{total } \Delta\text{PE} = \text{mass} \cdot \frac{\Delta\text{PE}}{\text{mass}}$$

in which the symbol Δ is to be read "change in," as usual. Thus we see that in our expressions mgh and Mgh, which represent the increments in the potential energy of the two bodies, the product gh represents the gain in energy per unit mass. This is called the ***difference of gravitational potential.*** Where no ambiguity will result, this term is shortened to ***gravitational potential,*** just as we refer to mgh as the potential energy of a body instead of its difference of potential energy, when the reference level is specified or agreed on.

Note that since the value of the gravitational potential is the product of g and h it has a definite and constant value for a specified vertical displacement at a given location in a gravitational field. It is independent of the mass of the body and so is identical for all bodies whatever their masses may be. Thus each of the two bodies in Fig. 20-5 has a gravitational potential gh equal to $9.80 \cdot 5.00 = 49.0$ joules/kg, though their masses differ considerably.*

* The whole discussion of gravitational potential has been in terms of *small* vertical displacements *near* the surface of the earth. For any situation outside of these limitations, g cannot be taken as a constant but must be evaluated in terms of Eq. (9-5): $g = GM/r^2$; also the methods of calculus must be used when the value of h is large.

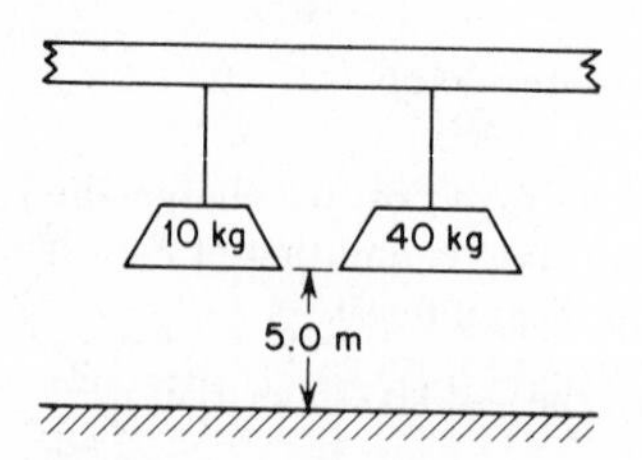

Fig. 20-5. The gravitational potential is the same, 49 joules/kg, for both masses.

Electrical potential is similar to gravitational potential in that it is characteristic of the electric field rather than of the charge. Thus we may define ***electric potential*** as energy per unit of electric charge. If V is the electric potential and W is the energy of an electric charge q in an electric field, the defining equation for electric potential is

$$V = \frac{W}{q} \tag{20-8}$$

Obviously it follows that*

$$W = qV \tag{20-9}$$

As in the case of gravitational potential, the definition of electric potential and the equations in which it appears actually deal with the *difference* of electric potential rather than with an absolute value of the electric potential. Any "absolute" value of electric potential, however, must be stated with reference to a specified or arbitrarily adopted reference potential; so in a sense *all* electrical potentials are *differences* of electric potential.

In the electrostatic system of units, electric potential may be expressed in terms of ergs per statcoulomb; but a less cumbersome unit is esu of potential, which is also termed a "statvolt." One ***electrostatic unit of potential,*** or 1 ***statvolt,*** is 1 erg per statcoulomb.

We shall make much more use of the practical system of units, which (for electrical units) is identical with the mks system. The practical unit of electric potential is the ***volt,*** which is 1 joule per coulomb. One v is $\frac{1}{300}$ of a statvolt (to three significant figures), and 300 v = 1 statvolt.

20-10 Comparison of Electric Field Intensity and Electric Potential

It is easy to become confused when we meet unfamiliar and intangible concepts, especially if they seem somewhat similar. Let's minimize the hazard by reviewing what we know of electric field intensity and electric potential.

The intensity of an electric field is measured by the *force* it will exert on a unit electric charge placed in the field, whereas the electric potential is the *energy* a unit charge will have in the field. Thus the basic difference between field intensity and potential is the difference between force and energy.

* The value of V may vary, as that of g may in the gravitational case; so some problems based on Eq. (20-9) are beyond the scope of this book.

If we multiply force per unit charge by the displacement *in the direction opposite that of the field intensity,* we obtain the work done on unit charge and hence the energy acquired by unit charge.* Thus, in terms of practical units,

$$\begin{aligned}(\text{newtons/coulomb}) \cdot \text{meters} &= \text{newton meters/coulomb} \\ &= \text{joules/coulomb}\end{aligned}$$

and, by definition, joules per coulomb is volts. Similarly,

$$\begin{aligned}(\text{dynes/statcoulomb}) \cdot \text{cm} &= \text{dyne cm/statcoulomb} \\ &= \text{ergs/statcoulomb}\end{aligned}$$

and ergs per statcoulomb is statvolts.

Summarizing these equations, we may write

$$(\text{newtons/coulomb}) \cdot \text{meters} = \text{volts}$$

and

$$(\text{dynes/statcoulomb}) \cdot \text{cm} = \text{statvolts}$$

and these may be rearranged to

$$\text{volts/meter} = \text{newtons/coulomb}$$

and

$$\text{statvolts/cm} = \text{dynes/statcoulomb}$$

Since newtons per coulomb is a measure of electric field intensity and the same is true of dynes per statcoulomb, it follows that the intensity of an electric field may be expressed in terms of volts per meter or statvolts per centimeter. Often, these new units of intensity are more convenient than the ones we met previously.

20-11 Difference of Potential between Two Points in an Electric Field

Consider an electric charge of one unit at some point A in an electric field. How much work will be required to move the charge to some other point B?

The distance between A and B is not significant in itself, any more than the slant height of an inclined plane is of primary importance in computing the useful work against gravity when a body is moved up the inclined plane. The significant distance is the *component* of the distance AB which is parallel with the electric field (but opposite in direction). If this component is d, and if the effective average value of the field intensity is E_{av}, the work required is $E_{av} \cdot d$. The energy expended to do this work will be acquired by the charge in the form of potential energy; and since this is

---

* Here also, only computations relative to a uniform electric field (constant field intensity) can be accomplished without calculus.

the increase in the potential energy of unit charge, by definition it is the increase in the electric potential. Thus the difference in electric potential between the two points is $E_{av} \cdot d$.

If the electric field is ***uniform,*** having a constant value of intensity everywhere, we can drop the restriction "average" from the intensity, and write

$$\Delta V = E \cdot d \tag{20-10}$$

in which ΔV is, of course, the potential difference. *It must not be overlooked or forgotten* that *this equation is valid only for a uniform electric field.*

The computation is quite different if the field is non-uniform. In general, non-calculus methods are incapable of producing the value of a potential difference in a non-uniform field. We shall consider only one important special case. For an electric field due to a single charge q in a medium which has a dielectric constant k, the methods of calculus produce the equation

$$\Delta V = \frac{q}{k} \cdot \left(\frac{1}{r_2} - \frac{1}{r_1}\right) \tag{20-11}$$

in which ΔV is the potential difference between two points at distances r_1 and r_2 from the charge, r_2 being greater than r_1. (If the charge q resides on a body having any appreciable dimensions, this equation is inaccurate except for values of r_1 and r_2 which are large compared to those dimensions.)

The definition of electric potential in Sec. 20-9 was somewhat intangible. We may make it a bit more concrete, with the aid of the concepts in this section. If 1 joule of energy must be expended to move a positive charge of 1 coulomb from point A in an electric field to point B, the electric potential at point B is 1 volt greater than that at point A; and if 1 erg of energy must be used to move a positive charge of 1 statcoulomb from A to B, the potential at B is 1 statvolt greater than at A. Note that these definitions are not dependent on the charge being carried along the straight line joining A and B. Since only the component of AB parallel to the field is pertinent, the charge may go on a world tour enroute, provided only that it starts at A and ends at B. (See Fig. 20-6.)

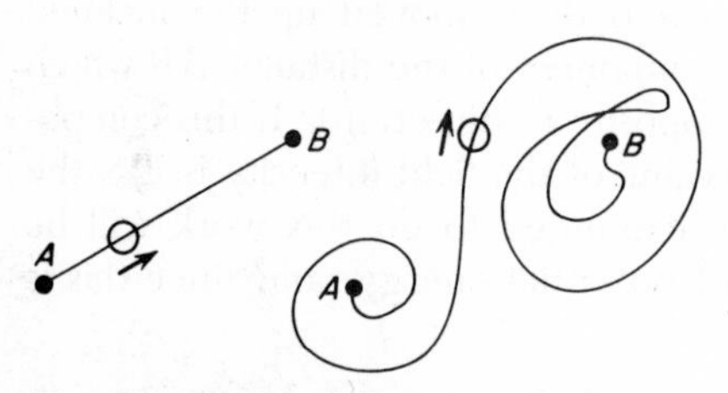

Fig. 20-6. The difference of electrical potential between two points is independent of the path followed.

Sample Problem 3

In the space between two parallel metal plates, the electric field intensity is 20.0 dynes per statcoulomb and the potential difference is 5.00 statvolts, due to the charges on the plates. Compute the distance between the plates.

In the space between parallel plates the field is uniform, so we may use Eq. (20-10):

$$\Delta V = E \cdot d$$

so
$$d = \frac{\Delta V}{E} = \frac{5.00}{20.0} = 0.250 \text{ cm}$$

We know from the equation that d must "come out" in centimeters, but *how* does it? If we use sc for statcoulombs and sv for statvolts,

$$\frac{\Delta V}{E} = \text{sv} \div \text{dynes/sc} = \text{sv} \cdot \text{sc/dynes}$$

But by definition a statvolt is 1 erg per statcoulomb:

$$\text{sv} = \text{ergs/sc}$$

so
$$\text{sv} \cdot \text{sc/dynes} = (\text{ergs/sc}) \cdot (\text{sc/dynes}) = \text{ergs/dynes}$$

and since an erg is a dyne centimeter

$$\text{ergs/dynes} = \text{dyne cm/dynes} = \text{cm}$$

Alternatively, we could have expressed the field intensity in statvolts/cm, since one dyne/statcoulomb = one statvolt/cm. Then, insofar as units are concerned,

$$\frac{\Delta V}{E} = \text{sv} \div (\text{sv/cm}) = \text{sv} \cdot (\text{cm/sv}) = \text{cm}$$

Obviously the latter approach is far simpler; the other was included only to help "tie down" the interrelationships of the units.

20-12 Some Final Details

Just what is meant by speaking of a "positive" electric charge, or a "negative" one? One of the original concepts of electricity, advocated by Benjamin Franklin, considered that bodies normally possess an electric fluid and that an excess of the fluid produces a positive charge on a body, whereas a negative charge is due to a subnormal quantity of the fluid. We know today that all matter contains positive charges of electricity (protons) and negative charges (electrons), and that normally these are present in equal quantities so that they balance each other; hence no macroscopic body gives any superficial evidence of the presence of either kind of charge. In principle, a positive charge could be put on a body by adding protons or by removing electrons. Similarly, adding electrons or removing protons could, in principle, produce a negative charge on a body. In either case, it is usually more practical to change the number of electrons present than to alter the number of protons; so a positive charge is most likely (but not necessarily) the result of a deficiency in the number of electrons, whereas the most probable cause of a negative charge is an excess of electrons.

Evidently the adjectives "positive" and "negative" cannot be interpreted as literally, when applied to electric charges, as they can when used in a mathematical sense. As a matter of fact, there would be just as much logic today in using the terms "black" and "white" as "positive" and "negative"; or we might use "Jack" and "Jill" or "east" and "west." We must consider the designations we use to be quite arbitrary, with no intrinsic meaning.

In general, gravitational, electric, and magnetic fields are independent, though (as noted in the footnote on page 358) this independence is not complete. Thus, if there is an electric field near the earth's surface a mass would not be affected by the electric field, and the gravitational field would have no effect on an electric charge. If a physical body carrying an electric charge is in the combined fields, its mass will be affected by the gravitational field, resulting in a force of gravitational origin. The electric field will act on the charge carried by the body, hence there will be a force of electric origin. As long as the charge remains on the body, the force on the charge will be transmitted to the body. The net effect on the body will be the resultant of the two forces, as indicated in Fig. 20-7.

Summary

A *field of force* is any region in which a *force acts without* any *apparent physical contact* with the entity (mass, magnetic pole, or electric charge) on which it acts.

The equation which describes the force between two magnetic poles is closely analogous with that for the gravitational force between two masses, and it is easily remembered if you know the equation for gravitational force. The same is true of the force between two electric charges. In all cases, the *force* is *directly proportional* to the *product* of *two appropriate quantities* (masses, magnetic pole strengths, or electric charges) and *inversely proportional* to the *square of the distance.*

Magnetic and electric forces may be either attractions or repulsions, and their magnitudes are influenced by any physical medium. The dielectric constant of a medium introduces the effect of the medium into the equation for an electric force, and the permeability of the medium has a similar function in the equation for a force of magnetic origin.

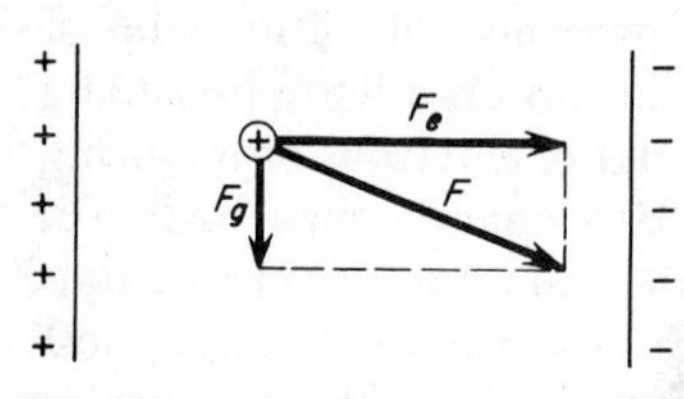

Fig. 20-7. The force on a body which carries a charge in an electric field is the resultant of the electrical and gravitational forces.

One statcoulomb is an electric charge of such magnitude that, if placed 1 cm from an equal charge, in a vacuum, there will be a force of 1 dyne between the two charges. The practical unit of charge is the coulomb, which is (approximately) $3.00 \cdot 10^9$ statcoulombs.

The *intensity* of a *gravitational field* is the *force* it exerts on *unit mass;* that of a *magnetic field* is the *force* it exerts on *unit magnetic pole;* and *electric field* intensity is the *force* the field exerts on *unit electric charge.* If the field is due to a single entity (mass, magnetic pole, or electric charge) in a homogeneous medium, the field intensity is directly proportional to the magnitude of the entity which is the source of the field, and inversely proportional to the square of the distance from it.

Electric potential is energy per unit charge.

Electric potential, and potential difference, may be measured in terms of volts or statvolts. One volt is (approximately) $\frac{1}{300}$ statvolt.

The direction of an electric field is the direction a positive charge tends to move. If W units of work are required to move a positive charge q from one point to another in the field, the second point is at the higher potential and the potential difference is W/q.

The designations positive and negative, used to distinguish between the two kinds of electric charge, are wholly arbitrary.

Field intensities are vector quantities. It is meaningless to try to find the resultant of (for example) a gravitational and an electric field, since the former affects only masses and the latter acts on electric charges. But if a mass carries a charge, forces of gravitational and electric origin acting on it may be added vectorially.

Self-Quiz

1. What is a "field of force"? What is meant by "action at a distance"? What is the present status of theories to explain action at a distance?

2. In a practical sense, the extent of any field of force is limited. Why? Is its extent limited in a theoretical sense? What determines the practical limit of (for example) the earth's gravitational field?

3. Write the equation for the gravitational force between two masses, and translate the equation into a verbal statement. Why is G called a *universal* gravitational constant?

4. Can you write an equation for the gravitational force between two electric charges? Explain.

5. Write the equation for the force between two electric charges, and translate the equation into English. What is k called? Compare the function of k in this relationship with that of G in the gravitational case. Is the value of k ever less than 1? Why?

6. What is the basis of the definition of unit charge? State and explain the definition. What is the unit of charge in the practical system, and how do the sizes of the two units compare?

7. What is meant by the *intensity* of a field? What is the intensity of the gravitational field in which you find yourself at the moment? Is it the same for this book as it is for you? Why? Would it be different on top of a mountain? On the moon? Explain.

8. When g is interpreted as gravitational acceleration, its dimensions are l/t^2. Determine its dimensions when it is interpreted as the intensity of a gravitational field.

9. How does the intensity of the earth's gravitational field (above the earth's surface) depend on the distance from the center of the earth? Does a similar relationship hold for an electric field? What restriction(s) are necessary in the latter case, and why?

10. Derive the equation for electric field intensity from the force equation.

11. By what process should the intensities of two electric fields be added? Why? Can you add an electric field intensity to a gravitational field intensity? Why? Can you add an electric force to a gravitational force? Was your answer the same as you gave for intensities? Why?

12. How is the direction of electric field intensity defined?

13. Define electric potential verbally, record its defining equation, and show that your verbal and algebraic statements are fully equivalent.

14. Compare and contrast electric field intensity and electric potential (a) in terms of the concepts themselves, and (b) in terms of the units in which they may be measured.

15. What significance, if any, do the terms "positive" and "negative" have, as applied to electric charges?

16. To what extent does the difference of electric potential between two points in an electric field depend on the path taken by a unit positive charge in going from one to the other? Explain clearly and give an analogy other than that in the text.

17. Compare Eq. (20-11) with the equation in Problem 8 of Chapter 9. Account for any similarities or differences.

Problems

1. A charge of 10.0 esu and one of 40.0 esu are 5.00 cm apart in a vacuum. Compute the force between them.

2. Two charges are 2.00 cm apart in water and the force between them is 30.0 dynes. If one of the charges is 100 esu, what is the magnitude of the other?

3. Three charges lie in a horizontal plane, in a vacuum: q_1 is $+8.00$ esu; q_2 is $+12.5$ esu and lies 5.00 cm due north of q_1; and q_3 lies 8.00 cm due east of q_1 and has a magnitude of -24.0 esu. Compute the magnitude of the force on q_1 and determine its direction.

4. (a) At the location of q_1, in Problem 3, determine the electric field intensity due to q_2. (b) Determine the intensity due to q_3, at the same point. (c) Determine the resultant field intensity at the location of q_1 (disregarding the effect of

q_1 on the field). (d) Apply the concept of field intensity to your answer to Problem 3, and compare with the answer to part (c) of this problem.

5. The charge on an electron is $4.80 \cdot 10^{-10}$ esu, and its mass is $9.11 \cdot (10^{-28})$ g. If at a certain instant, two electrons in a vacuum are 3.00 cm apart, (a) compute the acceleration of each. (b) Will this acceleration be constant? Why?

6. Assume that the electric field intensity in the "electron gun" of a TV tube is 1000 v/cm. Using the data in Problem 5, compute (a) the electrical force on an electron in the "electron gun," (b) the gravitational force on the electron, and (c) the ratio of the electric force to the gravitational force.

7. Compare the electrical force between the two electrons in Problem 5 with the gravitational force between them. Express the result as the ratio of the former to the latter.

8. In an evacuated space, an electron is moving through a uniform horizontal electric field. If the acceleration of the electron is 45.0° below the horizontal, calculate the intensity of the electric field. Take any necessary data from Problem 5.

9. From the conversion factor between coulombs and statcoulombs, and that between volts and statvolts, plus pertinent definitions, compute the number of ergs in a joule.

10. If 10.0 joules of work must be done to move a charge of -2.00 coulombs from point A to point B, (a) which of the two points is at the higher potential, and what is the potential difference? (b) If the two points are 4.00 cm apart, what is the component of the electric field intensity parallel to a line joining A and B?

21
ELECTRIC CURRENTS

21-1 Preview

In this chapter, you will meet the concepts of electric current and electrical resistance. An understanding of these and of electrical potential (Sec. 20-9) will lead to an obvious quantitative interrelationship of current, potential, and resistance. The concept of electric potential will lead also to expressions for electrical energy and electric power. (Power was originally defined in Sec. 6-11.) We shall make a brief investigation of why substances differ in their effectiveness as carriers of electric currents. Although, for the sake of simplicity, all basic concepts will be introduced in terms of unidirectional electric currents, we shall study also a very important type of current which reverses its direction periodically.

21-2 Electric Current

The concepts in the preceding chapter were presented in terms of static, or motionless, electric charges; but the term "currents" in the title of the present chapter implies some sort of motion or flow. This implication is valid; an ***electric current*** is any flow of electric charges. Thus we may consider an electric current to be somewhat analogous to a flow of water in a pipe or stream—though, like all analogies, this one has limitations.

A lover of nature, viewing a stream, may think of its current simply as a flow of water, but an engineer surveying the same stream from the standpoint of flood control considers the current in terms of the quantity of water passing any given location per unit time. To one, the significance of "current" is qualitative; to the other, it is quantitative. And as applied to electricity, the term "current" has this same double significance. It may merely indicate that there is motion of electric charge, or it may refer to the quantity of electric charge which passes a given point per unit time. As in the case of the stream, we can always tell from the context whether the term is being used in a qualitative or a quantitative sense. Since, however, the idea of a current in a stream probably is more familiar to you than the concept of a motion of electric charge, be careful to bear in mind the possible confusion from this double meaning of electric current.

Since, in its quantitative sense, electric current is the quantity of charge which passes any given point per unit of time,

$$I = \frac{q}{t} \tag{21-1}$$

in which the current is I, the charge q, and the time t. If, as is usually the case, q is in coulombs and t in seconds, I will be in coulombs per second, or ***amperes.*** We met the coulomb in Sec. 20-6.

One thing must be noted carefully. Nowhere has it been stated or implied that the flow of electric charge must occur *in a wire* or other conductor. True, we are more familiar with electric currents in wires, but *any* motion of electric charge is a current. The current in a fluorescent lamp tube flows through the gas in the tube rather than through a wire; and in a TV tube the stream of electrons traversing the length of the tube, through a vacuum, constitutes an electric current.

21-3 The Function of Electric Potential

It is helpful to compare an electric current with the flow of water, though we must be careful to avoid misusing the analogy or carrying it too far.

Consider two elevated water tanks which are identical in every way,

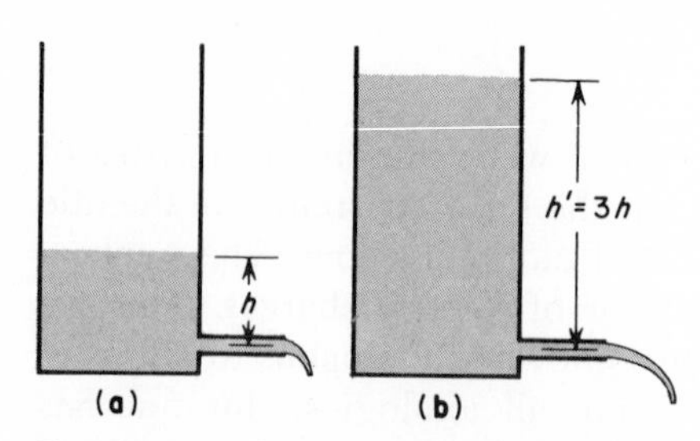

Fig. 21-1. When the depth of water is three times as great the rate of flow is also tripled.

including their outlets, except that one is full and the other only partly filled. Assume that the depth of water above the outlet of the tank in Fig. 21-1(b) is three times the corresponding depth in the tank in Fig. 21-1(a). From what we learned in Sec. 10-8, we know that the water pressure forcing water into the outlet in Fig. 21-1(b) is triple that in Fig. 21-1(a); so we would expect—correctly—that the rate of flow from the tank in Fig. 21-1(b) would be three times that from the other tank. That is, the rate of water flow is directly proportional to the pressure.

We shall find shortly that the magnitude of an electric current is directly proportional to the difference of electric potential, and because of this there is a temptation to think of electric potential as an electrical pressure. Though this point of view will lead to the correct conclusion (in a case of this sort), electric potential is energy per unit charge; there is no such thing as "electrical pressure."

Let's reconsider the two tanks of water. In Sec. 20-9, we met the concept of gravitational potential, or energy per unit mass due to a gravitational field. At points near the earth's surface, we found the gravitational potential to be gh. A particle of water at the surface in Tank A is three times as far above the outlet as a particle at the surface of Tank B. We found in Sec. 10-16, in developing Bernoulli's principle, that a small mass of fluid in a tank has the same energy wherever it may be in the tank, and whether it is moving or not; thus, the energy per unit mass of any and every particle in the tank is equal to the gravitational potential of a particle at the surface. We may summarize all this by saying that the gravitational potential in Tank A is three times that in Tank B; and since the flow rate from A is thrice that from B we may state that the rate of flow is directly proportional to the gravitational potential.

Although there can be no *pressure* in an electric circuit, there certainly can be an electric potential. This potential, which is energy per unit charge, has the same effect in an electric circuit as does gravitational potential, which is energy per unit mass, in the case of the two tanks. Thus electric potential is the cause of any electric current, and the magnitude or "strength" of the current is directly proportional to the electric potential as indicated in Fig. 21-2.

Electric potential is often presented as being analogous to fluid pressure because its *effect* is similar. The analogy is valid to the extent—and only to the extent—that there is a direct proportionality between potential difference and electric current, just as there is between hydraulic pressure and the flow rate of a fluid. In this sense, and to this degree, an employer withdrawing his weekly payroll from a bank and a gunman robbing the bank are analogous—each takes money from the bank; but few of us would consider the two transactions as equivalent. Electric potential *has an effect* in an electric circuit similar to the *effect* of pressure in a water system; but electric potential *is* not "electrical pressure" any more than the employer *is* the bandit.

21-4 Electrical Resistance

Although the strength of an electric current is directly proportional to the electric potential, it does not follow that each of two identical electric potentials will cause currents of equal size. Several influences tend to limit the current. The over-all effect of current limiting factors which arise from the chemical and physical nature of a conductor, and from its length and cross-sectional area, is what we call the ***resistance*** of that conductor.

The factors which affect resistance will be discussed at greater length in Sec. 21-7. At present, we shall ignore current limiting influences other than resistance and consider them in Chapter 25.

21-5 Units of Electric Current, Potential, and Resistance

The unit of current is the ***ampere,*** which is defined as a flow which carries 1 coulomb of electric charge past a given point in 1 second. The relationship of the coulomb to the statcoulomb was stated, and the latter defined, in Sec. 20-6. The basic definition of the coulomb will be given in Sec. 23-8.

The unit of potential is the ***volt,*** 1 v being 1 joule of energy per cou-

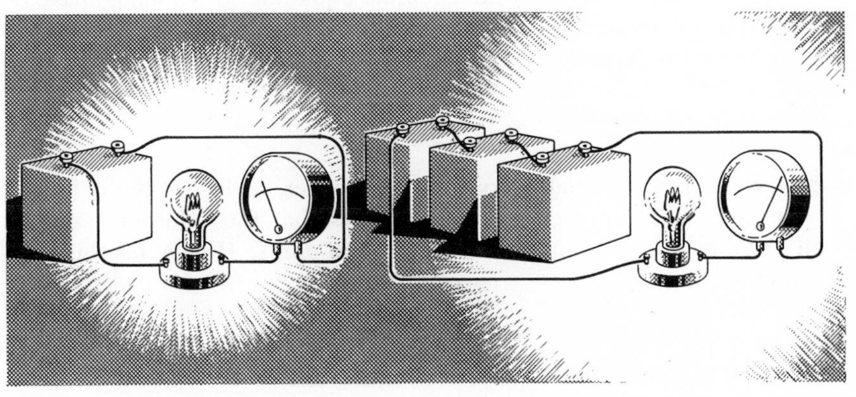

Fig. 21-2. Tripling the electrical potential triples the current.

lomb of charge (Sec. 20-9). For some purposes the ***statvolt,*** or erg per statcoulomb, is a more convenient unit of potential.

The term "volt" gives rise to the word ***voltage,*** which is an alternate name for either potential or potential difference. The term ***electromotive force*** (abbreviated emf) is widely used in place of voltage, or potential difference. There is an unfortunate implication here, for we know that potential difference is energy per unit charge, and is *not* in any sense a *force.* Because of this erroneous implication of the term, I prefer to avoid the use of emf insofar as can be done without leaving you open to confusion when you meet the term elsewhere.

The unit of resistance is the ***ohm.*** One ohm is a resistance such that if a potential difference of 1 v is applied to it the resulting current will be 1 amp.

Since the unit of potential difference is the volt, the term ***voltmeter*** is a logical name for an instrument designed to measure potential differences. On the same basis, one might expect an instrument designed to measure currents to be an amperemeter, or perhaps ampmeter; but instead it is called an ***ammeter.*** We shall consider these meters in Chapter 26.

21-6 Interrelationship of Current, Voltage, and Resistance

We have already seen, in Sec. 21-3, that the current flow is directly proportional to the electric potential responsible for that flow. This fact is an obvious and necessary result of the meanings of the terms "current" and "potential."

Also, we saw in Sec. 21-4 that, as the name implies, resistance is something which tends to hinder or limit the current flow; so obviously there is some sort of inverse relationship between current and resistance. Experiment reveals that this relationship is a simple inverse proportion.

On a number of occasions we have had to combine verbal statements of proportionality to produce an algebraic equation, so we should have no trouble. If V represents the potential difference, or voltage, if we use I to signify the current, and if the resistance is symbolized by R, in general

$$I = k \cdot \frac{V}{R}$$

where k is a proportionality constant. However, review of the definition of the ohm in the preceding section shows that the value of k will be unity if V is in volts, I in amperes, and R in ohms. Hence, for this combination of units,

$$I = \frac{V}{R} \tag{21-2}$$

Let us examine this equation on the basis of the *meanings* of the three quantities. There could be only three (first power) relationships among these quantities: $I = V/R$, $I = VR$, and $I = R/V$. The first one "makes sense" on the basis of what current, voltage, and resistance mean. The second is nonsense, for it says that an increase in resistance—an augmentation of the *hindrance* to the current—will *in*crease the current! The last compounds the asininity of the second by adding the requirement that the greater the voltage, which is what makes the current flow, the *smaller* the current will be. Equation (21-2) is so reasonable, and the others so obviously impossible, that there is never any possibility of your writing the equation incorrectly *if* you have any idea what voltage, current, and resistance mean *and if* you stop just a few seconds to think. Yet any physics teacher would probably expire from shock if a set of examination papers over this topic included neither of the perversions of Eq. (21-2), for some persons insist on relying *solely* on memory for the equation.

It is convenient, though never necessary, to rearrange the initial equation to either of two equivalent forms:

$$V = IR \tag{21-3}$$

$$R = \frac{V}{I} \tag{21-4}$$

Any one of these three equations may be considered to be an algebraic statement of ***Ohm's law:*** The current in an electric circuit is directly proportional to the voltage and inversely proportional to the resistance.

Since resistance is only one of the factors which may tend to hinder or impede an electric current, the validity of these equations and of this statement of Ohm's law is limited. When we consider the other factors in Chapter 25 and develop a more general quantitative relationship, we shall discover that Ohm's law is a special case of this more general relationship. We can use the relationship developed in this section with complete confidence whenever we are dealing with a current which is flowing steadily with no change of magnitude or direction. Some other situations can be handled by it but some cannot; so, for the present, we shall restrict our considerations to steady unidirectional currents.

21-7 Resistivity and Resistance

If you could measure the resistance between opposite faces of a cube of iron exactly 1 cm on a side and make a second measurement in which you use a similar cube of copper, you would find the resistance of the copper cube to be only about 17% of that of the iron cube. Measurements on similar cubes of other substances would yield other values. All these values would be indices of the intrinsic properties of the various substances as conductors of electricity.

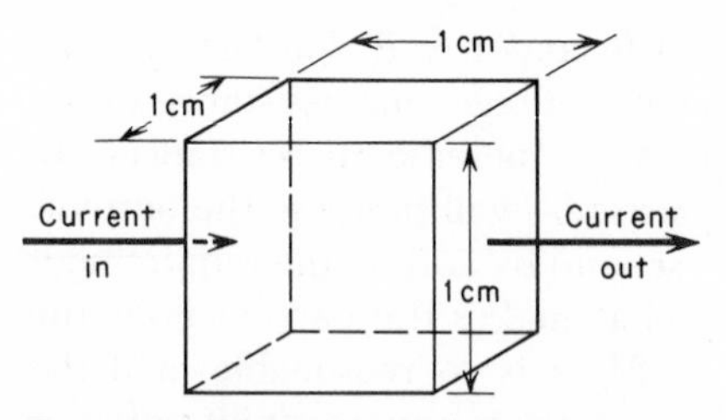

Fig. 21-3. The resistivity of a substance is the value of the resistance between opposite faces of a one centimeter cube of the substance.

A direct measurement of this sort is impractical, but an accurate measurement can be made of the resistance of a wire or rod of appropriate length and size, and the equivalent value for a 1 cm cube computed. Such a value is termed the ***resistivity*** of the substance. Resistivities of a number of substances appear in Table 21-1.

Just as two water pipes can carry more water than a single pipe, if electric current is flowing between two points we can get a larger flow by connecting additional wires between the two points. Since this increase of current is brought about without any increase in the voltage, the effective resistance must have been reduced. If we were to strip all insulation from the wires and compress them into a single larger wire or rod, the over-all effect would be no different than when they were separate. Thus we see that an increase in the cross-sectional area of a conductor reduces its resistance. In quantitative terms, the resistance of the conductor is inversely proportional to its cross-sectional area.

Suppose that we take several wires, each with a resistance R, and connect two of them together, obtaining a wire twice the length of either. Electric charges will encounter a resistance R in going through one segment, but they still have the other segment to go through, and it offers an additional resistance R; the total resistance of the wire is $2R$. If we join three segments, the resistance will be $3R$, etc. Thus we see that the resistance is directly proportional to the length of the conductor.

Combining the relationship of resistance to length and to cross-sectional area with the concept of resistivity, we have

$$R = \rho \frac{L}{A} \tag{21-5}$$

Table 21-1

RESISTIVITIES OF A FEW SUBSTANCES

(All values in ohm-centimeters)

Conductors		Non-conductors	
Aluminum	$2.83 \cdot 10^{-6}$	Bakelite (various kinds)	$2 \cdot 10^{7}$–$2 \cdot 10^{16}$
Brass*	$7 \cdot 10^{-6}$	Glass (various kinds)	$5 \cdot 10^{11}$–$1 \cdot 10^{16}$
Copper	$1.69 \cdot 10^{-6}$	Hard rubber (various kinds)	$2 \cdot 10^{15}$–$1 \cdot 10^{18}$
Gold	$2.44 \cdot 10^{-6}$	Fused quartz	over $5 \cdot 10^{18}$
Nichrome*	$100 \cdot 10^{-6}$	Sulfur	$8 \cdot 10^{15}$
Silver	$1.63 \cdot 10^{-6}$		

* Approximate value, due to variations among different alloys.

in which R is the resistance of a conductor made of a material which has a resistivity ρ, L is the length of the conductor, and A is its cross-sectional area. This equation is usable only if the value of A is constant or if it varies in a manner that can be described mathematically. We shall consider only examples in which the cross section is constant.

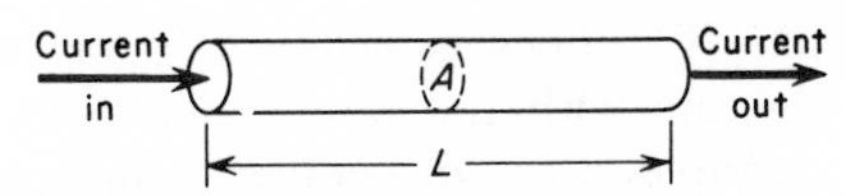

Fig. 21-4. Dimensions pertinent to the resistance of a conductor.

We can deduce the units appropriate to resistivity by rearranging Eq. (21-5) to the form

$$\rho = \frac{RA}{L} \tag{21-6}$$

and putting into this equation the units of R, A, and L. The result is

$$\rho = \text{ohms} \cdot \text{cm}^2/\text{cm} = \text{ohms} \cdot \text{cm}$$

so the unit of resistivity is ohm-cm.

Sample Problem 1

A copper wire has a cross-sectional area of 0.300 mm² and a resistance of 0.127 ohms. How long is the wire?

From Table 21-1 we obtain the resistivity of copper: $1.69 \cdot 10^{-6}$ ohm-cm. Solving Eq. (21-5) or (21-6) for L, we obtain

$$L = \frac{RA}{\rho}$$

Insertion of the data, after changing 0.300 mm² to $3.00 \cdot 10^{-3}$ cm², yields

$$L = \frac{(1.27 \cdot 10^{-1}) \cdot (3.00 \cdot 10^{-3})}{1.69 \cdot 10^{-6}}$$

$$= 2.25 \cdot 10^2 = 225 \text{ cm}$$

If you are less comfortable when juggling algebraic quantities than when using concrete numbers, you can substitute the data directly into Eq. (21-5) or (21-6) and obtain the same result.

21-8 Conductors and Insulators

Substances are classified as ***conductors,*** which will carry an electric current, and ***non-conductors,*** which will not. The latter are also termed ***insulators*** or ***dielectrics.***

This classification, however, is not so definite as the terms imply. The so-called insulators do not insulate perfectly, but they conduct so poorly that for many purposes we can ignore the minute currents they carry. We found conductors to differ considerably, in Sec. 21-7, and non-conductors vary much more widely, as the resistivities in Table 21-1 indicate. But the table also suggests that a "poor" conductor will conduct current something like 10^{11} times as well as a "poor" insulator. Comparison of the best conductors with the best insulators yields results which are fantastic: for example, a rod of copper 1 cm square and a billion times as long as the distance to the sun would have less resistance than a wafer of fused quartz 1 cm square and $\frac{1}{10}$ mm thick!

It is no accident that all the materials listed in Table 21-1 as conductors are metals and all the non-conductors are non-metals; all solids which are good conductors of electricity are metals. If this has a familiar ring, you haven't forgotten all you've learned previously; in Chapter 19 we found that metals are the best conductors of heat.

In Sec. 19-6, we ascribed the marked difference in the thermal conductivity of metals and non-metals to the difference in the tenacity with which atoms of the two substances hold onto their electrons, when any considerable number of atoms are grouped together. Whereas each atom of a non-metal, such as sulfur, zealously guards each of its electrons and allows none to escape, in a piece of metallic copper the outermost electron in each atom is virtually free to wander wherever it will so long as it remains within the confines of the piece of metal.

We shall find in Sec. 23-3, 23-4 that an electric battery can supply a potential difference because chemical processes within the battery cause an accumulation of electrons, and hence a negative charge, at one terminal, while a deficiency of electrons, and hence a positive charge, results at the other terminal. Therefore, if a conductor is connected between the terminals of the battery, one end of the conductor becomes positive and the other negative. This means that there is an electric field which causes a force on every electric charge in the conductor. The positive charges are in the nuclei of the atoms and hence are locked in the crystal lattice; they cannot move under the influence of the electric force applied to them. Each nucleus holds most of the electrons in the atom, preventing their escape; so they also are incapable of moving along the wire. But the "free" electrons have been roaming around much like molecules in a gas; and the application of the battery voltage repels them from the negative end of the conductor and attracts them toward the positive end. As they move away from the negative end of the conductor no deficiency develops there, for the excess electrons from the negative terminal of the battery move in to replace them. At the other end of the conductor, the electrons move to the positive terminal of the battery. If the chemical action within the battery maintains the charges on its terminals, there will be a continual march of electrons from the negative terminal, through the conductor, to the positive terminal of the battery. This flow of electrons constitutes, by definition, an electric current through the conductor.

If a non-conductor is connected between the terminals of a battery, the results are quite different because the atoms of the non-conductor hang onto their electrons too tenaciously; there are essentially no free electrons which can move and, by moving, carry a current.

Note an implication of this discussion of conduction in metals which is inconsistent with a common but erroneous concept of current flow. Many people feel that as a current flows through a circuit it weakens or "peters out" much as a flow of water in an irrigation furrow decreases along the furrow, because of water soaking into the soil. But no electrons are lost; over any appreciable interval of time the number of electrons entering the negative end of the conductor will be the same as the number leaving the positive end. Since they are "falling" through the difference of potential, the potential or energy of each electron is reduced. Neither the number nor the average speed of the electrons is altered, however; so the current is the same where it goes to the positive terminal as where it came from the negative terminal.

21-9 The Direction of Current Flow

In Franklin's one-fluid concept of the nature of electricity (Sec. 20-12) the fluid was considered to be positive. If some point A had a positive charge, this was due to an excess of the fluid; and if there was a deficiency of the fluid at a point B, there was a negative charge at that point. The flow which occurred if a wire was connected between the two points was considered to be a flow of the fluid—that is, a flow of positive charge. Thus the direction of flow was taken as the direction in which a *positive* charge moves. This convention regarding the direction of an electric current became firmly established in the literature of physics, engineering, and chemistry.

But we found in the preceding section that metals are the best conductors and that the positive charges in a metal cannot move; the electric current is due to a migration of electrons, which are *negative* charges. When these facts became known there was agitation to adopt a new convention, defining the direction of current flow as being from negative to positive.

If we investigate the nature of electric currents other than those in metals, the choice between the two conventions for current direction becomes less clear-cut. We shall find in Chapter 23 that when a current flows through a solution, such as table salt in water, for example, positive charges move in one direction and negative charges move the opposite way; so part of the current is due to motion of positive charge and part to movement of negative charge. A somewhat similar situation is found in an electric discharge through a gas.

For these reasons, and also because all the early literature and much modern literature employs the positive-to-negative convention, there is no universally accepted convention of current direction. According to the ***conventional direction of electric current*** the flow is from positive to negative, but on the basis of the ***direction of electron flow*** it is from negative to positive. In this book, the direction of an electric current will be taken as the direction of electron flow.

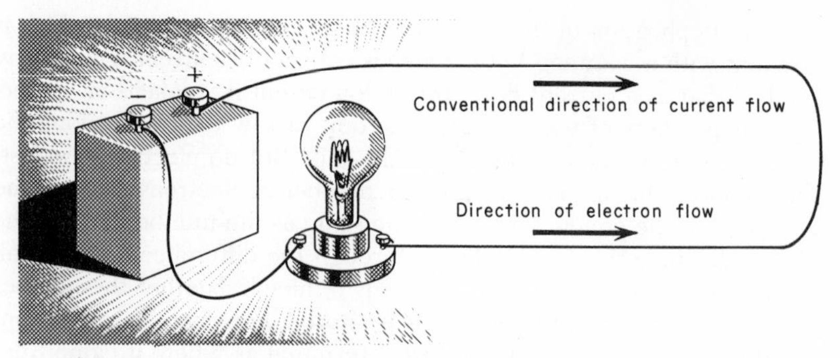

Fig. 21-5. Comparison of the conventional direction of an electric current with the direction of flow of electrons in a wire.

21-10 Energy and Power in an Electric Circuit

The definition of electric potential provides a means of evaluating the energy used (or produced) in an electric circuit. In Sec. 20-9, we found that electric potential is energy per unit charge, the algebraic definition being $V = W/q$, Eq. (20-8), in which V is the potential, W is the energy, and q the electric charge. As pointed out in that section, this may be rearranged to

$$W = qV \tag{20-9}$$

We may think of this relationship in terms of the units of the quantities:

$$\text{joules} = \text{coulombs} \cdot \text{volts}$$

which is obvious, if we recall that 1 joule/coulomb is 1 v, for

$$\text{joules} = \text{coulombs} \cdot (\text{joules/coulombs}) = \text{joules}$$

Note that Eq. (20-9) is based on the concept of electric potential as energy per unit charge rather than "electrical pressure." What would the product of charge and "electric pressure" (if there were such a quantity) be?! Note also that when we substitute units into the equation, any units of potential other than joules/coulomb would make the "equation" inhomogeneous and invalid.

We met the concept of power in Sec. 6-11, where power was defined as work or energy per unit time. Algebraically,

$$P = \frac{W}{t} \tag{6-4}$$

According to Eq. (20-9) for an electric circuit we may write qV in place of W:

$$P = \frac{qV}{t}$$

The right-hand side of this equation may be written as $(q/t) \cdot V$, and q/t is the current I, Eq. (21-1). Therefore

$$P = IV \tag{21-7}$$

The usual unit of electric energy is the joule. Time is measured in seconds, so the unit of power in Eq. (6-4) is joules per second. As defined in Sec. 6-11, 1 joule/sec is 1 watt, and 10^3 w, 1 kw. Thus power in Eq. (21-7) is expressed in watts, which may be converted to kilowatts by a simple shift of the decimal point.

Sample Problem 2

A heating unit on an electric stove is rated at 880 w. If the voltage is 220 v, (a) how many coulombs of electric charge will pass through the unit in 1 min, and (b) what is the value of the current?

We may proceed in either of two ways. First, since a watt is a joule per second, 880 w will be $880 \cdot 60$, or $5.28 \cdot 10^4$, joules in 1 min. Energy is the product of voltage and charge, Eq. (20-9) so charge is energy divided by voltage:

$$(5.28 \cdot 10^4) \text{ joules} \div 220 \text{ v} = 240 \text{ coulombs}$$

Current is coulombs per second:

$$240 \text{ coulombs} \div 60 \text{ sec} = 4.00 \text{ amp}$$

Alternatively, we may solve part (b) first, and this method requires only two computations instead of three. Since $P = IV$,

$$I = P/V = 880 \text{ w}/220 \text{ v} = 4.00 \text{ amp}$$

This is 4.00 coulombs/sec, so in 1 min the number of coulombs will be

$$4.00 \cdot 60 = 240 \text{ coulombs}$$

21-11 Modifications of the Equation for Electric Power

It often happens that we know the current *or* the voltage, but not both. In such a case, we cannot compute the power directly, though if the resistance is known we can compute the missing datum with the aid of Ohm's law, Eq. (21-2) and then calculate the power. It is convenient, however, to have a relationship among power, current, and resistance, and another among power, voltage, and resistance. These can be derived easily from Ohm's law and the equation for power.

Equation (21-7) is

$$P = IV$$

We may eliminate V from this equation by substituting the equivalent in terms of current and resistance as derived from Ohm's law, or we may eliminate I by a similar substitution of its equivalent in terms of voltage and resistance. According to Eq. (21-3), $V = IR$, so we may use IR in place of V in the original equation for electric power:

$$P = IV = I \cdot IR$$

$$P = I^2R \tag{21-8}$$

Or, according to the original form of Ohm's law, Eq. (21-2) $I = V/R$, so we may replace I in the power equation by V/R:

$$P = IV = \frac{V}{R} \cdot V$$

$$P = \frac{V^2}{R} \tag{21-9}$$

Though Eq. (21-8) and Eq. (21-9) are convenient, Ohm's law and the original equation for power will suffice for the solution of nearly any problem in which two of the four quantities, current, voltage, resistance, and power, are known and one or both the remaining quantities are to be found. However, if power and resistance are known but both current and voltage are unknown, Eq. (21-8) or (21-9) must be used (unless the solution is accomplished by the method of simultaneous equations—which many students prefer to avoid).

Sample Problem 3

An electric soldering iron is rated at 60.0 w and its resistance is 240 ohms. Compute the voltage and the current.

It is most convenient to use one of the derived equations, $P = I^2R$ or $P = V^2/R$. Choosing the former,

$$60.0 = I^2 \cdot 240$$

$$I^2 = \frac{60.0}{240} = 0.250$$

$$I = \sqrt{0.250} = 0.500 \text{ amp}$$

Now we have three choices: we may find the voltage with the aid of Ohm's law, from the basic power equation, or from the equation $P = V^2/R$. Using Ohm's law in the form $V = IR$,

$$V = 0.500 \cdot 240 = 120 \text{ v}$$

Obviously either of the other two choices would have yielded the same value of the voltage. Equally obviously, we might have chosen to begin with the other equation, $P = V^2/R$; this would have provided the value of V and left us a choice of three routes to follow to solve for the value of I. Thus, instead of there being *a* method of solution of the problem, there are at least *six!*

21-12 Direct Current and Alternating Current

Thus far we have been considering electric currents of the sort produced by batteries: currents which always flow in one direction. Such currents are ***direct currents,*** often abbreviated **DC.** Direct currents are used for electroplating and other electrochemical processes, for some kinds of electric motors, etc., and they find application in certain circuits used in radio, television and other electronic gear. There are also currents which reverse their direction of flow periodically; they are referred to as ***alternating currents,*** or **AC.** These also find a multitude of applications in electronic apparatus. Domestic power and lighting use alternating currents, and most electric power used in industry (except electrochemical industry) is AC.

The terms "frequency" and "period" are applicable to alternating electric currents, as they are to vibration and wave motion (Sec. 12-2, 13-6). The ***frequency*** of an alternating current is the number of complete cycles per second, one ***cycle*** consisting of a pulse of current in one direction and a pulse in the opposite direction, much as one compression and one rarefaction constitute a single sound wave. As always, the ***period*** is the reciprocal of the frequency, the time of one complete cycle.

Nearly all commercial AC in the United States has a frequency of 60 cycles per second (often referred to, incorrectly, as 60 cycle), and the waveform of the current is sinusoidal (Sec. 13-9). In other applications, however, frequencies as high as $3 \cdot 10^9$ cycles per second are used, and research is going on at still higher frequencies. In many applications, the waveform may be very complex rather than sinusoidal, and simple but non-sinusoidal forms, such as "square waves" and "saw-tooth waves," are used for special purposes. A sinusoidal AC is shown in Fig. 21-6.

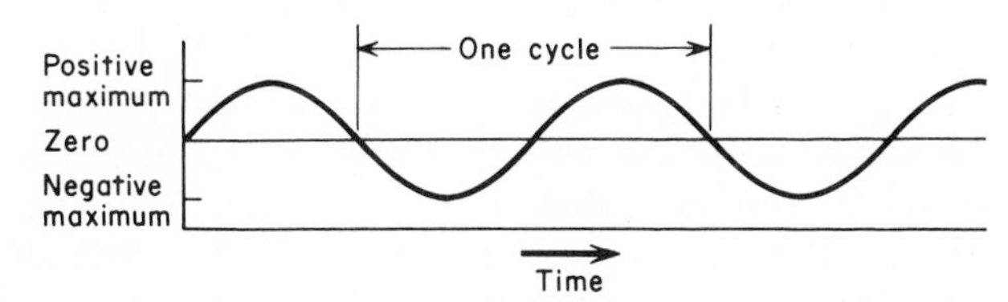

Fig. 21-6. Diagram of an alternating current which has a sinusoidal wave form.

21-13 Effective Values of Current and Voltage in an AC Circuit

Direct currents commonly are steady (though by no means always). There is no problem in measuring the constant voltage or current in a DC circuit carrying a steady current.

Alternating currents are quite another problem.* How can one obtain a meaningful value of a current if the current is perpetually changing in value and also in direction?

* So are pulsating direct currents, but these can be treated as a combination of a direct current and an alternating current.

Suppose that we take two identical heating coils, each associated with suitable equipment to measure the rate at which heat is produced and a suitable meter to measure the electric current. There must also be some means, such as a variable resistance, to control the current in one of the coils. A DC voltage may be applied to one heating coil and an AC voltage to the other. Since you can't change the heating coil through which direct current is flowing into a *refrigerating* coil by reversing the direction of the current, an alternating current will produce heat during both halves of the cycle, just as if it were a pulsating direct current. Therefore heat will be produced in both coils. The current in one of them may be adjusted so that the heating rate is exactly the same in both. The value of the direct current may then be read, and this value of DC which will have the same heating effect as the AC is defined as the ***effective value*** of the alternating current.

The effective value of the AC voltage may be defined, and determined, in an exactly similar manner. Obviously such cumbersome methods are not used in the actual measurement of AC voltages and currents, but these procedures constitute the ultimate basis on which AC meters are calibrated.

Since heat is a form of energy, the quantity of heat produced per unit time is a measure of power. The basic equation for electric power is $P = IV$, which indicates that the heating rate due to an alternating electric current will not be constant, since the values of both I and V are varying continuously. Over a time interval which is several times the period, however, there will be a definite *average* rate of heating. The electric power produced in a heating coil of resistance R, through which an alternating current is flowing, can be expressed as $P = I^2R$, Eq. (21-8). Thus the *average* power depends on the average value of I^2 rather than on the average value of I.* Similarly, since $P = V^2/R$, Eq. (21-9), the average power is determined by the average value of V^2 rather than the average value of V. Thus, if I_{eff} is the effective value of the current in an AC circuit,

$$I_{\text{eff}} = \sqrt{\text{average of values of } (I_{\text{AC}})^2} \qquad (21\text{-}10)$$

and similarly $$V_{\text{eff}} = \sqrt{\text{average of values of } (V_{\text{AC}})^2} \qquad (21\text{-}11)$$

in which the V_{eff} is the effective value of the AC voltage.

If the waveform of AC is sinusoidal, as is the case with commercial AC power supplies, the effective values of the current and the voltage are equal to the corresponding maximum or ***peak*** values divided by the square root of two:

---

* If the distinction between the average of (for example) I_{AC} and the square root of the average of $(I_{\text{AC}})^2$ isn't obvious, consider any pair of arbitrary values such as 0.50 and 10.00. Their average is 5.25. But the average of 0.50^2 and 10.00^2 is half of $(0.25 + 100.00)$, or 50.125, and the square root of this is about 7.08.

$$I_{\text{eff}} = \frac{I_{\max}}{\sqrt{2}} \approx 0.707\, I_{\max} \tag{21-12}$$

and

$$I_{\max} = I_{\text{eff}} \cdot \sqrt{2} \approx 1.414 I_{\text{eff}} \tag{21-13}$$

$$V_{\text{eff}} = \frac{V_{\max}}{\sqrt{2}} \approx 0.707\, V_{\max} \tag{21-14}$$

and

$$V_{\max} = V_{\text{eff}} \cdot \sqrt{2} \approx 1.414\, V_{\text{eff}} \tag{21-15}$$

The pulsations of both the current and the voltage result in somewhat similar pulsations of the power, as shown in Fig. 21-7. Since the effective values of both current and voltage are smaller than their peak values by a factor of $\sqrt{2}$, the effective power—the product of I_{eff} and V_{eff}—will be half of the peak power.* Thus

$$P_{\text{eff}} = \frac{P_{\max}}{2} \tag{21-16}$$

and

$$P_{\max} = 2 P_{\text{eff}} \tag{21-17}$$

It must not be overlooked that the validity of the relationships discussed in the last two paragraphs and expressed in Eq. (21-12) through Eq. (21-17) is confined to a sinusoidal waveform. In general the factors are different for other waveforms.

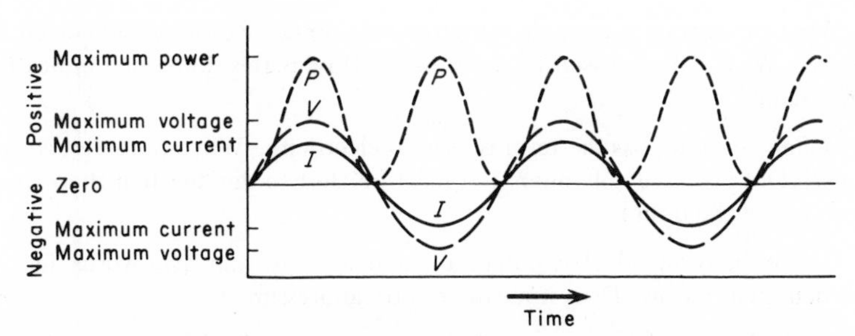

Fig. 21-7. Diagram showing current (I), voltage (V), and power (P) in an alternating current circuit. This is only an example; the relative values of the current and voltage might be quite different.

Summary

Any *flow* or *motion* of electric charge constitutes an *electric current.* In a *quantitative* sense, current is the *rate of flow* of charge. The cause of

* We shall find in Chapter 25 that the current and voltage may not be in phase with each other, in which case the relationships expressed in Eqs. 21-16 and 21-17 are invalid without appropriate modification.

current flow is electric potential. *Resistance* is a *hindrance* to *current flow* due to the chemical and physical nature, and the dimensions, of a conductor.

The resistance of a 1 cm cube of material is the measure of the *resistivity* of the substance. Substances which have relatively low resistivities are conductors; those with high resistivities are non-conductors. The presence of free electrons which conduct the current accounts for the relatively low resistivities of metals. As implied by the definitions of the concepts, electric current is directly proportional to the voltage and inversely proportional to the resistance. This is Ohm's law.

Any *general specification* of the *direction* of *current flow* is *arbitrary*. We shall consider the flow to be from negative to positive.

The energy used in an electric circuit is the product of the charge and the voltage; the power is the product of the current and the voltage. Power can be expressed also in terms of current and resistance, or in terms of voltage and resistance.

An alternating current reverses direction periodically. The effective values of the current and voltage in an AC circuit are determined by the heating effect, as compared with the heating effect of a known DC current or voltage.

Self-Quiz

1. What similarities, if any, are there between static electricity and current electricity? What is their essential difference? How is this difference indicated by their names?

2. Define "current," as the term is used in electricity. Why are there *two* definitions? (Did you give only one? You must be alert to the fact that there are *two* meanings of the term.)

3. Define the term "electric potential," and state, in your own words, just what this definition means. Does it mean "electrical pressure"?

4. On the basis of the true concept of electric potential, what relationship should exist between potential difference and current? (In what sense is "current" used here?)

5. Proceeding solely on the basis of what the pertinent terms really mean, by simple reasoning develop the relationship known as Ohm's law.

6. Define the ampere, the volt, and the ohm. In the algebraic statement of Ohm's law, why is no proportionality constant or conversion factor needed?

7. What is the essential meaning of the concept of resistivity?

8. Is the resistivity of a non-conductor higher, or lower, than that of a conductor?

9. In terms of the internal structure of the two types of substances, explain the great difference in the resistivities of non-conductors and conductors.

10. In what sense must the designations, "conductor" and "non-conductor," be interpreted? Is there any substance which refuses to conduct even a very minute electric current?

11. Outline the general mechanism of the conduction of an electric current by a metal.

12. As an electric current passes through a wire which has an appreciable resistance, does the current become progressively weaker because of the resistance? What *does* happen?

13. To what extent, if any, is a convention for the direction of an electric current arbitrary? To what extent, if any, is it based on something fundamental? Is any convention universally employed? What convention will be used in this text?

14. Solely on the basis of the definitions of the pertinent quantities, develop the basic method of computing electric power. Write the equation, and show that it is consistent with your method.

15. From other pertinent equations derive an equation for power in terms of voltage and resistance, and another in terms of current and resistance.

16. State, and define, the units of electric energy and electric power.

17. The electric "power" company bills you on the basis of the number of *kilowatt-hours* used. This means the company is *not* charging you for *power.* For what is it charging you?

18. What is an alternating current? How does it differ from a direct current? Is the value of the current constant? the value of the voltage? of the power?

19. What is meant by the frequency of an alternating current? In what terms is frequency expressed? How is it often *in*correctly expressed?

20. What is the basis for determining the effective value of an alternating current?

21. If the word "current" in the preceding question were replaced by the word "voltage," what modifications, if any, would be necessary in your discussion?

22. For commercial supplies of AC electric power, what numerical factor relates the effective value of the current to its peak value? How is the effective value of the voltage related to its maximum value? Are these factors applicable universally?

Problems

1. The current through a common type of Christmas tree lamp is 50.0 milliamperes (ma). (a) This is how many amperes? (b) How many coulombs of electricity pass through such a lamp in 3.00 hr? (c) The charge on an electron is $1.60 \cdot 10^{-19}$ coulomb. How many electrons pass through each second?

2. The current in a certain electronic gadget is exactly 1 ma. How long will it take for one billion electrons to pass?

3. If the lamp in Problem 1 is designed for use on 115 v, what is its resistance?

4. What current will flow through a lamp on a 120 v circuit if the resistance of the lamp is 240 ohms?

5. A current of 2.50 amp flows through a heating coil which has a resistance of 88.0 ohms. What voltage is applied to it?

6. Number 14 copper wire has a cross-sectional area of 2.08 mm^2. (a) Calculate the resistance of 1 km of this wire. (What additional datum do you need? See Table 21-1.) (b) What is the resistance of 1000 ft of the wire?

7. A copper wire is exactly 3 times as long as a silver wire of the same resistance. (a) Find the ratio of the cross-sectional area of the copper wire to that of the silver wire. (b) Compute the ratio of their diameters.

8. The resistance of a piece of No. 12 aluminum wire exactly 100 m long was found to be 0.855 ohms. The cross-sectional area of No. 12 wire is $3.31 \cdot 10^{-2}$ cm^2. Calculate the resistivity of aluminum.

9. A brass strip is 2.00 cm wide and 5.00 m long, and its resistance is 0.350 ohm. How thick is it?

10. What is the energy of an electron at the negative end of a wire if the potential difference between the two ends of the wire is 1.00 millivolt (mv)?

11. If an electric soldering iron is rated at 60.0 w on 120 v, (a) how much electrical energy does it use each second? (b) How much energy is used for each electron that goes through the heating coil? (c) How many electrons pass through each second?

12. (a) Using Eq. (21-7) compute the current passing through the heating coil in Problem 11. (b) From the answer to part (a) and the value of the electronic charge, calculate the number of electrons passing each second. Compare with the answer to part (c) of Problem 11.

13. From the definitions of the joule and the watt, and any appropriate conversion factors, determine the numerical relationship between joules and kilowatt-hours.

14. Sample Problem 3, page 388, was solved by one method and five others were suggested. Set up the method of solution by some of the other methods, and carry each far enough to see that it will yield the correct result.

15. An electric heater is rated at 1500 w on 120 v. Compute (a) its resistance, and (b) the current through it. Set up at least one alternate method of solution.

16. A radio parts catalog lists a particular resistor at $R = 2700$ ohms, $P = 2$ w. Assuming the power rating to be 2.00 w, determine (a) the maximum permissible DC current and (b) the maximum permissible DC voltage consistent with these ratings.

17. (a) In a sinusoidal 120 v AC, what is the peak value of the voltage? (b) What value would be read on a voltmeter?

18. The peak value of the current in a sinusoidal AC is 8.48 amp. What value of DC would give the same heating rate as this AC would?

19. If the effective value of a commercial AC is 120 v, what is the potential difference between the positive peak value and the negative peak value?

20. Alternating current is applied to one heating coil and DC is applied to another coil which is identical with the first one. The value of the DC is equal to the peak value of the AC. In which coil is the heating rate greater, and what is the ratio of the two rates?

22
SIMPLE ELECTRIC CIRCUITS

22-1 Preview

The first part of this chapter, through Sec. 22-5, deals with the components of simple electric circuits, how they are connected to form circuits of a few simple kinds, and the schematic representation of such circuits. The latter part deals with the resistance of a series circuit and that of a parallel circuit, the relationship of the currents in the parts of each type of circuit to the current in the circuit as a whole, and similar matters. The concept of conductance will appear.

22-2 Circuits in General*

An electric ***circuit*** is any arrangement whatever, simple or complex, in which electric charges flow out of some source, such as a battery or generator, through one or more conductors, back to the source, through the source, and continue circulating as long as the source continues to supply a potential difference and the path of flow remains complete.

It is important to note that the electric charges make a complete round trip of the circuit—which is why it is called a circuit. None are destroyed, and in a simple DC circuit none accumulate anywhere. Hence, as observed in the final paragraph of Sec. 21-8, the value of the current is the same where it reenters the source as it was where it issued from the source.

22-3 Analogies of Electric Circuits

Electric circuits are a mystery to many students, and many who have some understanding of simple circuits also have some *mis*understanding. It may be helpful to compare electric circuits with familiar traffic situations. This will furnish a concrete basis for discussion, and it will be instructive to note the similarities *and* the differences.

In Fig. 22-1, *R* denotes a popular and scenic vacation area. Tourist caravans go out to various points of interest or beauty. The roads are all good, but at all points of special interest, *A* through *E*, traffic is hampered by pedestrians, cars parking, etc.

One popular tour goes through *A* and returns. Traffic moves easily throughout this circle tour except at *A*, where it "piles up." There is no way of bypassing *A*, and the entire route is a one-way road; any car which leaves *R* must pass through *A* and return.

Another tour is similar to the first, except that it includes two points of interest, *B* and *C*. Some tourists may be interested in only one, but they can't go to *B* and return without passing through *C*, nor can they visit *C* without going through *B*, because this also is a one-way road.

A third tour is, in a sense, a combination of two different tours. All cars start out on the same road, and return to *R* by a common road; but some distance from *R* the road splits and part of the caravan goes through *D* whereas the remainder

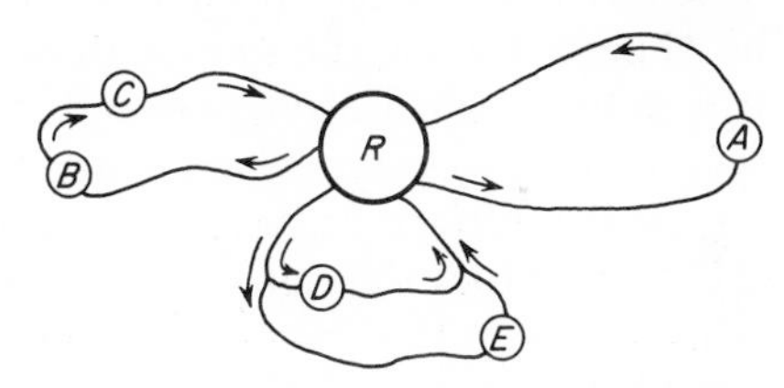

Fig. 22-1. Sight-seeing analogies of some simple electric circuits.

* Some acquaintance with electric circuits and their representation is necessary for the work in Sec. 22-6 – 22-10 and in some later chapters. Depending on the background of the class, Sec. 22-2 – 22-5 inclusive may be waived for part or all of the class.

go through E. No one car can go through both D and E on a single trip out of R, since all roads are one way; but it is quite possible to make a trip through either D or E and later make a second trip through the other.

Tourists take trips for any of a number of reasons, but the sole reason for an electric charge to take a trip around an electric circuit is an electric potential generated by some ***source.*** A very common source is a cell or a battery. Any device which uses the energy of a chemical reaction to generate electrical energy is a ***cell,*** and any combination of two or more cells is a ***battery.**** This conversion of chemical to electrical energy will be considered in the next chapter. Instead of a cell or battery, the source may be a ***generator*** of some sort, which transforms mechanical energy to electrical, as we shall see in Chapters 24 and 26. It may be any of several other devices, some of which we shall meet later.

There are no pedestrians or parking cars in an electric circuit: limitation of the current is due to some sort of ***load.*** For the present the only kind of load we shall consider is a ***resistor,*** or ***resistance,*** which is any device of relatively high resistance, such as a heating coil or the filament of an incandescent lamp. Current is led to, and out of, the load by low resistance conductors which correspond to the unobstructed roadways in Fig. 22-1. These conductors are usually wires, but need not be.

The cars of a tourist caravan may move rapidly in some portions of the tour, stop for indefinite periods, etc. There may be traffic jams where they "pile up" and move along slowly and spasmodically. A car may be wrecked and never complete the tour. In the morning, the number of cars leaving R each hour will be much greater than the number returning, and no matter how badly traffic may be hampered later, these early travelers could pass through the points of interest without slowing at all, if they wished.

On the contrary, in a simple DC circuit corresponding to the tour through A in Fig. 22-1, or that through B and C, the instant a current commences to flow at any point it commences at *all* points, and the flow rate is identical throughout. The effect of the load is "felt" equally by charges leaving the source, those entering the load or passing through it, and those which have passed through the load and are returning to the source. Every charge which leaves the source passes around the complete circuit and returns to the source. For an electric circuit corresponding to the divided tour through D or E in Fig. 22-1, all the remarks in this paragraph apply to the conductors which are common to both branches of the circuit.

---

* Note that a "dry battery" or a "flashlight battery" is far more likely to be a cell than a battery.

22-4 Terminology of Simple Circuits

For the present, only DC circuits will be considered, though all terms introduced in this section are applicable to AC circuits as well.

There is no special term for an electric circuit which contains only a single source and a single load (plus the necessary conductors, of course!) corresponding to the tour through A in Fig. 22-1. If there are two loads in a circuit, they may be connected in either of two ways. In a ***series*** circuit, the connections are such that all the current must go through one load and then the other, like cars on the tour through B and C. The current divides in a ***parallel*** circuit, part going through one load and the remainder through another; this corresponds to the divided tour through D or E in Fig. 22-1. Instead of the term "parallel," ***shunt*** and ***multiple*** are used sometimes, or in special applications.

In either series or parallel circuits, there may be more than two loads, just as there might have been several points of interest instead of only two on the route through B and C, or several branches of the main road, each with its own single point of interest, instead of only the branch through D and that through E.

The adjectives, series and parallel, were defined in terms of the manner in which two or more loads are connected in a circuit; but they are equally applicable, with the same meanings, if two or more sources are present in a circuit. Thus, the battery in a car is composed of cells connected in series, but in some applications it is preferable to connect cells in parallel to form a battery.

No source of potential can cause a current to flow unless the circuit is complete. When it is *in*complete, usually because of a switch, the circuit is said to be ***open.*** It is ***closed*** if it is complete so that current can flow. Some students confuse these terms because they think of an open or closed door; instead, you should imagine a river crossed by every tour in Fig. 22-1, with drawbridges over the river. Whenever a drawbridge on any route is opened, traffic on that route is stopped; but it can flow again as soon as the drawbridge is closed. Again, we must beware of "pushing" an analogy too far. Cars are stopped only as they arrive at the bridge; those in other parts of the route are unaffected. But when an electric circuit is opened, current flow ceases everywhere. All parts of the circuit connected to the positive terminal of the source acquire the potential of that terminal, so that no potential difference exists along that portion of the circuit; hence there is nothing to cause the electric charges to move. A similar situation exists in the portion of the circuit connected to the negative terminal. Thus the potential difference generated by the source is applied across the "open," or gap, in the incomplete circuit, which has an essentially infinite resistance and so blocks any current flow.

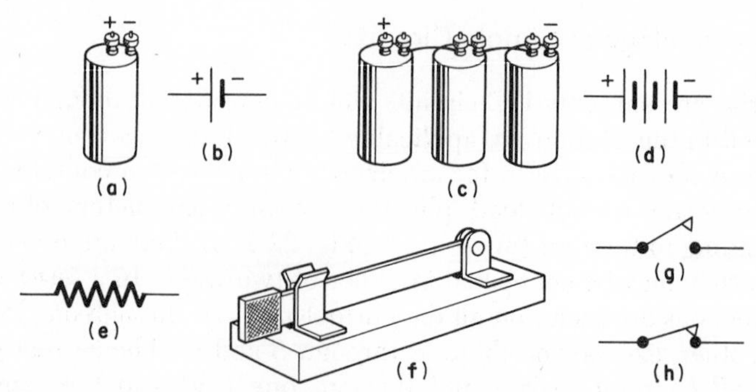

Fig. 22-2. Symbols for common circuit elements. (*a*) cell; (*b*) symbol for cell; (*c*) and (*d*) battery of three cells, and symbol; (*e*) symbol for resistor; (*f*) knife switch, in closed position; (*g*) symbol for open switch; (*h*) symbol for closed switch.

22-5 Schematic Representation of Electric Circuits

Figure 22-2 shows the symbols used for some common circuit elements. Part (a) of the figure is a dry cell, and part (b) is the symbol used to represent a single cell of any kind. The longer line always indicates the positive terminal of the cell, and the shorter and (usually) heavier line the negative terminal; thus the + and − signs are redundant, and often they are omitted. A battery of three cells in series and the corresponding symbol appear in parts (c) and (d) of the figure. Resistors may have any of a myriad of physical forms so only the general symbol for any resistor is shown in part (e). A knife switch is shown in Fig. 22-2(f); it is depicted schematically in the open position in part (g) of the figure, and symbolized in closed position in part (h). Note that the position of the switch is the basis for the terms *open* circuit and *closed* circuit.

Using these components, a simple DC circuit is shown, with switch closed, in Fig. 22-3(a); it consists of a battery composed of two cells

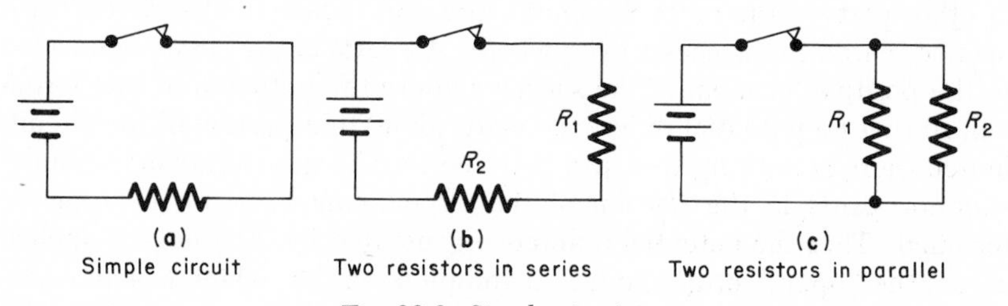

Fig. 22-3. Simple circuits.

in series, a switch, and a resistance. Figure 22-3(b) represents a similar circuit, but this circuit contains two separate resistors in series; since current which passes through either resistor must pass through the other, it is a series circuit. Part (c) of the figure depicts a circuit which also contains two separate resistors, but they are connected in such a manner that the current which flows through either one can *not* flow through the other. This is a parallel circuit.

It is possible to have some units in a circuit connected in series, and other parts in parallel. In fact, this is the situation in Fig. 22-3(c). Although the two resistors are in parallel, the battery consists of two cells in series. In Fig. 22-4(a) the circuit has two parallel branches, but one of the branches contains two resistors connected in series; and in the (b) part of the figure, R_2 and R_3 are in parallel but the combination of these two in parallel is in series with R_1. Either of these circuits is a *series-parallel* circuit.

22-6 Current and Voltage in a Part of a Circuit

As a rather rough approximation, in the circuit of Fig. 22-3(a) we may consider that all resistance except that of the load may be ignored. On the basis of this assumption, according to Ohm's law, Eq. (21-2), the current I in the circuit will be $I = V/R$, in which V is the potential difference supplied by the battery and R is the resistance of the load. Since there are no parallel branches in this circuit, the current is the same throughout the entire circuit. Rearranging the equation for Ohm's law to the form $V = IR$, we see that a potential difference V is required to force a current I through the resistance R. Though the current—the number of charges passing a given point per unit time—is the same everywhere in the circuit, the charges lose energy in passing through the resistance. The potential difference V which exists between opposite ends of the resistance while the current is flowing often is referred to as the "IR drop."

In a series circuit such as that in Fig. 22-3(b), the charges flowing around the circuit use up part of their energy in passing through R_1 and the remainder (again assuming that other resistances in the circuit are so

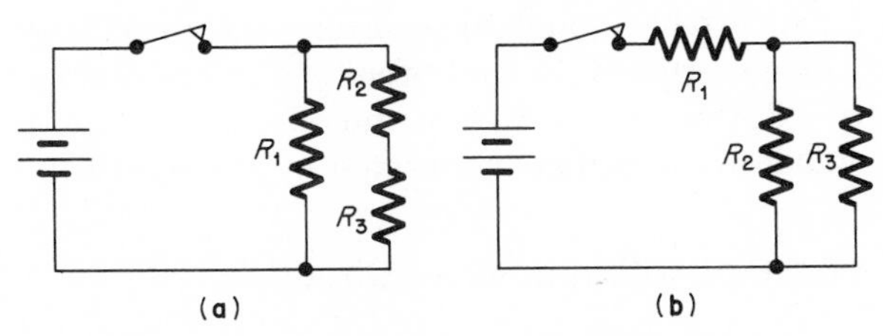

Fig. 22-4. Two kinds of series-parallel circuits.

small that they may be neglected) in passing through R_2. If there are more than two resistors in the circuit, there will be additional voltage drops IR_3, IR_4, etc., across them.

If the current in the circuit is I amperes, this means that during 1 sec Q coulombs leave the source, and at any other point in the circuit Q coulombs pass each second. If the source generates a potential of V volts, this means that each coulomb leaving the source has V joules more energy than one which is returning to the source; so in making a complete circuit each coulomb loses V joules of energy. According to Eq. (21-8), the power required to force a current I through the resistance R_1 is R_1I^2; and since energy is equal to power multiplied by time, the energy used up by the current in passing through R_1 is R_1I^2t. We may write this as $R_1I \cdot It$. If the source supplies Q coulombs at a potential V, the energy it delivers to the charges commencing their trip around the circuit is QV. Since they have used up all this energy when they return to the source, we may write, for a circuit with n resistors in series,

$$QV = (R_1I \cdot It) + (R_2I \cdot It) + (R_3I \cdot It) + \cdots + (R_nI \cdot It)$$
$$= (R_1I + R_2I + R_3I + \cdots + R_nI) \cdot It$$

But by the definition of current, $It = Q$; so we can cancel Q on the left side against It on the right, obtaining

$$V = R_1I + R_2I + R_3I + \cdots + R_nI \tag{22-1}$$

This equation says that the potential difference applied to a series circuit is equal to the sum of the voltage drops (since in general $V = IR$, each of the IR terms represents a voltage drop) across the separate units in the circuit.

Contrary to the situation in a series circuit, in which only part of the voltage generated by the source is available for any one unit of the circuit, the full voltage of the circuit is applied across each branch of a parallel circuit—provided that we assume, as before, that other resistances in the circuit are negligible. Thus, for a parallel circuit, such as that in Fig. 22-3(c),

$$V = I_1R_1 = I_2R_2 \tag{22-2}$$

wherein I_1 is the current through the resistor R_1, I_2 the current through R_2, and V the voltage applied to the circuit. If there are more than two branches, the IR drop across each of the others, like that across R_1 and R_2, will be equal to the voltage generated by the source.

22-7 Relationships within a Series Circuit

We have found in Eq. (22-1) that the voltage applied to the circuit is the sum of the voltage drops across the various parts of the circuit.

Since in general any voltage may be evaluated in terms of a current and a resistance, if the effective resistance of an entire series circuit is R_s, we may write $V = R_s I$, where V is the voltage applied to the circuit and I is the resulting current. Making this change in Eq. (22-1), we obtain

$$R_s I = R_1 I + R_2 I + R_3 I + \cdots + R_n I$$

But since the current is the same throughout the circuit all the I's are equal and may be canceled, giving

$$R_s = R_1 + R_2 + R_3 + \cdots + R_n \qquad (22\text{-}3)$$

Thus, the effective resistance of a series circuit is the sum of the resistances of its parts. Note the parallelism between this statement and that immediately below Eq. (22-1). We should expect this similarity, since only two minor changes were required to change Eq. (22-1) to Eq. (22-3).

It has been pointed out repeatedly that the current through any one part of a series circuit is identical with that in any other part, and also identical with the current in the circuit as a whole. And from the principle of conservation of energy, the energy supplied to the circuit must be equal to the sum of the quantities of energy used in the separate parts of the circuit. Since power is energy per unit time, a similar statement is valid for the relationship of total power to power used in the parts. Thus the same type of relationship applies to voltage, resistance, energy, and power; the only markedly different relationship involves the constancy of the current.

The facts that the current is the same throughout a series circuit and that in general $V = IR$, require that the voltage drops across the various units in a series circuit are directly proportional to the respective values of the resistances.

Sample Problem 1

Resistances of exactly 2, 3, and 5 ohms are connected in series with a 6.00 v battery. Find (a) the resistance of the circuit, (b) the current in the circuit, (c) the voltage drop across each resistor, and (d) check the sum of the voltage drops in part (c) against the voltage of the battery.

(a) The resistance of the circuit is the sum of the resistances:

$$R_s = 2.00 + 3.00 + 5.00 = 10.00 \text{ ohm}$$

(b) The current is voltage divided by resistance:

$$I = \frac{V}{R_s} = \frac{6.00}{10.00} = 0.600 \text{ amp}$$

(c) Across any resistor the voltage drop is IR, so

$$V_2 = 0.600 \cdot 2.00 = 1.20 \text{ v}$$

in which the subscript 2 is the resistance of the resistor under consideration. In like manner

$$V_3 = 0.600 \cdot 3.00 = 1.80 \text{ v}, \quad \text{and} \quad V_5 = 0.600 \cdot 5.00 = 3.00 \text{ v}$$

(d) The sum of the voltage drops is $1.20 + 1.80 + 3.00 = 6.00$ v which is equal to the applied voltage.

Sample Problem 2

An 80.0 ohm resistor and an 8.00 ohm resistor are connected in series on a 110 v circuit. What is the voltage drop across each?

This problem could be solved as the preceding one was, but there is an easier way—easier, at least, if you're willing to do a little thinking instead of using formulas blindly. Since the voltage drop across any unit in a series circuit is directly proportional to the resistance of that unit, the drop across the 80.0 ohm resistor is exactly ten times that across the 8.00 ohm resistor. If we call the latter value V_8, the total voltage drop is $10V_8$ across the 80 ohm unit plus V_8 across the 8 ohm one, or $11V_8$ total. But this must equal the applied voltage, which is 110 v, so $11V_8 = 110$ v and $V_8 = 10.0$ v. Then $10V_8$, the drop across the other resistor, is $10 \cdot 10.0$ or 100 v. These add up, as they should, to the applied voltage, 110 v.

22-8 Relationships within a Parallel Circuit

We have already seen, in the latter part of Sec. 22-6, that in a parallel circuit the voltage across any one branch is the same as that across any other, being equal in all cases to the voltage supplied by the source. Thus, if there are n parallel branches which have resistances $R_1, R_2, R_3, \ldots, R_n$, and if the respective currents through these branches are $I_1, I_2, I_3, \ldots, I_n$

$$V = R_1I_1 = R_2I_2 = R_3I_3 = \cdots = R_nI_n$$

We may denote the current in the circuit as a whole by I with no subscript. When we say that a current I leaves the source, we are saying that a certain number of electric charges flow out each second. Some of these will take the first turn and flow through R_1 but others will continue on, as in Fig. 22-5. Of those that don't flow through the first branch, some will take the path through R_2, but others (if there are more than two branches) will go on. Thus, at each junction the current divides. After passing through any one of the branches, the current will join the current(s) which flowed through other branch(es) forming one larger current which returns to the source. The fact that the charges are indestructible means that the total charge passing a

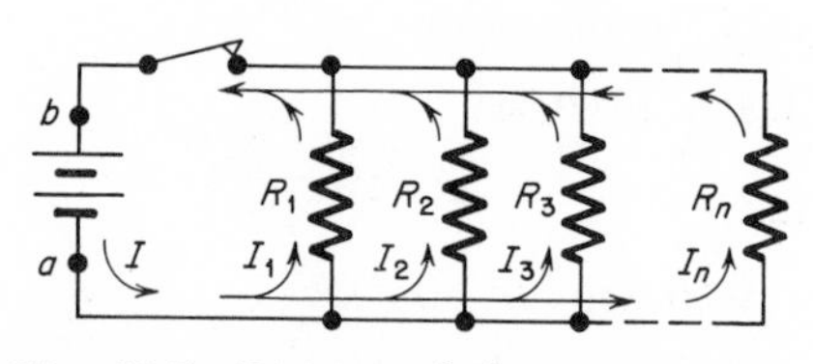

Fig. 22-5. Division of the current in a parallel circuit among the branches of the circuit.

point such as a or b in any given time must be the equal to the sum of the charges which pass through the several branches in that time. And since current is charge per unit time, we may write

$$I = I_1 + I_2 + I_3 + \cdots + I_n \tag{22-4}$$

According to Ohm's law, in general $I = V/R$; so if the effective resistance of a parallel circuit is R_p

$$\frac{V}{R_p} = \frac{V}{R_1} + \frac{V}{R_2} + \frac{V}{R_3} + \cdots + \frac{V}{R_n}$$

Because the voltage across any branch is equal to that applied to the circuit, all the V's represent the same voltage and may be canceled out. This gives

$$\frac{1}{R_p} = \frac{1}{R_1} + \frac{1}{R_2} + \frac{1}{R_3} + \cdots + \frac{1}{R_n} \tag{22-5}$$

Thus, the reciprocal of the resistance of a parallel circuit is equal to the sum of the reciprocals of the resistances offered by its individual branches. This means that the resistance of the circuit is *less* than the resistance of any one of its branches. We should expect this, for the addition of any parallel branch provides an additional path for the current without decreasing the current through the original path(s) (provided that the voltage applied to the circuit is unchanged). Thus, with no increase in voltage, the current is augmented by the addition of a parallel branch, and Ohm's law—and common sense—says that we can get *more* current with the *same* voltage *only* if the resistance is *de*creased.

The law of conservation of energy is not nullified by changing the type of connections used; the total energy consumption of the circuit is equal to the sum of the quantities of energy used in its branches, and the same relationship relates total power to the power used in the branches.

Since the voltage drop across any one branch is the same as that across any other, and because, as always, $I = V/R$, it follows that the currents in the various branches of a parallel circuit are *inversely* proportional to the respective values of resistance.

Sample Problem 3

The 2.00, 3.00, and 5.00 ohm resistors used in the series circuit in Sample Problem 1 are taken out of that circuit and connected in parallel, and voltage is supplied by the same 6.00 v battery as before. Find (a) the resistance of the circuit, (b) the current in the circuit, (c) the current through each branch, and (d) check the answers to parts (b) and (c).

(a)
$$\frac{1}{R_p} = \frac{1}{2.00} + \frac{1}{3.00} + \frac{1}{5.00} = \frac{15.0 + 10.0 + 6.00}{30.0} = \frac{31.0}{30.0}$$

$$R_p = \frac{30.0}{31.0} = 0.968 \text{ ohm}$$

Note that the resistance of the circuit is less than half that of the branch which has the *least* resistance.

(b) $$I = \frac{V}{R} = 6.00 \div \frac{30.0}{31.0} = \frac{6.00 \cdot 31.0}{30.0} = \frac{186}{30.0} = 6.20 \text{ amp}$$

We could have used R as 0.968 instead of 30.0/31.0, but this would have carried on the error involved in rounding off 0.9677+ ohm to 0.968 ohm. It would also have required a long division, or the use of logarithms or slide rule, whereas the other method involves only mental computations.

(c) $$I_2 = \frac{6.00}{2.00} = 3.00 \text{ amp}$$

in which I_2 is the current through the 2.00 ohm resistor. Similarly

$$I_3 = \frac{6.00}{3.00} = 2.00 \text{ amp}, \quad \text{and} \quad I_5 = \frac{6.00}{5.00} = 1.20 \text{ amp}$$

(d) The sum of the three currents in part (c) is

$$3.00 + 2.00 + 1.20 = 6.20 \text{ amp}$$

and this agrees with the answer to part (b).

Sample Problem 4

A total current of 5.00 amp is flowing in a parallel circuit which contains two branches. The resistance of one branch is 20.0 ohms, and the current through it is 1.00 amp. What is the resistance of the other branch?

The inverse proportionality between the currents and the resistances in the respective branches provides a very easy method of solution. The current in the other branch is 5.00 − 1.00 or 4.00 amp, and this is exactly four times the current in the first branch. If the current is four times as great, the resistance must be one-fourth as large, which is 20.0/4 or 5.00 ohms.

We can check the result very easily, since the voltage drops across the two branches must be the same. One of them is

$$20.0 \text{ ohms} \cdot 1.00 \text{ amp} = 20.0 \text{ v}; \quad \text{the other is} \quad 5.00 \text{ ohms} \cdot 4.00 \text{ amp} = 20.0 \text{ v}$$

Sample Problem 5

The circuit in Fig. 22-6 is neither a simple series circuit nor a simple parallel circuit. It consists of two parallel branches, but one branch contains two resistors connected in series. The values of the resistances are as marked, and the voltage supplied to the circuit is 6.00 v. Compute (a) the resistance of the circuit, (b) the total current, (c) the current through each resistor, (d) the voltage drop across each resistor, and (e) make any possible checks on the answers.

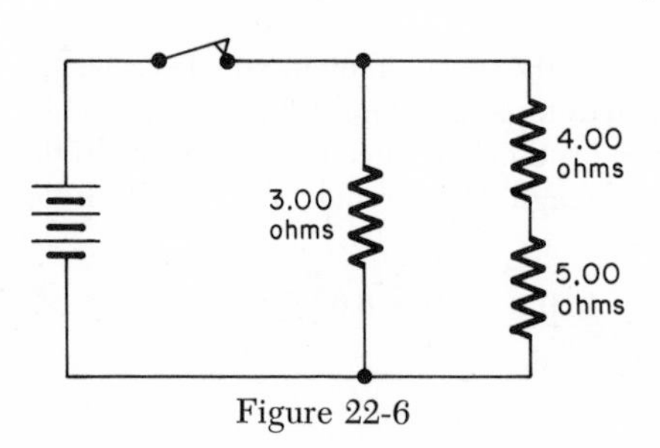

Figure 22-6

(a) First, consider only the branch which contains two resistors in series. Resistances in series are additive, so the resistance of this branch is 4.00 + 5.00 ohms, or 9.00 ohms. Thus we may imagine the two resistors in this branch to have been removed and replaced with a single 9.00 ohm resistor. We now have a branch with a resistance of 3.00 ohms and another with a resistance of 9.00 ohms, so

$$\frac{1}{R_p} = \frac{1}{3.00} + \frac{1}{9.00} = \frac{4.00}{9.00}$$

and

$$R_p = \frac{9.00}{4.00} = 2.25 \text{ ohms}$$

(b)

$$I = \frac{V}{R_p} = 6.00 \div \frac{9.00}{4.00} = 6.00 \cdot \frac{4.00}{9.00} = \frac{8.00}{3.00} \approx 2.67 \text{ amp}$$

(c) The current will divide between the two branches in such a way that the currents will be inversely proportional to the respective resistances. The branch with the 3.00 ohm resistance has exactly one-third the resistance of the other branch, so the current through it will be exactly thrice the current in the other. Thus exactly 3/4 of the current, which is $(3/4) \cdot (8.00/3.00)$, or 2.00 amp, will flow through the 3.00 ohm branch; and exactly $(1/4) \cdot (8.00/3.00) = 2.00/3.00$ amp, or approximately 0.667 amp, will flow through the other branch. Since the 4.00 ohm and 5.00 ohm resistors are in series in that branch, the current through each will be 0.667 amp.

(d) In general, $V = IR$. If the voltage drop across the 3.00 ohm resistor is V_3, that across the 4.00 ohm resistor V_4, and that across the 5.00 ohm resistor V_5,

$$V_3 = 2.00 \cdot 3.00 = 6.00 \text{ v}$$

$$V_4 = \frac{2.00}{3.00} \cdot 4.00 = \frac{8.00}{3.00} \approx 2.67 \text{ v}$$

and

$$V_5 = \frac{2.00}{3.00} \cdot 5.00 = \frac{10.00}{3.00} \approx 3.33 \text{ v}$$

(e) From part (c), the current through one branch is 2.00 amp and that through the other is 2.00/3.00 amp, giving a total of 8.00/3.00 amp, which we found in part (b) to be the total current.

In part (d), we found V_3 to be 6.00 v, which is equal to the applied voltage. V_4 was found to be 8.00/3.00 v and V_5 to be 10.00/3.00 v; and since these represent voltage drops across resistors which are in series, the total voltage drop across the pair is $8.00/3.00 + 10.00/3.00 = 18.00/3.00 = 6.00$ v. Thus the voltage drop across either of the two parallel branches is equal—as it should be—to the voltage applied to the circuit.

22-9 Open Circuit Voltage and Closed Circuit Voltage

Though at first it seems rather paradoxical, part of the voltage developed by any source of voltage must be used to force current through the source itself. No source is completely without resistance, which is called the ***internal resistance*** of the source, and electric currents don't flow *only* in the external circuit (outside of the source), they flow through the source as well. Within the source, just as outside, a potential difference is required to force a current through a resistance, as required by the equation $V = IR$.

When no current is flowing in the circuit, the value of I is zero, so the IR drop or potential difference required to force current through the source is zero also. The voltage between the terminals of the source under these circumstances is the ***open circuit voltage.*** As soon as current is allowed to flow, an IR drop appears within the source, its magnitude being directly proportional to the current. Part of the potential difference the source was able to maintain between its terminals on open circuit is wasted now in forcing current through the source itself, so the potential difference between its terminals is reduced. This reduced voltage is known as the ***closed circuit voltage.*** Its value is not constant, but varies according to the equation

$$V_c = V_o - Ir_i \tag{22-6}$$

in which V_c is the closed circuit voltage, V_o the open circuit voltage, I the current, and r_i the internal resistance of the source. A small r is used because the internal resistance usually is small as compared with the resistance of the external circuit.

Sample Problem 6

A dry cell has an open circuit voltage of 1.55 v and an internal resistance of $8.00 \cdot 10^{-2}$ ohm. What current is flowing when the voltage of the cell is 1.31 v?

The IR drop within the cell is 1.55 – 1.31 or 0.24 v. This is the product of the current and the internal resistance, so the current is equal to the IR drop divided by the internal resistance:

$$I = \frac{V_c - V_o}{r_i} = \frac{0.24}{0.0800} = 3.0 \text{ amp}$$

22-10 Conductance

It is convenient at times to think of the ease (to be very non-technical) rather than the difficulty which a current encounters in a circuit. For simple circuits of the sort we are considering, the "ease" a current encounters is reciprocally related to the "difficulty," and it is called the ***conductance*** of the circuit. Thus, if the conductance is G,

$$G = \frac{1}{R} \tag{22-7}$$

Obviously this concept is convenient in dealing with parallel circuits, for in terms of conductances Eq. (22-5), which is

$$\frac{1}{R_p} = \frac{1}{R_1} + \frac{1}{R_2} + \frac{1}{R_3} + \cdots + \frac{1}{R_n}$$

becomes simply

$$G_p = G_1 + G_2 + G_3 + \cdots + G_n \tag{22-8}$$

This equation is less helpful than first appears, however, because resistances are specified more commonly than conductances are. Knowing the value of a resistance, the corresponding conductance may be calculated; but if—as is often the case—the quotient doesn't "come out even" and has to be rounded off, error may be introduced.

Summary

An *electric circuit* consists of at least one *source* and at least one *load*, connected with wires or other conductors. Electric charges flowing in the circuit make one complete round trip of the circuit after another, as long as the circuit remains closed. If there is more than one load, the loads may be connected in series or in parallel; and the same is true if there is more than one source.

In a *series circuit*, the current is the same throughout the entire circuit, the resistance of the circuit is the sum of the resistances of its parts, the voltage applied to the circuit is equal to the sum of the voltage drops across the parts of the circuit, and the voltage drops across individual units of the circuit are directly proportional to the respective resistances of those parts.

In a *parallel circuit*, the voltage applied to one branch is the same as that applied to any other parallel branch, the current in the circuit is the sum of the currents through the separate branches, and the currents through the individual branches are inversely proportional to the respective resistances of the branches.

The energy supplied to a circuit is equal to the sum of the energy consumptions of its parts, and the power supplied to the circuit is equal to the sum of the power consumptions of its parts. These statements are true for any type of circuit.

In any schematic representation of an electric circuit, each unit in the circuit should be represented by a conventional symbol.

A circuit is *open* when it is *incomplete* and *no* current can flow. It is *closed* when it is *complete* so that current can flow.

Any source of electric energy has some internal resistance. Because of this, its closed circuit voltage will always be less than its open circuit voltage.

Conductance is the reciprocal of resistance.

Self-Quiz

1. What does the word "circuit" imply with respect to the flow of charges in an electric circuit? Does the magnitude of the current decrease along the circuit, as the size of a stream of water decreases along an irrigation furrow? Explain.

2. When an electric circuit is closed, do charges start to flow from the source and eventually establish flow throughout the circuit, or do they begin to flow in all parts of the circuit simultaneously?

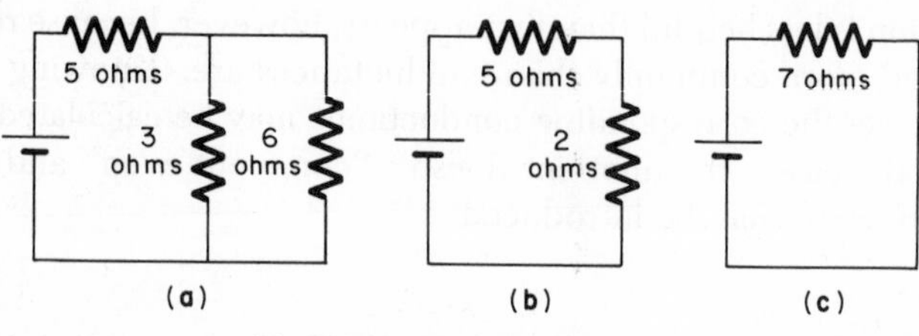

Fig. 22-7. (See Question 9.)

3. In what way does the current after passing through a resistor differ from current approaching a resistor? Or *is* there a difference? Explain.

4. Imagine a simple circuit with a switch connected to the negative terminal of the source by the shortest possible wire. We could expect electrons to flow over the switch the moment it is closed, but flow commences *everywhere* in the circuit *at the same instant.* How can electrons flow in a distant part of the circuit before they have had time to arrive from the negative terminal of the source? Why does flow start everywhere at the same instant?

5. Draw a diagram of each of the following circuits, including a switch in each. (a) One cell (not a battery) and one resistor. (b) A battery of three cells in series, and two resistors in series. (c) A battery of six cells in series, and three resistors connected in parallel. (d) Modify the circuit for part (c) by adding a switch which will enable the current through the first branch to be turned on or off without affecting the flow through the other branches. (e) Modify the same circuit by adding one switch which will control the currents through the second and third branches without affecting that through the first branch. (f) Why weren't you asked to control the current through the two resistors in part (b) individually, as you were for the circuit in part (c)?

6. Need the branches of a parallel circuit be parallel in a geometric sense? In what sense are they parallel?

7. Compare and contrast the following relationships in series circuits with those in parallel circuits: (a) current in circuit and current in parts of circuit, (b) voltage in circuit and voltage in parts of circuit, (c) resistance in circuit and in parts, (d) power in circuit and power in parts, and (e) energy in circuit and energy in parts.

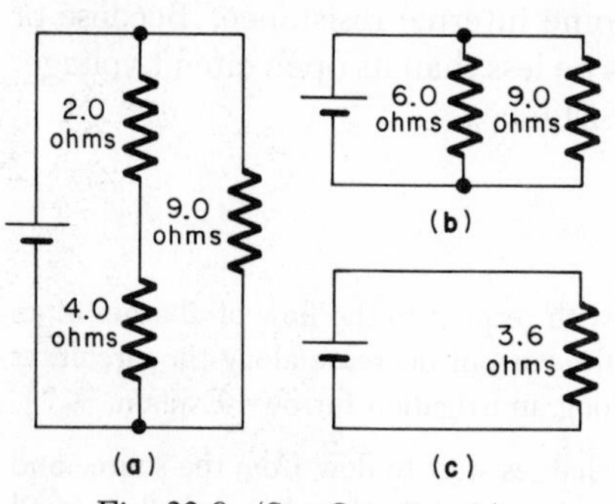

Fig. 22-8. (See Question 9.)

8. What quantitative relationship dictates the relative values of the currents in the branches of a parallel circuit? What relationship dictates the relative values of the potential differences across the parts of a series circuit? Why are both of these questions not asked with respect to both types of circuit?

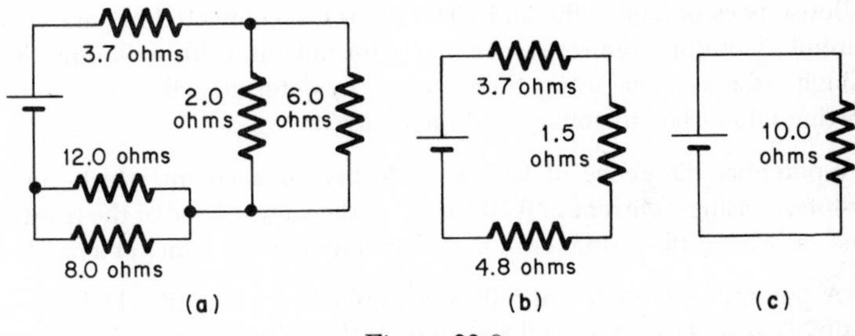

Figure 22-9

9. Show that the circuit in Fig. 22-7(a) is equivalent to those in parts (b) and (c) of the figure, and treat the circuits in Fig. 22-8, 22-9 in a similar manner.

10. Prove that the resistance of n resistors, each having the same resistance R, is equal to nR when they are connected in series. Prove also that their resistance is R/n when connected in parallel.

11. What is meant by the term "conductance"? What does the word "reciprocal" mean?

Problems

1. Find the resistance of the circuit in Fig. 22-10(a).

2. Find the resistance of the circuit in Fig. 22-10(b).

3. Find the resistance of the circuit in Fig. 22-10(c).

4. Find the resistance of the circuit in Fig. 22-10(d).

5. Resistances of 2.00, 5.00, and 8.00 ohms are connected in series on a 6.00 v circuit. (a) Compute the resistance. (b) Calculate the current. (c) Determine the voltage drop across each resistor.

6. Resistances of 6.00 and 12.00 ohms are connected in parallel on a 3.00 v circuit. (a) Determine the resistance. (b) Compute the current. (c) Calculate the current through each resistor.

7. Resistances of 1.00, 3.00, 5.00, and 11.00 ohms are connected in series on a 12.00 v circuit. Determine the voltage drop across each.

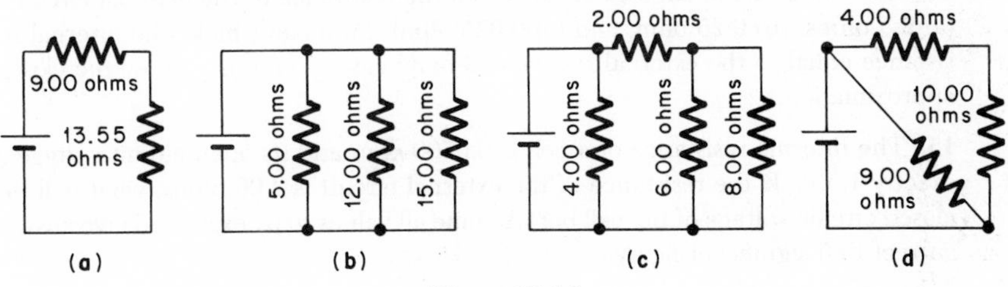

Figure 22-10

8. Resistances of 2.00, 5.00, and 10.00 ohms are connected in parallel on a 6.00 v circuit. Compute the resistance (a) by formula and (b) by finding the current through each branch, using these values to determine the total current, and applying Ohm's law to voltage and total current.

9. A potential difference of 6.00 v is applied to a circuit which contains two resistors, causing a current of 0.200 amp. If the value of one of the resistors is 10.0 ohms, (a) what is the resistance of the other, and (b) is it a series or a parallel circuit?

10. A potential difference of 6.00 v is applied to a circuit which contains two resistors, causing a current of 0.800 amp. If the value of one of the resistors is 10.0 ohms, (a) what is the value of the other, and (b) is it a series or a parallel circuit?

11. Resistors having values of 2.00, 6.00, and 12.00 ohms are connected in series. An identical set of resistors is connected in another circuit, in parallel. (a) The resistance of the series circuit is how many times as great as that of the largest single resistance in the circuit? (b) The resistance of the parallel circuit is what fraction of the smallest single resistance? (c) Determine the ratio of the resistance of the series circuit to that of the parallel circuit.

12. We shall find in Chapter 26 that a DC voltmeter, used for measuring potential differences, is composed of an instrument called a "galvanometer" and a resistance connected in series with the galvanometer. Assume that the galvanometer has a resistance of 25 ohms and that a current of 10^{-4} amp is just sufficient to cause a full-scale deflection of the galvanometer needle. Compute the resistance of the series resistor (a) if 1.5 v cause full-scale deflection and (b) if 3.0 v cause full-scale deflection. Assume all data to be exact and compute the values of the resistances to the nearest ohm.

13. The same galvanometer used in the preceding problem to make a voltmeter can also be used to make an ammeter for measuring DC currents. Instead of a resistor being connected in series with it as before, a shunt, or low resistance, is connected in parallel with it. What is the resistance of the shunt (a) if 0.2 amp causes full-scale deflection, and (b) if 1.0 amp causes full-scale deflection? Assume all data to be exact and express the answers correct to 5 significant figures.

14. Twelve dry cells can be connected in series, or in two parallel branches each containing 6 cells in series, 3 parallel branches of 4 cells in series, etc. It can be shown that the maximum current will flow when the cells are so arranged that the resulting battery has an internal resistance equal to the resistance of the external circuit. If each cell has an internal resistance of 0.0800 ohm, what arrangement of them will give the largest current when the resistance of the external circuit is (a) 2.5 ohms, (b) 0.25 ohm, and (c) 0.025 ohm? (You can't make the internal resistance equal to the external resistance in any case; you must choose the closest approximation.)

15. The internal resistance of a cell is 0.0500 ohm and its open circuit voltage is exactly 1.5 v. If the resistance of the external circuit is 4.00 ohms, what will the closed circuit voltage of the cell be? Assume all values to be exact and give answer correct to 5 significant figures.

16. The open circuit voltage of a battery is 12.00 v. The external circuit consists of two resistors with values of 1.70 and 2.20 ohms in series, the resistance of the connecting wires being negligible. The current in the circuit is 3.00 amp. What is the internal resistance of the battery?

17. A 1.50 v dry cell has an internal resistance of 0.0500 ohm. It is connected, by wires of negligible resistance, to a 0.500 ohm resistance and a 2.00 ohm resistance in parallel. Determine the *IR* drop within the cell.

18. A dry cell has an open circuit voltage of exactly 1.5 v and an internal resistance of 0.0493 ohm. A copper wire which is 5.00 cm long and has a mass of 0.600 g and a resistance of $7.00 \cdot 10^{-4}$ ohm is connected directly between the terminals of the cell. Calculate (a) the current, (b) the power used in the wire, and (c) the rate of temperature rise of the wire in C°/sec. (Assume that all heat generated in the wire remains in the wire.)

19. In Problem 2, (a) find the conductance of each resistor and use these values to compute the conductance of the circuit, and (b) find the conductance of the circuit directly from your answer to the original problem.

23

INTERCONVERSION OF CHEMICAL AND ELECTRICAL ENERGY

23-1 Preview

This chapter deals with the principles which underlie the production of electrical energy by cells and batteries, such as those used in flashlights, automobiles, etc. As the title of the chapter implies, and as the principle of conservation of energy requires, cells and batteries do not create *electrical energy; they convert chemical energy to electrical energy. The emphasis will be on basic principles; there will be no extensive discussion of various kinds of cells. The process by which a cell produces electrical energy may be reversed; electrical energy may be changed to chemical energy. This is important in many applications; of these we shall consider the charging of a storage battery and a few other electrochemical reactions. Use of some of the terminology and symbolism of chemistry is unavoidable; hence this chapter will be somewhat easier for those who have had chemistry than for those who have not. Non-chemists should not anticipate serious difficulty, however, because an attempt will be made to explain and clarify chemical matters as they appear in the discussion.*

23-2 Ions

Let's review briefly some of the things we've learned about atoms. There is a core, or nucleus, which is positively charged. Outside the nucleus there are one or more electrons, each electron being essentially a charge of negative electricity and the magnitude of this charge being identical for all electrons. Normally, the total negative charge of the electrons surrounding the nucleus is equal to the positive charge on the nucleus, so that the atom as a whole is electrically neutral.

Most substances are compounds rather than pure elements. This means that they are composed of two or more atoms of different elements, chemically combined. For example, water is a compound of hydrogen and oxygen. The smallest unit of a compound is the molecule, and each molecule of water is a chemical combination of two atoms of hydrogen and one atom of oxygen. The chemical symbol for hydrogen is H, and that for oxygen is O, so this structure of water molecules is represented by the chemical formula H_2O. Ordinary table salt is made up of equal numbers of atoms of sodium and chlorine. This structure is represented by the formula NaCl, Na being the symbol for sodium (from the Latin name for sodium, *natrium*) and Cl the symbol for chlorine. An example of a substance which has a somewhat more complex structure is zinc sulfate, which contains one atom of zinc (Zn), one of sulfur (S), and four of oxygen in each molecule, thus having the chemical formula $ZnSO_4$.

If table salt is dissolved in water, it is not present as molecules of NaCl; instead there are atoms of sodium which have lost one electron each, and atoms of chlorine, each with an extra electron.* Thus the sodium particles will be positively charged and the chlorine particles negatively charged; and these electrically charged particles have entirely different chemical and physical properties than electrically neutral atoms of sodium and chlorine would have. Similarly, a solution of zinc sulfate contains electrically charged particles. One kind of particle is a zinc atom which has lost two electrons and hence carries a double positive charge. The other is made up of the remainder of the molecule plus the two electrons lost by the zinc atom.

These electrically charged particles we have discussed in the preceeding paragraph, and all similar charged particles, are called ***ions.*** Thus, a sodium ion is a sodium atom minus an electron, so it may be represented by the symbol Na^+; a chloride ion is an atom of chlorine with an extra electron, or Cl^-; a zinc ion is Zn^{++}; and a sulfate ion is SO_4^{--}.

---

* This loss of electrons by the sodium and gain of electrons by the chlorine does not occur when the salt is dissolved, as was once believed. In solid crystalline table salt, the particles which comprise the crystal are these same electrically charged particles rather than electrically neutral atoms. Dissolving the salt merely allows the two kinds of particles to separate and wander around, their random migrations being similar to those of the molecules of a gas.

23-3 Active Metals, Inactive Metals, and Equilibrium

The chemist describes any metal which has a relatively strong tendency to enter into a chemical reaction as an ***active*** metal, and one which is relatively inert chemically as an ***inactive*** metal. For example, zinc is considered to be a fairly active metal because if a piece of zinc metal is put into an acid, such as dilute sulfuric acid, it will dissolve. Copper is considered to be relatively inactive because under the same circumstances a piece of clean copper metal is unaffected by the acid.

As is so often the case, qualitative designations like active and inactive are inadequate for any but a rather superficial qualitative consideration. To lay a foundation for a quantitative understanding, consider an arrangement like that in Fig. 23-1(a). A solution of zinc sulfate is put into a chemically inert vessel. Since the solution contains equal numbers of zinc ions and sulfate ions, it is electrically neutral. The sulfate ions take no part in the process we are investigating, however; so they are not shown. A piece of zinc metal is partly immersed in the solution.

Since zinc is an active metal, there is a marked tendency for atoms of zinc to leave the metal strip and become zinc ions in solution. But zinc atoms are electrically neutral, whereas a zinc ion lacks two electrons and hence is positively charged. Thus the conversion of a single atom of zinc in the metal to a zinc ion in the solution leaves two extra electrons in the metal and adds an equal positive charge to the solution. Therefore continuation of this process builds up a negative electric charge on the metal and a positive charge in the solution. But as always, opposite electric charges attract, and the positive zinc ions will be attracted to the metal. If a zinc ion is attracted to the metal and picks up two of the extra electrons on the metal, it is no longer an ion but an atom of zinc.

Therefore there are two opposing processes: zinc atom to zinc ion, caused by the chemical activity of the metal, and zinc ion to zinc atom, caused by electrostatic attraction. At first, the former process is much more rapid because no electric charges have built up on the metal and in

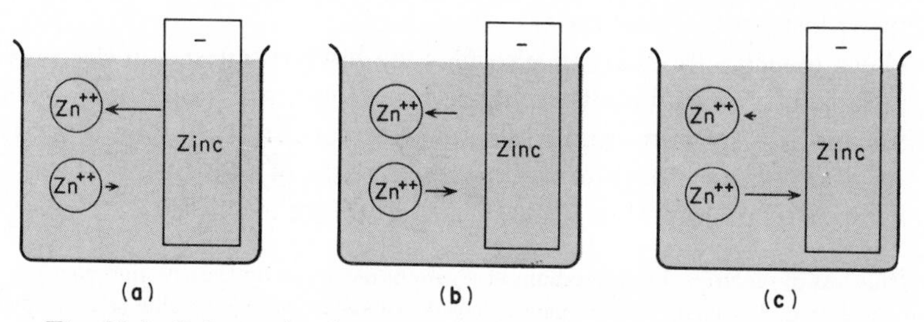

Fig. 23-1. Relationship between zinc metal and zinc ions in solution. (a) Potential difference less than 0.7628 v; (b) Potential difference 0.7628 v; (c) Potential difference greater than 0.7628 v.

the solution, but as these charges accumulate the rate of the second process increases, and eventually the two processes will proceed at identical rates. This is analogous to the evaporation of a liquid in a sealed container until the recondensation rate equals the vaporization rate. Both processes continue, but there is no net change. In the case of the zinc metal and zinc sulfate solution, equilibrium is reached when the charges on the metal and in the solution have built up until the potential difference between the two is 0.7628 v, the solution being positive with respect to the metal.*

We may symbolize all of this by writing

$$Zn \rightleftarrows Zn^{++} + 2e^{-} \qquad +0.7628 \text{ v} \tag{23-1}$$

in which Zn is the symbol of zinc atoms, Zn^{++} that for zinc ions, and e^{-} the symbol for an electron. The equation states (a) that a zinc atom may produce a zinc ion and two electrons, (b) that a zinc ion and two electrons may produce a zinc atom, and (c) that the two processes are in equilibrium when the solution is 0.7628 v positive with respect to the metallic zinc. If the potential difference is less, zinc will go into solution as zinc ions, spontaneously. If it is greater than 0.7628 v, zinc ions will be forced out of solution as zinc atoms. Figure 23-1(a) represents the situation when the potential difference is smaller than 0.7628 v, the equilibrium situation is indicated in part (b) of the figure, and part (c) shows the situation when the potential difference exceeds the equilibrium value.

A system similar to that we have been discussing, except that the solution is copper sulfate and the metal is copper, is shown in Fig. 23-2.† Copper is a relatively inactive metal, so the normal tendency is ion → atom, whereas the reverse was true with the $Zn - ZnSO_4$ system. The chemical symbol for copper is Cu (Latin, *cuprum*). Like a zinc ion, an ion of copper lacks two electrons, so its symbol is Cu^{++}.

As copper ions come out of solution and change to atoms of metal, positive charges are withdrawn from the liquid and transferred to the metal; thus the solution acquires a negative charge and the metal a positive charge. The resulting potential difference will tend to repel the positive Cu^{++} ions from the metal, slowing the $Cu^{++} \rightarrow Cu$ reaction. Equilibrium is reached when the potential difference is 0.3460 v.‡ Thus

$$Cu \rightleftarrows Cu^{++} + 2e^{-} \qquad -0.3460 \text{ v} \tag{23-2}$$

* This is the value of the voltage at equilibrium if the zinc ions have a standard concentration (1 molar). The equilibrium voltage will be somewhat different at other concentrations.

† As in Fig. 23-1, sulfate ions are not shown because, though present, they take no part in the reaction. They will be omitted also from all later figures in which they are present but take no part.

‡ Again, this is the voltage at a standard concentration (1 molar) of the ions.

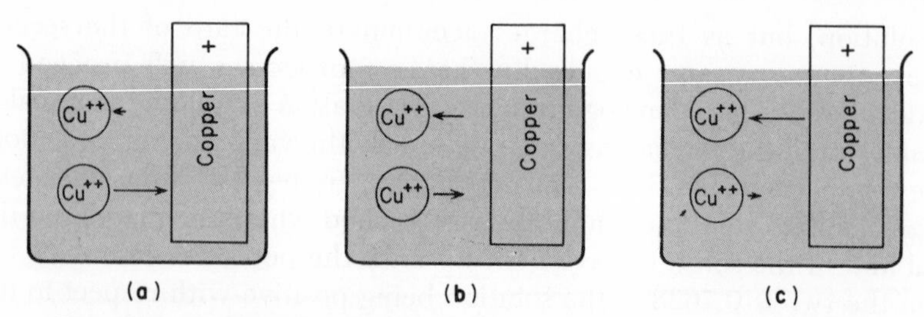

Fig. 23-2. Relationship between copper metal and copper ions in solution. (a) Solution less than 0.3460 v negative to copper; (b) Solution 0.3460 v negative to copper; (c) Solution more than 0.3460 v negative to copper.

which says that a copper atom may produce a copper ion plus two electrons, or the reverse reaction may occur, and that the two opposing reactions will be in equilibrium when the potential difference between the metal and the solution is 0.3460 v, the solution being negative with respect to the metal. If the potential difference has a value nearer zero than 0.3460, Cu^{++} will plate out as Cu atoms, spontaneously, as in Fig. 23-2(a). When the voltage is 0.3460 v there will be equilibrium as in part (b) of the figure; and if the solution is more than 0.3460 v negative with respect to the metal, atoms will be forced to become ions as in part (c).

23-4 Energy from a Chemical Reaction; an Electric Cell

Suppose that we have pieces of copper and zinc metals touching each other in the same container, immersed in a solution which contains zinc sulfate and copper sulfate, as in Fig. 23-3. We have seen that zinc atoms will pass into solution as zinc ions spontaneously, unless an adverse potential prevents them. This leaves excess electrons on the zinc and tends to make the solution positive. At the same time, copper ions will come out of solution, as noted above, tending to leave the solution negatively charged and cause a positive charge on the copper metal.

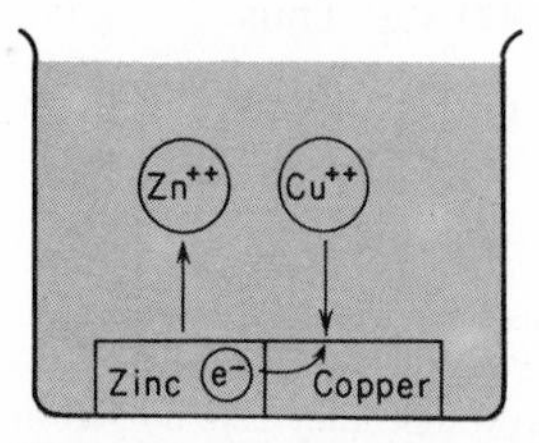

Fig. 23-3. Reaction of zinc and copper with solution of their salts when the metals are in contact.

In a situation like that in Fig. 23-3, the excess electrons left on the zinc by the $Zn \rightarrow Zn^{++}$ reaction will flow to the copper, compensating for the positive charge which tends to develop there as the result of the $Cu^{++} \rightarrow Cu$ reaction. At the same time, the addition of the positive charges on newly formed Zn^{++} ions to the solution will compensate for the removal of the positive charges of the Cu^{++} ions from the solution. Thus the zinc will dissolve, and the amount of copper in the solution will be decreased.* All this occurs spontaneously, because of the difference in the chemical activity of zinc and copper as indicated by the difference in their equilibrium potentials.

In the system as arranged in Fig. 23-3, the spontaneous reaction uses chemical energy of the substances, converting it into heat energy. This is hardly an ideal heating device, economically or otherwise! But note that the process involves a transfer of electrons from the zinc to the copper. Let us rearrange the system as in Fig. 23-4, so that the two metals are not in direct contact. On the left is a strip of zinc metal immersed in a solution of zinc sulfate; at the right, a strip of metallic copper is immersed in copper sulfate. Mixing of the two solutions is minimized by a porous barrier indicated by the dashed line.

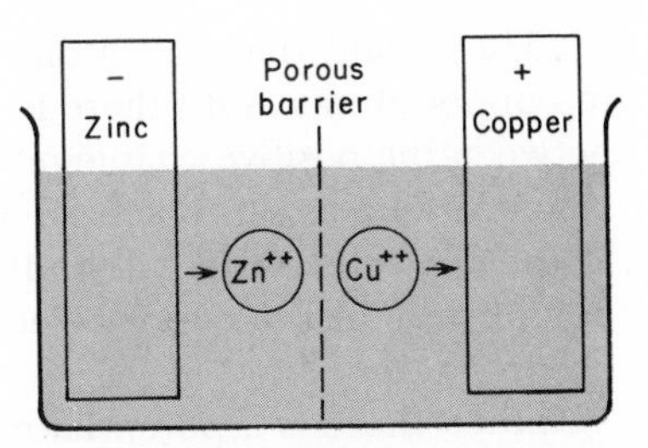

Fig. 23-4. Reaction of zinc and copper with solutions of their salts when the metals are not in contact.

Reactions occur between the zinc and zinc sulfate, and between the copper and the copper sulfate, exactly as we discussed in Sec. 23-3; the left half of Fig. 23-3 is equivalent initially to Fig. 23-1(a) and the right half to Fig. 23-2(a). Thus the zinc metal will acquire a negative electric charge and a positive charge will accumulate on the copper. Migration of zinc ions through the porous barrier will keep the solutions electrically neutral throughout. The chemical reactions which cause these charges will proceed until the solution is 0.7628 v positive to the zinc and 0.3460 v negative to the copper. We may represent these situations, as we did before, by Eq. (23-1) and Eq. (23-2). It will be convenient to reverse the order of Eq. (23-2):

$$Cu^{++} + 2e^- \rightleftarrows Cu \qquad +0.3460 \text{ v}$$

The potential difference is positive, since we have changed it from the side of the equation with Cu^{++} and $2e^-$, where it was before, to the side with Cu; and, as always, changing something from one side of an equation to the other reverses its sign.

Like mathematical equations, chemical equations may be added, and equal quantities on opposite sides of the resulting equation may be canceled:

$$\begin{array}{llll} Zn & \rightleftarrows Zn^{++} + 2e^- & 0.7628 \text{ v} & (23\text{-}1) \\ Cu^{++} + 2e^- & \rightleftarrows Cu & 0.3460 \text{ v} & (23\text{-}2 \text{ reversed}) \\ \hline Zn + Cu^{++} & \rightleftarrows Zn^{++} + Cu & 1.1088 \text{ v} & (23\text{-}3) \end{array}$$

* Actually, all that is necessary is the zinc metal and the copper sulfate solution. Zinc ions formed from the metallic zinc will replace the copper ions, and the copper ions will come out as metallic copper in contact with the zinc. In Fig. 23-3, and in the discussion, zinc sulfate and metallic copper were included for parallelism with the previous discussion, and also as a basis for the discussion in the next paragraph.

This means that zinc atoms will change to zinc ions, and copper ions to copper atoms, until there is a potential difference of 1.1088 v built up between the positive charge on the copper and the negative charge on the zinc. As long as this potential difference exists the two opposing reactions at the zinc electrode will be in equilibrium, and there will be a state of equilibrium at the copper electrode also, so no further net reaction can occur.

Since there is a potential difference between the two metal strips, a current will flow through any conductor connected between them. This flow will remove electrons from the zinc strip and transfer them to the copper strip, thus tending to reduce the charge on each and hence lower the potential difference between them. But any reduction of the potential difference will upset the equilibrium at the electrodes, with the result that the chemical reactions will tend to build the charges up again. Thus the reactions will produce current as long as there is a closed external circuit (and copper ions and unused zinc metal remain).

An arrangement of this sort, or any other system which changes chemical energy to electrical energy in a similar manner, is called a ***voltaic cell,*** or simply a ***cell.*** Aside from the vessel which contains it, the essential parts of such a cell are a positive and a negative ***electrode***—the copper strip and the zinc strip, respectively, in the cell we have been discussing—and a solution called an ***electrolyte,*** which contains appropriate ions to react with the electrodes. The positive electrode is called the ***anode;*** the ***cathode*** is the negative electrode.

As in this instance, both electrodes may be metals, and the electrolyte a solution of a salt of a metal; but many other arrangements are possible. A very common type of voltaic cell, used in modified form in most "dry cells," uses zinc for the negative electrode, a carbon rod for the positive electrode, and a solution of ammonium chloride as the electrolyte. The carbon doesn't react chemically at all, but merely acts as a conductor to supply electrons for the reaction $H^+ + e^- \rightarrow H$, which takes place at the carbon electrode.* In another very common type of cell, one electrode is

Table 23-1

APPROXIMATE POTENTIAL DIFFERENCES FOR EQUILIBRIUM BETWEEN A METAL AND IONS OF THE METAL

A positive value means that the solution is positive with respect to the metal.

Aluminum	Copper	Lead	Silver	Tin	Zinc
+1.67	−0.346	+0.126	−0.800	+0.141	+0.763

* It may seem that the *positive* electrode would not supply *electrons,* but it is positive only because it has *lost* electrons *in this reaction.*

lead and the other is a compound of lead, and the electrolyte is sulfuric acid. We shall consider this kind of cell further, in Sec. 23-5, 23-6.

A review of the present section, especially the second paragraph on page 420, will reveal that, in effect, the net chemical reaction within a voltaic cell can be "turned on" and "turned off" by a switch. Startling as this may seem, it is exactly what we should expect. Though the opposing reactions at the electrodes are always going on, they will be in equilibrium—hence, there can be no net reaction—except when the flow of current causes the potential differences at the electrodes to fall below the equilibrium values. Thus, the net chemical reaction within the cell can occur, and produce electric energy, only when that electric energy is being consumed. Here, again, we are dealing with the principle of conservation of energy.

23-5 Primary Cells and Secondary Cells

The process by which the cell in the preceding section produces electric current involves erosion of the zinc cathode as zinc atoms change to zinc ions, and removal of copper ions as they change to copper atoms. When the zinc has been consumed, or the copper ions removed, by the chemical reactions which produce the current, no more electric current can be produced by the cell. The discussion, however, implies that the chemical actions which cause the current could be reversed and the cell restored to its original condition by imposing (from some outside source) a potential difference in excess of 1.1088 v on the cell, with the copper electrode positive.

In the case of the sort of cell we have been discussing, this regeneration is impossible, as it is for many other voltaic cells. Instead of re-forming a metal electrode, the ions forced out of solution as atoms in our attempt to regenerate or recharge the cell may form a useless sludge of loose fine particles, or unwanted side reactions may interfere with the reversal of the reactions which produced the current.

But in certain types of cells, the chemical reactions responsible for the production of the current can be reversed exactly, and the cell restored essentially to its original condition.

Cells of a nature such that they cannot be restored to their original condition and used again to produce electrical energy are called ***primary cells.*** Those which can be restored to their initial condition, and reused repeatedly, are known as ***secondary cells.*** The latter are also called—unfortunately, for reasons we shall soon see—***storage cells.*** A cell is said to be ***discharging*** when it is producing current at the expense of its store of chemical energy. If it is a secondary cell, the process of restoring it, after it has been partially or completely discharged, is called ***charging,*** or ***recharging,*** the cell.

Note that the process of charging a cell makes use of electrical energy from an outside source to cause non-spontaneous chemical changes within the cell. During the discharge of any cell, chemical energy is being used to produce electrical energy, but when a secondary cell is being charged electrical energy is being used to produce chemical energy. *No electricity is stored* in the cell; *energy* is stored in the form of *chemical* energy. Unfortunately, the term "storage battery" carries, for many people, the completely erroneous implication that the battery stores electricity.

23-6 A Secondary Cell

The most familiar type of secondary cell, to most of us, is found in the "storage" battery of an automobile. A cell of such a battery, when fully charged, consists of lead dioxide as the anode, metallic lead as the cathode, and sulfuric acid as the electrolyte—Fig. 23-5(a). The hydrogen ions in the solution tend to react with the lead dioxide, forming water and lead (mon)oxide, in the process leaving their positive charges on the electrode. The lead oxide thus formed then reacts with the sulfuric acid to form more water and lead sulfate, but this reaction has no influence on the production of an electric charge on the electrode. The over-all reaction at the anode when the cell is discharging is summarized in Eq. (23-4) below. The chemical symbol for lead is Pb (Latin, *plumbum*); lead dioxide is PbO_2; and lead sulfate is $PbSO_4$. We have met the other symbols earlier.

At the cathode, the situation is considerably simpler. Sulfate ions react with the metallic lead, producing lead sulfate and leaving the extra electrons on the electrode, thereby producing its negative charge. This reaction is recorded in Eq. (23-5). Equations (23-4) and (23-5) are summed to derive the equation for the over-all chemical reaction during discharge.

$$PbO_2 + 4\,H^+ + SO_4^{--} + 2e^- \rightarrow PbSO_4 + 2\,H_2O \qquad (23\text{-}4)$$

$$Pb + SO_4^{--} \rightarrow PbSO_4 + 2\,e^- \qquad (23\text{-}5)$$

$$PbO_2 + Pb + 4\,H^+ + 2\,(SO_4)^{--} \rightarrow 2\,PbSO_4 + 2\,H_2O \qquad (23\text{-}6)$$

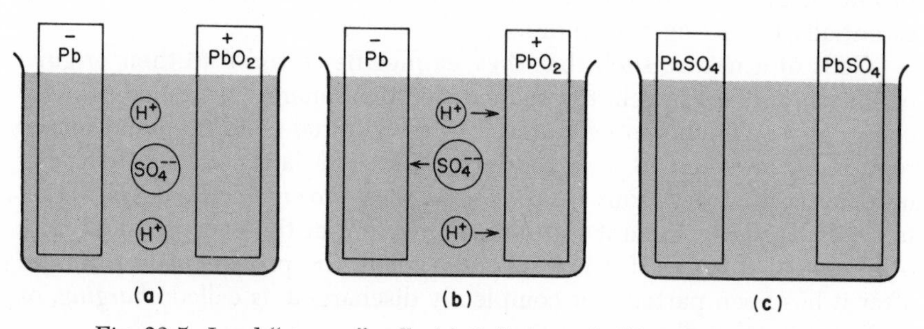

Fig. 23-5. Lead "storage" cell. (a) Cell charged; (b) Cell discharging; (c) Cell discharged.

Insofar as the chemical reaction is concerned, the $2e^-$ on the left cancels with the same term on the right, and the essential process is a conversion of lead, lead dioxide, and the ions in sulfuric acid to lead sulfate and water. As the result of this chemical process, however, an electric potential is generated and used to create an electric current in some useful circuit.

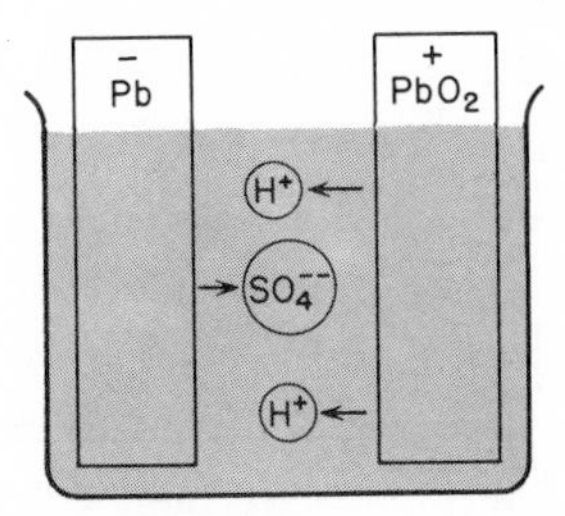

Fig. 23-6. Lead "storage" cell being charged.

The chemical reactions during recharging are the exact opposites of those in Eqs. (23-4)–(23-6). The lead sulfate is changed back to lead dioxide on the anode, and to free metallic lead on the cathode. The SO_4 from the lead sulfate is changed again to SO_4^{--} ions. Oxygen for the lead dioxide comes from the water, and the hydrogen of the water furnishes the H^+ ions. Figure 23-6 represents the process of charging in the same way Fig. 23-5(b) indicates the discharge.

23-7 Electrochemical Reactions

Some chemical reactions, like those which generate an electric current in a voltaic cell, occur spontaneously, releasing energy in some form. In many other reactions, the products contain more energy than did the substances entering the reaction; obviously these cannot occur spontaneously. Energy in some form must be used to "make the reaction go." The recharging of a secondary cell, discussed in the preceding section, is an example of such a reaction. Any of various energy sources may be used to make non-spontaneous reactions occur. Heat is used for many reactions, pressure for others, and light for some. Electricity is the source of energy for many reactions, and such reactions are described as ***electrochemical*** reactions. An obvious example of an electrochemical reaction, already mentioned, is the recharging of a secondary cell.

A very important kind of electrochemical reaction is ***electrolysis,*** which is the decomposition of a chemical compound by an electric current. Thus, the passage of current through a cell containing water to which a small percentage of an acid, such as sulfuric acid, has been added to reduce the resistance, produces hydrogen gas at the cathode and oxygen gas at the anode.* Aluminum is won from its chemical compounds in ores by sending a current through molten aluminum ore. Many metals, including copper, silver, gold, nickel, chromium, and cadmium, may be plated onto an object by using the object as the cathode and a solution contain-

* Pure water ionizes to so slight a degree that ions from some other source are necessary for any but a very minute current, and the sulfuric acid furnishes H^+ and $(SO_4)^{--}$ ions. Though it is these ions which carry the current and react at the electrodes, the discharged (SO_4) groups react with the water to form H^+ and $(SO_4)^{--}$ ions plus free oxygen; so the over-all reaction leaves the acid unchanged, but changes water into hydrogen and oxygen gases.

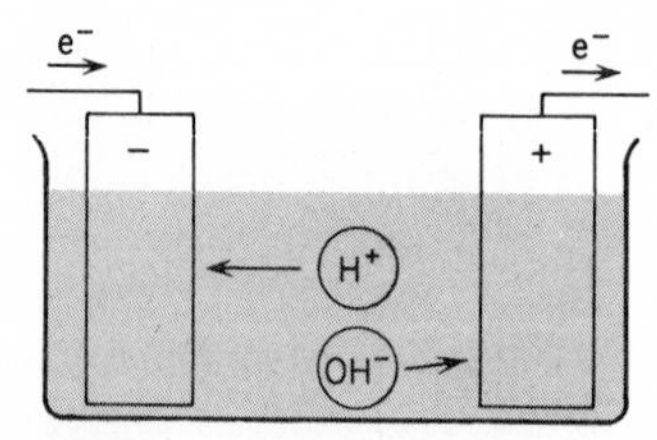

Fig. 23-7. Electrolysis of water.

ing ions of the metal as the electrolyte. If the anode is made of the metal being plated, ions of the metal will leave the positive electrode at the same rate at which they are being removed at the negative electrode, and thus the strength of the plating solution (electrolyte) may be maintained. Copper is refined by what is essentially an electroplating process; impure copper metal is used as the anode and plated out in nearly pure form on the cathode.

23-8 Electrochemical Equivalents, and the Coulomb

Since the electric charge on any ion is due to the loss of one or more electrons, or to the addition of one or more electrons, the magnitude of any ionic charge is always some small whole number times the electronic charge; that is,

$$q = \pm ne \tag{23-7}$$
$$= \pm n \cdot 4.80 \cdot 10^{-10} \text{ esu}$$
$$= \pm n \cdot 1.60 \cdot 10^{-19} \text{ coulomb}$$

in which n is a small integer and e represents the charge on an electron, which is $4.80 \cdot 10^{-10}$ statcoulomb or $1.60 \cdot 10^{-19}$ coulomb. A silver ion is an atom of silver which has lost one electron, so the passage of any number of electrons through a solution containing silver ions will cause an exactly equal number of atoms of silver to be plated out on the negative electrode.* Each atom of silver has a definite mass† so the passage of a certain number of electrons will deposit a definite mass of silver. Since the charge on 1 electron has a fixed value, 1 coulomb of electricity will contain a definite number of electrons, and therefore the passage of 1 coulomb of electricity through a solution containing silver ions will cause a definite mass of silver to be plated out. This is (to four significant figures) 0.001118 g, and the ***coulomb*** may be defined as the quantity of electric charge which will deposit this mass of silver.

The mass of any element which will be liberated by the passage of one coulomb of electricity, such as 0.001118 g of silver, is the ***electrochemical equivalent*** of that element.

---

* Of course, this will be true only if conditions are such that no other positive ions are discharged by the passage of the current.

† Actually this "definite mass" is a statistical average of the masses of two different kinds of silver atoms, but this need not concern us here. We shall investigate the matter of atoms of the same element having different masses in Chapter 36.

Chemists have established a system of *relative* masses of single atoms of the various elements, *arbitrarily* based on an atom of carbon as 12;* these relative masses are called the ***atomic weights*** of the elements. Table AD-2, on page 760, gives data on atomic weights. One ***gram atomic weight*** of an element is a quantity of the element such that its mass, in grams, is numerically equal to its atomic weight. Thus the atomic weight of oxygen is 16.000, so 1 gram atomic weight of oxygen is 16.000 g; the atomic weight of silver is 107.880, so 1 gram atomic weight of silver is 107.880 g, etc. By means we shall meet in Chapter 36, it has become possible to make very accurate, though indirect, determinations of the masses of individual atoms; and these have verified a principle stated by Avogadro a century and a half ago, which says in effect, that 1 gram atomic weight of any element must contain the same number of atoms as 1 gram atomic weight of any other element. Thus, the number of atoms in 16.000 g of oxygen is the same as the number of atoms in 107.880 g of silver, or in 1 gram atomic weight of any other element. This number, known as ***Avogadro's number,*** is $6.02486 \cdot 10^{23}$.

The charge on a single silver ion is $1.602 \cdot 10^{-19}$ coulomb. The number of ions of silver in 1 gram atomic weight is $6.025 \cdot 10^{23}$, both values being correct to four significant figures. Therefore the number of coulombs of electricity required to deposit 1 gram atomic weight is the product of these two values, or $9.652 \cdot 10^4$ coulombs. It is tempting to say that $9.652 \cdot 10^4$ coulombs should liberate 1 gram atomic weight of *any* element, but this is not a valid generalization. Recall that each copper ion has lost *two* electrons. This means that *two* electrons will be required to change *one* copper ion to an atom of copper, and twice $9.652 \cdot 10^4$ coulombs will be necessary to liberate 1 gram atomic weight of copper. To generalize the statement we must not speak of the gram atomic weight of the element, but of the gram atomic weight divided by the number of electronic charges on each ion.† This is the ***gram equivalent weight*** of the element. Thus $9.652 \cdot 10^4$ coulombs of electricity, a quantity called 1 ***faraday*** of electricity, will liberate 1 gram equivalent weight of an element.

We now have a means of determining the value of the electrochemical equivalent of an element. It is the gram atomic weight of the element divided by the number of electronic charges carried by one ion, and divided also by the value of the faraday.

---

* Until recently the scale was based on oxygen (16) rather than on carbon. See the last two paragraphs of Sec. 36-6.

† The chemist would say that the gram atomic weight is to be divided by the *valence* of the element.

Summary

Solutions of some compounds in water contain positively and negatively charged particles called *ions*. The charge on an ion is always a small whole number of electronic charges, and the total positive charge is identical with the total negative charge.

Atoms of some metals have a tendency to lose one or more *electrons* and go into solution as *positive ions*, leaving electrons behind and hence making the body of metal negative. Ions of other metals tend to come out of solution as atoms, taking the necessary electrons from a piece of the solid metal and thus making the metal body positive. Either process develops a potential difference between the solution and the metal, the metal body being negative with respect to the solution in the former case, and positive in the latter. A *voltaic cell* may consist of a *cathode* made of a metal which has a relatively strong tendency to form ions (or a relatively weak tendency for its ions to form atoms), an *anode* of a metal with relatively weak ion-forming tendencies (or relatively strong atom-forming tendencies), and an *electrolyte*. In some cells, one or both electrodes may be non-metallic. In any type of voltaic cell, chemical energy is transformed to electrical energy.

Primary cells *cannot* be *recharged; secondary* cells *can*. The cells in a "storage battery" are secondary cells. Such a battery stores chemical energy, not electricity.

Many important chemical reactions use electrical energy to create chemical energy. These include the charging of secondary cells, or batteries, the electrolysis of solutions or of molten ores or salts, and electroplating and electrolytic refining.

One coulomb is the quantity of electric charge required to deposit 0.001118 g of silver by electrolysis. The electrochemical equivalent of an element is the mass of the element which will be liberated by 1 coulomb of electricity; it is equal to the gram atomic weight of the element divided by the value of the faraday and the number of electronic charges on 1 ion of the element. One faraday is the quantity of electric charges required to deposit 1 gram equivalent weight of an element; it is $9.652 \cdot 10^4$ coulombs.

Self-Quiz

1. What is an ion? In what essential way does it differ from an atom? How is a positive ion formed? A negative ion? What can you say about the magnitude of the charge on an ion?

2. For the purposes of this chapter, what is the essential difference between an active metal and an inactive one?

3. Does a piece of an active metal in contact with a solution containing its ions tend to remain electrically neutral, to acquire a positive charge, or to acquire a negative charge? Why? Answer the same questions with respect to an inactive metal.

4. Why do reactions of the sort suggested by the preceding question come to equilibrium? How does the condition necessary for equilibrium if the metal is active differ from that required if the metal is inactive?

5. Describe a simple form of voltaic cell. Explain in detail how it produces an electric current.

6. Does a voltaic cell use chemical energy when no current is flowing? Does it maintain a potential difference when there is no current? Should the answers to these two questions be the same, or different? Explain.

7. Compare and contrast the terms "electrode," "anode," and "cathode."

8. Compare and contrast primary cells and secondary cells. Give at least one example of each type. If considerable quantities of electrical energy are required, which type would be more economical? Why?

9. To recharge a battery, to which terminal of the battery should the positive terminal of the charger be connected, and why?

10. The specific gravity of relatively concentrated solutions of sulfuric acid is greater than that of relatively dilute solutions. You may have noticed that the attendant at a service station or garage usually tests the condition of an automobile battery with a hydrometer, which measures specific gravity rather than any electrical quantity. Explain the basis of this test clearly, including as much of the processes of charging and discharging as necessary for complete clarity.

11. Define each of the following, and make a table or chart to show their interrelationships: atomic weight, gram atomic weight, gram equivalent weight, ionic charge, coulomb, electrochemical equivalent, electronic charge, faraday, Avogadro's number.

Problems

1. (a) Using data from Table 23-1, find the voltage to be expected from a voltaic cell using tin and zinc electrodes; (b) repeat for a cell with copper and lead electrodes; and (c) state the combination which should give a higher voltage than any other combination from the table, and determine the voltage.

2. An advertisement rates an automobile battery as "capacity, 100 ampere-hours." Convert this to more suitable units, and state its value in those units.

3. With the help of data from Table AD-2, p. 760, compute the electrochemical equivalent of (a) copper, (b) magnesium, and (c) zinc. Ions of each of these carry two electronic charges.

4. The symbol for aluminum is Al, that for silver is Ag (Latin, *argentum*), and that for tungsten is W (German, *Wolfram*). The electrochemical equivalents of these

metals, in *milli*grams per coulomb, are 0.0932, 1.12, and 0.318, respectively. Determine the number of electronic charges on an ion in each case, and record the symbol, including charges, for each ion.

5. Compute the value of the faraday from the value of the electronic charge and Avogadro's number. Use the values from Sec. 23-8. Check with the value given in Sec. 23-8.

6. The electrochemical equivalent of cadmium is $5.82 \cdot 10^{-4}$ g/coulomb. Compute the mass of cadmium which will be plated out by a current of 3.50 amp in 25.0 min.

7. Calculate the electrochemical equivalent of hydrogen and compute the time required for a current of 5.00 amp to produce 2.50 g of hydrogen by electrolysis.

8. What volume will the hydrogen produced in Problem 7 occupy at a pressure of 740 mm of mercury and a temperature of 37°C? The density of hydrogen is $8.99 \cdot 10^{-2}$ g/liter at 760 mm of mercury and 0°C.

9. The electrochemical equivalent of platinum is $5.06 \cdot 10^{-4}$ g/coulomb. An object with a surface area of 15.0 cm^2 is plated with platinum, the current being 0.300 amp and continuing for 50.0 min. What is the average thickness of the platinum plating? The density of platinum is 21.4 g/cm^3.

10. A cell is made, using a zinc cathode with a mass of 100 g, the anode being of copper. Assuming that current is drawn until the cathode is entirely consumed and that the current is used exclusively to produce heat, how many calories of heat are produced?

24

MAGNETISM AND ELECTROMAGNETISM

24-1 Preview

Many inter-related topics comprise this chapter. We commence with permanent magnets, natural and artificial. We shall consider the concept of a magnetic field, "understanding" it in terms of fictitious lines of force. We shall meet again the property of permeability, which distinguishes magnetic materials from those that are not magnetic. We shall observe the two-fold process by which a crystal of iron becomes magnetized, and consider the implications of this process in practical applications. The mystery of the earth's magnetic field will be noted. We shall investigate the magnetic field which is the inseparable companion of an electric current, and the means by which a magnetic field may be used to cause an electric current.

24-2 Permanent Magnets

Historically, magnetic phenomena were first observed in connection with certain varieties of an iron ore called "magnetite." Two remarkable properties of this ore were discovered: a piece of it would always orient itself in the same position relative to geographical directions, if free to do so, and it attracted objects made of iron. Its property of directional orientation gave a tremendous boost to extensive voyages of exploration. The old Anglo-Saxon word for journey, *lode,* formed part of the name ***lodestones*** given to such pieces of ore.

Lodestones are mere curiosities today, since we have learned to make much stronger magnets of iron or other materials; also because electromagnets (Sec. 24-9, 24-10) are even stronger, and much more convenient. We still use the directional properties of magnets in magnetic compasses, which are small permanent magnets pivoted so that they may rotate in a horizontal plane.

24-3 "Lines of Magnetic Force"

It is convenient to think of magnetic phenomena in terms of "lines of magnetic force," and to depict a magnetic field by drawing such lines. In making use of the concept, we must realize that such lines are hypothetical; they have no actual existence. But they do provide a very convenient crutch for our minds and our imaginations to lean on while exploring this rather intangible topic.

For example, imagine that we have a bar magnet lying on a piece of paper, and that we have a very small magnetic compass with a stub of a pencil attached beneath it. We could set the pencil point near the north pole of the magnet and move the compass (with pencil), always keeping the direction of motion parallel with the compass needle. The pencil would trace a line like one of those in Fig. 24-1. Repeating with a different starting point, always near the pole, we could produce each of the lines in the figure. If the paper were large enough, lines which appear to stop at the edges of the diagram would make continuous loops instead.

This seems to imply that the lines are "real." But the influence of the magnet isn't limited to the lines drawn; it is present between these lines as well. With unlimited time and patience, we could trace a line between any two of the original lines and continue this until the entire paper outside the magnet is blackened.

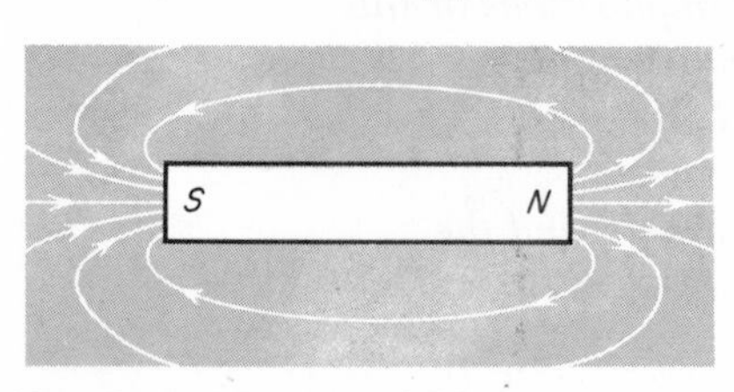

Fig. 24-1. Magnetic field around a bar magnet.

Observations and experimental

results in the field of magnetism are in accord with what would be expected *if* these hypothetical lines of force were real and *if* they were endowed with the following properties:

The lines invariably are continuous loops rather than line segments. (In our imaginary experiment, developing a magnetic field pattern similar to Fig. 24-1, the small compass couldn't reveal the presence of lines *inside* the magnet; but we must consider them to be there.)

The lines issue from the north pole and re-enter the magnet at the south pole.

They tend to shorten and to straighten, like stretched rubber bands.

They tend to expand laterally, pushing away from each other.

No two lines ever cross.

Lines pass far more "easily" through iron and a few other substances than through most materials.

These imaginary lines of magnetic force, and their assumed properties, "explain" many phenomena.

It is well known that it is impossible to obtain an isolated north pole or a lone south pole by using a hacksaw midway between the poles of a magnet; such an attempt always produces *two* magnets, each with two opposite poles. Figure 24-2(a) "explains" this, the newly appearing poles being shown in dotted letters. The lines are shown inside the magnets as well as outside. Since the lines are always continuous, cutting the magnet doesn't sever the lines; it merely causes them to issue at one face of the cut and re-enter the other face. But any region from which the lines issue is a north pole, and there is a south pole wherever they enter.

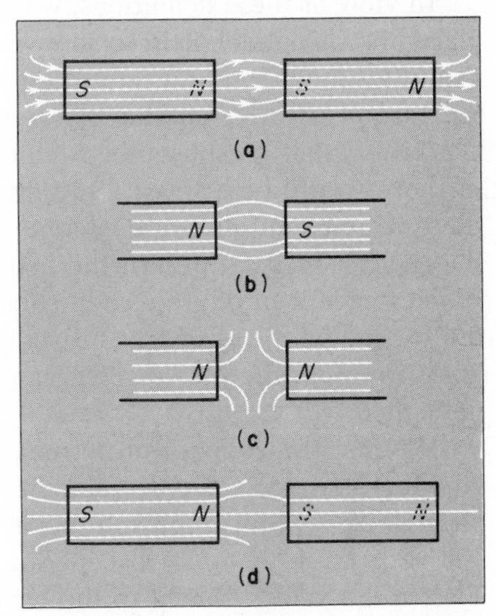

Fig. 24-2. (a) Appearance of two new poles when a magnet is cut in two; (b) Attraction of unlike poles; (c) Repulsion of like poles; (c) Induction of magnetism in an iron bar placed in a magnetic field.

The tension of the lines of force "explains" the force tending to move unlike poles toward each other, Fig. 24-2(b), and the repulsion of like poles is "explained" by the tendency of the lines to push apart laterally, Fig. 24-2(c).

A piece of soft iron placed in a magnetic field provides a much "easier" path for the lines of force than does the air, so the lines tend to pass through the iron. This causes (temporarily, while the iron is in the field) a south pole where they enter and a north pole where they exit, endowing the iron with ***induced magnetism,*** Fig. 24-2(d).

24-4 Permeability

In the list of characteristics of the hypothetical lines of magnetic force, in the preceding section, the last one states that the lines pass far more "easily" through iron than through most other substances—about as naïve and nontechnical a statement as one could imagine. In more appropriate terminology, the iron is more ***permeable,*** or its ***permeability*** is greater. Because of its high permeability, an iron rod placed in a magnetic field becomes an induced magnet [Fig. 24-2(d)] and is subjected to a considerable torque tending to align it with the magnetic field; and the same is true, for the same reasons, of any other body which has a high permeability. Since this property was first observed in iron (for which the Latin name is *ferrum*) the adjective ***ferromagnetic*** is used to describe any substance of high permeability. Conversely, any substance with a low permeability is said to be ***non-ferromagnetic.***

In view of these definitions, we would expect a rod of low permeability placed in a magnetic field to show far less induced magnetism, if any, than would a similar rod of a ferromagnetic substance at the same location, so the torque (if any) on the non-ferromagnetic rod would be very small. The fact is that no substance is completely devoid of magnetic properties, so there would be at least a minute torque in all cases. But the sense of the torque is not always the same. Rods of some substances tend—very sluggishly—to line up with the field, thus resembling ferromagnetic substances except in degree; such substances are called ***paramagnetic.*** But the torque on a rod of any substance described as ***diamagnetic*** actually tends to orient the bar—again very sluggishly—*perpendicular* to the magnetic field.

We met the concept of permeability very briefly in Sec. 20-3; in Sec. 20-5 it was stated that the value of the permeability of a vacuum is taken (arbitrarily) as unity, the values for all physical media being positive and not very far from unity except for a minority of relatively high values. These high values belong to the ferromagnetic substances. Relatively low values which are larger than one characterize paramagnetic substances, and the values for diamagnetic substances are less than one (but larger than zero). A sampling of values is given in Table 24-1. We shall return to the topic of permeability in Sec. 24-6, 24-10.

Table 24-1

PERMEABILITIES OF VARIOUS SUBSTANCES*

Ferromagnetic substances		Non-ferromagnetic substances	
Substance	Permeability	Substance	Permeability
Cobalt	240	Air	1.00000037
Iron	5,000	Aluminum	1.000021
Nickel	1,000	Antimony	0.999952
Permalloy	100,000	Bismuth	0.999983
		Liquid oxygen	1.0040
		Platinum	1.0003
		Water	0.999992

* Values are only approximate. They depend strongly on the purity, or on the composition of an alloy, and on heat treatment. The values given are the maximum values.

24-5 Magnetic Pole Strength and Magnetic Intensity

In Sec. 20-3 we found the force between two magnetic poles to be given by the equation

$$F_m = \frac{m_1 m_2}{\mu d^2} \tag{20-1}$$

in which F_m is the force, m_1 and m_2 are the strengths of the two magnetic poles, μ is the permeability of the medium between the poles, and d is their distance apart.

Consider two magnetic poles 1 cm apart in a vacuum, the poles being of equal strength, and the force between them being 1 dyne. Under these conditions, every quantity other than the pole strengths would have a value of unity; so the only possible value for the product of the two pole strengths would be unity. We assumed them to be of equal strength, so each must have a pole strength equal to 1.* Thus ***unit magnetic pole*** is a pole strength such that there would be a force of 1 dyne between two such poles placed 1 cm apart in a vacuum.

You will find it interesting and instructive to compare this discussion of the unit of magnetic pole strength with that of unit electric charge (Sec. 20-6). One marked difference will be noted: whereas the unit of electric charge is endowed with two alternate names (esu and statcoulomb), unit magnetic pole hasn't even one such name.

Just as electric field intensity is defined as the force the electric field

* In an operational sense this definition is unsatisfactory. It is impossible to obtain *isolated* magnetic poles for the measurement, since every magnet has *two* poles. Also, a "pole" is not a point but a somewhat diffuse region, making an exact measurement of the distance impossible. However, pole strengths measured by more practical methods are consistent with the value defined on the basis of Eq. (20-1).

would exert on unit electric charge in a vacuum (Sec. 20-7), ***magnetic intensity*** is the force a magnetic field would exert on unit magnetic pole in a vacuum. The symbol for magnetic intensity is H, so if F_m is the force, in a vacuum, on a magnetic pole of strength m,

$$H = \frac{F_m}{m} \tag{24-1}$$

Like the intensity of a gravitational or an electric field, magnetic intensity is a vector quantity.

Magnetic intensity, as given by Eq. (24-1), is measured in oersteds, if the force is in dynes.

24-6 Permeability Again, and Flux, and Flux Density

The vast majority of forces of magnetic origin do not occur in a vacuum; and Eq. (24-1) is inadequate for these cases. We have seen in Sec. 24-3, 24-4 that a magnetic field tends to concentrate in media of high permeability. In terms of lines of force there would be vastly more lines of force through a ferromagnetic substance than through a vacuum, under the same circumstances. This artificial concept gives rise to the term ***flux density,*** which is related to the magnetic intensity H and the permeability μ by the equation

$$B = \mu H \tag{24-2}$$

B being the flux density in gauss.* In a sense, we may think of the flux density as the effect induced by the magnetic intensity. For this reason, the flux density is also called the ***magnetic induction.***

In terms of lines of force, either 1 oersted or 1 gauss may be considered to represent one line of force per square centimeter of area normal to the field, the lines being in a vacuum for intensity (oersteds) and in a physical medium for flux density (gauss). In a field which has either a uniform or an average flux density B, if the ***total flux*** is ϕ it is obvious that

$$\phi = BA \tag{24-3}$$

in which the area of the field normal to the field direction is A. For B in gauss and A in square centimeters, ϕ will be in maxwells.

24-7 Magnetization of a Piece of Iron

Only ferromagnetic substances can be magnetized to any significant degree. We'll have to take the reasons for this as experimental facts and

* Some authorities use the plural as gausses, but others employ gauss for the plural as well as the singular. Since the use of the word gausses is so awkward, the latter usage has been adopted in this text.

forego any attempt at a real understanding. We shall have a hint in Sec. 24-9, but it will fall far short of an explanation.

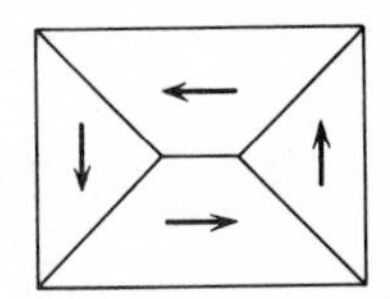

Fig. 24-3. Relative orientation of magnetic domains in unmagnetized iron cancels their magnetic fields.

Ordinarily, the only forces of attraction between two pieces of iron* are gravitational, and so minute as to be imperceptible in any practical sense. But if they are magnetized, forces many orders of magnitude greater than gravitational forces appear. What causes this difference, and how is it brought about?

Careful and ingenious studies have shown that the iron, whether magnetized or not, is made up of ***magnetic domains.*** Each of these domains, which have an average volume of the order of 10^{-6} mm^3, is completely magnetized; all the atoms, each of which is itself an extremely tiny magnet, are lined up with their north poles pointing the same way. Ordinarily, these magnetized domains themselves are *not* lined up with their north poles all pointing in the same direction, for much the same reason that coins dropped onto a table don't all stand on edge. More energy is required to tip a coin up onto its edge than to make one fall from that position, so the total energy of the coins is less when they are lying flat than when on edge. This is an example of the general fact that the stability of any system is at a maximum when its energy is at a minimum. Similarly, the energy of a myriad of magnetic domains all lined up with their magnetic axes parallel is greater than their energy when not arranged in that manner; so the more stable—and thus more probable—situation finds the magnetic axes of the domains oriented in various directions. But the orientations are not random; the domains are arranged somewhat as suggested by Fig. 24-3, which represents only two dimensions and therefore cannot give the full picture of the arrangement of the domains in the iron. In terms of lines of magnetic force, an arrangement similar to that in this figure would result in the shortest possible length of the loops formed by the lines, and this is in accord with the tendency of these hypothetical lines to shorten as much as possible.

Figure 24-4 is an adaptation of original photographs generously furnished by Dr. R. W. DeBlois and Dr. C. D. Graham, Jr., of the General Electric Research Laboratory. The photographs were obtained by spreading a suspension of extremely finely powdered magnetite over the surface of a single crystal of iron. The powder collected at the domain boundaries, where there are strong magnetic fields. In Fig. 24-4(a) the crystal is unmagnetized, since the domains which have their magnetic axes directed toward the right are matched by others with their axes to the left.† The

* This discussion will apply to any ferromagnetic substance, iron being used as a concrete example.

† There appears to be an uncompensated magnetic axis directed downward; but the diagram can reveal only the condition at the surface, and this probably is compensated by an upwardly directed magnetic axis of a domain lying beneath the surface.

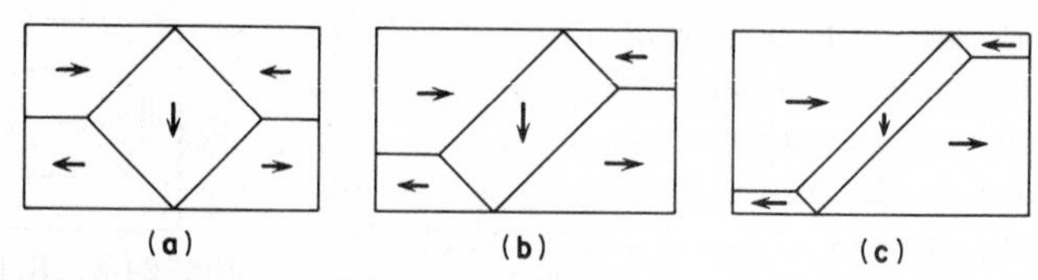

Fig. 24-4. Migration of domain walls as a magnetic field to the right is applied and increased. (a) No applied field; (b) Relatively weak field applied; (c) Relatively strong field applied.

application of an external magnetic field directed to the right changes the pattern as indicated in parts (b) and (c) of Fig. 24-4. The walls of the domains shift, as the field is applied, in such a way as to increase the sizes of those domains with magnetic axes in the direction of the field and decrease the sizes of domains which have unfavorable directions of their magnetic axes. Since domains with magnetic axes toward the right now predominate, the crystal has become magnetized, in the sense that it will exhibit an external magnetic field. Increasing the intensity of the applied field shifts the domain walls farther, increasing the magnetization of the crystal.

Though the magnetization increases with the strength of the applied field, the relation between them is not a simple direct proportion. This is evident in Fig. 24-5, in which flux density B is plotted against magnetic intensity H. Approximately up to the "knee" of the curve, this graph represents the magnetization due to the shift of the domain walls—a process indicated schematically by the diagrams in Fig. 24-4. Somewhere in the vicinity of the "knee" the domain walls will have moved until essentially all of the iron is in domains which have their magnetic axes in the preferred direction. In general, however, various crystals will be oriented somewhat at random, so that in most cases no domains within the crystal will have a magnetic axis exactly parallel with the direction of the applied field. Though the migration of the domain walls causes the growth of those domains which have their magnetic axes closest to the direction of the applied field, this wall migration does not alter the directions of the magnetic axes of the domains. But when magnetization due to wall migration has proceeded about as far as possible, further increase of the intensity of the applied field causes rotation of the magnetic axes of the domains. It was believed originally that the domains rotated as units, but at present the atoms within the domain are considered to rotate so that their individual magnetic axes—and hence that of the

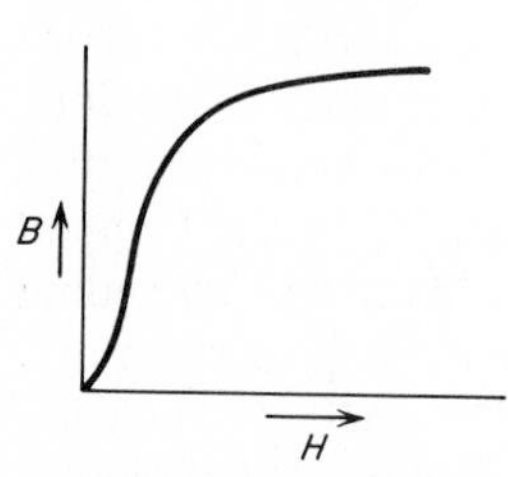

Fig. 24-5. Magnetization curve. This figure is greatly compressed in the vertical direction: the values of B may be three or more orders of magnitude greater than those of H.

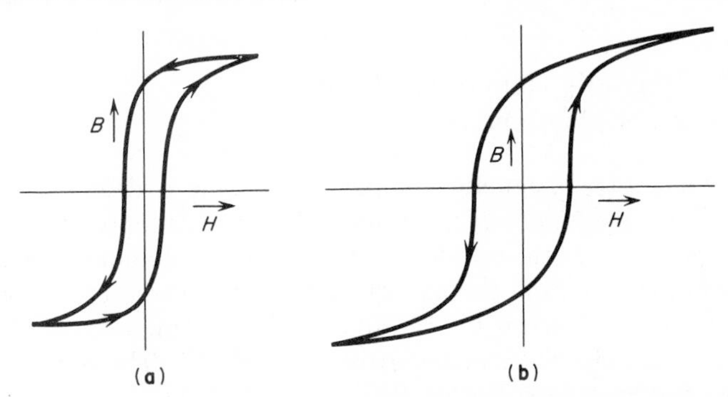

Fig. 24-6. Hysteresis loops of two types of ferromagnetic materials.

domain—are in the direction of the applied field. The diagrams in Fig. 24-4 can give no hint of this rotation of the magnetic axes of the individual atoms, but the increase in magnetization resulting from this process is revealed by the gently rising portion of the curve above the "knee" in Fig. 24-5. When the processes of domain wall shifting and rotation of magnetic axes within the domains are complete, the substance is said to be magnetically ***saturated.***

Energy must be expended to shift domain walls, and to rotate magnetic axes to saturate the magnet. Once saturated, this is the *status quo,* and energy must be used to change conditions back toward the initial situation. Thus, as the intensity of the applied magnetic field is reduced, the relationship between B and H is different from what it was during the magnetizing process; so a graph of the demagnetization would not coincide with the curve in Fig. 24-5. Some magnetization will remain when the applied field is again zero, and to obtain zero magnetization an adverse field must be applied. The iron may be magnetized in the opposite polarity by increasing this reverse field, but again B will not become zero when H is zero. If we begin with the iron saturated and carry it through a complete cycle of magnetization (or several such cycles), the graph would appear somewhat like Fig. 24-6(a) or 24-6(b). A material suitable for a permanent magnet would have a B-H relationship similar to that in part (b) of the figure, requiring a relatively strong reversed magnetic field to demagnetize it. The curve in part (a) would indicate that the material is not suitable for permanent magnets, but we shall see (Sec. 25-2) that such substances are useful for other purposes.

The lag of the magnetization behind the strength of the applied field is called ***hysteresis,*** and the closed curves in Fig. 24-6 are ***hysteresis loops.*** The energy expended during one complete cycle of magnetization is directly proportional to the area of the hysteresis loop. This "lost" energy reappears as thermal energy within the iron.

24-8 The Magnetic Field of the Earth; Names of Magnetic Poles

The ability of a magnetic compass to assume a definite orientation relative to geographic directions requires that the earth possess a magnetic field. There is ample other evidence of such a field, including the existence of the aurora borealis and the aurora australis, the variation of cosmic ray intensity from the Equator to the Poles, and the configuration of the Van Allen radiation belts revealed by artificial satellites. There is a magnetic pole some distance from the north geographic pole, and another in the vicinity of the south geographic pole. The naming of these magnetic poles is wholly arbitrary. It would seem logical to call the former the north magnetic pole, and the latter the south magnetic pole. However, this would require that, to go *north,* one would have to follow the *south* pole of a compass, since *un*like magnetic poles attract. So we reverse the terms, naming the end of a compass which points northward the ***north*** pole and the other end the ***south*** pole. Note that this means that the *south* magnetic pole of the earth is in the *North*ern Hemisphere, and vice versa.

Actually, at very few places on the earth's surface does a compass point exactly north (or south). In the continental United States, the ***declination,*** or difference between "magnetic north" and geographic north, varies from more than 20° W (which means that the compass points more than 20° west of north) in upper Maine to more than 25° E in Washington. And the earth's field is more nearly vertical than horizontal in this same region; the *dip* varies from 57° in Florida and Texas to 77° in North Dakota. It was once believed that a portion of the earth's interior was a permanent magnet and that this was the source of the earth's magnetic field. But though in some respects the earth *acts as if* it were a permanent magnet, such cannot be the case, for various reasons. It is known that the temperature of the earth's interior is high, and no substance can retain its magnetism above a certain temperature, characteristic of the material, called the ***Curie point.*** This is true because the thermal agitation destroys the orderly lining up of the magnetic axes, so that the material reverts to the condition indicated in Figs. 24-3, 24-4(a). Another difficulty is the inconstancy of the earth's field, of which there are three aspects. An erratic variation of the field, sometimes great enough to be called a magnetic storm, is one of these. Another is a daily excursion of a magnetic needle back and forth over several minutes of angle. The third is a long-term drift of the location of the magnetic poles, and hence of the direction indicated by a compass. For some two centuries before 1800, the declination at London shifted westward at an average rate of more than $\frac{1}{7}$° a year and since that time it has shifted eastward at an average rate about half this value.

An acceptable theory of the earth's magnetism must account for all these complications; but to date none of the many theories presented has been able to do so.

24-9 Magnetic Fields from Electric Currents

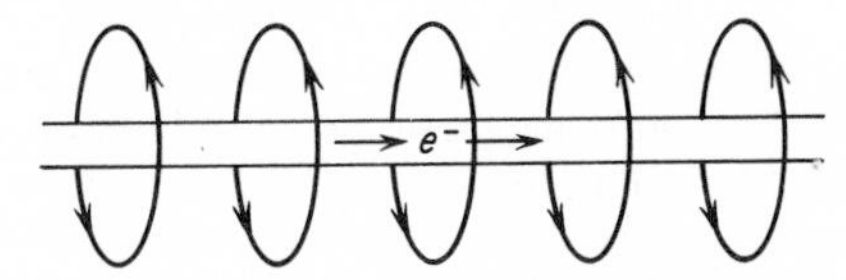

Fig. 24-7. The relationship between the direction of electron flow and the direction of the magnetic field surrounding the flow.

Today, magnetic fields due to permanent magnets are less common, and far less useful, than those which accompany an electric current. If a direct current flows in a straight wire, as in Fig. 24-7, there is always a circular magnetic field accompanying it. Reversing the direction of current flow also reverses the magnetic field direction, so there is a definite relationship between the two directions. This may be expressed by one of several "hand rules." *Don't* ever grasp a wire or coil when a current is flowing unless you are *certain* that it is well insulated *and* that you are well insulated from the ground. But *imagine* grasping the wire with your *left* hand, in such a way that your extended thumb points along the wire in the direction of current flow; the direction in which your fingers would encircle the wire is the direction of the magnetic field.

Magnetic effects are more prominent if, instead of using a straight wire, the wire is formed into a loop as in Fig. 24-8.* Application of the above rule at various points around the loop shows that, everywhere inside the loop, the direction of the field is to the right. Since a north magnetic pole is merely a region from which magnetic lines issue, and a south pole one into which the lines enter, the right face of the loop must be a north magnetic pole and the left face a south pole. Thus the loop might be called an ***electromagnet***, though this term is usually reserved for coils of many turns wound on a ferromagnetic core.

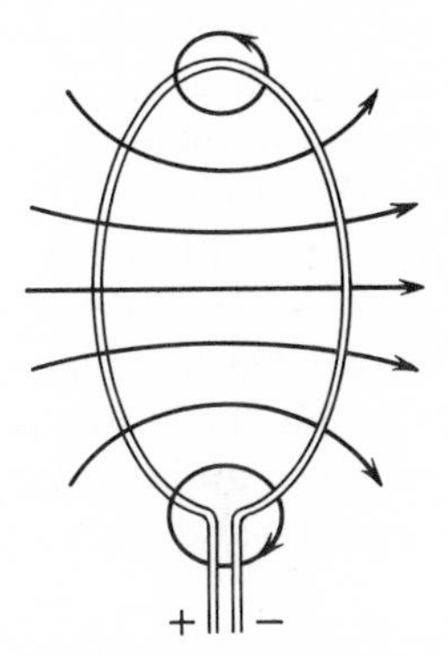

Fig. 24-8. Magnetic field due to a current in a loop of wire.

There is also a left-hand rule for the magnetic polarity of such a device, whether a single loop or a "powerful" electromagnet. Imagine grasping the coil with the left hand, the fingers encircling the coil in the direction of current flow around the coil; then the extended thumb will point in the direction of the north pole. Note that it is the direction of current flow *around* the coil that is pertinent. Stu-

* The lines of the field are continuous, but are shown broken in an attempt to produce an illusion of three dimensions, the right limb of the loop being nearer you and the left limb farther away.

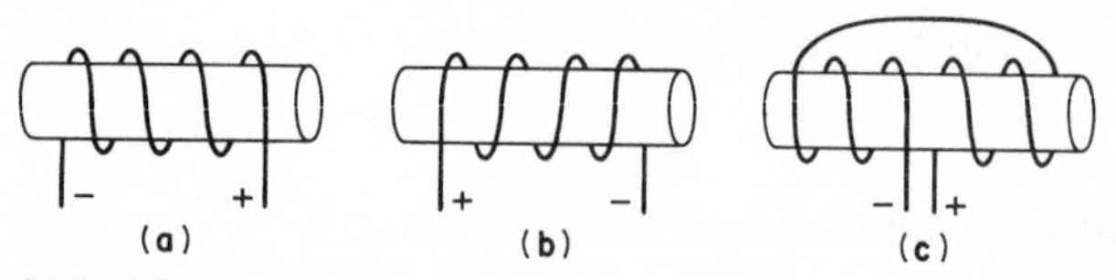

Fig. 24-9. The magnetic polarity of a coil is determined by the direction of current flow around the coil. The coils in (a) and (b) have the same magnetic polarity, both opposite the magnetic polarity of the coil in (c).

dents tend to confuse themselves by thinking of the totally irrelevant direction of flow from one end of the coil to the other. In Fig. 24-9(a), the current flows from left to right and in part (b) of the figure it flows from right to left, but in both cases the direction of flow *around* the coil is the same; and the north pole is at the left in both cases. The current enters the coil in part (c) of the diagram at essentially the same point from which it leaves, but the coil has a definite polarity; the north pole is at the right.

One must be careful to realize, and remember, that there are *two* left-hand rules relating the directions of current flow and magnetic field; and we shall meet another left-hand rule soon.

Though these rules were stated in a form appropriate for finding the direction of the magnetic field when the current direction is known, they may also be used to yield the current direction if that of the field is known.

The effects discussed in this section are characteristic of the current, not of the conductor. Thus, there is a circular magnetic field surrounding the stream of electrons in a TV tube as they shoot from the "electron gun" toward the screen of the tube. And any circular motion of charge will give the effect of a current in a coil; an effect like that in Fig. 24-8 may be obtained by charging a disk with electrons and rotating it in a counterclockwise sense as seen from the left, or by putting a positive electrostatic charge on it and rotating it in a clockwise sense as seen from the left.

We have met the fact that any atom consists of a positively charged nucleus with one or more electrons—up to 92 in naturally occurring elements—outside the nucleus. These electrons whirl around the nucleus somewhat like planets journeying around the sun, and they also seem to spin on their own axes as a planet does. Both the orbital motion of an electron and its spin constitute rotary motion of electric charge; so each should—and does—give the atom the properties of a magnet, very much as in Fig. 24-8. This, however, suggests that *all* substances should be ferromagnetic, whereas in fact relatively few are.

24-10 Quantitative Relationships between the Current and the Magnetic Field

If a current of I amp flows in a long straight wire in a vacuum, at a point d cm distant from the wire the magnetic intensity H, in oersteds, is given by the equation

$$H = \frac{I}{5d} \tag{24-4}$$

provided that d is small compared with the length of the wire; and more generally, if a medium of permeability μ is present

$$B = \frac{\mu I}{5d} \tag{24-5}$$

where B is the flux density in gauss.

If the wire is wound into a flat coil, there being n turns of radius r,

$$H = \frac{\pi n I}{5r} \tag{24-6}$$

and

$$B = \frac{\pi \mu n I}{5r} \tag{24-7}$$

Sample Problem 1

At a distance of 4.50 cm from a long straight wire the magnetic field due to the current is 0.300 gauss. Compute the current.

Equation (24-5) may be solved for I:

$$I = \frac{5dB}{\mu}$$

Since nothing is said about the medium, if any, the best thing to do is to make the most logical assumption and consider that the wire and the field are in air. For air under normal conditions, the value of μ is about 1.00000037, which we may safely round off to 1.00. Thus

$$I = \frac{5 \cdot (4.50) \cdot (0.300)}{1.00} = 6.75 \text{ amp}$$

Sample Problem 2

A current of 0.849 amp flows in a coil of 4.00 cm radius which is wound on a core with a permeability of $5.00 \cdot 10^4$. The flux density is $2.00 \cdot 10^4$ gauss. How many turns are there in the coil?

Solution of Eq. (24-7) for n yields

$$n = \frac{5rB}{\pi \mu I}$$

$$= \frac{5 \cdot (4.00) \cdot (2.00) \cdot 10^4}{\pi \cdot (5.00) \cdot 10^4 \cdot (0.849)}$$

$$= 3.00 \text{ turns}$$

24-11 Conservation of Energy, Again

Since there always is a magnetic field surrounding a conductor in which an electric current is flowing, it might appear that this situation should be reversible: there should always be an electric current in a conductor which is in a magnetic field. But such is *not* the case! Since the conductor has resistance, energy is necessary to force a current through it, and no energy is being expended when the conductor is lying motionless in the magnetic field. To obtain electrical energy in the form of a current in the wire, we must expend mechanical energy by moving the wire relative to the field, but the motion requires energy only if there is a resisting force. What is the source of this force?

To get a start on this question, consider a bar magnet and a coil with its ends connected so that a current could flow in it, as in Fig. 24-10. Initially, there is no motion between the coil and the magnet, so no current can result. Suppose that we use a small amount of energy to give the coil or the magnet—it makes no difference which—a slight velocity toward the other. A slight ***induced current*** will flow in the coil; this can be observed by an appropriate measuring device. Because of the current, the coil will acquire a magnetic polarity; let us *assume* that the end toward the magnet will be unlike the near end of the magnet, and see where the assumption leads us. There would be attraction between the coil and the magnet, so the velocity of relative approach would be increased, and this in turn would induce a stronger current. With an increased current, the coil would become a stronger magnet, further accelerating the relative approach, etc. Commencing with a minute quantity of energy, we obtain an ever-increasing kinetic energy of motion, and an increasing strength of electric current, and a magnetic field which builds up—all spontaneously! But of course nothing of the sort happens; it would be an egregious contraversion of the principle of conservation of energy. Our assumption of the magnetic polarity of the coil was incorrect—as you may have realized at the time.

The only alternative is that the induced current must make the end of the coil facing the magnet the *same* as that on the near end of the magnet. This will result in a force of repulsion between the coil and the magnet, and we can cause an induced current only by moving the magnet toward the coil (or the coil toward the magnet), *against* this force. This situation is stated and generalized by ***Lenz's law,*** which states that the direction of an induced current is *always* such as to oppose the influence which caused the current to be induced. This opposition is in the form of a force arising from the interaction of the original magnetic field and that of the induced current.

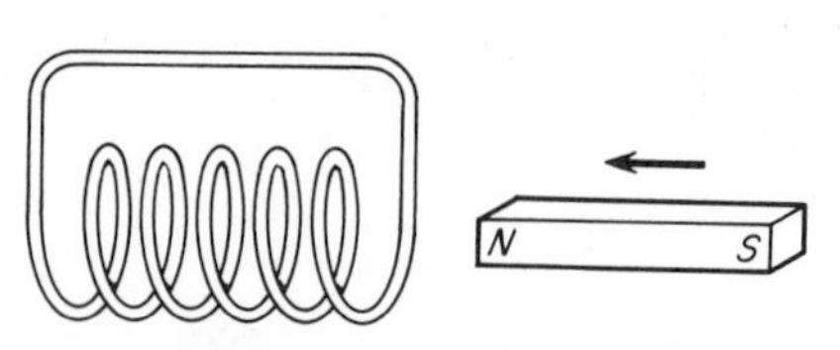

Fig. 24-10. Diagram for development of Lenz' law.

Now let's return to the induction of a current in a straight wire moving relative to a magnetic field. It happens that the directions of the magnetic field, the relative motion, and the induced current are mutually perpendicular, so that

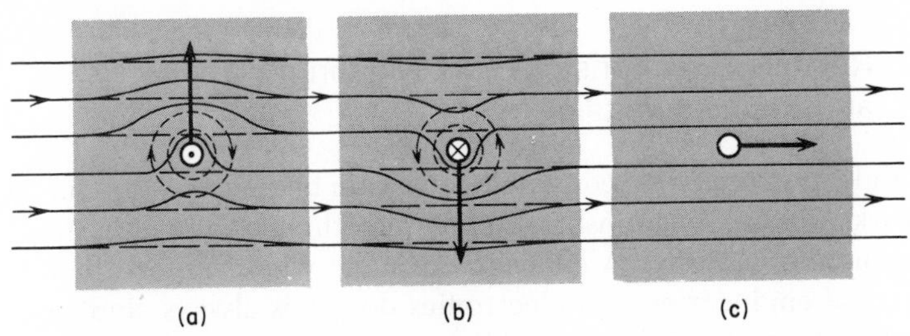

Fig. 24-11. Magnetic field of induced current causes opposition to motion which induces current. Arrows attached to wires indicate direction of motion. Dotted circles show fields of currents; dashed lines show original field where it differs from resultant field; solid lines show resultant field. Motion parallel to the field encounters no opposition and no current is induced.

only the first two lie in the plane of the paper. The current direction is perpendicular to the paper, so some convention is necessary to indicate which way it is going. The conductor itself is shown as a small circle; if the current direction is up out of the paper, this is indicated by a dot in the circle which represents the tip of an arrowhead just puncturing the paper from below. A current going down into the paper is symbolized by a cross in the circle, which represents the feathered end of an arrow.

Thus, in Fig. 24-11(a) a wire is moving toward the top of the page as indicated by the arrow. It moves across a magnetic field directed toward the right, as shown by the dashed lines. The induced current is upward, and it causes the circular magnetic field shown by dotted lines. But, as with two waves on the same string, only the resultant is apparent, and the resultant magnetic field is shown in solid lines. Since we consider that these hypothetical lines tend to shorten and straighten, they exert a force which opposes the motion of the wire—as Lenz's law requires. If the direction in which the wire moves is reversed, as in Fig. 24-11(b), the current direction is reversed also, and the interaction of the magnetic fields again opposes the motion. In both these cases, the situation is crudely analogous to a boy walking across rows of heavy plants in a field; the rows of vegetation impede his feet. But this trouble disappears if he walks between the rows. Similarly, a wire moving parallel with a magnetic field as in Fig. 24-11(c) doesn't cross any lines of force and encounters no opposition; and since no expenditure of energy is required, no current is induced.

Because this topic is somewhat intangible, the discussion has been in terms of induced currents, but the fundamental phenomenon is the production of an ***induced voltage,*** which occurs whenever there is relative motion between a conductor and a magnetic field (the motion not being parallel with the field), whether the conductor is part of a complete circuit or not. *If* it is part of a complete circuit, there is also an induced current.

24-12 Relative Directions of Field, Motion, and Induced Voltage

It is always possible to construct a diagram like Fig. 24-11(a) or 24-11(b) and work out the relationship among the three pertinent directions in any given case logically. A colleague of mine who is an excellent teacher of electrical engineering and electronics does this always, and can state a rule only if he first derives it in this manner. Most people, however, find it convenient to have a rule for such relationships.

The rule is another left-hand rule, but very different from the other two. Extend the forefinger of your left hand, bend the center finger down so that this finger is straight but at right angles to the forefinger, and extend the thumb so that it is perpendicular to both. The relative directions of the forefinger, the middle finger, and the thumb are now the same as the relative directions of the magnetic field, the induced voltage (or current), and the relative motion of the wire with respect to the field, respectively.* Knowing the directions of any two of the three quantities, you can determine the remaining direction immediately. However, you should also be able to do so without the rule, on the basis of logic.

24-13 The Magnitude of the Induced Voltage

Consider the arrangement in Fig. 24-12. There is a uniform magnetic field, indicated by the dots, perpendicular to the paper. A bare wire in the shape of a U with parallel sides a distance L apart lies in the field, and a straight bare wire, also of length L, lies across the open ends of the U. If this wire is moved at right angles to its length so that it crosses the field with a velocity v, intuitively we should expect—correctly—that the induced voltage will be directly proportional to the flux density of the field, the length of the wire, and the velocity of its motion relative to the field. Algebraically,

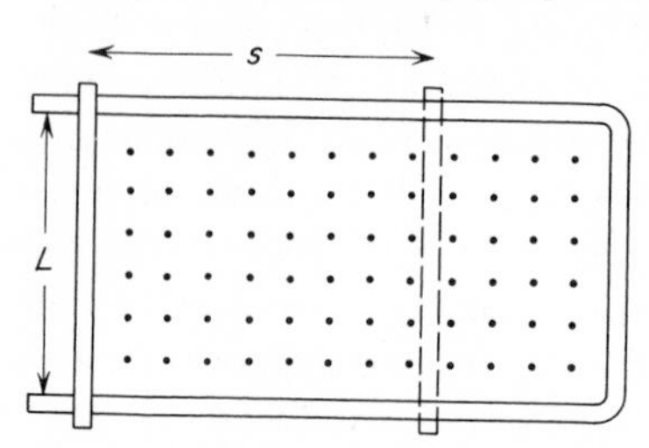

Fig. 24-12. Diagram for determining the voltage induced in a wire moving across a magnetic field.

$$V = kBLv$$

wherein V is the induced voltage, k is a proportionality constant, B is the flux density, L the length of the wire, and v the relative velocity. If the units of B, L, and v are gauss, cm, and cm/sec, respectively, and if V is in volts,

* Rather than blindly memorizing this rule by rote, try this alliterative mnemonic trick: *fore*finger, *field*; *c*enter finger, *c*urrent; and *th*umb, *th*rust (of the wire across the field).

the value of k is 10^{-8}.* Thus

$$V = BLv \cdot 10^{-8} \tag{24-8}$$

This equation† is valid only if the directions of the magnetic field, the conductor, and the relative motion between the conductor and the field are mutually perpendicular.

In the original position of the straight wire in Fig. 24-12, this wire and the U-shaped wire enclose a definite area of the field—a definite quantity of magnetic flux, or a definite number of lines of force. If in a time t the wire is moved with uniform velocity v a distance s to the position shown in dashed lines, there will be a change, ΔA, in the enclosed area. This change in area is equal to Ls and also to Lvt, since $v = s/t$. Thus $Lvt = \Delta A$, or $Lv = \Delta A/t$. Making this substitution in Eq. (24-8) yields

$$V = \frac{B\,\Delta A}{t} \cdot 10^{-8}$$

but according to Eq. (24-3), $BA = \Phi$; so $B\,\Delta A = \Delta\Phi$,

and

$$V = \frac{\Delta\Phi}{t} \cdot 10^{-8} \tag{24-9}$$

V being in volts, $\Delta\Phi$ in maxwells, and t in seconds.

Equation (24-9) says that the magnitude of the voltage induced in a coil is determined solely by the rate at which the total flux through the coil is changing. It is applicable to any coil and, in fact, to any closed circuit through which the flux is changed.

Summary

It is convenient to think of *magnetic phenomena* in terms of *lines of force* which have certain definite properties, but such lines of force are purely hypothetical.

A substance which has a *high permeability* is (*ferromagnetic*). If its permeability is low it may be (*paramagnetic*) or (*diamagnetic*).

The force between two equal magnetic poles 1 cm apart in a vacuum will be 1 dyne if each has unit pole strength.

Magnetic intensity is *force* per *unit pole*. *Flux density* is the *product*

---

* In the electromagnetic system of units, the unit of potential is defined so that $k = 1$; but we shall not consider this system.

† Many authorities prefer to include a minus sign in this and similar equations, to imply the opposition required by Lenz's law; perhaps your instructor will ask you to modify the equations in this way. I prefer to have students (who are not physics or engineering majors) interpret the equations in a numerical sense only, considering the direction of the induced voltage logically on the basis of Lenz's law, or in terms of the left-hand rule for induced voltages.

of *magnetic intensity* and *permeability*. It is also the total flux divided by the area normal to the flux.

Ferromagnetic substances, whether magnetized or not, consist of *very small magnetic domains*. Magnetization of an initially unmagnetized ferromagnetic body involves shifting of domain walls, followed by rotation of the magnetic axes of the atoms within the domains. Either magnetization or demagnetization lags behind the applied magnetic field, giving rise to *hysteresis losses*.

The magnetic field of the earth exhibits variations inconsistent with the idea that the field is due to a permanent magnet within the earth. At present there is no fully satisfactory explanation of the source of this field.

Any *motion* of *electric charge generates* a *magnetic field*. This finds manifold uses in electromagnets for various purposes. Motion of a conductor relative to a magnetic field generates a voltage within the conductor. The principle of conservation of energy dictates both the conditions under which electrical energy can be produced by this method and the direction of the induced voltage.

The *voltage induced* in a coil is determined by the *rate of change* of the *magnetic flux* through the coil.

Self-Quiz

1. Explain induced magnetism on the basis of lines of force. Is this actually explanation, or is it rationalization? On the same basis, consider the attraction of unlike poles, the repulsion of like poles, and what happens when a magnet is cut in two.

2. Discuss permeability from a qualitative standpoint. Discuss it in terms of B and H. Classify ferromagnetic, paramagnetic, and diamagnetic substances on the basis of permeability. Classify them also on the basis of their actions in a magnetic field. Show that this last classification is consistent with your qualitative discussion of permeability.

3. Compare and contrast the following: magnetic intensity, flux density, total flux, magnetic induction.

4. What is hysteresis, and what causes it? What is a hysteresis loop? Of what importance is a hysteresis loop?

5. Would a permanent magnet be much good after it had gone through a fire? Explain fully, in terms of magnetic domains. What *are* magnetic domains? Have they been involved in any previous question?

6. How many left-hand rules have you met in this chapter? State each, and state clearly the circumstances under which it should be used.

7. Make a diagram similar to one of those in Fig. 24-9 and mark an assumed direction of current flow. Show that the rule for the magnetic polarity of a coil can be derived from the rule for the field direction around a current.

8. State Lenz's law. Why is it considered to be a special case of the principle of conservation of energy? On the basis of energy considerations determine whether the magnetic polarity of the coil in Fig. 24-10 will remain unchanged, or reverse, as the magnet is passed through the coil and carried toward the left. Check your conclusion with Lenz's law.

9. Assume that the magnetic field in Fig. 24-12 is directed downward into the page. Using logical analysis, with the aid of a diagram similar to the one in Fig. 24-11, determine the direction of the current induced in the straight wire as it moves to the right. Check by applying the appropriate rule.

Problems

1. A bar magnet with a pole strength of 500 units lies in an east-west direction, with its N pole at the east end. The distance between the poles of the magnet is 12.0 cm. A north pole with a strength of 200 units lies 8.00 cm due south of the midpoint of this magnet. Determine (a) the force on this pole due to the N pole of the magnet, (b) the force due to the S pole of the magnet, (c) the resultant force on the 200 unit pole, and (d) the magnetic intensity due to the magnet at the location of the 200 unit pole.

2. A bar magnet of 6.00 units pole strength and a distance of 10.0 cm between its poles lies in a horizontal north-south position, with its N pole to the north. The horizontal intensity due to the earth's field is 0.200 oersted. Compute the horizontal intensity at a point 5.00 cm due south of the S pole of the magnet.

3. A bar magnet lies in a horizontal north-south position with its S end to the north. The distance between the poles of the magnet is 15.0 cm. The horizontal intensity of the earth's field is 0.200 oersted, but it is found that the horizontal intensity at a point 5.00 cm due north of the magnet's S pole is zero. Compute the pole strength of the magnet.

4. The magnetic flux in an iron bar 2.00 cm thick and 6.00 cm wide is $1.80 \cdot 10^4$ maxwells. (a) What is the flux density in the bar? (b) If the magnetic intensity is 1.20 oersteds, what is the permeability?

5. At a certain location the horizontal component of the intensity of the earth's field is 0.200 oersted, and the dip is 60.0°. Determine the intensity of the field.

6. At a location where the horizontal intensity of the earth's field is 0.200 oersted a vertical wire carries a current of 3.00 amp downward. Compute the horizontal intensity 3.00 cm from the wire at each of these points: (a) due north of the wire, (b) due east of it, (c) due south, and (d) due west.

7. Three fine wires, each part of a different DC circuit, are brought together to form a small straight bundle. One carries a current of 5.00 ma to the right and another has a current of 2.00 ma to the left. The field due to the bundle has an intensity of 0.0160 oersted exactly $\frac{1}{2}$ cm from the wires. Determine the magnitude and direction of the third current.

8. A current of 2.00 amp flows in a flat coil which contains 12 turns and has a diameter of 3.00 cm. (a) What is the magnetic intensity within the coil? (b) If the flux density is $1.10 \cdot 10^4$ gauss, what is the permeability of the core of the coil?

9. A coil of 5 turns is wound on a core which has a diameter of 1.20 cm and a permeability of 250. If the flux density is 4000 gauss, calculate the current strength.

10. A plane with a metal wing 10.0 m long (about 33 ft) is flying in a region where the vertical component of the earth's field has an intensity of 0.300 oersted. The speed of the plane is 150 m/sec (roughly 340 mph). Compute the potential difference developed between the wing tips.

11. A metal rule 30.0 cm long is balanced on end on a table. It falls over, eastward, requiring 2.50 sec to do so. If the horizontal component of the earth's field is 0.200 oersted, what average potential difference is developed?

12. A wire is bent to form a rectangle 10.0 cm wide and 20.0 cm long. In 0.500 sec, it is turned from a position perpendicular to a magnetic field with a flux density of 25.0 gauss to a position parallel with the field. Calculate the average value of the induced voltage.

13. A flux of 5000 maxwells passes through a coil when it is normal to the field. The coil has 400 turns and is being rotated at 30.0 revolutions per second. (a) Compute the average voltage induced in the coil. (b) Is the voltage alternating or direct?

25

ALTERNATING CURRENT CIRCUITS

25-1 Preview

The first topic in this
chapter is the transformer and some
of the reasons it is so useful.
This will lead to the concept of inductance
and inductive reactance. Next we
shall meet capacitors, capacity, and capacitive
reactance. Development of the concept of
impedance from inductive and capacitive
reactance and resistance will enable us to generalize
Ohm's law, obtaining a relationship applicable
to any circuit. It will develop that power
in an AC circuit depends on the phase angle
between the current and the voltage;
and this fact will lead to the concept
of resonance in an AC circuit,
with a few examples of its importance.
This list of strange terms and new concepts
and relationships may be somewhat
frightening; but you can take them one at a time,
and if you keep your thinking cap on you
shouldn't find this chapter nearly
so difficult as it sounds.

25-2 Transformers

We found in Sec. 24-9, 24-10 that a current flowing in a coil gives rise to a magnetic field within the coil. The direction of the magnetic field is determined by the direction of the current, and the flux density is directly proportional to the magnitude of the current. This means that if we put an *alternating* current through a coil there will result within the coil a magnetic field which will be continuously varying, both in flux density and in direction. From what we learned of permeability, we know that if a continuous path of high permeability is provided, this magnetic flux will remain almost completely within that path.

In Sec. 24-11 and Sec. 24-13, we found that any change of magnetic flux through a coil would induce a voltage within that coil. Our quantitative study was in terms of the rather artificial arrangement in Fig. 24-12, but the conclusions are applicable to any coil. And they are applicable without regard to the means by which the change of flux through the coil is produced.

Thus if, as in Fig. 25-1, we send an alternating current through a coil wrapped around the left limb of an open square made of soft iron, it will generate a magnetic field throughout the iron core; and this field will vary continuously in direction as well as in strength. Therefore, the coil on the right limb of the square core will have a constantly changing magnetic field threading through it, so an electric voltage will be induced in it. Since there will be a reversal of the direction of this magnetic field for each reversal of the AC in the left-hand coil, the voltage induced in the right-hand coil will also reverse in direction at the same rate; that is, it will be an AC voltage with a frequency identical with that of the current supplied to the left-hand coil.

The whole arrangement in Fig. 25-1 is a ***transformer.*** The electric energy supplied to the transformer is the ***input,*** and the coil through which the current supplied by the input flows is the ***primary coil,*** or simply the ***primary***. The coil within which an AC voltage is induced is the ***secondary coil,*** or ***secondary,*** and the electrical energy in the secondary circuit is the ***output.***

Thus, a transformer can transfer AC electrical energy from one circuit to another with no electrical contact between the two circuits. If this were all, however, it would be of relatively little importance. Its major usefulness lies in the fact that the voltage induced in the secondary is not the same (usually) as that delivered to the primary. As a good first approximation, the

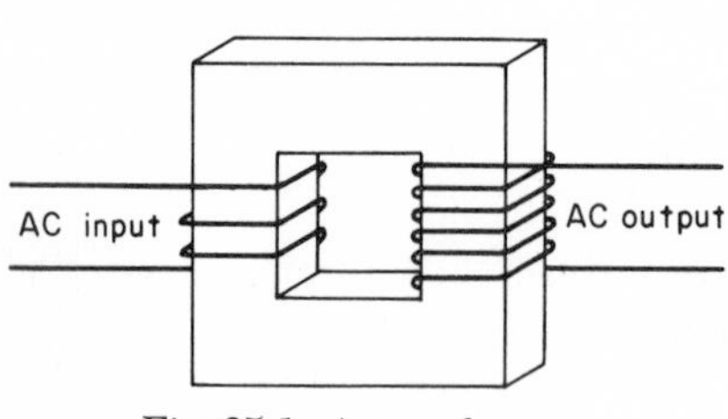

Fig. 25-1. A transformer.

ratio of the voltages is the same as the ratio of the numbers of turns in the respective coils. Thus, if the subscript p identifies quantities pertinent to the primary and s serves the same purpose for the secondary,

$$\frac{V_s}{V_p} = \frac{n_s}{n_p} \tag{25-1}$$

V representing voltage and n the number of turns.

A transformer designed to increase the voltage is called a ***step-up*** transformer, and a ***step-down*** transformer is designed to reduce the voltage. The ratio of change may be very large, but it has practical limits.

Each cycle of current carries the core of the transformer through a complete cycle of magnetization, first in one sense and then in the opposite; hence, to be suitable for use in such cores, a material must have a hysteresis loop of relatively small area (see latter portion of Sec. 24-7).

25-3 Reduction of Line Loss by Transformers

Electric energy usually is generated some distance from where it is to be used; generating plants must be located where adequate water power is available, or where fuel can be obtained, or delivered, cheaply. The energy is generated at one voltage, stepped up to far higher voltages by transformers, delivered over transmission lines at these high voltages, and then stepped down to voltages which are relatively safe and useful. Why isn't it generated and delivered at the voltage desired for its final use?

The power generated is equal to the product of the current and the power, Eq. (21-7); the voltage may be low and the current large, or there may be a smaller current at a high voltage. Any combination of values of current and voltage which has the same product will represent the same power. If the maximum percentage of the power generated is to reach its destination—as profitable operation requires—loss of power in the transmission line must be kept to a minimum. According to Eq. (21-8), if the current is I and if the resistance of the transmission line is R, RI^2 watts of power, or RI^2 joules of energy per second, will be lost in the line as heat. This means that if the voltage at which power is delivered to the line is increased by a factor f the current will be reduced by the same factor, and the loss in the line will be reduced by a factor f^2. For example, a hundredfold increase in the voltage will cut the current to 1% of its former value, and the line loss to 0.01% of what it would have been at the lower voltage.

25-4 Inductance and Inductive Reactance

Were you bothered, in the discussion of the transformer in Sec. 25-2, by the fact that nothing was said about providing any resistance in the primary circuit to reduce the current? For example, the primary of an ordinary bell-ringing transformer is connected directly across the 110 v AC power line; won't it burn out if there isn't a resistor to limit the current? It *would,* on a 110 v *DC* circuit, but it's quite safe on a 110 v AC circuit, because of something called "inductive reactance."

Recall the argument in Sec. 25-2 by which we justified the induction of an AC voltage in the secondary; the cause was the variation of the magnetic flux through the coil. But the primary coil is wound on the same core as the secondary, so the same variation of flux is occurring within it, just as in the secondary. True, the current in the primary is the cause of this flux, but this can't alter the fact that an AC voltage is induced *always* when there is a variation of flux within a coil. Thus the input is inducing an AC voltage in the primary itself, as well as in the secondary; and as Lenz's law—that is, the principle of conservation of energy—requires, the direction of the voltage induced in the primary is such as to oppose the effect which caused it. That is, the *induced* voltage in the primary is exactly opposite the voltage *applied* to the primary. In a well-designed transformer, when the circuit associated with the secondary is open, the induced voltage is very nearly equal to the applied voltage; so the net voltage available to cause current in the primary is almost zero.

Since the induced voltage in the primary opposes the applied voltage, it may be called the ***back voltage*** or ***back emf.*** Its opposition to the applied voltage may be indicated by saying that it is ***180° out of phase*** with the applied voltage—terminology reminiscent of our study of sound waves.

The characteristic of a coil which is revealed by the induction of a back voltage when the current within the coil is changing is the ***inductance*** of the coil.* The unit of inductance is the ***henry,*** which is the inductance of a coil such that a back voltage of 1 v will be induced when the current is changing at the rate of 1 amp per sec. The henry is a very large unit, so the millihenry (mh) is more convenient.

As we have seen, the inductance of a coil is responsible for limiting the current by producing a back voltage, the net effect being a limitation of the strength of the current. This current-limiting effect of a coil is called ***inductive reactance***—*inductive,* for obvious reasons, and *reactance* because the back voltage is a dynamic reaction to the variation of the current strength in the coil. It is evident that inductive reactance has an effect similar to that of resistance, but we shall see (Sec. 25-7) that its effect is quite different in one important aspect.

If the inductive reactance of the primary of a transformer reduces the primary current almost to zero, how can any energy appear in the second-

---

* Inductance often is called "self-inductance" to distinguish it from a similar quantity called "mutual inductance." This distinction is not important for us since we shall not consider the latter.

ary? None can under the conditions we have been discussing—the circuit through the secondary being open. When the secondary circuit is closed so that a current flows, this current also will cause a magnetic flux in the core of the transformer. A moment's consideration of Lenz's law shows that this flux will oppose that of the primary, reducing the flux in the core and thereby reducing the back voltage induced in the primary. This increases the *net* voltage on the primary and allows a significant primary current to flow; so energy is delivered to the primary and converted, through the agency of the magnetic flux in the transformer core, to electric energy in the secondary. Thus we see that a switch in the *secondary* circuit will control, automatically, the current in the *primary* circuit.

The higher the frequency of the AC supplied to a circuit, the shorter time is required for each cycle; so, other things being equal, the rate of change of the current will be directly proportional to the frequency. This means that the induced back voltage also is directly proportional to the frequency, and it is this back voltage which is the source of the inductive reactance. Thus, the inductive reactance is directly proportional to the frequency of the applied AC, as well as to the value of the inductance. If the inductive reactance in ohms is X_L, the frequency in cycles per second f, and the inductance in henries L, the equation is

$$X_L = 2\pi f L \tag{25-2}$$

Since the inductive reactance is a current-limiting quantity analogous to resistance, if an AC voltage V_L is applied across an inductance L, the current I should be given by the equation

$$I = \frac{V_L}{X_L} \tag{25-3}$$

in parallelism with Ohm's law, Eq. (21-2).*

25-5 Capacitors and Capacity

Suppose that we have two sheets of aluminum separated by a thin layer of air, a sort of aluminum and air sandwich as seen from the edge in Fig. 25-2. If we connect one plate to the positive terminal of a battery and the other plate to the negative terminal, the mutual attraction of opposite electric charges will cause them to "condense" on the plates as shown. Any such arrangement of two conductors of appreciable area, the two not being in electri-

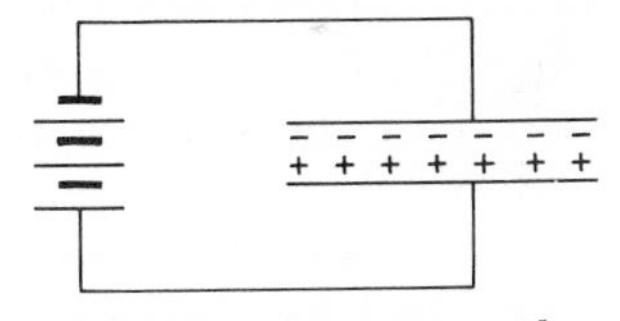

Fig. 25-2. Capacitor with charge.

* It is assumed here that the resistance is negligible, if there is appreciable resistance, Eq. (25-8) or (25-9) must be used instead of Eq. (25-3).

cal contact (except perhaps through a battery or some other source of voltage), is a ***capacitor*** or a ***condenser.***

The quantity of the charge which will collect on the plates of a capacitor depends on several factors. Associated with the capacitor itself are the factors of effective surface area, distance of separation of the plates, and the dielectric constant of any insulating medium between the plates; these determine what is called the ***capacity,*** or ***capacitance,*** of the capacitor. But this capacity is by no means analogous to the capacity of a bucket, for example. When a bucket is full of water it is full, "period"! But when a capacitor is "full," it merely contains all the charges it can *at that particular voltage;* if a higher voltage is used, more charges will accumulate in the condenser. Hence, the capacity of a capacitor resembles the capacity of a compressed air tank rather than that of a bucket. We might rate the "capacity" of such a tank in terms of mass of air per unit of pressure. In a somewhat similar way, the capacity of a capacitor is the quantity of charge it will contain per unit of electric potential difference. If the capacity of the condenser is C, the charge on it Q, and the voltage difference between the plates V,

$$C = \frac{Q}{V} \qquad (25\text{-}4)$$

If Q is in coulombs and V in volts, C will be in ***farads.*** This unit also is so large as to be impractical; capacitances are usually expressed either in microfarads ($1\ \mu\text{f} = 10^{-6}$ f) or in micromicrofarads ($1\ \mu\mu\text{f} = 10^{-6}\ \mu\text{f} = 10^{-12}$ f).

25-6 Displacement Current and Capacitive Reactance

If the plates in Fig. 25-2 were separated by a large distance, the charges on them would be negligible. Each would be at the potential of the battery terminal to which it is connected so the upper plate would have a slight excess of electrons and the lower plate would have a slight deficiency of them. The repulsion of like charges, however, would prevent a considerable excess of electrons on the upper plate, and the attraction of unlike charges would minimize the electron deficiency on the lower plate. But if the two plates were brought toward each other, to their positions in the figure, the situation would be much different. Electrons on the upper plate would repel those on the lower plate, increasing the positive charge on that plate. The unlike charges on the two plates would attract each other, and the increase of the positive charge on the lower plate would augment this attraction. Thus more electrons would flow into the upper plate, increasing the negative charge there and repelling more electrons out of the lower plate. This would continue until the increased mutual repulsion of the like charges on each of the separate plates balances the mutual attraction of the unlike charges on the two different plates. At this point all change will cease.

Obviously no current of any kind can flow through the capacitor; the insulation between the plates presents essentially an infinite resistance.

The capacitor can be discharged only by a flow of electrons out of the negative plate and into the positive plate, and a continuation of this flow will recharge the capacitor with reversed polarity. A second discharge requires an electron flow in a direction opposite the original, and if flow is continued in this direction, the capacitor again becomes charged with its initial polarity. Thus a complete cycle of discharge of the capacitor, recharging with reversed polarity, discharging and recharging with the original polarity will require a complete cycle of electron flow in the wires leading to the capacitor plates; that is, one complete cycle of AC in the circuit associated with the capacitor will carry the condenser through the complete charge-discharge cycle.

Thus, *even though no current can pass through a capacitor, an alternating current can flow in the circuit* of which it is a part; for AC, the circuit is, in effect, complete even though it actually is open between the plates of the capacitor. If a dielectric, such as paraffin, is present between the plates, the alternation of the voltage on the plates causes positive electric charges within the dielectric to be displaced slightly toward the negative plate, and negative charges toward the positive plate. For this reason, the current "through" a capacitor (which doesn't really pass through it at all!)—is called the ***displacement current.***

The strength of the alternating current in a circuit which contains only a condenser is limited by the capacitor somewhat as a resistor limits the current in a DC circuit or inductive reactance limits AC current through a coil. The effect of a capacitor in limiting current is called ***capacitive reactance.*** Like inductive reactance, its value depends on frequency; but in this case the relationship is an inverse proportion. If X_C symbolizes the capacitive reactance, f the frequency, and C the capacitance,

$$X_C = \frac{1}{2\pi f C} \tag{25-5}$$

As in the case of inductive reactance, by parallelism with Ohm's law we can write

$$I = \frac{V_C}{X_C} \tag{25-6}$$

where I is the current due to an AC voltage V_C applied across a capacitive reactance X_C.*

* Like Eq. (25-3), this is a special case of Eq. (25-8) and Eq. (25-9).

25-7 The Difference of Phase between Current and Voltage in a Coil

An inductance in an AC circuit is analogous to a mass in vibratory motion; since the latter is considerably more tangible, let's consider first the phase difference between force and velocity in a massive vibrating body. Figure 25-3 represents a massive body on a perfectly frictionless car, and we're going to put a boy on either side of it to push it back and forth between the stops, the motion to be simple harmonic. After the boys have become skilled, let's examine the situation, commencing (arbitrarily) at the instant the car passes the midpoint, moving to the right. Going back to the concept of simple harmonic motion (Sec. 12-3 and 12-4), we know that the velocity toward the right is at its maximum, and Hooke's law (Sec. 11-4) tells us that the force on the mass is zero. To decelerate the mass, a force toward the left must be applied, and if the motion is to be simple harmonic, this force must increase directly with the displacement. At the point of maximum displacement to the right, the velocity is zero, and the leftward force is at a maximum. The body is accelerated toward the left, its velocity increasing and the force decreasing until, as the car passes the midpoint of its range, the velocity toward the left has reached its maximum value, and the force has become zero. The excursion to the left extremity and the return to the center may be described by the statements detailing the first half of the cycle of vibration, if in every case "right" is changed to "left," and vice versa. If we tabulate these facts at quarter-period intervals, all the values of force or velocity will be either zero or maximum, so a properly directed arrow will indicate a maximum value in the indicated direction. Symbolizing the period by t,

Time	*Force*	*Velocity*
0	0	$\rightarrow$
$t/4$	$\leftarrow$	0
$t/2$	0	$\leftarrow$
$3t/4$	$\rightarrow$	0
t	0	$\rightarrow$

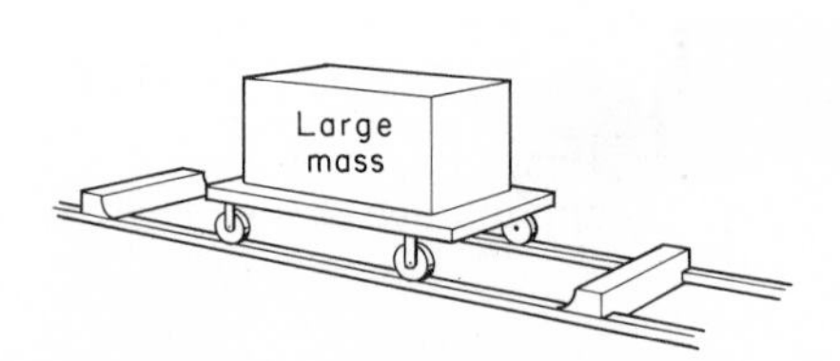

Fig. 25-3. Mechanical analog of an inductance.

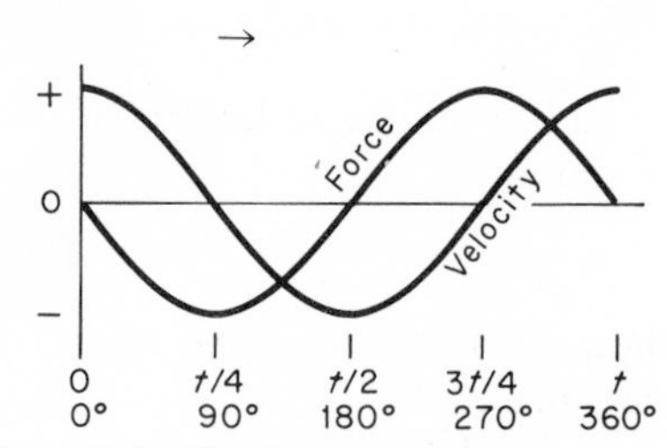

Fig. 25-4. The force on a body moving with simple harmonic motion leads the velocity by one-fourth of a cycle.

Examination of this table shows that the force on the mass is always exactly one-fourth of a cycle ahead of the velocity. We may express this by saying that there is a phase angle of 90°, the force leading the velocity.

Remembering that the motion is simple harmonic, so that the quantities vary in a sinusoidal manner, we may plot these results to obtain Fig. 25-4. Values of quantities directed toward the right are arbitrarily considered positive, those directed to the left being negative. In terms of the circle of reference (Sec. 12-3), zero time corresponds to 0°, $\frac{1}{4}$ period to 90°, $\frac{1}{2}$ period to 180°, $\frac{3}{4}$ period to 270°, and a full period to 360°.

When AC is applied to an inductance, something occurs which is very similar to the mechanical situation we have been discussing. We may think of voltage as analogous to the force on the mass, since potential is energy per unit charge, and energy must be exerted to apply a force over a distance. And since current is the rate of flow of electric charge, we may consider it analogous to the velocity of the mass.

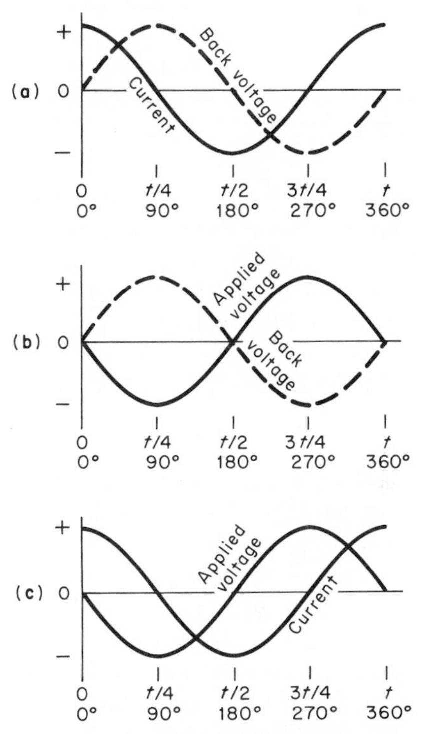

Fig. 25-5. (a) The back voltage in an inductance lags the current by 90°; (b) Phases of applied voltage and back voltage in an inductance differ by 180°; (c) The applied voltage in an inductance leads the current by 90°.

When the current has its maximum positive value, corresponding to $t = 0$ in Fig. 25-5(a), the rate of change of the current is zero momentarily.* Zero change of current means zero induced back voltage, as shown for $t = 0$ in Fig. 25-5(a). As the strength of the current begins to decrease, a back voltage appears; and since the positive value of the current is decreasing, the back voltage will be positive, opposing the decrease of current. At $t = \frac{1}{4}$ period, the current is decreasing at its maximum rate, so the back voltage has its maximum positive value. As

* If we plot an unchanging quantity, such as a steady direct current, on axes arranged like those in Fig. 25-5, the plot is a straight horizontal line. Thus any point on a curve where the curve is tangent to the horizontal is a point at which there is no change with time (at that instant). Conversely, the greatest rate of change with time occurs where the curve is the steepest.

the current continues to decrease toward its negative maximum, its change is still in the same sense but the rate of change is decreasing, so the induced voltage remains positive but decreases; and at $t = \frac{1}{2}$ period, the current is at its negative maximum and the induced voltage is zero. The instant the current starts to increase toward zero an induced voltage appears, in the negative direction, opposing this increase of current. This negative induced voltage reaches its maximum at $t = \frac{3}{4}$ period, when the rate of increase of the current is a maximum, then tapers off to zero at the end of the period, when the current is again at its maximum positive value and unchanging.

If the circuit contains only a source of AC voltage and an inductance, with no resistance (a situation which is impossible to achieve, but which can be considered theoretically and approached closely in practice) there is no opposition to the voltage of the source except the induced back voltage, so these must be 180° out of phase, as in Fig. 25-5(b). If we take the applied voltage from part (b) of Fig. 25-5 and the current from part (a), we can represent the relationship between the applied voltage and the current; this is done in part (c) of the figure. Study of this figure shows that the applied voltage is always $\frac{1}{4}$ period ahead of the current; thus in a pure inductance, the voltage leads the current by 90°, or the current lags 90° behind the voltage.

25-8 The Difference of Phase between Current and Voltage in a Capacitor

Here, again, it will help to commence with a mechanical analog. This time, we assume a car which has neglible mass, connected by a stiff spiral spring to a solid bulwark, as in Fig. 25-6. When the car is at the midpoint of its range of vibration, the spring exerts no force on it. Our team of boys is operating again, moving the car with simple harmonic motion.

As the car passes the rest position, moving toward the right, it has its maximum velocity, but the force on it is zero. To continue this motion, a force toward the right must be exerted to compress the spring, and according to Hooke's law, this force will increase to a maximum at the point of maximum displacement to the right. Meantime, the rightward velocity decreases to zero. To prevent the spring from accelerating the car far more rapidly than simple harmonic motion dictates, a force toward the right must be maintained on the car until it again reaches its rest position; this will allow it to accelerate smoothly toward the left, attaining a maximum velocity at the rest position. At this juncture, a force to the left is required to stretch the spring and

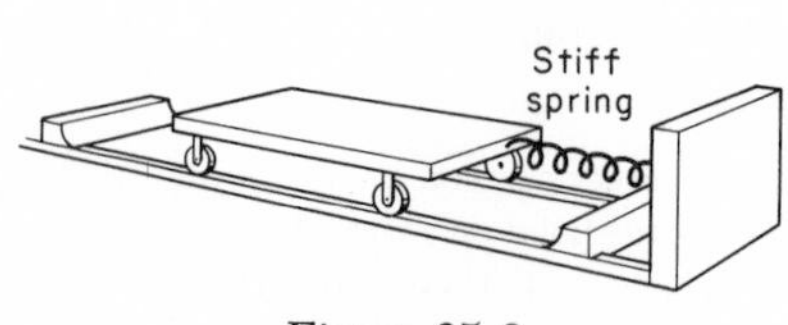

Figure 25-6

carry the car beyond the rest position; the force increases to a maximum, and the velocity becomes zero, at the point of maximum leftward displacement. Again a force opposing the motion must be maintained to control the return of the car to the rest position, this leftward force decreasing to zero as the rightward velocity reaches its maximum at the rest position. These facts are summarized below, for intervals of $\frac{1}{4}$ period, or 90°, and plotted in Fig. 25-7.

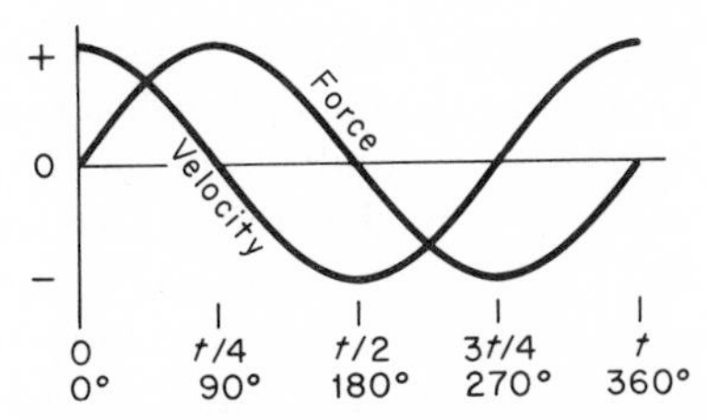

Fig. 25-7. In simple harmonic motion of a very small mass controlled by a stiff spring, the force applied to the spring lags one-fourth cycle behind the velocity.

Time	*Force*	*Velocity*
0	0	→
$t/4$	→	0
$t/2$	0	←
$3t/4$	←	0
t	0	→

We find the situation to be the exact opposite of that found for the mechanical analog of inductance; here the applied force is always $\frac{1}{4}$ period behind the velocity, or lags 90° behind the velocity.

As before, we may consider the applied force to be analogous to the AC voltage supplied to a circuit, and the velocity to be the analog of the current.

A full cycle of alternating current in a circuit containing only a capacitance is indicated, at intervals of $\frac{1}{4}$ period, or 90°, in Fig. 25-8. The circle with a wavy line in it is the conventional symbol for the generator of an alternating current. An arrow or a zero above this symbol indicates the direction of the applied voltage, or the absence of any applied voltage; and an arrow or zero above a connecting wire serves the same purpose with respect to current.

It will be simplest to consider part (b) of the figure first. There has been an inrush of electrons to the left plate and an outrush from the right

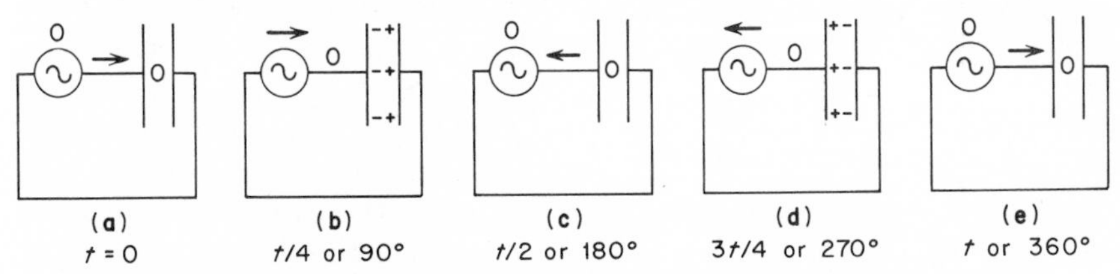

Fig. 25-8. Relationship among applied voltage, current, and charge in a capacitive circuit.

plate, so that the plates carry charges as indicated, and at this instant the charge on the condenser has reached its maximum. The applied voltage has also attained its maximum value. Any reduction of the applied potential will allow the mutual repulsion of like charges on the left plate to force electrons off the plate, and the excess positive charge on the right plate to attract electrons from the wire; so a current flow *opposite* the applied potential commences the instant the value of the potential passes its maximum. This flow will reach its maximum when the potential tending to "hold" the charges on the plates has become zero; part (c) of Fig. 25-8 represents this situation. Having dropped to zero, the polarity of the applied voltage reverses and commences to increase, causing a rush of electrons into the right plate and out of the left plate. But the mutual repulsion of the increasing excess of electrons on the negative plate reduces the inflow of electrons to that plate, and the attraction for electrons of the growing positive charge on the other plate decreases the electron outflow from that plate; so despite the increase of applied voltage, the current becomes smaller. In part (d) of the figure, the charge has reached its maximum, the current has dropped to zero, and the applied voltage is at a maximum. Subsequent reduction of the voltage allows outflow of electrons from the right plate and their flow into the left plate, the resulting current reaching a maximum at the end of the period, at which the applied voltage has decreased to zero. This is indicated in part (e) of Fig. 25-8, which is identical with part (a) because the cycle repeats. As the second cycle begins, the applied voltage has reversed and is increasing, causing a rush of electrons out of the right plate and into the left plate; but, as happened half a cycle earlier, the increasing charges on the plates tend to oppose further accumulation of charge, so the current decreases to zero at $\frac{1}{4}$ period, just as the applied voltage reaches its maximum.

Figure 25-9 shows all this graphically, the values of currents and voltages in one direction arbitrarily being considered positive and the values of oppositely directed quantities negative. The current in an AC circuit which contains only a capacitor leads the voltage by 90°, or the voltage lags 90° behind the current.

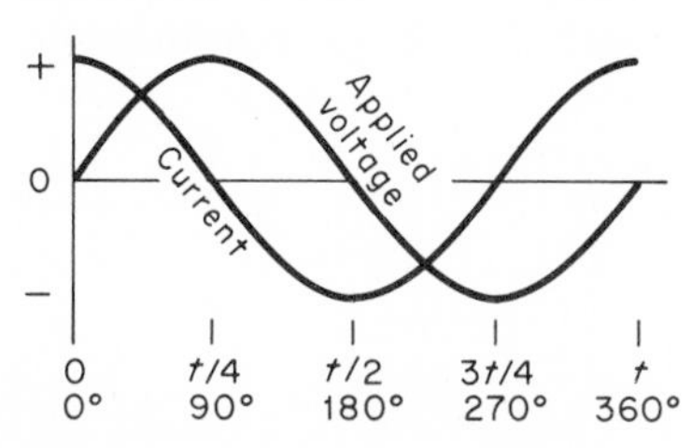

Fig. 25-9. The voltage applied to a capacitance lags 90° behind the current.

At a specified voltage, the charge on a capacitor is directly proportional to its capacitance, since $C = Q/V$ according to Eq. (25-4); so for a given period or frequency of AC, the current in a circuit containing only the capacitor and a voltage source is directly proportional to the capacity. And since the current is the flow of charge per unit time, the greater the number of times a capacitor is charged and discharged in 1 second the greater the effective value of the current must be. Thus the current is directly proportional to the capacity and also to the frequency; so the capacitive reactance, or hindrance to current flow, must be inversely proportional to both. This is in agreement with Eq. (25-5).

25-9 Electrical Quantities as Vector Quantities

Previous to this chapter, except for a hint or two of future complications we have assumed without question that the current and the voltage are perfectly in phase with each other. This tacit assumption is valid for any DC circuit in which the current is constant. It is valid also, whatever the type of current, for any ***non-reactive*** circuit, which is purely resistive, containing no inductance or capacitance. But we have found in this chapter that in a ***reactive*** AC circuit, containing an inductance or a capacitor or both, the voltage across an inductance leads the current by 90° and the voltage across a capacitance lags 90° behind the current.

Using the subscripts *R*, *L*, and *C*, respectively, to identify the voltage across a resistance, an inductance, and a capacitance, and with the aid of the convention for relative directions adopted in Chapter 3 and recorded in Fig. 3-8(a), the relative directions of these voltages may be represented as in Fig. 25-10(a). Note that V_L and V_C lie along the same line but are oppositely directed; that is, their directions differ by 180°. This is to be expected, since one is 90° ahead of V_R and the other is 90° behind.

If an AC circuit contains a resistor with a resistance *R*, an inductance with an inductive reactance X_L, and a capacitor with a capacitive reactance X_C (not necessarily in that order) in series, as in all series circuits the current *I* will be the same throughout.* The current flow through the resistance will involve a voltage difference *IR*, according to Ohm's law. Similarly, there will be a voltage drop IX_L across the inductance, Eq. (25-3), and a potential difference IX_C across the condenser, Eq. (25-6). Thus, for a series circuit, the designations V_R, V_L, and V_C in Fig. 25-10(a) could be replaced by *IR*, IX_L, and IX_C respectively; and since *I* is common to all three, it can be canceled out. The result is represented in Fig. 25-10(b).

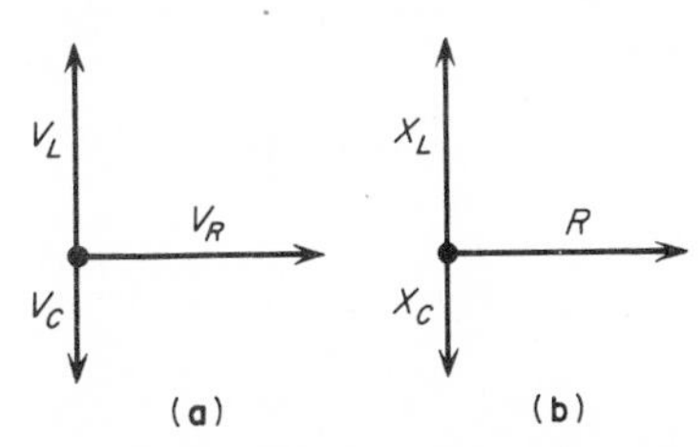

Fig. 25-10. (a) Conventional representation of relative phases of voltages across a resistance (V_R), an inductance (V_L), and a capacitance (V_C); (b) Corresponding vectorial interrelationship of resistance (*R*), inductive reactance (X_L), and capacitive reactance (X_C).

---

* Of course, no current will actually flow through the capacitor, but the situation will be exactly as if a displacement current equal to *I* were doing so.

Thus we see that the voltages across the various units in a reactive circuit are vector quantities, and the same is true of resistance and reactance.

25-10 Impedance

If an AC circuit contains resistance, inductance, and capacitance in series as in Fig. 25-11(a), each of these will have an influence on the strength of the current in the circuit. The combined effect of all of them is the ***impedance.*** Since resistance, inductive reactance, and capacitive reactance are all vector quantities, the impedance must be their vector sum or resultant, and it must be itself a vector quantity.

Thus we find ourselves back in Chapter 3, adding vectors, but we are concerned only with a special and relatively simple kind of vector addition. Assumed values of the resistance, inductive reactance, and capacitive reactance are plotted in their proper directions in Fig. 25-11(b), corresponding to the circuit in part (a) of the figure. X_L and X_C are 180° apart, and it is assumed that the latter is the larger; so the resultant of these two reactances will lie along X_C, its magnitude being the difference between the magnitudes of X_C and X_L. Hence part (b) of the figure may be simplified as in part (c), in which the resultant of X_L and X_C is labeled X_{net}, for effective, or net, reactance.

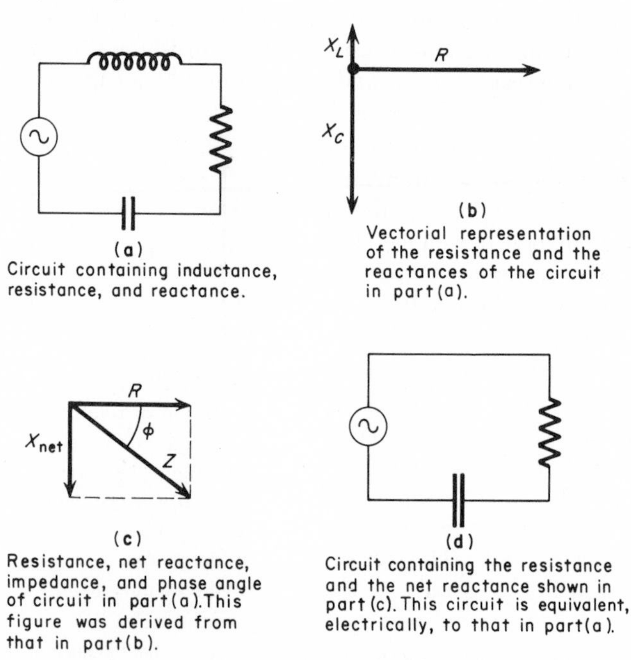

(a) Circuit containing inductance, resistance, and reactance.

(b) Vectorial representation of the resistance and the reactances of the circuit in part (a).

(c) Resistance, net reactance, impedance, and phase angle of circuit in part (a). This figure was derived from that in part (b).

(d) Circuit containing the resistance and the net reactance shown in part (c). This circuit is equivalent, electrically, to that in part (a).

Fig. 25-11. An example of the analysis of an AC circuit.

Thus the circuit in Fig. 25-11(a) is equivalent to that in part (d) of the figure, in which the inductance has been removed and the capacitor of the original circuit has been replaced by one with a smaller reactance. The net reactance and the resistance are added by the polygon method, as in part (c) of Fig. 25-11, and the resultant is the impedance Z.

Review of the discussion and the vector diagrams shows that the algebraic relationship of the impedance to the other quantities is:

$$Z = \sqrt{(X_L - X_C)^2 + R^2} \qquad (25\text{-}7)$$

The order of X_L and X_C is of no importance, since the square of their difference always must be positive.

We can now write a law more general than Ohm's law:

$$I = \frac{V}{Z} \qquad (25\text{-}8)$$

or, combining this with the preceding equation,

$$I = \frac{V}{\sqrt{(X_L - X_C)^2 + R^2}} \qquad (25\text{-}9)$$

When we developed Ohm's law in Sec. 21-6 for a non-reactive circuit, it was stated that this was but a special case of a more general law. Now we see that this is true, for in a non-reactive circuit both X_L and X_C are zero, and Eq. (25-9) reduces to $I = V/R$.

In Fig. 25-11(c), the angle between R and Z is the ***phase angle*** ϕ. In this case, the phase angle is negative, showing that the voltage lags behind the current and thus indicating that the net reactance of the circuit is capacitive—which agrees with our previous conclusion.

Trig

Evidently the phase angle is the arc cosine of R/Z, or the arc tangent of X_{net}/R.

Sample Problem 1

An AC generator supplies 130 v at a frequency of 1000 cycles per second. It is connected to a series circuit consisting of a 100 ohm resistance, an inductance of $150/\pi$ mh (millihenries), and a condenser of $100/12\pi$ μf (microfarads). Determine (a) the inductive reactance, (b) the capacitive reactance, (c) the impedance, (d) the phase angle, (e) the current in the circuit, (f) the potential difference across each part of the circuit, and (g) compare the answers in part (f) with the value of the applied voltage.

This problem is much less difficult than it seems.

(a) $X_L = 2\pi f L = 2\pi \cdot 1000 \cdot 150/\pi \cdot 10^{-3} = 300$ ohms

(b) $X_C = \dfrac{1}{2\pi f C} = \dfrac{1}{2\pi \cdot 1000 \cdot (100/12\pi) \cdot 10^{-6}} = 60.0$ ohms

(c) $$Z = \sqrt{(X_L - X_C)^2 + R^2} = \sqrt{(300 - 60)^2 + 100^2}$$
$$= \sqrt{240^2 + 100^2} = \sqrt{57{,}600 + 10{,}000}$$
$$= \sqrt{67{,}600} = 260 \text{ ohms}$$

(d) A graphical solution similar to Fig. 25-12 or 25-13 yields ϕ = about $+67.4°$.

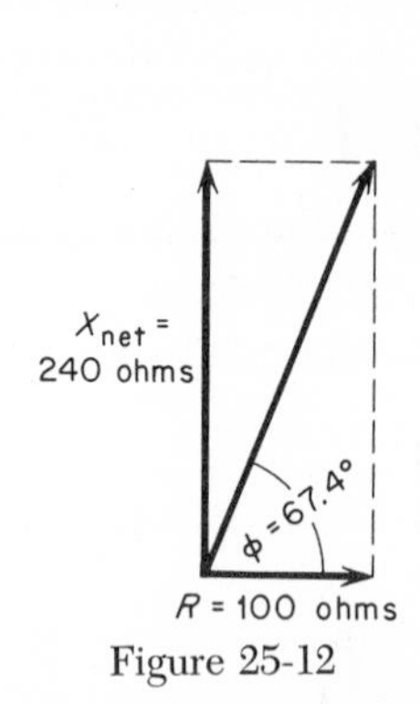

Figure 25-12

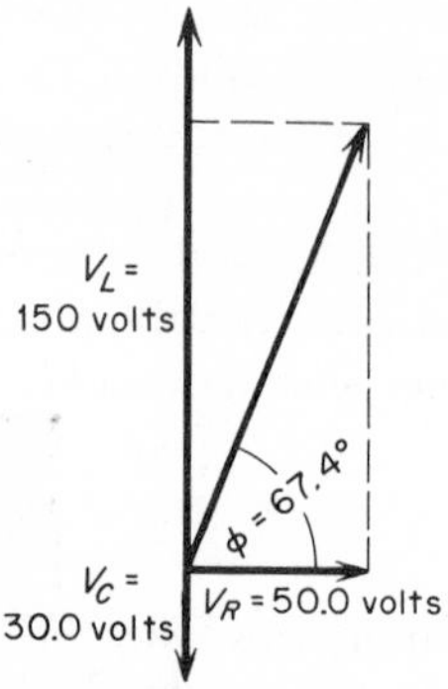

Figure 25-13

(e) $$I = V/Z = 130/260 = 0.500 \text{ amp}$$

(f) $$V_R = IR = 0.500 \cdot 100 = 50.0 \text{ v}$$
$$V_L = IX_L = 0.500 \cdot 300 = 150 \text{ v}$$
$$V_C = IX_C = 0.500 \cdot 60.0 = 30.0 \text{ v}$$

(g) It appears that we are in trouble, since V_L *alone* is greater than the applied voltage, and the sum of all the voltages is 230 v, whereas the applied voltage is only 130 v. But these voltages are *vector* quantities, so only their *vector* sum has any significance. According to Fig. 25-13, this vector sum is

$$\sqrt{(150 - 30)^2 + 50^2} = \sqrt{120^2 + 50^2} = \sqrt{14{,}400 + 2500}$$
$$= \sqrt{16{,}900} = 130 \text{ v}$$

Magic!

25-11 Resonance

In connection with vibration and sound, the term "resonance" was used to describe any situation in which the pertinent factors are so related that the amplitude of the vibrations or waves is at a maximum. Similarly, an AC circuit is in ***resonance*** when the relative values of the inductive reactance and capacitive reactance in the circuit are such that the current is at a maximum.

This means that, since $I = V/Z$, the circuit will be resonant when the impedance is minimized. We may use a graphical or an algebraic approach to find the conditions which will reduce the impedance to a minimum. First, study of Fig. 25-11(c) and Fig. 25-12 indicates that Z can never be smaller than R, and always will be greater than R unless the phase angle is zero. Second, consideration of Eq. (25-9) shows that the impedance becomes equal to the resistance if—and only if—$(X_L - X_C) = 0$; for all other situations, the value of Z exceeds that of R.

Thus we arrive at two different but fully equivalent criteria of resonance: a circuit is resonant if the phase angle is zero, and it is resonant if the value of the inductive reactance is equal (disregarding signs) to that of the capacitive reactance.

Stating the latter criterion algebraically, we have, *for a resonant circuit,*

$$X_L = X_C, \quad \text{or} \quad 2\pi fL = \frac{1}{2\pi fC} \tag{25-10}$$

Solving the latter equation for f, we obtain

$$f = \frac{1}{2\pi\sqrt{LC}} \tag{25-11}$$

Whenever you "tune" a radio or television receiver, you vary the value of the capacity (or sometimes the inductance) in the tuning circuit, to satisfy Eq. (25-11), thus adjusting the natural or resonant frequency of the circuit to the frequency of the broadcast station.

Sample Problem 2

If the tuning circuit of a radio receiver contains a 20.0 mh coil in series with a variable capacitor, what value of the capacity is required to tune the set to a broadcast station with a frequency of 800 kilocycles per second (kc/sec)?

We can solve the problem either on the basis of Eq. (25-10) or Eq. (25-11); it makes no real difference. Using the latter,

$$800 \cdot 10^3 = \frac{1}{2\pi\sqrt{20.0 \cdot 10^{-3} \cdot C}}$$

$$(800 \cdot 10^3)^2 = \frac{1}{4\pi^2 \cdot 20.0 \cdot 10^{-3} \cdot C}$$

$$C = \frac{1}{4\pi^2 \cdot 20.0 \cdot 10^{-3} \cdot (800 \cdot 10^3)^2}$$

$$= 1.98 \cdot 10^{-12}\ \text{f} = 1.98\ \mu\mu\text{f}$$

25-12 Power in a Reactive Alternating Current Circuit

In Sec. 21-10, we developed the equation for electric power in terms of current and voltage:

$$P = IV \tag{21-7}$$

There, however, we were dealing with non-reactive circuits; so perhaps, like Ohm's law, this equation is invalid for reactive circuits. A glance back at Fig. 25-5(c) confirms our doubts. During the second and fourth quarters of the cycle, I and V have like signs and their product is positive, but dur-

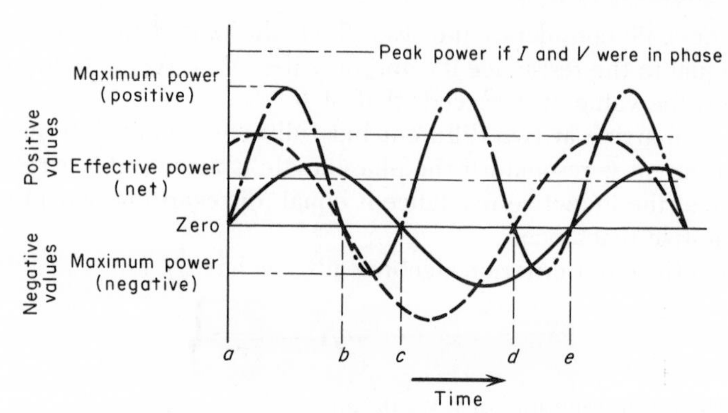

Fig. 25-14. When current (dashed line) and voltage (solid line) are not in phase, the power (dot and dash line) is negative part of the time. This reduces the net or effective power.

ing the first and third quarters of the cycle, their signs are opposite and their product negative. Thus during 50% of the cycle, the power used by the circuit is positive, but during the other 50%, the power is negative; that is, for half the time the circuit draws energy from the power line but the other half of the time the circuit delivers the energy back to the line. The net power consumption is zero!* Figure 25-9 reveals a similar situation. This sort of thing was implied in the discussion of inductance in Sec. 25-4, but it's still surprising.

Figure 25-14 is a more detailed representation of the situation in a circuit which contains resistance and a net capacitive reactance. The time for one cycle extends from a to e. There is a pulse of positive power from time a to time b, and another from time c to time d; but from b to c and from d to e the power is negative. The energy during any one interval is proportional to the area between the corresponding lobe of the power curve and the axis, so there is a larger quantity of "positive energy" than "negative energy." Thus the circuit is using energy and power, but both are reduced by the fact that the phase angle between current and voltage is not zero. Compare Fig. 25-14 with Fig. 21-7.

To compensate for differences of phase between current and voltage, it is necessary to include in the power equation (21-7) a factor k, which is called the ***power factor.*** The equation becomes

$$P = kIV \tag{25-12}$$

More advanced texts prove that the power factor is equal to the ratio of the resistance to the impedance: $k = R/Z$. Thus

$$P = \frac{IVR}{Z} \tag{25-13}$$

* These figures were constructed on the assumption that the resistance in the circuit is zero. Since this can never be realized, the power can never be *quite* zero.

Trig

Since $R/Z = \cos \phi$, $P = IV \cos \phi$

Summary

By the use of transformers an AC voltage may be increased or decreased, the ratio of voltages being approximately the same as the ratio of the numbers of turns in the respective coils of the transformer.

Because of the *inductance* of the *coil*, a *back voltage* is *induced* in any coil through which an alternating current is flowing. This results in an inductive reactance which is directly proportional to the inductance of the coil and to the frequency of the AC.

A *capacitor* is any arrangement of two conductors of considerable area *insulated* from each other. The mutual attraction of unlike charges causes charges to "condense" on the capacitor when a voltage is applied. The *capacity* of a capacitor is not a measure of charge, but of charge per unit potential difference.

A DC circuit containing a capacitor would always be open; but a displacement current has the *effect* of passing an AC current through a capacitor, even though no current actually flows through it. A capacitor in an AC circuit has a capacitive reactance which is inversely proportional to the capacitance and to the frequency.

Voltages in a reactive AC circuit are *vector quantities*, and so are resistance and both kinds of reactance. The vector sum of the resistance and the two types of reactance is the *impedance* of the circuit. The current is equal to the voltage divided by the impedance.

An inductance would cause the current to lag 90° behind the voltage if there were no resistance whatever in the inductance, and a pure capacitance would cause the current to lead the voltage by 90°.

The angle between the resistance and the impedance is the *phase angle*. An AC circuit is resonant if the phase angle is zero, which can occur only if the net reactance is zero.

The *power factor* of a reactive circuit is the quotient of the resistance divided by the impedance. Power in a reactive circuit is equal to the product of the current, the voltage, *and* the power factor.

Self-Quiz

1. Explain clearly how an alternating current in the primary of a transformer can cause an AC voltage in the secondary. Why aren't transformers used on DC?

2. Why is the loss of energy in a transmission line less if power is transmitted at a relatively high voltage? Since power can be expressed as V^2/R, Eq. (21-9), why doesn't the use of high voltage *in*crease the line loss?

3. Why doesn't the primary of a transformer burn out? As used in this connection, what does "180° out of phase" mean? Is the induced voltage ever in phase with the applied voltage? Why?

4. What is inductive reactance, and why is it so called? How is its value related to inductance, and why? To frequency, and why?

5. What is a capacitor? What is the capacity of a capacitor? What erroneous implication may the term "capacity" carry, if you aren't careful?

6. Does any current pass through a capacitor in a DC circuit? Does any pass through a capacitor in an AC circuit? Does any current flow in an AC circuit which contains a capacitor? Explain any similarities and differences among your three answers.

7. What is capacitive reactance, and why is it so called? How is its value related to capacitance, and why? to frequency, and why?

8. Either on the basis of energy considerations or by applying Lenz's law, show that, as the flux through a coil commences to decrease, the induced voltage tends to maintain the current. Show that when the flux has dropped to zero and begins to build up in the opposite direction, the induced voltage tends to oppose the current. Do these effects tend to advance the phase of the current, or to cause it to lag? Compare this result with the discussion in Sec. 25-7.

9. Outline the mechanism which causes the current in a capacitive circuit to lead the applied voltage by 90°; illustrate with appropriate diagrams.

10. Why are voltages in a reactive circuit vector quantities? Why are reactances and resistance vector quantities? How are the voltages across the parts of a reactive series circuit related to the applied voltage? How are the reactances and the resistance related to the impedance?

11. Outline the method of determining the impedance, the phase angle, and the power factor of a reactive series circuit.

12. Write the equation for current in terms of impedance and voltage. Make a vector diagram of resistance, inductive reactance, and capacitive reactance, and with the aid of the diagram modify your original equation so that it gives current in terms of voltage, resistance, inductive reactance, and capacitive reactance.

13. Rewrite Eq. (25-9), expressing X_L and X_C in terms of f, L, and C. Reduce this modified equation to Ohm's law by setting L equal to zero and C equal to infinity.

14. Just how is it possible for the voltage across a single element of a series circuit which contains a single generator to exceed the voltage delivered by the generator?

15. What is a resonant circuit? Explain how resonance may be achieved (a) in geometrical terms, (b) in algebraic terms, and (c) in terms of experimental procedure. Would it be correct to say that a resonant circuit is one which has a power factor of 1.00? Explain.

16. How is the power factor related to other quantities characteristic of the circuit? Is the power factor ever negative? Is its value ever greater than 1? Explain.

17. Assume that a circuit has a current of several amperes but a phase angle of almost 90°. Will the circuit use an appreciable amount of power? Will there be any power loss in the lines feeding the circuit? Were your two answers the same or different? Explain clearly.

Problems

1. Compute the ratio of the number of turns in the secondary of a step-down transformer to the number in the primary if the input is at 22.0 kv and the output is at 550 v.

2. The input of a transformer is 5.00 amp at 220 v and the output is at 550 v. What is the current in the secondary (a) on the assumption that the efficiency is 100%, and (b) if the efficiency actually is 98.0%?

3. A transformer on a 120 v line has an efficiency of 98.5% and its output is 2.00 amp at 15.0 v. Calculate the current in the primary.

4. Assume that the voltage applied to the primary of a transformer is 220 v, and that, due to the inductance, the net voltage is only 1 v. (a) What is the rate of change of flux through the coil? (b) If the frequency is 60.0 cycles per sec, compute the maximum flux through the coil.

5. (a) Compute the reactance of a 0.0500 mh coil if the frequency is 600 kilocycles (kc) per second. (b) What voltage is required to maintain a current of 1.50 milliamperes (ma) through the coil (at this frequency)? (c) What voltage would be required if the frequency were doubled?

6. (a) Calculate the reactance of a 1200 $\mu\mu$f capacitor if the frequency is 600 kc/sec. (b) What voltage across this condenser is necessary to maintain a current of 1.50 ma in the circuit of which it is a part? (c) What voltage would be required if the frequency were doubled?

7. Find (a) the net reactance and (b) the impedance of a circuit of 600 kc/sec frequency if the circuit contains the coil of Problem 5, the condenser of Problem 6, and a 50.0 ohm resistor in series. If the current in the circuit is 1.50 ma find (c) the voltage across the resistor and (d) the voltage applied to the circuit.

8. An inductance of $500/\pi$ mh and a condenser of $500/\pi$ μf are connected in series with a 40.0 ohm resistance in a 60.0 cycle per sec 120 v circuit. Compute (a) the impedance of the circuit and (b) the current.

9. Compute the resonant frequency of a circuit which contains a 0.0500 mh coil and a 6.00 $\mu\mu$f condenser in series.

10. A circuit contains a 4.00 mh coil in series with a variable condenser. To what capacitance should the condenser be adjusted to make the circuit resonant (a) at 800 kc/sec, and (b) at 1200 kc/sec?

11. A current of 2.50 amp flows in a reactive series circuit on a 120 v line. (a) Calculate the impedance of the circuit. (b) If the resistance of the circuit is 12.0 ohms, determine the power factor. (c) Compute the power.

12. Calculate the power consumption of the circuit in Problem 8.

13. Power at 220 v, with a frequency of 60.0 cycles per sec, is supplied to a circuit. The current is 0.400 amp and the power is 44.0 w. Determine (a) the power factor, (b) the impedance, (c) the resistance, and (d) the capacity of the condenser, if the net reactance is capacitive and the inductance is $90/\pi$ mh.

26

GENERATORS, METERS, AND MOTORS

26-1 Preview

Although all the topics in this chapter are new, we already have essentially all the basic information required to understand them. Generators employ the principle of induced currents, and a new look at the process of inducing a current will reveal that there must be a force on any electric charge which is moving in a magnetic field. This will lead us to the principle of the galvanometer and, combined with some of the properties of parallel and series circuits, to the ammeter and the voltmeter. It will also lead us to the principle of simple motors.

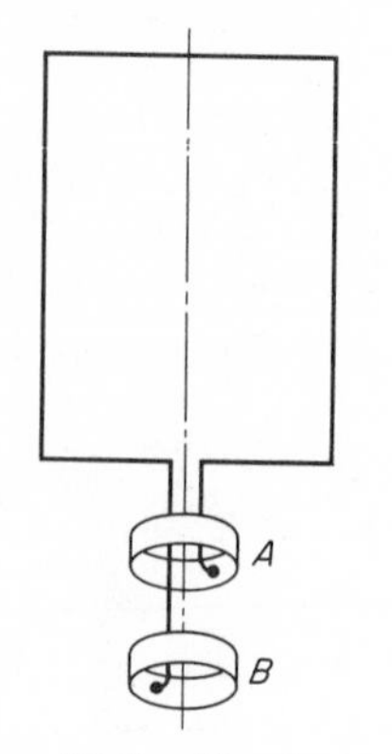

Fig. 26-1. Single-turn coil, with slip rings, for an AC generator.

26-2 A Simple AC Generator

Imagine that we have a device similar to that in Fig. 26-1. There is a hollow metal ring *A* connected to one end of the wire. The wire is bent so that it forms a rectangle, and the other end is fastened to a ring *B*, similar to the ring *A*. These rings are known as ***slip rings.*** All segments of the wire lie in the same plane; and the axis of the coil, shown by a dot-and-dash line, is perpendicular to both slip rings, and passes through their centers. To allow a current to flow when a voltage is induced, a flexible metal strip, or ***brush,*** is brought into contact with the outer surface of ring *A;* another brush is provided for ring *B.* These brushes, which are shown in Fig. 26-2, lead the current generated in the rectangular wire out into the external circuit. The whole arrangement constitutes a one-turn coil, with provision for connections to an external circuit.

Suppose that we place the wire rectangle in a uniform magnetic field, its axis being at right angles to the field, and rotate it about its axis. We know, from Sec. 24-11, that a voltage will be induced in segments *a* and *b* of the wire when they are moving across the field, but none when they are moving parallel with it; and Eq. (24-8) tells us that the voltage will be directly proportional to the velocity normal to the field.

Let's commence a study of the induced voltage when the plane of the coil is vertical, the segment *a* being at the top. This situation appears in the upper left part of Fig. 26-2, where it is labeled 0°. At the moment, the limbs *a* and *b* are moving parallel with the field, so the induced voltage is zero. When the rectangle has turned clockwise 90°, limb *a* will have its maximum velocity downward across the field and limb *b* its maximum upward speed, so the induced voltage will be at a maximum. The direction of the induced voltage in limb *a* will be away from ring *A*, making that ring and the corresponding brush positive. The direction in limb *b* will be toward ring *B*, making it and its brush negative. At 180°, the situation is essentially the same as at 0°. The induced voltage has its maximum value at 270°, as it had at 90°, but limb *a* is now moving upward and limb *b* downward, exactly the opposite of what they were half a cycle earlier; so the direction of the induced voltage has been reversed, and the same is true of the polarities of the brushes. At 360°, the situation is an exact duplication of that at 0°.

If the rotation proceeds with a uniform angular velocity, the limbs of the wire will describe uniform circular motion. Hence the effective component of their velocity—the component normal to the field—will vary sinusoidally, exactly as the velocity in simple harmonic motion does (Sec. 12-4). And the direct proportionality between velocity normal to the field and induced voltage requires that the induced voltage be sinusoidal also. The lower portion of Fig. 26-2 illustrates this, and also the relationship between the position of the coil in the field and the value of the induced voltage. It will be instructive to compare this portion of the figure with Fig. 12-1 and Fig. 13-7.

No electric power company could avoid bankruptcy with an arrangement of this sort; nevertheless it constitutes an ***AC generator.*** In practical form, the rotating coil would consist of many turns instead of a single one, and it would be provided with a core of high permeability and low hysteresis loss. For power production, AC generators are provided with electromagnets fed with DC to generate the magnetic field; these are sometimes called ***dynamos.*** For special purposes, especially gasoline engine ignition systems, permanent magnets may be employed to provide the field; such generators are called ***magnetos.*** The *source* of the magnetic field, whether it be permanent magnets or electromagnets, is called the ***field,*** and the coil in which the voltage is induced is the ***armature.*** The armature may rotate in a stationary field, as in our example; or the field may rotate, the armature being associated with the stationary frame of the generator.

In Sec. 24-13, we considered the magnitude of an induced voltage, and

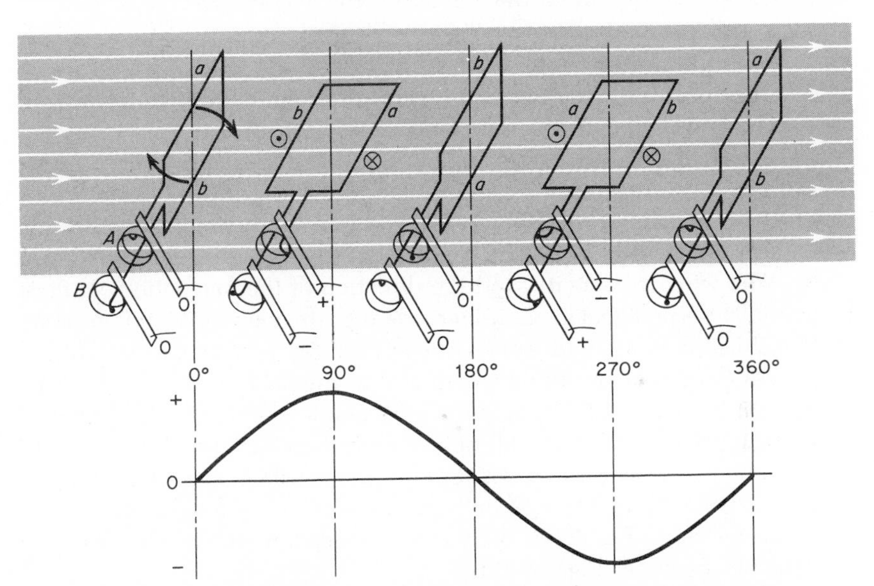

Fig. 26-2. A coil rotating in a magnetic field produces an AC voltage. The field direction is toward the right, and the direction of rotation is clockwise.

developed two equations to relate it to other quantities. One of these was Eq. (24-9):

$$V = \frac{\Delta\Phi}{t} \cdot 10^{-8}$$

In this equation, V is the voltage induced in a coil and $\Delta\Phi$ is the change of flux through the coil in a time interval t. Let us represent the maximum flux passing through the loop in the upper left of Fig. 26-2 by Φ. After a 90° turn, the plane of the coil is parallel to the field, so the flux passing through the coil is zero; hence for this 90° turn of the coil, $\Delta\Phi = \Phi - 0 = \Phi$. The magnitude of the flux change is the same in each successive quarter; the *sign* of $\Delta\Phi$ changes, causing the direction of the induced voltage to reverse, but we are concerned only with the magnitude of the voltage. Hence for a complete revolution of the coil $\Delta\Phi$ is 4Φ; and if there are n revolutions in 1 sec, $\Delta\Phi$ is $4n\Phi$, and t is 1. Thus

$$V = 4n\Phi \cdot 10^{-8}$$

In any practical generator, however, there are many turns in the coil, rather than one, and they are in series so that the voltages induced in them are additive. Also, the rate of change of the flux through the coil varies greatly during a quarter-turn, producing the varying values of the voltage discussed above and shown in the lower part of Fig. 26-2. Hence the equation yields only the average value of the voltage. Therefore, if there are N turns of wire in the coil and if the average voltage is V_{av},

$$V_{av} = 4N\Phi n \cdot 10^{-8} \tag{26-1}$$

We may determine the maximum value of the induced voltage, instead of its average value, with the aid of Eq. (24-8), which is

$$V = BLv \cdot 10^{-8}$$

in which V, in volts, is the voltage induced in a conductor of length L cm when the conductor has a velocity of v cm/sec in a magnetic field of B gauss. The wire, its velocity, and the direction of the magnetic field must be mutually perpendicular. Consider side a of the loop in the 90° position in Fig. 26-2; it is at right angles with the field, and at this instant, its velocity is perpendicular to its length and to the field. If the width of the loop, from limb a to limb b, is w cm, any point on either limb of the coil is following a circular path of radius $w/2$; hence if the loop is rotating steadily at a rate of n revolutions per second, the limbs have a tangential velocity of $2\pi nw/2$ or πnw cm/sec. If the length of a limb is L cm, according to Eq. (24-8) the voltage induced in limb a when the loop is in the 90° position (Fig. 26-2) is

$$V = \pi BLnw \cdot 10^{-8}$$

At the same time, an equal potential difference is being induced in limb b, and these two voltages are additive, doubling the voltage of either. Hence, for a coil of N turns, instead of the single loop in the figure,

$$V = 2\pi NBLwn \cdot 10^{-8}$$

The product Lw is the area A of the coil, and according to Eq. (24-3) $BA = \Phi$; so the maximum voltage V_{max} induced in a coil of A cm² area rotating steadily n revolutions per second in a magnetic field of B gauss (the axis of rotation being normal to the field) is

$$V_{max} = 2\pi N\Phi n \cdot 10^{-8} \qquad (26\text{-}2)$$

This equation is applicable to a coil of any shape as well as to one of the rectangular shape assumed, but the mathematics of the derivation would be far less simple.

Comparison of Eq. (26-1) and Eq. (26-2) yields the relationship of the average value of the induced voltage to the maximum value:*

$$\frac{V_{av}}{V_{max}} = \frac{4N\Phi n \cdot 10^{-8}}{2\pi N\Phi n \cdot 10^{-8}}$$

$$\frac{V_{av}}{V_{max}} = \frac{2}{\pi} \qquad (26\text{-}3)$$

Sample Problem 1

A coil of 500 turns has a cross-sectional area of 400 cm² and is rotating 20.0 times per second in a magnetic field. The average value of the induced voltage is 6.00 v. Determine the values of the magnetic flux, flux density, the maximum voltage, and the effective voltage.

Equation (26-1) may be rearranged to the form

$$\Phi = \frac{V_{av} \cdot 10^8}{4Nn}$$

and insertion of the data yields

$$\Phi = \frac{6.00 \cdot 10^8}{4 \cdot 500 \cdot 20.0} = 1.50 \cdot 10^4 \text{ maxwells}$$

Since the area of the coil is 400 cm²,

$$B = \frac{\Phi}{A} = \frac{1.50 \cdot 10^4}{400} = 37.5 \text{ gauss}$$

From Eq. (26-3)

$$V_{max} = V_{av} \cdot \frac{\pi}{2} = \frac{6.00\pi}{2} = 9.42 \text{ v}$$

---

* Note that Eq. (26-3), which relates the maximum and average values of the voltage, is different from Eq. (21-14) and Eq. (21-15), which relate the maximum and effective values. There is no disagreement here, however, for the effective value is based on the average power rather than on the average voltage (Sec. 21-13).

Finally, according to Eq. (21-14)

$$V_{\text{eff}} = \frac{V_{\text{max}}}{\sqrt{2}} = 9.42 \cdot 0.707 = 6.66 \text{ v}$$

26-3 A Simple DC Generator

The simple AC generator of the preceding section can be converted into a DC generator by providing some means of reversing the connections between the armature and the external circuit each time the polarity of the voltage induced in the armature reverses.

Let's use the same rectangular wire as before, but snip off the slip rings. In their place, we may connect two halves of a single slip ring, as in Fig. 26-3, the two halves being electrically insulated from each other (except through the single-loop rectangular coil). This arrangement of two halves of a single ring is a simple ***commutator.*** As before, brushes will provide the connections between the armature and the external circuit; but instead of making contact with different slip rings they rub against opposite sides of the same split-ring commutator.

Rotation of the coil in a magnetic field will induce an alternating voltage in the armature exactly as before, as indicated in the upper part of Fig. 26-4. Again we commence with the coil in the 0° position, perpendicular to the field, the induced voltage being zero. The brushes are so positioned that each barely makes the contact with *both* segments when the coil is in this position. As the coil rotates clockwise slightly past this position, the brush at the left will touch only the commutator segment connected with limb b of the wire, and the brush on the right will make contact with the segment to which limb a is attached. Simultaneously, an induced voltage appears and increases to a maximum at the 90° position of the coil. The direction of the induced voltage makes the commutator segment attached to limb a positive, so the right-hand brush is positive also; and the commutator segment connected to limb b and the left brush are both negative. At the 180° position, after one-half cycle, the induced voltage is again zero. At this instant the commutator segment attached to limb a is on the point of losing contact with the brush on the right and making contact with the left-hand brush, and the other commutator segment is shifting from the left brush to the one on the right. As the coil turns toward the 270° position, the induced voltage will make the commutator segment connected to limb a negative rather than positive as before, so the left brush will be negative; and the segment connected to

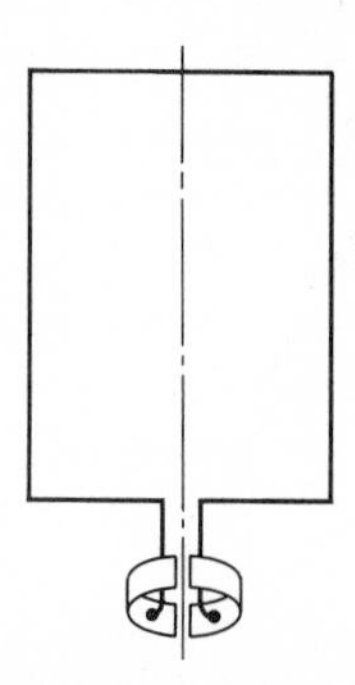

Fig. 26-3. Single-turn coil, with commutator, for a DC generator.

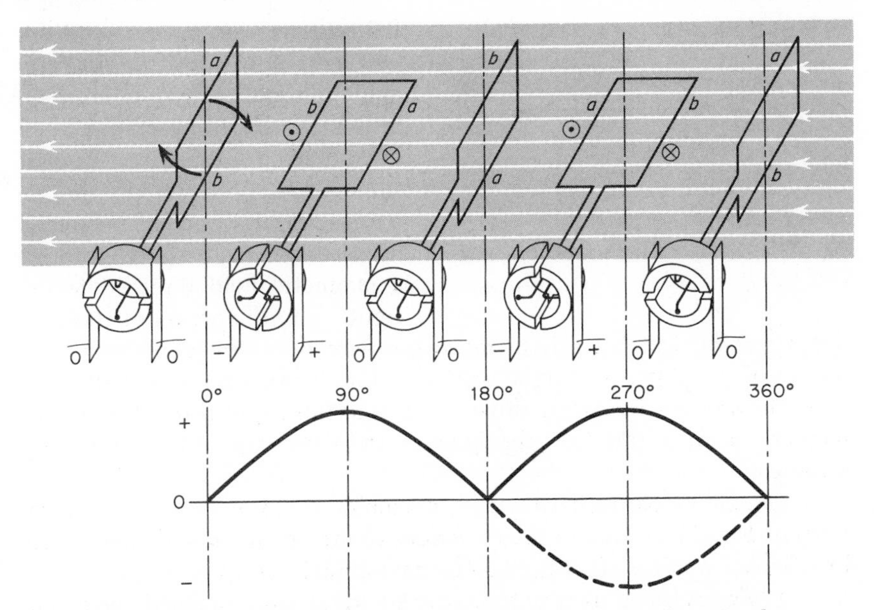

Fig. 26-4. By using a commutator instead of slip rings, the AC voltage induced in the rotating coil is changed to pulsating DC in the external circuit.

limb *b* will be positive, making the right-hand brush positive. These polarities of the brushes are the same as they were before. When the 360° or 0° position is reached, the direction of the induced voltage will reverse again, but the connections to the brushes will be changed at the same time, so the polarities of the brushes will remain unchanged. In the lower portion of Fig. 26-4, the dashed line indicates the voltage induced in the armature; the voltage applied to the brushes—and hence to the external circuit—is shown by the solid line.

Obviously the DC produced by this generator differs from that supplied by a cell or battery; though it is unidirectional, its magnitude varies like that of an alternating current. In any practical DC generator, however, there are many armature coils instead of the one we have been discussing, the planes of the various coils being distributed symmetrically about their common axis and each coil having its pair of commutator segments. The effect of this is that the voltage supplied to the brushes is "smoothed out" a great deal, though some "ripple" always remains. By means of filter circuits, the "ripple" may be reduced virtually to zero.

26-4 Force on a Charge Moving in a Magnetic Field

Consider a current flowing in a wire at right angles to a uniform magnetic field. Surrounding the wire there will be a circular magnetic

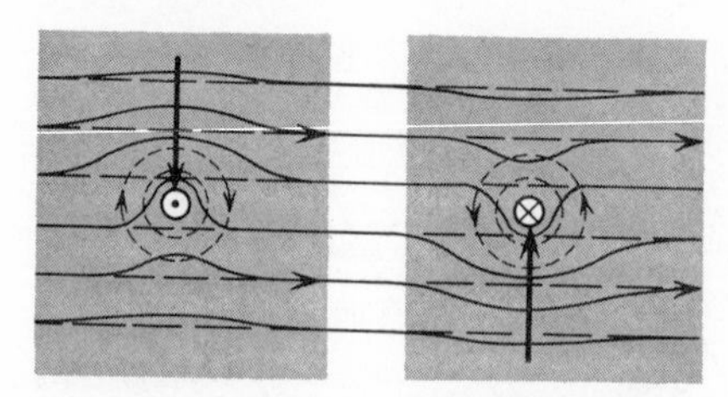

Fig. 26-5. Force on a current in a magnetic field.

field due to the current, and this will combine with the uniform field to produce a resultant field in which the lines of force are kinked around the wire. The left side of Fig. 26-5 depicts the situation when a current is flowing upward (out of the page) through a magnetic field directed to the right. The distortion of the field causes a force which tends to move the wire in a direction toward the bottom of the page. The right portion of the diagram shows the situation when the current is flowing downward (into the page) through the same magnetic field; in this case, the force on the wire urges it toward the top of the page.

If Fig. 26-5 looks rather familiar, it should. It differs from the left two-thirds of Fig. 24-11 only in the directions of the arrows which indicate the direction of motion. In Fig. 24-11, mechanical energy in the form of a moving force is being used to transport a wire across a magnetic field, and as a result a current (or at least a voltage) is being generated. But in Fig. 26-5 the current is supplied from some appropriate source, and as a result the wire is subjected to a force tending to cause mechanical motion. Thus either situation is the opposite of the other. We may consider the principle of conservation of energy, or invoke Newton's third law of motion, or apply Lenz's law; in any case, we see that the forces in the two diagrams must be oppositely directed, as they are.

Your two hands are mirror images of each other, so if you extend the thumb, forefinger, and center finger of either hand so that they are mutually perpendicular, do the same with the other hand, and twist your wrists so that the two forefingers are parallel and the same is true of the two center fingers, the two thumbs will be antiparallel. Thus the rule stated in Sec. 24-12 as a *left*-hand rule for the direction of an induced current may be restated as a *right*-hand rule and used to express the relative directions of the magnetic field, the current, and the force on the current.

Once again there is a possibility of a misunderstanding, since this discussion was couched in terms of a current *in a wire* in order to make the discussion less abstract. But the wire is merely a channel for the current, and the current is a flow of charge. The *essential* thing is the motion of electric charges relative to the magnetic field, and the force which results acts on the electric charges. Since the charges are contained in the wire and can't get out, the force which tends to cause them to be accelerated at right angles to their initial velocity *appears* to act on the wire, but it does so only indirectly.

The fact that the wire plays no essential part can be demonstrated by bringing a strong magnet near the tube of a TV set, perhaps about midway of the length of the tube. You will find that the image on the screen is shifted, because each individual electron in the stream moving through the vacuum between the "electron gun" and the screen of the tube is accelerated at right angles to the axis of the tube—and also at right angles to the field of the magnet. In fact, the application of magnetic fields is one of the two possible methods of deflecting the electron stream and thus forming an image instead of having the stream fall continuously at the center of the screen. By changing ends of the magnet and moving it around the tube, you can easily verify the validity of the right-hand rule in the second paragraph above.

26-5 The Magnitude of the Force on a Moving Charge, or Current, in a Magnetic Field

It is obvious that the force arising from the interaction of a uniform magnetic field and the field surrounding the current will be greater for larger currents, and a greater length of wire in the field would experience a larger force. These relationships are included in the equation

$$F = \frac{BIL}{10} \tag{26-4}$$

in which F is the force acting on a wire, B is the flux density of the magnetic field, I the strength of the current, and L the length of the wire in the field (*if* the wire is at right angles to the field; otherwise L represents the *component* of the length *normal* to the field). F is in dynes when B is in gauss, I in amperes, and L in centimeters.

Instead of thinking of the current, let us consider the charges which are involved in the current. By definition, $I = q/t$. If the charges flow a distance L in a time interval t, by definition $v = L/t$, in which v is their velocity; so $L = vt$. Thus $IL = (q/t) \cdot vt = qv$. Hence Eq. (26-4) may be rewritten

$$F = \frac{Bqv}{10} \tag{26-5}$$

if F is in dynes, B in gauss, q in coulombs, and v in cm/sec. One coulomb is equal to $3 \cdot 10^9$ statcoulombs, which may be expressed as $c/10$, where c is the speed of light (in cm/sec); so we may rewrite Eq. (26-5) in the form

$$F = \frac{Bqv}{c} \tag{26-6}$$

in which q is in statcoulombs and the other units are as before.

Very commonly, as in the TV tube used as an example in the preceding section, we are concerned with the force on a single electron. We may symbolize any charge q as ne, n being the number of electrons which comprise the charge and e the charge on each electron. Thus Eq. (26-6) becomes

$$F = \frac{Bnev}{c} \tag{26-7}$$

Units in this equation are the same as in Eq. (26-6), the electronic charge e being equal to $4.80 \cdot 10^{-10}$ esu. For a single electron, this reduces to

$$F = \frac{Bev}{c} \tag{26-8}$$

These last equations are *not* new equations; in fact all five equations are simply different forms of the same basic equation.

26-6 The Galvanometer

The principle of a galvanometer is illustrated in Fig. 26-6. A rectangular coil is placed between the pole pieces of a permanent magnet. A cylinder of highly permeable material acts as a core to intensify the magnetic field due to any current in the coil, and it also increases the magnetic flux between the pole pieces by reducing the air gap. The coil is suspended or mounted in such a way that it is able to turn, its axis of rotation being the same as the axis of the cylinder.

Suppose that a direct current is led into the coil so that it flows down the right side, up the left, and out. Application of the right-hand rule shows that the force on the right limb of the coil will be down into the page, and the force on the left side, up out of the page; thus the coil is subjected to a torque which tends to rotate it counterclockwise as seen from the top of the coil. Alternatively, we may apply the left-hand rule for the magnetic field of a coil, finding that the north pole of the coil is on the near face, and again coming to the conclusion that the coil must experience a counterclockwise torque. If the current direction had been the reverse of what we assumed, the result would have been a torque in a clockwise direction as seen from above the coil.

In any practical galvanometer, the coil would have many turns instead of the single turn shown in Fig. 26-6. The coil may be mounted on pivots, or it may be suspended by a fine metallic fiber or ribbon. Commonly there is provision for some elastic restraint on the rotation of the coil, so that it will turn through some angle and remain there, the angle being directly proportional to the torque in accordance with Hooke's law (Sec. 11-4).

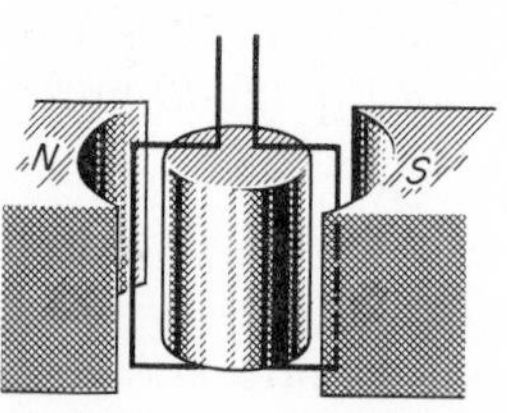

Fig. 26-6. The principle of the galvanometer.

Since the sense of the torque on the coil reverses with reversal of the current direction, it is evident that the galvanometer cannot be used for alternating currents. The same is true of other instruments employing the principle of the galvanometer.

26-7 The DC Ammeter

A galvanometer will indicate the presence of a current, and the discussion in the preceding section might indicate that we could use it to measure the strength of a current. If currents of practical magnitude were put through a galvanometer, however, they would burn out the fine wires of the coil; hence a galvanometer cannot be used as an ammeter.

We might evade this difficulty by sending only a small *part* of the current in a circuit through the galvanometer, "bypassing" nearly all the current around it. We can accomplish this by connecting between the terminals of the galvanometer a ***shunt*** which has a resistance much lower than that of the galvanometer; thus the galvanometer and the shunt constitute the two branches of a parallel circuit—branches with widely different resistances. We found in Sec. 22-8 that the magnitudes of the currents in parallel branches are inversely proportional to their respective resistances, so only a trickle of current will flow through the galvanometer and nearly all the current will go through the shunt.

If the potential difference between the terminals of the galvanometer is V, the resistance of the galvanometer R_g, that of the shunt R_s, and the respective currents I_g and I_s,

$$I_g = \frac{V}{R_g}, \quad \text{and} \quad I_s = \frac{V}{R_s}$$

Dividing the second equation into the first,

$$\frac{I_g}{I_s} = \frac{V}{R_g} \div \frac{V}{R_s} = \frac{V}{R_g} \cdot \frac{R_s}{V}, \quad \text{so} \quad \frac{I_g}{I_s} = \frac{R_s}{R_g} \tag{26-9}$$

This means that the total current I, which is the sum of I_g and I_s, will bear a definite numerical relationship to the current through the galvanometer:

$$I = kI_g \tag{26-10}$$

The value of the proportionality factor k is determined by the values of R_g and R_s, so for any specific combination of a galvanometer and a shunt k will have a definite value. This means that the galvanometer may be calibrated to read the total current I, rather than the relatively minute current I_g actually passing through it.

Thus, a ***DC ammeter*** consists of a galvanometer provided with a low-resistance shunt. The maximum current the ammeter can measure safely, which is the upper limit of its ***range,*** is determined by the relative values of the galvanometer resistance and shunt resistance. Commonly, an internal shunt is used, housed within the case of the galvanometer and

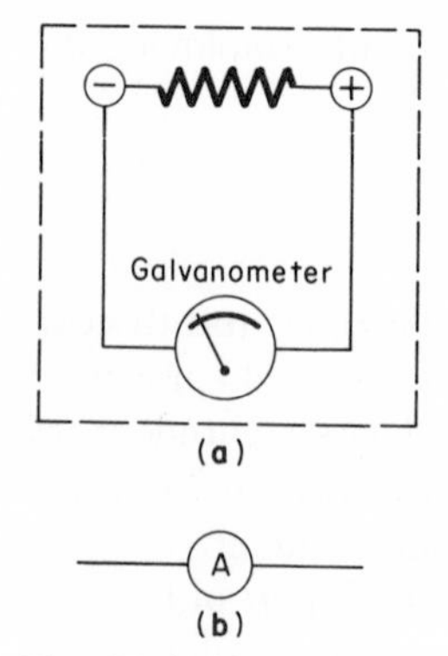

Fig. 26-7. (a) Construction of an ammeter; (b) Symbol for an ammeter.

permanently connected across the terminals of the galvanometer, as in Fig. 26-7(a). Figure 26-7(b) shows the conventional symbol for an ammeter. Often an ammeter has more than one range, which means that it has more than one shunt; the desired range is selected by the proper choice of a shunt. A range switch may be provided, or there may be a separate terminal associated with each shunt. Some ammeters use external shunts.

26-8 The DC Voltmeter

Since, according to Ohm's law, $I = V/R$, the potential drop across a given resistance is directly proportional to the current through it. Thus, we could measure the difference of voltage between two points by connecting a galvanometer between them *if* the current wouldn't ruin the galvanometer; but this limitation restricts the galvanometer to measurements in which the current is extremely small. However, we can reduce the current due to any given voltage by increasing the resistance; so we connect a high resistance in series with the galvanometer. What we learned in Sec. 22-7 is pertinent here.

Because it is a series circuit, the current through the resistor is identical with that through the galvanometer. Since $I = V/R$ and therefore $V = IR$, the voltage drops across the resistor and the galvanometer are directly proportional to their respective resistances:

$$\frac{V_r}{V_g} = \frac{R_r}{R_g} \tag{26-11}$$

in which V_r is the potential drop across the series resistor, that across the galvanometer is V_g, and the respective resistances are R_r and R_g. For a specific combination of galvanometer and series resistor, the voltage drop across the galvanometer will be a definite fraction of the total potential difference; so if the total voltage difference is V,

$$V = kV_g \tag{26-12}$$

where k is a proportionality constant determined by the relative values of R_r and R_g. Hence the galvanometer can be calibrated to read the total voltage drop V rather than the drop V_g across it alone.

Any combination of a galvanometer and a series resistor of relatively high value constitutes a ***DC voltmeter.*** As with the ammeter, the resistor commonly is internal, and there may be more than one resistor to provide different ranges. External resistors may be used.

Figure 26-8(a) represents a voltmeter with a single internal resistor, and part (b) of the figure is the conventional symbol for a voltmeter.

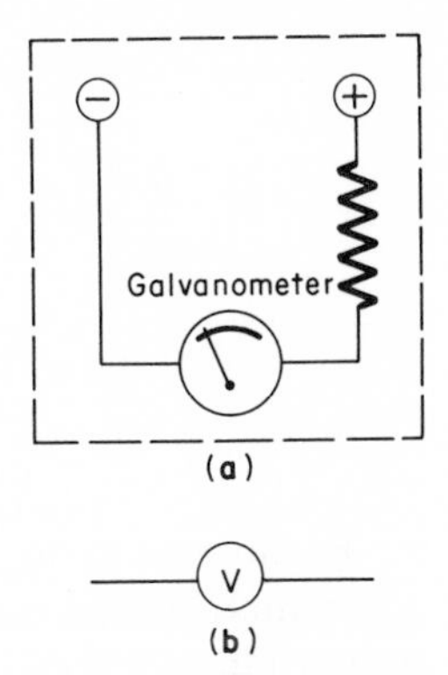

Fig. 26-8. (a) Construction of a voltmeter; (b) Symbol for a voltmeter.

26-9 AC Meters

Since the periodic reversal of current direction in AC would reverse the torque on a galvanometer coil periodically, no instrument based on a galvanometer which employs permanent magnets can be used on an AC circuit. There are three general types of AC instruments. They may use an electromagnet in place of the permanent magnet; they may employ the heating effect of a current to cause thermal expansion and use this expansion to move a pointer over a scale; or they may make use of the magnetic effect of the current to draw a soft iron vane into a coil. No new principles are involved in any of these instruments, and lack of space precludes any detailed discussion.

26-10 Proper (and Improper) Connections of Ammeters and Voltmeters

Carelessness, lack of thought, or lack of understanding has made many an ammeter a casualty in a physics laboratory. The low resistance shunt makes the resistance of an ammeter extremely low; so any considerable voltage applied to it will cause a very large current, and what *was* an ammeter will be only a smoking ruin. *An ammeter must **always** have a resistance*—the load—*in series with it,* as in Fig. 26-9(a). If it is connected in parallel with the load as in Fig. 26-9(b) it will be ruined. Even if it were not ruined, it wouldn't read the current *through* the load; to measure current through the load, the ammeter must be in *series* with the load. Of course, care must be exercised habitually to be sure that an ammeter of sufficiently high range is chosen.

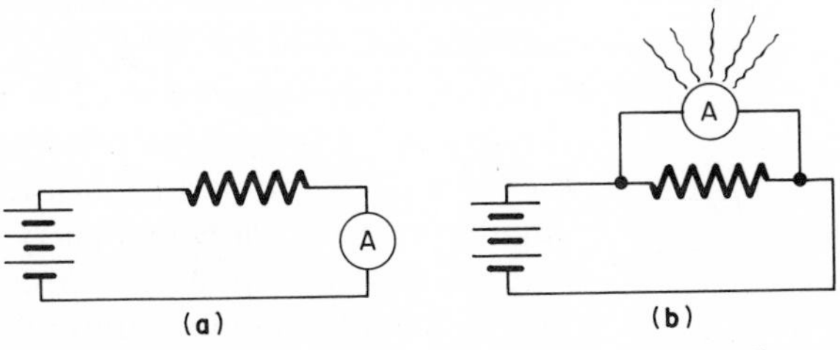

Fig. 26-9. (a) Proper connection for an ammeter; (b) An effective way to ruin an ammeter.

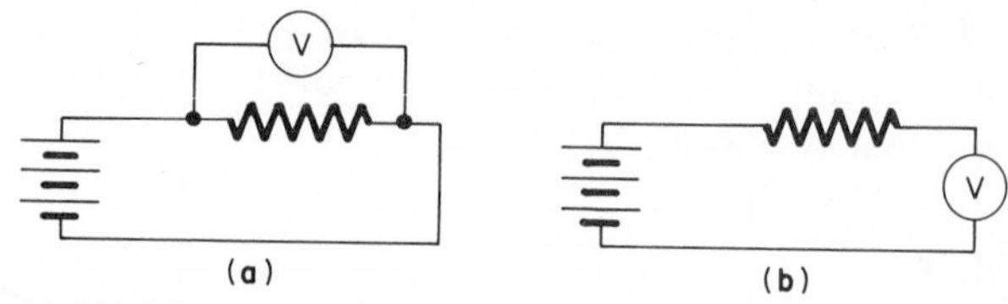

Fig. 26-10. (a) Proper connection for a voltmeter; (b) Incorrect way to connect a voltmeter.

Because of its high resistance, a voltmeter is perfectly safe on a voltage which would burn out an ammeter (provided that a voltmeter of proper range is used). The purpose of a voltmeter is to measure a voltage, such as the potential drop across a load. To do this, it must be connected across—in parallel with—the load, as in part (a) of Fig. 26-10. To connect it as you would an ammeter, in series with the load as in part (b) of the figure, would harm only the experimental results. The high resistance of the voltmeter would reduce the current through the load to a very small value, and the reading of the voltmeter would *not* be the value of the voltage drop across the load. A voltmeter should always be connected so that it is in parallel with the circuit element across which the voltage is to be measured.

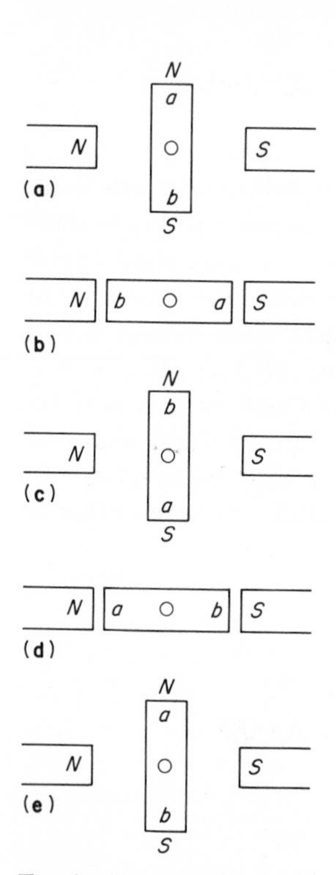

Fig. 26-11. Basic of operation of a simple electric motor.

26-11 A Simple Motor

A DC motor is a rather close relative of the galvanometer in Fig. 26-6. It consists of a coil wound on a soft iron core, mounted between the poles of a magnet in such a way that it can rotate. The field of this magnet reacts with that due to a current in the coil, producing a torque which tends to rotate the coil. When the magnetic axis of the coil is at right angles to the field of the magnet, the situation is essentially as if the coil and its core were a permanent magnet, as in Fig. 26-11(a); a torque tends to rotate it clockwise. But when it has turned through 90°, the opposite poles are as close as they can get, as in part (b) of the figure. The angular momentum would carry the rotating magnet—or coil—past this position, but the torque would become counterclockwise, opposing the motion. Thus, after a period of decreasing vibration about the position of closest approach of unlike poles, there would be no further motion. Continued rotation would be impossible. But if at the instant the rotating coil reaches this position, we reverse the current direction in the coil—exactly as we did the current *out* of the coil to make a DC generator in Sec. 26-3—we shall have *like* poles together. Its angular momentum will carry the coil past the position in Fig. 26-11(b), and the repulsion of like poles will produce a torque which is in a clockwise direction, continuing the rotation in the original direction. In part (c) of the figure, the coil has turned through 180° and both the attraction of unlike poles and the repulsion of like poles maintain the clockwise torque. At the position in part (d) of the figure, the magnetic polarity of the coil is reversed again, and the repulsion of like poles carries it on to the position in part (e), which duplicates part (a) of the figure and is the starting position for a second rotation.

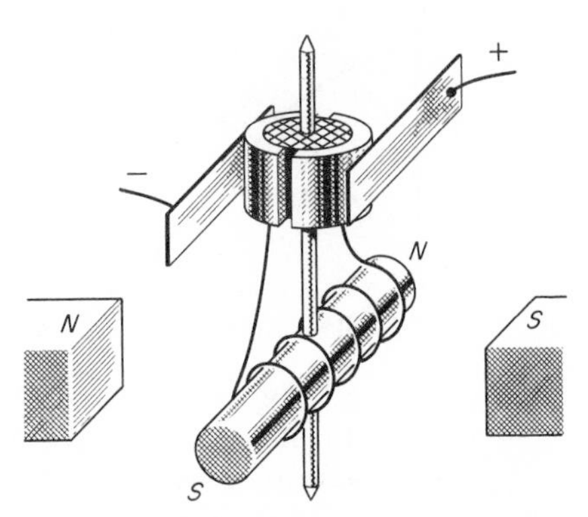

Fig. 26-12. A simple DC motor. The commutator and brushes are shown abnormally large so that their construction and arrangement may be seen more easily.

The means by which this reversal of current is achieved is diagramed in Fig. 26-12. The supports on which the brushes are mounted are not shown, nor are the bearings which support the shaft. As in a generator, the rotating coil and its core are called the ***armature.*** The motor in this diagram should be considered to be purely schematic, since a motor so designed would have a low efficiency; however, motors similar to the diagram are used for demonstration purposes.

Nearly all practical motors have electromagnets rather than permanent magnets to furnish the field within which the armature rotates.

Though we have been discussing DC motors, if the field magnets of a motor are electromagnetic it can be used on AC. Although this means that all polarities are being reversed periodically, reversal due to the alternations will occur simultaneously in the field and in the armature. Where *N* was repelling *N* before reversal, S repels S after reversal; and where *N* had been attracting S, S attracts *N*. Thus the *mutual* reactions of the armature and field are unaffected by the reversal of the current. Hence the motor will operate on AC. However, considerations of hysteresis loss in the core of the field magnet arise, which are not a factor if the motor is used on DC.

26-12 Three-phase AC

Imagine a generator similar in principle to that shown schematically in Fig. 26-2, but provided with three coils instead of one, the coils being

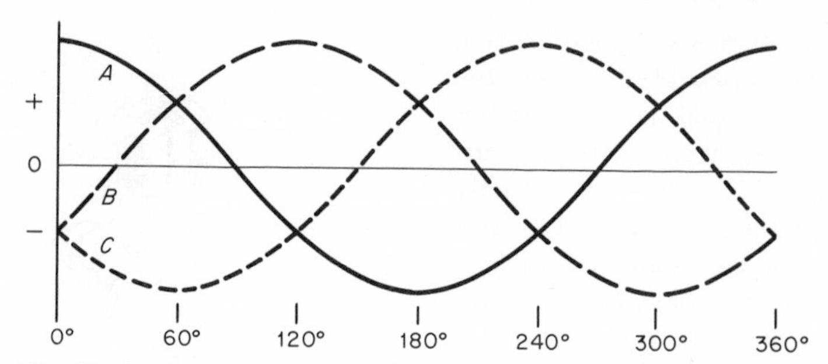

Fig. 26-13. Relative phases of voltages (and currents) produced by a three-phase AC generator.

arranged symmetrically about the axis of rotation. Each would generate a sinusoidal voltage like that in the lower part of Fig. 26-2, and the phases of these three voltages would differ by 120°. Thus the three would produce voltages as diagramed in Fig. 26-13, in which the letters *A*, *B*, and *C* identify the voltages from the separate coils.* A generator so designed is a ***three-phase generator.***

The advantages of a three-phase generator are not immediately obvious, but we can discover one of them by studying Fig. 26-13. If we fix our attention on phase A, *at every instant the algebraic sum of the values of phases* B *and* C *is numerically equal to the value of phase* A *but of opposite sign.* If we arbitrarily call the maximum value 2, at 0° phase B and phase C have values of −1 each, or −2 together; and the value of phase A is +2. At 30°, phase B has a value of zero, and those of phases A and C are equal and opposite. The value of phase B is +1 at 60° but that of phase C is −2, giving an algebraic sum of −1; and phase A has a value of +1. You can carry the check on for as many additional points as you wish; barring error, you will find no discrepancies. Furthermore, you can show in the same manner that the value of phase B is always numerically the same as the algebraic sum of the values of phases A and C but of opposite sign; and a similar relationship exists between phase C and phases A and B.

Trig

You can verify these relationships among the currents in the three phases easily and beautifully by expressing phase A as $I \cos \theta$, phase B as $I \cos (\theta + 120°)$, and phase C as $I \cos (\theta + 240°)$, then proving that

$$I \cos \theta + I \cos (\theta + 120°) + I \cos (\theta + 240°) = 0$$

* It would be *possible* to connect the brushes so that the relative phases would be 0°, 60°, and 120° rather than 0°, 120°, and 240°; but this is not desirable.

This means that *you don't need six wires to deliver the power from the three coils* in the three-phase generator. We may connect the coils as in Fig. 26-14 and *use only three wires in the transmission line;* for the current going out over the wire from coil A is the combined currents for phases B and C returning, the outgoing current on the wire from coil B is the combined return currents of phases A and C, and the current going out on the wire from coil C constitutes the combined return currents of phases A and B.

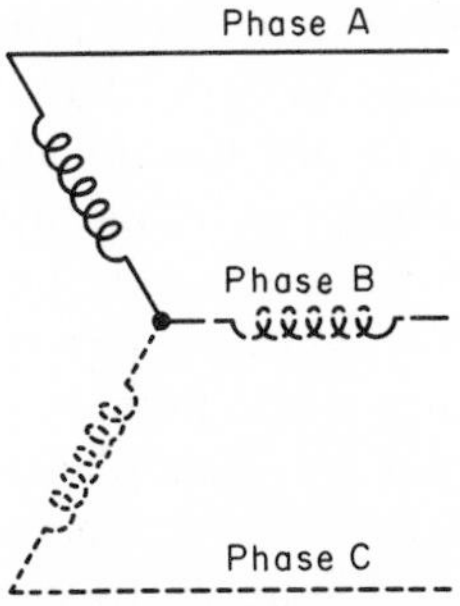

Fig. 26-14. One way of connecting the armature coils in a three-phase AC generator.

26-13 The Three-phase Induction Motor

Delivery of current to the rotating armature of a motor, such as those discussed in Sec. 26-11, requires that it be fed in and out through brushes rubbing against a rotating commutator. This may cause difficulty when motors of relatively large power are needed. The three-phase induction motor is the most common answer to this problem. There are no brushes and no commutator, and not even any windings—in the ordinary sense—in the armature. The windings may be a cast "squirrel cage" of aluminum or copper, with a soft iron core, and the current in the armature is induced by the rotation of the magnetic field.

How can the magnetic field of stationary coils be made to rotate?! Actually, the principle is very simple; the discussion of the principle is more complex than the principle itself.

Figure 26-13 and the series of diagrams in Fig. 26-15 constitute the basis of the discussion. The designations of angle in Fig. 26-15 correspond

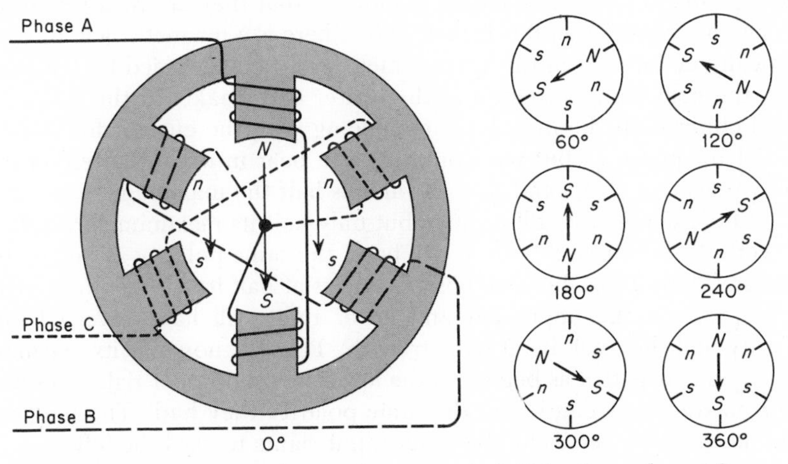

Fig. 26-15. Creation of a rotating magnetic field by three-phase AC.

to those in the earlier figure, and the coding of the different phases is the same in both. The diagram for 0° in Fig. 26-15 shows the way the various coils are wound and connected. Obviously the wires are tucked down along the frame rather than crossing from coil to coil directly, as shown, for the armature must occupy this space; but they're a *little* easier to follow when they're redrawn directly across. All three wires are connected at a single point marked with a heavy dot; they are *not* in electrical contact at other places where the lines cross. Details of wiring are shown only in the 0° diagram in Fig. 26-15.

Figure 26-13 shows that at 0° phase A has its maximum positive value. Let's follow the wire carrying this phase into the 0° diagram in Fig. 26-15. It enters the top coil, goes around it in such a direction that, applying the appropriate left-hand rule, we find the inner end of the coil to be a north pole. Going across to the bottom coil, it makes the inner end of that coil a south pole. Both of these poles are at maximum strength, since the current in them is at a maximum. Leaving the bottom coil, the current flows to the junction with the other two wires; here it splits, half going out over the wire for phase B and half over that for phase C. A glance at Fig. 26-13 shows that at 0° both these phases are negative, so the currents for them should be going out of the motor rather than in. It also shows that each is half the strength of the current in phase A. All this is in accord with what we have deduced by following phase A to the junction.

The current for phase B will leave the junction and flow through the upper left coil, and application of the rule shows that the inner end of this coil will be *N*. The current then goes through the coil at the lower right, making the inner end of that coil S. Following the current out on the phase C wire in the same manner, we find that the inner end of the upper right coil is *N* and that of the lower left coil is S. Thus the polarities of the various coils are as marked, the designations on the coils fed by phases B and C being in lower-case letters to indicate that they are relatively weak.

The net result of all this is that, at 0°, there is a magnetic field directed vertically downward in the space which would be occupied by the armature, the field being strongest at the center and weaker at the sides. We could confirm our findings by commencing with the current for phase B or that for phase C, but we would have to bear in mind that either current is negative at 0°, and that its value is half the maximum.

At 60°, phase A is still positive but only half its maximum strength, so the coils at the top and bottom will be of the same polarity as before, but weaker. Phase B has become positive and is at half its maximum strength, so the coils at the upper left and lower right will have reversed their polarity and they will be at half strength. Phase C now has its maximum value and is negative as before, so the lower left and upper right coils have their maximum strength and the same polarity they had. The magnetic field no longer is vertically downward, but slants toward the left.

At 120°, phase A has changed from positive to negative and is at half strength; phase B has its maximum positive value; and phase C is still negative but weaker. The result is shown in the diagram for 120°. Continuation of the analysis yields the results shown in the other diagrams in Fig. 26-15. During the cycle, the magnetic field makes one complete rotation in a clockwise direction.

Now suppose that we mount a "squirrel cage" armature on a shaft between the poles. The "windings" would be somewhat as indicated in Fig. 26-16, and they would be associated with a soft iron core which is not shown. At 0° (Fig. 26-15) the rotation of the magnetic field would induce currents toward the far end of the upper bars and toward the near ends of the lower bars. These would flow down through the far end portion of the "squirrel cage" and up through the near portion, and the magnetic effect of these currents would make the right side of the armature a north pole and the left side a south pole. Comparison of this fact with the 0° situation shown in Fig. 26-15 shows that the magnetic field of the armature will interact with that of the coils to produce a clockwise torque on the armature. Analysis for the other situations in Fig. 26-15 would show that this effect persists; there is always a clockwise torque on the armature. And this is exactly what Lenz's law requires; since the rotation of a magnetic field causes induced currents which result in a torque on the armature, the direction of the torque should be such as to oppose the angular advance of the rotating field—that is, the conductors in which the currents are induced should tend to retreat from the advancing field.

We saw in Sec. 25-4 that the power input to the primary of a transformer is controlled automatically by the power used in the secondary circuit. In like manner, and for very similar reasons, the power used by the motor is governed by the power required by the load. Very little power is used when the motor is running without a load. This automatic adjustment of electric power to mechanical power output is characteristic of electric motors in general.

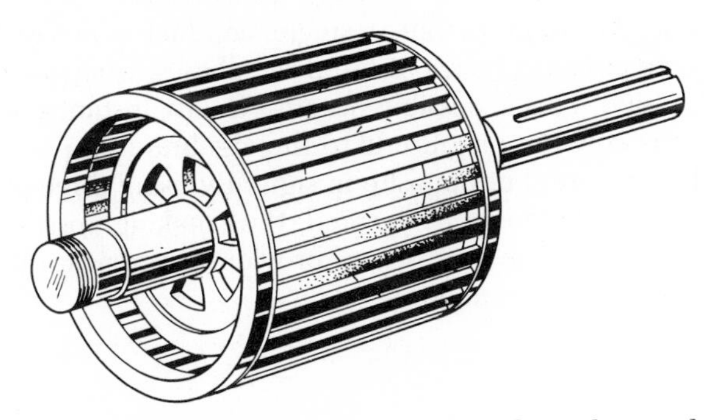

Fig. 26-16. "Squirrel cage" armature for a three-phase induction motor.

There are ways in which an induction motor can be designed to run on a single-phase power supply, instead of three-phase. Such motors are usually of relatively low power, however, and the three-phase induction motor is the standard motor wherever relatively high power is required and three-phase current is available.

Summary

An AC *generator* consists essentially of a *coil rotating* in a *magnetic field,* each end of the coil being connected to a separate slip ring, and the current being taken off the slip rings by brushes. If the slip rings are replaced by a commutator, the current in the external circuit will be DC but not steady.

Any *electric charge moving* in a *magnetic field* is subjected to a *force* which is determined by the *magnitude* of the *charge,* its *velocity normal* to the field, and the *strength* of the *field.* The *force* is *perpendicular* to the *velocity* and to the *field.* If the charges are flowing in a conductor, the force acts, indirectly, on the conductor.

The force of a magnetic field on a moving charge is employed to create a *torque* on a *coil* placed between the poles of a magnet when any current flows in the coil; such an arrangement is a *galvanometer.* A DC ammeter is a galvanometer provided with a low-resistance shunt to bypass nearly all the current, and calibrated to read total current. A DC voltmeter is a combination of a galvanometer and a high resistance in series, calibrated to read the voltage drop across the galvanometer *and* the resistance. An *ammeter must always* be connected in *series* with the load; a *voltmeter* is connected in *parallel* with the load.

A simple electric motor operates on the basis of the *force* acting on an *electric current* in a *magnetic field,* the current being led to the armature through brushes and a commutator which reverses the magnetic polarity of the armature periodically by reversing the current.

Three-phase AC requires but a single conductor for each phase to make a complete circuit for each of the three phases, whereas six would be required ordinarily. This is possible because at any instant the current on any one phase is equal in magnitude to the algebraic sum of the currents in the other two phases, but opposite in sign. By using three-phase power, a rotating magnetic field can be created, thus making possible induction motors which eliminate the necessity of providing current for the armature through brushes and a commutator.

Self-Quiz

1. Define each of the following terms, and compare and contrast any comparable terms: slip rings, brush, commutator, armature, field, AC generator, DC generator,

magneto, dynamo, induced current, induced voltage, motor, induction motor, phase, single-phase, three-phase, galvanometer, voltmeter, ammeter, shunt, series, parallel.

2. Review the conditions under which a voltage may be induced in a wire, the relative directions of pertinent quantities, and energy considerations relative to induced currents.

3. Thus far we have met three different left-hand rules and one right-hand rule. State each one and specify what it is used for.

4. Sometimes the term "motor rule" is applied to one of the "hand" rules, and another is called the "generator rule." State these, compare and contrast them, *and account for* their similarities and differences.

5. With the aid of a series of rough diagrams show that when a coil is rotated in a magnetic field the induced voltage must be AC. Show how this coil can be made to supply AC to an external circuit, and how it can be made to supply DC to the external circuit. In each case, clearly explain *why* the voltage in the external circuit is of the type specified.

6. What would happen, and why, if a coil such as that in Fig. 26-2 were rotated while its axis was parallel with the magnetic field?

7. Show that the phenomenon of induced currents necessarily requires that a force must act on any electric charge which is moving across a magnetic field.

8. There is a common statement that whenever an electric motor is "running" it is acting as a generator. Discuss the validity of this statement, making use of the principle of energy conservation.

9. As the load on a three-phase induction motor is increased, its angular velocity decreases slightly, causing the rotating field to sweep more rapidly over the bars of the "squirrel cage" armature; and as the load is decreased, the armature speeds up, decreasing the relative motion between the field and the bars. Combine these facts with your discussion for the previous question to show that the current to the motor is controlled automatically by the load—much as the energy used in the primary of a transformer is controlled by the load in the secondary circuit.

10. Derive Eq. (26-4) from Eq. (26-5).

11. If there is a *force* on a current in a magnetic field, why is the discussion of the galvanometer and electric motors in terms of *torque*? What is the difference, if any, between force and torque?

12. In the derivation of Eq. (26-9) the two V's were canceled out. This implies that their values must be identical. *Why* are they identical?

13. In an ammeter the resistance of the shunt may be much less than one-millionth of that of the galvanometer. Why doesn't this extremely low resistance cause *all* the current to go through the shunt?

14. If the deflection of a galvanometer is determined by the *current* through it, how can any instrument based on a galvanometer measure *voltage*?

15. Why is a commutator necessary in a simple electric motor? With the aid of a series of rough diagrams explain the operation of a motor through one full revolution.

16. If the current through a practical DC motor is reversed, will the direction of rotation reverse? Explain.

17. When a motor is used on AC, why doesn't the direction of the torque on the armature reverse with each reversal of current direction? Do you wish to reconsider your answer to Question 16?

18. Discuss, *with reasons*, the proper method of connecting an ammeter in a circuit. Repeat for a voltmeter.

19. State two practical advantages of three-phase AC over single-phase AC.

20. Discuss any practical advantages AC may have over DC, or vice versa, from the standpoints of generation, transmission, and use.

21. Make a graph of the voltages over one complete cycle of three-phase AC.

22. Copy the large diagram in Fig. 26-15 but interchange phases B and C. What change, if any, would result in the magnetic field at 0°? Continue the analysis for each 60° through a complete cycle, referring to Fig. 26-13 for the necessary information on the currents. What is your final conclusion?

Problems

1. A circular coil has 40 turns and a diameter of 2.40 cm. It is located in a magnetic field with a flux density of $1.5 \cdot 10^4$ gauss, the plane of the coil being normal to the field. If the coil is jerked out of the field in 0.125 sec, what average voltage will be induced in the coil?

2. A coil of 5 turns is in the form of a square loop 8.00 cm on each side. If its axis of rotation is normal to a field of $1.20 \cdot 10^4$ gauss, and the coil is rotated exactly once each second, compute the maximum and the effective values of the induced voltage (a) if the axis of rotation is midway between two sides, and (b) if the axis of rotation coincides with one side of the coil.

3. A rectangular coil of wire is 12.0 cm wide and 15.0 cm long, and contains 4 turns. It is rotated 360 times a minute in a field of $2.20 \cdot 10^3$ gauss, the axis of rotation being normal to the field. Calculate the instantaneous value of the voltage (a) when the plane of the coil is parallel with the field, (b) when it is at 60° to the field, and (c) when it is at 90° to the field. (d) Also calculate the effective voltage.

4. If the coil in Problem 3 forms a closed circuit with a resistance of 2.50 ohms, compute (a) the effective current and (b) the quantity of heat produced in the coil per minute.

5. A generator armature has a coil of 200 turns. If the effective voltage generated when the armature is turning at 1200 rpm is 120 v, (a) calculate the total flux (assume that the entire flux of the field passes through the coil). (b) If the

poles of the field have faces with an area of 40.0 cm^2 each, determine the flux density of each face.

6. A 12.0 cm length of a wire which carries a current of 2.00 amp lies in a uniform magnetic field, the field direction being normal to the wire. The force on the wire is 1500 dynes. Determine the flux density.

7. Two wires are arranged so that 50.0 cm segments of each lie alongside each other, parallel and 2.50 cm apart. If each carries a current of 0.800 amp, compute the force between them.

8. A magnetic field of 600 gauss exerts a force of 200 dynes on an electron which is moving at right angles to the field. Calculate the speed of the electron.

9. An electron has a velocity of 1.50 cm/sec in a direction at right angles to a magnetic field of 2.50 gauss. Compute the lateral acceleration of the electron. The mass of the electron is $9.11 \cdot 10^{-28}$ g.

10. If an electric field is applied, and it is just sufficient to prevent any lateral force on the electron in Problem 9, calculate the electric field intensity. If the electron velocity is horizontally to your right and the magnetic field is horizontal and directly away from you, what is the direction of the electric field?

11. A current of $5.00 \cdot 10^{-5}$ amp in the coil of a galvanometer which has a resistance of 20.0 ohms causes the needle of the galvanometer to move to the upper limit of the scale. Compute the resistance of the shunt which should be used to convert this galvanometer to (a) a microammeter with a range of 0–500 μa, (b) a milliammeter with a range of 0–200 ma, and (c) an ammeter with a range of 0–10.0 amp.

12. The galvanometer of Problem 11 is to be employed to construct a voltmeter instead of an ammeter. Calculate the value of the resistance to be employed if the range of the voltmeter is to be (a) 0–200 mv, (b) 0–1.00 v, and (c) 0–150 v.

13. A 220 v motor has an efficiency of 96.0% and delivers 5.00 hp. Compute the value of the current (1 hp = 746 w).

14. A 220 v motor with an efficiency of 95.0% requires a current of 2.30 amp to rotate a load with an angular velocity of 200 rad/sec. Calculate in meter newtons the torque applied to the load.

15. A hoist driven by an electric motor lifts a 500 lb load 12.0 ft in 25.0 sec. If the over-all efficiency is 60.0% and the voltage is 120 v, calculate the current.

16. Prove that in Eq. (26-10) the value of k is $(R_s + R_g)/R_s$ (the symbols having the meanings specified in Sec. 26-7) and use this relation to solve Problem 11.

17. Prove that in Eq. (26-12) the value of k is $(R_r + R_g)/R_g$ (the symbols having the same significance as in Sec. 26-8) and rework Problem 12 on the basis of this relationship.

27
LIGHT

27-1 Preview

We shall review briefly the different ideas of the nature of light which have been proposed in the last few centuries, and meet the present concept of its nature. Next we shall consider the earliest recorded attempt to measure the speed of light and compare it with a much more recent and successful method. The history of theories of the nature of light, and of attempts to measure how fast it travels, will give us a new outlook on the nature of science and how it advances. It will develop that the value of the speed of light has an importance which is suprisingly broad. We shall then consider the relationship between color and wavelength of frequency, the concepts of spectral and non-spectral colors, and the additive and subtractive processes of color production. Finally, we shall have evidence that science is still changing—an amazing development which will force us to modify our concept of how the eye "sees" color.

27-2 The Physical Nature of Light

A complete report on the history of the various theories of the nature of light, and a thorough discussion of the present concept, would fill several volumes. This chapter offers only a brief outline of the historical aspect, followed by an introduction to the present concept. We shall return frequently to various aspects of the modern concept of light, in later chapters.

The inquiring mind of man has been intrigued by this most familiar and useful physical phenomenon for centuries, and two diametrically opposed—apparently!—ideas emerged. One regarded light as a wave motion analogous to the wave motions we have met previously; the other concept held that it is a rain of particles or corpuscles of energy. According to the ***wave theory,*** you can see this page because it is being washed by light waves somewhat as a beach is washed by ocean waves or your ear is "washed" by sound waves. According to the ***corpuscular theory,*** the page is being illuminated in somewhat the same way a shower wets a pavement.

In relatively modern times, the strongest advocate of the corpuscular concept was our friend Sir Isaac Newton. Somewhat as the prestige of the ancient Greeks resulted in an authoritarian point of view and interfered with the advance of scientific knowledge during the Middle Ages, Newton's eminence lent an aura to the corpuscular concept of light; but minds were much more free than they had been a very few centuries earlier, and the wave theory was by no means dead.

In general, a beam of light is bent as it passes from one medium into another (Sec. 28-8), and any such phenomenon furnishes a potential means of testing the validity of a concept or theory; but this particular contest between the wave and particle concepts ended in a draw. Newton was able to account for the bending on the basis of an assumed force, analogous to those responsible for surface tension (Sec. 10-18), which accelerates the corpuscles of light as they enter a more dense medium and decelerates them as they leave. Huygens* was able to account for the same phenomenon on the basis of the wave theory by assuming that the waves travel more slowly in denser media. Thus neither theory was invalidated. The ground was laid for another test, since Newton's explanation of the bending of light required that its speed be greater in dense media than in less dense media, whereas Huygens' explanation required the exact reverse to be true. However, it was some two centuries later that Foucalt made the first experimental measurements and thereby validated the wave concept of the nature of light. We shall see, though, that the concept of light as a particulate phenomenon did not die.

---

* Pronounced High′-genz or Hoi′-gens.

Meantime, two other investigators, Young and Fresnel, found incontrovertible evidence that light must have a wave character. We found in Sec. 14-12 that when two trains of sound waves meet they may strengthen or weaken each other, depending on their relative phases. We called this phenomenon "interference"—constructive interference when the two trains aid each other and destructive interference when the reverse is true. Interference is a characteristic property of wave motion; given appropriate conditions, interference may be observed with wave motion of any kind whatever, but it *never* occurs except in connection with wave motion. And both Young and Fresnel were able to demonstrate interference between two rays or beams of light. We shall see something of how this is done in Sec. 28-12 and 28-13.

The researches of Young and Fresnel, together with the later work of Foucalt (which showed that as light passes from air, or a vacuum, into a relatively dense medium its speed is *de*creased) combined to put the wave theory on a fairly sound foundation. Then, in 1864, Maxwell published a mathematical description of light based on the concept that it is a wave phenomenon which is electromagnetic in nature. It was in complete accord with all experimental data, but it went beyond mere agreement with existing knowledge; Maxwell found that his equations predicted waves similar to visible light but of much greater wavelength, and no such waves had ever been observed. Spurred by this prediction, however, attempts were made to discover these waves, and in 1881 Hertz succeeded.

Hertz used a resonant circuit (Sec. 25-11) with a source of AC energy. Nearby he placed a similar circuit, resonant at the same frequency but containing no source of energy; and in this second circuit, he had a narrow spark gap. He found that pulses of energy in the first circuit could cause a spark to jump the gap in the second circuit. Energy in the form of electromagnetic waves was being sent out from one circuit and received by the other. Here were the world's first radio transmitter and receiver! Hertz was able to demonstrate interference of the waves, and to use this interference to measure their wavelength. Thus was the final nail driven into the coffin lid of the corpuscular theory. (Or so it was thought!)

Hertz was a careful scientist, however, and he investigated the effect of inserting sheets of various materials between his "transmitter" and his "receiver." In the course of this, he noticed that the response of the "receiver" was reduced markedly by any obstruction, no matter what the material or how small its area, which shaded the spark gap of the "receiver" from the light emitted by the spark in the "transmitter" circuit. He could not account for this, but he recorded it; and it later proved to be the first recorded observation of the photoelectric effect. And it developed that the photoelectric effect could *not* be explained on the basis of the wave theory of light! Instead, Einstein, in 1905, stated a beautiful explanation of the photoelectric effect on the basis of a resurrected and refurbished version of the *corpuscular* theory.

Thus, *the very experiment which seemingly had removed the last shred of doubt concerning the wave theory simultaneously revealed a previously unknown phenomenon incompatible with that theory; and whereas it had been thought that the experiment had consigned the corpuscular concept to eternal oblivion, it actually caused the resurrection of that point of view.* What supreme irony!

27-3 The Quantum Concept

The "corpuscles" on which Einstein based his explanation of the photoelectric effect are much less nebulous than those in Newton's theory of light. In Sec. 19-12, we saw that Planck had found it necessary to assume that energy is emitted and absorbed in definite and discrete amounts, in order to develop a mathematical description of the way energy radiated from a hot body is distributed among the various wavelengths. In general, the quantity of energy in a given bundle or packet—in a particular "corpuscle," to use Newton's term—is different than the quantity in other packets. Since the Latin word for "how much" is *quantum,* Planck called an individual packet of energy a quantum of energy, or simply a ***quantum.*** (The plural is ***quanta.***)

Though Planck was forced to adopt a quantized mechanism of emission and absorption of radiant energy, he considered that the transmission of energy was due to continuous and unquantized waves. Einstein extended the idea of quantization of energy to the transmission of radiant energy as well as its emission and absorption.

Thus, in Einstein's view, light is a rain of particles called quanta, rather than a wave phenomenon. Yet we have seen ample evidence that it *is* a wave phenomenon. Furthermore, Einstein made use of the relation stated by Planck,

$$W = h\nu \tag{27-1}$$

in which W is the energy of a single quantum of light, h is a constant known as Planck's constant, and ν is the frequency of the light; but *frequency,* being the speed of light divided by the *wave*length, has no meaning except in connection with a wave phenomenon! Thus we find the new version of a particulate concept of light to be inextricably entwined with the wave concept. Mutually exclusive as the ideas seem, light is at once a particulate phenomenon and a wave phenomenon. The concept of quantization is much broader than this, however; just as all matter is "granular" rather than continuous, since it is composed of atoms, all energy is "granular" rather than continuous, since it is composed of quanta. It is only the minute energy value of an individual quantum that prevents this quantization of energy from being obvious, just as the minuteness of the atom obscures the granular nature of matter.

We shall discover other strange and perhaps disturbing characteristics of light quanta as we proceed.

In Eq. (27-1) the unit of the frequency is 1/sec. For energy in ergs, Planck's constant is $6.63 \cdot 10^{-27}$ erg sec, or for energy in joules Planck's constant is $6.63 \cdot 10^{-34}$ joule sec.

The term quantum has largely superceded the terms "particle" and "corpuscle." Quantum, however, is a general term; there may be a quantum of light energy or a quantum of vibrational energy or a quantum of angular momentum, etc. The specific term for a quantum *of light* of any frequency or wavelength in the entire electromagnetic spectrum is ***photon.***

We shall investigate these photons further in later chapters.

27-4 The Determination of the Speed of Light

Here, also, there is a long and fascinating history, but space limits us to only two "laboratory" methods and two astronomical methods. First, however, let us pause and consider the difficulty of the problem. The speed of light is about 186,000 *miles* a *second;* if a beam of light could be bent to follow the earth's equator, it would go almost seven and a half times around the earth in one second! How would you go about measuring such a speed?!

Galileo made the earliest recorded attempt. He ascended one of the fabled hills of Rome with a lantern, and an assistant, with a lantern, climbed another hill a known distance away. Both lanterns were to be covered; then suddenly Galileo was to uncover his. The instant the assistant on a distant hill saw the gleam of Galileo's lantern he was to uncover his own lantern. Galileo was to note the lapse of time between the uncovering of his own lantern and his first glimpse of his assistant's lantern. Obviously (*to us,* knowing the speed of light) this method was foredoomed to dismal failure.

But let's examine the *principle* of the method. A signal of light was to be sent over a path of a known length, returned over the same path, and the time required for the round trip noted. And Galileo was not so naïve as it may appear, for he realized that human reaction time would be involved, and he planned to minimize this by carrying out the experiment using different combinations of hilltops. In a specific case, the time observed would be the sum of an interval required for transit, which would depend on the distance, and an interval due to reaction time, which should be essentially the same whatever the distance; thus the reaction time could be determined and eliminated. For example, the data might, if plotted, appear like the small circles and solid line in Fig. 27-1. The reaction time would be given by the distance *ab,* and subtraction of this value from each of the observed times would give the relationship between distance and actual transit time as shown by the dashed line.

Thus, the *principle* is entirely valid. The only trouble is that the error which had to be eliminated was tremendously greater than the value which was to be measured.

Jumping over many intervening and highly ingenious methods which gave meaningful and increasingly accurate values, we come to Michelson's method. *This is identical, in principle, with Galileo's method,* though one was a complete failure and the other was highly precise. Michelson also used two mountain tops—Mt. Wilson and Mt. San Antonio. A special survey established the distance accurately.

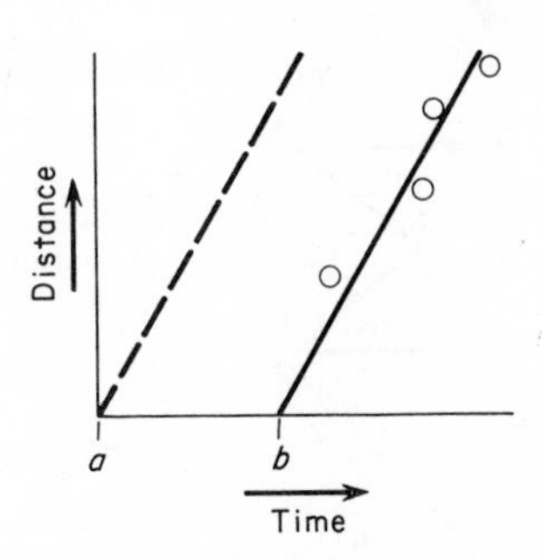

Fig. 27-1. The type of data Galileo hoped to obtain, and the method by which human reaction time was to be eliminated.

On Mt. Wilson, Michelson sent a powerful beam of light against an array of eight plane mirrors mounted so that, seen from above, their edges formed a regular octagon. This array formed an eight-sided mirror, and it was mounted so that it could be rotated about a vertical axis. This is shown (minus many essential accessories and refinements) in Fig. 27-2. As this octagonal mirror rotated, light was reflected, first from one face and then from the next. As shown in the figure, the direction of the reflected beam changes as the orientation of the mirror face with respect to the incoming light beam changes; so that the reflected beam is caused to sweep clockwise (as this diagram is set up) much as the rotating beam of a lighthouse or airway beacon does. At one precise position of a face, the beam will be directed exactly toward Mt. San Antonio. Thus, as the mirror rotates, at one very precise *instant* a face will send a light signal in the desired direction; the tiniest instant earlier or later the beam is directed too far to the left or right. Exactly one-eighth of a revolution later the adjacent face will have moved into the proper position and will send a second signal. Thus eight signals are sent out to Mt. San Antonio each revolution, automatically timed by the rotation of the mirror.

For an "assistant" on Mt. San Antonio, Michelson used a combination

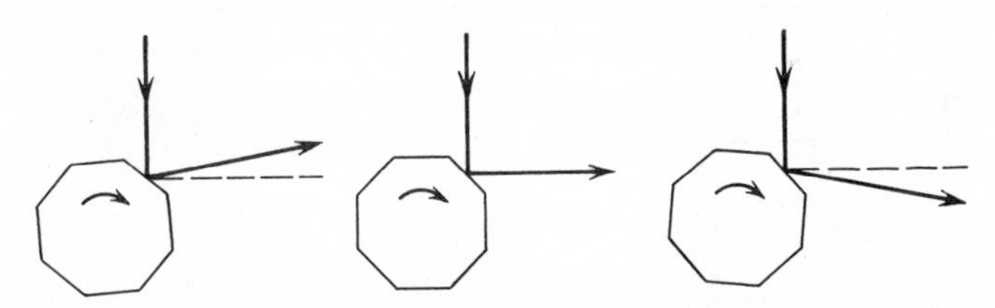

Fig. 27-2. Michelson's method of sending intermittent light signals to Mt. San Antonio. As the octagonal mirror rotates clockwise the reflected beam sweeps past Mt. San Antonio, which is in the direction of the dashed line.

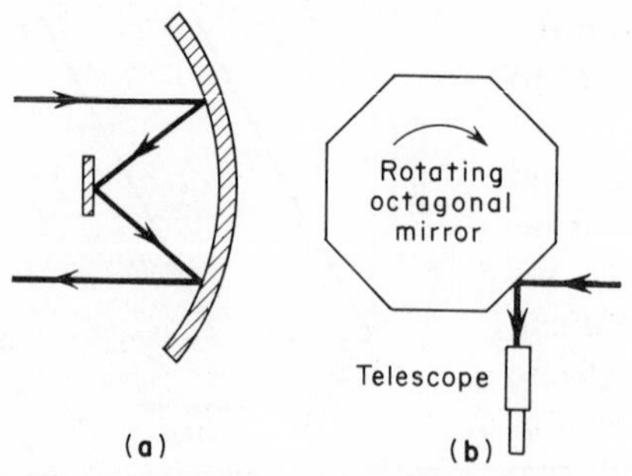

Fig. 27-3. (a) Mirror arrangement on Mt. San Antonio (schematic); (b) Reflection of returning signal into telescope.

of mirrors somewhat as in Fig. 27-3(a), to return the signal to Mt. Wilson. The returning signal would strike a face of the rotating mirror, and *if* at that instant the mirror was properly oriented it would be reflected into a telescope as in Fig. 27-3(b). The whole experimental setup is indicated schematically in Fig. 27-4.

Preliminary adjustments were made with the octagonal mirror not spinning. It was carefully oriented so that the light beam was reflected to Mt. San Antonio and back, and the telescope was positioned so that the returning beam fell on a cross hair in the telescope field. Then the mirror was started spinning. This caused the beam to disappear from the telescope, because if the outgoing signal was reflected from face *a* (Fig. 27-4), it wouldn't complete the round trip until face *c* had turned far enough so that the beam would be reflected to the left of the telescope. But the rate of rotation was increased steadily, until the mirror was making just one-eighth of a revolution while the light signal made the round trip. This meant that after the signal was sent out from face *a* the mirror moved so that face *b* occupied the position where face *c* had been when the signal was sent out. That is, the signal was sent out from face *a* and, on returning, it was reflected into the telescope by face *b;* at this instant, another signal went out from face *h* and on its return it was reflected from face *a* into the telescope, etc. Final adjustment of the rate of rotation made the

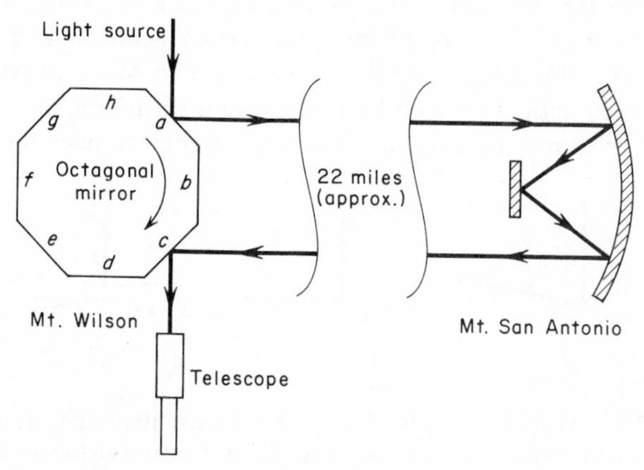

Fig. 27-4. Schematic representation of apparatus for Michelson's method of measuring the speed of light.

image of the returning beam coincide with the cross hair in the telescope. Thus the time required for exactly one-eighth of a rotation of the mirror was made equal to the time necessary for one round trip of the light. To evaluate the time of one-eighth of a revolution, the revolutions of the mirror were compared by a stroboscopic method with the vibrations of an electrically maintained tuning fork. The round trip distance was roughly 44 miles, and the mirror made roughly 530 revolutions per sec (see Problem 5).

The value Michelson obtained by this method was in error by only a few thousandths of 1%—quite a different result from Galileo's attempt. Comparison of the two shows that the vast improvement was due to refinement of a basically valid method by eliminating the factor of human reaction time and minimizing even the influence of human judgment.

Meantime, two independent astronomical methods had yielded reasonable values of the speed of light. The earlier measurement—the first successful one by any method—was made by Roemer in 1675. Astronomical observations of the moons of Jupiter showed that, like our moon, they were eclipsed periodically. But the eclipses weren't *exactly* periodic; when Jupiter and the earth were in the relative positions shown in Fig. 27-5(a), the eclipses came a few minutes earlier than one would expect from their *average* periodicity, but they were late when the two planets were in the relative positions shown in part (b) of the figure. Roemer deduced that these deviations were due to the time required for light to cross the earth's orbit, and on this basis he found the speed of light to be about $1.4 \cdot 10^5$ miles per second. In terms of modern data, to three significant figures, the eclipses occur as much as 4 min and 18 sec ahead of, or behind, the average; so light takes 8 min 36 sec to cross the earth's orbit, which is $9.29 \cdot 10^7$ miles. These data give (to three significant figures) $1.87 \cdot 10^7$ miles/sec. Thus Roemer's value was about 25% low (which isn't bad at all for the *first* measurement, three centuries ago).

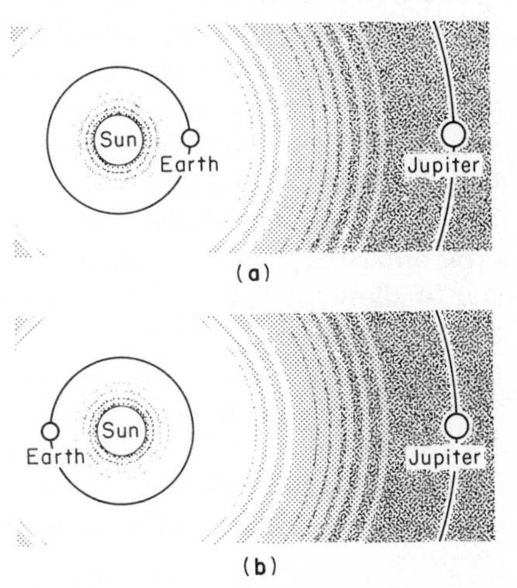

Fig. 27-5. Basis of Roemer's method of determining the speed of light (*not* drawn to scale).

Another astronomical method was due to Bradley. You observe the basis of his method whenever you drive in the rain, with a window rolled up. Even if the rain is falling vertically, the streaks it makes on the window are slanted because of the motion of the car. If you were to hold a piece of stove-

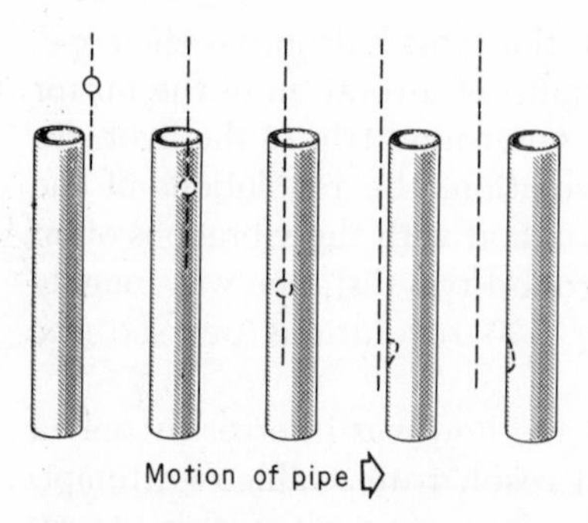

Fig. 27-6. If a pipe is held in a vertical position and moved horizontally, vertically falling raindrops cannot pass through it. The line of fall of the drops, shown by the dashed lines, remains fixed in space as the pipe moves to the right.

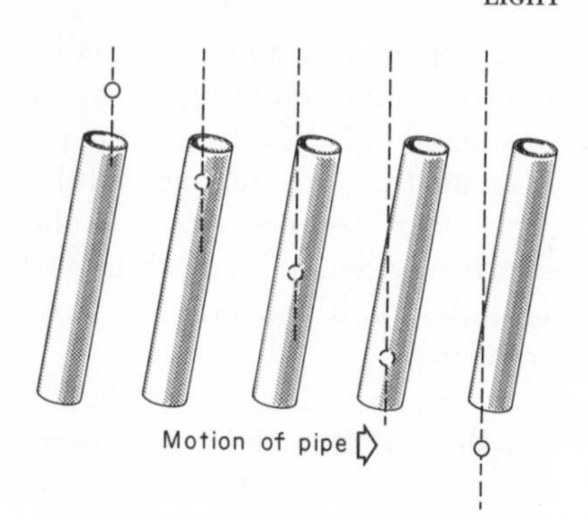

Fig. 27-7. If the pipe in Fig. 27-6 is tilted forward the vertically falling drops can pass through it. The angle of tilt is determined by the ratio of the velocity of fall to the horizontal velocity of the pipe.

pipe out of the window of the moving car, in a vertical position, vertically falling raindrops couldn't pass through; the drops would be intercepted by the advancing interior wall of the pipe as indicated for a single drop in a series of diagrams in Fig. 27-6. To allow the drops to fall through, the pipe must be tilted forward as in Fig. 27-7. For a given speed of the car and a given rate of fall of the drops, there is one definite orientation of the pipe which would allow the raindrops to fall cleanly through the pipe; hence by reading the speedometer and noting the angle of inclination of the pipe you could determine the vertical velocity of the raindrops.

Bradley did essentially the same thing. Astronomical observations had shown that though a distant star appears to remain in approximately the same place, it seems to shift its position very slightly, the shift during one half of our year being the opposite of the shift the remainder of the year. The star doesn't actually shift, but because of the earth's motion in its orbit an astronomer must point his telescope a bit off the direct line to the star to allow the light to "fall" through the telescope just as you had to tilt that pipe off the vertical to let the rain fall through. The deviation of the telescope from the true line to the star is at a maximum when the earth's velocity is perpendicular to the direction of the star, as in Fig. 27-8. Measurement of this angle, and knowledge of the earth's orbital speed (which is the circumference of its orbit divided by the time for it to make a circuit of the orbit), will yield the value of the speed of light.

27-5 The Nature, and the Progress, of Science

The topic of light constitutes a wonderful basis for orientation to physical science. The history of the various theories of the nature of light illustrates the way ideas develop and are compared and tested, how they often have to be modified, sometimes rather suddenly and drastically, and how sometimes the modifications seem to complicate matters rather than to simplify them. This history also shows that "useless" research—such as a search for waves predicted by a theory, for no reason except to test the theory—may have tremendous "practical" consequences.

At the same time, the history of the attempts to measure the speed of light is an inspiring and fascinating story. The diversity of effective methods developed to attack an apparently impossible problem is nothing short of amazing. The same is true of the improvement of instrumentation which—in the case of Galileo and Michelson, many others during the intervening centuries, and still others after Michelson—changed an utterly useless method into one capable of at least six-digit accuracy.

You may find it interesting to reread this chapter thus far with this point of view in mind. You will certainly find it fascinating if you follow the history of the theories of light, or of the attempts to measure its speed—or both—in other sources.

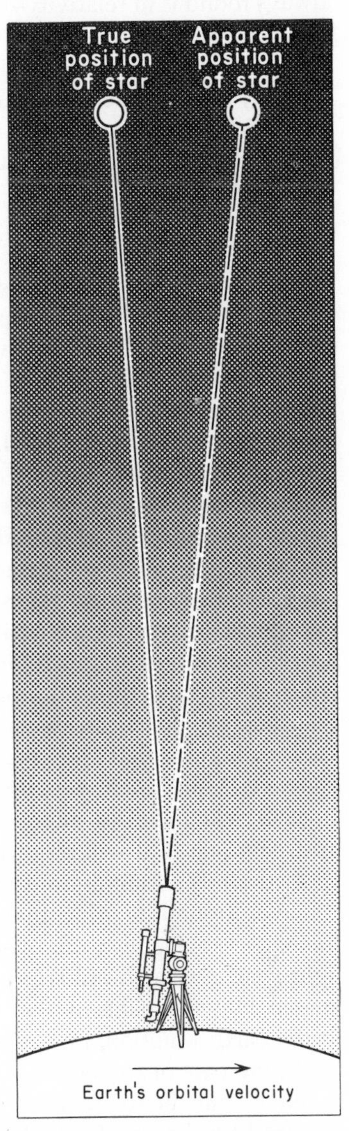

Fig. 27-8. Bradley's application of the raindrop-and-pipe experiment to the determination of the speed of light.

27-6 Importance of the Speed of Light; Forerunners of Relativity

The speed of light in a vacuum is now given as

$$2.997930 \cdot 10^{8} \text{ m/sec}$$

or

$$2.997930 \cdot 10^{10} \text{ cm/sec}$$

For all ordinary purposes we may consider it to be

$$3.00 \cdot 10^{8} \text{ m/sec}, \quad 3.00 \cdot 10^{10} \text{ cm/sec}$$

or

$$1.86 \cdot 10^{5} \text{ miles/sec}$$

either in a vacuum or in air.

The accurate value given is a "best value" based on many precise determinations. What possible purpose can there be in making all these different measurements, or in establishing the value with such high accuracy?

In fact, this is not merely the speed of light; it turns out to be a fundamental constant of nature. It keeps popping up in unexpected places until one reaches the point of expecting it almost anywhere. One place it is always found is in relativity—which may seem most impractical, but which must be considered in many very practical situations.

This story goes back to the controversy over the nature of light. If it is a wave, what is the medium through which it is propagated? The best "medium" is a vacuum, but in the ordinary sense of either word, there is *no* medium in a vacuum. Yet waves in sheer nothingness were inconceivable, so "luminiferous ether" was invented to serve as a medium. It had to pervade all space through which light would travel, including the entire solar system—the whole universe. Yet the planets must be able to move through it with no loss of energy, since they continue in the same orbits. Remarkable as these properties were, physicists generally accepted them in preference to the idea of waves in nothingness.

Consider for a moment a somewhat unusual boat race on a wide river. The rate of flow of the river is the same everywhere, and the two boats are exactly matched in speed. But boat A follows a course at right angles to the bank, making a round trip, while boat B makes a round trip over a course of equal length parallel with the bank. The stream aids boat B on the downstream trip and hinders it when it returns upstream, but the two effects do *not* cancel out because, owing to the lesser speed relative to the bank, the upstream trip takes longer than the trip downstream. Thus the *average* velocity of this boat is reduced considerably by the rate of stream flow. Boat A will be much less affected by the stream flow and invariably will win the race. For example, suppose that the stream flow is 6 miles an hour and the boats can move at 10 mph in still water. You can show by a vector diagram that the cross-stream velocity of boat A is 8 mph; if the course is 1 mile each way, boat A will need $\frac{2}{8}$ or $\frac{1}{4}$ hour for the round trip. Boat B will have an effective speed of only $10 - 6$ or 4 mph on the upstream leg, so it will require $\frac{1}{4}$ hr for this part of the race alone.

If there is a luminiferous ether, the earth must be moving through it as it moves around its orbit; that is, the ether must have a velocity relative to the earth, analogous to the velocity of the river past the bank. A signal of light sent over a round trip parallel with the earth's motion should take longer than a signal sent over a path of the same length but perpendicular to the earth's motion, just as boat B loses the race to boat A.

In the case of the boats, if one knows the length of the race course, the speed of the boats relative to the water, and the difference of time required by the two boats, he can compute the speed of the stream flow. In the case of the earth and the light signals sent over different paths, similar data would yield the speed of the earth's motion relative to the luminiferous ether. Michelson and Morley devised a clever and very precise piece of apparatus to determine the difference of time required by the two signals of light over two mutually perpendicular courses. Each course was along an arm of the apparatus, there being mirrors at the ends to reflect the signals; and the two arms were mutually perpendicular. One arm was set parallel with the earth's motion in its orbit, corresponding to the course followed by boat B in the example, and the other was perpendicular to the earth's velocity. To eliminate any effect arising from lack of exact equality of length of the two arms, the whole apparatus was rotated so that what had been course A became course B, and vice versa. By analogy with the boats, the signal traveling parallel with the earth's velocity should always lose the race to the other signal. The expected difference was very small, but was well within the capability of their equipment to detect and to measure with fair accuracy. But the investigators failed to find any difference whatever, and repeated experiments by them and others stubbornly persisted in giving negative results! This was most astonishing, and very embarrassing.

Of the many tentative explanations offered for this surprising result, the only one which withstood critical analysis was the seemingly foolish suggestion that the motion of the earth automatically shortened the arm of the apparatus which was parallel with that motion, and that this shortening was just sufficient to allow the two signals to complete their journeys simultaneously. Furthermore, this suggestion required that when *any object whatever* is in motion its dimension in the direction of the motion is reduced, dimensions perpendicular to the velocity being unaltered. This effect is called the ***Lorentz-Fitzgerald contraction.***

What could possibly cause such a remarkable effect; and *if* it occurs, why don't we notice it?

We have found that any atom has a positive nucleus surrounded by electrons in some sort of stable configuration. We have seen also that any *moving* electric charge is surrounded by a magnetic field of an intensity directly related to its velocity. This means that the structure of a motionless atom must be stable under the influence of electric forces, whereas that of a moving atom must be stable under the influence of electric *and magnetic* forces.* Application of appropriate equations in the fields of electricity and magnetism shows that the effect of these magnetic forces is to flatten the atom, making the diameter in the direction of the motion less than the diameters in other directions. This change is exactly the

* There are magnetic effects due to the motion of electrons *within* the atom, regardless of any motion of the atom. But if the atom is moving, a magnetic effect due to its motion is superimposed on the other effects.

same as the Lorentz-Fitzgerald equation requires; and if each atom is distorted in this way, it is logical that any body made of atoms—as all bodies are—must undergo a similar distortion.

But why are such contractions never observed? There are two excellent reasons. One is that the effect is extremely small except at velocities comparable with the speed of light. This is evident from the equation for the Lorentz-Fitzgerald contraction:

$$L = L_0 \cdot \sqrt{1 - v^2/c^2} \tag{27-2}$$

L_0 is the length of a body when it is motionless, L its length when moving with a velocity v parallel with its length, and c is the speed of light. The ratio of the speed of a body to that of light will be met so frequently that it is convenient to represent it by the special symbol β:

$$\beta = \frac{v}{c} \tag{27-3}$$

In these terms, the equation for the Lorentz-Fitzgerald contraction is

$$L = L_0 \cdot \sqrt{1 - \beta^2} \tag{27-4}$$

Suppose, then, that we have a jet plane traveling at 600 mph; at this snail's pace—compared to the 186,000 miles/sec speed of light—the length of the plane would be reduced less than 0.0001%. But if the plane could go at half the speed of light, β would be $\frac{1}{2}$, β^2 would be $\frac{1}{4}$, $1 - \beta^2$ would be $\frac{3}{4}$, and the square root of this would be 0.866; thus the length of the plane would be reduced to 86.6% of its normal length.

But suppose that there is a plane which can go that fast, and that you measure the distance between successive seats along the aisle while the plane is on the ground, finding it to be perhaps 32 in. You remeasure the distance when the plane is flying at top speed and find it to be—still 32 in.! The distance has been reduced, but your yardstick or measuring tape has shrunk also—when extended in the direction of motion—so that it gives exactly the same reading as before. In fact, everything has been contracted in the direction of motion, yourself included. But as with the distance between the seats, there is no way you can detect the change; everything appears quite normal to you. To everyone on the ground, however, the plane appears foreshortened.

There may seem to be something wrong here (aside from the intuitive implausibility of all this), for it has been emphasized that only relative motion is significant, and you may feel that the discussion of the Lorentz-Fitzgerald contraction has overlooked this. But on reconsideration you will realize that the speed of the plane has been expressed *relative* to the ground. This reminds you that the ground has a very high velocity relative to you, so you look out of the window just as you pass over a city which has a large circular lake in a park. But the lake doesn't *appear* circular; it has become oval! Although people on the ground see everything unchanged, you see all dimensions parallel with the plane's path reduced.

The ideas illustrated by this example of the plane appearing foreshortened to those on the ground, and features of the landscape below appearing distorted to persons on the plane, have been accepted for over half a century. However, it has been suggested recently that this overlooks the fact that if an observer on the ground has a momentary glimpse of the approaching plane, the photons which give this glimpse were reflected from the plane at different times; those for the tail have to travel farther than those from the nose, so the former must have left the plane earlier. Detailed consideration of this sort of thing suggests that instead of a distorted view of the sort in this example an observer would see the object undistorted but rotated from its actual position, with the result that the object may appear to approach with its tail forward. Nevertheless, whatever the true description of what the observer *sees* may be, there is agreement that the Lorentz-Fitzgerald *contraction* is *real.*

This business of the Lorentz-Fitzgerald contraction will seem to be just someone's bad dream, at first. We must realize that none of our experiences has involved relative velocities comparable with the fantastic speed of light and that therefore our intuitive feelings in the matter are wholly unreliable. For all ordinary velocities, Eq. (27-2) and Eq. (27-4) reduce, in any practical sense, to $L = L_0$; so there should be no *observable* contraction in our ordinary experiences. Thus, to this extent, our experiences *do* agree with what the theory requires.

We shall return to further considerations of this sort in Chapter 32 and later chapters. To make these ideas a little less strange, in the meantime, recall our experience with Ohm's law. We found that we could not apply it to a reactive circuit; but when we developed a more general relationship which was valid for such circuits, we found that this general relationship contained Ohm's law as a special case. In an analogous manner, we must accept the fact that the every-day experiences which make the Lorentz-Fitzgerald contraction seem so unreasonable are simply special cases of the general relationship, and that they do not contradict it in any way.

27-7 The Electromagnetic Spectrum

The term "light" has two somewhat different meanings. Its significance may be limited to radiations to which our optic nerves are sensitive, thus excluding those which do not contribute to our vision; in this sense, the term includes a relatively narrow band of wavelengths or frequencies. In a different sense, it applies to all electromagnetic radiations, whatever their wavelength or frequency. The entire gamut of radiations, arranged in order of wavelength, is called the electromagnetic ***spectrum.*** It is

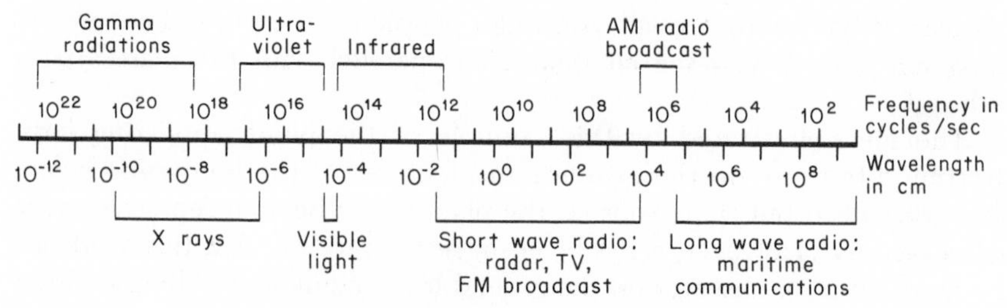

Fig. 27-9. The electromagnetic spectrum.

shown in Fig. 27-9. Note that different categories of waves may not be mutually exclusive. In fact, no boundary between categories is sharp and definite. The unit of wavelength used in this figure is the centimeter; but for wavelengths in and near the visible range the usual unit is the ***angstrom*** (abbreviated Å), which is 10^{-8} cm or 10^{-10} m.

27-8 Spectral Colors and Non-spectral Colors

Within the very restricted portion of the spectrum to which our eyes are sensitive there is a unique relationship between a particular wavelength and a color. We see this in the rainbow, which is the spectrum of visible light. The red is due to the longest wavelength we can see; the violet, to the shortest. The colors shade gradually from one to the other, and each color corresponds to one specific wavelength. Thus, any one wavelength of light in the visible spectrum produces a particular ***spectral color.***

If you open your eyes under water, you see things in their normal colors. Yet as the light entered the water its velocity was reduced because of a lessening of the wavelength, the frequency remaining unaffected. Thus it is evident that, although it is customary to relate each specific wavelength to a particular spectral color, actually it is the frequency, rather than the wavelength, which is significant.

Many colors, however, do not appear in the spectrum; a rainbow includes no brown, for example. All such colors are ***non-spectral colors*** and are due to a combination of frequencies.

We find here a response of the eye which is quite different from that of the ear. Presented with a complex stimulus composed of a combination of frequencies, the ear analyzes the stimulus and perceives the separate components; each contributes to the tone quality even though we do not consciously perceive all of them. But when a complex stimulus is presented to the eye, the individual wavelengths are not perceived; instead the eye makes a single over-all response to the complex stimulus.* It is as if the

* Apparently this statement is not true under certain circumstances which will be discussed in Sec. 27-10.

ear would hear neither C nor G when both are sounded, but would hear (perhaps) E instead. For example, if red light and green light of appropriate relative intensities are caused to fall on a white screen, the unaided eye will see the color as yellow even though no yellow light whatever is present. When you look at a lemon, your eye receives all colors of the spectrum except blue and violet, but your eye reports only the sensation of yellow.

27-9 The Additive and Subtractive Processes of Color Formation

As the term implies, the ***additive process*** of color formation involves the combination of various wavelengths or frequencies to produce a color. The production of yellow by combining red and green lights, cited in the final paragraph of the preceding section, is an example. It is *lights,* not *pigments,* which are combined; and the eye makes a single over-all response to the combination.

The term ***subtractive process*** is equally suggestive; this process produces a color by subtracting part of the light. The color of a lemon, mentioned at the end of the last section, is due to the subtractive process, for the pigment of the lemon absorbs the blue and violet light, subtracting them from the stimulus the lemon presents to your eye. Usually, as here, the subtractive process involves the additive process as well, for the eye makes an over-all response to all the colors *not* subtracted by the pigment—in this case, the green, yellow, orange, and red, the eye seeing the combination as yellow.

Either a single pigment or a combination of pigments may be involved in the subtractive process. For example, you know what happens when blue and yellow paints are mixed. *Why* it happens is that blue paint absorbs red, yellow, and orange, and yellow paint absorbs blue and violet; thus, when we mix them, only green escapes absorption and is left to be reflected to the eye.

The fact that in the subtractive process the color observed is due to the colors of light *not* absorbed is responsible for the effect sometimes observed when a colored light is used to illuminate a colored object. If, for example, a girl has a lovely blue dress, its color is due to its ability to reflect blue, green, and violet. But suppose that she wears it to a party at the home of a hostess who likes amber lighting. There is little color in the light which the dress can reflect, so it appears a rather *un*lovely bluish-greenish gray.

27-10 New Developments in Color Vision

Recent researches by Land and associates indicate that the familiar world of color, as described briefly in the preceding sections, is but a special case of something much broader and more general, somewhat as the familiar world of *non*-contracting objects is a special case of a universe subject to the Lorentz-Fitzgerald contraction.*

If you photograph a colorful scene on black and white film, you get a colorless image. If you put a red filter in front of the camera lens, you still get a colorless image but the gradations of gray are somewhat modified; a black and white (colorless) transparency made from this is known as a "long record" because it was photographed with red light, which has a relatively long wavelength. Suppose that you photograph the same scene through a green filter and make a colorless transparency; this is called a "short record" because it was made with light of relatively short wavelength.

If either the long or the short record is projected onto a screen, the result is a colorless picture. Placing a red filter over the projector with the long record produces a picture in reds, reddish grays, and black. Similarly, projection of the short record through a green filter yields a picture in green, greenish gray, and black. If both projectors, with filters but *without* the transparencies, are turned on, the result will be a yellow, as we have seen before, with no suggestion of red or green. Thus far, all is as we would expect. But if the transparencies are now placed in their respective projectors, the filters remaining in place, and the two images brought exactly together on the screen, the whole gamut of colors from red to blue appears! If the filters on the projectors (or the transparencies) are interchanged, color is present but blue is changed to yellow and vice versa, green becomes red, and red becomes green, etc.

Surprising as this is, more is to come; the filters used in projecting the two transparencies need not be the same as those used in taking the original photographs. Fair color, including red and blue, has been obtained when only two wavelengths were used, that for the long record having a wavelength only 200 Å longer than that used for the short record, both wavelengths being in the yellow part of the spectrum. In terms of older ideas, *only* yellow was present, but all colors were seen. In fact, any of a wide range of combinations can be used to produce full color. This is indicated in Fig. 27-10.† Furthermore, the relative intensities of the "long-wave stimulus"—the light used to project the long record—and the "short-wave stimulus" may be varied over a wide range with very little effect on the observed colors.

The net effect of this seems to be that the color at a particular point in the projected image is determined not by wavelength or frequency, not

---

* Something of these color phenomena was known at least as far back as 1914, but their study has been greatly broadened by the Land group.

† This figure, and also Fig. 27-11, are adapted from those in an article by Edwin H. Land in *Scientific American*, May, 1959.

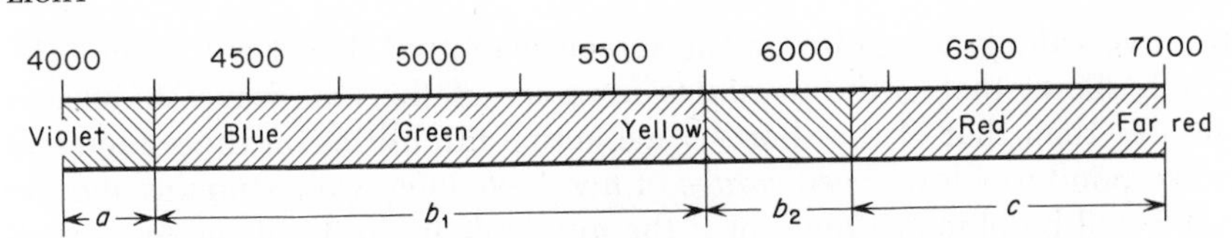

Fig. 27-10. Single wavelengths give colors as labeled, but combinations of wavelengths projected through a "short record" and a "long record" may give a full range of color. A wavelength in a can serve as a short-wave stimulus with any longer wavelength. Any wavelength in b_1 as short-wave stimulus plus any longer wavelength will give full color; one in b_1 as long-wave stimulus with one in a will give a limited range of color. Any wavelength in b_2 can serve either as the long-wave or the short-wave stimulus, giving a full color range in either case. Wavelengths in c may be used only as long-wave stimuli.

by the intensity of either of the two stimuli (long and short), and not even by their relative intensities. It seems to be determined, instead, by the relationship between the percentage of the available long-wave stimulus and the percentage of the available short-wave stimulus. Figure 27-11 will make this more clear. If at a specific point the intensity of the long-wave stimulus is 10% as great as it would be if the long record transparency were absent, the color will be red if the intensity of the short-wave stimulus is about 1.8% of what it would be if the short record transparency were absent; the color will be gray if the intensity of the short-wave stimulus is 10% of the maximum available; and the color will be blue if the short-wave stimulus has an intensity about 14% of its maximum. Other combinations of percentages of available intensities yield other colors. In general, combinations toward the lower left of Fig. 27-11 produce relatively deep, saturated colors, whereas those toward the upper right produce unsaturated tints.

It is important that we realize that the *intensity* of a stimulus is relatively unimportant; the significant factor is the *percentage* of the *available* intensity of that stimulus. It would be easy to conclude that equal intensities of the two stimuli result in gray, since any point of the line labeled "gray" has the same value on both axes of the graph; but this is not a valid conclusion. Equal intensities of

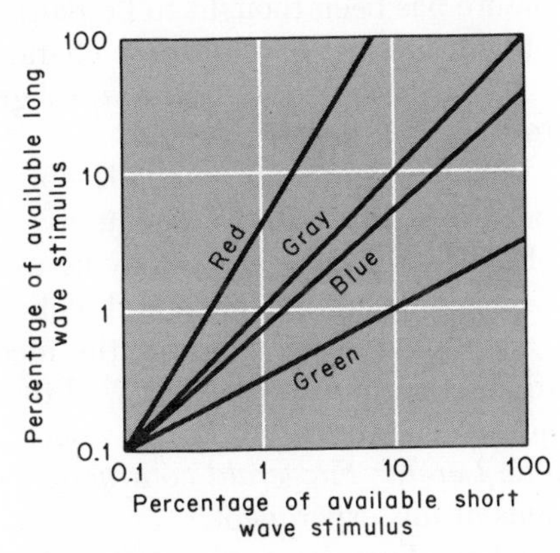

Fig. 27-11. Approximate representation of the dependence of observed color to the ratio of the percentages of the available stimuli.

the two stimuli at a point on the screen may give almost any color. The graph shows that if the *available* intensity of the long-wave stimulus is greater than that of the short, equal actual intensities on the screen will correspond to a lower *percentage* of *available* long-wave stimulus and the color will be blue or green; or if the *available* intensity of the long-wave stimulus is less than that of the short-wave stimulus, equal actual intensities on the screen will causes an orange or red color, since the *percentage* of *available* long-wave stimulus is greater than that of the *available* short-wave stimulus. Grays are due to equal *percentages* of *available* stimuli, *not* to equal *intensities* of the two stimuli.

Notice that these results are entirely different from what happens if the lights are present without the transparencies. In the latter case, the eye sees but a single color or, if the intensities vary somewhat from one part of the screen to the other, a uniform and fairly slight gradation of color; under no circumstances is a full spectrum of color observed. But the introduction of the colorless transparencies alters the situation drastically, and a full range of color may appear.

An interesting factor is that the result is somewhat similar if, instead of superimposing the images of the long and short records, one is presented to the right eye alone while the other is presented to the left eye only.

Lack of space prevents our pursuing these fascinating developments further.

Summary

Light has been considered to be a *wave phenomenon,* and also its nature has been thought to be *particulate.* Our present view of the nature of light ascribes *both* of these characteristics to it.

The energy of a *quantum* of light, or *photon,* is directly proportional to the *frequency* of the light.

A wide variety of methods—both "laboratory" and astronomical—has been developed for the seemingly impossible task of measuring the speed of light. A given method may be useless or highly accurate, depending on details of instrumentation and technique.

Speculations concerning the medium for the transmission of light led to an experiment which showed that *if* such a medium exists the earth is not moving through it at any velocity comparable with the expected value. The *Lorentz-Fitzgerald contraction* was conceived to account for the results of this experiment.

The *electromagnetic spectrum* includes a tremendous range of wavelengths or frequencies, of which visible light constitutes an extremely small fraction. Within the visible band, frequency determines color. Nonspectral colors are due to a combination of wavelengths.

The eye makes a *single response* to a *combination* of wavelengths instead of perceiving a combination of colors. Thus, different colors of light may be combined to generate a new color. Any pigment absorbs some color or colors, allowing others to be reflected to the eye.

Recent findings show that color is not related to frequency in so simple a way as has been thought. Under certain circumstances, just two frequencies, projected through appropriate colorless transparencies so that the two images are superimposed on the screen, may produce a full range of color.

Self-Quiz

1. Major contributions to theories of light were made by Newton, Huygens, Young, Fresnel, Maxwell, Hertz, and Einstein. Discuss the part played by each.

2. Compare and contrast the terms "wave," "quantum," and "photon."

3. Compare and contrast the immediate results of Hertz's experiment with its eventual results.

4. Write the equation for the energy of a photon. Rewrite it in terms of wavelength, (λ), instead of frequency, using c to represent the speed of light.

5. In all examples of fluorescence, the light emitted by the fluorescent material has a longer wavelength than that of the light which causes the fluorescence. Why is this?

6. Show clearly why Galileo's and Michelson's attempts to measure the speed of light had such different results, including any necessary details of instrumentation and technique.

7. Compare the theory of Roemer's method with that of Bradley's.

8. Discuss the Michelson-Morley experiment and its results.

9. What is the Lorentz-Fitzgerald contraction, and why are we not aware of it ordinarily? Suppose that the speed of light were 1860 miles an hour instead of 186,000 miles a second; would the Lorentz-Fitzgerald contraction be obvious to everyone? Would it be obvious to a jet pilot?

10. If a plane could be accelerated to the speed of light, what would its length be, Eq. (27-2)? What conclusion can you draw?

11. Name a number of kinds of electromagnetic radiations other than visible light, and arrange them in order of increasing wavelength. Did you list them in the order of increasing, or decreasing, frequency? Explain, on the basis of pertinent definitions. Also explain on the basis of the units.

12. Define the angstrom. If the range of visible light is about 4000 Å to 7000 Å, what is its range in centimeters? Check your result against Fig. 27-9.

13. Discuss the reaction of the eye to a complex stimulus (in general).

14. Compare the additive and subtractive processes of color formation.

15. Will the result of mixing two colors of light be the same as that of mixing the same two colors of pigments? Explain clearly.

16. Discuss the means by which full color may be obtained in an image when only two specific wavelengths are present.

Problems

1. Compute the energy of a photon near (a) the long-wave (7000 Å) end of the visible spectrum and (b) the short-wave (4000 Å) end.

2. What is the energy of a single "photon" of the energy sent out by a radio station which broadcasts on a frequency of 1250 kc/sec?

3. If a gamma ray photon has an energy of $2.00 \cdot 10^{-6}$ erg, calculate its frequency and its wavelength.

4. At the earth's surface one square centimeter of area normal to the sun's rays receives about 3.4 joules of energy each minute. If the average wavelength were 6000 Å, this would require how many photons per minute?

5. In one of his measurements, Michelson found the octagonal mirror to be rotating at 528.76 rps. The one-way distance was 35,426 m. Compute the speed of light in air from these data.

6. Suppose that while rain is falling vertically you have someone hold a stovepipe out the window of your car while you drive. If he finds that the raindrops fall through the pipe when it is tilted 35° from the vertical, find graphically the factor by which the speedometer reading should be multiplied to give the rate of fall of the rain.

28
PROPAGATION OF LIGHT

28-1 Preview

First we shall consider some
of the consequences of the fact that light
travels in straight lines. This will lead
to the relationship between the illumination
and the distance from a point source of light;
it will lead also to the phenomenon of pinhole images.
We shall see that, quite paradoxically,
the propagation of light in a straight line can be explained
by assuming continuous production of circular wavelets
from every point on a wavefront. Like sound,
light may undergo a change of direction caused by reflection,
refraction, or diffraction; we shall consider
each of these phenomena. We shall find that when light
goes from one point to another the path it follows
is always such that the time of travel between
the two points is a minimum, even in cases which
involve reflection or refraction. We shall
encounter the phenomena of interference
and polarization, which not only are interesting
and important in themselves, but which also
tell us much about the nature of light.

28-2 The Rectilinear Propagation of Light

Whenever a hunter aims a gun, or a carpenter sights along the edge of a board to see whether it is straight, he is assuming that the light which reaches his eye has followed without deviation a path which is a straight line. This assumption is valid, and the straight-line propagation of light is described as ***rectilinear propagation.*** Although the hunter and the carpenter will encounter no difficulties as the result of their assumption of rectilinear propagation, it is by no means true that light invariably follows a straight line. But before we consider deviations from straight-line propagation, let's investigate two consequences of rectilinear propagation.

28-3 The Inverse Square Law of Illumination

Suppose that we have a fairly bright, but very small, source of light sending rays out in all directions. Most of the rays may be blocked by a flat sheet of cardboard which has a rectangular opening cut out of it as in Fig. 28-1, the width of the opening being w and its height h; but an expanding "cone" of light of rectangular cross section will pass through. If the opening is at a distance d from the source and the cone of light falls on a screen twice that distance from the source, it will illuminate a rectangle $2w$ wide and $2h$ high, or $4wh$ in area. This doubling of linear dimensions of the "cone" of light is the necessary consequence of the properties of similar triangles and the fact that light travels in straight lines. Since the area of the opening is only wh, evidently *doubling* the distance has *quadrupled* the area covered by the expanding cone of light. If the screen is placed at a distance $3d$ from the source, the illuminated area will be $3w$ wide and $3h$ high, so its area will be $9wh$. At the distance of nd, the width of the cone will be nw and its height nh, making its area n^2wh. Thus the area covered by the cone of light is directly proportional to the square of the distance.

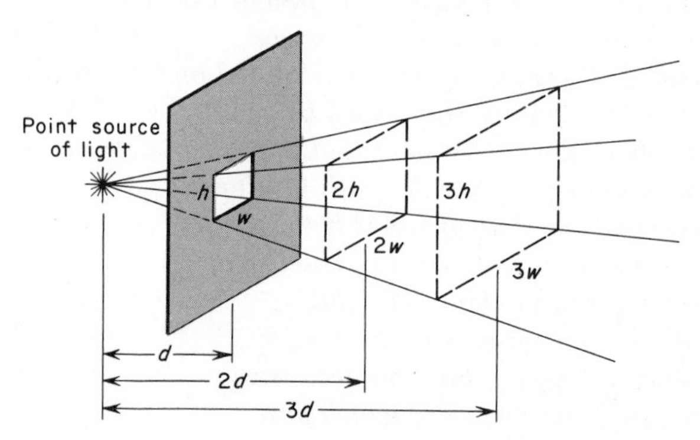

Fig. 28-1. Basis of the inverse square law of illumination.

In clear air, the energy of the light must be constant; no more light energy is available en route, and none is being absorbed. In the situation we have been considering, however, the energy *per unit area* is not constant, for the energy is being spread over a rapidly increasing area; so the energy per unit area must decrease. Thus the ***illumination,*** or ***illuminance,*** which is the measure of the luminous energy per unit area, is inversely proportional to the square of the distance from the source. Obviously the illumination will also be directly proportional to the brightness, or ***luminous intensity,*** of the source. If we represent the luminous intensity by L, the illumination by I, and the distance by r,

$$I = \frac{L}{r^2} \tag{28-1}$$

provided that consistent units are employed so that no proportionality constant is required. The customary unit of luminous intensity is the ***candle,*** or ***candlepower,*** which is an arbitrary unit based not on a candle but on a specially designed oil lamp. If r is in feet, the unit of illumination is the ***foot candle*** or ***lumen per square foot,*** which is equivalent to the illumination at a distance of 1 ft from a source of 1 candle luminous intensity. A corresponding unit is the ***lumen per square meter,*** used when r is in meters.

Sample Problem 1

What is the luminous intensity of a source if it produces an illumination of 5.00 foot candles (ft-c) at a distance of 4.00 ft?

Equation (28-1), when solved for L, becomes

$$L = Ir^2$$

so

$$L = 5.00 \cdot 4.00^2 = 5.00 \cdot 16.00 = 80.0 \text{ candles}$$

It must not be overlooked that the entire discussion in this section has been in terms of a point source of light. The quantitative relationships are invalid if the source is extended, like a fluorescent tube or a luminous panel. They are invalid also under any circumstances in which reflections from walls or other surfaces or objects contribute to the illumination.

28-4 Pinhole Images

An object can be seen only because light comes from it to the eye. In general, whether the object is self-luminous or reflects light to the eye, the rays leaving it go out in all directions. However, a screen placed at one side of the object will block off the light going in that general direction. Suppose that we punch a small hole in such a screen; this will allow only those light rays directed toward this hole to pass on, all others being blocked. If a second screen is placed behind the pinhole, the result will be

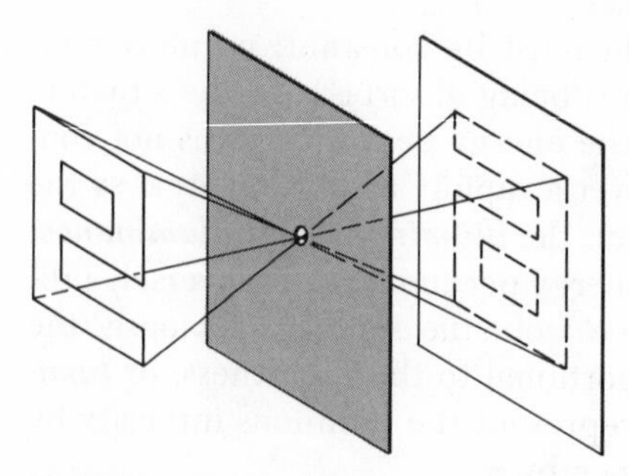

Fig. 28-2. Formation of an image by a pinhole.

as shown in Fig. 28-2. Because each ray travels in a straight line, rays from different parts of the object cross as they pass through the pinhole. A ray from the top of the object will strike the lower part of this second screen, a ray from the far side of the object will fall on the near side of the screen, etc. Each point on the object will send a ray of light which will pass through the pinhole and go straight on to the screen. Thus the screen will be illuminated by a pattern of rays of light arranged exactly as the corresponding points in the object are, except that top and bottom are interchanged and the same is true of right and left. We say that there is an ***image*** of the object on the screen, and that the image is ***inverted.*** In general, the ray leaving any given point on the object will have a color and an intensity characteristic of that point, and it will illuminate the corresponding point on the screen with the proper color and relative intensity. Thus the pinhole image will be a faithful full-color reproduction of the object.

An examination of Fig. 28-2 shows that (in terms of linear dimensions) the relative sizes of object and image must be the same as their relative distances from the pinhole.

28-5 Rectilinear Propagation as a Consequence of Huygens' Principle

In the second paragraph of Sec. 14-10, we met Huygens' principle—the fact that any point on a wave front acts as a source of circular wavelets. As an illustration, we considered a water wave meeting a barrier which has a narrow opening in it. When a short segment of a wave crest passes through the opening, momentarily it is a "hill" of water above the general level; so it flows outward in all directions, forming a semicircular wave beyond the barrier. And by a similar process the short segment of a trough penetrating the barrier forms a semicircular wave beyond it.

If, instead of a single opening, the barrier has several, a series of semicircular wavelets will be generated at each opening as in Fig. 28-3. In general, the wavelets from one opening will interfere destructively with those from the others, but in the forward direction they are in phase and interfere constructively. The two types of interference, plus the fact that as the waves expand beyond the openings their wave fronts become less curved, nullify the wavelets in most directions but cause them to form a wave front parallel with those which haven't yet encountered the barrier. Thus, except for some reduction in energy (because some is reflected at the barrier) and therefore a lessened amplitude, the waves some distance beyond the barrier show no evidence of having encountered the barrier. You have observed this if you have ever watched waves passing through a line of pilings.

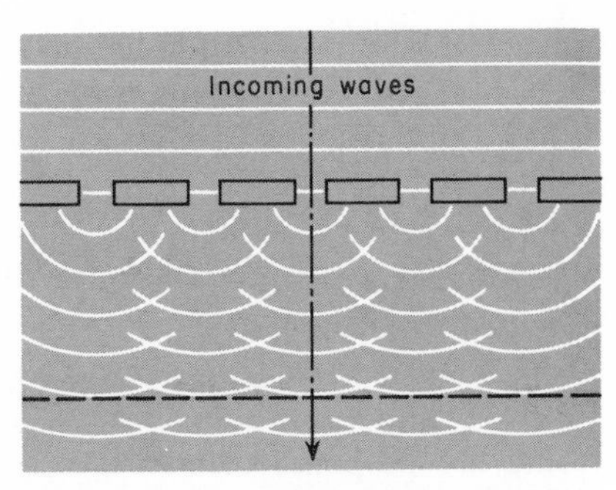

Fig. 28-3. Use of Huygens' principle to demonstrate rectilinear propagation of waves.

Huygens' principle tells us that this sort of thing occurs with all waves even though no barrier is present; at all times every point is the source of spherical wavelets, and the advancing wave front is created by the constructive interference of these wavelets. In any isotropic medium, the speed of the wavelets emanating from any point is the same as that of all other such wavelets; hence the advancing wave front created by their constructive interference must always be parallel with its previous position. Thus, in an isotropic medium, the direction of propagation must remain constant; it could change only if the wave front did *not* remain parallel with its previous positions.

28-6 Reflection of Light

In Fig. 28-4, we have a beam of light approaching a mirror from above and the left, the letters p, q, r, and s identifying four of the myriad of rays in the beam. Lines at right angles to the beam represent wave fronts, and the lower edge of the wave front labeled AB has just reached the mirror; thus ray p has gone as far as it can. Ray p immediately generates a circular wavelet at A, which starts out in all directions above the mirror; and at this same instant ray s is at B, and rays q and r are on the line AB. A moment later, ray s will reach the mirror at C, having traveled the distance BC. Since the wavelet generated at A is traveling in the same medium as ray s is, it also must have traveled a distance BC during this interval; that is, the wavelet centered at A must have a radius equal to BC. Similarly, wavelets will have been generated where rays q and

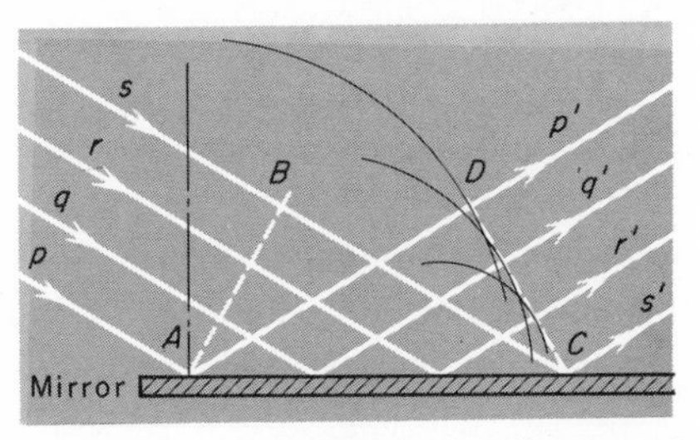

Fig. 28-4. Mechanism of reflection of waves.

r struck the mirror—and at all intermediate points between A and C, since the beam of light contains countless rays, of which only four are shown. When ray s reaches C, rays p, q, and r will have generated the wavelets shown, and these are in phase along the line DC—and *only* along this line are they in phase. Hence constructive interference builds up a wave front DC which moves upward and to the right. The beam of light has been ***reflected*** from the mirror.

In Fig. 28-4, triangles ADC and CBA have a common side AC and the sides AD and CB are equal; also, both are right triangles, since the wave fronts are perpendicular to the light rays. Hence the two triangles are congruent. Therefore angle BCA is equal to angle DAC; that is, the incoming and reflected rays make the same angle with the mirror. This fact is part of the law of reflection, but we are not quite ready to state the law yet. The ***angle of incidence*** is the angle between the incoming or ***incident*** ray* and the *normal* to the mirror; it is *not* the angle between the ray and the mirror itself. Similarly, the ***angle of reflection*** is the angle between the normal to the mirror and the ***reflected*** ray. These definitions are illustrated in Fig. 28-5, $\angle i$ being the angle of incidence and $\angle r$ the angle of reflection. The ***law of reflection*** states that the angle of incidence is equal to the angle of reflection and that the incident ray, the normal to the surface at the point of the reflection, and the reflected ray all lie in the same plane. The proviso in the latter portion of the law means that a ray coming down from due east onto a horizontal mirror will be reflected upward and due west; it will *not* be reflected north or southeast!

28-7 Formation of an Image by a Plane Mirror; Virtual Images

If an object, such as the arrow AB in Fig. 28-6, is placed in front of a mirror, a person in an appropriate position can "see" the object "in the mirror." This is the direct result of the law of reflection. A ray from A will strike the mirror at such a point that it will be reflected to the left eye at L, and another ray from A will be reflected to the right eye at R. All other rays from A will be reflected in directions which miss the viewer's eyes. Likewise, two rays from B will be reflected to the watcher's eyes; and every point on the object between A and B contributes its two rays. As the law of reflection requires, and as Fig. 28-6

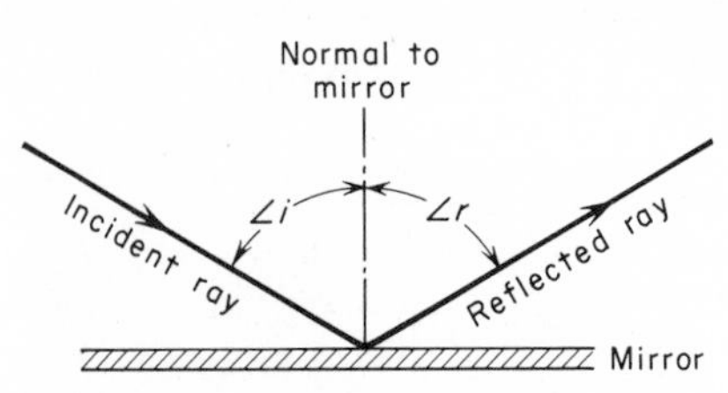

Fig. 28-5. Illustration of the definitions of the incident and reflected rays, and the angles of incidence and reflection.

* In terms of the Latin roots from which it comes, the incident ray is the in-falling ray—the ray which falls on the mirror.

shows, the two rays from a given point on the object diverge as they travel from the mirror toward the two eyes.

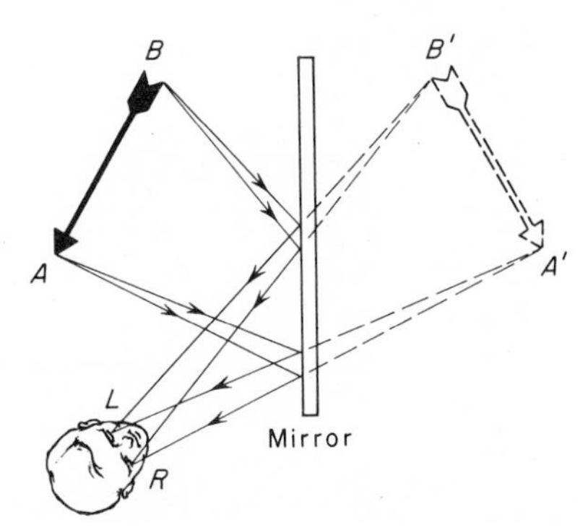

Fig. 28-6. Formation of a virtual image by a plane mirror.

When we view an object directly, we judge its direction in terms of the direction from which light from the object enters our eyes. Also, the ray which reaches the right eye from any given point on the object must diverge from that which reaches the left eye from the same point; and it is in terms of this divergence of the approaching rays that we judge the distance of the object. Hence, the eyes naïvely assume that the two rays which actually came from point B in Fig. 28-6 had their origin at B' and that A' is the source of the rays which really came from A; and the light rays aren't ethical enough to inform our eyes that this assumption is invalid or that the rays turned a corner en route. Hence the eyes conclude that they are not seeing something in front of the mirror, but behind it, as indicated by $A'B'$. Thus $A'B'$ is the image of AB.

By considering two viewers* (each with one eye closed, to simplify the diagram) with the object between them, you can construct a diagram somewhat like Fig. 28-6; and adding lines such as AA' and BB' will enable you to prove that the mirror is the perpendicular bisector of any line between a point on the object and the corresponding point on the image. This means that the object and image are of the same size and are equidistant from the mirror. It is a common fallacy that the image is *on* the mirror; but—aside from the geometrical proof—you can convince yourself that this is not so by focusing your eyes on a flaw in the mirror (or a dusting of powder, or an ink spot), reducing the distance of the mirror until it goes out of focus, and then shifting your attention to your image.

The rectilinear propagation of light and the law of reflection combine to limit the field of view which can be observed with the aid of a plane mirror. In Fig. 28-7(a), a driver has a rearview mirror mounted on the fender about as far forward as the radiator. He can see only the reflections of such objects as are within the angle α, for rays from objects farther to the right or left will not be reflected to his eye. Part (b) of the figure is similar except that the mirror is mounted much nearer the driver's eye; obviously his angle of view is much greater. Evidently the angle of view

* You can do this by using Fig. 28-6 instead of drawing a diagram with two different observers, but it is convenient to increase the sizes of angles $LA'R$ and $LB'R$ by choosing viewpoints separated by a greater distance than that between L and R.

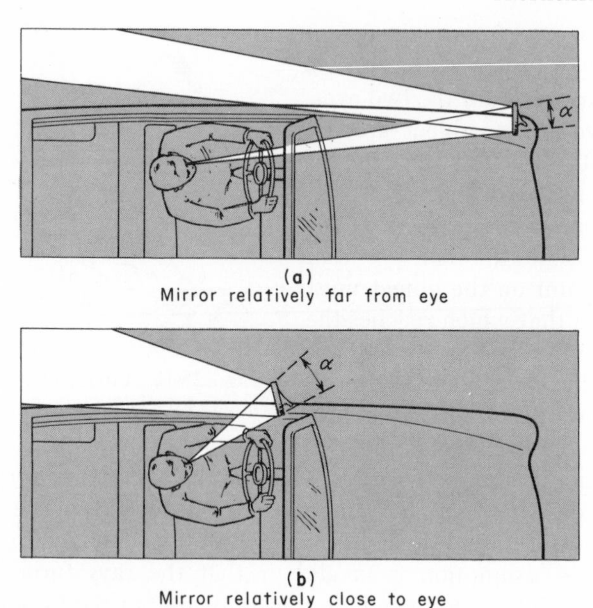

Fig. 28-7. The field of view seen in a mirror depends strongly on the distance of the mirror from the eye.

provided by the mirror is determined by the angle the mirror subtends at the eye, so it is increased markedly as the distance between the eye and the mirror is reduced. It appears that, before deciding where such a mirror should be placed, one should decide whether he really wants an ornament or a functional mirror.

Note that the rays in Fig. 28-6 and Fig. 28-7 bounce off the mirror and back to your eye: they do *not* penetrate behind the mirror. If you were to hold a cardboard screen behind the mirror, as we did behind the pinhole in Fig. 28-4, nothing would appear on the screen. *Physically,* there is *nothing whatever* at $A'B'$ in Fig. 28-6, and this is true of all images formed by plane mirrors. Images of this sort, which have no physical existence and result only from the eye being fooled, are called ***virtual images.***

(To many of us, it is a very comforting thought that what we see whenever we look into a mirror is only an optical illusion!)

28-8 Refraction of Light

The expression "the speed of light," if unqualified, means the speed of light *in a vacuum.* When light travels in any physical medium, even air, its speed is less than in a vacuum, although in air the difference is so small that for many purposes it may be ignored. In general, the speed of light is less in a relatively dense medium and greater in a medium of comparatively low density.

It is because of the change of speed which occurs when light penetrates the interface between two media that light is bent by lenses and prisms and its direction changed as it enters or leaves water, etc. Bending of light caused by a change of speed as it goes from one medium to another is called ***refraction.*** We can understand the mechanism of this alteration of direction with the help of Fig. 28-8.

The argument here is much like that employed in connection with Fig. 28-4 to account for reflection. Again we have an incident beam, with our attention focused on four rays in the beam. When the ray p reaches the surface it doesn't bounce off as before, but passes from the air into the water.* An instant later, ray s will reach the surface, having traveled a distance BD. Meantime, a wavelet will have started downward, into the water, from A. However, the speed of light in water is only about three-fourths of its speed in air, so when ray s reaches the surface, the radius of the wave front of this wavelet will be only $\frac{3}{4}$ of BD. Meantime, rays q and r—and all other rays between p and s—have penetrated the surface and generated relatively slow-moving wavelets. The various wavelets are in phase along the line CD, so constructive interference builds up a wave front on this line. Each point on this wave front acts as a source of wavelets, so the ***refracted*** ray is propagated down into the water. However, the new wave fronts, such as CD, are *not* parallel with those in the air, such as AB, so the direction of propagation in the water is different than in air.

The angle of incidence is defined exactly as for reflection. The ***angle of refraction*** is the angle between the normal to the surface at the point of entry and the refracted ray, as shown in Fig. 28-9.

Review of the mechanism of refraction shows that the relationship between the angle of incidence and the angle of refraction is determined by the relative velocities of light in the two media. If a circle is drawn with its center at the point of entry into the new medium, a normal to the surface at the point of entry constructed, and lines such as A and B constructed, the lengths of these two lines will be in the same ratio as the speeds of light in the respective media.

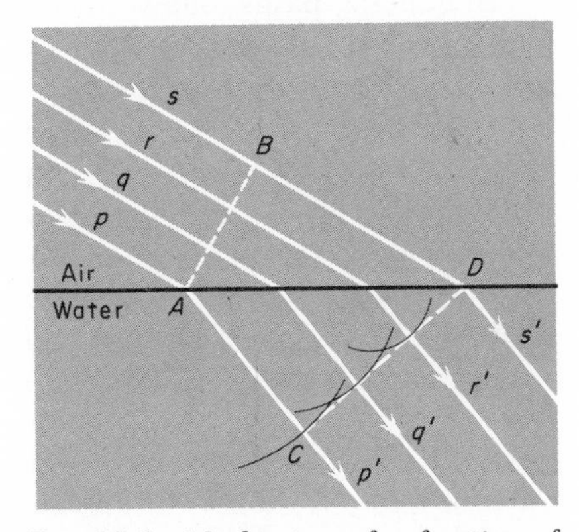

Fig. 28-8. Mechanism of refraction of waves.

The result of dividing the speed of light in vacuum by the speed in a particular medium is called the ***index of refraction*** of the medium. If this index is sym-

* Some of the light will be reflected from the surface, exactly as from the mirror, and for the same reasons. However, we are restricting our attention to refraction, so only the part which is *not* reflected concerns us at the moment.

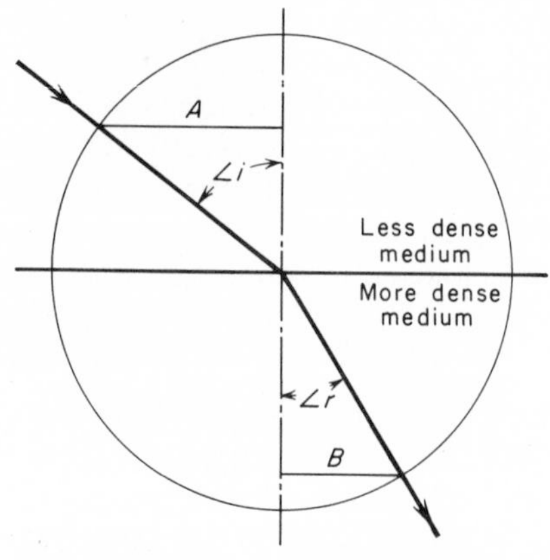

Fig. 28-9. The ratio of the speed of light in the less dense medium to that in the more dense medium is equal to the ratio of the length of A to the length of B; either quotient is equal to the index of refraction.

bolized by n, the speed of light in the medium by v, and its speed in a vacuum by the customary c,

$$n = \frac{c}{v} \tag{28-2}$$

The ***relative index*** of refraction, applicable when light passes from one medium to another, is the quotient of the speeds of light in the two media, the larger always being the dividend. If the greater speed is v_g and the smaller is v_s,

$$n_r = \frac{v_g}{v_s} \tag{28-3}$$

in which n_r represents the relative index of refraction.

Though the relative index of a medium with respect to air differs from its index with respect to vacuum, the two values will agree in the first four significant figures, so the difference may be neglected for most practical purposes.

Trig

From the discussion above, and Fig. 28-9, it is evident that $n = \sin i/\sin r$.

In general, paths followed by light beams are reversible; in Fig. 28-8 and Fig. 28-9 only the directions of the arrowheads need be reversed to make the figures correct for rays approaching the surface from below. This leads to an inconsistency in terminology. The refractive index often is defined in terms of the angles of incidence and refraction; and although this definition was used only under the heading *Trig*, it has been implied in the discussion. But the definitions and equations for the index of refraction require that its value must exceed unity. Hence it becomes necessary, when dealing with refraction, to call the ray in the less dense medium the incident ray, and that in the more dense medium the refracted ray, *regardless of the actual direction of propagation along the path.*

Table 28-1

INDICES OF REFRACTION

(The values given are for a wavelength of 5890 Å)

Substance	Index
Air	1.0002765
Calcite	1.658
Carbon disulfide	1.630
Diamond	2.417
Glass, crown	1.517–1.520
Glass, light flint	1.575
Glass, dense flint	1.650
Ruby	1.768
Water (20°C)	1.33299

Refraction is a phenomenon of great practical importance. The next section deals with one application of refraction. Also, refraction is the principal basis of the ensuing three chapters, and the sole basis of two of them.

28-9 Dispersion

To minimize complications, a very important detail was omitted from the discussion of refraction and refractive indices. You may have noted its omission, for you are familiar with the ability of a prism to produce a spectrum from white light. Obviously this is due to refraction, but the discussion gave no hint of it.

In a vacuum, all frequencies of light have the same speed. The speed of light in any physical medium is less than in a vacuum, and different frequencies of light do *not* have the same speed. The speed of light near the violet end of the spectrum is appreciably less than that near the red end.

Since all refraction is due to a change of speed, and because the angle of bend depends on the ratio of the speeds in the two media, inequality of speeds of various colors of light in a medium results in inequality of the angles of bending, as light enters that medium. Thus, if white light enters a prism as in Fig. 28-10, it is refracted, but the colors are refracted unequally, so they emerge in somewhat different directions, separating or dispersing. Any such analysis or separation of a combination of wavelengths or frequencies into its separate components is ***dispersion.*** In this diagram, it is assumed that the light enters from air into a glass prism. All colors of light are slowed and hence refracted; the blue is slowed most, however, and hence refracted most; the red, with a higher velocity in the glass than blue (or any other color), is slowed least and refracted least. Hence a medium does not have one definite index of refraction; it has a range of indices, corresponding to the range of frequencies of light. It was for this reason that the heading of Table 28-1 specified that the values recorded were appropriate for a particular wavelength.

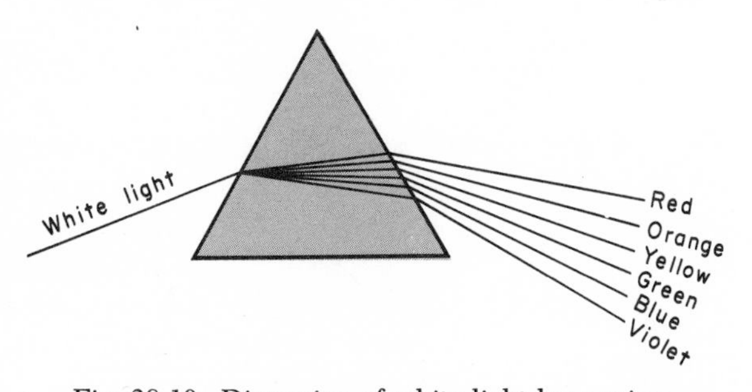

Fig. 28-10. Dispersion of white light by a prism.

28-10 Fermat's Principle of Least Time

An interesting sidelight on what we have studied so far in this chapter is afforded by ***Fermat's principle of least time*** which simply says that in passing between any specific point A and another point B a ray of light will follow that path which will enable the journey to be completed in the least possible time.

This principle is in obvious agreement with the rectilinear propagation of light, since a straight path is the shortest distance between two points and (in a homogeneous medium) passage over the shortest path will require a minimum of time. Part (a) of Fig. 28-11 represents this. If a barrier prevents light from going directly from one point to the other and a mirror is present, as in Fig. 28-11(b), it can be shown that the shortest path from A to the mirror and thence to B is the one for which the angles of incidence and reflection are equal. You can see that the result is reasonable by making a diagram similar to Fig. 28-11(b) but with the angles of incidence and reflection very dissimilar and then drawing a different path with the angles equal.

If the two points are in different media, the path will be such as to take advantage of the higher speed of light in one of the media. Thus, the segment of the path which is in the less dense medium will be longer than it would be if the path were a straight line between the two points, and the reverse will be true in the less dense medium. This becomes more obvious if you draw the straight line AB on Fig. 28-11(c) or any similar figure.

With the aid of differential calculus, Fermat's principle ceases to be an interesting curiosity and becomes a very useful tool. Though it has been introduced in connection with light, it is applicable to any wave phenomenon and to such things as a runner who can choose any course between two points, one of which is on hard ground and the other in a plowed field.

28-11 Interference

We met the concept of interference in our study of sound (Sec. 14-12), and in Sec. 27-2 we learned that Young's and Fresnel's experiments on the interference of light showed that light is a wave phenomenon.

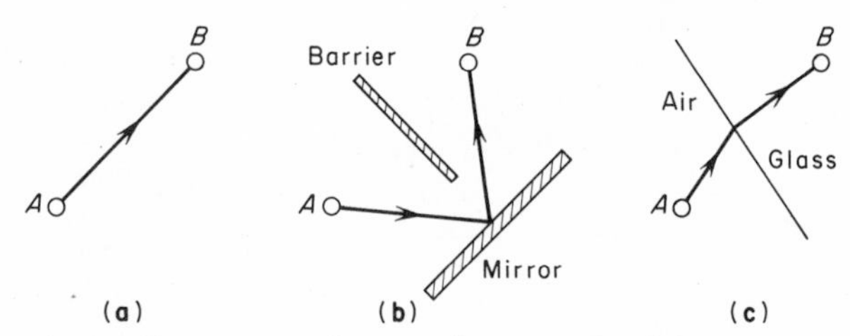

Fig. 28-11. Illustrations of Fermat's principle of least time for (a) Rectilinear propagation; (b) Reflection; (c) Refraction.

A very common type of interference is that which occurs with thin transparent films. To see how such interference occurs, consider Fig. 28-12(a). The line $BDB'D'$ represents the upper surface of a very thin film of glass, and the line CC' represents the lower surface. A beam of light, including rays AB, FD, $A'B'$, and $F'D'$, is shining on the film from above and to the left. Part of ray AB will be reflected, but to simplify matters we shall ignore this; and similarly we shall overlook any portion of any ray which is not pertinent to the discussion.

(a)

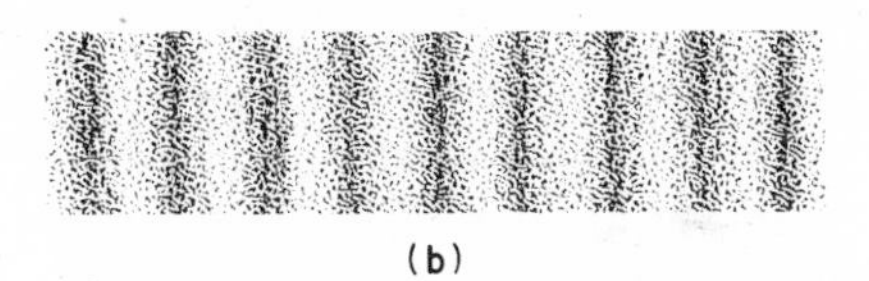

(b)

Fig. 28-12. Interference of light caused by a thin film. (a) Mechanism of interference in a thin film; (b) Type of interference pattern.

The part of ray AB which is refracted will follow the path BC. At C, part will pass out of the film but part will be reflected. The situation is closely analogous to that of a sound pulse reaching the open end of a pipe (Sec. 14-9, 15-13); as the ray is reflected at the surface of a less dense medium, its phase is reversed. The reflected portion proceeds to D, where part of it emerges and is refracted toward E.

Part of ray FD will be reflected at D, in the direction of E. Thus there will be not one, but *two*, rays directed from D toward E. At the instant ray AB entered the film, the wave front was as shown by the line BG, so ray FG had gone from G to D and been reflected before ray AB was able to go to C and back up to D. Suppose that the path BCD is a whole number of wavelengths greater than the path GD. In this case, the phase reversal at C will cause any crest which arrives at D directly from G to encounter a trough which came by way of BCD, so the two rays will interfere destructively.

At some point where the thickness of the film is a little greater, there will be a ray $A'B'$ which, after refraction and reflection, will reach D' and be refracted toward E', and another ray $F'G'D'$ which is reflected from D' toward E'. If the difference between the number of wavelengths in the path $B'C'D'$ and the path $G'D'$ is any *odd* number of *half* wavelengths, the extra half wavelength will compensate for the reversal of phase which occurred at C'; hence the two rays traveling toward E' will be perfectly in phase and will interfere constructively. If the film continues to thicken toward the right there will be a location at which the two rays will again interfere destructively as they did at D, another where the interference is constructive as at D', etc. Viewed from above, if the thickness of the film increases uniformly, the film would show a pattern of light and dark bands as in Fig. 28-12(b), the dark bands corresponding to D in Fig. 28-12(a) and the bright bands corresponding to D'.

However, since the ***interference pattern*** in Fig. 28-12(b) depends on whether rays which arrived at a given point by different routes are in phase or out of phase, it depends also on the wavelength of the light. Only ***monochromatic*** light—light of a single wavelength or frequency—would give a clearly marked pattern like Fig. 28-12(b), and review of the discussion associated with Fig. 28-12(a) shows that (if the thickness of the film increases uniformly) the spacing of the bands is directly proportional to the wavelength. This means that if a mixed light such as white light is used, the spacing of the light and dark bands will be different for different colors of light; what is a dark band for one wavelength may be a bright band for another. This is the source of the irridescent colors of very thin films of glass, cellophane, oil, etc.

28-12 Diffraction

While studying sound, we met the phenomenon of diffraction (Sec. 14-11). What we learned there implies that if light undergoes diffraction it should be propagated behind an obstruction as sound is diffracted around a building, and should spread after passing through an opening as sound diffuses after passing through an open door. Instead, we observe that buildings cast rather sharply defined shadows and that sunlight passing through openings is restricted to beams of parallel rays. But the longest of visible light waves is much less than one ten-millionth of the length of the shortest audible sound wave. If we use obstructions and openings only about 10^{-7} as large as those involved in the diffraction of sound, we find that light *is* diffracted. Whatever the nature of the waves—sound, light, water, etc.—diffraction is appreciable only if the dimensions of the obstructions or openings are comparable with the wavelength.

It is somewhat frustrating, and not very convincing, to read of such things as diffraction if one is unable to observe them. You *have* observed diffraction, however, probably without knowing that there is such a thing as diffraction. Whenever you look at a distant street lamp through a window screen, or through a fabric such as a handkerchief, you see not just a point of light but two rows of points of light arranged symmetrically around the brightest central point. The rows are parallel with the strands of the fabric; if you use a handkerchief, you can rotate them by rotating the handkerchief; and though normally the diffraction pattern has the two rows mutually perpendicular, you can distort the pattern by pulling outward on opposite corners of the handkerchief.

What is called "double-slit diffraction" is represented in Fig. 28-13. Light is moving downward toward a barrier which is pierced by two narrow parallel slits (which are seen from the upper end of the slits) at A

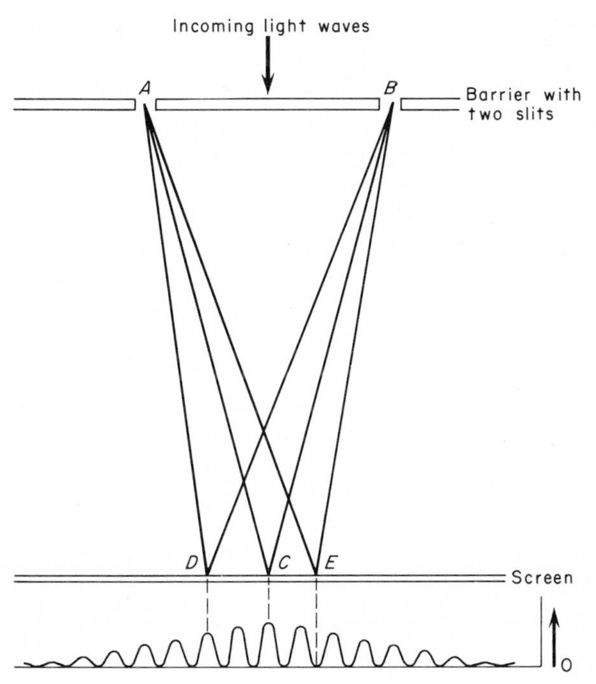

Fig. 28-13. Mechanism of two-slit diffraction, with schematic graphical representation of spacing and relative intensities of bright and dark bands.

and *B*.* The light which has penetrated the openings falls on a screen. If the light is monochromatic, a symmetrical pattern of alternate light and dark bands appears on the screen, the bands being mutually parallel and also parallel with the slits. At the bottom of Fig. 28-13 is a graph of the intensity of light in the various portions of the pattern. The distance from *A* to *C* is identical with that from *B* to *C*, so the number of wavelengths in *AC* is identical with that in *BC;* hence rays from the two slits interfere constructively, and the line in the pattern at *C* is bright. On either side of this line, the distances from the two openings will be unequal so the number of waves along one path will differ from that along the other. Constructive interference, and a bright line, will result wherever the path difference is a whole number of wavelengths; where the difference is any odd number of half wavelengths, the rays arriving over the two paths will be in opposite phase and the destructive interference will result in a dark line. For example, the second bright line to the left of the center is at *D;* since it is a bright line, the difference between *BD* and *AD* must be

* For simplicity, it is assumed that the wavefronts are straight, and that they are parallel to both the barrier and the screen; however, none of these conditions is an essential restriction.

a whole number of wavelengths, and because it is the *second* bright line from the center, the difference must be two wavelengths. On the other hand, there is a dark line at E, so AE must exceed BE by an odd number of half wavelengths; and since E is between the first and second bright lines to the right of the center, this difference in path length must be one and a half wavelengths.

Note that the light through either opening spreads out instead of going straight forward; this is fully in accordance with Huygens' principle. The wavelets emanating from the openings have their greatest intensity in the forward direction, however, the intensity decreasing toward the sides. Because of this, the pattern fades out at the edges rather than being of indefinite width.

It is possible to obtain a pattern much like that in the lower part of Fig. 28-13 with a single opening instead of the two slits. The mechanism of this, and the importance of this phenomenon, will be discussed in Sec. 30-8, 30-9.

28-13 The Diffraction Grating

The earliest ***diffraction gratings*** were made of many very fine wires mounted mutually parallel, with very narrow spaces between them. Modern gratings are prepared by special machines which rule extremely fine scratches on glass or metal—as many as 25,000 evenly spaced lines to the inch. If you use a diffraction grating in the laboratory, almost certainly it will be a replica rather than an original, formed by flowing collodion or some similar substance over a ruled grating, allowing it to harden, stripping off the resulting film, and mounting it on glass.

The sequence of rectangles in Fig. 28-14 represents a portion of a diffraction grating—a portion much less than 0.001 in. wide. This resembles Fig. 28-3, in Sec. 28-5, where the rectilinear propagation of light was shown to be in accord with Huygens' principle. At that time, mention of what is now the key fact was purposely avoided: wave fronts, such as that indicated by the dashed line in Fig. 28-3, are not the only loci along which the various wavelets are in phase.

Waves approaching the diffraction grating in Fig. 28-14 are traveling in the direction AB. Each of the openings will be the source of circular wavelets. As in Fig. 28-3 these will build up new wave fronts parallel with the original ones, but these are not shown because we are interested in other wave fronts. A straight line GH drawn from opening G tangent to the fourth wavelet below opening C will also be tangent to the first wavelet from F, the second one from E, and the third one from D. This means that the wavelets from the various openings are in phase along this line; and, this being true, their constructive interference will build up a wave front along GH. In similar manner, other wave fronts parallel with

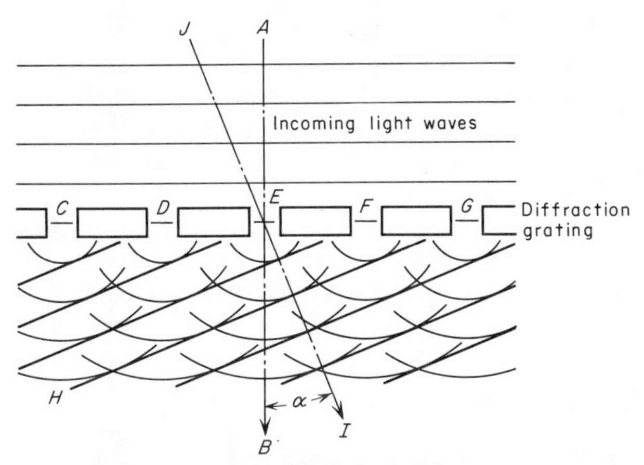

Fig. 28-14. Deviation of light by a diffraction grating.

GH will be built up. Since they are not parallel with the original wave fronts, they have a new direction of propagation; instead of proceeding in the direction *EB*, they travel along the direction *EI*. Therefore these diffracted waves will *seem* to have come from the direction of *J* rather than *A;* the direction of propagation has been altered by the angle α.

Obviously, the story doesn't end here. A line drawn from *C* tangent to the fourth wavelet below *G* would also be tangent to wavelets from intermediate openings, so a series of diffracted wave fronts is built up like the series parallel with *GH*, and this other series will travel at the angle α to the left of the original direction. Also, a line from *G* could be drawn tangent to the *second* wavelet below *F* and the *fourth* wavelet below *E;* this would represent one of a set of wave fronts which had been deviated through an angle of the order of 2α.

But more important is the fact that the angle of deviation, α, is determined by the wavelength. A portion of the diffraction grating containing only two openings which correspond to *E* and *F* in Fig. 28-14 is shown schematically in Fig. 28-15. A single wavelet of blue light and a lone wavelet of red light are shown, the radius of each being the wavelength (tremendously magnified) of light of that color. A wave front of diffracted blue light, and one of red light, are shown in solid lines, and the cor-

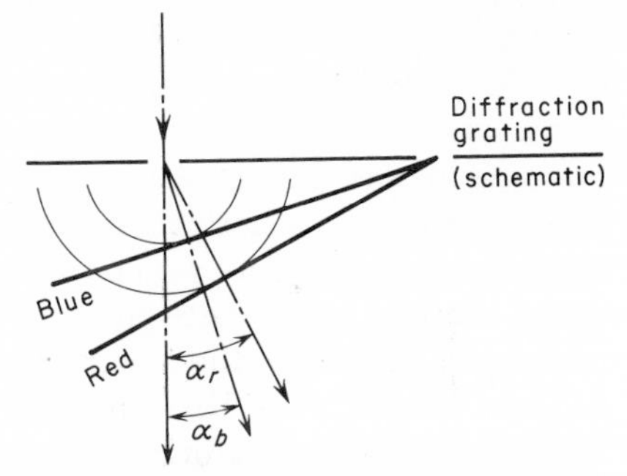

Fig. 28-15. The angle of deviation is greater for light of relatively long wavelength—the reverse of the situation when the deviation is caused by a prism (Fig. 28-10).

responding directions of propagation are indicated by dot-and-dash lines. Because of the greater wavelength, the angle α_r through which red light is deviated is greater than the angle of deviation α_b of the blue light. Thus a diffraction grating can disperse light somewhat as a prism does, so such gratings are useful in any spectrographic work. They have the great advantage that there is a definite mathematical relationship among (1) the distance between adjacent lines on the grating, (2) the angle of deviation, and (3) the wavelength. There is no general relationship between the angle of deviation caused by a prism and the wavelength.

Trig

If the wavelength is λ, the distance between adjacent lines on the grating is a, and the angle of deviation is α,

$$\lambda = a \sin \alpha \tag{28-4}$$

28-14 Polarization of Light

The waves of the electromagnetic spectrum are transverse waves. As a ray passes a point in a vacuum or in any transparent medium, an electric field at that point oscillates at right angles to the direction of propagation, the frequency of oscillation being the frequency of the waves. Simultaneously, the magnetic field oscillates, also perpendicularly to the direction of propagation and at the frequency of the waves; in addition, the directions of the electric and magnetic fields are mutually perpendicular.

Although for any photon passing a point the directions of the ***electric vector*** and the ***magnetic vector***—the directions of the electric and magnetic fields—are at right angles to each other, it does not follow that the electric vector for one photon is parallel to that for another photon. In general, the orientations of the electric vectors, hence of the magnetic vectors also, are random. We can make this more tangible by imagining a large group of children, each shaking one end of a rope and sending waves to the other end, which is tied to a post. Some youngsters would shake the rope up and down, generating waves in a vertical plane; others would produce waves in a horizontal plane by shaking the end of the rope from side to side; still others would not use either a perfectly vertical or horizontal motion. Thus waves in all possible planes might appear on the various ropes. Similarly, the electric vector or the magnetic vector of a light wave ordinarily may have any orientation, provided only that each is normal to the direction of propagation and that the electric and magnetic vectors are mutually at right angles. Thus there usually is a random orientation of corresponding vectors of different waves or rays or photons. In this case, the light is said to be ***unpolarized.***

By any of several means, the commonest of which now is to pass the light through a sheet of one of the substances known as Polaroid, the random orientation of the vectors may be reduced essentially to zero; that is, part of the light is removed, and in what remains, the electric vectors are all mutually parallel and so are the magnetic vectors. The light is then said to be ***plane polarized.*** This is the commonest type of polarization and light so modified often is simply called ***polarized*** light. Other types of polarization—which this book has no room to treat—are circular and elliptical polarization.

28-15 Evidence of the Transverse Nature of Light Waves

When scientists had so much difficulty in trying to discover whether light is a wave phenomenon or is particulate, how can we say with confidence that the waves are transverse? One justification is that light can be plane polarized, and no one has been able to conceive how the concept of polarization could apply to longitudinal waves; furthermore, longitudinal waves, such as sound waves, cannot be polarized.

A rather simple experiment furnishes additional and convincing proof that light waves must be transverse. Consider first a mechanical analog, as shown in Fig. 28-16(a); here we have a system of three mutually perpendicular ropes which are fastened together at a common point. If we send a longitudinal wave down the vertical rope, no longitudinal waves will appear in either horizontal rope, for there is no transverse motion of rope AB to disturb rope CD or EF in the direction of its length. But if we send a transverse wave down AB, its plane of vibration being parallel with EF, the motion of point G will cause longitudinal waves in EF but will generate transverse waves in a horizontal plane along CD.

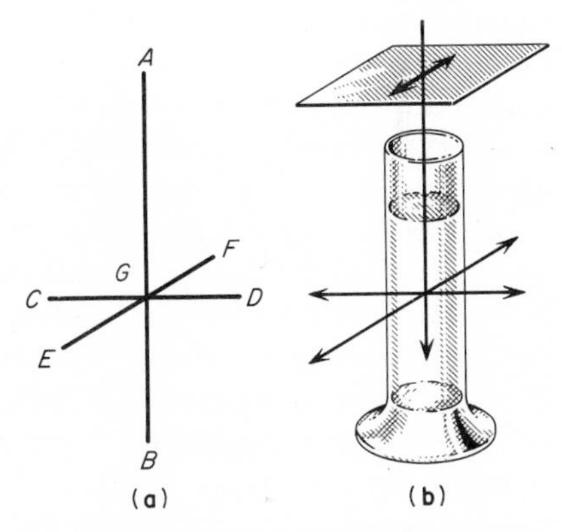

Fig. 28-16. Light-scattering experiment (b) which proves that light waves are transverse, and (a) a mechanical analog of the experiment. If polaroid is present, and if it is oriented so that waves in a plane parallel with the double-ended arrow can pass, no light will be scattered in that plane but light will be scattered to right and left.

If you shine light down into a glass cylinder of water which contains just a little milk, the contents of the cylinder appear luminous because the minute particles of milk scatter light out to the sides. If light were a longitudinal wave phenomenon, no light could be scattered laterally, for the same reason we have seen in the case of the ropes. Hence light must be due to transverse waves. We can check this by placing a piece of

Polaroid over the cylinder, as in Fig. 28-16(b), so that the light entering the cylinder is plane polarized. The result is that the liquid will appear luminous in some directions but not in others. Either changing your position or rotating the Polaroid film above the cylinder will vary the degree of luminosity, and the directions of maximum luminosity—maximum scattering of light—will be found to be 90° from the orientations of minimum luminosity—no scattered light. These results are in accord with what we found with the rope analogy. As a final check, the cylinder may be viewed through a second Polaroid film from a position where the luminosity is at a maximum, and this sheet of Polaroid rotated. It will be found that light will come through when the second Polaroid film is in a position to pass light polarized in a horizontal plane, but not when it is rotated to pass only light in a vertical plane.

28-16 Rotation of the Plane of Polarization

Various substances have the peculiar property of rotating the plane of polarization of plane-polarized light; a beam of plane-polarized light twists or "corkscrews" through the substance. This property provides a very convenient basis of analysis of such substances. A sample is put into a ***polariscope***, which is simply a device for measuring the angle through which the plane of polarization is rotated. The standard means of measuring sugar concentrations in the syrups in a sugar refinery is a saccharimeter, which is simply a polariscope calibrated to read per cent sugar rather than angle of rotation.

It happens that a strain in a transparent solid will alter its tendency to rotate the plane of polarization, with the result that when such a solid is viewed with polarized light while under stress an interference pattern will appear, the bands or "fringes" being narrow and close together at points of greater strain but wider and farther apart where the strain is less. Based on this, a technique has been developed for testing the design of parts of machines, etc., by making models of transparent plastic and studying them under polarized light as stress is applied.

A very interesting device is the Kerr cell, which uses an electrical field to cause, or alter, the rotation of the plane of polarization. In Fig. 28-17 there is a container with windows at either end and a pair of parallel plates like those of a capacitor. If this cell is filled with nitrobenzene (or any of many other substances) and plane-polarized light passed through from one end to the other, there is no effect on the plane of polarization, so long as no potential difference exists between the plates. But if a voltage is applied across the plates, the plane of polarization is rotated, the angle of

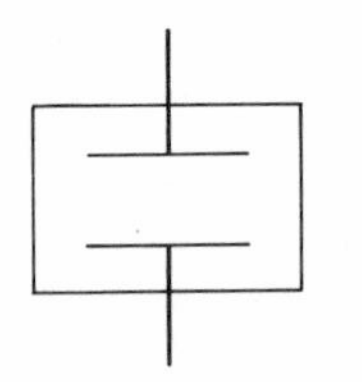

Fig. 28-17. The Kerr cell.

the rotation depending on the length and separation of the plates and on the value of the applied voltage. This so-called Kerr effect is one of many independent phenomena which testify to the electromagnetic nature of light.

Summary

Light normally travels in a *straight line.* The inverse square law of illumination and the formation of pinhole images are consequences of this rectilinear propagation.

Huygens' principle provides a convenient means of accounting for the *rectilinear propagation* of *light* and also for the direction taken by a *reflected* or a *refracted ray.*

The angles of incidence and reflection are equal, and the incident ray, the normal to the surface at the point of reflection, and the reflected ray all lie in the same plane.

An image may be formed by a plane mirror, but invariably the image is virtual.

Refraction is caused by a *change* in the speed of light as it passes from one medium to another. The *index of refraction* of a medium is the quotient of the speed of light in a vacuum and its speed in the medium. If it passes from one medium to another, division of the greater of the speeds in the two media by the smaller will give the relative index of refraction.

Dispersion is the *unequal bending* of the various components of non-monochromatic light. In the case of a prism, it occurs because different colors of light have unequal speeds in a physical medium. In the case of a diffraction grating, it is an interference phenomenon.

Since light is a wave phenomenon, interference may occur. Diffraction occurs if light encounters obstructions, or openings in a barrier, which have dimensions comparable with the wavelength.

Light may be polarized, and passage of polarized light through some substances causes the plane of polarization to rotate. This rotation of the plane of polarization has many useful applications.

Self-Quiz

1. Cite examples other than those in Sec. 28-2 which illustrate our acceptance and application of the fact that the propagation of light is rectilinear.

2. Discuss the "reasonableness" of Eq. (28-1) on the basis of the definitions of the quantities and the fact of rectilinear propagation. Is this equation applicable if the source is a fluorescent tube? Why?

3. With the aid of a diagram, describe in some detail the formation of a pinhole image. Is each point on the object represented by a *point* of light in the image?

Explain. How will the "sharpness" of the image be affected if the pinhole is enlarged? How will the brightness of the image be altered?

4. Discuss the propagation of a wave in terms of Huygens' principle.

5. Name the three phenomena which cause the path of a ray of light to be bent, and outline the process which is responsible for the bending. Point out any similarities and any differences among the three.

6. State the law of reflection, including any pertinent definitions. Illustrate the law, *especially* the latter portion of it, by considering the desk or table top to be a mirror and three pencils or pens to be the two light rays and the normal to the surface.

7. A ball being bounced off a frictionless surface may come close to obeying the law of reflection, but it never can obey it exactly, regardless of what material the ball is made of. Explain. A spinning tennis ball, bouncing off a hard court, may violate the law of reflection rather obviously. How, and why?

8. What is a virtual image, and why is it given this name? Why does a virtual image appear in a plane mirror, and why does it appear where it does? If you are three feet from a vanity or shaving mirror on the outside wall of a room, where is the image you are looking at? If the scene a cameraman is photographing includes a virtual image in a mirror, will that image appear in the photograph? Explain.

9. What is likely to happen to the orientation of a car at the instant the driver suddenly slams on the brakes while the left wheels are on dry concrete and the right wheels are in slippery mud? Compare this with what occurs when a beam of light passes obliquely from one medium into another in which the speed of light is reduced.

10. A quiz includes a diagram of a ray of light *AB* passing from air to water, as in Fig. 28-18, the line *CD* being the normal to the surface at the point of entry. The students are asked to indicate the approximate direction of the refracted ray, and the instructor finds the responses to include the five possibilities shown by the lines *BE–BI*, inclusive. On the basis of the fact that the speed of light is less in water than in air, and the mechanism of refraction as indicated in Fig. 28-8, show that four of these five responses are incorrect; and in each case show *why* the path indicated is impossible.

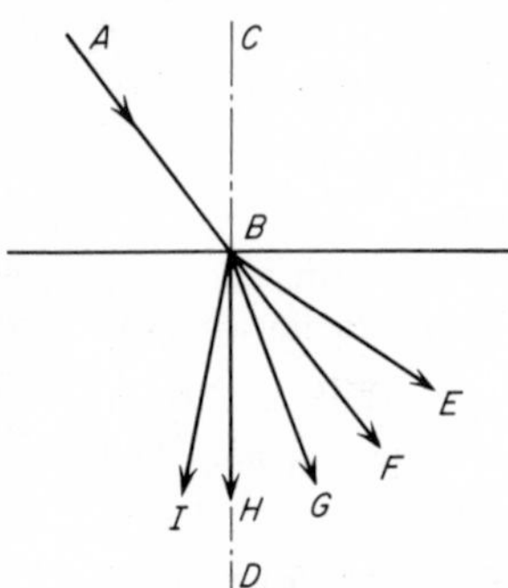

Figure 28-18

11. Define, compare, and contrast the two terms "index of refraction" and "relative index of refraction."

12. What is dispersion, and how does a prism cause dispersion?

13. A student finds that on passing through a prism color A is deviated more than color B. Outline each step of the logical process of thought by which he can determine which color has the greater velocity in the prism, and state the conclusion.

14. Show that if light of 5000 Å wavelength produces an interference pattern on a thin film with bands 1.0 mm apart, light of 6000 Å will give a pattern on the same film with the bands 1.2 mm apart.

15. With the aid of a diagram, explain the production of a diffraction pattern by two slits. Exactly what determines whether a given point on the screen will be in a light band or a dark band? If there are five bright bands between a given dark band and the central bright band, what is the difference in path length from the two slits to the position of the dark band?

16. Explain clearly the deviation of light by a diffraction grating. Is all the light deviated? Is monochromatic light all deviated in one direction? Explain the dispersion of light by a grating.

17. How does polarized light differ from unpolarized light? Which is more common? Of what use is polarized light?

18. Discuss the experiment on the scattering of light. What does it show with regard to the nature of light? Explain in some detail.

19. Discuss briefly an experiment which tends to verify the electromagnetic character of light.

Problems

1. Compute the illumination at a distance of (a) 5.00 ft, and (b) 10.0 m from a 30.0 candlepower (cp) lamp.

2. What is the luminous intensity of a lamp which gives an illumination of 5.00 lumens/m^2 at a distance of 175.0 cm?

3. A 100 w lamp gives an illumination of 6.00 ft-c at a distance of 4.00 ft. Calculate the luminous efficiency of the lamp, in candlepower per watt.

4. Light falls normally on the same surface from two lamps, the illumination being 10.0 ft-c. One lamp has a luminous intensity of 90.0 cp and is 5.00 ft from the surface. If the other lamp is 3.00 ft from the surface, determine its intensity.

5. Two lamps, one having an intensity of 25.0 cp, are 1.00 m apart. When a screen is placed directly between them, 35.0 cm from the 25.0 cp lamp, the two sides of the screen are illuminated equally. Calculate the intensity of the other lamp.

6. A lamp of 90.0 cp and one of 30.0 cp are 1.00 m apart. At what distance from the 30.0 cp lamp should a screen be placed between them if the illumination must be the same on both sides of the screen?

7. An object 2.00 ft wide and 5.00 ft high is 10.0 ft from a pinhole, and its image appears on a screen 6.00 in. behind the pinhole. Determine the dimensions of the image.

8. The frontal area of an object is 6.25 times as great as the area of its pinhole image. If the image is 15.0 cm from the pinhole, how far from the pinhole is the object?

9. A motorist has a rearview mirror 4.00 in. wide exactly 1.50 ft from his eye. At a distance of 50.0 ft behind the mirror, how wide is his field of view?

10. If the mirror in the preceding problem were moved 2.50 ft farther forward, by what per cent would the width of view at the same distance behind the car (not behind the mirror) be reduced?

11. The father of a family is 6 ft 2 in. tall, his wife is 5 ft 1 in., and they have a boy 5 ft 3 in. tall and a girl 3 ft 8 in. tall. He buys a mirror 62.0 in. high to mount on a door. Assuming the most favorable height of mounting, who is the tallest member of the family who can see his full height in the mirror?

12. In the preceding problem, the father's eyes are 5.00 in. below the top of his head. (a) What is the shortest mirror in which he could see his entire image? (b) How far above the floor should the bottom of the mirror be?

> NOTE: Use graphical methods for the remaining problems. You may have to be satisfied if your results check the first two digits of the answers given. If you know trig, do at least some of the problems graphically but check them trigonometrically.

13. Light falls on a block of glass at an angle of 45° from the normal. If the index of refraction of glass is 1.50, find the angle of refraction.

14. Determine the angle of refraction if the angle of incidence is 60.0° and the index of refraction is 1.60.

15. What is the angle of incidence if the index of refraction is 1.50 and the angle of refraction is 20.0°?

16. If the angles of incidence and refraction are 70.0° and 40.0° respectively, what is the index of refraction?

17. In Fig. 28-14 the angle of deviation, α, is equal to the angle between the grating and the diffracted wave front. If the openings of the grating are $1.67 \cdot 10^{-4}$ cm apart and the wavelength is 6000 Å, determine the angle of deviation.

18. In the same figure, and assuming the same distance between openings, what is the wavelength if the angle of deviation is 16.0°?

29
LENSES

29-1 Preview

This chapter is based almost entirely on the refraction of light (Sec. 28-8). It will deal briefly with the types of simple lenses. Next comes a discussion of the convergence of light by a lens, with some new terms. We shall meet the concept of a real image and renew acquaintance with the virtual image. Techniques will be developed for finding the location and characteristics of an image graphically, in different situations and with different kinds of lenses, and for solving simple lens problems mathematically. The chapter will close with a brief discussion of curved mirrors, in terms of analogies with lenses.

29-2 Types of Simple Lenses

By a ***simple lens*** one usually means a single piece of glass shaped in such a way that it can cause a beam of initially parallel light rays to converge to a point or to make such a beam diverge as if from a point. Lenses of the former type are ***converging*** lenses; the others are ***diverging*** lenses. For reasons to appear in Sec. 29-10, these two classes of lenses are also called ***positive*** and ***negative*** lenses, respectively. Simple lenses are subject to various defects, some of which we shall meet in the next chapter; to minimize defects, two or more simple lenses commonly are combined to from a ***compound*** lens. The unadorned term, "lens," is applied to either a simple or a compound lens, since the latter is optically equivalent to a simple lens except that it lacks some of the defects of a simple lens. Though glass is the most common material for lenses, they may be made of any transparent material.

There are three kinds of simple converging lenses, and three of the diverging type. In Fig. 29-1, each type is shown in cross section, and labeled.*

29-3 Convergence of Light by a Lens

From what we learned in Sec. 28-8 it is evident that if we put two prisms together, base to base, as in Fig. 29-2(a), the combination would refract the beam in such a way that, at some point behind the prisms, the beam would be reduced to only about half its initial width. The effect would be enhanced if we used portions of four prisms, as in part (b) of the figure. The more prism segments we added, if we chose them properly, the more effectively the beam would be concentrated; and the end result with an infinite number of infinitesimally thin sections would be a smoothly curved body as in part (c) of the diagram. Thus we may consider the double convex lens to be closely related to the prism.

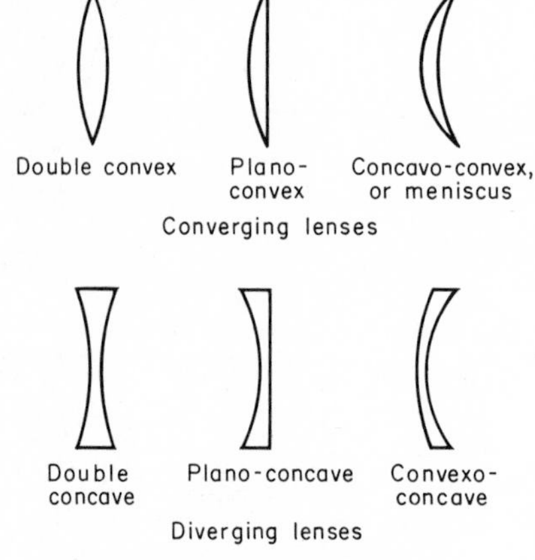

Fig. 29-1. Types of lenses.

Figure 29-3 is similar to Fig. 29-2(c), but more informative. The lens is AB, its center being at C.

* Many students have difficulty in avoiding confusion between the terms "convex" and "concave." This may be eliminated if you think of "concave" as "with cave"—that is, hollowed out; in fact, this is very close to the literal meaning of the Latin roots of the word.

The line *DE*, which passes through the center of the lens and is perpendicular to the plane which contains the rim of the lens, is the lens ***axis.*** *GA* and *HB* are the margins of a beam of rays which are all parallel with the axis—hence mutually parallel also. The ***principal focal point*** of a converging lens is defined as the point at which light will converge if it approaches the lens as a beam composed of rays which are mutually parallel, and parallel with the lens axis. *GA* and *HB* are the marginal rays of such a beam, so the principal focal point of the lens is at *F.* It is important to note that *any* ray which is parallel with the axis as it approaches the lens will be refracted so that (if it is not intercepted) it will cross the axis at the principal focal point.

(a)

(b)

(c)

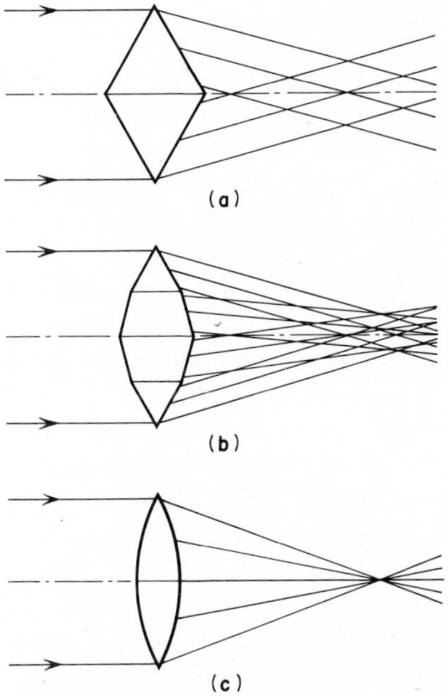

Fig. 29-2. Relative effectiveness of differently shaped pieces of glass in concentrating a beam of parallel light rays.

The distance between the optical center of a simple lens and the principal focal point is the ***focal length*** of the lens. This is the distance *CF* in Fig. 29-3, and is also labeled *f* in the upper part of the diagram.

The figure could have been drawn with the bundle of parallel rays coming from the right and converging to a point at the left; such a diagram would be a mirror image of Fig. 29-3, and all of our definitions would be correct for it. Thus a lens has not one principal focal point, but two; they are located on opposite sides of the lens, on the axis and equidistant from the optical center of the lens.

29-4 Conventions Employed in Making Lens Diagrams

Before we begin on the problem of determining the location and characteristics of the image, we must examine a special case of refraction which will be helpful. Part (a) of Fig. 29-4 shows a ray of light passing through a sheet of glass. In passing through the glass, the ray is offset from its

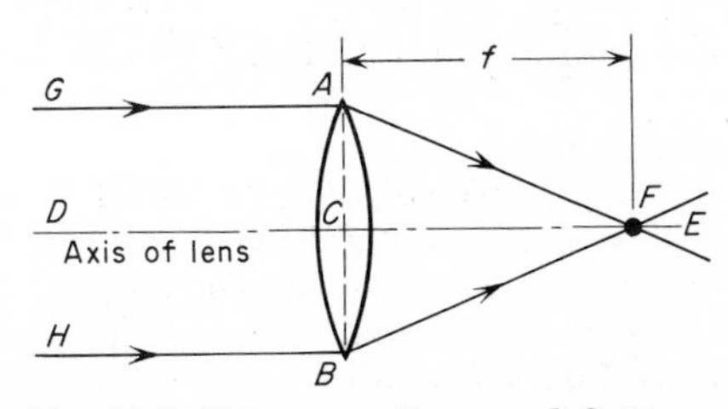

Fig. 29-3. Diagram to illustrate definitions.

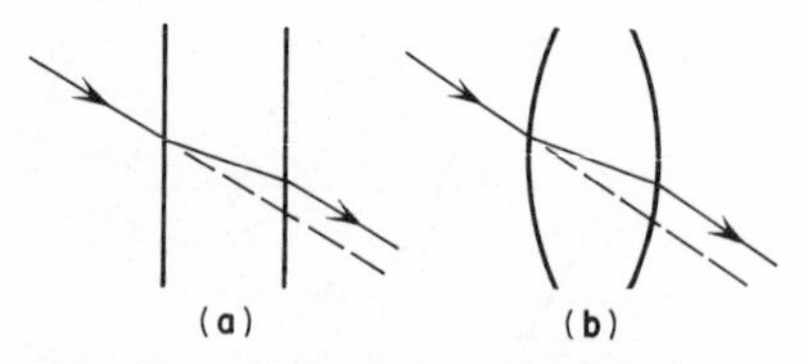

Fig. 29-4. Offset of path of light ray when surface at point of entry is parallel to surface at point of emergence.

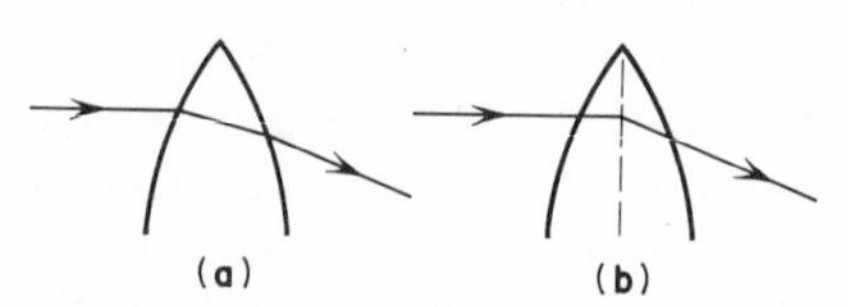

Fig. 29-5. (a) Actual path of a light ray through a lens; (b) conventional representation of path.

former path, which is shown by the dashed line; but because the two surfaces of the glass sheet are parallel, the emergent ray travels parallel with its former direction. It is evident that the thinner the glass is, the smaller the offset in the path of the ray will be.

Part (b) of Fig. 29-4 shows a ray approaching a symmetrical lens at an angle to the axis. In general, the surfaces of the lens certainly are not parallel; but because of the symmetry of the lens, *if a ray passes through the center of the lens,* the surface of the lens at the point of entry *of that ray* is parallel to the surface at the point of emergence. Thus the situation is the same as in part (a); the ray is offset but continues parallel with its original path, and for a thin lens the offset may be so small that we may disregard it.* Hence we may use a simple straight line to represent any ray which passes through the center of the lens.

One other simplification is commonly employed. A ray is bent as it enters the lens and is bent again when it emerges, as in Fig. 29-5(a); and these two different bends complicate the construction of diagrams. Hence the incoming ray is drawn, with no bend, to the midplane of the lens as in part (b) of the same figure; and the outgoing ray is drawn as a straight line from the midplane. You must not let the habitual use of this convention generate the idea that any bending actually *occurs* at the midplane; the true situation is represented in part (a), not part (b), of the figure.

29-5 Formation of an Image by a Converging Lens: Object Distance Greater than Focal Length

In Fig. 29-6, the arrow *AB* represents an object, the distance of the object from the lens being greater than the focal length of the lens.

---

* Of course, disregarding the offset limits us to approximations rather than exact relationships, and by no means all lenses are "thin" lenses. Furthermore, most lenses are not symmetrical double convex lenses. For many lenses, however, the approximate relationships involve less uncertainty than the average laboratory experiment. Discussions which take into account the thickness and assymmetry of lenses may be found in advanced texts—where they belong. Our concern is with the basic principles, plus an awareness that an approximation is involved.

An image can be formed only if the object is illuminated or is self-luminous. Light rays may leave the object in all directions, but only those which travel toward the lens are of interest to us. In general, we are at a loss to predict the paths of these rays after they have passed through the lens. They could be worked out, in terms of angles of incidence and index of refraction, but it would be quite a chore. However, we can always predict, with complete confidence, the paths of three particular rays which reach the lens from a given point on the object. Two of these are usually more convenient, so the third will be left for you to deal with in Self-Quiz Question 5. Once we have found where our two chosen rays from a given object point converge, we may be sure that this is also the point of convergence for all other rays which originate at the same object point and pass through the lens—that is, there is *approximate* convergence at this particular point, and all of them would meet there exactly if the lens were perfect.

The two rays whose paths we can predict are one parallel with the axis and one through the center of the lens. From the definition of the principal focal point, we know that the ray from point A in Fig. 29-6 which approaches the lens parallel with the axis must, after passing through the lens, cross the axis at the principal focal point; thus we obtain the ray ADF. And in the preceding section we found that we may draw a central ray through the center of the lens, and on with no deviation; this gives us the straight line through A and C in the figure. If we continue both of these rays they converge at the point labeled A'.

Suppose that we hold a cardboard or ground-glass screen at the location of $A'B'$ in the figure. The rays $ADFA'$ and ACA', *and all other rays from* A which passed through the lens, will fall on the screen at point A', illuminating it with a color and relative brightness characteristic of point A on the object. We could draw a pair of rays analogous to $ADFA'$ and ACA' for each of the infinite number of points on the object (if we had infinite time and patience!), showing that each object point on AB is represented by an image point of $A'B'$. The spatial arrangement of the image points, their color, and their relative brilliance would correspond to those in the object, so $A'B'$ is the image of the object AB. Object points above the axis of the lens yield image points below the axis, and there is a similar reversal of right and left, so the image is said to be ***inverted.***

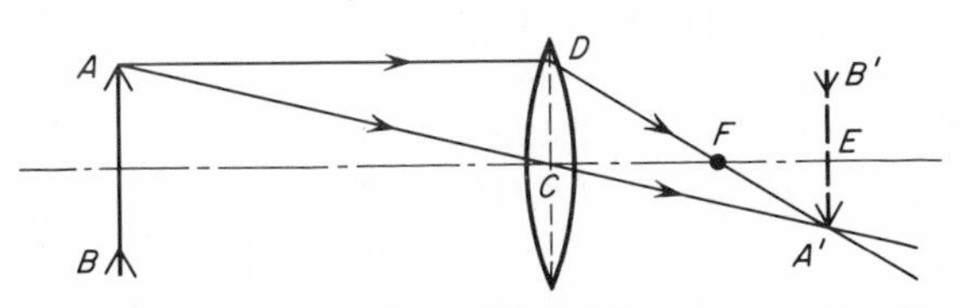

Fig. 29-6. Formation of a real image by a converging lens.

Because of a potential source of confusion which will be pointed out in Sec. 29-8, I prefer my students to locate B' by symmetry rather than by drawing rays from B as I have done from A; however, most instructors prefer to have the second set of rays constructed. You can easily add them to Fig. 29-6.

Compare the image we find here with that formed by a plane mirror (Sec. 28-7). In that case there were no light rays from the object at the location of the image; the image was merely an optical illusion and consequently was described as virtual. But in the present case, the light rays not only are present, they converge in such a way as to illuminate a screen (if one is present), painting, in pinpoints of light, a full-color facsimile of the object. This is a ***real*** image.

The point on the axis where the axis intersects the image—E, in Fig. 29-6—is the ***focal point*** for the object. Obviously this is not the *principal* focal point, which is at F rather than at E. We must be very careful to avoid confusing the two. The principal focal point has a fixed position (which is why the lens has a definite focal length), but a focal point, in general, may be almost anywhere on the axis. For example, imagine the object in Fig. 29-6 being moved farther from the lens. Without altering the path of the ray from D through F, the change in object position would make the angle between ray ACA' and the axis more acute. Hence the two rays would converge closer to F; that is, the focal point would be moved nearer to the *principal* focal point. You can see that as the object distance is increased ray ACA' becomes more nearly parallel with the axis, moving the image ever nearer to F; but since this ray crosses the lens axis at the center of the lens, its intersection with the ray through DF must remain on the far side of F. In theory, the image is exactly at F if the object distance is infinite, and in a practical sense it may be considered to be at F if the object distance is large compared with the focal length.* Hence we may consider the focal length—the distance from the lens to the *principal* focal point—to be equal to the image distance *when the object is at a great distance.* This provides a convenient basis for obtaining an approximate value of the focal length of a converging lens.

29-6 The Lens Equation

The terms "object distance," "image distance," and "focal length" have been used, but only the last has been defined formally. As indicated in Fig. 29-7, the distance of the object from the lens is the ***object distance,*** and the ***image distance*** is the distance of the image from the lens. Both of these distances, as well as the focal length, are measured from the center

* The image distance exceeds the focal length by 1% when the object distance is 100 times the focal length, 0.1% when the object distance is 1000 times the focal length, etc.

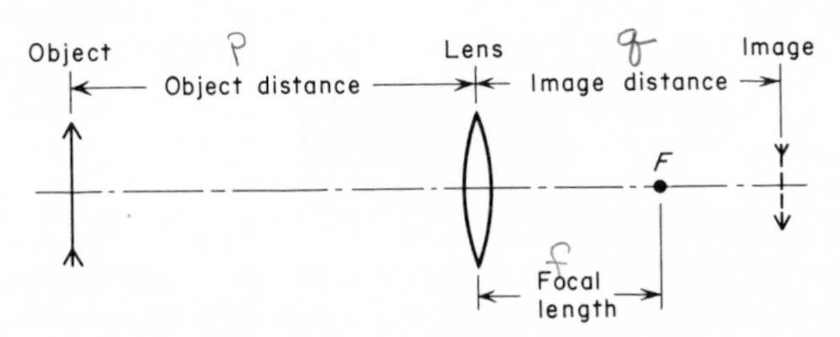

Fig. 29-7. Diagram to illustrate definitions.

of the lens.* The symbol p stands for object distance, the image distance is symbolized by q, and f represents the focal length of the lens.

By applying a bit of geometry to Fig. 29-8 we can derive the mathematical relationship among these three quantities. Triangles CDF and GEF are similar; and since corresponding parts in similar triangles stand in the same ratio to each other, we can write

$$\frac{GE}{CD} = \frac{FG}{CF}$$

Triangles BAC and GEC are similar also, so

$$\frac{GE}{BA} = \frac{CG}{BC}$$

The ray AD is parallel with the axis, for otherwise it would cross the axis, after refraction, at some point other than F; hence $BA = CD$, and we may make this substitution in the last equation above. Thus it becomes

$$\frac{GE}{CD} = \frac{CG}{BC}$$

The left side of this equation is identical with that of our initial equation, so the right-hand members of the two equations must be equal:

$$\frac{FG}{CF} = \frac{CG}{BC}$$

Referring to Fig. 29-8, we see that we may use $(q - f)$ for FG, f for CF, q for CG, and p for BC. Thus,

$$\frac{q-f}{f} = \frac{q}{p}$$

This simplifies to

$$\frac{q}{f} - 1 = \frac{q}{p}$$

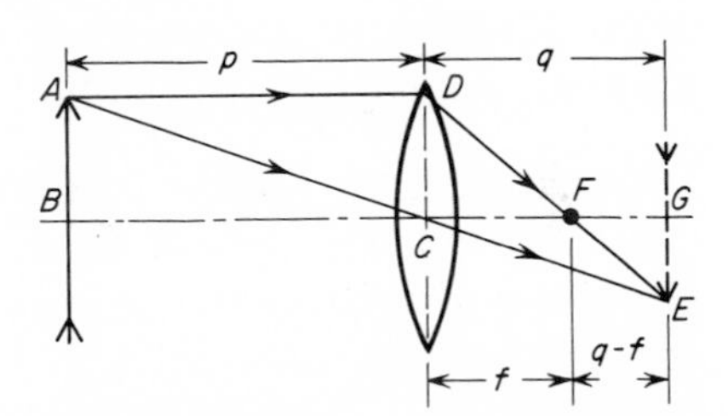

Fig. 29-8. Diagram for derivation of lens equation.

* Here, again the situation is more complicated if unsymmetrical lenses are used.

and, on transposing and dividing through by q, we obtain

$$\frac{1}{f} = \frac{1}{p} + \frac{1}{q} \tag{29-1}$$

This is the most common form of the simple ***lens equation.***

Much can be learned by studying this equation. Evidently, the values of p and q could be interchanged without violating the equation. The physical implication of this is that if the object is moved from its position in Fig. 29-6, 29-7, or 29-8, and placed where the image was, an image will appear at the former location of the object. This agrees with the fact that light paths are reversible, as noted in Chapter 28. Because the positions of object and image are interchangeable, any object position and the corresponding image position are called ***conjugate foci.***

The reversibility of light paths implies that if a point source of light is placed at the principal focal point of a lens (Fig. 29-3) the refracted light should form a parallel beam. Mathematically, this is equivalent to setting p equal to f, in which case Eq. (29-1) requires that $1/q = 0$, which can be true only if the value of q is infinite. This means that the refracted rays converge only at an infinite distance if the object distance equals the focal length; that is, the refracted rays form the parallel beam we predicted by considering the reversibility of rays in Fig. 29-3. Finally, suppose that the object is at an infinite distance; then $1/p = 0$ so $q = f$. This agrees with our finding in the last paragraph of Sec. 29-5.

Before we leave this equation, one additional point must be emphasized. In the derivation, all distances have been taken as positive; thus the values of p, q, and f are all positive if the principal focal point and the image are on the side of the lens opposite the object. Following the usual convention, a minus sign is applied to any distance which must be measured in a direction, relative to the object direction, which is opposite that assumed in the derivation, and shown in the figures thus far. Hence, p, q, and f all have positive values in Fig. 29-6; but in Fig. 29-9, p and f are positive, whereas q is negative. In Fig. 29-11, f is negative; and in Fig. 29-12, p is positive, but both f and q are negative.

29-7 An Alternate Form of the Lens Equation

Though Eq. (29-1) is the most common form of the equation for simple lenses, sometimes an equivalent equation formulated by Newton is useful. This makes use of the distances of the object and image from the principal focal points, rather than from the lens. Thus, $p - f = x$, where x is the distance of the object from the principal focal point nearer the object, and $q - f = y$, where y is the distance of the image from the principal focal point. (If the value of the image distance is less than that of the focal length, y is negative, and similarly x may have a negative value.)

To derive the Newtonian lens equation, we may take Eq. (29-1) and multiply through by pqf, obtaining

$$pq = qf + pf$$

Expressed in terms of x and y instead of p and q, this becomes

$$(x + f)(y + f) = (y + f)\cdot f + (x + f)\cdot f$$

$$xy + xf + yf + f^2 = yf + f^2 + xf + f^2$$

Canceling common terms on opposite sides of the equation, we obtain

$$xy = f^2 \tag{29-2}$$

Sample Problem 1

An object is 30.0 cm from a converging lens of 10.0 cm focal length. Where is the image?

The usual equation is

$$\frac{1}{f} = \frac{1}{p} + \frac{1}{q}$$

so

$$\frac{1}{10.0} = \frac{1}{30.0} + \frac{1}{q}$$

$$\frac{1}{10.0} - \frac{1}{30.0} = \frac{1}{q} = \frac{3}{30.0} - \frac{1}{30.0}$$

$$\frac{1}{q} = \frac{2}{30.0} = \frac{1}{15.0}$$

$$q = 15.0 \text{ cm}$$

On the basis of the Newtonian lens equation,

$$x = 30.0 - 10.0 = 20.0 \text{ cm}$$

Then

$$xy = f^2$$

so

$$20.0y = 10.0^2 = 100$$

$$y = 100/20.0 = 5.00$$

Hence the image distance exceeds the focal length by 5.00 cm, so it is 10.0 + 5.00 = 15.0 cm.

29-8 Formation of an Image by a Converging Lens: Object Distance Less than Focal Length

We saw in the last paragraph of Sec. 29-5 that, as the object distance increases, the image moves closer to the principal focal point, reaching that point when the object is at infinity. Because the light paths are reversible, this means that, as an object is moved toward the lens from well beyond the principal focal point, the image moves farther back, being at infinity when the object is at the principal focal point. We deduced the same fact in the latter part of Sec. 29-6 by setting p equal to f in Eq. (29-1). But what becomes of the image if the object is moved still closer to the lens?

A diagram will answer this question, and we know how to construct *any* such diagram: a ray which is parallel to the axis as it approaches the lens will pass through the principal focal point after leaving the lens, and a ray through the center of the lens will be undeviated. Proceeding on this basis, we obtain the solid lines in Fig. 29-9. After passing through the lens the rays are neither convergent nor parallel; instead, they diverge. This situation is reminiscent of the one we met in Sec. 28-7, in the case of rays reflected from a plane mirror; and as in that case, the eye is fooled into thinking that the rays originated at the common point on their extended direction lines. Hence the eye assumes that all rays which originated at A came instead from A', and in the same way it is tricked into taking for granted that rays came from B' whereas they actually came from B; and a similar situation exists for rays from all other points on the object. Thus an image of AB is seen at $A'B'$. Unlike the inverted image formed when the object distance was greater than the focal length (Fig. 29-6 and Fig. 29-8), this image is "right side up" or ***erect.*** Like that seen in a plane mirror, it is an optical illusion; it is a virtual image, instead of the real image produced by the lens when the object distance exceeds the focal length.

There is a very common error which may occur if you include rays from both ends of the object in your diagram. It is very easy to see an intersection of rays, as at C and D in Fig. 29-10, and conclude that there is an image CD. But intersections such as those at C and D involve rays from *different* points on the object, and only rays from the *same* point on the object can generate a corresponding point in an image; so the chance crossing of unrelated rays as at C and D is utterly meaningless. Possibly you could give such points some significance by emulating the great hybridizer Luther Burbank, drawing a plum at A and an apricot at B and obtaining a plumcot at C (or would it be at D?); but since this book deals with physics rather than plant breeding this possibility will not be pursued.

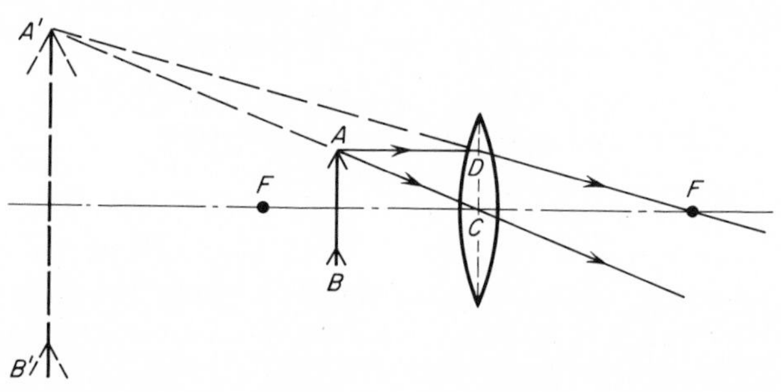

Fig. 29-9. Formation of a virtual image by a converging lens.

Equations (29-1) and (29-2) are valid, without change, for the situation discussed in this section. If, for example, an object is 15.0 cm from a lens which has a focal length of 20.0 cm, according to Eq. (29-1)

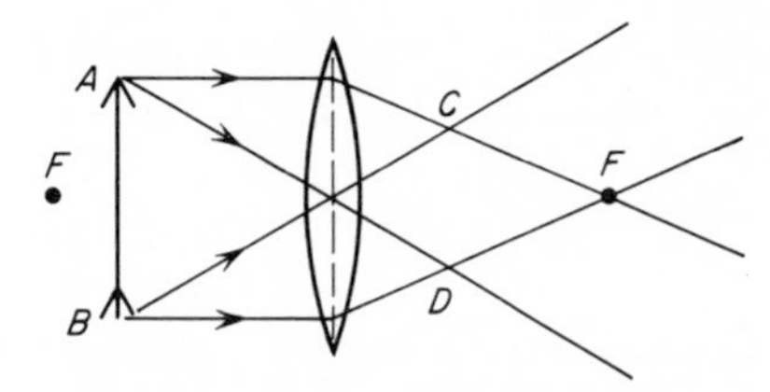

Fig. 29-10. The intersection of rays from A and B, as at C or D, does *not* produce an image point.

$$\frac{1}{20.0} = \frac{1}{15.0} + \frac{1}{q}$$

$$\frac{1}{20.0} - \frac{1}{15.0} = \frac{1}{q} = \frac{3}{60.0} - \frac{4}{60.0}$$

$$\frac{1}{q} = -\frac{1}{60.0}$$

$$q = -60.0 \text{ cm}$$

The negative sign on the image distance may be unexpected, but we should have anticipated it. Relative to the direction of the object distance, the image distance in Fig. 29-9 has to be measured in a direction opposite that in Fig. 29-6 and Fig. 29-8, and from Chapter 3 on we have interpreted a minus sign associated with a vector quantity as indicating reversal of direction. Thus *a negative image distance identifies the image as a virtual image.* Similarly, *a real image is identified by a positive value of the image distance.*

Sample Problem 2

An object 20.0 cm from a lens produces a virtual image 50.0 cm from the lens. Compute the focal length of the lens.

Putting the data into Eq. (29-1), we have

$$\frac{1}{f} = \frac{1}{20.0} + \frac{1}{50.0} = \frac{5}{100} + \frac{2}{100} = \frac{7}{100}$$

$$f = \frac{100}{7} = 14.3 \text{ cm}$$

But this is *not* correct, and I hope that you knew it was wrong. The image is *virtual*, so the image distance is -50.0 cm instead of $+50.0$ cm. Hence

$$\frac{1}{f} = \frac{1}{20.0} + \frac{1}{-50.0} = \frac{1}{20.0} - \frac{1}{50.0}$$

$$= \frac{5}{100} - \frac{2}{100} = \frac{3}{100}$$

$$f = \frac{100}{3} = 33.3 \text{ cm}$$

Just as you must habitually interpret a negative image distance as the distance of a *virtual* image, you must school yourself to include a minus sign

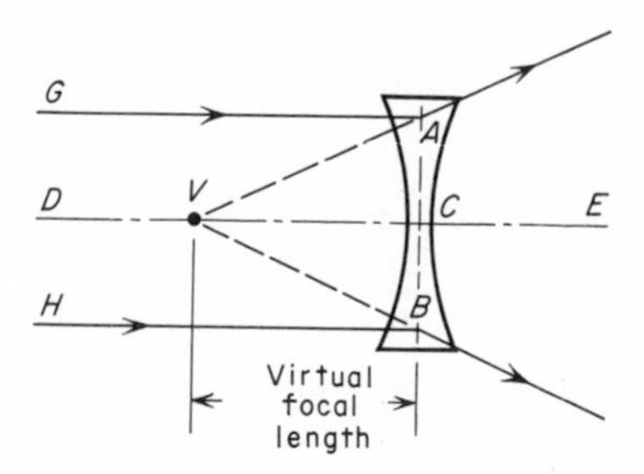

Fig. 29-11. Diagram to illustrate definitions.

automatically when you record the distance of a virtual image. Note, however, that the equation itself is unchanged for this new situation; with proper attention to signs, it is valid for *any* problem relating object distance, image distance, and focal length.

29-9 Diverging Lenses

Had the lens in Fig. 29-3 been a diverging lens, the beam of parallel rays would have spread out after passing through the lens; there would have been no principal focal point, and no focal length, in the sense of their definitions in Sec. 29-3.

Figure 29-11 indicates the analogous situation when a diverging lens is employed. The ray *GA* is refracted upward and the ray *HB* is bent downward, the directions of the refracted rays being such that they seem to have come from a common point *V* on the axis; and (assuming a perfect lens) all other rays in the parallel bundle will be refracted so that they appear to have had a common origin at *V*. Thus, instead of being refracted *toward* a common point, the rays are refracted *away from* a common point. This common point, *V* in Fig. 29-11, is the ***virtual focal point*** of the lens, and the distance of the virtual focal point from the center of the lens is the ***virtual focal length.****

29-10 Formation of an Image by a Diverging Lens

Here again, the method of constructing a diagram to locate the image is no different. In Fig. 29-12 a ray *ADE* is drawn parallel with the axis, and then outward from the virtual focal point *V*. Another ray *AC* is drawn through the center of the lens without bending. These two rays will *seem* to have originated at *A′*, where the projected direction line of the refracted ray *DE* intersects the path of the ray *AC*. Thus *A′* is an image point corresponding to the object point *A;* and similar divergence of rays from other points on the object *AB* will produce the image *A′B′*. Since the ray *ADE* does not pass through *A′* but only *seems* to have come from there, this is a virtual image.

If the object *AB* were moved from its position in Fig. 29-12 to a point between the virtual focal point *V* and the lens, the path of the refracted

* Most authorities use the term "principal focal point" or "principal focal point (virtual)" instead of "virtual focal point," and "focal length" rather than "virtual focal length." Until you are thoroughly familiar with these concepts, however, the habitual inclusion of the word "virtual" in these terms may reduce confusion.

ray DE would be unaffected, but the path of the ray AC would slant more sharply downward; hence the rays beyond the lens would diverge and the image would be virtual as before. Such a change of position does not affect the type of image given by a diverging lens, as we found it does in the case of a converging lens.

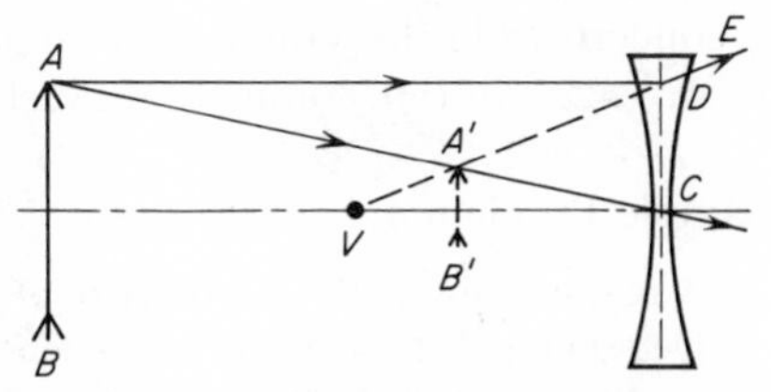

Fig. 29-12. Formation of a virtual image by a diverging lens.

Sample Problem 3

Suppose that an object 25.0 cm from a diverging lens gives an image 10.0 cm from the lens. What must the virtual focal length of the lens be?

The image can only be virtual, as we have just seen, and we must avoid the trap set in Sample Problem 2; the image distance is *minus* 10.0 cm. Insertion of the data into Eq. (29-1) gives

$$\frac{1}{f} = \frac{1}{25.0} + \frac{1}{-10.0} = \frac{1}{25.0} - \frac{1}{10.0}$$

$$= \frac{2}{50.0} - \frac{5}{50.0}$$

$$\frac{1}{f} = \frac{-3}{50.0}$$

$$f = \frac{-50.0}{3} = -16.7 \text{ cm}$$

Here, at last, is the reason a diverging lens is called a "negative" lens. A *negative value* of a *focal length identifies* the *lens* as a *diverging* lens and the *focal length* as *virtual.* Similarly, a lens is *converging* if the *value* of *its focal length* is *positive.*

29-11 Relative Sizes of the Object and the Image

A glance at the figures which represent the formation of an image by a lens reveals that in every case there is a pair of similar triangles formed by segments of the object and the image, the central ray, and the lens axis, regardless of the type of lens or the kind of image. Invoking the properties of similar triangles, we may write

$$\frac{\text{image size}}{\text{object size}} = \frac{\text{image distance}}{\text{object distance}}$$

or

$$\frac{\text{image size}}{\text{object size}} = \left|\frac{q}{p}\right| \qquad (29\text{-}4)$$

The vertical bars bracketing q/p signify that only the magnitudes of p and

q concern us in this equation, so signs (+ or −) may be disregarded. The term "size" in this connection must be interpreted as a *linear* dimension.

Sample Problem 4

A real image exactly 1/5 the size of the object is formed 9.00 cm from a lens. Determine the focal length of the lens.

From Eq. (29-4), the image distance is 1/5 the object distance. So

$$p = 5q = 5 \cdot 9.00 \text{ cm} = 45.0 \text{ cm}$$

Then

$$\frac{1}{f} = \frac{1}{45.0} + \frac{1}{9.00} = \frac{1}{45.0} + \frac{5}{45.0}$$

$$= \frac{6}{45.0} = \frac{2}{15.0}$$

$$f = \frac{15.0}{2} = 7.50 \text{ cm}$$

29-12 Discussion of the Locations and Characteristics of Images

Let us summarize the qualitative aspects of our findings:

If the object distance exceeds the focal length, a positive lens will produce an image which is real, inverted, and located on the side of the lens opposite the object. It may be larger or smaller than the object.

If the object distance is less than the focal length, a positive lens will produce a virtual image which is erect, larger than the object, and on the same side of the lens as the object.

The image produced by a negative lens invariably is virtual, erect, on the same side of the lens as the object, and smaller than the object.

This summary indicates that real images are inverted and virtual ones are erect. Though this is true *if* the optical device contains but a single lens (or curved mirror), it is unsafe if two or more lenses are involved. If you are a biologist, you know that a compound microscope gives an inverted image, but this is a virtual image. A criterion much safer than erectness or inversion is convergence or divergence of the rays. If the rays *con*verge to form the image, the image is *real;* if the image is due to the *di*vergence of rays, it is *virtual.*

29-13 An Alternate Point of View of the Action of Lenses

Instead of thinking only of rays going through lenses, it is instructive to consider waves.

In Fig. 29-13(a), a series of circular wavelets of light is sent from an object point A toward a positive lens. Since the lens is thickest at the axis and becomes progressively thinner toward the edges, and because of the lessened speed of light in the glass, the waves are retarded most along the axis and least at the edges. The result is that the wave fronts emerging from the lens are concave rather than convex, so instead of continuing to diverge they converge toward their common center of curvature A'.

The lens in part (b) of the figure also retards the waves along the axis more than at the edges, but because A is so close to the lens the wave fronts are more sharply convex when they reach the lens than were those in (a). Hence the lens is only able to reduce, rather than to overcome, the convexity of the wave fronts. The emergent wave fronts are still divergent, but are diverging as if from a point A', farther from the lens than point A.

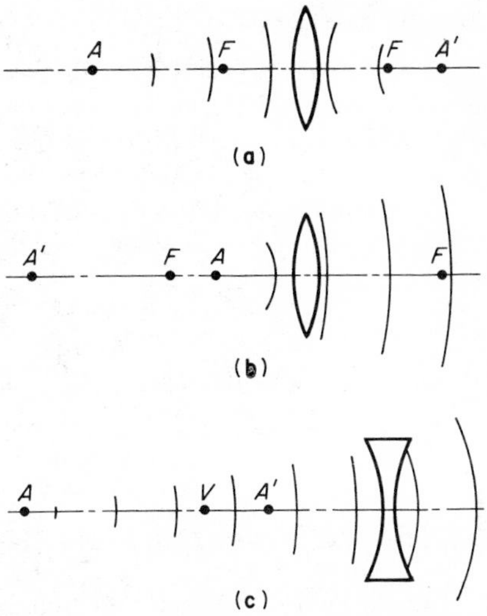

A negative lens appears in part (c) of Fig. 29-13. It retards the waves most near its rim and least along the axis; thus it increases the convexity of the wave fronts rather than reducing or reversing it. The emergent wave fronts seem to come from a point A', closer to the lens than A.

Fig. 29-13. A positive lens retards the center of the wave fronts, making them concave as in part (a) or reducing their convexity as in part (b). A negative lens retards the edges of the wave fronts as in part (c), making the wave fronts more convex. The wave fronts originate at A, but after passing through the lens their center of curvature is at A' instead.

29-14 The Lens Maker's Equation

Quantitative analysis of the action of a lens from the point of view in the preceding section leads to a relationship among the focal length of a lens, the index of refraction of the lens material, and the radii of curvature of its surfaces; but the derivation belongs in more advanced texts. The equation is

$$\frac{1}{f} = (n - 1) \cdot \left(\frac{1}{R_1} + \frac{1}{R_2} \right) \qquad (29\text{-}5)$$

in which f is the focal length, n the refractive index of the medium in the lens, and R_1 and R_2 are the radii of curvature of its two faces. Values of the radii are positive for convex lens surfaces, and negative for concave surfaces.

Sample Problem 5

A plano-convex lens is made of glass which has a refractive index of 1.600. The focal length is 30.0 cm. Compute the radius of curvature of the convex surface.

No value is given for the radius of curvature of the plane surface, but since the curvature of a sphere flattens as the size increases, a plane surface may be considered to be part of the surface of a sphere of infinite radius. With this, and the specified values of other quantities, Eq. (29-5) becomes

$$\frac{1}{30.0} = (1.600 - 1)\left(\frac{1}{\infty} + \frac{1}{R}\right) = 0.600 \cdot \frac{1}{R}$$

since $1/\infty = 0$. Rearrangement of the equation gives

$$R = 0.600 \cdot 30.0 = 18.0 \text{ cm}$$

29-15 The Power of a Lens

Those who prescribe or manufacture lenses for eyeglasses do not describe the lenses in terms of focal length. Instead, they speak of the ***power*** of the lens, which is the reciprocal of its focal length when the focal length is expressed in meters. The power is expressed in ***diopters.*** Thus a lens which has a focal length of 40.0 cm or 0.400 m has a power of 1/0.400 or 2.50 diopters; or a lens with a power of (exactly) half a diopter will have a focal length of 1/0.500 or 2.00 m, or 200 cm.

Algebraically, the definition of the power of a lens is $D = 1/f$, D being the power in diopters and f the focal length in meters. Combining this with Eq. (29-1), we obtain

$$D = \frac{1}{p} + \frac{1}{q} \tag{29-6}$$

in which the object and image distances, p and q, must be expressed in meters.

29-16 Curved Mirrors

If a beam of parallel light rays falls on a concave mirror, the rays will be reflected so that they are convergent; a diagram would be similar to Fig. 29-3, with the part of the diagram to the right of the lens folded back over the part at the left, and the lens replaced by a concave mirror. Thus, a concave mirror is essentially equivalent, optically, to a positive lens. Similarly, a convex mirror is the analog of a negative lens.

The summary of characteristics of images formed by lenses in Sec. 29-12 can be made to apply to mirrors by changing "same" to "opposite," and vice versa, in the specifications of the relative positions of object and image, and replacing "positive lens" by "concave mirror" and "negative lens" by "convex mirror."

Equations (29-1) and (29-2) are valid for curved mirrors, if f is considered positive for a concave mirror and negative for a convex mirror, and if q is considered positive when the image is on the same side of the mirror as the object and negative when it is behind the mirror.

Summary

A lens may be any one of several types, and it may be simple or compound; but all lenses may be classified as *converging* or *diverging*. Converging lenses are also called *positive* lenses, and diverging lenses are *negative* lenses.

If a ray initially is *parallel* with the axis of a positive lens, the point at which the ray crosses the *axis* after passing through the lens is the *principal focal point* of the lens. The distance from the center of the lens to the principal focal point is the *focal length* of the lens. A *negative* lens bends a similar ray *away* from the *axis*, and the point on the axis from which the refracted ray *seems* to come is the *virtual focal point* of the lens. Its virtual focal length is the distance from the center of the lens to the virtual focal point.

Depending on the situation and the lens used, an *image* may be *real* or *virtual*. *Real* images are due to the *convergence* of *refracted* rays, and *virtual* images are due to *divergence* of such rays. Commonly, the former are inverted and the latter erect, but this is not always a valid criterion.

Virtual focal lengths, and image distances of virtual images, always have *negative* values.

In general, an *image* may be located graphically, and its type and relative size determined, by considering a ray *parallel* with the *axis* and another through the *center* of the *lens*. The former will be refracted toward the principal focal point, or away from the virtual focal point; the latter will pass through without deviation.

The *ratio* of the *sizes* of object and image are the *same* as the *ratio* of their *respective distances* from the lens.

Three different mathematical relationships are available for lens problems; two of them relate the focal length to the positions of the object and image, and the other relates it to the design of the lens.

The power of a lens in diopters is the reciprocal of its focal length in meters.

Curved mirrors are essentially equivalent to lenses, a concave mirror being analogous to a positive lens and a convex mirror to a negative lens.

Self-Quiz

1. Make a diagram of the six kinds of simple lenses and label each. Classify each as converging or diverging and as negative or positive.

2. Compare and contrast the terms "focal point" and "principal focal point." Give two definitions of principal focal point. Define focal length.

3. Compare and contrast the terms "principal focal point" and "virtual focal point." Compare and contrast focal length and virtual focal length.

4. When a spotlight "throws" a beam of parallel light rays, where is the source of light with respect to the lens? How do you know this to be true? What kind of a lens is used?

5. Draw a diagram similar to Fig. 29-6 but omit ray ACA'. Instead, mark and label the position of the principal focal point on the side toward the object, and draw a ray from A through this point. Where will it go after it passes through the lens, and why? Locate the image with the aid of this ray and the ray $ADFA'$. Repeat, omitting ray $ADFA'$ but showing ray ACA' and drawing the ray through the near principal focal point.

6. Define the two terms, "real image" and "virtual image." Compare and contrast the two kinds of images.

7. What is the simplest way of finding the approximate value of the focal length of a positive lens? Why is this method valid? Within what limits is it valid?

8. What is meant by the expression, "reversibility of light paths"? Of what importance, if any, is this reversibility?

9. Discuss the significance of signs (+ and −) in Eq. (29-1) and Eq. (29-2). If for a given situation p is positive in Eq. (29-1), will x necessarily be positive in Eq. (29-2)? If q is positive will y necessarily be positive?

10. Derive Eq. (29-2) directly from the figure called for in the first part of Question 5. (This derivation is similar to that in Sec. 29-6, but simpler.)

11. Proceeding with the least possible reference to the diagrams in the text, make a diagram which will definitely show the position, relative size, type, and erectness or inversion of the image when (a) the lens is positive and f is greater than p; (b) the lens is negative; and (c) the lens is positive and p is greater than f. Why was the relationship between p and f not specified in part (b)?

12. Prove, for each diagram in the preceding question, that the ratio of the sizes of the object and image equals the ratio of their respective distances from the lens.

13. Summarize the properties of the image—type, erectness or inversion, size relative to that of the object, and location relative to the lens and the object—for all possible combinations of lens types and locations of the object relative to the principal focal point. Check against your diagrams for Question 11.

14. Discuss the facts in your summary (Question 13) in terms of the effect of the lens on the expanding waves coming from a point on the object.

15. Make a rough diagram to show that a concave mirror will cause a beam of parallel rays to converge, and one to show that a convex mirror will cause such a beam to diverge.

16. A ray of light striking a curved mirror at the axis will be reflected so that the reflected ray makes the same angle with the axis as the incident ray, since the axis is normal to the mirror at that point. A ray approaching the mirror parallel with the axis will be reflected toward the principal focal point, or away from the virtual focal point. On the basis of these facts, construct diagrams similar to Figs. 29-6, 29-9, 29-11. Discuss the analogies between curved mirrors and lenses, on the basis of your diagrams.

Problems

1. An object 80.0 cm from a lens produces a real image 15.0 cm from the lens. Compute the focal length (a) by Eq. (29-1) and (b) by Eq. (29-2).

2. Determine, by both equations, the object distance if a real image is formed 25.0 cm from a lens of 15.0 cm focal length.

3. Again using both equations, calculate the location of the image produced by a lens of 80.0 cm focal length when the object is 60.0 cm from the lens.

4. Work out Sample Problem 4 (Sec. 29-11) for a virtual image instead of a real image.

5. An object is 2.00 m from a lens which forms an erect image one-quarter (exactly) the size of the object. Determine the focal length of the lens.

6. A lens has a focal length of 45.0 cm. Determine the image distance (a) if the object is 5.00 cm outside the principal focal point (that is, 5.00 cm farther from the lens), and (b) if it is 5.00 cm inside the principal focal point.

7. A diverging lens of 20.0 cm focal length forms an image 15.0 cm from the lens. Compute the object distance.

8. Determine the value of p in terms of f when the object and image are of equal size.

9. What is the focal length of a lens which produces an image one-third (exactly) the size of the object when the object distance is 2.70 m? (There are *two* correct answers; find both.)

10. Compute the focal length of a lens which forms an image exactly three times the size of the object when the object distance is 2.70 m. Why is there only one answer, whereas there were two in the previous problem?

11. (a) A double convex lens is made of glass with a refractive index of 1.650, and the radii of its surfaces are 50.0 cm and 75.0 cm. Compute the focal length. (b) Recompute the focal length of the lens in part (a), if the flatter surface of the lens is concave.

12. A plano-convex lens is made of light flint (Table 28-1) and the convex surface has a radius of curvature of 1.50 m. Calculate (a) the focal length and (b) the power of the lens.

13. A plano-convex lens has a radius of curvature of 80.0 cm and an index of refraction of 1.600. Determine the image distance when an object is 50.0 cm from the lens.

14. For an object distance of 60.0 cm the image distance is 20.0 cm. The lens has a refractive index of 1.500, and one face has a radius of curvature of +18.0 cm. Calculate the radius of curvature of the other surface.

15. An object 30.0 cm from a lens produces a virtual image five times (exactly) as large as the object. The lens is double convex, with radii of curvature equal to 40.0 cm and 24.0 cm. Calculate the index of refraction.

30
DEFECTS IN IMAGES

30-1 Preview

In the preceding chapter we were concerned with finding how images are formed, and there was a tacit assumption that the images were perfect. Actually, a perfect image is very rare. Defects in an image may arise from any of many different causes. Among these is the fact that if the object is "deep," parts of it at different distances from the lens will have unequal image distances. Also, light coming to a simple lens from a point off the axis is not focused as cleanly as if it came from a point on the axis. Image defects may also have their origin in the inability of a simple lens to refract all colors of light equally, or in the fact that rays passing through the peripheral portions of a simple lens will not be focused at the same point as rays which go through the center. Superimposed on all these factors is the wave nature of light itself, which prevents even a perfect lens from producing a perfect image. Investigation of this peculiarity of light will lead us to an understanding of why much greater magnification may be obtained with an electron microscope than with an optical microscope.

30-2 The Circle of Confusion

According to Fig. 29-6, 29-9, 29-12, and Eq. (29-1) and Eq. (29-2), there is a unique relationship between the location of a "flat" object and that of the image (for a given lens). Hence, if the object is "deep," various parts of it being at unequal distances from the lens, it will be impossible for the lens to form a perfect image of every portion of the object. In Fig. 30-1, for example, the three object points *A*, *B*, and *C* are at different distances from the lens, causing the distances of the corresponding image points *A′*, *B′*, and *C′* to be unequal. If we place a screen so that object point *B* is focused perfectly on the screen at *B′*, the rays from *A* will have converged at *A′* and diverged slightly before they strike the screen; hence *A* will be represented on the screen by a small circle rather than by a point. Object point *C* also will be represented by a circle instead of a point, but for a different reason; the screen intercepts the rays from *C* before they reach the point of convergence at *C′*. Light rays from object points contiguous with *B*, and at the same distance from the lens, will converge to points adjacent to *B′* on the screen, forming a sharp image of this portion of the object. On the contrary, light from points adjacent to *A* will not come to points on the screen; what *should* be a point will be a small circle, and these circles of light will overlap. Thus the image of this portion of the object will be blurred. The same is true of the part of the object near *C*.

These circles of light which appear on the screen where, ideally, there should be a *point* of light, are called ***circles of confusion***, since they confuse, or blur, the image. Obviously, the smaller the circles of confusion are, the clearer the image will be.

If the lens in Fig. 30-1 is considerably farther from the same object, the discrepancy among the distances of the image points will be reduced. You can prove this by diagrams or by applying one of the lens formulas.

The image can also be sharpened by blocking off the outer portions of the lens with a ***stop***, or ***diaphragm***, as shown in Fig. 30-2. The points of convergence are unchanged from those in Fig. 30-1, but the smaller

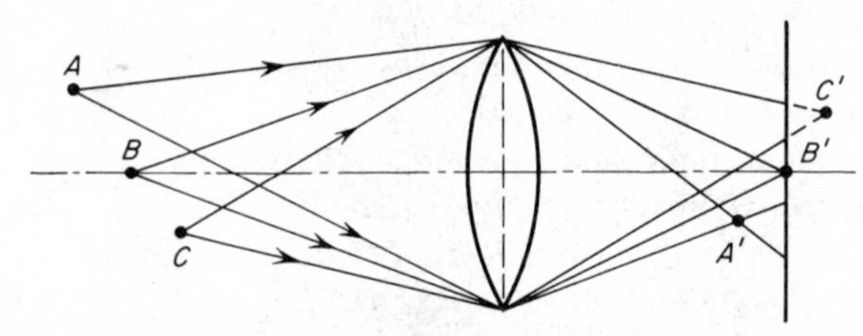

Fig. 30-1. Object points on a "deep" object produce image points at unequal distances from the lens, causing circles of confusion on the screen.

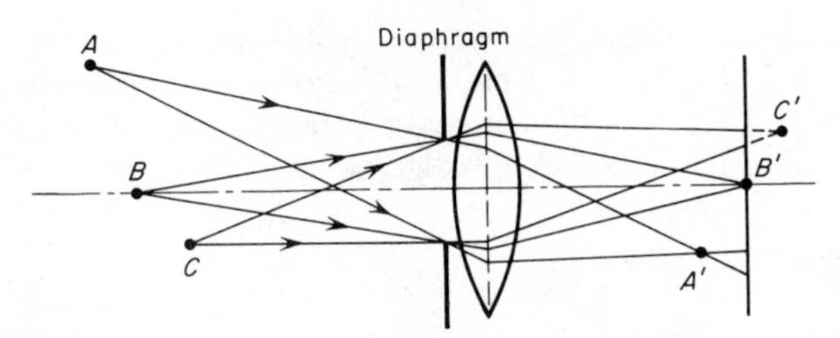

Fig. 30-2. The diameters of the circles of confusion are reduced by using a stop.

angular spread of the rays able to pass through the stop results in smaller circles of confusion.

Actually, this discussion has been oversimplified by assuming that under ideal conditions light from an object point will be focused to a perfect point on the screen. A circle *always* results, instead of a point, for reasons we shall investigate in Sec. 30-8, 30-9; but in general this effect is minor compared to the effect we have been discussing.

30-3 Astigmatism

Another image defect may result either from the location of the object or from an imperfection of the lens.

Consider first a double convex lens whose surfaces have more curvature in the vertical plane than in the horizontal, as shown—exaggerated!—in parts (a) and (b) of Fig. 30-3; such a lens will have no definite focal length. If there is a point of light at *O*, and if one explores the region behind the lens with a screen, nowhere will he find the rays to come to a point. Instead, the patterns in Fig. 30-3(c) will appear at the indicated positions of the screen. Any horizontal lines in the object will focus at *B* (if the object is at *O*), and vertical lines will focus at *D;* but no sharp image can be found anywhere, and even the lines at *B* and *D* will be less clean than a normal lens would produce.

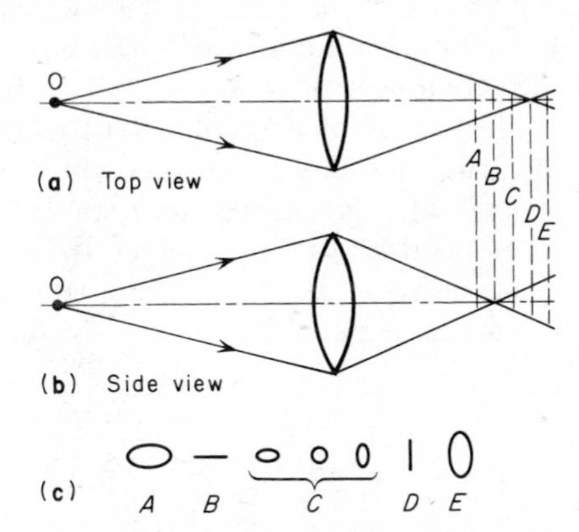

Fig. 30-3. An astigmatic lens, and patterns produced by the refracted rays on a screen at various locations behind the lens.

A lens of the sort discussed is said to be ***astigmatic,*** or to have ***astigmatism;*** and the same terms may be applied to the image.

Now consider a "perfect" converging lens and an object point a considerable distance to the right or left of the lens axis. In effect, this makes the curvature of the lens greater in the vertical plane than in the horizontal plane, for rays from this point, so the image of such a point will be astigmatic.

30-4 Spherical Aberration

The easiest, and hence the most economical, method of grinding lenses produces surfaces which are curved exactly as a portion of the surface of a sphere would be. Such a surface is not ideal, however, for rays through the peripheral portions of the lens are refracted more than they should be —or those through the central portion are refracted too little. Hence, as indicated—and exaggerated—in Fig. 30-4, F_p, the principal focal point for peripheral rays, is closer to the lens than F_c, that for the rays through the central portion of the lens. In effect, the lens has a longer focal length for central rays than for those through the outer portions of the lens. Thus every object point will be represented on the other side of the lens by a circle of confusion rather than by an image point.

As in the case of a "deep" object (Sec. 30-2), the diameter of the circles of confusion can be reduced by using a stop in front of the lens to block off the peripheral parts of the lens. Alternatively, of course, the center could be blocked off and the peripheral portions used, but the use of a diaphragm is far more common.

This type of imperfection of a lens is known as ***spherical aberration.***

30-5 Chromatic Aberration

Thus far, the discussion of lenses and image formation has ignored something we found in Sec. 28-9: the dispersion of light due to unequal refraction of various wavelengths of light.

If a beam of parallel rays of white light approaches a lens as in Fig. 30-5, light of all wavelengths will be slowed as it enters the lens and will resume its original speed as it emerges; so all of the light will be refracted. The speed of the violet light is reduced more than that of any other color, however, so it is refracted more on entering the lens; and on emerging, its increase in speed exceeds that of any other, so again it undergoes

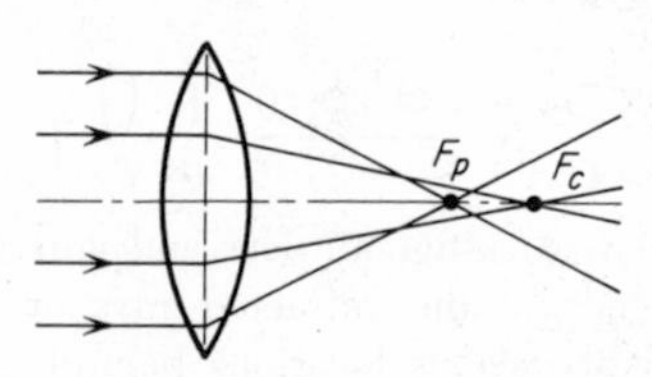

Fig. 30-4. Spherical aberration.

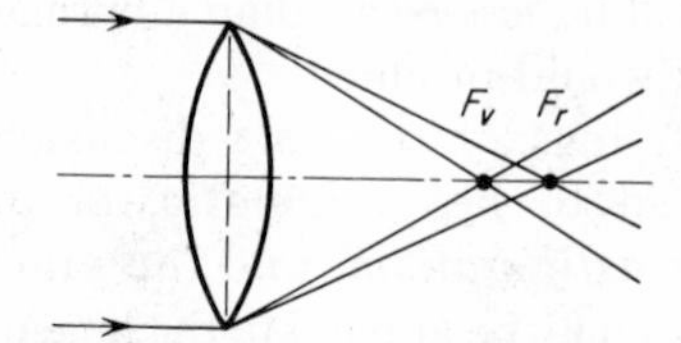

Fig. 30-5. Chromatic aberration.

the greatest refraction. This means that the focal length of the lens is less for violet light than for light of any other color. Red suffers the minimum change of speed as it enters or leaves the lens, since its speed in the lens is greater than that of any other color. Hence red is refracted the least of all the colors, and the principal focal point for red is farthest from the lens. These facts are the basis of Fig. 30-5, in which a beam of initially parallel rays of white light is refracted to give the principal focal points F_v and F_r for violet light and red light, respectively. In your imagination, you can add an infinite number of other principal focal points between F_v and F_r, one for each intermediate wavelength, in the general order of violet, blue, green, yellow, orange, and red.

Hence a simple lens will have a definite focal length, and will give a clean image, only for monochromatic light; and its focal length for any one monochromatic light will differ from that for any other single spectral color. For white light, the lens will give a whole series of sharp images in the spectral colors, arranged in order at slightly different distances from the lens. It is impossible to get a perfectly focused image; the best one can do is to focus light of an intermediate wavelength sharply so that the circles of confusion of the out-of-focus red image will be of about the same size as those of the violet image.

This defect of a lens is ***chromatic aberration.***

30-6 Some Other Defects of Images

If the object is flat and lies in a plane perpendicular to the lens axis, the distance from the center of the lens is less for the object point on the axis than for any off-axis point, and the distance increases with the displacement of the object point from the axis. Equations (29-1) and (29-2) require that greater object distances produce smaller image distances. Hence, though the object lies in a plane, its image does not; the image lies on a curved surface, concave toward the lens. This effect is called ***curvature of field.***

In addition to the astigmatism which is expected when the object is not on or very near the lens axis (Sec. 30-3), ***coma*** may be observed. This term comes from the word "comet" and is applied because a point source yields an image which, when focused as well as possible, resembles a comet. Perhaps a better description would be beet-shaped or pear-shaped, the large part being toward the axis of the lens and the tail of the beet or elongated stem end of the pear extending away from the axis.

If a stop is placed either in front of the lens—that is, on the side toward the object—or behind it, the lens may magnify or reduce different portions of the object unequally, with the result that straight lines in the object (except those passing through, or near, its center) appear as curved lines in the image. This is ***distortion***: ***barrel*** distortion if lines which should be straight bow out from the center like the staves of a barrel, or ***pincushion*** distortion if they sag toward the center like the edges of a pincushion.

30-7 The Reduction of Image Defects

The reduction of the blurring of the image of a "deep" object by the use of a diaphragm has been discussed, and shown schematically in Fig. 30-2. Astigmatism, coma, and curvature of field may be reduced by avoiding the inclusion of object points which are far off the axis, when possible. Their effects may be minimized by proper design of a compound lens, but in general, we shall not consider what kinds of simple lenses are used, or how they are combined, to construct a compound lens. Treatment of spherical aberration, other than its minimization by the use of a diaphragm, also calls for a compound lens, though it may be controlled if the lens surfaces are ground with less curvature toward the edges than at the center—a relatively difficult and expensive process. Distortion is minimized by placing the stop between the elements of a compound lens instead of either in front of the lens or behind it.

A fuller discussion of the reduction of chromatic aberration will be more fruitful for us than would be the case for any of the other image or lens defects. The possibility of controlling chromatic aberration lies in the fact that the ratio of the refractive indices of two kinds of glass is not the same as the ratio of their dispersions. Thus the angle of dispersion, α, is the same for the crown glass prism in Fig. 30-6(a) as for the flint glass

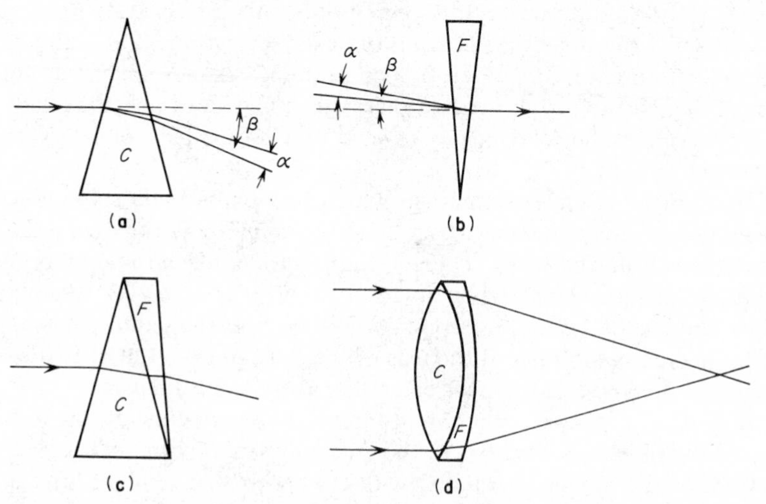

Fig. 30-6. Development of an achromatic prism and an achromatic lens. *C* stands for crown glass, *F* for flint glass.

prism in part (b) of the figure, even though the mean angle of deviation, β, is considerably greater for the former. Since the paths of light rays are reversible, rays of appropriate colors approaching the prism in Fig. 30-6(b) from the left would be combined to a ray of white light issuing from the right side of the prism. Hence if the two prisms in parts (a) and (b) of the figure are combined as in part (c), the dispersion caused by the crown glass prism will be canceled out by the flint prism, but some deviation will remain. Thus it is possible to combine a strong positive lens of crown glass with a relatively weak diverging lens of flint glass as in Fig. 30-6(d), obtaining a compound converging lens in which the dispersion is largely canceled. Such a lens is an ***achromatic lens.***

This is too bright a picture, however, for such a combination of two lens elements will produce exact achromatization for only two wavelengths; there will be some residual, though relatively minor, dispersion of other wavelengths. More highly corrected lenses include three elements instead of two; they bring the images of the corresponding three colors into exact superposition and further minimize the residual dispersion of other colors.

30-8 Optical Images as Diffraction Patterns; Single-slit Diffraction

A glance at any of the diagrams which show image formation by a positive lens shows that the various paths from a given object point to the corresponding image point are unequal in length. The shortest path passes through the thickest portion of the lens, and the ray which goes through the thin edge of the lens travels the greatest distance. Recall, though, that the light travels less rapidly in the lens and that when the speed of light is reduced it is the wavelength which is affected, the frequency remaining unchanged. Thus the waves in the lens have a shorter wavelength than those outside. Hence, despite the inequality of path lengths, the number of wavelengths between the object point and the corresponding image point is the same for all paths. Since the time required for the trip is the number of wavelengths in the path divided by the frequency, it follows that the journey along any path requires the same time interval as along any other; each path is in accord with Fermat's principle of least time (Sec. 28-10).

In Sec. 28-12, we discussed diffraction and found that it is the agreement in phase, or lack of such agreement, among light waves arriving at a given point which results in the diffraction pattern, and the phase relationships are determined by the numbers of wavelengths along the different paths. Since we have just seen that all waves arriving at a point in the image have traveled over paths containing the same number of wavelengths, we may consider any such image to be a diffraction pattern.

To follow this idea a bit further, let us forget lenses for the moment

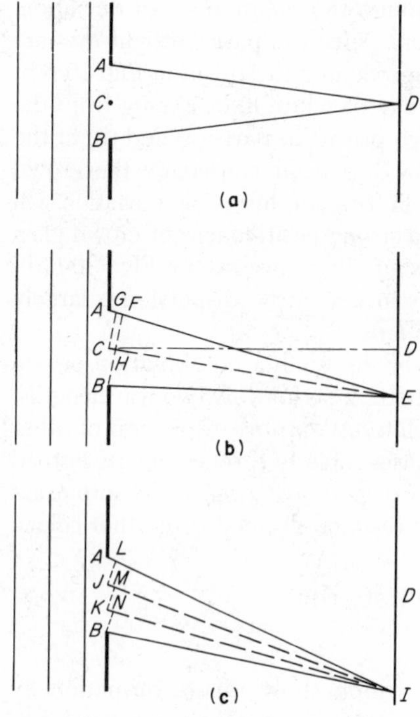

Fig. 30-7. Single-slit diffraction. There is a bright line at D, a dark line at E, and another bright line at I.

and consider light passing through a narrow slit in a screen. In Fig. 30-7, waves from the left approach a barrier in which there is a narrow slit. You are looking along the length of the slit, its width being AB. For simplicity, the approaching wave fronts are plane, and parallel with the barrier. Light passing through the slit and falling on the screen at the right will produce a diffraction pattern somewhat like that resulting from double-slit diffraction (shown in the lower portion of Fig. 28-13); but the central bright line is twice the width of the other lines and is much brighter, and the series of "bright" lines on either side of the central one fades much more rapidly than in double-slit diffraction. Also the mechanism of the formation of this diffraction pattern is different.

Point D on the screen is equidistant from A and B, so the paths AD and BD in Fig. 30-7(a) contain the same number of wavelengths. Thus a wavelet originating at A (in accordance with Huygens' principle) and one starting from B will be in phase when both reach D. Similarly, there will be constructive interference at D between any two rays which come from points equidistant from C (and on the line AB); *any* wavelet originating in the upper half of the slit will interfere constructively with a corresponding wavelet which comes from the lower half of the slit.

Figure 30-7(b) indicates the situation at a point E on the screen, point E being so situated that the distance AE exceeds that along BE by exactly one wavelength.* Thus AF is one wavelength; so AG is half a wavelength, and the same is true of CH. Hence a ray along AE will interfere destructively at E with a ray along CE. Similarly, a ray from just below A and one from an equal distance below C will cancel each other at E; in fact, for *every* ray proceeding from the upper half of the slit toward E there will be one of opposite phase traveling toward E from the lower half of the slit. The end result is that there will be no illumination at E.

* The dot-and-dash line CD in this figure has no special significance for us at present, so it may be disregarded until it is needed in the last paragraph of this section.

Still farther from D, at point I in part (c) of the figure, the path AI will exceed BI by three halves of a wavelength. We may imagine the slit to be divided into three parts, instead of the two assumed for part (b) of the figure. This makes each of the distances AL, JM, and KN just half a wavelength. As in the paragraph above, for each ray originating between A and J there will be one of exactly opposite phase coming from between J and K, so that rays coming through the upper third of the slit will be canceled by those coming through the middle third; but this leaves nothing to interfere with rays coming from the lower third of the slit, between K and B, so these illuminate the screen at I and produce a bright line in the diffraction pattern.* There will be another dark line where the difference in path length for the two marginal rays is two wavelengths, rays through the upper fourth of the slit canceling those through the next lower fourth, and those through the two lower quarters nullifying each other. Where there is a difference of five halves of a wavelength between the paths of the marginal rays, rays through four-fifths of the width of the slit will cancel out, leaving those through the remaining fifth to produce a bright line. Obviously the term "bright" is relative; the illumination at I will be much less than at D, and the brightness of lines farther from D falls off very rapidly.

Though the diagrams and the discussion would have been somewhat more complicated, we could have considered the light approaching the slit to have come from a point source; and we would have found that the same sort of diffraction pattern would have resulted.

In all the diagrams in Fig. 30-7, the slit width is greatly magnified as compared with the distance between the slit and the screen, with the result that there is a severe exaggeration of the angular displacement of the lines, such as the angle ECD by which the first dark line in part (b) of the figure is displaced from the central bright line. Bearing in mind this distortion of the figure, consider the triangles AFB and EDC in Fig. 30-7(b); they are approximately similar. Hence, as an excellent approximation, $ED/EC = AF/AB$. Let us represent ED, the displacement of the first dark line from the central bright line (the measurement being between the centers of the lines), by symbol S; the distance between the slit and the screen, which is essentially the distance EC, by L; the distance AF by λ, since it is exactly one wavelength; and the slit width AB by w. Then

$$\frac{S}{L} = \frac{\lambda}{w}, \quad \text{or} \quad S = \frac{\lambda L}{w} \tag{30-1}$$

This equation shows clearly that (other things being equal) the lines of the

---

* We could have considered the rays through the central portion to be nullified by those in the lower portion, leaving rays in the upper third unhindered to form the bright line, or we could consider that any ray through the middle portion *half* cancels a ray through the upper third *and* one through the lower third, leaving these *half*-canceled rays to combine and produce the bright line.

diffraction pattern are closer together when the slit is relatively wide and when the wavelength of the light is relatively small.

30-9 The Limit of Resolution: the X-ray and Electron Microscope

The rather extended discussion of single-slit diffraction is not out of place in a chapter on lenses, as it seems; it provides a basis for considering the limit of resolution of a lens and the factors which determine that limit.

The slit on which we based the discussion of the preceding section was very narrow and relatively long, but suppose that we replace the slit with a pinhole; this will be a sort of two-dimensional slit, and it will produce a diffraction pattern in which a central bright circle of light will be surrounded by a succession of alternate dark and bright rings corresponding to the dark and bright lines on either side of the central bright line in the preceding section. This is a necessary and unavoidable consequence of the fact that light has the characteristics of waves. Since the brilliance of the bright lines, or circles, decreases very rapidly from the central image outward, we may ignore everything except the bright central circle. The essential thing is that even though the source of the light is a point, the image of that point will be a small circle rather than a point. This is not the circle of confusion we met in Sec. 30-2; it is the result of diffraction rather than imperfect focusing.

Thus a single point of light will give a pinhole image which is a small circle, the circle being brightest at the center and fading toward the edges, as in Fig. 30-8(a). The other parts of the figure represent pairs of points, and the corresponding images. In part (d), the points are separated by a distance greater than the radius of the diffraction circle; though the images are somewhat "smeared," one can perceive that there are two circles. In part (b), however, the fact that two points of light contribute to the image is not at all obvious, because of the degree of overlap of the two circles in the image. In practice, it is considered that two points on an object are just distinguishable if they are separated by a distance equal to the radius of the circles which result from diffraction; this situation is depicted in part (c) of Fig. 30-8.

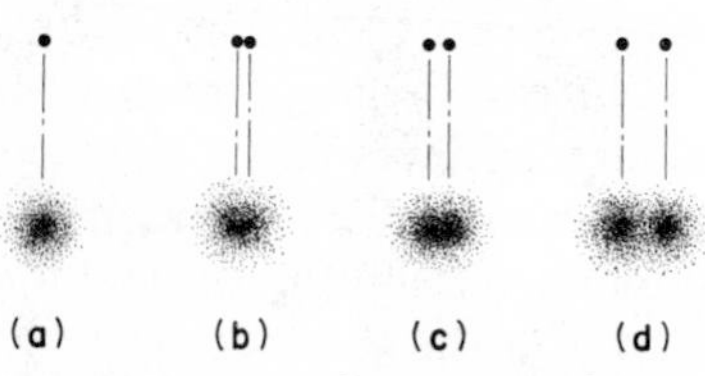

Fig. 30-8. A single point, and pairs of points, in the upper line, and the corresponding images in the lower line. (a) Single-point and diffraction pattern; (b) Two points separated by distance less than radius of diffraction circle, points not resolved in image; (c) Separation of points equal to radius of circle, points just resolved; (d) Separation greater than radius of circle, points easily resolved.

Perhaps surprisingly, these considerations apply to the most highly refined optical instruments. The fact that a lens refracts light to form a better image than can be obtained with a pinhole does not alter the fact that the lens constitutes an aperture through which the light must pass, and in this sense the lens is equivalent to a pinhole of large diameter. Consequently, though a microscope could be designed to give extremely great magnification, any magnification beyond a certain point would be useless because the image is a diffraction pattern.

The ***limit of resolution***, or the ***resolving power***, of any optical instrument is the minimum separation of two objects which the instrument is able to ***resolve***, or reveal as separate. As we have just seen in the case of the pinhole, this limit of resolution is a distance such that the central bright circles of the diffraction patterns overlap by just their common radius, and this criterion applies to the most sophisticated optical device just as it does to a pinhole.

The quantitative specification of the limit of resolution is based on Eq. (30-1), which was derived for a long and narrow opening; but since the "opening" of a lens is circular, the equation must be modified. The result (the derivation belongs in advanced texts in optics) is

$$\theta = 1.22 \frac{\lambda}{D} \tag{30-2}$$

in which θ is the angular separation in radians of the closest points which can be resolved (that is, the angle between rays to the center of the lens from the two points), λ is the wavelength as always, and D is the diameter of the lens.

Since the usable magnification of an instrument is limited by its resolving power, we must consult Eq. (30-2) for suggestions on increasing the useful magnification. The equation tells us that, in principle, there are two approaches: use light of shorter wavelength, or lenses of greater diameter. For visual observation, the sensitivity of the eye sets an obvious limit on the reduction of the wavelength. For photographic observation, ultraviolet light may be used; one type of microscope is "achromatized" in the sense that when it has been focused visually, using a selected portion of the visible spectrum, it is in focus for ultraviolet light. If the ultraviolet light has half the wavelength of the visible light, the limit of resolution is halved and the useful magnification doubled. There are obvious limits also in augmenting usable magnification by using larger lenses. Since correction of a lens for the defects mentioned earlier in this chapter becomes much more difficult and expensive as the diameter of the lens is increased, there is a practical limit.

Though the discussion of the limit of resolution has been in terms of microscopes, the same principles apply to the resolution of the two members of a binary star system, or other stars very close together, by an astronomical telescope, and to the resolution of lines in a spectrum by a spectroscope; in short, to any optical instrument.

Relatively recently in the history of optical science, two new methods of increasing the resolution of microscopes have been developed, both based on the reduction of the wavelength employed. One of these is the X-ray microscope, which employs X rays rather than visible light to form the image. Since the wavelength of X rays is very small as compared with that of visible light (Fig. 27-9), the limit of resolution is greatly reduced and the useful magnification correspondingly enhanced. X rays are not refracted as visible light is, so quite different principles of image formation must be employed.

The other breakthrough is, in a sense, an outcome of the long controversy over the wave versus the particulate nature of light, and the present acceptance of its dual nature. As we shall see in Sec. 33-9, this duality of nature extends to "ordinary" particles, such as electrons; a moving electron is accompanied by waves, the equation being

$$\lambda = \frac{h}{mv} \tag{30-3}$$

in which the wavelength is λ, h is Planck's constant, which we met in Sec. 19-12, 27-3, m is the mass of the electron, and v is its speed. Since an electron can be given almost any desired velocity by allowing it to "fall" through a sufficiently high potential difference, it can be given any momentum within a very wide range; and this is a way of saying that its waves may be given any of a wide range of wavelengths, including values of the order of 1 angstrom. This is very roughly one-thousandth of the wavelength of visible light; hence it represents a great increase in the useful magnification obtainable. To form the image, these "electron waves" must be focused, and this is done by using electric or magnetic fields, or both, to focus the electron streams, very much as the electron stream in a TV tube is focused.

Summary

Imperfections of an image may result from the *configuration* of the object, its *position* relative to the lens, *aberrations* of the lens itself, or the *wave nature* of *light*.

A lens cannot produce a clear image of all parts of a "deep" object near the lens, because of the *variation* of *object distance* among *points* on the *object*. An object off the axis of the lens may produce an astigmatic image, and a similar image defect will result from unequal curvature of a lens surface in different planes. The focal length of the peripheral portion of a lens with spherical surfaces will differ slightly from that of the central portion. A simple lens will have unequal focal lengths for the various colors of light; this *chromatic aberration* may be minimized by combining two or more lenses of different kinds of glass. Other image defects include curvature of field, coma, and distortion.

Any optical image is necessarily a diffraction pattern, and the *overlapping* of the *diffraction patterns limits* the *usable magnification* of any optical instrument. To increase the useful magnification a shorter wavelength may be employed or a lens of larger diameter used. Reduction of wavelength through the use of X rays or "electron waves" increases the usable magnification of special microscopes far beyond the limit obtainable with microscopes which employ visible light.

Self-Quiz

1. What is a circle of confusion? (A group of physics students, possibly? I hope not!) Of what significance is the circle of confusion?

2. Assuming a camera with a perfect lens (!) and optimum focusing of the camera, how will the "sharpness" of a photograph of a flower garden extending 5 ft to 20 ft from the camera compare with that of a picture of a landscape which extends from 5 miles to 20 miles from the camera, if both pictures are made with the lens "wide open"? Explain clearly, with the aid of diagrams.

3. Which of the photographs in Question 2 would have been improved more by "stopping down" the lens? Justify your answer by appropriate diagrams.

4. What is astigmatism, and what are its causes?

5. Make a fairly accurate diagram like Fig. 30-4. Using a pencil or pen of a different color, draw a lens over the one in your diagram, its thickness and curvature coinciding with the original lens near the axis but flattening appreciably toward the edges. Bearing in mind the relationship between the angle of incidence and the angle of refraction, draw the new paths of the peripheral rays. How does the position of the new focal point of these rays compare with the previous location? (On a rough freehand drawing it is impossible to determine exactly where it will be; but it should move away from the lens and, *ideally*, should coincide with the focal point of the central rays.)

6. Define "chromatic aberration," and explain clearly what causes it.

7. Assume that you know nothing of the relative speeds of blue and red lights in glass. Deduce which travels more rapidly in glass from the phenomenon of chromatic aberration, with the aid of Fig. 30-5.

8. Newton believed that there was no way of reducing the chromatic aberration of a lens. What erroneous idea of the properties of lens materials must have led him to this conclusion?

9. Discuss the correction of chromatic aberration in some detail.

10. Though the term "correction" of chromatic aberration is used almost exclusively, "reduction" would be a better term. Why?

11. What is curvature of field, and what causes it?

12. Why is diffraction pertinent to the study of lenses and images?

13. A bright line appears in the pattern resulting from double-slit diffraction at the location where the distance from one slit exceeds that from the other by one wavelength. In single-slit diffraction, a dark line results where the path difference of the marginal rays is one wavelength. Account for this difference.

14. Fermat's principle of least time ordinarily predicts a single path between two points, but if there is a (perfect) lens between the points, *any* path through the lens satisfies Fermat's principle as well as any other such path. Explain.

15. An optical microscope could be constructed which gives far greater magnification than is available in any such instruments now in use. Why doesn't some optical manufacturer produce such instruments?

16. In terms of the characteristics of the image, what determines the minimum separation between points on an object which can be resolved?

17. What two avenues are available for increasing usable magnification, and just what is the basis of each? What practical limitations are there, if any, for each of these approaches?

18. Why are the X-ray microscope and the electron microscope able to produce greater usable magnification than an optical microscope can?

Problems

1. A lens of 20.0 cm focal length is 40.0 cm above the top of a table, the lens axis being vertical. A dime lies on the table directly beneath the lens and a penny lies 30.0 cm to one side. Compute the image distance of (a) the dime, and (b) the penny. (c) By what percentage does the image distance of the penny differ from that of the dime, and is this difference positive or negative?

2. For thin lenses in contact, $1/F = 1/f_1 + 1/f_2$, where f_1 and f_2 are the focal lengths of the two lenses and F is the effective focal length of the combination. If a crown glass lens of 3.00 diopters and a flint glass lens of -1.20 diopters are combined to produce an achromatic lens, compute the power and the focal length of the combination.

3. Light falls on a slit exactly 10^{-1} cm wide, producing a diffraction pattern on a screen 2.50 m behind the slit. If the center of the first dark line is 0.125 cm from the middle of the central bright line, compute the wavelength of the light.

4. Compute the slit width necessary, in the preceding problem, to produce a 3.00 cm displacement of the first dark line at a distance of 5.00 m.

5. (a) If the diameter of a lens is 0.500 cm, and if light of 5000 Å is used, what is the minimum angular separation of objects which can be resolved? (b) If the effective distance of the object is 0.200 cm, what is the minimum separation, in Ångstroms, of points which can be resolved?

6. Taking the value of Planck's constant as $6.63 \cdot 10^{-27}$ erg sec and the mass of an electron as $9.11 \cdot 10^{-28}$ g, compute the wavelength of an electron which has a speed of $5.00 \cdot 10^{8}$ cm/sec.

7. Calculate the wavelength of an electron which has fallen through a potential difference of 100 v.

31

THE EYE AND OTHER OPTICAL INSTRUMENTS

31-1 Preview

The first topic in this chapter is that most important of optical instruments, the eye. We shall consider some of the defects of abnormal eyes (limiting our attention to errors in the refraction of light by the eye), and the type of corrective glasses needed for each refractional defect. This will be followed by a discussion of the simple magnifier. Next we shall combine the simple magnifier with another lens to obtain, first, an astronomical telescope, and later a compound microscope. We shall consider briefly two modifications of the astronomical telescope, and a different type of telescope commonly employed in opera glasses. In the case of each basic type of instrument (other than the eye) we shall investigate how the magnification produced by the instrument is related to such factors as the focal lengths of the lenses.

31-2 The Normal Eye

By far the most common of all optical instruments is the eye, without which other optical instruments would have little value. Insofar as physics is concerned, the eye consists of a positive lens and a screen on which a real image is formed, plus means of varying the focal length of the lens and controlling the quantity of light passing through it. Vision requires biochemical and biophysical processes at the "screen" and interpretation of nerve impulses by the brain, but these factors lie in the fields of advanced physical sciences, physiology, or psychology.

The lens is not a simple lens. On entering the eye, light first passes through the ***cornea,*** then through the ***aqueous humor,*** through the ***crystalline lens*** (which isn't crystalline at all), and finally through the ***vitreous humor.*** These are shown schematically in Fig. 31-1, and all of them play a part in the refraction which produces the image. The "screen" on which the image falls is the ***retina.***

Since the outer surface of the cornea is convex, it tends to cause light rays to converge. The index of refraction of the aqueous humor is slightly less than that of the cornea, so it makes the rays slightly less convergent. The vitreous humor has the same index of refraction as that of the aqueous humor, and the refractive index of the crystalline lens is appreciably higher, so the effect of the crystalline lens is similar to what one would expect of a positive lens in air, if the lens had a low index of refraction.* Thus the rays are made to converge more sharply, focusing on the retina.

We have found that, for a given lens, the image distances will be unequal for objects at various distances from the lens. A photographer must focus his camera differently for close-ups than for distant scenes; to do so he adjusts the distance between the lens and the film. No comparable adjustment is possible in the eye, so it would seem that only objects at some definite distance from the lens can be seen clearly. However, we have also found that, for a given object distance, the image distance will be greater with a lens of relatively great focal length, and vice versa.

It is true that when you are looking at a distant object you do not see near objects clearly, and vice versa. Nevertheless, if your eye is normal you can see clearly at any distance beyond perhaps 10 cm or a bit less. You focus your eye by altering its focal length. The capsule of the crystalline lens is supported by suspensory ligaments attached to the ciliary muscle (Fig. 31-1), which is in the shape of a ring surrounding the lens. When this muscle is relaxed, images of distant objects will focus on the retina of

---

* The index of refraction for the aqueous and vitreous humors is 1.336. That for the crystalline lens is 1.413 when the eye is relaxed, and 1.424 when the eye is focused on the nearest object which can be seen clearly. Thus the refractive index of the lens, relative to that of the humor on either side of it, varies between 1.058 and 1.066.

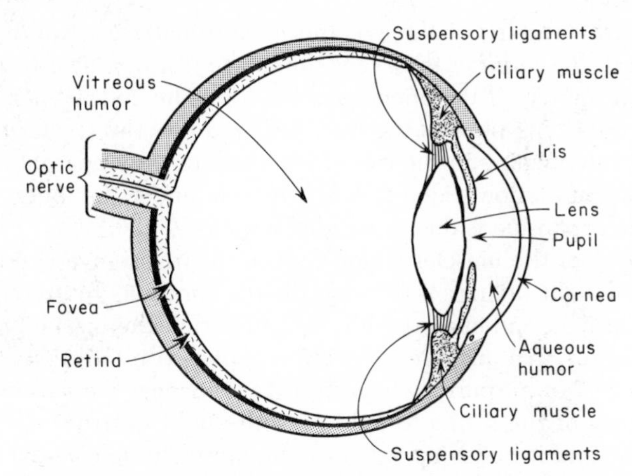

Fig. 31-1. Diagram of the eye. Courtesy of National Society for the Prevention of Blindness, Inc. (Diagram slightly modified.)

the normal eye. Contraction of the muscle relaxes the tension of the suspensory ligaments, and this allows the elasticity of the lens capsule to make the front surface of the crystalline lens bulge forward. Thus the curvature of the front surface of the lens is increased, the rear surface being relatively unaffected. In this way the focal length is decreased, enabling the eye to focus on relatively near objects.

This ability of the eye to adjust its focal length in accordance with the distance of the object under observation is called ***accommodation.*** The degree of accommodation of the eye decreases with age, the change being most rapid between roughly 45 and 50 years. The minimum distance of distinct vision at various ages is indicated in Fig. 31-2, which shows also the accommodation required to focus at the minimum distance. The curve represents an average; values for individuals with otherwise normal eyes may vary somewhat from this curve. The condition of decreased accommodation which is normal beyond the age of about 45 years is termed ***presbyopia,*** the first two syllables coming from the Greek root meaning "old." Primarily, loss of accommodation is usually considered to be caused by a decrease in the elasticity of the crystalline lens.

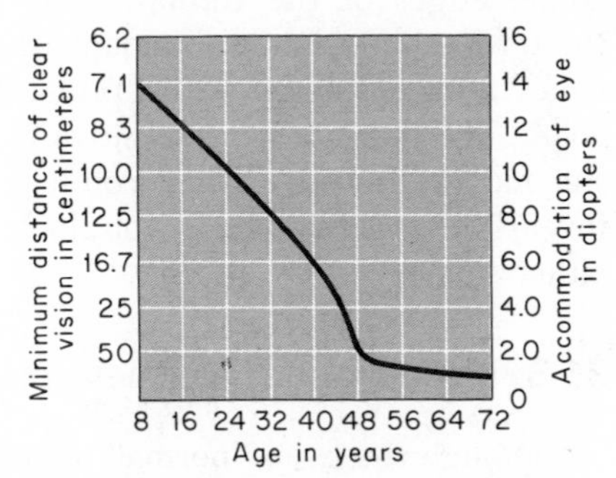

Fig. 31-2. Average accommodation at various ages.

The "automatic" cameras which use an "electric eye" to adjust the diaphragm according to the existing illumination are patterned after the iris of the eye and its automatic control mechanism. What we call the ***pupil*** of the eye is the image (formed by the cornea and the aqueous humor) of the opening in the iris. The colored portion of the eye surrounding the pupil is the iris itself, and it is the expansion or contraction of the opening in the iris which changes the apparent size of the pupil. This contraction is due to a ring muscle under the inner rim of the iris, and the expansion is due to a radial muscle.

The action of the muscles which control the iris is governed by the intensity of the light falling on the eye; the iris contracts to protect the eye from brilliant light and opens in dim light to permit the maximum quantity of light to enter. An analogous function is played by a substance called "visual purple," or purpurin, which strongly influences the sensitivity of the nerve endings of the retina to light. Intense light destroys the purpurin very rapidly, and it builds up again—comparatively slowly—when the intensity is low. This accounts for the fact that, when driving or riding, you can see much better in either sunlight or shade than you can if your motion causes rapidly flickering shadows of roadside objects.

Decrease in the diameter of the iris opening has the incidental effect of decreasing the spherical and chromatic aberrations of the eye, its astigmatism, and the accommodation necessary for clear vision. Since the iris responds only to light intensity, often the individual cannot make voluntary use of these effects. For objects close at hand, however, he can bring these effects into play by increasing the level of illumination.

The retina, on which the image falls, is a structure too complex to be treated in any detail in a physics book. For our purposes we may consider the principal features to be specialized cells of two types called ***rods*** and ***cones.*** The cones are found in the greatest numbers in the ***fovea,*** which is a small portion of the retina centered on the optical axis of the lens. It is here that both visual acuity and color perception are best. With increasing distance from the fovea, the abundance of the cones decreases according to a regular pattern; no cones are found at the extreme edges of the retina. Rods are found in nearly all portions of the retina, but are less abundant where the cones are most common. The cones are considered to be primarily responsible for the perception of color. The rods are more sensitive than the cones to very dim light; a faint star may be invisible when you look directly at it (image focused on the fovea) but visible when you look a little above or below it, or to either side.

31-3 Myopia and Hypermetropia

Though the term "normal" is regularly used, as in the preceding section, to signify that the eye is free from defects, "perfect" or "ideal" would be more realistic.* Various defects of vision are so common that they might well be considered to be normal.

Two common defects of vision are farsightedness, or ***hypermetropia,*** and nearsightedness, or ***myopia.*** When the "normal" eye is relaxed, light from an object at infinity will focus on the retina, as in Fig. 31-3(a). The focal length of a hypermetropic eye is too great for the length of the eyeball, with the result that rays from infinity tend to focus behind the retina as in part (b) of the figure. Thus what should be a point of light focused on the retina is a circle of confusion instead. On the other hand, in a myopic eye the focal length is too short for the length of the eyeball. Rays from a distant object come to a focus in front of the retina as in Fig. 31-3(c), then diverge to form circles of confusion on the retina.

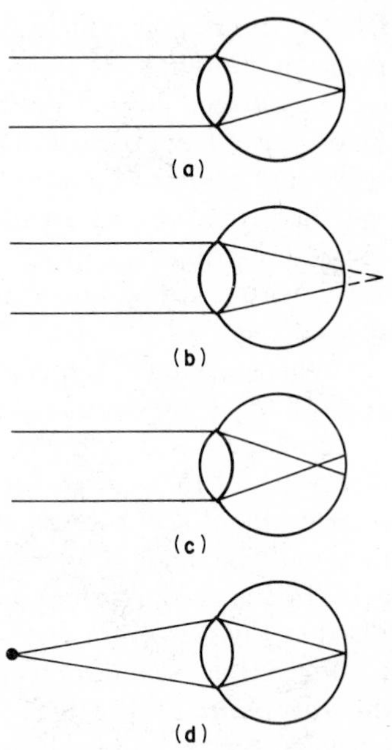

Fig. 31-3. Normal and abnormal eyes. (a) Normal eye, relaxed; (b) Hypermetropic eye, relaxed; (c) Myopic eye, relaxed; (d) Normal eye, accommodated, or Myopic eye, relaxed.

The accommodation of the "normal" eye enables it to bring light rays from a relatively near object to a focus on the retina, as in Fig. 31-3(d). An individual afflicted with farsightedness must use some of the eye's accommodation to bring rays from a distant object into focus, as in part (a) of the figure, and for objects closer to the eye, an abnormal degree of accommodation is required. Hence some eyestrain is involved, its degree being greater for relatively close objects, and the minimum distance of clear vision is greater than for a "normal" eye. We have seen that the eye has its maximum focal length when relaxed, however. Since accommodation cannot further increase the focal length, a myopic individual is unable to compensate his visual defect by accommodation.

31-4 The Correction of Myopia and Hypermetropia

Part (a) of Fig. 31-3 shows that the relaxed "normal" eye will cause light rays from infinity to focus on the retina. In order that they may focus on the retina of a myopic eye, the object must be relatively close; Fig.

* Professionals in this field call the "normal" eye *emmetropic* and one which is not "normal" *ametropic.*

31-4(a) shows rays which diverge from an object at P being brought to a focus on the retina. If a myopic individual is provided with a negative lens (of the correct power) the lens will cause rays from a distant object to diverge as if from point P, as in part (b) of Fig. 31-4; hence the relaxed eye will cause them to focus on the retina. Since the rays enter the eye as if they had come from P rather than from infinity, the effect of the lens is to replace the object, which the individual cannot see because it is too far away, with a virtual image at the most convenient viewing distance of the relaxed eye.

When relaxed, a hypermetropic eye cannot focus an object clearly at any distance, not even at infinity. As indicated in Fig. 31-5(a), rays must be convergent if they are to focus on the retina. If we extend the original directions of these rays, they meet at P, behind the eye. If rays from a distant object are to focus on the retina of a relaxed hypermetropic eye, they must be made to converge in the direction of P before they enter the eye. This is accomplished by a positive lens of appropriate power, as indicated in Fig. 31-5(b).

For either type of defect, the point P in Fig. 31-4(a), 31-5(a) is called the ***far point*** of the eye. The reciprocal of the distance, in meters, between the eye and the far point is the ***static refraction*** of the eye, in diopters. Since the far point of the myopic eye is in front of the lens, its distance, and hence the power of the eye, is positive. However, the far point of a hypermetropic eye is behind the eye so its distance is taken as negative and the power of the eye has a negative value. The far point of a "normal" eye is at infinity, and $1/\infty = 0$, so the static refraction of such an eye is zero.

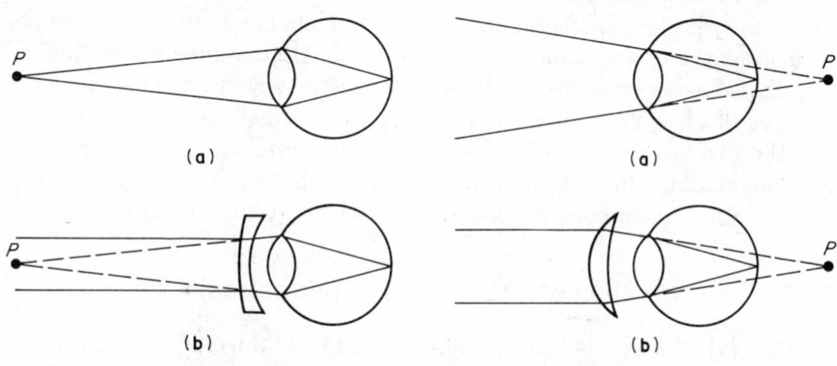

Fig. 31-4. Myopic eye and its correction. (a) To focus on the retina, rays must diverge from P; (b) A negative lens causes parallel rays to diverge as if from P, so they focus on the retina.

Fig. 31-5. Hypermetropic eye and its correction. (a) To focus on the retina, rays must converge toward P; (b) A positive lens causes parallel rays to converge toward P, so they focus on the retina.

Correction of either type of vision defect involves the use of a lens such that the eye and the lens combined have the static refraction of a "normal" eye—that is, zero. When two thin lenses are in contact, the power of the combination is the algebraic sum of their individual powers (see Problem 1). Obviously the correcting lens is an appreciable distance ahead of the eye (except for a contact lens), so this relationship is not exact, for our present purpose; nevertheless, it yields a fairly good approximation except where rather powerful corrective lenses are needed. (The necessary refinement will be left to books in the field, and to those who have reason to follow the matter further.)

Since the static refraction of the "normal" eye is zero, if that of a myopic or hypermetropic eye is D_e diopters, and if the power of the corrective lens is D_l diopters,

$$D_l + D_e = 0$$

so

$$D_l = -D_e \tag{31-1}$$

as a first approximation.

If, for example, the far point of a myopic eye is 250 cm, D_e is $1/2.50 = 0.400$ diopters, so the corrective lens should have a power of approximately -0.400 diopters.

On the other hand, if the far point for an individual with hypermetropia is -66.7 cm or $-2/3$ m (the value being negative since the far point is behind the eye), the power of his eye is -1.50 diopters. This individual should be provided with positive, or converging, eyeglasses of 1.50 diopters power.

This method of computing the power of a corrective lens must be considered only approximate, since it ignores the distance between the optical center of the eye and that of the corrective lens, and also because it does not consider lack of accommodation or other possible complications.

31-5 Astigmatism

As with a non-biological lens, astigmatism results from unequal curvatures, in different planes, of some part of the lens system of the eye (Sec. 30-3). Correction involves the use of a properly oriented astigmatic lens. If, for example, the curvature of the eye's lens system is greater in the vertical plane than in the horizontal plane, the correcting lens should reduce the convergence of rays in the vertical plane, or increase that of those in the horizontal plane, or both; in effect, it must be a negative lens in the vertical plane and a positive lens in the horizontal plane. These characteristics may be combined with a positive power, for an astigmatic and hypermetropic eye, or with a negative power, for an astigmatic and myopic eye.

31-6 Other Comments on the Abnormal Eye

Hypermetropia, myopia, and astigmatism are all due to imperfections of refraction which result in a "fuzzy" image on the retina. This lack of clarity occurs because the image is composed of circles of confusion or, in the case of astigmatism, ellipses or lines of confusion, instead of points of light. We have found that such images may be made more clear by "stopping down" the lens with a diaphragm, since this decreases the diameter of the circles of confusion; and it will affect the imperfections due to astigmatism similarly. This means that, in case of emergency, even a person with very poor eyesight can see without glasses well enough to read an address or telephone number in a directory, for example, if he pokes a small hole in a piece of paper with a pencil point and uses this as a diaphragm in front of one eye. This assumes, of course, that the illumination is sufficiently high and that the defect of vision has no cause other than refraction.

The imperfections of vision discussed in the preceding sections are by no means all the defects to which the eye is subject, but the others are material for a physiology rather than a physics textbook.

We are now ready to consider optical devices other than the eye.

31-7 The Simple Magnifier

A ***simple magnifier*** may be a single positive lens of relatively short focal length, or it may be a compound lens. Since the basic principle is the same in either case, the discussion will assume a simple lens.

We found in Sec. 29-8 and Fig. 29-9 that whenever the distance of an object from a positive lens is less than the focal length of the lens an enlarged virtual image results; and though the lens obviously has no effect on the dimensions of the object, we say that the object is "magnified" by the lens. Thus any positive lens acts as a magnifier when the object distance is less than the focal length.

Equation (29-1), which is $1/f = 1/p + 1/q$, may be rearranged to

$$\frac{-1}{p} = \frac{-1}{f} + \frac{1}{q}$$

and on multiplying through by q this becomes

$$\frac{-q}{p} = \frac{-q}{f} + 1$$

In practice, a simple magnifier usually is adjusted so that the virtual image is about at the distance you would hold a photograph to examine it carefully. This usually would be about 25 cm, and since this image is virtual, we may take $q = -25.0$ cm, or $-q = +25.0$ cm. Insertion of this value

into the equation yields
$$\frac{25.0}{p} = \frac{25.0}{f} + 1$$

in which both p and f must be expressed in centimeters (unless $-q$ is evaluated other than in centimeters).

The left-hand side of this equation is the ratio of the image distance to the object distance, and according to Eq. (29-4), this is equal to the ratio of image size to object size. Obviously this latter ratio is a measure of the ***magnification***, m, so

$$m = \frac{25.0}{f} + 1, \quad \text{for } f \text{ in cm} \qquad (31\text{-}2)$$

or

$$m = \frac{0.250}{f} + 1, \quad \text{for } f \text{ in m} \qquad (31\text{-}3)$$

The latter may be expressed as

$$m = \frac{D}{4} + 1 \qquad (31\text{-}4)$$

where D is the power of the lens in diopters.

31-8 The Basic Principle of Instruments Which Use More than One Lens

The instruments considered in the following sections differ in their function and in the details of their construction, but all are based on the same general principle. There are at least two lenses (each of which usually is a compound rather than a simple lens), the lens nearer the object being the ***objective*** lens and that the nearer the eye being the ***ocular*** lens. The function of the objective lens is to form a real image of the object. This image then serves as the object for the ocular lens. For visual observation, the instrument is so adjusted that the image formed by the objective falls just inside the principal focal point of the ocular, so that what the eye sees is a virtual image of the real image. For photographic observation, additional lenses must be used, or the instrument must be readjusted so that the ocular produces a real image. Since basic principles rather than details are our primary concern, we shall consider only visual observation.

31-9 The Astronomical Telescope

The ***astronomical telescope*** employs positive lenses for the objective and the ocular, or a concave mirror for an objective with a positive lens for the ocular. The principle is the same in either case, but the discussion will be in terms of an instrument that has a lens for the objective.

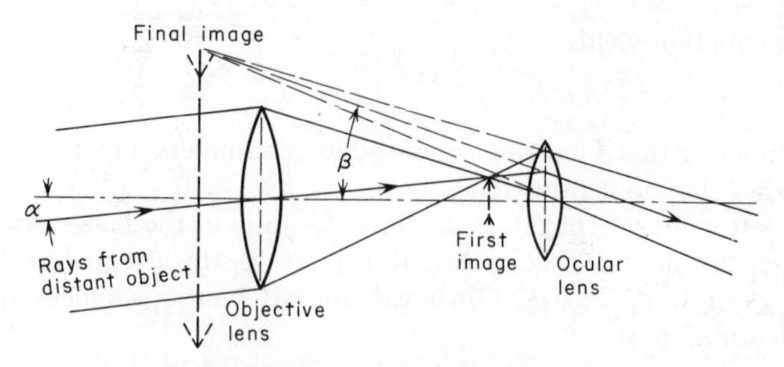

Fig. 31-6. The astronomical telescope.

The normal function of a telescope is to view some distant object; hence the real image formed by the objective lens will fall essentially at the principal focal point of the objective. The position of the ocular is adjusted so that it produces an enlarged virtual image of the real image.

Figure 31-6 depicts this situation schematically, but this diagram differs from those we have met previously. Heretofore, all lens diagrams involving an image were constructed by following from a given object point two rays, these rays being chosen so that we could predict their directions easily. On this basis, we could reproduce Fig. 29-6 to show the formation of the real image by the objective lens and combine this with Fig. 29-9, using the image in the former figure as the object in the latter, to show how the objective forms the virtual image. However, this combination of the two diagrams would show the light rays making sharp turns at the location of the real image. Since there is nothing at that location to bend the light, such a diagram is confusing. Hence, in Fig. 31-6, no attempt has been made to *construct* the image in the sense in which it was constructed in Fig. 29-9.

Thus far, we have considered the magnification to be given by the ratio of the size of the image to that of the object. The most powerful telescope, however, can give only a pinpoint of light as the image of a distant star, though the star may be far larger than our sun. What kind of "magnification" is this?! Yet the telescope does "magnify," for if we view a portion of the moon with it we see a tremendous amount of detail imperceptible to the unaided eye.

To resolve this paradox, consider a line of telephone poles stretching away into the distance. To see all of the nearest one, you may have to tilt your head up and down, but you needn't even move your eyeball to see the full height of a more distant one. You know that all the poles are about the same height, but their heights *appear* very different. We judge the relative sizes of things in terms of the angle they subtend at the eye; that is, in terms of the angle between a ray from one extremity of the object to the eye, and a ray from the opposite extremity to the eye.

In Fig. 31-6, the rays coming from a point on the distant object make an angle α with the axis of the telescope, and after refraction by both lenses they make an angle β with the axis. Thus, the final image subtends a much larger angle than the object does, so there appears to be magnification. Evidently the magnitude of the magnification (in this sense) is the ratio of angle β to angle α. It can be shown that this ratio is equal to the ratio of the focal length of the objective to that of the ocular. Using m to represent the magnification, f_o for the focal length of the objective, and f_e to indicate the focal length of the ocular or eye lens, we have

$$m = \frac{f_o}{f_e} \tag{31-5}$$

31-10 The Terrestrial Telescope and Prism Binocular

In the astronomical telescope, the objective gives an inverted image and the ocular leaves it inverted. This is of little moment in observing a star, but it is somewhat disconcerting when watching a football game or trying to shoot a rifle with a telescopic sight. For such earth-bound or terrestrial functions, we prefer an erect image.

The astronomical telescope is modified in either of two ways to yield an erect image. One method involves the use of a third positive lens as an erecting lens. It is placed between the objective and the ocular, at such a position that the inverted real image formed by the objective serves as the object for the erecting lens. This additional lens produces an inverted real image of the first real image, and this double inversion makes the second real image the same side up as the object. The ocular then uses this second, erect, real image as its object, forming an erect virtual image. A telescope modified in this fashion is a ***terrestrial telescope.***

The other means of erecting the image is employed in the ***prism binocular*** (there are also some monocular instruments based on the same principle). Figure 31-7 shows a prism in which the near face makes a 45° angle with each of the other vertical sides; thus these other sides are mutually perpendicular. The near face is clear, but the other two are silvered so that they act as mirrors. If a pair of rays of light, A and B, enter the clear face with ray A at the left, after a double reflection the rays emerge with ray A now to the *right* of ray B.

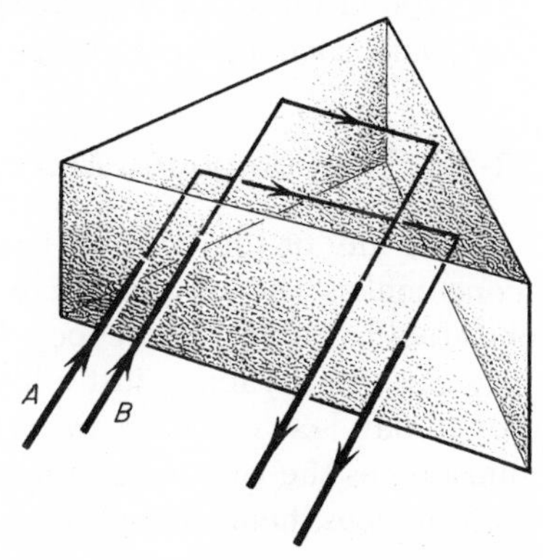

Fig. 31-7. Reflection, and right-left reversal, of rays by a 90° prism.

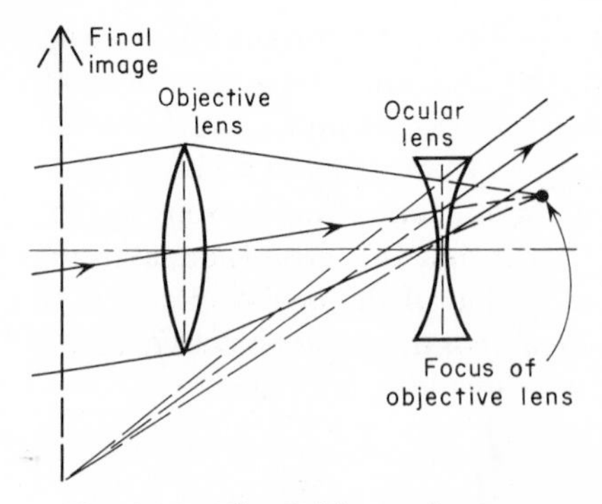

Fig. 31-8. The Galilean telescope.

Thus such a prism will do two things to the rays: it will reverse their direction of travel and it will interchange their relative lateral positions. If you rotate the page 90° you will see that a properly oriented prism of this sort can reverse the direction of propagation and interchange the relative vertical positions of the two rays. If we use two prisms, one in the position shown and the other rotated 90°, placing them so that the second one receives the rays reflected from the first, one will interchange right and left and the other will interchange top and bottom. Thus the two of them will invert the image. Since the image given by the astronomical telescope is inverted, such a combination of prisms will reinvert it, the final image being erect. Each half of a prism binocular is equivalent to Fig. 31-6 with a pair of prisms interposed between the lenses. In addition to erecting the image, the prisms "fold" the optical path so that the instrument is much shorter than the telescope.

31-11 The Galilean Telescope or Opera Glass

Both erectness of image and compactness are achieved if a negative ocular is employed in place of the positive ocular which the astronomical telescope uses. This ocular is placed so that it intercepts the converging rays from the objective before they converge to form a real image, diverging them so that a virtual image is formed.* This is indicated in Fig. 31-8. This type of telescope was developed by Galileo, and it is the basis of all binoculars, such as opera glasses, which are not prism binoculars.

31-12 The Compound Microscope

Like any of the types of telescopes discussed, the ***compound microscope*** makes use of a positive lens as the objective. The microscope objective has a very short focal length, however, and the object is placed very close to the lens—just a little beyond the principal focal point. The Newtonian lens equation $xy = f^2$ (Eq. 29-2) shows that under these circumstances the real image formed by the objective will be relatively far from the lens; hence it will be considerably magnified, since the magnifica-

* When, as here, rays are intercepted by a lens before they can form a real image, the image which *would* have been formed is called the *virtual* object for the lens. As with a virtual image, the value of the distance of a virtual object is negative.

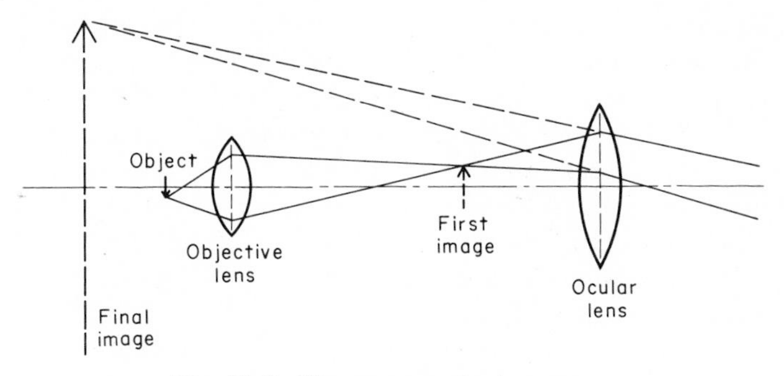

Fig. 31-9. The compound microscope.

tion is equal to q/p. As with the astronomical telescope, a positive ocular, also of short focal length, is used as a simple magnifier to view the real image; thus the final image is virtual and is further enlarged. Figure 31-9 is a schematic representation of a compound microscope.

If we call the distance between the objective and ocular lenses d, the distance of the real image from the objective q is approximately equal to $d - f_e$, where f_e is the focal length of the eye lens or ocular; for the image must be just inside the principal focal point of the ocular if the ocular is to produce a virtual image with the maximum magnification. Hence, for the magnification m_o produced by the objective, we may write,

$$m_o = \frac{q}{p} = \frac{d - f_e}{p}$$

Since the ocular acts as a simple magnifier, its magnification is given by Eq. (31-2), (31-3), or (31-4). Eq. (31-2) is

$$m_e = \frac{25.0}{f_e} + 1$$

the subscript e being appended to f to emphasize that this expression applies to the eye lens rather than to the objective. The magnification of the compound microscope will be the product of the magnifications of its components; so, if the over-all magnification is m,

$$m = m_o \cdot m_e$$

$$m = \frac{d - f_e}{p} \cdot \left(\frac{25.0}{f_e} + 1\right) \qquad (31\text{-}6)$$

Summary

The *eye* is a structure in which a *complex lens system* focuses an image on the *retina.* Muscles acting on the *crystalline lens* change its focal length, enabling the normal eye to see clearly at various distances. The degree of this accommodation decreases with age. The *iris* automatically adjusts the size of the pupil to the intensity of the illumination.

Hypermetropia is *farsightedness* and results from the *focal length* of the lens system being *too great* for the length of the eyeball; its correction involves positive lenses. *Myopia* is *nearsightedness* and is due to the *focal length* being too *small* relative to the length of the eyeball; it is corrected by negative lenses. In either case, the function of the corrective lens is to provide a *virtual image*, at a convenient viewing distance, of the object. Astigmatism is corrected by an astigmatic lens.

A *simple magnifier* is any positive lens placed so that the object distance is *less* than the focal length. It gives an *enlarged* and magnified *virtual image.*

The *astronomical telescope* uses a positive objective plus a simple magnifier as an ocular. The *magnification* of a telescope is determined by the *ratio* of the sizes of the *visual angles* subtended by image and object, rather than by the ratio of their actual dimensions. The inverted image given by the astronomical telescope may be erected by a supplementary lens or by using two prisms. The Galilean telescope makes use of a negative ocular, which gives an erect image directly.

The objective of a compound microscope produces an enlarged real image of an object placed just outside its principal focal point, and the ocular is a simple magnifier which views this real image.

Self-Quiz

1. Compare the eye with the camera, including the lens, the retina (or film), the type of image, the method of focusing, and the control of the brightness of the image.

2. What is accommodation, and what is its importance? How does accommodation usually vary with age? What relationship, if any, is there between presbyopia and hypermetropia?

3. Compare and contrast hypermetropia and myopia.

4. Give the common name for myopia. Explain the cause of myopia. What type of corrective lens is used, and why?

5. Answer Question 4, substituting hypermetropia for myopia.

6. Discuss astigmatism and its correction.

7. Assume that your eyes are farsighted and astigmatic. If you lost your glasses, how could you manage to read the 'phone number of your eye doctor? Why does this method work?

8. Derive Eqs. (31-2)–(31-4), inclusive, from Eq. (29-1), explaining clearly any steps which are not obvious.

9. What is meant by the power of a lens, and what is a diopter?

10. What is the function of the objective in a telescope or a compound microscope? What is the function of the ocular? In what way, if any, is the function of the ocular in a Galilean telescope similar to that in an astronomical telescope? In what ways, if any, are they different?

11. Make a diagram of an astronomical telescope, constructing the images as suggested in the third paragraph of Sec. 31-9. In what way is this diagram misleading? In what way is it preferable to Fig. 31-6?

12. Compare and contrast the term "magnification" as used in connection with a microscope and as used in relation to a telescope.

13. Consideration of Fig. 31-6 shows that the distance between the two lenses is approximately equal to the sum of their focal lengths. Is this relationship valid for the Galilean telescope in Fig. 31-8? Explain.

14. Show that if, in converting an astronomical telescope to a terrestrial telescope by adding an erecting lens, the length of the telescope is increased by four times the focal length of the erecting lens, the magnification will be unchanged.

15. Describe the essential features of the compound microscope, and explain how it magnifies.

16. In Eq. (31-6) the focal length of the objective lens does not appear, yet the magnification of the microscope depends strongly on this factor. Resolve this paradox.

17. In answering Question 13 did you overlook the fact that in a Galilean telescope the focal length of the ocular is negative? If so, does this fact change your original answer?

Problems

1. If D_1 is the power of a thin lens and D_2 is the power of another, prove that $D_c = D_1 + D_2$, where D_c is the power of the two lenses in contact. To do this, make use of the fact that the image formed by the first lens serves as the object for the second lens. If the first lens is assumed to be positive, the object for the second must be considered to be virtual and given a negative sign. Consider the distance between the lenses to be zero.

2. The far point for an individual is 80.0 cm in front of his eye. Determine the type and power of the correcting lens, and state the type of visual defect.

3. Repeat Problem 2 for a person whose far point is 25.0 cm behind the eye.

4. A young person who has normal eyesight has 12.5 diopters of accommodation. Determine his minimum distance of clear vision.

5. The person in Problem 3 has 8.50 diopters of accommodation. When wearing proper glasses, what is his minimum distance of distinct vision?

6. A draftsman feels no eyestrain when he works with his eyes at a distance of 15.0 cm from the drafting table, but his shoulders ache; a distance of 30.0 cm relieves the ache but is impossible because of his vision defect. Compute the minimum power of the glasses he should wear when drafting.

7. The power of a simple magnifier is 20 diopters. What is its magnification?

8. If the linear magnification of a positive lens is 4.50, what is its focal length?

9. A boy has lenses of +5.00, −10.0, +15.0, and +30.0 cm focal length. Which combination will he find to give the greatest magnification as a telescope, and what will the value of the magnification be?

10. A telescope which has an ocular of 7.50 cm focal length is in focus when the lenses are 50.0 cm apart. What is the magnification of the telescope?

11. A Galilean telescope with a 20.0 cm objective has a magnification of 4.00. What is the focal length of the ocular? (A "20.0 cm lens" means a lens of that focal length, not one of that diameter.)

12. A compound microscope has a 2.00 cm ocular and the distance between the ocular and the objective is 20.0 cm. If the instrument is in focus when the object is 0.500 cm from the objective, calculate the magnification.

32
SOME ASPECTS OF RELATIVITY

32-1 Preview

From Chapter 1 on, you have met occasional warnings that the treatment of a subject was incomplete. No satisfactory explanation of action-at-a-distance forces has been offered. The statement that the mass of a body is an intrinsic and independent property of the body was qualified by the statement that this independence disappears if the body attains a speed comparable with that of light. Similar qualifications were appended to limit the validity of Newton's second law of motion and the equation for the kinetic energy of a body. In this chapter, we shall investigate briefly Einstein's special theory of relativity, stated in 1905. This will furnish new quantitative relationships free of the limitations which impaired the validity of those we met earlier. The general theory of relativity, which Einstein stated about a decade later, provides an "explanation" of action-at-a-distance forces; but unfortunately the sophistication of the general theory, both mathematically and conceptually, is beyond us.

32-2 The Postulates of Einstein's Special Theory of Relativity

We have seen (Sec. 27-6) that the negative results of the Michelson-Morley experiment led Fitzgerald and Lorentz to the concept of a contraction of a moving body in the direction of its motion, Eq. (27-2). Einstein found that a more extended analysis indicated that quantities other than length are affected. The analysis was restricted to unaccelerated motion, and this lack of generality was reflected in the names ***special theory of relativity*** and ***restricted theory of relativity*** given to the theory. Its basic postulates may be stated thus:

> If two systems are moving at a constant velocity with respect to each other, laws of mechanics which are valid in one system are valid in the other.
>
> The speed of light in empty space has a constant value which is not dependent on any motion of the source or of the observer.

In effect, the first postulate says that any experiment performed within a system will give the same result, whatever the velocity of the system. That is, no experiment can give information regarding the system's absolute velocity. This being the case, the concept of absolute velocity—the velocity of the system itself, without reference to anything outside the system—loses all significance. Only the velocity of a system *relative to another* has any meaning. This is the source of the theory's title. You realize that we have taken the stand, early in the text, that all motion is relative; this feature of relativity is not new to us, but the theory furnishes a solid foundation for a familiar concept.

If we think of a bullet fired from a plane as analogous to light coming from a moving source, Einstein's second postulate seems incomprehensible; certainly the speed of the bullet with respect to the ground is affected by the motion of the plane. A better analogy is the sound of the plane. If there is no wind, this sound is carried to us through the air at a speed which is determined entirely by the pressure and density of the air, Eq. (14-2); it is wholly independent of the speed of the plane and of any motion of the listener.* In terms of this analogy, the lack of influence of any motion of the source or the observer on the speed of light is quite reasonable.

Because we must use the equations of the theory of relativity when speeds comparable with that of light are encountered, such speeds are termed ***relativistic.*** Speeds such that the equations we have met previously are valid are called ***non-relativistic.*** These adjectives are applied

---

* It is true that the *pitch* of the sound is affected by the motion of the source and by that of the observer. This however, is due to an alteration of the wavelength or the frequency, and not to any change in the speed of sound through the air. (See Doppler effect, Sec. 14-14.)

also to the equations themselves, and to concepts such as relativistic mass, for example (Sec. 32-5).

The implications of relativity just don't "make sense" at first. This is because of the limitation of our experiences to speeds which, compared to the speed of light, are like the speed of a snail which was born tired. Perhaps the next section will make matters seem a bit less unreal.

32-3 The Lorentz-Fitzgerald Contraction

In a world in which the speed of light is comparable with other speeds, the Lorentz-Fitzgerald contraction would be obvious.* Let us imagine ourselves at a railway station in a suburb, in such a world, just as a commuter train commences to leave. In this hypothetical world the speed of light is only 10.0 ft/sec, and we shall assume that, for an appreciable period, the train has a constant speed of 5.00 ft/sec.

A commuter, C in Fig. 32-1(a), has seated himself midway of the length of a car when he notices that his wife W, who drove him to the station, is waving from the platform. Just at the instant the train carries the man past her position, a latecomer makes a flying leap from a point A on the platform to the rear steps of the car, and another jumps from a point B on the platform onto the front steps of the car.† Light is reflected from both jumpers, but because in this world it travels at only 10.0 ft/sec, it requires an appreciable time to reach the man or his wife.

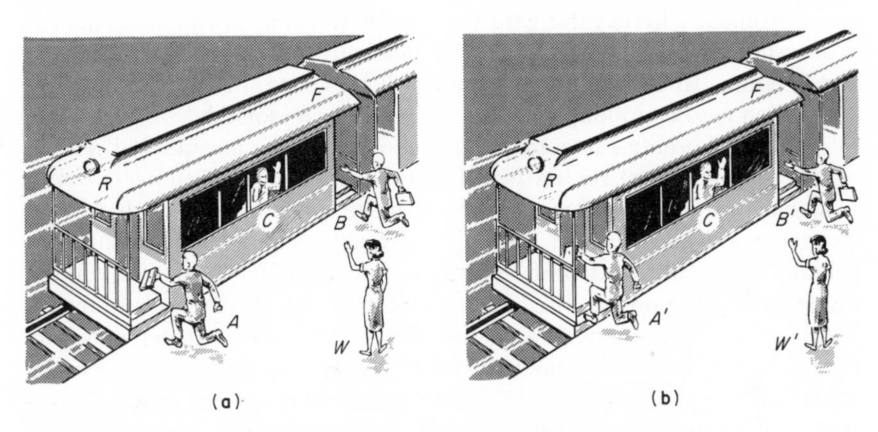

Fig. 32-1. Diagram to show the Lorentz-Fitzgerald contraction.

---

* See the third paragraph from the end of Sec. 27-6.

† Placing the husband and wife at the stated locations and having the latecomers jump at the moment specified simplifies the argument, and analysis of less simple situations would yield the same final conclusions.

The man was midway between points A and B when light was reflected from the jumpers, but as it travels toward him, the train carries him forward toward B. Hence light from A has to travel farther to reach him than light from B does; so it reaches him later. Because the husband in the moving car perceives the light reflected from the jumper at A after he perceives the light reflected from the jumper at B, and since each of these two latecomers gets onto the car safely, the husband concludes that the rear steps of the moving car passed point A after the front steps passed point B. This can only be possible if the distance AB is less than the distance between the front and rear steps of the car, so he concludes that this is the actual fact.

Since the train is moving slowly, the wife decides to run ahead to W' in Fig. 32-1(b), stop, and wave again to her husband. Tardy commuters are still trying to catch the train, and again two jump from points A' and B' onto the opposite ends of the car, but the husband observes these two to jump simultaneously. Since, owing to the motion of the train, light requires longer to reach him from the rear of the car than from the front, the man at the rear must have jumped a little before the one at the front did. Hence the wife, who is not moving, sees the light from A' arrive before that from B' reaches her; and since both commuters made the jump safely she observes that the rear steps passed A' before the front steps had reached B'. That is, she sees the distance between the front and rear steps as shorter than the distance $A'B'$.

Thus, the husband sees the moving car as normal and the platform foreshortened, whereas the wife sees the platform as normal and the car as foreshortened. However, this will *not* cause any argument when he comes home. In fact, neither of them will bother to mention an observation which is so commonplace and so obviously reasonable!

That the Lorentz-Fitzgerald contraction would be accepted as normal by the inhabitants of such a world, yet seems so strange to us, is a consequence of the tremendous difference in the speed of light in that hypothetical world and in ours; they differ by a factor of almost a hundred million. Thus, substitution of 5.00 ft/sec for v and 10.0 ft/sec for c in the equation for the Lorentz-Fitzgerald contraction, Eq. (27-2), leads to the result that in our hypothetical world the train—or the platform, depending on the point of view—is shortened by about 13.4%, or over one-eighth. On the other hand, as we saw in Sec. 27-6 the actual shortening of a plane flying at 600 mph is less than 0.0001%. Small wonder we don't notice such contractions, as the inhabitants of our hypothetical world did.

It is important that we realize the relative and reciprocal nature of all this. If any two systems are in uniform motion with respect to each other, at a relativistic velocity, any observer at rest in system *1* will observe all dimensions in his system to be normal and those in system *2* to be foreshortened in the direction of the relative motion. On the other hand, to any observer at rest in system *2*, all dimensions in system *2* will be normal, but those in system *1* parallel with the relative motion will be reduced.

32-4 Simultaneity and Time Dilation

Did you notice, in the discussion of the Lorentz-Fitzgerald contraction in the preceding section, that when the leaps of two late commuters appeared simultaneous to the wife they did not appear so to the husband, and vice versa? Events which are simultaneous in one system are not simultaneous in another system if the two systems are moving with respect to each other at relativistic velocities. This is a necessary corollary of the relativistic contraction and is an essential feature of the theory of relativity.

Note that this means that such terms as "just at the instant," "before," and "after," in the discussion of the Lorentz-Fitzgerald contraction in Sec. 32-3 really are indefinite and ambiguous. They seemed definite to you only because you are accustomed to time intervals being equal in different systems.

Lack of simultaneity implies inequality of time intervals in the two systems. Relativistic velocities cause time to be extended, or dilated. We might have expected this from the fact that, in spite of the difference in the length of a given body as seen from the two systems, the velocity of the relative motion is obviously the same. If system A is moving past system B at a relative speed equal to $c/2$, how could system B be moving past system A at any rate *other* than $c/2$? In fact, we can use this agreement on the relative speed to determine the quantitative description of time dilation.

An observer in either system would determine the relative speed by choosing the length, parallel with the motion, of some object in the other system, and noting how long it takes this object to pass some point in his own system. Naturally, he would time the interval by his own clock. If the lengths are represented by L and the times required by t, with appropriate subscripts, to an observer in the system A the relative velocity would be L_B/t_A, and L_A/t_B to an observer in B. Since these speeds are the same,

$$\frac{L_B}{t_A} = \frac{L_A}{t_B}$$

which may be rearranged to

$$t_B = t_A \cdot \frac{L_A}{L_B}$$

Because of the Lorentz-Fitzgerald contraction, an observer in A would see the length of an object in B as shorter than that of an identical object in A; according to Eq. (27-2)

$$L_B = L_A \cdot \sqrt{1 - \beta^2}$$

Substitution of this value in the preceding equation gives

$$t_B = t_A \cdot \frac{L_A}{L_A \cdot \sqrt{1 - \beta^2}}$$

which reduces to

$$t_B = \frac{t_A}{\sqrt{1 - \beta^2}}$$

Of course, an observer in system B would see time intervals in A altered in a similar manner, so in general,

$$t = \frac{t_o}{\sqrt{1 - \beta^2}} \tag{32-1}$$

where t_o is the duration of a time interval in one system and t is its duration as observed from another system. As always, β is the ratio of the relative velocity of the two systems to the speed of light.

In our imaginary world where the speed of light is 10.0 ft/sec (Sec. 32-3), a clock in a train moving past the station at 5.00 ft/sec would run at a rate less than seven-eighths of the rate of an identical clock in the station, as seen by a person at the station. In the real world, however, a perfect clock in a plane kept in continuous flight at 600 mph for a year would lose less than half a minute as observed by persons on the ground.

32-5 The Dependence of Mass on Velocity

We have been able to see some degree of "reasonableness" in the Lorentz-Fitzgerald contraction by imagining a world in which the speed of light is a very small fraction of its speed in the actual universe. There seems to be no way of making use of this hypothetical world to help us with other seemingly strange relationships in the theory of relativity, and no simple mathematical derivations are available to "tie" these relationships to those pertinent to our everyday experience. We are faced with the necessity of accepting them on the basis of rather extensive experimental verification plus the fact that we can reduce one of them to the usual form without great difficulty. Unfortunately, those relationships which have been shown to be reasonable are less important than those we have yet to meet.

The first of these is the dependence of the mass of a body on its speed. If when at rest a body has a mass m_0, when moving at a speed v its mass m will be given by the equation

$$m = \frac{m_0}{\sqrt{1 - (v^2/c^2)}} \tag{32-2}$$

or, in terms of β, where

$$\beta = \frac{v}{c}$$

$$m = \frac{m_0}{\sqrt{1 - \beta^2}} \tag{32-3}$$

Thus, the mass of a body increases as its speed increases, and the form of the equation which describes this effect is the same as that which describes the dilation of time.

The quantity m_0 is called the ***rest mass*** of the body, and m is its ***relativistic mass.***

Returning once more to the example of a plane flying at 600 mph and our hypothetical train with a speed half that of light, we find that Eq. (32-3) requires that the rest mass of the plane be increased less than 0.0001% but that the rest mass of the train be augmented by about 15.5%.

32-6 The Kinetic Energy of a Body Moving at a Relativistic Speed

We met the concept of kinetic energy in Sec. 6-4 and learned to evaluate it with the aid of Eq. (6-2):

$$KE = \frac{mv^2}{2}$$

in which m is the mass of the body and v its speed. However, a warning appeared in Sec. 6-9: Eq. (6-2) is valid only for values of v which are small compared to the speed of light. Since we know now that at relativistic speeds the mass of a body increases, we are able to see the basis of that warning.

We cannot, however, replace m in Eq. (6-2) by the value of m as given by Eq. (32-2) or (32-3); it turns out that a more sophisticated derivation is necessary. The result of this is

$$KE = m_0c^2 \cdot \left[\frac{1}{\sqrt{1 - \beta^2}} - 1\right] \tag{32-4}$$

Since our original and unsophisticated equation for kinetic energy is valid for non-relativistic speeds, Eq. (32-4) must reduce to Eq. (6-2) for small values of β. We shall proceed to prove that it does so. However, unless you are interested in mathematical demonstrations, or your instructor wishes you to follow the proof, you may skip to the next section.

For the moment, we shall ignore all of Eq. (32-4) except the first term within the brackets. This term may be written in the form $1/(1 - \beta^2)^{1/2}$, and in turn this may be expressed as $(1 - \beta^2)^{-1/2}$. This is a binomial which may be expanded according to the usual procedure. The result is:

$$(1 - \beta^2)^{-1/2} = 1 - \left(-\frac{1}{2}\beta^2\right) + \frac{(-\frac{1}{2})(-\frac{3}{2})}{2}\beta^4 - \frac{(-\frac{1}{2})(-\frac{3}{2})(-\frac{5}{2})}{2 \cdot 3}\beta^6 + \cdots$$

$$= 1 + \frac{\beta^2}{2} + \frac{3\beta^4}{8} + \frac{5\beta^6}{16} + \cdots$$

Since we are interested in whether Eq. (32-4) is equivalent to Eq. (6-2) for non-relativistic speeds, we are concerned only with very small values of β. If β is small, the values of β^4 and β^6 will be negligible in comparison with β^2, so all terms to the right of the one containing β^2 may be dropped. Thus,

$$(1 - \beta^2)^{-1/2} = 1 + \frac{\beta^2}{2}$$

and the whole quantity within the brackets in Eq. (32-4) becomes just $\beta^2/2$. Hence,

$$\text{KE} = m_0c^2 \cdot \frac{\beta^2}{2} = \frac{m_0(c\beta)^2}{2}$$

but

$$\beta = \frac{v}{c}$$

so

$$c\beta = v, \quad \text{and} \quad \text{KE} = \frac{m_0v^2}{2}$$

If we recall that m_0 is the rest mass and m in Eq. (6-2) is the mass at non-relativistic speeds, we see that this equation is identical with our original equation for kinetic energy. Hence it is evident that the non-relativistic equation for kinetic energy is a special case of the relativistic equation, and is contained within the latter.

The kinetic energy of a body moving at 600 mph would have to be evaluated to a dozen significant figures before any difference between the values given by the relativistic and non-relativistic equations would appear. On the other hand, for a value of β equal to 0.500, the kinetic energy of a body as given by Eq. (32-4) exceeds that computed by Eq. (6-2) by about 23.8%.

32-7 The Equivalence of Mass and Energy

Section 6-5 included a statement that the principles of conservation of energy and conservation of mass are but special cases of a more general law which considers mass and energy to be intraconvertible. With the aid of Eq. (32-3) and Eq. (32-4) we can derive Einstein's equation for the equivalence of mass and energy. This equation has been called the most important equation in the science of physics.

Equation (32-4) can be rewritten in the form

$$\text{KE} = c^2 \cdot \left[\frac{m_0}{\sqrt{1 - \beta^2}} - m_0\right]$$

but according to Eq. (32-3), the quantity $m_0/\sqrt{1 - \beta^2}$ is the mass m which a body of rest mass m_0 has when the body is moving with a speed v such that $v/c = \beta$. Hence the equation becomes

$$\text{KE} = c^2 \cdot (m - m_0) = \Delta mc^2$$

where Δm is the increase in the mass of the body due to its velocity.

Since energy of one kind can be converted into another, the restriction to kinetic energy becomes meaningless, and we may use the symbol E for energy in general. The equation thus becomes

$$E = \Delta mc^2 \tag{32-5}$$

This famous equation of Einstein* states that matter and energy are intraconvertible, and thus forms a bridge between the older principles of conservation of mass and conservation of energy; these principles now become special cases of this more general law. At the same time, the equation defines the quantitative relationship between mass and energy. If the value of c is in the cgs system, E is in ergs, m is in grams, and the numerical value of c^2 is $9.00 \cdot 10^{20}$, since in this system $c = 3.00 \cdot 10^{10}$ cm/sec.† When mks units are used, E is in joules, m in kilograms, and c^2 is $9.00 \cdot 10^{16}$.

Sample Problem 1

When at rest, an electron has a mass of $9.11 \cdot 10^{-28}$ g. Compute its mass and its kinetic energy when its speed is $0.950c$.

Substituting these data in Eq. (32-3), we have

$$\begin{aligned} m &= \frac{9.11 \cdot 10^{-28}}{\sqrt{1 - 0.950^2}} = \frac{9.11 \cdot 10^{-28}}{\sqrt{1 - 0.90\overline{2}5}} \\ &= \frac{9.11 \cdot 10^{-28}}{\sqrt{0.097\overline{5}}} = \frac{9.11 \cdot 10^{-28}}{0.31\overline{2}} \\ &= 9.11 \cdot 10^{-28} \cdot 3.2\overline{0} = 2.9\overline{2} \cdot 10^{-27} \text{ g} \end{aligned}$$

According to Eq. (32-4),

$$\text{KE} = 9.11 \cdot 10^{-28} \cdot 9.00 \cdot 10^{20} \cdot \left[\frac{1}{\sqrt{1 - 0.950^2}} - 1\right]$$

We have evaluated the quantity $1/\sqrt{1 - 0.950^2}$ in the first part of the problem; it is equal to $3.2\overline{0}$. Using this value,

$$\begin{aligned} \text{KE} &= 9.11 \cdot 10^{-28} \cdot 9.00 \cdot 10^{20} \cdot (3.2\overline{0} - 1) = 81.99 \cdot 10^{-8} \cdot 2.2\overline{0} \\ &= 1.8\overline{0} \cdot 10^{-6} \text{ erg} \end{aligned}$$

Had we computed the kinetic energy by the non-relativistic equation, the result would have been only $3.70 \cdot 10^{-7}$ erg, which is only about 20% of the true value.

---

* Einstein's original statement of this equation was $E = mc^2$, and this is the usual form in the literature today. For this reason E was used in Eq. (32-5) for energy, instead of the W heretofore employed. The m in Einstein's equation, however, referred to *change* of mass, rather than to *mass;* so it seems advisable to follow a fairly common practice in introductory books and use Δm rather than the naked m, to reduce the danger of misinterpretation.

† If the more accurate number sequence 2.99793 is used in place of the approximation 3.00, the corresponding number sequence for c^2 is 8.98758.

32-8 An Upper Limit to Velocities

We have seen that the motion of a body causes a contraction in the direction of the motion, a stretching out of time, an increase in the mass of a body, and an augmentation of its kinetic energy over the value given by a non-relativistic equation. In all cases, these effects are more prominent at higher speeds. What happens if the velocity becomes equal to the speed of light?

Each of the equations which describe these effects contains the expression $\sqrt{1 - \beta^2}$. At the speed of light, the value of β^2 is one, so the value of $\sqrt{1 - \beta^2}$ becomes zero. The equation for the Lorentz-Fitzgerald contraction contains $\sqrt{1 - \beta^2}$ as a multiplier, Eq. (27-2); so at speeds equal to that of light, a body would contract to zero length in the direction of its motion. The equations which describe time dilation, the mass of a moving body, and its kinetic energy—Eq. (27-2) and Eqs. (32-1–32-4), inclusive—contain $\sqrt{1 - \beta^2}$ in the denominator. Division of any quantity (except zero) by zero yields infinity as the quotient; so a body moving with the speed of light would have infinite mass and infinite kinetic energy, and in a system moving at such a speed time would stand still. None of these results is possible.* Hence we must conclude that no body can attain a speed equal to that of light.

Care must be taken to avoid misinterpreting this velocity limitation. In any of the relativistic equations, $\beta = v/c$ or u/c, where c is the speed of light *in empty space.*

In certain phases of nuclear research and technology, a luminous glow may be observed where high-energy particles are moving through transparent matter. This is known as "Cherenkov radiation" and is the result of particles moving through matter at a speed in excess of the speed of light *in that medium.* This does *not* constitute a violation of the limitation of the speeds of physical bodies to values less than the speed of light, for in relativity "the speed of light" *always and invariably* means its speed *in a vacuum.* Since the index of refraction of water is about $\frac{3}{4}$, light travels at about $2.25 \cdot 10^8$ m/sec in water, and Cherenkov radiation would be produced by particles having velocities greater than this value; however, all such speeds would be less than "the speed of light," which is not $2.25 \cdot 10^8$ m/sec but $3.00 \cdot 10^8$ m/sec.

---

* If any body, even a single electron, were to attain the speed of light, its mass would be infinite, as we have seen. According to the law governing gravitational forces, there would be an infinite gravitational force between the body and each other body in the finite universe. This would require an infinite acceleration of all such bodies toward the one which had infinite mass, completely destroying the organization of the astronomical universe.

32-9 The Addition of Velocities

Suppose that a spaceship is moving away from the earth at a speed of $2.00 \cdot 10^8$ m/sec and that it fires a projectile in the forward direction at a speed of $2.00 \cdot 10^8$ m/sec with respect to the ship. Since only relative velocities are significant and since each of these relative velocities is less than the speed of light, nothing in the theory of relativity says that this is impossible. However, the theory does say that no velocity can equal that of light, and it appears that the projectile must be moving away from the earth at

$$2.00 \cdot 10^8 + 2.00 \cdot 10^8 \text{ m/sec}, \quad \text{or} \quad 4.00 \cdot 10^8 \text{ m/sec}$$

and this is far above the speed of light.

The seeming paradox is no paradox at all; we have assumed that relativistic speeds can be added arithmetically, just as non-relativistic speeds are. We have found in many situations that the methods we employ for the non-relativistic domain are inapplicable when relativistic velocities are encountered, and this is just another example of that fact. For such velocities, the law of addition is quite different. If a body has a velocity u_1 relative to an observer and a second body has a velocity u_2 with respect to the first one, the velocity v of the second body relative to the observer will be

$$v = \frac{u_1 + u_2}{1 + (u_1 u_2/c^2)} \tag{32-6}$$

in which c, as always, is the speed of light.* Thus, in the example given, the velocity of the projectile with respect to the earth is

$$v = \frac{2.00 \cdot 10^8 + 2.00 \cdot 10^8}{1 + (2.00 \cdot 10^8 \cdot 2.00 \cdot 10^8)/(3.00 \cdot 10^8)^2} = \frac{4.00 \cdot 10^8}{1 + 4.00/9.00}$$

$$= \frac{4.00 \cdot 10^8}{13.00/9.00} = \frac{9.00 \cdot 4.00 \cdot 10^8}{13.00} = 2.77 \cdot 10^8 \text{ m/sec}$$

and this speed is not outlawed by the theory of relativity.

32-10 When Is an Accelerating Force Not an Accelerating Force?

In Secs. 5-10, 5-14, and 5-15, we dealt with Newton's second law of motion, which says, in part, that the acceleration of a body is directly proportional to the force applied to it; and in Sec. 5-13 there was a tentative definition of "force" as something which tends to accelerate a body. There was a warning, however, in Sec. 5-15, to the effect that the direct pro-

* This equation is valid only if the paths of the two bodies lie along the same line. We shall not consider more complicated situations.

portionality between force and acceleration does not hold at velocities comparable with the speed of light.

At non-relativistic speeds, the effect of an unbalanced force acting on a body is to accelerate it. As the speed becomes comparable with the speed of light, the acceleration decreases even though the force does not; and when the speed of light is approached closely, the force can cause virtually no acceleration. Instead, the energy expended in applying the force appears as an increase in the mass of the body. Alternatively, we could consider that kinetic energy above that predicted by the non-relativistic equation is being stored up in the body; the two points of view are equivalent, since, according to Einstein's equation relating mass and energy, the additional mass and the additional kinetic energy are but different aspects of the same thing.

32-11 A Couple of Warnings

Any group of ideas as new and strange as those encountered in this chapter contains the seeds of confusion. Such sources of confusion will be pointed out in the hope that your difficulties may be minimized.

In the very midst of the study of relativity, it is easy to forget that magnitudes of quantities other than velocities are relative. For example, systems *1* and *2* are moving relative to each other at a speed $\frac{3}{5}$ that of light, and there is a mass of 100 g at rest in system *1*. An observer in system *1* observes its mass as 100 g, of course, but an observer in system *2* observes it as 125 g instead. You can verify this value easily with the aid of Eq. (32-2) or (32-3). Question: Is the mass really 100 g or is it really 125 g? Reasonable as this question seems, it has no meaning. It is exactly like asking whether system *1* is moving and system *2* at rest, or vice versa. Only the velocity of one system *relative to the other* has any significance whatever. Similarly, a body has one mass relative to one system and a different mass relative to another system which is moving with respect to the first system. It is impossible to specify a "real" mass except with respect to one system, and the 100 g and 125 g masses of the body in the example are equally "real" with respect to the appropriate systems. Only because all bodies on the earth are at rest with respect to the earth (insofar as relativistic velocities are concerned) can we assign definite values to their masses.

In a similar manner, a dimension of any body, its kinetic energy, and the duration of a time interval have definite values only with respect to a particular system; any such quantity has different values relative to different systems, if relativistic velocities are involved.

Another matter is the interpretation of Δm in the equation for the intraconversion of mass and energy. In later chapters, we shall meet a very few examples of the complete conversion of mass into energy, but such things are extremely rare. Far more common are situations in which there is a *slight reduction* of mass, with the appearance of an equivalent quantity of energy. Nothing in the theory of relativity suggests that the mass of a macroscopic quantity of matter can be annihilated and converted completely into energy; and both theoretical considerations and practical experience indicate that this cannot be expected.* Hence you should be careful to think of the conversion of mass to energy as being due nearly always to a *reduction* of mass rather than to the *annihilation* of mass.

Summary

The *restricted theory* of *relativity* accounts for the *Lorentz-Fitzgerald contraction* and for other seemingly strange phenomena, including time dilation, the increase of mass with velocity, and the fact that as the velocity of a body approaches the speed of light the continued application of a force increases the energy of the body without a commensurate increase in the speed. The foundations of the theory are the *relative nature* of *all velocities*, and the *constancy* of the *speed* of *light* in a *vacuum*. As used in connection with relativity, "the speed of light" always means its speed in a vacuum.

A *relativistic velocity* causes a *dilation* of time which is governed by the same factor involved in the contraction of a dimension. At such velocities, the mass of a body is *increased*, and its kinetic energy may be much greater than the non-relativistic equation would indicate. For ordinary speeds, however, the relativistic equation for kinetic energy, like all equations pertinent to relativity, reduces to the non-relativistic equation.

Mass and energy are intraconvertible according to the equation $E = \Delta mc^2$.

No body which possesses mass can attain a speed equal to that of *light*. Relativistic velocities cannot be added in the way we add non-relativistic velocities.

All *relativistic effects* are *mutual*. For example, if an observer in system A sees clocks in system B running half as fast as identical clocks in his own system, an observer in system B will see those in A running only half as fast as the clocks in B.

---

* True, in theory the masses of matter and antimatter could be annihilated, with the production of energy, if the two types of matter were brought together. Because of this very fact, however, there is no naturally occurring antimatter on the earth or our astronomical neighbors, and artificial antimatter can be created only in submicroscopic quantities—which immediately are destroyed by contact with ordinary matter.

Self-Quiz

1. State the two postulates of the restricted theory of relativity and discuss briefly the meaning of each.

2. Carry out the argument in Sec. 32-3, on the Lorentz-Fitzgerald contraction in a world where light travels very slowly, as far as you can without reference to the text. Don't expect to go clear through it, at first, without checking the text.

3. Discuss briefly the matter of simultaneity. Work out a derivation similar to that in the latter part of Sec. 32-4, from the standpoint of an observer in system B.

4. The quantity $\sqrt{1 - \beta^2}$ occurs very commonly in equations pertinent to relativity. For what does the symbol β stand? Restate the original quantity in a form which contains the symbol c. For what does c stand, and what restrictions always apply to its interpretation?

5. It is very easy to show that the Lorentz-Fitzgerald expression for the length of a moving body reduces to the "normal" length of the body for speeds which are non-relativistic. Carry out this demonstration, and similar demonstrations, on the expression for time dilation, for the relativistic mass of a body, and for the sum of two velocities. For these non-relativistic speeds, do any of the relativistic equations we've met differ from those we have used previously?

6. Why is the symbol Δm used in the equation for the equivalence of mass and energy, instead of the simple m Einstein used?

7. The quantitative aspects of chemistry are based on the observation that the total mass of the substances entering a chemical reaction is equal to the total mass of the products. Since virtually every chemical reaction either absorbs or releases energy, this is contrary to the principle of relativity which says that energy and mass are equivalent. What is the explanation of this paradoxical situation?

8. The heat of combustion of petroleum products is of the order of 10^4 cal/g. Very roughly, this is $4 \cdot 10^4$ joules or $4 \cdot 10^{11}$ ergs. This quantity of energy is equivalent to how many grams of mass? Does the result help to answer the preceding question?

9. What is the cause of Cherenkov radiation? What is the source of confusion of persons who feel that Cherenkov radiation is evidence of a violation of the limit placed on velocities by the theory of relativity?

10. System B has a velocity of $0.9c$ with respect to system A. An observer in system A finds that there is a serious violation of Newton's second law in system B. What is the nature of this violation, and what is its cause? Does an observer in system B observe this violation, which the observer in A noticed? Explain.

11. A manufacturer of weights for analytical balances adjusts the mass of such a weight exactly (we'll assume) to 50 g. In what sense is this mass definite? In what sense is it indefinite, and why—aside from the assumption of exactness?

Problems

1. The speed of the boats discussed in Sec. 27-6 is v and the stream is flowing at a velocity u. The one-way length of the course is L. (a) Show that the time required for boat A to finish the race is $2L/\sqrt{v^2 - u^2}$. (b) Show that the time for boat B is $2vL/(v^2 - u^2)$. (c) Assume that L_B for boat B is unchanged and that the course for boat A is shortened to L_A, so that the times for the two boats are exactly equal; and solve for L_B in terms of L_A. Compare the result with Eq. (27-2).

2. A spaceship is 50.0 ft long when at rest. If it is traveling in a direction parallel with its length at a speed of (exactly) $3c/5$, (a) what is its length, and (b) by what per cent has its length been reduced?

3. This problem can be solved most easily by solving the appropriate equation for β. Determine the speed in m/sec necessary to reduce the length of a body to each of the following (exact) fractions of its normal value, if the body moves parallel with its length: (a) $\frac{9}{10}$, (b) $\frac{1}{2}$, (c) $\frac{1}{10}$.

4. A motionless body has a length of exactly 100 ft. When moving parallel with its length, what is the value of its length when its velocity is (a) less than the speed of sound; (b) 186 mi/sec; (c) $1.86 \cdot 10^3$ mi/sec; (d) $1.86 \cdot 10^4$ mi/sec; (e) $5 \cdot 1.86 \cdot 10^4$ mi/sec; and (f) $9 \cdot 1.86 \cdot 10^4$ mi/sec?

5. The dimension of a body in the direction of its motion is 60.0% of the "normal" value. Calculate the speed of the body.

6. If a spherical body were given a velocity of $2.90 \cdot 10^8$ m/sec, by what per cent would its volume be reduced?

7. Sixty cycle AC is used in system A, and 50 cycle in system B. At a certain relative speed, an inhabitant of one of the systems would observe the two frequencies to be identical. In which system does he reside, and what is the value of the relative speed?

8. In a linear accelerator, electrons pass down a straight tube 500 ft long. If the effective average speed of an electron with respect to the tube is exactly 99.5% of the speed of light, how long will the tube "appear" to the electron?

9. The rest mass of an electron is $9.11 \cdot 10^{-28}$ g. What is the mass of the electron in the preceding problem?

10. What is the kinetic energy of the electron in Problem 8 as computed by (a) the relativistic equation and (b) the non-relativistic equation?

11. Through what potential difference would an electron have to fall to acquire a velocity exactly 99% that of light?

12. Compute the speed in m/sec of an electron which has fallen through a potential difference of 30.0 v.

13. (a) At what speed in m/sec will the mass of a body be exactly 5 times its rest mass? (b) What will the ratio of its mass to its rest mass be, when its speed is exactly $2.90 \cdot 10^{10}$ cm/sec?

33

THE INTERNAL STRUCTURE OF AN ATOM: INTRODUCTION

33-1 Preview

We have taken brief glimpses into the internal structure of the atom on previous occasions, chiefly in connection with heat conduction by metals (Sec. 19-6) and the electrical conductivity of metals (Sec. 21-8). The major portion of this and the remaining chapters will be devoted to this fascinating field. This chapter presents something of the history of the concept of atomicity, and of the study of the internal structure of the atom, and then introduces subatomic particles and associated concepts.

33-2 Origins of the Concept of Atomicity

The word "atom" comes from the Greek. We can deduce its meaning by considering familiar words containing the same roots: an *a*chromatic lens is one which does not have chromatic aberration, and an appendec*tomy* is the separation of the appendix from the rest of the body. Hence "atom" means, literally, indivisible. We already know that this is a misnomer, for we have found that any atom contains at least two kinds of subatomic particles, protons and electrons, and that under appropriate circumstances some electrons may be separated from the remainder of the atom. Thus it is evident that the ancient Greek concept of an atom differs from ours.

Democritus considered that all matter consists of indivisible particles, with a different kind of atom for each kind of matter; thus his "atoms" correspond more closely to our concept of molecules than to what we call an atom—except that his "atoms" were indivisible. Some other Greeks, including Aristotle, rejected the concept of atomicity.

The ***atom*** may be defined as the smallest particle of an element which retains the chemical properties of the element, but this is not a very satisfying statement. Since an individual atom is far too small to be observed, even with the best microscopes, how can we determine its chemical properties? This will have to do for the present, however; as we progress through the next few chapters, you will find your idea of what an atom is becoming more definite.

33-3 Early "Models" of the Atom

The great majority of the human race finds it difficult to understand a novel idea in terms of abstract symbols and equations alone; we feel that we are on more solid ground if we can visualize what is under discussion.* Thus we have tried to get a mental picture of how an atom is made, how it would look if we could magnify it enough so that we could see it.

The atoms of Democritus were solid particles in a great variety of the regular geometrical shapes of which the Greeks were so fond. This picture, and the idea that all the different kinds of atoms Democritus envisioned were indivisible, faded when the misguided efforts of the alchemists paid off in an accumulation of chemical facts. Following the work of Dalton and other true chemists who followed him, the molecular concept emerged. It was evident that these molecules were built from two or more atoms, and the term "atom" was restricted to elements. Thus the almost infinite number of atoms required by Democritus' ideas was reduced to

* Workers in the higher levels of physics find that such models becloud the matter rather than clarify it, but for most of us models are of considerable help.

the number of different elements then known. This new kind of atom retained its forebear's property of indivisibility.

The discovery of electricity spurred research of many kinds, including the discharge of electricity through gases. It was found that if a metal wire was sealed into one end of a glass tube and a similar wire sealed into the other end, an electrical discharge would occur when the tube was partially evacuated and a sufficiently high potential applied between the wires at the opposite ends of the tube. This was the forerunner of "neon" lights. At very low pressures, the visible discharge disappeared, but if a sufficiently high voltage was used, fluorescence of the walls of the tube would occur. It developed that whatever caused this fluorescence came from the cathode, so the unknown emanations were called "cathode rays." By various means, these cathode rays could be restricted to a narrow beam, and it was found that this beam could be deflected by an electric or a magnetic field. This was a strong implication that the beam bore electric charges; and when it was deflected so that it impinged on a metallic collector, the collector acquired a negative charge. The path of the deflected beam was not angular, like that of a reflected or refracted light ray; instead, the path was more gently curved, like that of a body tossed horizontally. This suggested that the rays had mass. Hence the rays seemed to consist of a stream of electrified physical particles. Moreover, a study of the relationship between the deflection due to an electric field of known strength and that caused by a known magnetic field made it possible to determine the ratio of the electric charge on a cathode ray particle to the mass of the particle.

Thus these experiments showed that, under proper conditions, electrically charged particles could be separated from a metal. Furthermore, they could be obtained from *any* metal used as the cathode; and *regardless of what metal was employed for the cathode the charge-mass ratio of the cathode ray particles invariably was the same.* Hence there must be some component of the atoms of a metal which was "pulled out" by the electric field, and which was the same in the atoms of all metals. Atoms were *not* indivisible, and the newly discovered particles were common to the atoms of all metals. By other techniques it was learned that particles of the same sort are present in all atoms, not just in those of metallic elements.

These particles were named ***electrons.***

Since matter is electrically neutral under ordinary conditions, it was evident that if every atom contains electrons (or at least one electron) it must also contain a positive electric charge equal in magnitude to the total negative charge of its electrons. Other lines of research had shown that the charge-mass ratio of the electron is a great deal larger than that of the rest of the atom, so nearly all the mass of the atom had to be in the portion which contained the positive charge. This led Thompson to propose that an atom is constructed along the lines of a plum pudding which has raisins scattered through it; the electrons corresponded to the raisins, and the rest of the atom with its relatively great mass and positive electric charge was analogous to the pudding within which the raisins were embedded. Since plum pudding is not a common food in this country, Thompson's atom was likened to a pumpkin, the electrons being the seeds of the pumpkin. Hence this concept of the structure of the atom came to be known as "Thompson's pumpkin atom."

33-4 Rutherford's Nuclear Atom

By 1912, radioactivity had been discovered and it was known that the alpha particles shot out by a decaying atom of radium bore a positive electric charge. Rutherford made use of a stream of such alpha particles to test the validity of the "pumpkin atom" concept. This he did by causing the stream to fall on a thin gold foil and observing the scattering pattern of the alpha particles.

If the positive charge of an atom is "smeared" throughout the atom, in general an alpha particle which penetrates the atom will be affected more by the positive charge nearby than by the more distant negative charges concentrated in the electrons. Nearly all of the positive charge lies at one side of the path of an alpha particle which penetrates a nucleus near the edge, as in Fig. 33-1(a), and the repulsion of like charges deflects it as shown. On the other hand, if an alpha particle makes a "dead center" hit as in part (c) of the figure, the charge of the nucleus will be distributed symmetrically about its path and no deflection will occur. Part (b) of the figure represents an intermediate situation. Evidently particles which pass through the foil will be scattered at various angles, and it is possible to compute the angular distribution of the scattered particles.

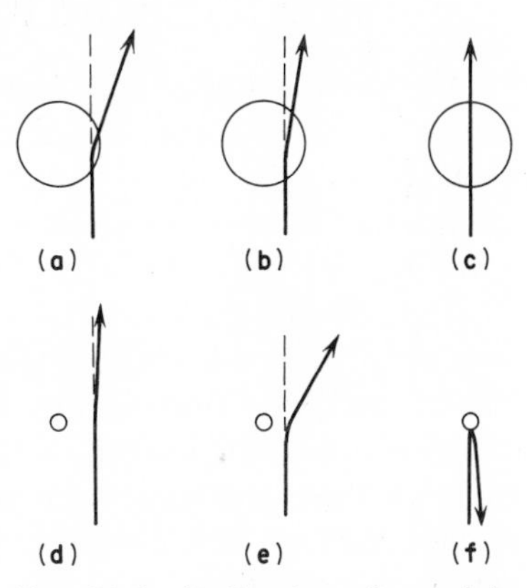

Fig. 33-1. Deflection of an alpha particle, on the assumption that the positive charge is distributed throughout the atom (a), (b), and (c); and on the assumption that the positive charge is concentrated in the nucleus (d), (e), and (f).

Suppose, however, that the positive charge is concentrated at the center of the atom. In this case, the electrostatic forces will be greatest on those alpha particles which pass close to the center—just the opposite of what we deduced for the other situations. The paths of the approaching particles in parts (d), (e), and (f) of Fig. (33-1) are the same as those in parts (a), (b), and (c) respectively; but the deflections are very different. Again, it is possible to compute the pattern of the angular scattering of the alpha particles to be expected.

When Rutherford sent a stream of alpha particles through a very thin foil of gold, he found the scattering pattern to agree with the assumption that the charge was concentrated at the center of the nucleus. The agreement was good even for particles turned almost directly back; and since the computation of the scattering pattern considered only electrostatic forces, this showed that no "mechanical" contact occurred—that is, the particles were not bounced back by a mechanical collision. Knowledge of the energy of the alpha particles, and of the law governing the electrostatic repulsion, made it possible to determine that particles turned back nearly 180° had come to within about $3 \cdot 10^{-12}$ cm, or $3 \cdot 10^{-4}$ Å, of the center of the atom—this without suffering a "mechanical" collision. Hence the mass of the atom, except for the almost negligible fraction represented by the mass of the electrons, was concentrated within a sphere of less than $3 \cdot 10^{-4}$ Å radius. It had been established, by various means, that the diameter of an atom is of the order of 1 Ångstrom, so the space occupied by the positive charge, and nearly all the mass, of an atom is an extremely small fraction of the total volume of the atom. Later determinations show that this core or ***nucleus*** of any atom has a radius between 10^{-4} Å and 10^{-5} Å, depending on the element.

33-5 The Measurement of the Electronic Charge and the Mass of the Electron

We have seen that early workers with cathode rays were able to determine the charge-mass ratio of the electron, but they could not deduce an explicit value for either the charge or the mass. Determinations of the charge on the electron have a long and fascinating history, but we have space for only the most widely known determination, that by Millikan.

This determination is based on familiar laws of electrostatic and gravitational forces, plus the phenomenon of terminal velocity. The progress of any body through any fluid, including air, is opposed by a force which is due to the viscosity of the fluid. For a spherical body, the magnitude of this opposing force is directly proportional to the speed of motion through the medium. Hence if the body is moving under the action of a constant force, it will accelerate, but this acceleration will increase the opposing force; in a practical sense, at some particular velocity the increasing resisting force becomes equal to the unchanging driving force, and acceleration ceases. The resulting constant velocity is the ***terminal velocity.*** A parachute designer tries to minimize the terminal velocity by producing a parachute which will cause a relatively large resisting force as it falls through the air with its load; an airplane designer tries to minimize the resistance of an aircraft to increase its "top speed"—that is, its terminal velocity.

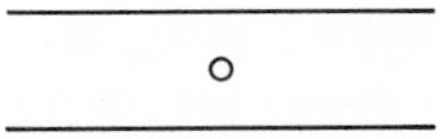

Millikan used an apparatus within which a fine droplet of oil could fall at its terminal velocity—which was very low, because of the small mass of the droplet—between two horizontal plates in an enclosed space. The droplet could be watched and its speed of fall measured. It was then given an electric charge by irradiating the space with X rays (Sec. 35-2, 35-4) or exposing the droplet to radiations from some radioactive substance. An electric field was then established between the plates, in such a direction that the electric force on the droplet caused it to rise; and its velocity of rise was determined. From these data and the viscosity of air, the magnitude of the charge on the droplet could be computed. It turned out that the charges were not equal; however, the larger values were integral multiples of the smallest one, indicating that some drops carried two or more charges rather than a single one. The modern value of this smallest unit of electric charge, the charge on a single electron, is $4.80 \cdot 10^{-10}$ esu or $1.60 \cdot 10^{-19}$ coulomb, and Millikan's value was in good agreement with this.

Fig. 33-2. Schematic representation of Millikan oil drop apparatus.

The existence of this ***electronic charge*** as the smallest possible charge of electricity means that electricity, like matter, is "granular"; it cannot be obtained in arbitrary quantities, for all quantities are multiples of this basic charge. The electronic charge is an "atom" of electricity in a more literal sense than the smallest particle of an element is an atom of the element.

Once the electronic charge was known, it was a simple matter to determine the mass of the electron from the charge and the charge-mass ratio. The mass is $9.11 \cdot 10^{-28}$ g.

33-6 Protons and Neutrons

The "atomic" character of any electric charge implies that the positive charge on the nucleus of an atom must not only be equal to the total negative charge of the electrons; it must consist of separate charges, the number of positive charges being identical with the number of electrons in the atom. Hence it is reasonable to suppose that each of these positive charges is associated with a particular particle within the nucleus, and this is borne out amply by experimental evidence. The particle is the ***proton,*** which has a mass 1836 times that of the electron and a positive charge equal in magnitude to the negative charge on the electron.

For some time it was considered that any atom is made up wholly of protons and electrons. However, after Moseley's work in 1914 (Sec. 34-11) the number of positive charges on the nucleus was known. It turned out that an atom with a nucleus composed solely of protons would have a smaller mass (with the sole exception of hydrogen) than the masses previously established by chemical methods; actual masses of individual atoms range from 2.0 to more than 2.5 times what might have been expected. This discrepancy was taken care of by assuming that the nucleus contained some electrons along with the protons, and that the law discovered by Moseley applied to the *net* positive charge on the nucleus. In this way, theorists were able to crowd enough extra protons into the nucleus, (each accompanied by an electron to neutralize its charge) to achieve fair agreement with the masses determined by chemists.

Although there were theoretical considerations at variance with this concept, there was no better way out of the dilemma until 1932, when Chadwick's discovery of the neutron removed the difficulty. The ***neutron*** is a particle of essentially the same mass as the proton (its mass exceeds that of the proton by about 0.14%), but as its name implies, it is devoid of any electric charge. Thus it became possible to "build" an atomic nucleus by combining the number of protons required by Moseley's law with the necessary number of neutrons to give the atom the mass which chemical evidence required, though there were still relatively slight discrepancies. Just before World War I, a method of making a determination of the mass of an individual atom by physical means was initiated, and after the war it was developed to a high degree of accuracy. Values obtained by this method agreed with those computed on the basis of the proton-neutron-electron model of the atom much better than chemical data did, through no fault of the chemists. See Sec. 36-6.

Since in the structure of the atom, protons and neutrons are found only in the nucleus, they are called ***nucleons.***

33-7 "Elementary" or "Fundamental" Particles

With Chadwick's discovery of the neutron in 1932, our array of the subatomic particles which comprise atoms seemed to be complete, and in a sense it was. Today we say, for example, that an atom of berylium is made up of a nucleus which contains 4 protons and 5 neutrons, with 4 electrons outside the nucleus. The proton, neutron, and electron were the fundamental, or elementary, particles of which all atoms are composed.

But the same year that saw the discovery of the neutron also saw Anderson discover a new particle which had been predicted by Dirac, though it isn't a component of ordinary matter. This was the positive electron, or ***positron,*** an identical twin of the ordinary electron except that its charge is positive. When one of these positrons meets an ordinary electron, the two of them immediately carry out a mutual suicide pact; that is, charge and mass are annihilated, and in their stead appear two photons of equal energies, traveling in exactly opposite directions! Not only that; under appropriate conditions, a photon of sufficient energy disappears and in its place there appear an electron and a positron! The electron commences to appear much less "fundamental" and "elementary" than we had thought it. The production of photons when an electron and a positron are annihilated is called ***annihilation radiation,*** and the creation of such a pair from a photon is ***pair production.***

Nor is this the end of the story. Nearly all atoms are stable over the ages, so to all external appearances the components of an atom are stable. But if you could obtain a leakproof container full of neutrons newly freed from nuclei, only about 4% of them would be left after an hour; the remainder would have decayed into protons and electrons! Thus

$$\text{neutron} \rightarrow \text{proton}^{+} + \text{electron}$$

And this process can be made to go the other way; neutrons can be created from protons and electrons.

This is reminiscent of a chemical reaction and its reverse, in which a compound can be dissociated into its elements, or they can be combined to form the compound. The compound isn't "fundamental"; it is a combination of "fundamental" atoms. Is this the relationship of the neutron to the proton and electron? There is good evidence for a negative answer. The neutron is just as fundamental—or as *un*fundamental!—as the proton or the electron. The fact that an electron can "come out of" a neutron is no better evidence that it existed as such in the neutron than the "evidence" that liquid water must exist within an ice cube because liquid water comes from the ice.

But it *is* very evident that we shall have to modify our concepts of the adjectives "elementary" and "fundamental," as applied to such particles.

33-8 Other Particles

Observations since about the beginning of this century have indicated the presence of effects which are now grouped under the classification of cosmic radiation, and a great deal of research is still under way in this field. The stimulus of this and various theoretical considerations, plus the impact of pioneer work in artificial transmutation, led to the development of complex machines able to accelerate atomic and nuclear particles to speeds at which they have very high energies. These particles are caused to strike a target of some sort, and the results analyzed in a great number of ways.

Cosmic ray research, and research based on these high-energy machines, have increased tremendously our array of "elementary" particles. One of these is the antiproton, which differs from the proton principally in having a negative instead of a positive charge. There is also an antineutron. Thus there arises the possibility of antimatter, in which the atomic nuclei contain negative protons and antineutrons, and the electrons are positive.

A wide variety of other "elementary" particles appears when matter is bombarded with subatomic missiles of great energy. Some of these carry no electric charge, some are charged positively, and some negatively. Their masses range from essentially zero to over 2500 times the mass of an electron. Almost without exception they are unstable, decaying into other particles, the eventual products being neutrons, protons, electrons, neutrinos, and photons. We have met all of these but the neutrino, which is a particle with no charge, like the neutron, but also with essentially zero mass.

These relatively familiar particles and all other "elementary" particles, including those of antimatter as well as matter, total about 30 particles.

33-9 More on the Duality of Nature: de Broglie Waves

If the inclusion of photons in the list of elementary particles startled you, perhaps it will be well to review Sec. 27-2, 27-3, in which we found that though light very definitely has a wave nature, it is equally definite that it consists of bundles of energy called quanta. This duality of its nature can not be rationalized away or ignored.

In 1924, de Broglie suggested that since light, which had been considered a wave phenomenon, has particulate properties, perhaps "ordinary" particles may have wave properties; and he developed an equation for the wavelength of such ***de Broglie waves,*** or ***matter waves.***

The Einstein mass-energy equivalence equation (32-5) is

$$E = \Delta mc^2$$

If a photon is changed into mass (as in pair production, Sec. 33-7), the photon ceases to exist; the only mass it ever had is the mass equivalent of its energy. Hence, *for a photon,* Δm is the entire mass, m, of the photon; so

$$E = mc^2$$

The quantum concept of light was treated in Sec. 27-3, and the energy of a photon is given by Eq. (27-1):

$$W = h\nu$$

where W is the energy of the photon, h is Planck's constant, and ν is the frequency of the photon. Comparing this with the equation above, we see that the left side of each stands for the energy of the photon, so the right-hand members must be equal:

$$mc^2 = h\nu$$

The frequency is related to the wavelength and the velocity by Eq. (13-4):

$$c = \nu\lambda$$

in which symbols appropriate to light have been used rather than those used for other types of waves. From this equation

$$\nu = \frac{c}{\lambda}$$

so that

$$mc^2 = \frac{hc}{\lambda}$$

Cancellation of one c on each side yields, after rearrangement,

$$\lambda = \frac{h}{mc}$$

The denominator of the term on the right is the product of the mass of the photon and its speed. According to Eq. (6-7), this is the momentum of the photon. Hence, *if* particles partake of the character of waves, the length of such waves should be given by the equation

$$\lambda = \frac{h}{mv} \tag{33-1}$$

where h is Planck's constant, as before, m is the mass of the particle, and v its speed.

Wild as such a concept might seem, it was put to the test by directing a fine beam of electrons at a crystal of nickel, and a diffraction pattern was obtained. And a diffraction pattern is the result of interference, so it can be produced only by waves! De Broglie's novel idea was validated not only qualitatively but quantitatively, for the wavelength can be determined from a diffraction pattern and it agreed with what Eq. (33-1) would predict.

It is these matter waves, or de Broglie waves, which are the basis of the electron microscope.

Research has shown that particles more massive than electrons also have wave properties. This characteristic appears to be limited to particles of submicroscopic size, however. We must consider a moving proton from this standpoint, but we needn't concern ourselves with the wavelength, or frequency, of a ten-ton truck barreling down the highway at 50 mph!

Matter waves constitute a new and striking validation of the quantum concept. Schroedinger and Heisenberg built on the foundation laid by de Broglie and worked out theoretical treatments which appeared to be different, but proved to be equivalent. The approach pioneered by them is known as ***wave mechanics*** and is an essential tool for any study of subatomic physics above the elementary level. The mathematics necessary for wave mechanics puts it beyond our reach; thus our study of much of the remaining material will be on a basis somewhat like our study of nonrelativistic mechanics—informative, not too misleading, but by no means the whole story.

Summary

The atomic concept is ancient, but present ideas of atoms differ greatly from those held earlier.

The first evidence that the atom is not indivisible was the discovery of the *electron*, which is a *negatively charged particle* of very small mass found in all atoms. Its charge is the basic unit of electric charge.

By observing the *scattering* of *alpha particles* shot through matter it was found that the *positive charge* of the atom and nearly all its *mass* are concentrated in an *extremely small nucleus*. At *first* it was thought that this nucleus was composed of *protons*, or of a number of protons and a smaller number of electrons, the proton being a relatively massive particle with a positive charge equal to the negative charge of the electron. The discovery of the *neutron*, an electrically neutral particle of about the same mass as a proton, led to the present concept of a nucleus composed of *protons* and *neutrons*. A number of electrons sufficient to equal the positive charge of the nucleus completes the atom.

Though the electron, proton, and neutron are considered to be *fundamental particles*, they are *not* necessarily permanent and unchangeable. There are more than a dozen other elementary particles, but nearly all are unstable.

Moving particles have a wave character in addition to their more familiar particulate character, the wavelength being inversely proportional to the momentum of the particle.

Self-Quiz

1. In terms of its origin, what is the meaning of the word "atom"? Try to find a pair of words, other than those in Sec. 33-2, from which this meaning may be deduced.

2. Compare and contrast atoms as visualized by Democritus and by Thompson.

3. What are cathode rays? How was their nature determined? What effect would a horizontal electric field have on a horizontal beam of cathode rays, if the beam enters the field at right angles? What effect would be observed if the electric field were replaced by a magnetic field?

4. Discuss Rutherford's alpha scattering experiment in some detail. What did it indicate with regard to the internal structure of the atom? How was it deduced that nearly all the mass of the atom, as well as the positive charge, is confined within the nucleus?

5. What does the expression "terminal velocity" mean, and why is there a terminal velocity? If the accelerator of a car is depressed to a certain point and kept exactly there, on a level road, will the car continue to accelerate indefinitely? Explain.

6. Explain Millikan's method of determining the value of the electronic charge. Why didn't all his determinations give the same value (within experimental error)?

7. Define, compare, and contrast: electron, positron, proton, antiproton, neutron. Which are components of normal matter?

8. What is a nucleon, and why is it so called? How many kinds of nucleons are there?

9. What is the relationship of pair production to annihilation radiation?

10. Why must a photon possess at least a certain minimum energy to cause pair production? If the photon has this amount or more, and produces an electron pair, *all* the energy of the photon is used. What does this suggest relative to the speeds of the electrons created? How should the direction of the velocity of the electron compare with that of the positron, and why?

11. Derive the equation for de Broglie waves.

12. A high-speed electron shot into air loses speed and stops after a fairly short distance. What happens to the length of its de Broglie waves in the meantime?

Problems

1. (a) Determine the wavelength of an electron which has a speed of exactly 10^8 cm/sec. (b) Determine the wavelength of a proton of the same speed. (Take the masses of the particles from the table in Appendix A, p. 756.)

2. Assume that the electron in the hydrogen atom has a speed of $2.20 \cdot 10^6$ m/sec. What is its wavelength? If the electron is in a circular orbit such that the circumference of the orbit is equal to the wavelength of the electron, compute the radius of the orbit.

3. What wavelength will electrons in an electron microscope have if they are accelerated by a voltage of 250 v? (Use the non-relativistic expression for kinetic energy. The computations will be greatly simplified and the error will not be large.)

4. What accelerating voltage would be required in an electron microscope to obtain waves with a length of 0.500 Å?

5. Prove that the wavelength in an electron microscope is inversely proportional to the square root of the accelerating voltage.

34

THE BOHR ATOM: OPTICAL SPECTRA AND X-RAY SPECTRA

34-1 Preview

In the preceding chapter, we found that an atom has a positive nucleus with a diameter a great deal smaller than that of the atom, and one or more electrons, depending on the element, outside the nucleus; but we gained no information on how these are "put together" to form the atom. This chapter gives us a brief glimpse at how the problem of the internal structure of the nuclear atom was attacked and reports something of the results. It has been said, rather aptly, that in approaching this problem a researcher is like a blind man faced with the task of discovering the details of the structure and operation of a wristwatch with a crowbar as his sole tool. Since we are less fortunate than a theoretician who has wave mechanics at his command, our view of the internal structure of the atom must be on a basis somewhat like our use of hypothetical lines of magnetic force to "understand" magnetic phenomena. Yet our incomplete view of the internal structure of the atom will be both interesting and useful, much as the incomplete view of mechanics was very useful even before it was broadened by a glimpse of relativistic mechanics.

34-2 Difficulties in the Problem of the Internal Structure of the Atom

Since the diameter of the largest atom is less than one-thousandth of the wavelength of visible light, direct visual observation is obviously impossible. All evidence bearing on the problem of the atom's internal structure must be indirect. Hence it is a matter of detective work—and no fictional detective was ever more clever than the real-life detectives in this field, nor was any detective novel more fascinating. It is a pity that space is available for only a bare outline.

Superimposed on the fact that only indirect evidence is available were two discrepancies between what was known of the atom and known physical principles. First, the electrostatic attraction between the positive nucleus and an electron would cause an electron to "fall" to the nucleus unless this were somehow prevented; in the case of the hydrogen atom, the initial acceleration of the electron toward the nucleus would be about $9 \cdot 10^{24}$ cm/sec^2! If this occurred, how could the atom maintain its diameter of something like 10^5 times the diameter of the nucleus? The electron must be either vibrating or moving around the nucleus in an orbit. The other conflict with known laws arises from the fact that either a vibratory or an orbital motion of an electron involves acceleration of the electron.* If we think of the electric field around an electron as consisting of lines of electric force radiating out from the electron, any acceleration of the electron must send a "kink" along lines of force just as the acceleration of a hand holding the end of a rope sends a "kink" along the rope. This phenomenon has a solid theoretical and practical foundation; it is in this way, for example, that the AC currents surging into and out of the antenna of a radio or TV station generate the electromagnetic waves which bring the program into our homes. Since the waves carry energy away from their source, any acceleration of the electron in an atom should cause it to lose energy by radiation. If it is vibrating, energy loss must result in a reduced amplitude, vibration ceasing when all the energy has been radiated. If the electron is in an orbit, loss of energy would cause it to spiral down toward the nucleus like a "dying" artificial satellite. In either case, the structure of the atom would be impermanent; yet the atoms of most elements are stable over the ages.

As we shall see in the next section, an incandescent element emits

---

* We found in Sec. 12-3 and Sec. 12-5 that in simple harmonic vibration the vibrating body is always being accelerated (except at the instant it passes through its rest position); and the same is true for any type of vibration whatever, for the velocity is never constant and the direction alters periodically. In the case of motion in a circular orbit, the speed is constant but the direction is constantly changing; hence, as we found in Sec. 8-8, a centripetal acceleration is required to keep the body in the circular path, so an orbital motion of an electron would necessarily involve acceleration.

certain frequencies of light; and here there is another discrepancy. No wave produced by a mechanical vibrator has a frequency different from a frequency of the vibrator itself; and though the source may have more than a single frequency, each frequency is an integral multiple of the fundamental frequency (Sec. 15-12 – 15-14, inclusive). And it seems that there could be but a single frequency of wave generated by a body moving in an orbit—the frequency of its trips around the orbit. Yet the light produced by an incandescent element has more than one frequency, and the frequencies are *not* related to each other by integral ratios.

34-3 Spectra and Spectral Series

When an element in gaseous form is made incandescent by any means, such as extreme temperature or an electric discharge, it emits certain discrete frequencies of light rather than a continuous spectrum of frequencies. "Light," as used here, includes the ultraviolet and infrared as well as the visible. Dispersion of this light by a prism or diffraction grating yields an ***emission spectrum*** consisting of bright lines (in the visible region) and lines detectable by non-visual methods (in the other regions). This is also called an ***optical*** spectrum, to distinguish it from the ***X-ray*** spectrum, which is composed of much shorter wavelengths.

The spectrum of any element is a characteristic "fingerprint" different from that of any other. Since the frequencies emitted by a certain kind of atom must depend somehow on the internal structure of the atom, they offer an avenue for the investigation of that structure.

Chemical evidence long ago established that the least massive atoms are those of hydrogen, and this implies that their structure should be the simplest. The spectrum of hydrogen proves to be relatively simple, and the first marked advance after Rutherford's discovery of the nucleus was based on a study of the spectrum of atomic hydrogen by Neils Bohr (Secs. 34-4, 34-5). Before anything at all was known of atomic structure, however, four lines in the visible portion of the hydrogen spectrum, plus a number of lines in the near end of the ultraviolet, had been observed and their wavelengths determined. In 1885, Balmer worked out a relationship among the wavelengths of these lines, known as the "Balmer formula." Stated in terms of frequencies rather than wavelengths, it is

$$\nu = cR\left(\frac{1}{4} - \frac{1}{n^2}\right) \tag{34-1}$$

in which ν is the frequency, c is the speed of light, R is a constant called the "Rydberg constant," and n may have any integral value greater than 2. The value of R, to four significant figures, is $1.097 \cdot 10^5$ when c is in cm/sec or $1.097 \cdot 10^7$ when c is in m/sec.

Further research and better instrumentation revealed more lines in both the infrared and the ultraviolet. Part of the spectrum is shown in the upper part of Fig. 34-1, and considerable order is apparent. The lines are grouped in ***series,*** as shown and identified in the lower part of the figure. The series in the visible and near infrared is the Balmer series, which is described by Eq. (34-1). It was found that the frequencies of the lines in any one of the other series could be described by a similar formula, the only difference being that instead of 4 in the denominator of the first term in parentheses some other integer was necessary. Like 4, each integer which replaced it was a perfect square. Hence the Balmer formula could be generalized to apply to any series, as follows:

$$\nu = cR\left(\frac{1}{n_s^2} - \frac{1}{n_l^2}\right) \tag{34-2}$$

in which ν, c and R have the same meanings as before, n_s is an integer characteristic of the series, and n_l an integer, larger than n_s, which is characteristic of a particular line in any series. Appropriate values of both integers are recorded in Fig. 34-1.

If we divide both sides of Eq. (34-2) by c, the left side becomes $1/\lambda$, since $c = \nu \cdot \lambda$; so the equation may be written

$$\frac{1}{\lambda} = R\left(\frac{1}{n_s^2} - \frac{1}{n_l^2}\right) \tag{34-3}$$

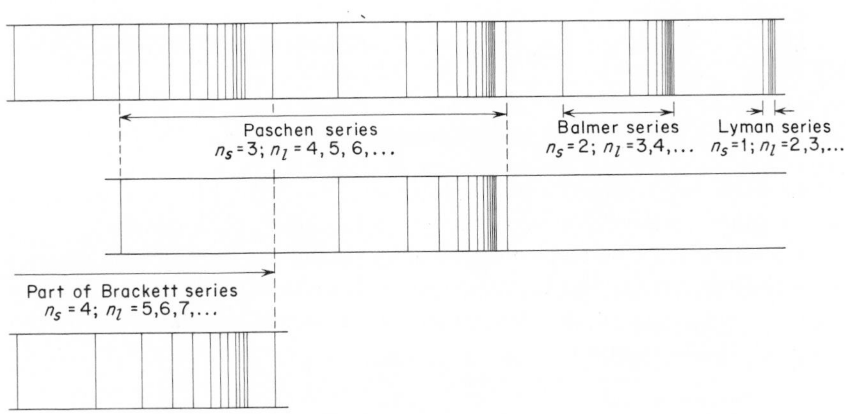

Fig. 34-1. The Lyman, Balmer, and Paschen series, plus part of the Brackett series. Dots near the right end of a series represent many lines which are too close together to show. Not included in the figure are the Pfund series ($n_s = 5$; $n_l = 6, 7, \ldots$) and the Humphreys series ($n_s = 6$, $n_l = 7, 8, \ldots$). Wavelength increases toward the left, frequency increases toward the right.

These relationships were of great value to "practical" spectroscopists and to theorists, but they left much to be desired because they were purely empirical and gave no hint of how the hydrogen atom was constructed. In fact, as we have seen, the relationship among the frequencies they gave was not in accord with what theoretical considerations indicated the relationship should be.

Sample Problem 1

Find the values of the longest and shortest wavelengths in the Brackett series.

For this series, $n_s = 4$, and the smallest possible value of n_l is 5. Use of this value will give the expression in parentheses its minimum value, so it will yield the maximum wavelength. The minimum wavelength will be given by the largest possible value of n_l, which is infinity.

For the longest wavelength,

$$1/\lambda = R\left(\frac{1}{4^2} - \frac{1}{5^2}\right) = R\left(\frac{1}{16} - \frac{1}{25}\right)$$

$$= R\left(\frac{25}{400} - \frac{16}{400}\right) = \frac{9R}{400}$$

$$\lambda = \frac{400}{9R} = \frac{400}{9 \cdot 1.097 \cdot 10^5} = 4.05 \cdot 10^{-4}\ \text{cm} = 4.05 \cdot 10^{+4}\ \text{Å}$$

For the shortest wavelength,

$$1/\lambda = R\left(\frac{1}{4^2} - \frac{1}{\infty^2}\right) = R\left(\frac{1}{16} - 0\right) = \frac{R}{16}$$

$$\lambda = \frac{16}{R} = \frac{16}{1.097 \cdot 10^5} = 1.46 \cdot 10^{-4}\ \text{cm} = 1.46 \cdot 10^{+4}\ \text{Å}$$

34-4 Bohr's Solution of the Dilemma: Postulates

In 1913, Bohr offered a way around all these difficulties, one which required much courage as well as exceptional insight and cleverness.

He stated that the electron circles the nucleus in any one of a number of permitted orbits, the criterion for a permitted orbit being that the angular momentum of the electron in an orbit should be related to Planck's constant by the equation

$$mvr = \frac{nh}{2\pi} \tag{34-4}$$

wherein m is the mass of the electron, v is its speed in an orbit of radius r, n is an integer, and h is Planck's constant.* Normally the electron occupies

* From Eq. (8-19) in Table 8-3, angular momentum $= I\omega$. According to Eq. (8-8), the moment of inertia I of the electron is mr^2, and from Eq. (8-5) its angular velocity ω is v/r. Hence its angular momentum $= mr^2 \cdot v/r = mvr$.

the orbit of minimum radius, for which $n = 1$, but the atom may be ***excited*** by acquiring extra internal energy (by some sort of a collision); and in the excited atom, the electron is in one of the other orbits.

Bohr stated that while in any of these permitted orbits the electron does not radiate; he stated this as a simple fact with no attempt to account for it.

The other basis of his concept was that radiation occurs only when the electron in an atom "jumps" from an excited orbit to the normal orbit, or to an excited orbit closer to the nucleus. Since the larger the orbit, the greater is the energy possessed by the electron, in making a jump to a smaller orbit the electron must lose energy; and this appears as a photon.

The energy of a photon is equal to $h\nu$, so

$$h\nu = W_o - W_i \tag{34-5}$$

where W_o is the energy of the electron in any relatively large or outer orbit, and W_i is its energy in any inner orbit.

34-5 Bohr's Solution: The Bohr Equation

The proton which constitutes the nucleus of a hydrogen atom carries a charge of magnitude e, and the electron carries a charge of the same magnitude. When the electron is in an orbit of radius r, the electrostatic force on it will be e^2/r^2, Eq. (20-2). This furnishes the centripetal force required to keep the electron in its orbit, where m is the mass of the electron and v is its speed; and this force is mv^2/r, Eq. (8-23). Hence

$$\frac{mv^2}{r} = \frac{e^2}{r^2}$$

or

$$mv^2 = \frac{e^2}{r} \tag{34-6}$$

Equation 34-4 may be written

$$v = \frac{nh}{2\pi mr}$$

If this value of v is squared and substituted in Eq. (34-6) for v^2, the result is

$$m \cdot \frac{n^2h^2}{4\pi^2m^2r^2} = \frac{e^2}{r}$$

and solution of this equation for r yields

$$r = \frac{n^2h^2}{4\pi^2me^2} \tag{34-7}$$

This equation defines the radii of the permitted orbits. Since n is in the numerator, the value of r will increase as n increases; and since n is

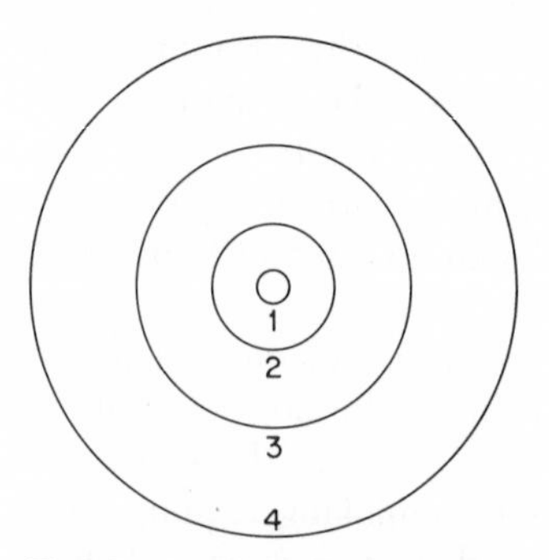

Fig. 34–2. The relative sizes of the first four "permitted" orbits in the hydrogen atom.

squared and can have only integral values, the relative values of the radii of the permitted orbits are 1, 4, 9, 16, and so on. The first few orbits are shown, to scale, in Fig. 34-2.

Now we must express the energy of the electron in any orbit in terms of the radius, so that we may evaluate W_o and W_i in Eq. (34-5). We found in Sec. 6-9 that any energy value is relative; it is referred to a specified (or understood) condition or situation. Conventionally, the electron is considered, for a good but somewhat obscure reason, to be zero when it is at an infinite distance from the nucleus. Hence in any orbit its energy is negative. This is like referring the energies of an ore bucket at the various levels of a mine shaft to the top of the mine shaft; all values will be negative, but the *difference* in energy between any two specified levels is quite independent of our choice of a reference level.

The potential energy is the product of the force and the distance, the force being e^2/r^2. Since the force varies with distance in this manner, we cannot compute the potential energy without calculus. The result of such a computation is $-e^2/r$.* Thus,

$$\text{PE} = -\frac{e^2}{r} \tag{34-8}$$

The kinetic energy of the electron is $mv^2/2$, so, according to Eq. 34-6

$$\text{KE} = \frac{e^2}{2r} \tag{34-9}$$

The total energy W of the electron is the sum of its potential and kinetic energies, so

$$W = -\frac{e^2}{r} + \frac{e^2}{2r} = -\frac{e^2}{2r} \tag{34-10}$$

We have the value of the radius of any permitted orbit in Eq. (34-7). Insertion of this value of r into Eq. (34-10) gives

$$W = -\frac{e^2}{2} \cdot \frac{4\pi^2 me^2}{n^2h^2} = -\frac{2\pi^2 me^4}{n^2h^2} \tag{34-11}$$

All values in Eq. (34-11) are constants except n, which is the number of the orbit as indicated in Fig. 34-2. If we factor $1/n^2$ out of Eq. (34-11)

---

* If you have had integral calculus you can derive this result; it is a matter of integrating $(e^2/r^2) \cdot dr$ between infinity and r.

and subtract the values of the energies in two different orbits, as in Eq. (34-5), we obtain

$$h\nu = -\frac{2\pi^2 me^4}{h^2}\left(\frac{1}{n_o^2} - \frac{1}{n_i^2}\right)$$

or

$$\nu = \frac{2\pi^2 me^4}{h^3}\left(\frac{1}{n_i^2} - \frac{1}{n_o^2}\right) \tag{34-12}$$

where n_i and n_o are numbers of the inner and outer orbits, respectively.

This bears a marked resemblance to the empirical Eq. (34-2). In effect, Eq. (34-12) *is* the generalized Balmer formula, except that instead of being wholly empirical it is based on theoretical considerations. Comparing the two equations, we see that

$$R = \frac{2\pi^2 me^4}{h^3 c} \tag{34-13}$$

34-6 Experimental Support for the Bohr Concept

Any concept which agrees with the observed stability of atoms is better than one which does not, even if its agreement is based on an arbitrary assumption; but the strongest support for the Bohr concept is the very close agreement between experimentally determined wavelengths and those given by the Bohr equation.

Another source of support is the ***absorption spectrum.*** When light containing a continuous range of frequencies in the optical range is passed through hydrogen gas and then dispersed, the resulting spectrum contains dark lines due to the absorption of light of certain frequencies by the hydrogen. The frequency of each line in the absorption spectrum coincides with one in the emission spectrum. This means that hydrogen can absorb energy from light only in specific quantities—quantities identical with the energy of photons it can emit. The conclusion is that it can absorb a photon if—and only if—the energy of the photon is just sufficient to "lift" the electron from one permitted orbit to another.

More direct evidence comes from measurements of the current carried through hydrogen gas by a stream of low energy electrons. The electrons are "boiled off" a filament which is heated by current from a battery, and a variable voltage is applied between this filament and a plate at the opposite end of a tube. The apparatus is shown, minus refinements, in Fig. 34-3(a). Part (b) of the figure indicates the peculiar manner in which the current varies as the voltage is increased. The even spacing of the maxima along the voltage axis indicates that when electrons in the stream have been accelerated until they have a certain critical quantity of energy, they lose that energy; and the only way they can lose it is in a collision with a hydrogen atom. (Collisions, in this sense, are not mechanical impacts; each one is an interchange of energy which occurs when an electron in the stream passes near, or perhaps through, an atom.) Measurement of the

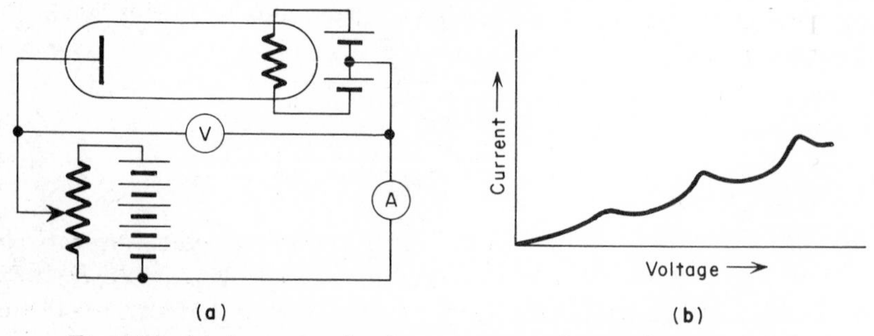

Fig. 34-3. (a) Apparatus for determination of excited states, and (b) the manner in which the current varies with the voltage.

voltage difference between two successive maxima leads to the fact that in such a collision a free electron in the stream loses just enough energy to "lift" the electron in a hydrogen atom from its normal orbit to the next orbit. Further research with more refined apparatus reveals that other discrete quantities of energy may be lost by an electron in a collision with an atom, each such quantity coinciding with the energy of a photon in the emission spectrum. Thus we have direct and independent confirmation of the energy levels which are a basic feature of the Bohr concept.

All atoms other than those of hydrogen have more than one electron, so their spectra are different. If one of the two electrons of a helium atom is removed, however, this singly ionized helium behaves much like hydrogen, spectroscopically, except that the double charge on the nucleus increases the energy of the electron in any given orbit. Thus the spectrum of singly ionized helium has a spectrum closely resembling that of hydrogen except that it is shifted in the direction of higher frequencies. Similarly, the spectrum of doubly ionized lithium, in which the atoms retain only a single electron each, is hydrogen-like but shifted still farther toward higher frequencies because of the triple charge on the nucleus.

34-7 A New Unit of Energy

In such applications as the measurement of energy levels within an atom by sending a stream of electrons through a gas composed of the atoms under investigation (third paragraph of Sec. 34-6), it is customary to employ a unit of energy which we have not met. This is the ***electron volt,*** which is defined as the energy an electron, or any other body carrying one electronic charge, would acquire in falling through a potential difference of exactly one volt. According to Eq. (20-9), $W = qV$, where W is the energy a charge q will acquire in falling through a potential difference V. The value of q is $1.60 \cdot 10^{-19}$ coulomb; so, for $V = 1.000$ v,

$$W = 1.60 \cdot 10^{-19} \cdot 1.000 = 1.60 \cdot 10^{-19} \text{ joule} = 1.60 \cdot 10^{-12} \text{ erg}$$

Thus 1 electron volt (abbreviated ev) is $1.60 \cdot 10^{-12}$ erg or $1.60 \cdot 10^{-19}$ joule. The unit abbreviated as Mev is 1 million electron volts, and that abbreviated as Bev is 1 billion electron volts.

Though the electron volt is defined in terms of a particle which carries one electronic charge falling through a potential difference of 1 volt, its size is convenient for many other applications, such as the energy acquired by any other charged particle in falling through a potential difference, the energy of a photon, and many other applications in molecular, atomic, and subatomic physics.

34-8 An Initially Arbitrary Assumption Becomes Logical

It appears that Bohr had no more basis, on theoretical ground, for his choice of permitted orbits than for the non-radiation of the electron; the justification for both assumptions was that they gave the right results. We are in a much more favorable position than Bohr was, for de Broglie's proposal of matter waves came eleven years after Bohr's concept of the atom.

Equation (34-4), which describes the permitted orbits, may be written

$$\frac{nh}{mv} = 2\pi r$$

but according to Eq. (33-1),

$$\frac{h}{mv} = \lambda$$

Hence the restriction stated by Eq. (34-4) becomes

$$n\lambda = 2\pi r$$

Thus the initially arbitrary restriction on the orbits turns out to be merely a requirement that the circumference of the orbit must include some whole number of wavelengths! To see the significance of this, think of the necessity of constructive interference in the establishment of standing waves on a string or in an air column (Sec. 15-7 – 15-14, inclusive). The existence of standing waves, or resonance, is possible in an orbit only if there is a whole number of waves in the circumference, as shown in the permitted orbits 1, 2, and 3, in Fig. 34-4. No

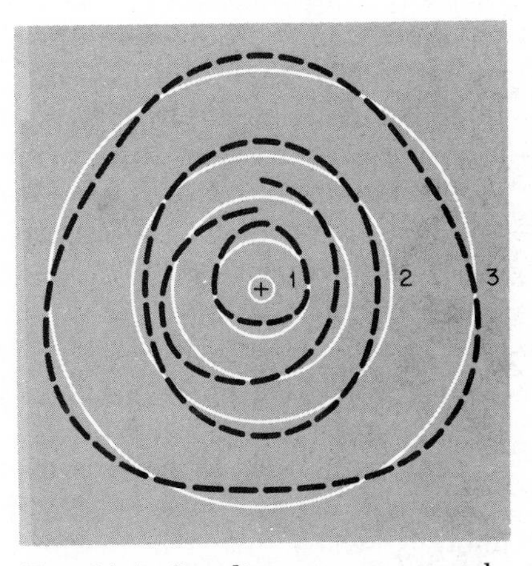

Fig. 34-4. Standing waves are established in the "permitted" orbits 1, 2, and 3; but destructive interference prevents their establishment between "permitted" orbits, such as between orbits 1 and 2. (The diagram is not to scale.)

wave pattern can be established between orbits 1 and 2 because of destructive interference, and this is equivalent to saying that no electron can exist in an intermediate orbit.

34-9 The Concept of Atomic Number and the Definition of an Element

In the last paragraph of Sec. 34-6, it was assumed, in discussing the hydrogen-like spectra of singly ionized helium and doubly ionized lithium, that an atom of helium normally contains two electrons, and an atom of lithium, three. From a different point of view, the fact that the spectrum of singly ionized helium is hydrogen-like shows that in this condition a helium atom must contain a single electron; hence it must contain two normally. Since any atom normally has no net electric charge, the helium nucleus must contain two protons. Similarly, the normal lithium atom must contain three electrons, and there must be three protons in its nucleus. Thus the distinction between elements lies in the number of protons in the nucleus, which therefore is called the ***atomic number.**** Any ***element*** is a substance in which all atoms have the same number of protons in their nuclei.

Since there are 92 natural elements, atoms of the various elements contain anywhere up to 92 protons in their nuclei, with an equal number of electrons outside the nucleus. Spectroscopic and other data show that in a Bohr orbit characterized by the number n there can be $2n^2$ electrons but no more; thus there may be up to 2 electrons in the first orbit, 8 in the second, 18 in the third, and so on. The first orbit is "filled" with electrons in all elements except hydrogen, and the second is "filled" in all but the nine elements of lowest atomic number. As one goes to elements of higher atomic number, however, an outer shell may contain electrons even though one nearer the nucleus is incomplete. The most massive atoms contain electrons in seven orbits, although the fifth and sixth orbits are both "unfilled."

34-10 X Rays and X-Ray Spectra

The "jump" of an electron from an excited orbit to a normal one (or to one with a lower level of excitation) produces a photon, and it is such photons which give rise to the characteristic optical spectrum of an element. Only the outer electrons are involved in the production of optical spectra, however, and as the number of electrons goes up, the problem of

---

* The term atomic "number" must not be confused with the term atomic "weight." The distinction between these terms will be discussed in Sec. 36-6.

relating the internal structure of the atom to the optical spectrum rapidly becomes very difficult. However, similar information can be obtained from X rays, with much less difficulty.

When a stream of high-energy electrons impinges on a target, electromagnetic radiations of very high frequency (short wavelength) are produced. These were discovered quite accidentally by Roentgen in 1895, and are sometimes called Roentgen rays, but the more common term is ***X rays.*** Though their character depends on the voltage used to accelerate the electrons which strike the target, in general a spectrum of X rays consists of a ***continuous spectrum*** of frequencies and a ***characteristic spectrum*** of a limited number of fairly definite frequencies, the two types of spectra being superimposed.

Though they are interesting and very important in practical applications, the radiations of the continuous spectrum contribute nothing to the problem of the internal structure of the atom; so we shall not consider them further.

Radiations in the characteristic spectrum have an origin closely analogous to that of optical spectra, except that their production involves electrons closer to the nucleus. Thus, if an electron in the stream bombarding the target knocks an electron out of one of the inner orbits of an atom, an electron from farther out will drop into the "hole" left in the inner orbit. In so doing, it will lose energy, and the energy loss is much greater than would be the case for a similar jump between orbits farther from the nucleus. Hence the photon produced will have a relatively large energy, which means a high frequency and short wavelength.

In the terminology of X rays, the innermost orbit is called the *K* orbit, or the *K* shell, the next is the *L* shell, etc. If an electron is knocked out of the *K* shell, a photon belonging to the *K* series will be produced when the vacancy is filled by the arrival of an electron from outside the *K* shell. Similarly, a vacancy in the *L* shell results in a photon belonging to the *L* series. The terminology is recorded in Fig. 34-5. A vacancy may be filled by one jump, with the production of a single photon, or by several jumps and therefore several photons. Obviously the total energy of the photons must be the same in any case. For example, Fig. 34-5 shows that the total energy of a K_α photon and an L_β photon must be the same as that of a single K_γ photon, since in either case the electron vacancy is tranferred from the *K* shell to the *N* shell.

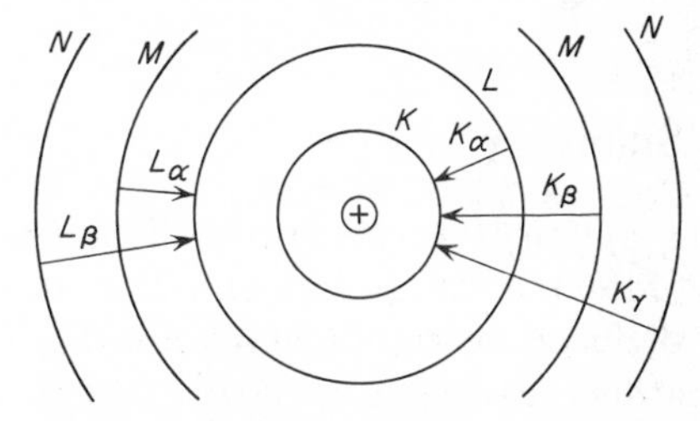

Fig. 34-5. Designations of orbits, and of lines in X-ray series. (Orbits are not drawn to scale.)

34-11 Moseley's Law

The concept of atomic number and its significance to atomic structure, and all the beauty, simplicity, and practical values which result, are due to the work of Moseley, who died a young man in the trenches of World War I.

Chemists long ago worked out a system of relative weights of individual atoms of the various elements, and arranged the elements in the order of increasing relative weight. Moseley noted that there was a definite relationship between the frequency of any characteristic X-ray line, such as the K_α line, and the number of the element in the chemists' list. He was able to state a law such that, when the constants were properly evaluated, the frequency of any characteristic X-ray line of any element could be predicted. The law may be stated thus:

$$\nu = a(Z - b)^2 \tag{34-14}$$

where ν is the frequency of the line, a is a constant characteristic of the series, b is a constant characteristic of the line, and Z is the atomic number. For example, for the K_α line, a is $24.7 \cdot 10^{14}$ and b is very nearly 1; so if these values are inserted into Eq. (34-14), together with the atomic number Z of any element, the equation will give the frequency of the K_α line of that element.

It was on this basis that the number of charges on the nucleus of the atom of a particular element became definitely known. Chemical evidence can predict the number of electrons in atoms of the various elements, but not on such direct evidence as that on which Moseley's law is founded. In fact, Moseley had to alter the order of the chemists' list in at least one case.

In more advanced texts, it is shown that Moseley's law may be derived from the Bohr equation, with modifications to account for the difference in the nuclear charge and the effects of the other electrons. Hence the validity of Moseley's law adds further confirmation of Bohr's basic concepts.

Summary

Optical spectra furnished the *first evidence,* after Rutherford's discovery of the nucleus, pertinent to the *internal structure* of the atom. *Balmer* had deduced an *empirical relationship* for the *frequencies* in one *series* of the atomic hydrogen *spectrum,* but there was no theoretical basis for it; and the observed frequencies and the long-term stability of atoms both were contrary to what would have been expected.

Bohr was able to derive an equation equivalent to Balmer's by making certain assumptions which seemed highly arbitrary. He considered that an electron emitted a photon when it jumped from a larger permitted orbit to a smaller one, but did not radiate otherwise. This concept was bolstered by independent experimental verification of the existence of different energy levels in the atom.

Comparison of the optical spectrum of the ionized form of one element with that of the normal form of an element of slightly lower atomic weight led to the concept of an element's being distinguished by the number of positive charges on the nuclei of its atoms; this number is the atomic number of the element. Evidence from *X-ray spectra,* with the aid of Moseley's law, contributed the bulk of the information on the atomic numbers of the elements.

Characteristic X rays are produced much as radiations in the optical range are, except that orbits nearer the nucleus are involved in X-ray production.

On the basis of de Broglie waves, one of *Bohr's* arbitrary restrictions becomes a statement of the conditions required for resonance of the de Broglie waves in an orbit.

Self-Quiz

1. Why can't an atom be magnified by some sort of microscope so that it will be visible?

2. In the second paragraph of Sec. 34-2, it was stated that if the electron in a hydrogen atom were able to "fall" to the nucleus its initial acceleration would be $9 \cdot 10^{24}$ cm/sec^2. Give two reasons why the qualification "initial" is necessary in this statement.

3. Why was there considered to be a conflict between the concept of an atom in which an electron either vibrates or moves in an orbit, and the fact that an atom is stable?

4. Why were the observed frequencies in the spectrum of atomic hydrogen thought to be inconsistent with either a vibratory or an orbital concept of the structure of the atom?

5. Which has more energy, a photon in the infrared or one in the ultraviolet? Why?

6. Discuss the value of the Balmer formula and the limitations of that value.

7. State the three assumptions on which the Bohr concept was based; discuss briefly the meaning of each.

8. Which of these assumptions does the concept of matter waves support? Carry out the algebraic proof and show how it justified the relationship arbitrarily assumed by Bohr.

9. Referring to equations in Sec. 34-5 as necessary, in each of the following cases make an accurate verbal statement of how the first quantity depends on the

second: radius of orbit, number of orbit; velocity in orbit, number of orbit; velocity in orbit, radius of orbit; energy in orbit, number of orbit; energy in orbit, radius of orbit.

10. On the basis of the discussion of the Balmer series, and the corresponding equations, make a diagram somewhat like Fig. 34-5 to show the generation of several lines in the Balmer series and label the series. On the same diagram add and label the Lyman and Paschen series.

11. What determines the energies of the photons an atom can produce? What determines the energies of those it can absorb?

12. How can the spectroscopic evidence of excited states be verified by other means?

13. Define the term "atomic number." What does it represent?

14. Why is it assumed that the number of electrons in a normal atom is the same as the number of protons in the nucleus? Why is the charge on the proton considered to be equal in magnitude to that on the electron?

15. What was the principal source of positive proof on the atomic number of any given element?

16. Discuss the production of an X-ray photon. Point out similarities with the production of a photon in the optical spectrum and also state any differences.

17. Discuss the terminology of series in characteristic X-ray spectra, and that of lines in a series.

18. What is an element?

Problems

In these problems use the following values: mass of the electron, $9.11 \cdot 10^{-28}$ g; electronic charge, $4.80 \cdot 10^{-10}$ esu; Planck's constant, $6.63 \cdot 10^{-27}$ erg sec; 1 ev $= 1.60 \cdot 10^{-12}$ erg.

1. Compute (a) the frequencies of the longest and shortest lines in the Lyman spectrum, and (b) their wavelengths.

2. Compute the longest and shortest wavelengths in the Paschen series.

3. From your answers to the preceding questions determine (a) the ratio of the wavelength of the longest Paschen series line to that of the longest Lyman series line, and (b) the ratio of the two shortest lines in the two series. (c) Verify both answers by dividing the equation for Paschen series lines by that for Lyman series lines, canceling out common terms, and putting the necessary data into the resulting ratio.

4. Considering only the term in parentheses in Eq. (34-3) or (34-12), determine the ratio of the highest frequency to the lowest frequency (a) in the Brackett series and (b) in the Lyman series. Check your answer to part (b) against your answer to Problem 1(a).

5. Compute the value of R as given in Eq. (34-13) and check against the value given below Eq. (34-1).

6. Calculate the radius of the first Bohr orbit ($n = 1$) and from this determine the radii of the next three orbits. Compare your first answer with the answer for part (b), Problem 2, Chapter 33, p. 615.

7. (a) Compute the velocity of the electron in the first Bohr orbit. (b) How many times does the electron go around the orbit in 1 sec?

8. (a) Using Eq. (34-8) and Eq. (34-9) compute the potential energy, the kinetic energy, and the total energy of an electron in the first Bohr orbit. (b) Repeat for the second Bohr orbit.

9. From the results of Problem 8 determine (a) the energy loss in ergs and in electron volts of an electron which drops from the second orbit to the first, (b) the frequency of the resulting photon, and (c) its wavelength.

10. Compute the frequency of the photon emitted when an electron drops from the second to the first orbit by Eq. (34-12), and compare the result with Problem 9.

11. If the energy difference between a normal and an excited orbit of an atom is $8.00 \cdot 10^{-12}$ erg, through what voltage must electrons fall between collisions to gain enough energy to enable them to excite the atoms on collision?

12. If, after excitation by collision with a stream of electrons, hydrogen atoms emit the longest line of the Lyman series, 1216 Å, through what voltage must the electrons in the stream fall between collisions?

13. Using the values given below Eq. (34-14), determine the frequency and the wavelength for the K_α line of (a) copper and (b) tungsten. (See Table AD-2, p. 760.)

14. From your answers to Problem 13 calculate the energy difference, in electron volts, between the K and L orbits in (a) copper and in (b) tungsten.

35

INTERACTIONS OF PHOTONS WITH MATTER

35-1 Preview

The interactions of photons with matter are of both theoretical and practical importance, and their results range from the acquisition of a suntan (or a sunburn!) to investigations of the internal structure of the nucleus. Some of the most striking evidence of the particulate nature of light comes from such interactions, and we shall investigate some of these. In one case, this will lead to the principle of uncertainty, which greatly modified the philosophy of physics.

35-2 The Photoelectric Effect

The first type of interaction we shall consider is the emission of electrons which may occur when light falls on a substance. This is the ***photoelectric effect.*** You may recall that the first recorded observation of this phenomenon was made by Hertz when he was carrying out an experiment which was considered to be the final nail in the coffin of the particulate concept of light (Sec. 27-2). Ironically, the photoelectric effect, discovered under these circumstances, is quite incomprehensible if viewed from the standpoint of the wave theory but readily understandable on the basis of the particulate concept.

The effect can be demonstrated by attaching a zinc plate to the top of each of two identical electroscopes, and charging one negatively and the other positively, as in part (a) of Fig. 35-1. If a lamp which produces ultraviolet light is turned on so that the light falls equally on the zinc plates of the two electroscopes, the results will be as shown in part (b) of the figure; the positively charged electroscope retains its charge, but the negative charge disappears from the other electroscope. Research with considerably more sophisticated instrumentation established beyond doubt that the ultraviolet light causes electrons to leave the zinc. Recall that in a metal some electrons are essentially free, and if one of these acquires sufficient energy it can leave the body of the metal, much as a molecule can leave the body of a liquid if the molecule has sufficient energy. On the other hand, the positive charges are in the atomic nuclei, locked in the crystal lattice of the metal. Hence energy acquired from the light enables electrons to escape, carrying away the charge on the negative electroscope; but protons are unable to escape, so the positive charge remains on the other electroscope.

The photoelectric effect has a tremendous variety of practical uses, ranging from TV cameras to the automatic grading of oranges, and from

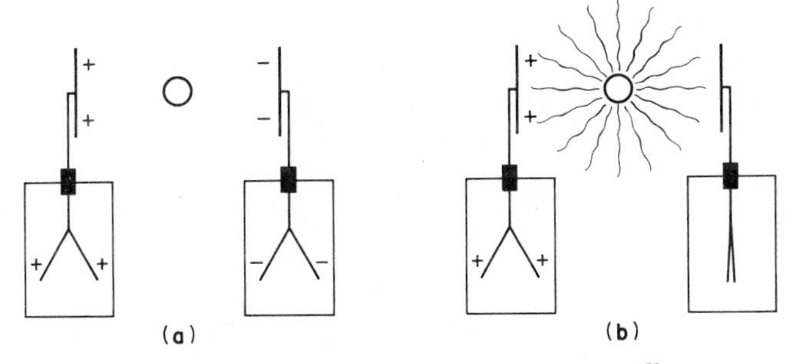

Fig. 35-1. (a) Either a positive or a negative charge will remain in an electroscope when the ultraviolet lamp is turned off; (b) When the lamp is on, the positive charge still remains but the negative charge leaks off.

automatic inspection of can labeling to burglar alarms and door openers. Though this introduction has been in terms of ultraviolet light, any other kind of electromagnetic radiation will be effective if the wavelength is short enough.

35-3 Characteristics of the Photoelectric Effect

From the standpoint of the wave theory, it would be appropriate to speak of the peculiarities of the photoelectric effect rather than its characteristics, for the situation is not at all what the wave theory would predict.

The removal of an electron from a body leaves a small positive charge on the body, and this attracts the departing electron. Hence, if the electron is to escape, it must have at least a definite minimum quantity of energy, just as a molecule requires a definite quantity of energy to overcome the force of surface tension and escape from a liquid. Any excess of energy above the minimum required would be retained by the electron—or the molecule—as kinetic energy.

Since illumination is measured by the quantity of light energy per unit area, it appears that a sufficiently high illumination should always produce the photoelectric effect and that the effect should disappear at some low level of illumination. Also, the speeds of the emitted photoelectrons* should increase as the level of illumination increases.

Nature, however, stubbornly refused to observe these relationships. Light of any particular spectral composition may, or may not, produce the photoelectric effect, and this is quite independent of the level of illumination. Also, raising the level of illumination increases the number of photoelectrons produced per unit time but has no effect whatever on their speeds.

The fact is that the effects which the wave theory would predict for the level of illumination depend instead on the frequency. If one commences an investigation with monochromatic light of relatively low frequency—say the near infrared—he will obtain no photoelectrons. If the frequency is gradually increased (by employing a different portion of the spectrum) there will be a certain minimum frequency at which photoelectric emission will be initiated, whatever the level of illumination may be; this is the ***critical frequency*** for the material being used. At this frequency, the photoelectrons have essentially no kinetic energy. Continued increase in the frequency of the light used results in a regular increase in the speeds of the electrons emitted. Augmentation of the level of illum-

---

* The term "photoelectron" furnishes an example of the use of a prefix, or sometimes a quite different term, to indicate the recent history of a particle. A photoelectron is identical with all other electrons in its mass, charge, and all other properties.

ination makes the photoelectric emission more copious, but has no effect on the speed of the photoelectrons. All of these things are unexpected and incomprehensible on the basis of the wave theory.

The lack of any perceptible time lag adds to the failures of the wave theory. Provided that the frequency of the light exceeds the critical value, photoelectrons will be emitted at very low levels of illumination. It is not difficult to determine the quantity of luminous energy passing through any particular area per unit time. On the basis of an assumption of the effective cross-sectional area of an electron, one can compute for how long a time a level of illumination which is low, but sufficient to produce observable photoelectric emission, should be maintained in order that an electron may receive and store up enough energy to enable it to escape. Depending on the assumptions made, such a calculation indicates that a matter of weeks or months or even years would be necessary. However, techniques which can measure rather small fractions of a microsecond (1 μsec $= 10^{-6}$ sec) fail to reveal any lag whatever between the arrival of light on a surface and the ejection of the first photoelectrons.

35-4 Einstein's Explanation of the Photoelectric Effect

The plot of the experimental results of an investigation of photoelectric emission would appear like Fig. 35-2(a). For light of any frequency less than the critical frequency ν_c, no emission whatever occurs. Emission takes place with light of all higher frequencies, giving a straight line graph. This means that the kinetic energy of the emitted electron is directly proportional to the difference between the frequency used and the critical frequency.

Let us extrapolate the line in Fig. 35-2(a) back to zero frequency; it will intersect the energy axis at w as shown in the figure. Evidently the existence of a minimum effective frequency, ν_c, means that a photon must have an energy at least equal to $h\nu_c$, Eq. (27-1) in order to liberate an electron. Hence the distance from w to the zero of the energy axis

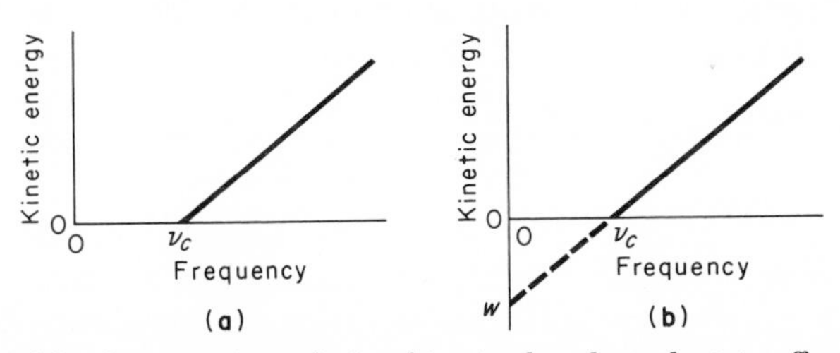

Fig. 35-2. Quantitative relationships in the photoelectric effect. (a) Plot of typical experimental data. (b) Extrapolation of experimental data yields the value of the work function.

must represent the quantity of energy an electron needs in order to escape. This quantity is called the ***work function.***

On this basis it appears that, if a photon has sufficient energy, part is used to free the electron and the remainder is converted to kinetic energy of the electron. The photon itself ceases to exist. Stated otherwise, the kinetic energy, KE, of the photoelectron is the difference between energy $h\nu$ of the photon and the work function w of the material from which the electron comes. Thus,

$$KE = h\nu - w \tag{35-1}$$

which is Einstein's photoelectric equation.

Though Planck had originated the concept of the quantization of energy being radiated from a hot body, or being absorbed, Einstein's statement of the photoelectric equation in 1906 made the quantum concept more general and spurred its development.

On the basis of Einstein's theory of the photoelectric effect, all its characteristics are quite reasonable. Regardless of how *many* photons may be striking a surface, no electrons can emerge unless some photons have individual energies at least equal to the work function. If any photons have this much energy, photoelectric emission will occur no matter how dim the light. The more the energy of a photon exceeds the work function, the more energy will be left to give the electron kinetic energy. A higher level of illumination means more photons, and therefore more photoelectrons will appear; but their individual kinetic energies will be unchanged (unless the spectral composition of the light is changed). Since photoelectric emission is a process which takes place between an individual photon and an individual electron, no time lag should be expected.

It would be just as valid to discuss all these matters in terms of wavelength rather than frequency. Thus there is a critical wavelength, λ_c, which is equal to c/ν_c; light of this wavelength or less will be effective, but all waves of greater than this critical length will be incapable of producing the photoelectric effect.

The value of the work function, and hence that of the critical frequency, varies considerably among different elements. These values may be affected by any surface contamination of the substance. Values of a few work functions are given in Table 35-1.

Table 35-1

WORK FUNCTIONS OF SOME ELEMENTS

Elements	Values
Cesium	1.9 ev
Sodium	2.28 ev
Platinum	6.30 ev
Tungsten	4.54 ev
Zinc	4.3 ev

Sample Problem 1

A photoelectron is ejected from a clean surface of platinum with a speed of (exactly) 10^8 cm/sec. Determine the wavelength of the light used.

The mass of the electron is $9.11 \cdot 10^{-28}$ g, so its kinetic energy is

$$9.11 \cdot 10^{-28} \cdot (10^8)^2 \div 2 = 4.56 \cdot 10^{-12} \text{ erg}$$

The work function of platinum, from Table 35-1, is 6.30 ev or $10.0\bar{8} \cdot 10^{-12}$ erg, so the total energy required of the photon is $14.6\bar{4} \cdot 10^{-12}$ erg. Hence,

$$h\nu = \frac{hc}{\lambda} = 14.6\bar{4} \cdot 10^{-12}, \quad \text{and} \quad \lambda = \frac{hc}{14.6\bar{4} \cdot 10^{-12}}$$

Insertion of the values for h and c yields

$$\lambda = 1.36 \cdot 10^{-5} \text{ cm} = 136\bar{0} \text{ Å}$$

35-5 The Inverse Photoelectric Effect

Had you noticed the relationship between photoelectric emission and X-ray production? In the former, photons strike a substance and cause electrons to be emitted, and in the latter, photons are emitted as the result of bombarding a substance with electrons. Thus, either phenomenon can be considered to be the inverse of the other.

We shall find in Sec. 37-2 and Sec. 37-3 that certain rays, called "gamma rays," are emitted in some types of radioactive decay, and that the nature of these gamma rays is indistinguishable from that of X rays. Hence what follows is applicable to gamma rays as well as to X rays, though the discussion will be in terms of the latter since we have not as yet had a formal introduction to gamma radiation.

Equation (35-1) may be written

$$h\nu = \text{KE} + w$$

in which $h\nu$ is the energy of an X-ray photon, KE the energy of an electron the instant before it strikes the target, and w the work function of the material in the target. Note that the work function adds to the energy of the X-ray photon; an electron entering the target evolves energy, much as a molecule in the vapor phase evolves energy when it returns to the liquid phase (Sec. 18-7). However, the value of w is of the order of a few electron volts, whereas the value of KE is of the order of 10^4 ev or higher. Thus, in a practical sense, the term w usually may be ignored, making the equation $h\nu$ = KE. The kinetic energy may be evaluated in terms of the voltage and the electronic charge: KE = Ve. Thus $h\nu = Ve$, or

$$\nu = \frac{Ve}{h} \tag{35-2}$$

and, since

$$\lambda = c/\nu$$

$$\lambda = \frac{hc}{Ve} \tag{35-3}$$

These relationships define the maximum frequency and minimum wavelength of X rays obtainable at any specified voltage. They apply to both the continuous and the characteristic X-ray spectra.

35-6 Compton Collisions

Perhaps the most striking evidence that we must accept the quantum concept of the nature of light comes from a study of the scattering of X rays by matter. If a well-defined pencil of monochromatic X rays (for example, the K_α line of tungsten) is passed through matter, most of the photons may emerge with their directions and energies unchanged (depending on the frequency of the X rays, and the thickness and density of the material). However, some photons will be scattered at various angles to the initial direction. This is not surprising, but Compton and others found that the frequency of the scattered photons was reduced. For a given angle of scattering, the effect was the same for all frequencies of X rays and independent of the material used to scatter the rays, but the reduction of frequency was greater at larger angles of scattering.

The reduction in frequency constituted a loss of energy, since the energy of a photon is $h\nu$. Compton considered that this loss occurred as the result of some interaction of the photon with an electron in the matter. Since Einstein's mass-energy equivalence equation states that the energy of a photon is equal to mc^2, while the quantum concept gives the energy as $h\nu$,

$$mc^2 = h\nu$$

which can be written

$$mc = \frac{h\nu}{c}$$

The left side of this equation is the product of the mass of a photon and its velocity, which by definition is its momentum; so the momentum of a photon can be expressed by $h\nu/c$.

Compton found that computations based on the assumption of conservation of both kinetic energy and momentum, during the interaction of the photon and the electron, were in agreement with experimental data. Yet conservation of both momentum and kinetic energy are the criteria of a perfectly elastic mechanical collision! In X-ray scattering, the electron and photon obey the same laws which apply to the collision of billiard balls, and the electron and photon obey them better!

Planck originated the concept of radiant energy being emitted and absorbed in quanta, and Einstein's explanation of the photoelectric effect supported the idea of quantization. However, it remained for Compton collisions to furnish the first strong evidence that quantization is not limited to emission and absorption, and to establish the fact that radiant energy travels in quanta or photons.

35-7 Heisenberg's Uncertainty Principle

Until about 1927, it was possible to say that *if* one could obtain complete information on every particle in the universe, it would be theoretically possible to learn the future history of a particle by applying physical laws; and since this could be done for every particle, the entire future of the whole universe could be predicted. This deterministic philosophy was shattered by Heisenberg's ***uncertainty principle.***

To see the basis of this principle of indeterminacy, let us borrow one of Heisenberg's examples. We wish to observe an electron in a microscope, and determine its speed by timing its passage over a certain distance. We must observe it at a point A and again at a point B.

From Sec. 30-9 we know that the image produced by light reflected from the electron will be a diffraction pattern. To be sure of the exact instant when the electron passes point A or arrives at point B, we must reduce the diameter of the diffraction pattern by using light of the shortest possible wavelength, Eq. (30-2). However, the reflection of a photon from the electron constitutes a Compton collision, and this will alter the velocity of the electron. This can be minimized by using photons of relatively low energy; but this means relatively low frequency and comparatively long wavelength. Hence any attempt to reduce the uncertainty in the position of the electron increases the indefiniteness of its velocity, and vice versa.

Heisenberg worked out a quantitative statement of this indeterminacy. If Δp represents the uncertainty in the momentum of a particle and Δs the uncertainty in its position, the equation as modified by Schrodinger is

$$\Delta p \cdot \Delta s \geqslant \frac{h}{4\pi} \qquad (35\text{-}4)$$

in which h is Planck's constant and the symbol $\geqslant$ is to be read "is equal to or greater than."

We may look at the situation in a different and instructive way. Since $\lambda = h/(mv)$—Eq. (33-1), the wavelength of an electron is inversely proportional to its velocity. Hence if the velocity may have any value between v and v', its wavelength may have any value from λ' to λ. Suppose that v' exceeds v by 1%; then for every hundred waves of length λ there will be 101 waves of length λ', so one "beat" will contain about 100 waves. If v' is 25% larger than v there will be 4 waves of length λ to 5 lengths λ', so the length of one "beat" will be about 4.5 times the average wavelength. A "beat" between two waves whose lengths are in the ratio of 9 to 10 is shown in Fig. 35-3(a), and one resulting from a wavelength ratio of 4 to 5 appears in part (b) of the figure. Either of these is somewhat analogous to the group of waves or "wave patch" which accompanies an electron. However, only two specific wavelengths were used in

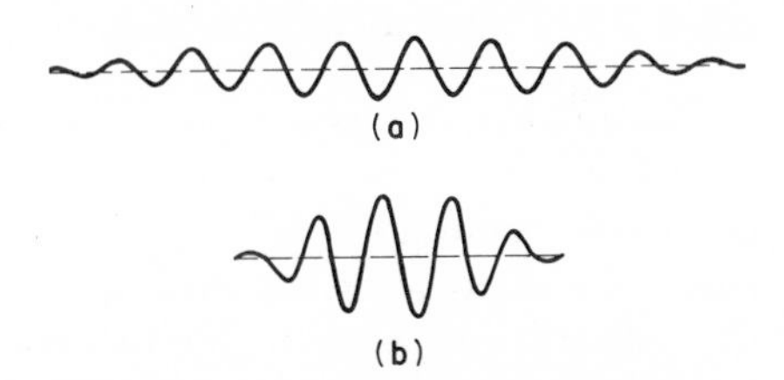

Fig. 35-3. One "beat" or "patch" of waves produced by two wave trains with wavelengths in the ratio of 9 to 10, part (a); and 4 to 5, part (b).

constructing either part of the figure, whereas the lengths of the various waves accompanying an electron may have any of an infinite number of values between λ and λ'.

Theory indicates that the amplitude of the waves at any location within the wave patch is a measure of the probability that the electron is at that point.* The electron *must* be *somewhere* within the patch, but it may be *anywhere* that the wave amplitude is not zero. If you know something is hidden in one of three places, the chance of its being in any one you choose is ten times as great as it would be if there were thirty possible hiding places. Similarly, the relative amplitudes in parts (a) and (b) of Fig. 35-3 reveal that the probability of the electron being at any given location is greater if the wave patch is short. However, the wave patch can be shortened only by allowing a greater variation in wavelength, and the wavelength is determined by the velocity of the electron. Thus we see, again, that when the indeterminacy of location of the electron is reduced, the indefiniteness in its velocity is increased proportionally, and vice versa. And the same argument applies to any other small particle.

Further consideration shows that an equation similar to Eq. (35-4) relates the uncertainty in the energy of a particle to the indeterminacy in the time at which it has that energy.

It is important to realize that these things are not the result of faulty observations, imperfect equipment, or any similar cause. Like the limit on the resolving power of any optical system, they stem from the very nature of nature itself.

Because of Heisenberg's principle of indeterminacy, statistics has become an increasingly important tool in physics. It is no longer possible, even in theory, to predict when or where a particular molecule of gas will strike the wall of a container, but it *is* possible to predict the *average* number of molecules which will strike a given area of surface in one second. The statistical approach to this problem antedates Heisenberg, but this approach is essential to a thorough understanding of many fields in which statistics would not have been applied before 1927. We shall see something of this in Sec. 36-3 and Sec. 37-9.

35-8 Photochemical Reactions

Many chemical reactions occur spontaneously once they are started, though energy must be supplied to start them; a log in the fireplace does not ignite spontaneously, but it will burn after it is set afire. In other cases, energy must be supplied continuously to make the reaction "go," as in the recharging of a storage battery. With certain reactions, the energy may be supplied in the form of light; these are called "photochemical" re-

* The square of the amplitude determines the probability.

actions. For example, a mixture of hydrogen and chlorine gases is inert, but the two combine very rapidly after being illuminated by a flash of light of sufficiently short wavelength. Energy from light causes some compounds to decompose, and in the case of relatively complex molecules it may alter the internal structure of the molecule.

Here we have a situation reminiscent of the photoelectric effect: light of a frequency below a certain critical value is incapable of producing any effect, no matter how high the level of illumination may be; but even dim light is effective if its frequency is above the critical frequency. The reasons are similar. In a photochemical reaction, a photon delivers all its energy to one atom or molecule, which can then react with another; and if the energy of the photon is insufficient—its frequency too low—to cause the reaction, no reaction can occur.

Thus the characteristics of photochemical reactions contribute additional evidence—if more is needed—of the particulate nature of light.

35-9 Pair Production

In Sec. 33-7, we met the concept of pair production very briefly. Einstein's equation which defines the intraconvertibility of mass and energy may be interpreted as predicting that matter can be created out of energy, and this occurs in the phenomenon of pair production. If a photon has sufficient energy it may disappear, leaving in its place an electron-positron pair. This takes place in the vicinity of a nucleus, which takes up some of the momentum. The electron and positron created may or may not have appreciable kinetic energy, depending on the energy of the photon.

The energy required to create the mass of either particle is mc^2, m being the mass of the electron or positron (these two masses being identical). Thus, if the kinetic energy of the electron is KE_- and that of the positron is KE_+

$$h\nu = 2mc^2 + \mathrm{KE}_- + \mathrm{KE}_+ \tag{35-5}$$

Evidently the minimum photon energy which will cause pair production, without endowing the particles with appreciable kinetic energy, is

$$h\nu_{\mathrm{min}} = 2mc^2 \tag{35-6}$$

Since the mass of the electron is $9.11 \cdot 10^{-28}$ g and the speed of light is $3 \cdot 10^{10}$ cm/sec, this minimum energy required of the photon is $1.640 \cdot 10^{-6}$ erg or 1.024 Mev. This corresponds to a wavelength of about 0.0121 Å, which is a fairly high energy X-ray photon. It is found that X rays of longer wavelength than this never cause pair production, and that those shorter may do so. This constitutes very strong evidence that the concept of mass-energy equivalence and that of the quantization of light energy are valid.

It is interesting to note, in passing, that after a very short existence the positron enters into a suicide pact with an electron, both disappearing with the appearance of two photons. This is almost, but not quite, the reverse of the process represented by Eq. (35-6). The total light energy produced is 1.024 Mev, but conservation of momentum requires that this be divided between two photons which travel in opposite directions from the site of their origin. Thus each has 0.512 Mev of energy; and this is confirmed experimentally. Hence pair production followed by the annihilation of an electron-positron pair has the over-all result of splitting a 1.024 Mev photon into two 0.512 Mev photons!

Summary

In the *photoelectric effect,* light having a *frequency above* a certain *critical value ejects electrons* from matter. The process is instantaneous. The number of electrons produced is determined by the level of illumination, and their velocities by the frequency of the light. A *definite quantity* of *energy,* different for each substance, is required to free the electron. X-ray production is the inverse of the photoelectric effect.

A photon passing through matter may collide with an electron, the collision obeying the laws which govern a perfectly elastic collision between macroscopic physical bodies.

It is impossible to determine both the position of a particle and its momentum, or both its energy and the time at which it has that energy, with exactness.

A photochemical reaction can be initiated by light only if the frequency of the light is above a certain critical value. The reason is much the same as in the photoelectric effect.

A single photon of sufficient energy may produce an electron and a positron.

All of these phenomena support the particulate concept of the nature of light.

Self-Quiz

1. What is the photoelectric effect? Of what importance is it, if any?

2. Outline the discrepancies between the requirements of the wave theory of light and the facts observed in photoelectric emission.

3. Show how each of the difficulties pertinent to the preceding question disappears when the photoelectric effect is considered in terms of the quantum theory of light.

4. What is the work function? On what factors does its value depend?

5. Record the Einstein photoelectric equation, explain the meaning of each term, and show that it constitutes an explanation of experimental data on the phenomenon.

6. In Eq. (35-2) and Eq. (35-3), why is the work function disregarded? Suppose the voltage on an X-ray tube is 10,000 v, and that the target is tungsten. About what per cent error is introduced by ignoring the work function (see Table 35-1)?

7. Explain why the collision of a photon with an electron increases the wavelength of the photon.

8. What value did the explanation of Compton collisions have, aside from accounting for the increase in the wavelength of the X ray?

9. Discuss Heisenberg's principle of indeterminacy. Why can't improved techniques and instrumentation reduce the uncertainty the principle specifies?

10. In what important respect does a photochemical reaction resemble photoelectric emission? Explain clearly the basis of this similarity.

11. Discuss the phenomenon of pair production. Might pair production occur with photons of 0.97 Mev energy? With photons of 1.024 Mev energy? With photons of 2.73 Mev energy? Explain your answer in each case.

Problems

NOTE: Use of the non-relativistic equation for kinetic energy will involve little error and is much simpler.

1. Compute the critical wavelength for photoelectric emission from (a) sodium and (b) tungsten.

2. Calculate the kinetic energy and the speed of a photoelectron ejected by the Balmer line of wavelength 4862 Å from (a) sodium and (b) tungsten.

3. Photoelectrons emitted from tungsten are observed to have a speed of (exactly) 10^8 cm/sec. Determine the minimum wavelength of the light used.

4. When ultraviolet light of 2450 Å wavelength falls on a metal, electrons are emitted with speeds of $3.00 \cdot 10^7$ cm/sec. Compute the value of the work function, in ergs and in electron volts.

5. The shortest wavelength in the Lyman series is 912 Å. Photoelectrons have energies of 7.13 ev when this light falls on a metal, which is one of those listed in Table 35-1. What is the identity of the metal, and what percentage error is involved?

6. Compute the maximum frequency and the minimum wavelength of the X rays produced when a potential difference of 5.00 kilovolts (kv) is applied to the X-ray tube.

7. If the voltage across an X-ray tube is 22.0 kv, what are the values of the minimum wavelength and the maximum frequency?

8. If the uncertainty in the position of an electron is (exactly) 0.1 mm compute the minimum uncertainty in its speed.

9. (a) What is the minimum uncertainty in the position of an electron when the uncertainty in its speed is $5.00 \cdot 10^{-2}$ cm/sec? (b) What is the minimum uncertainty in the position of a proton under the same circumstances? Take the mass of the proton as 1840 times that of an electron.

10. If the uncertainty in the speed of a 10.0 g bullet is exactly 0.1 mm/sec, what is the minimum uncertainty in its position?

11. Just below Eq. (35-6) the minimum energy required for pair production by a photon is given in ergs and in electron volts, and the minimum wavelength is given also. Verify each of these three values.

36

FURTHER CONSIDERATIONS OF THE STRUCTURE OF THE ATOM

36-1 Preview

The uncertainty principle forces us to revise the Bohr concept of the structure of the atom, and other modifications of that concept must be mentioned. Next we shall discover that the statistical point of view has an application important other than in the principle of indeterminacy. This will lead to the necessity of determining the masses of individual atoms, and the consideration of one method for making such determinations will bring us back to Einstein's principle of the equivalence of mass and energy. In turn, this will reveal the fundamental basis of nuclear energy.

36-2 Refinements of the Original Bohr Concept

Though Bohr's concept of the structure of the hydrogen atom, and his equation describing the lines of the hydrogen spectrum, were remarkably successful, careful spectroscopic studies revealed shortcomings. The causes of these will only be mentioned here; detailed treatment belongs in more advanced texts.

Elliptical as well as circular orbits are possible; and in atoms with several electrons, some of the orbits are normally elliptical, the degree of ellipticity being quantized. The energy of an electron in an elliptical orbit differs slightly from that in an equivalent circular orbit, giving rise to photons of slightly different energies. According to what we found in the last paragraph of Sec. 9-5, the speed of an electron in an elliptical orbit is greatest when its distance from the nucleus is least. This may result in a relativistic increase in the mass of the electron, causing the axis of the elliptical orbit to precess. Finally, the electrons themselves are spinning, some in one sense and others in the opposite direction. All of these result in complications of the spectrum; or, looking at it from the other point of view, these refinements of structure were deduced from complications in the spectrum.

36-3 Implications of the Uncertainty Principle

A brief review of the uncertainty principle (Sec. 35-7) indicates plainly that we must revise our concept of a Bohr orbit. We have considered an electron in its orbit to be essentially like the moon in its orbit around the earth, or the earth in its orbit around the sun; but these astronomical bodies are directly observable, and their orbits are definite. On the other hand, it is impossible to know exactly the location or the speed of an electron. Instead of thinking of the electron as a particle which can be located definitely, even in principle, we must think of it as being "smeared" around the orbit. Also, this orbit ceases to be a simple orbit and becomes a hollow shell, for the waves can go in all directions around the nucleus somewhat as waves for a radio broadcast station spread around the earth. The radius of this shell is not precise, as that of the pre-Heisenberg orbit was, for although the circumference of the shell still must be an integral number of wavelengths, the uncertainty in the speed of the electron introduces a proportional uncertainty in its wavelength. Hence a permitted electron orbit becomes a most probable electron shell. The nature of the probability function, however, is such that the uncertainty in the radius of the shell is extremely small; for most purposes, the radii of the old Bohr orbits may be assigned to these shells and considered to be definite.

This section and Sec. 34-8 are fruits of wave mechanics, a powerful tool. It is unfortunate that we cannot follow this discipline farther.

36-4 Atomic Weights

Since the atoms of a given element contain a different number of protons than those of any other element (Sec. 34-9), it is not surprising that in general the atoms of different elements have unequal masses. A tremendous accumulation of data over a long period of time has enabled chemists to determine the relative masses of atoms of the various elements.* Since there was no way to determine directly the actual masses of individual atoms, a value of exactly 16 was assigned to the oxygen atom and the masses of atoms of all other elements were expressed with respect to this value.† Thus, the carbon atom is about 75.087% as massive as the oxygen atom, so its value on this relative scale is

$$16.000 \cdot 0.75087 = 12.014$$

and a chlorine atom is about 2.2167 times as massive as an oxygen atom, so the chlorine atom is assigned a relative mass of

$$16.000 \cdot 2.2167 = 35.467$$

Note that these are not 16.000 g, 12.014 g, etc., nor are any other mass units assigned; such values are only relative and therefore dimensionless, like values of specific gravity.

The relative masses of atoms, on this arbitrary scale, are known as the ***atomic weights*** of the elements.

The values of the atomic weights of many elements are whole numbers or nearly so; these include such common elements as calcium, gold, hydrogen, iodine, nitrogen, sulfur, and many others. None of those listed has an atomic weight which differs from an integer by as much as 0.5%; most differ by smaller percentages. This situation suggested that perhaps more accurate determinations would reduce all atomic weights to integers, and a great deal of chemical research was carried out to see whether this degree of order actually exists. Since the masses of the proton and the neutron are essentially equal, and that of the electron is almost negligible, we should expect the masses of different atoms to be related by whole numbers; non-integral relationships would seem to imply the presence of a *half* of a proton or a *third* of a neutron, or some equally unreasonable situation. However, these facts were unknown to investigators until relatively recently.

The concept of integral values of all atomic weights proved invalid; the

---

* For about a half a century, it has been possible to compute the actual masses of atoms by making use of the values of the faraday, Avogadro's number, and the valence of the atom; but no *direct* measurement of actual atomic masses by chemical means is available.

† We shall see in Sec. 36-6 that the present basis of atomic weights differs slightly from this.

more carefully the determinations were made, the more evident it became that many atomic weights differ greatly from integral values. The development of instruments called "mass spectrographs" furnished the reason for major deviations, and the concept of the intraconvertibility of mass and energy accounted for minor ones. We shall discuss the mass spectrograph and the implications of its findings in the next two sections, and the matter of mass-energy equivalence in Sec. 36-8.

36-5 The Mass Spectrograph

The term ***mass spectrograph***, or ***mass spectrometer***, is applied to any of a number of devices which enable the masses of individual atoms to be determined. Though their variety is great, the general principle is the same. By some appropriate means, ionized (electrically charged) atoms of an element are introduced into a vacuum chamber and given rather high velocities by allowing them to fall through a potential difference. The stream of ions produced in this way is passed through an electric or a magnetic field, or some combination of the two, with the result that the path of the ions is altered. Other things being equal, the more massive the atom is, the less it will be deflected. The deflected ion stream falls onto an ion collector or a strip of photographic film; in either case the deflection can be determined, and from this and measurements of the pertinent electric and magnetic quantities, the mass may be computed.

One type of instrument will be discussed, as an illustration of some of the basic principles. It is an early form, usually credited to Bainbridge, though it is an improvement of a type used by others. In Fig. 36-1 there is an ion source S which produces positive ions. (For negative ions the electric and magnetic fields would be the reverse of those shown; otherwise the apparatus would be the same.) The source is in an electric field supplied by a battery, and the field accelerates the ions toward a slit which restricts them to a narrow stream. This stream of ions passes through a uniform magnetic field directed upward out of the page. The force of the magnetic field on the moving electric charges deflects the stream of ions to the right. Since this force is always at right angles to the magnetic field and to the velocity, the ions must follow a path which is a circular arc. It is assumed that ions of two different masses are present; the lighter ions will strike a photographic film at P_1 and the more massive ones will fall on it at

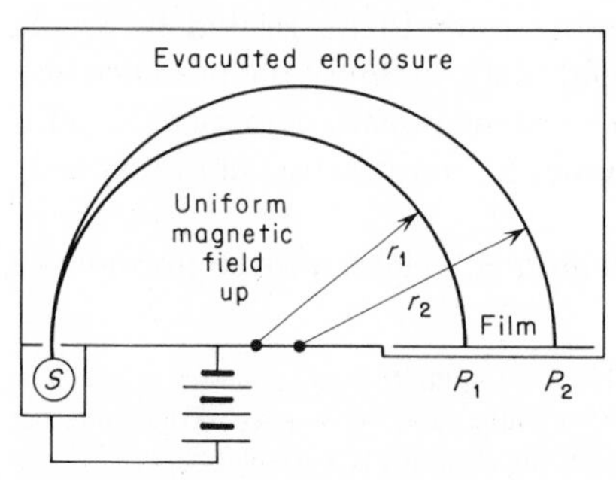

Fig. 36-1. Schematic representation of a mass spectrograph.

P_2. The charged ions "expose" the film as photons would; hence after being developed the film will show a "line" at P_1 and another at P_2.

The centripetal force required to constrain a particle in the ion stream to a circular arc is, according to Eq. (8-23),

$$F_c = \frac{mv^2}{r}$$

where F_c is the centripetal force, m the mass of the particle, v its speed, and r the radius of the circular arc. The action of the magnetic field on the moving charge supplies the centripetal force. According to Eq. 26-6,

$$F = \frac{Bqv}{c}$$

in which F is the force in dynes on a charge of q statcoulombs when the charge is moving with a velocity v cm/sec at right angles to a magnetic field of intensity B gauss. Hence,

$$\frac{mv^2}{r} = \frac{Bqv}{c}, \quad \text{or} \quad mv = \frac{Bqr}{c}$$

The kinetic energy of the ion is determined by its charge and the potential difference used to accelerate it:

$$\frac{mv^2}{2} = qV$$

where m is the mass of the ion in grams, v its speed in cm/sec, q the charge it carries in statcoulombs, and V the accelerating potential in statvolts. If the preceding equation is squared and divided by this last equation, we have

$$\frac{m^2v^2}{mv^2/2} = \frac{B^2q^2r^2/c^2}{qV}$$

or

$$m = \frac{B^2qr^2}{2Vc^2} \tag{36-1}$$

The values of B and V can be measured, and they will be kept constant for any given determination. As in the Millikan oil drop experiment, q can only be equal to e or a small multiple of e, where e is the electronic charge; and most ions will carry a single electronic charge. Measurement of r, which is half the distance between the entrance slit and the point where the ions strike the film (Fig. 36-1) will make the computation of m possible.

In practice, the ions do not all have identical velocities, and this tends to widen the "line" on the film, thereby limiting the accuracy of the determinations. Bainbridge added a "velocity selector," as shown schematically in Fig. 36-2. After being accelerated, the ions must pass through this selector before entering the spectrograph. The magnetic field of the spectrograph (or a separate field) is applied, in a direction up out of the

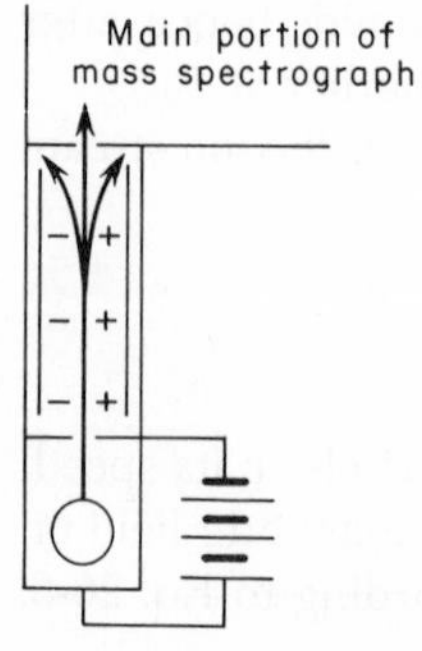

Fig. 36-2. Velocity selector for mass spectrograph.

paper; this tends to deflect the ions to the right. A pair of plates is placed so that the ion stream must pass between them, and a voltage is applied to them in such a direction that the resulting electric field tends to deflect the ions to the left. According to Eq. (26-6),

$$F = \frac{Bqv}{c}$$

and Eq. (20-5) may be rewritten as

$$F_e = Eq$$

These forces act in opposite directions on the ions, so if no deflection is to result their magnitudes must be equal:

$$\frac{Bqv}{c} = Eq$$

which may be written

$$v = \frac{Ec}{B} \qquad (36\text{-}2)$$

Only those ions which have velocities in agreement with this equation can pass through the velocity selector and into the mass spectrograph. Proper adjustment of the relative values of E and B will allow ions of any desired velocity to be passed, and will block all others.

Other more refined forms of the mass spectrograph yield more accurate results than this relatively early design. Accuracy is further improved by introducing ions of known mass (such as those of oxygen) and comparing the lines given by the ions of unknown masses with lines due to the ions of known mass, rather than basing the determination on measurements of voltages and magnetic field intensities. In this way, amazingly high accuracies have been obtained; six- and seven-digit accuracy is common, and at least one value is known to nine significant figures with an uncertainty of only three in the last digit!

36-6 Some of the Fruits of the Measurement of Atomic Masses

Using the relatively crude apparatus in 1913, Thompson found evidence that neon may contain atoms of different masses. After World War I, Aston designed the first true mass spectrograph, and with this device he established the fact that three different kinds of neon atoms exist. In round numbers, their masses were 20, 21, and 22 on the atomic weight scale.

The existence of atoms of different masses which nevertheless belong to the same element is not peculiar to neon; nearly every element has naturally occurring atoms of different masses. Atoms which contain the same number of protons in their nuclei and therefore belong to the same element, but differ in mass because of unequal numbers of neutrons, are called ***isotopes.*** All isotopes have masses, on the atomic weight scale, which are very nearly whole numbers. It is convenient to identify a particular isotope of an element by specifying its ***mass number***, which is the whole number nearest its mass on the atomic weight scale. Thus, the three isotopes of neon discovered by Aston have atomic weights* of 19.9987979, 21.0005241, and 21.9983771; and the mass numbers of these isotopes are 20, 21, and 22, respectively.

The complete symbolization of a particular isotope includes three parts: the symbol of the element, the atomic number Z of the element, and the mass number A of the isotope. Thus if X represents the generalized symbol for any element, the complete symbol for a particular isotope is ${}_ZX^A$. For example, ${}_{10}Ne^{20}$, ${}_{10}Ne^{21}$, and ${}_{10}Ne^{22}$ are the symbols for the three neon isotopes above.† This symbolization is redundant, since the name of the element uniquely determines its atomic number, and vice versa. However, few students or physicists can immediately state the atomic number of every element or identify every element from its atomic number, so this redundancy often is desirable.

Any particular nuclear species, distinguished by specific values of both Z and A, is called a ***nuclide.*** Thus ${}_{10}Ne^{20}$, ${}_{10}Ne^{22}$, and ${}_{11}Na^{22}$ are three different nuclides. Since the first two have the same atomic number, the corresponding atoms are isotopes (of neon). The latter two have different atomic numbers, so they belong to different elements (neon and sodium) but they have the same mass number. Nuclides (or atoms) which have the same mass number are called ***isobars.***

How does the existence of isotopes bear on the problems of the physicist and the chemist?

The mass of either a proton or a neutron is very nearly 1, on the atomic weight scale, and either is almost $2 \cdot 10^3$ times as massive as an electron. Hence the essentially integral value of the atomic weight of any isotope is to be expected, since any isotope is made up of these components. The existence of different kinds of atoms of the same element doesn't complicate the study of the chemical properties of the element, because the electronic structure of all isotopes of any given element is the same, and chemical properties are determined by that structure.‡ Finally, the

* These are recent data. Naturally, Aston's mass spectrograph did not have the precision of today's instruments.

† Many foreign publications, and some in this country, place the mass number ahead of the element symbol, thus: ${}_Z^AX$. Though there is some trend in this direction, the majority of American publications place the mass number at the right.

‡ In reactions where the mass of an atom is a factor in the mechanism of the reaction, the *rate* of the reaction may differ slightly for the various isotopes.

obviously non-integral values of the atomic weights of some elements, which had bothered chemists for a long time, prove to be statistical averages of the atomic weights of the isotopes of the element.

Chlorine is an excellent example of the statistical nature of an atomic weight determined by chemical procedures. The atomic weight of this element is 35.467. It is found to consist of two isotopes, 75.53% of it being ${}_{17}Cl^{35}$ and the other 24.47% being ${}_{17}Cl^{37}$. The atomic weights of these isotopes are 34.9799720 and 36.9776573, respectively. Let us round them off to five digits and find their statistical average:

$$\begin{aligned} 0.7553 \cdot 34.980 &= 26.42\bar{0} \\ 0.2447 \cdot 36.978 &= \underline{9.04\bar{8}} \\ \text{Total} & 35.46\bar{8} \end{aligned}$$

This value differs from the chemical atomic weight by less than one part in 3500. In view of the fact that the chemical atomic weight is determined by methods completely independent of those used in obtaining the other data, and since the percentages are given only to four digits, this is remarkable agreement.

Oxygen, which was the arbitrary basis of the atomic weight scale, has three isotopes; hence the atomic weight scale developed from chemistry is based on the statistical average of three atomic weights, rather than on a single atomic weight. For this reason, physicists established a slightly different system of atomic weights, based on the mass of the O^{16} isotope as exactly 16. More recently this isotope has been deposed from its position of eminence by the carbon isotope C^{12}, which has been assigned a value of exactly 12.

Except for the matter of proper definition, these changes in the basis of atomic weights are of no great practical concern to us in this course because values in the three systems differ only slightly. Those based on O^{16} exceed the older values derived from chemical investigations by less than 0.03%, and atomic weights based on C^{12} are only about 0.004% lower than those referred to O^{16}.

To avoid ambiguity, or the necessity of specifying that the value of an atomic mass is a relative value based on the mass of the C^{12} isotope as exactly 12, an ***atomic mass unit*** has been defined which is exactly one twelfth of the mass of the C^{12} isotope. Thus, for example, instead of saying that a helium atom has a relative mass of 4.0039 on the physical scale we may say that it has a mass of 4.0039 atomic mass units (abbreviated amu).

36-7 The Periodic Table

Long ago chemists noticed "families" of elements whose members resemble each other in physical and chemical properties. As such evidence accumulated, it became possible to arrange the known elements in a table now called the ***periodic table,*** leaving blanks in many places where no element with appropriate properties was known. One form of this table appears in Table 36-1. This orderliness in the properties of elements spurred research for elements to fill the blanks, and led to the discovery of many new elements. Thus the table was a powerful tool, and at the same time a satisfying assurance of a sort of neatness in nature.

There were difficulties, however. In Table 36-1, it is evident that in general the elements are arranged in the order of increasing atomic weight, but

Table 36-1

PERIODIC TABLE OF THE ELEMENTS*

1 H 1.008										2 He 4.004
3 Li 6.942	4 Be 9.015	5 B 10.82	6 C 12.01	7 N 14.01	8 O 16.00	9 F 19.01				10 Ne 20.19
11 Na 23.00	12 Mg 24.33	13 Al 26.99	14 Si 28.10	15 P 30.98	16 S 32.07	17 Cl 35.47				18 A 39.96
19 K 39.11	20 Ca 40.09	21 Sc 44.97	22 Ti 47.91	23 V 50.96	24 Cr 52.02	25 Mn 54.95	26 Fe 55.87	27 Co 58.96	28 Ni 58.73	
29 Cu 63.56	30 Zn 65.40	31 Ga 69.74	32 Ge 72.62	33 As 74.93	34 Se 78.98	35 Br 79.94				36 Kr 83.82
37 Rb 85.50	38 Sr 87.65	39 Y 88.94	40 Zr 91.24	41 Nb 92.94	42 Mo 95.98	43 Tc (99)	44 Ru 101.7	45 Rh 102.9	46 Pd 106.4	
47 Ag 107.9	48 Cd 112.4	49 In 114.8	50 Sn 118.7	51 Sb 121.8	52 Te 127.6	53 I 126.9				54 Xe 131.3
55 Cs 132.9	56 Ba 137.4	Rare earths	72 Hf 178.5	73 Ta 181.0	74 W 183.9	75 Re 186.3	76 Os 190.3	77 Ir 192.2	78 Pt 195.1	
79 Au 197.1	80 Hg 200.7	81 Tl 204.4	82 Pb 207.3	83 Bi 209.1	84 Po 210	85 At (210)				86 Rn 222
87 Fr 223	88 Ra 226.1	89 Ac 227	90 Th 232.1	91 Pa 231	92 U 238.1	Transuranic elements				

Rare earths

57 La	58 Ce	59 Pr	60 Nd	61 Pm	62 Sm	63 Eu	64 Gd	65 Tb	66 Dy	67 Ho	68 Er	69 Tm	70 Yb	71 Lu
139	140	141	144	(145)	150	152	157	159	163	165	167	169	173	175

Transuranic elements

93 Np	94 Pu	95 Am	96 Cm	97 Bk	98 Cf	99 E	100 Fm	101 Md	102 No	103 Lw
(237)	(242)	(243)	(245)	(249)	(249)	(255)	(255)	(256)	(253)	(257)

* The number to the left of the symbol of an element is the atomic number of that element. The atomic weight is given beneath. Values of atomic weights in parentheses are uncertain. Elements may be identified from the symbols in this table by referring to Table AD-2, Appendix D. Values of atomic weights in this table are on the older basis, not the new system described in the latter portion of Sec. 36-6.

there are discrepancies. The most obvious of these involves argon and potassium. It is necessary to put argon in the column with helium, neon, and krypton, because all of these are gases which are completely inert chemically. Similarly, potassium is a metal like lithium, sodium, and rubidium, and like these its chemical reactivity is very high. This disruption of order bothered chemists and physicists, but attempts to remove it by determining the atomic weights more accurately merely confirmed the inversion of order.

Moseley's concept of atomic number, however, combined with the discovery of isotopes and the realization of the statistical character of the atomic weight of an element, clarified the situation. There are no inversions of atomic number in the table, and inversions of atomic weight are due to nothing more fundamental than the percentages of the various isotopes which comprise a given element. Hence it is evident that the atomic number of an element is a far more fundamental quantity than the atomic weight.

36-8 Mass Defect and Nuclear Stability

The symbol ${}_2He^4$ indicates that this helium atom contains two protons (since the atomic number is 2) and two neutrons (since the mass number is 4, and two of the four nucleons are protons). It also contains two electrons to balance the charges of the protons. Thus 2 protons, 2 neutrons, and 2 electrons comprise the "parts list" of this atom. The symbol ${}_1H^1$ indicates that a hydrogen atom has a single proton as a nucleus, and one electron. Thus two ${}_1H^1$ atoms plus two neutrons will furnish exactly the parts needed for one atom of ${}_2He^4$. To five digits, the mass of a ${}_1H^1$ atom is 1.0081 amu, and that of a neutron is 1.0090 amu. Thus we may compute the total mass of the parts necessary to build a ${}_2He^4$ atom as follows:

$$\begin{aligned} 2 \cdot 1.0081 &= 2.0162 \\ 2 \cdot 1.0090 &= \underline{2.0180} \\ \text{Total} \quad & 4.0342 \end{aligned}$$

However, the mass of a ${}_2He^4$ atom is *not* 4.0342 amu; it is 4.0039 amu (to five digits). Thus the mass of this atom is less than the total mass of its parts! The discrepancy is 0.0303 amu.

Though at first glance this situation may be surprising and disturbing, a little thought shows that it should be expected, and that the stability of the ${}_2He^4$ atom actually requires such a discrepancy.

A uniform ball on a horizontal surface is in neutral equilibrium; it can move in any direction with no increase or decrease in its potential energy. A meter stick can be stood on end if care is taken, but its equilibrium is rather unstable. It is much more stable when lying on one edge, but it has its maximum stability when lying flat. A moment's consideration shows that this is equivalent to saying that the meter stick is most stable when its potential energy is at a minimum. This proves to be a general criterion; any system has its maximum stability when it has minimum energy.

Returning to the helium atom, we must account for the apparent loss of mass, or ***mass defect.*** Mass cannot be destroyed, but it *can* be converted to energy; 0.0303 amu of mass has been converted into energy, and this energy has been evolved. Thus the system of particles when arranged to form a ${}_2He^4$ atom has less energy than when it exists as two ${}_1H^1$ atoms and two neutrons; and this is a way of saying that the ${}_2He^4$ atom is more stable than a system composed of its parts. If there had been no decrease of mass, the atom would have been no more stable than the combination of separate particles; it would be in neutral equilibrium with them, like the ball on the table. Thus there would have been nothing to hold it together; it could "come apart" spontaneously.

Any and every stable atom has a mass which is less than the total mass of the nucleons and electrons which comprise it, and the magnitude of the mass defect is a measure of the stability of the atom.

The energy required to divide a ${}_2He^4$ atom into two ${}_1H^1$ atoms and two neutrons can be computed from the mass defect. From the concepts of a gram atomic weight and Avogadro's number, (Sec. 23-8) the actual mass of 1 amu is one gram divided by Avogadro's number, which is $6.06 \cdot 10^{23}$ (to three significant figures). According to the mass-energy equivalence equation, the energy is the mass multiplied by the square of the speed of light. Thus,

$$E = \frac{9.00 \cdot 10^{20}}{6.06 \cdot 10^{23}} = 1.48 \cdot 10^{-3} \text{ erg}$$

This may seem like a small quantity of energy, but it is possessed by an extremely small particle. If it were in the form of kinetic energy, it would give the He atom six-tenths of the speed of light. Expressed another way, this quantity of energy is $9.25 . 10^8$ ev; that is, a singly ionized helium atom would have to fall through a potential difference of almost a billion volts to give it an energy equivalent to its mass defect.

36-9 Binding Energy, and Binding Energy per Nucleon

The ***binding energy*** of any atom is the quantity of energy which would be required to break it up into ${}_1H^1$ atoms and neutrons. Its value may be computed from the mass defect, as was done for the ${}_2He^4$ atom in the preceding section. For some purposes the ***binding energy per nucleon*** is more useful; this may be thought of as the average energy required to extract one nucleon from the nucleus. Its value is obtained by dividing the binding energy by the mass number, since the mass number represents the total number of protons and neutrons. The usual units for these quantities are the electron volt and its multiples. For example, from the last paragraph of the preceding section, the binding energy of $_2He^4$ is $9.25 \cdot 10^2$ Mev and its binding energy per nucleon is $2.31 \cdot 10^2$ Mev.

In Fig. 36-3, the binding energy per nucleon is plotted against the mass number. Obviously there is considerable regularity. Evidently atoms with mass numbers of approximately 60 are the most stable, since the curve shows that the average energy required to remove a nucleon from such an atom is greater than for atoms of appreciably higher or lower mass numbers.

36-10 Nuclear Energy—an Open Secret

By 1927, Aston's work with the mass spectrograph had yielded accurate values of the masses of isotopes of nearly all the elements, and he published a "packing fraction" curve which was essentially equivalent to Fig. 36-3 except that it was an index of mass defect per nucleon rather than binding energy per nucleon. The important thing was that it revealed the relative stability of atoms much as Fig. 36-3 does.

Looking at Fig. 36-3—or at Aston's original curve—we see immediately that very heavy atoms are less stable than those of mass number nearer 60. This means that if a heavy atom could be broken into two less massive atoms, the stability would be increased. But this means a reduc-

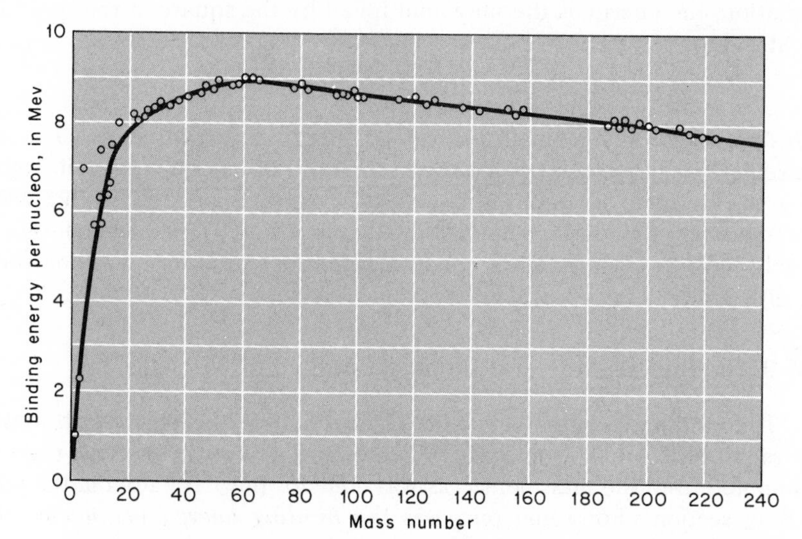

Fig. 36-3. The Relationship between the binding energy per nucleon and the mass number. This figure is reproduced (with slight modifications) from *Introduction to Modern Physics,* by Blanchard, Stoner, and Weber (Prentice-Hall) with the permission of the authors and the publisher.

tion in the energy of the system must occur if such a splitting takes place: *the splitting of a heavy atom should release energy!* Thus data widely published in 1927 contained a suggestion of the possibility of nuclear energy—miscalled "atomic energy." Furthermore, since Einstein's equation defining the intraconversion of mass and energy was already over two decades old, it was possible in 1927 to compute the quantity of energy which would be released if a way could be found to split a massive atom. This is the basic "secret" of nuclear energy obtained by "fission," as the splitting of atoms is called.

But this is not all. The data also predicted even greater emission of energy if relatively light atoms could be fused into more massive ones, as a glance at the left portion of Fig. 36-3 shows. Thus the basic "secret" of fusion, or "thermonuclear" reaction, which underlies the so-called H-bomb and the extensive research for a method of carrying on a controlled fusion process for the production of commercial power, was available to physicists throughout the world in 1927. What remained to do before energy from either fusion or fission could be obtained was more a problem of technology than of physical principle, and it is in this field rather than in science that any real secrets lie.

Summary

Though the basic concepts of the Bohr theory of atomic structure are valid, instead of orbits there are *electron shells;* and in other respects, the situation is more complex than originally supposed.

In general, an *element* consists of *isotopes* which have the *same nuclear charge* but *unequal masses.* The *atomic weight* of an element is a *statistical average* of the atomic weights of its isotopes.

The mass of a particular species of atom can be determined with high precision by a *mass spectrograph.*

Any stable atom has a mass which is *less* than the sum of the masses of its components. This *mass defect* is a measure of the *binding energy* which holds the atom together. For some purposes it is convenient to consider the *binding energy per nucleon* rather than the total binding energy of the atom.

A plot of the binding energy per nucleon against the mass number predicts the possibility of obtaining nuclear energy from fission processes and from fusion processes.

Self-Quiz

1. Why does the relativistic increase in the mass of the electron in an elliptical orbit cause the axis of the orbit to precess? (Consider the effect which Eq. (8-23) predicts that an increase in the value of m would have on the value of r.)

2. Explain why the concept of a shell must replace the concept of a definite electron orbit.

3. What is meant by the atomic weight of an element? Is "weight" the proper term, or would "mass" be preferable? Why? The chemist uses no unit when he expresses an atomic weight. Why doesn't he?

4. Why do chemists and physicists have different values for the atomic weight of the same element? How serious is this difference? Is one system of atomic weights correct and the other wrong? Explain. What unit is often used by physicists? Is this in terms of grams or any similar unit? Explain.

5. Why do the atomic weights of many elements differ markedly from integers?

6. How does the mass of an atom compare with the total mass of its subatomic components? What is the significance of this difference?

7. Compare and contrast the concepts of mass defect, binding energy, and binding energy per nucleon. How is the stability of the atom related to these?

8. For each of the following nuclides state the number of protons and the number of neutrons contained in the nucleus:

$$_{6}C^{12}, \quad _{29}Cu^{63}, \quad _{47}Ag^{107}, \quad \text{and} \quad _{92}U^{238}$$

9. Referring as necessary to the periodic table (Table 36-1) write symbols similar to those in Question 8 for each of the following nuclides: lithium (Li) containing 4 neutrons, aluminum (Al) containing 14 neutrons, zirconium (Zr) containing 50 neutrons, and tungsten (W) containing 108 neutrons.

10. Compare and contrast the terms "isotope" and "isobar."

11. What is the meaning of Avogadro's number?

12. Show clearly that Fig. 36-3 reveals the possibility of energy production by fusion and by fission. What do the terms "fusion" and "fission" mean as used here?

Problems

1. Magnesium is composed of three isotopes, there being 78.8% of an isotope of 23.99 amu, 10.1% of one of 24.99 amu, and 11.1% of one of 25.99 amu. Calculate the atomic weight of magnesium.

2. The atomic weight of potassium is 39.111, and it is composed of two isotopes* which have masses of 38.976 and 40.975 amu. Compute the percentage of each isotope.

3. The two isotopes of bromine have masses of 78.943 and 80.942 amu, and the atomic weight of bromine is 79.938. Compute the percentage of each isotope.

---

* There is also an isotope with a mass of 39.977, but it constitutes only about 0.01% of potassium so it may be disregarded for our present purposes.

4. (a) With the aid of Avogadro's number compute the mass, in grams, of 1 amu. (b) Compute the energy equivalent of this mass. (If you use the usual "rounded off" values for c and for the relationship between electron volts and ergs, your answer will be higher than the true value of 931.14 Mev.)

5. The mass of an electron is $5.488 \cdot 10^{-4}$ amu. From this and the number of Mev equivalent to 1 amu as specified in Problem 4 compute the energy equivalent of the mass of an electron. Compare this with the minimum energy of a photon which can cause pair production (Sec. 35-9).

6. Taking the mass of $_{17}Cl^{35}$ as 34.9800 amu, that of $_1H^1$ as 1.0081 amu, and that of a neutron as 1.0090 amu, and making use of the fact that 1 amu = 931 Mev, compute (a) the energy in Mev which would be released if one $_{17}Cl^{35}$ atom could be constructed from $_1H^1$ atoms and neutrons; (b) the energy in kilowatt hours which would be produced if 1.00 kg of this isotope of chlorine could be made in that manner; and (c) the binding energy per nucleon in the $_{17}Cl^{35}$.

7. If the binding energy per nucleon of $_{28}Ni^{60}$ is 8.77 Mev per nucleon, compute the mass of the atom. (Take 1 amu = 931 Mev.)

37

NATURAL RADIOACTIVITY

37-1 Preview

The goal of the alchemists was the transmutation of elements—the production of one element from another. With the dawn of modern chemistry, that hope vanished; an element became a unique substance different from any other, and not convertible to any other. It was composed of indivisible atoms which had existed since the beginning of time and always would exist. What we have learned of the internal structure of atoms has annihilated the concept of their indivisibility and raised again the possibility of transmutation by somehow altering the "parts list" of the nucleus. In this chapter, we shall consider some spontaneous changes of this sort; Chapter 39 deals with artificially produced changes.

37-2 The Discovery of Radioactivity

We have seen, in Chapter 33, that experiments on the discharge of electricity through gases led to the discovery of cathode rays, with the discoveries of the electron and X rays following. There was much activity in this field during the last decade of the last century, and Becquerel, among others, was studying the properties of X rays. This involved the use of photographic plates and of many different kinds of materials. He happened to leave a substance containing uranium in a drawer with unexposed photographic plates, and when he used these plates he found that they were "fogged." In the course of tracing the cause of the "fogging," he found that the mere presence of a uranium compound would "fog" a photographic plate even though the plate was in a lightproof package.

Thus was the phenomenon of radioactivity discovered. It was a quite accidental discovery, stumbled on in an attempt to learn the nature of X rays. Since X rays had been discovered accidentally in connection with the study of cathode rays, the discovery of radioactivity was doubly accidental.

There was a rush of workers interested in Becquerel's discovery. They soon found that some sort of radiations were emanating from any substance containing uranium. Very shortly the emanations were proved to consist of three kinds, which differ in their ability to penetrate matter. One kind was stopped by a few inches of air; since it was stopped first, the term ***alpha rays*** was applied to it. Another component had markedly greater ability to penetrate matter, but could be blocked completely by a few centimeters of wood or a few millimeters of lead; this second component was called ***beta rays.*** The third component had still greater ability to penetrate matter; it was weakened by passage through matter, but no thickness of absorbing material could absorb it completely. This component was labeled ***gamma rays.*** These gamma rays were found to travel in straight lines.

Continued research revealed that radioactivity is fairly common, though it is confined principally to nuclides of relatively high atomic number. There seems to be but one stable nuclide of atomic number 83, and none of higher atomic number. On the other hand, among over twenty-three dozen naturally occurring nuclides of atomic number 82 or less, only some ten are radioactive; and the radioactivity of these is so slight that half of the atoms of the most active nuclides among them will still be left undecayed a billion years from now.

37-3 The Nature of Alpha, Beta, and Gamma Rays

A great deal of research went on in an attempt to determine the nature of the alpha, beta, and gamma radiations. One of the methods used

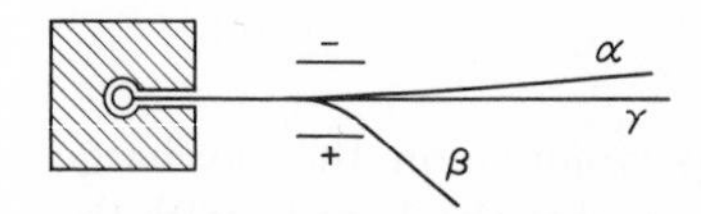

Fig. 37-1. Differences in the effect of an electric field on alpha, beta, and gamma rays.

was to pass a stream of radiations through an electric or a magnetic field, or through a combination of the two. Such a stream could be produced by encasing a radioactive substance in a thick shield of lead with just one opening. The lead blocked all the alpha and beta radiation and most of the gamma radiation, except through this opening. Figure 37-1 is a schematic representation of one arrangement, and it indicates the approximate results. As the radiations pass through the electric field between two plates, the alpha rays are deflected slightly toward the negative plate and the beta rays are deflected strongly toward the positive plate. The gamma rays are quite unaffected. Evidently there is a positive charge associated with the alpha rays, so alpha rays must be a stream of positively charged particles. Similarly, beta rays must consist of negatively charged particles. The gamma rays could be waves, uncharged particles, or particles which carry a small charge but aren't deflected appreciably because of a relatively great mass.

More sophisticated equipment failed to show any charge associated with gamma rays, and it revealed the ratio of the charge to the mass for alpha particles and the charge-mass ratio of beta particles. From these data, and as the result of many other observations, the nature of an alpha particle and that of a beta particle have been established.

An ***alpha particle*** is a particle composed of two protons and two neutrons, the protons being responsible for its positive charge. In the symbolism of Sec. 36-6, ${}_2\alpha^4$ represents an alpha particle. However, the subscript 2 before the α is the atomic number, and 2 is the atomic number of helium. In fact, ${}_2\text{He}^4$ symbolizes the most common isotope of ordinary helium. The helium atom is electrically neutral, however, since it contains two electrons; but the alpha particle has no electrons associated with it. Hence we see that an alpha particle is identical with the nucleus of a ${}_2\text{He}^4$ atom. This fact was definitely established in a very clever manner, with an apparatus equivalent to that in Fig. 37-2. A bit of radium, which emits alpha particles as it undergoes radioactive decay, was sealed into a very thin-walled glass tube. In turn, this capsule was placed in a larger tube supplied with electrodes, and the large tube was evacuated and sealed off. Alpha particles from the radioactive decay passed through the thin walls of the capsule, but couldn't pass through the heavy walls of the outer tube. After a considerable time, a high voltage was applied, and the light from the resulting discharge in the tube was analyzed spectroscopically. It proved to be the

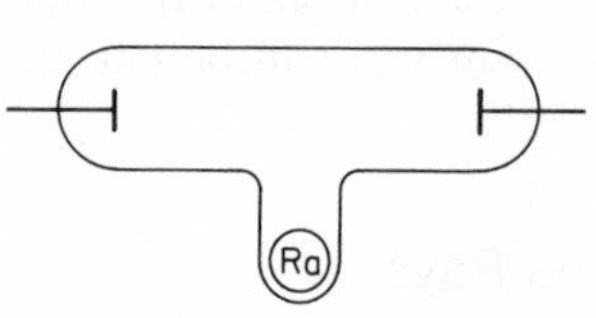

Fig. 37-2. Device by which alpha particles were proved to be helium nuclei.

characteristic spectrum of helium! The alpha particles had stolen electrons from atoms of the glass or of the electrodes and had become typical atoms of helium.

In a similar but perhaps a less dramatic manner, research established that the ***beta particles*** which comprise beta rays are ordinary electrons. The term, "beta particle," is still used, rather than "electron," to call attention to the fact that the electron or electrons under discussion result from radioactive decay. You must not let the use of a different term for such electrons confuse you. You use the term "American" to describe any specimen of *Homo sap* who is a citizen of the United States, and terms such as "New Yorker" and "Texan" to call attention to the origin of a particular American; but you automatically include the concept "American" along with "New Yorker" or "Texan." Similarly, "beta particle" carries with it the concept "electron."

Application of the techniques which proved useful in investigating X rays to the problem of determining the nature of gamma rays revealed that gamma rays are identical in nature with X rays. Here again the use of different terms provides information about the source of the radiation. A gamma ray photon comes from the nucleus as a result of radioactivity, and an X-ray photon comes from outside the nucleus as the result of an electron "jump" to an orbit or shell near the nucleus; but both are photons of the same nature, just as an Iowan and a Californian are both human beings.

37-4 Types of Radioactive Decay

Certain radioactive nuclides, or ***radionuclides,*** exhibit ***alpha decay,*** in which a decaying nucleus emits an alpha particle. Other radioactive nuclides exhibit ***beta decay,*** in which the nucleus emits a beta particle. Less commonly, a certain percentage of the decaying nuclei of a particular nuclide will emit alpha particles and the others will emit beta particles.

After the emission of an alpha or a beta particle, the nucleus may be in an excited state. Though we do not suppose that the nucleons are moving in orbits or shells within the nucleus as the electrons outside the nucleus do, there are definite energy levels of an excited nucleus just as there are for an excited atom. As with the excited atom, the return to the normal state is accompanied by the loss of the excitation energy in the form of a photon—a gamma ray photon, in the case of the excited nucleus. Thus gamma emission is not an independent process, but is the immediate aftermath of alpha decay or beta decay. Many nuclides yield nuclei which are not excited after radioactive decay; such nuclides produce alpha rays or beta rays (depending on the nuclide) but no gamma radiation.

A relatively uncommon type of radioactive decay called "*K* electron capture" is discussed briefly in Sec. 39-11.

37-5 Alpha Decay

Early in the history of radioactivity the Curies discovered the new element, radium, by separating it from uranium, which contained a very small portion of this previously unknown element. Radium is a typical alpha emitter. Since alpha emission removes two protons and two neutrons from the nucleus, the resulting nucleus must belong to a different element. This element can be identified by simply noting its atomic number. In the case of ${}_{88}\mathrm{Ra}^{226}$ the decay process may be represented as follows:

$$
{}_{88}\mathrm{Ra}^{226} \rightarrow {}_{2}\alpha^{4} + {}_{86}\mathrm{Rn}^{222} \tag{37-1}
$$

Since no nucleons are destroyed, the determination of the atomic number and the mass number of the nuclide is a matter of the simplest arithmetic. Reference to Table 36-1 or to Table AD-1 in Appendix D, p. 759, will give the identity of the element, since the atomic number is known.

In any radioactive decay process, the original nuclide is called the ***parent*** and the resulting nuclide is known as the ***daughter.*** If we use Pn as a generalized symbol for the parent nuclide, and symbolize the daughter nuclide by Dn, we may generalize the equation for the alpha decay process in this manner:

$$
{}_{Z}\mathrm{Pn}^{A} \rightarrow {}_{2}\alpha^{4} + {}_{(Z-2)}\mathrm{Dn}^{(A-4)} \tag{37-2}
$$

This equation says that when a parent nuclide emits an alpha particle, the atomic number of the daughter nuclide is two less than that of the parent, and the mass number of the daughter nuclide is four less than that of the parent.

37-6 Beta Decay

You may have been worried about what has been said of beta decay and beta particles, for the nucleus is composed of protons and neutrons. How *can* an electron be emitted from a nucleus?! We met the "fundamental" or "elementary" particles in Sec. 33-7, and found that they aren't so fundamental or elementary as these adjectives imply. Among other things, we found that when neutrons are free they decay according to the scheme

$$
\text{neutron} \rightarrow \text{proton}^{+} + \text{electron}^{-}
$$

and this reaction within the nucleus is the source of the electrons in beta decay. However, both experimental findings and theoretical considerations show that this cannot be a complete description of the neutron decay process because there appear to be violations of certain conservation laws. For example, since all neutrons are alike, and the same is true of all protons and all beta particles, the decay of a neutron should always yield the same energy. This should appear as kinetic energy of recoil of the nucleus and kinetic energy of the emergent beta particle. For a particular nuclear species, all nuclei have the same mass, so it appears that the recoiling nucleus should always have a specific velocity, and that each beta particle should have the same speed as any other (from the same radioactive species). Yet in fact, the beta particles emerge with a wide range of different speeds, up to, and including, the expected value; but since in general their speeds are below the expected value, it appears that some energy and some momentum have disappeared.

This situation was rectified by the assumption that a hitherto undiscovered particle is emitted along with the electron; in fact, it may not be putting it too strongly to state that a new particle was invented to salvage the conservation laws. The new particle to which this task was assigned is called the ***neutrino***, or "little neutron," because it has no electric charge and its mass is essentially zero. If there were such a particle, it would be virtually impossible to detect it, but it could carry off the (apparently) missing energy and momentum, thus reestablishing the validity of the conservation laws. Though the circumstances of its advent invite skepticism, the neutrino does eliminate a number of difficulties in nuclear theory, and experimental investigations are generally considered to have established the reality of this new particle. Thus we must write

$$\text{neutron} \rightarrow \text{proton}^+ + \text{electron}^- + \text{neutrino}$$

Since the neutron carries no electric charge, we may consider its "atomic number"—the number of positive charges it carries—to be zero, and the same is true of the neutrino. The beta particle carries one *negative* charge, so its "atomic number" is -1. The mass number of any particle is the total number of neutrons and protons it contains, so the mass numbers of the neutron, proton, beta particle, and neutrino are respectively one, one, zero, and zero. In these terms, the neutron decay process may be symbolized by writing

$$_0\text{n}^1 \rightarrow {}_1\text{p}^1 + {}_{-1}\beta^0 + {}_0\nu^0 \qquad (37\text{-}3)$$

in which n represents the neutron, p the proton, β the beta particle, and ν the neutron. Since the nucleus of the most common isotope of hydrogen is a single proton, the symbol H may be used in place of p; and e, for electron, may be employed instead of β:

$$_0\text{n}^1 \rightarrow {}_1\text{H}^1 + {}_{-1}\text{e}^0 + {}_0\nu^0$$

Because of this process within the nucleus, beta decay increases the nuclear charge, and hence the atomic number, by 1, but the mass number is unchanged. For example,

$$_{82}\text{Pb}^{214} \rightarrow {}_{-1}\beta^0 + {}_{83}\text{Bi}^{214} + {}_0\nu^0 \qquad (37\text{-}4)$$

The generalized equation for beta decay is

$$_Z\mathrm{Pn}^A \rightarrow {}_{-1}\beta^0 + {}_{(Z+1)}\mathrm{Dn}^A + {}_0\nu^0 \qquad (37\text{-}5)$$

in which Pn and Dn represent the parent nuclide and the daughter nuclide, respectively, as before. This equation states that the atomic number of the daughter nuclide resulting from beta decay exceeds that of the parent nuclide by one, and that the mass number is unaffected.

37-7 Radioactive Series

In general, the daughter of a radioactive decay process is radioactive. Thus the daughter becomes a parent and then perhaps a grandparent, a great-grandparent, and so on. The various nuclides which are involved in the successive decay processes constitute a ***radioactive series,*** or a ***radioactive family.*** Each series ends with a stable nuclide, after a number of successive decays.

There are three radioactive series which have as their original progenitors nuclides which occur naturally on the earth, and one which has an artificially produced progenitor.* The first three are the uranium, thorium, and actinium series, and the last is the neptunium series. The first three end with a stable isotope of lead (a different isotope in each case); the final daughter product of the neptunium series is a stable isotope of bismuth.

On a grid constructed of horizontal lines which represent mass numbers in "steps" of four and vertical lines which represent successive atomic numbers, as in Fig. 37-3(a), an arrow which slants downward to the left, traversing two horizontal spaces and one vertical space, is a graphical representation of an alpha decay, since it represents a reduction of Z by 2 and of A by 4. An arrow drawn horizontally to the right across a single space as in Fig. 37-3(b) is a graphical representation of a beta decay, since it signifies an increase of 1 in the value of Z, with no change in A. This provides a very convenient way of recording the pattern of a radioactive series.

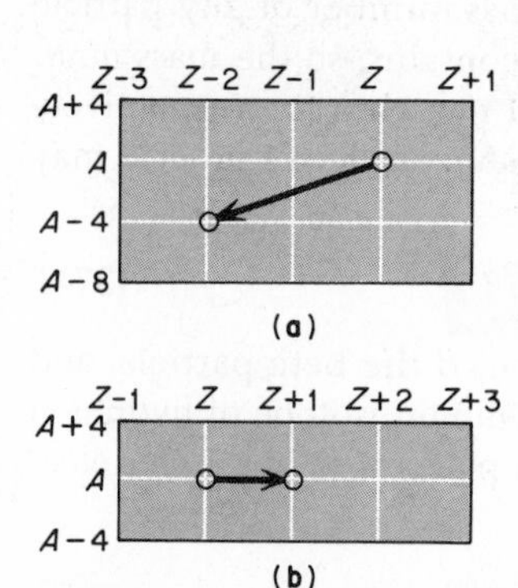

Fig. 37-3. (a) Graphical representation of an alpha decay; (b) of a beta decay.

The uranium series is represented graphically in Fig. 37-4, the thorium series in Fig. 37-5, and the actinium series in Fig. 37-6. Note that in each series there is at least one nuclide which can undergo either alpha or beta decay, causing the series to branch. In

* If this fourth series ever existed as a natural series its radioactive members seem to have decayed completely. This is not impossible, since the progenitor of the series has a half life less than $\frac{1}{300}$ of that of the progenitor of any other.

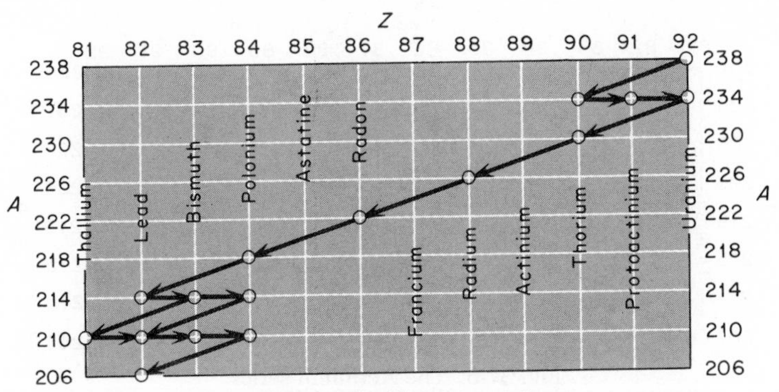

Fig. 37-4. The Uranium series.

the thorium series, about a third of the $_{83}Bi^{212}$ undergoes alpha decay, and the rest decays by beta emission; but this is very unusual. Usually 98% or more decays by one process and less than 2% by the other. The uranium and actinium series branch otherwise than as shown, but in no case of branching do more than 0.15% of the atoms undergo a type of decay not recorded in the diagram.

Note also that in each series a given element may be represented by two or more isotopes. Among the three series, four different radioactive isotopes of lead appear, in addition to the three different stable isotopes of lead which terminate the series. Isobars are common also in the series. There are three isobars of mass number 234 (thorium, protoactinium, and uranium) near the head of the uranium series; and there are three of mass number 214, and four of mass number 210. There are two groups of three isobars in the thorium series, plus one group of two; and four pairs and one group of three isobars appear in the actinium series.

37-8 The Rate of Radioactive Decay

The present existence of appreciable quantities of U^{238}, U^{235}, and Th^{232}, which head the uranium, actinium, and thorium series, respectively,

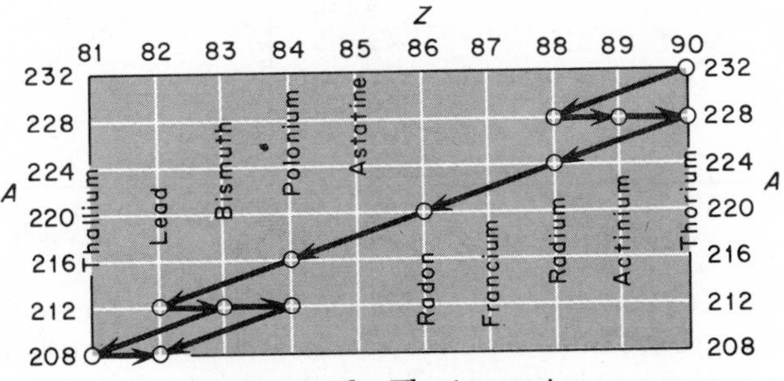

Fig. 37-5. The Thorium series.

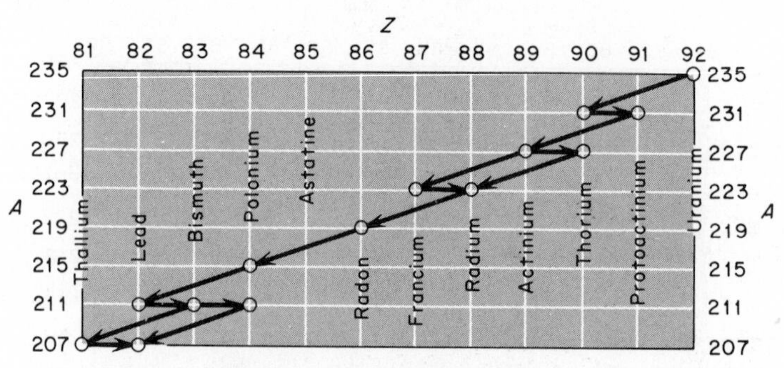

Fig. 37-6. The Actinium series.

is ample evidence that the rate of decay of these nuclides is extremely low. On the other hand, a few members of the various series decay with extreme rapidity. Thus it becomes necessary to have some quantitative index of the rate of decay.

Suppose that some wealthy eccentric were to deposit a large sum in your name with the stipulation that you must draw from it constantly in such a way that you would reduce the account by 50% each year. You would *not* be "broke" at the end of two years. If the initial amount was \$1000 you would have \$500 left at the end of the first year. During the second year you must reduce your *account—not* the initial sum—by 50%; and 50% of \$500 is \$250. Thus \$250 would be left at the end of the second year, \$125 at the end of the third year, and so on. This might be summarized by saying that at the end of the nth year $(\frac{1}{2})^n$ of the initial money would remain; for example, at the end of 3 years $(\frac{1}{2})^3$ or $\frac{1}{8}$ would remain, and $\frac{1}{8}$ of \$1000 is \$125. During any year, the amount you withdraw would be less than for any previous year, but it would always represent the same *fraction* of what was left at the beginning of the year. The status of the account at any time is plotted in the usual manner in Fig. 37-7(a). The same data are replotted in part (b) of the figure, but here the

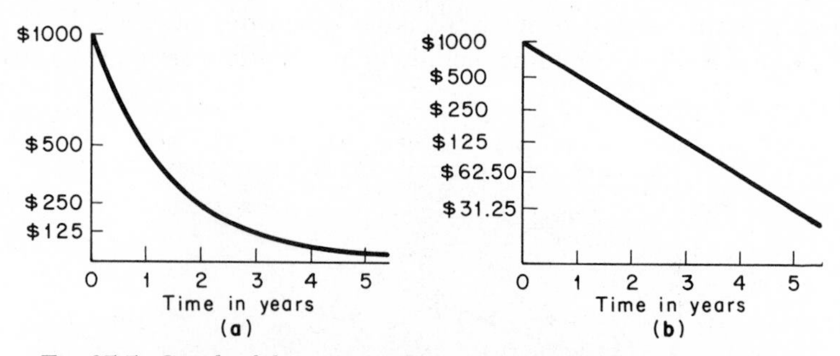

Fig. 37-7. Graph of the money in an account which is reduced 50 per cent each year. Part (a) is plotted on a linear scale, but in part (b) the quantity of money is plotted on a logarithmic scale.

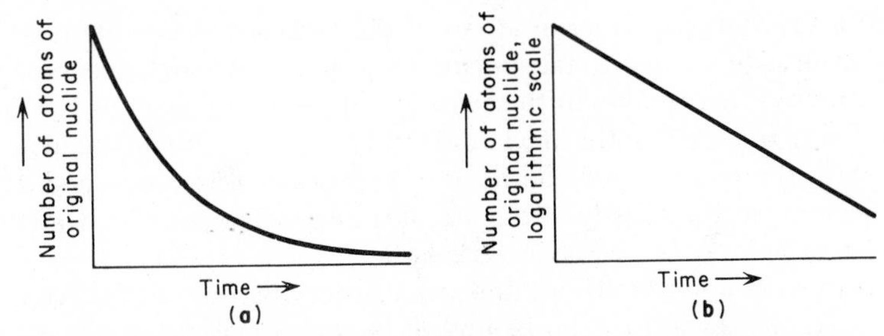

Fig. 37-8. Graphs showing the reduction in the quantity of a radionuclide with time. The number of remaining atoms of the original nuclide is plotted on a linear scale in part (a) and on a logarithmic scale in part (b).

amount of money is plotted on a logarithmic scale rather than on a linear scale; and the graph is a simple straight line. Obviously this graph is easier to draw, and to use, than the curved graph in part (a).

If someone else were left the same initial amount of money with the stipulation that he withdraw 10% each year, \$900 would be left at the end of the first year, \$810 at the end of the second, \$729 after three years, and so on. After n years, $(9/10)^n$ of the original sum would remain.

Radioactive decay follows laws similar to those we've assumed for these unusual bank accounts. The number of atoms that will decay during any specified period will be directly proportional to the number of atoms present at the beginning of the period.* For a given nuclide, the fraction decaying during any given period will be the same as that during any other equal period. In general, this fraction will not be the same for different nuclides.

These relationships may be symbolized by writing

$$-\Delta N = \lambda N_0 t, \quad \text{or} \quad \frac{-\Delta N}{N_0} = \lambda t \tag{37-6}$$

in which N_0 is the number of atoms initially present, $-\Delta N$ is the *de*crease in this number which occurs in a short time interval t, and λ is a ***decay constant*** characteristic of the particular nuclide. This decay constant is simply the fraction of the atoms undergoing decay per unit time, as is evident if we rearrange Eq. (37-6) thus:

$$\frac{-\Delta N/N_0}{t} = \lambda \tag{37-7}$$

It must be realized that radioactive decay is a statistical process, and that, because of this, all equations pertinent to the rate of decay are valid

* Thus we need only do some relabeling of Fig. 37-7 to obtain Fig. 37-8, which represents the decay of a radioactive nuclide.

only if a very large number of atoms of the radioactive nuclide is present. A life insurance company statistician can predict with high accuracy what percentage of the people in the nation will die in a year, but it is highly improbable that the deaths in a hamlet of fifty persons would be in accordance with that percentage. So far as one individual is concerned, the insurance company's statistics are quite meaningless; he may be dead within minutes or he may live to be a centenarian.

From such considerations, and from observing how the curve in Fig. 37-8(a) trends toward the horizontal, it becomes evident that it is impossible to state the life of any radioactive sample, if by its life we mean the time which will elapse before the last atom decays.* It is possible, however, and quite useful, to state the ***half life*** of any radioactive nuclide, the half life being the time required for one-half of the atoms initially present to undergo decay.

We may represent the half life of a nuclide by the symbol $T_{1/2}$. By definition, when half of the atoms originally present have decayed, t in Eq. (37-7) is $T_{1/2}$; that is, for $t = T_{1/2}$, the value of $-\Delta N/N_0$ is 0.500. Thus it would appear that $\lambda = 0.500/T_{1/2}$, and $T_{1/2} = 0.500/\lambda$. However, we must remember that t in Eq. (37-6) is defined as a *short* time; if the time is at all comparable with the half life, the value of N_0 will change appreciably, and therefore the number of atoms decaying per unit time will not be constant. In such a case, an effective average value of $-\Delta N$ must be used. The methods of calculus enable one familiar with them to compute such an average, and when this average is employed the true relationship between the decay constant and the half life is

$$\lambda = \frac{0.693}{T_{1/2}}, \quad \text{or} \quad T_{1/2} = \frac{0.693}{\lambda} \tag{37-8}$$

The calculus also yields an expression for the number of atoms remaining after any time t in terms of their initial number and the half life. The equation is

$$N = N_0 e^{-0.693t/T_{1/2}} \tag{37-9}$$

in which e is the base of natural logarithms, its value being 2.7183. This equation is awkward to use; equivalent, and more convenient, equations are

$$\log N = \log N_0 - \frac{0.301t}{T_{1/2}} \tag{37-10}$$

and

$$\log \frac{N}{N_0} = -\frac{0.301t}{T_{1/2}} \tag{37-11}$$

* The graph in Fig. 37-8(b) may appear to predict a definite life, since the straight line will intersect the time axis if extended. We must remember, however, that distances on the vertical axis in this graph represent the *logarithm* of the number of dollars, *not* the *number* of dollars. When the logarithm of a quantity is zero, the quantity is 1. Extension of the line below the time axis would give negative values of the *logarithm* of the number of atoms, but these negative values of the logarithms correspond to positive fractions of an atom—which is meaningless.

The half lives of different radioactive nuclides vary greatly. At least one has a half life of the order of 10^{15} years—very roughly 100,000 times the age of the universe! The half life of some others is of the order of 10^{-20} seconds! Other values of half lives range within these approximate limits.

The rate of a chemical process may be influenced by such factors as temperature and pressure. The process of radioactive decay, however, takes place within the nucleus of the atom and therefore is insensitive to such factors. We have no way of altering the decay constant or half life of any radioactive substance.

Sample Problem 1

The activity of a radioactive substance is reduced to 6.25% of its initial value in 12.4 min. What is the half life?

We need no complex equations to solve this; 6.25% is 1/16, and 1/16 is $(1/2)^4$. Thus the number of atoms has been halved four times, which necessarily required a total time of four half lives. Hence the half life is

$$12.4 \text{ min}/4 = 3.10 \text{ min}.$$

Sample Problem 2*

The activity of a sample decreases 17.3% in 30.0 min. What is the half life?

The sample retains (100.0 − 17.3)% or 82.7% of its initial activity, so the fraction of the original atoms still left is 0.827. Insertion of this, and the time, into Eq. (37-11) gives

$$\log 0.827 = -0.301 \cdot \frac{30.0}{T_{1/2}} = -\frac{9.03}{T_{1/2}}$$

The logarithm of 0.827 is 9.9175 − 10 (from Appendix I, p. 779, and inspection), and this simplifies to −0.0825. Hence,

$$-0.0825 = -\frac{9.03}{T_{1/2}}$$

$$T_{1/2} = \frac{9.03}{0.0825} = 109 \text{ min}$$

37-9 Other Evidence of the Statistical Character of Decay

Since all kinds of rays produced in radioactivity—alpha, beta, and gamma—have some ability to penetrate matter (Sec. 37-2), it is obvious that they possess energy. The very fact of radioactivity requires that energy be evolved, since any spontaneous process must tend toward a more stable system, and a more stable system must contain less energy (Sec. 36-8). Hence it is not surprising that, for example, alpha particles are

* If you are unfamiliar with logarithms, the material in Appendix H will enable you to handle simple problems like this. Some instructors, however, may wish to waive problems which require logarithms for their solution.

ejected with considerable energy. However, the relationship between the rate of decay of an alpha emitter and the energy of the alpha particles it gives birth to is not what might be expected.

To get an idea of the anticipated relation between alpha particle energy and decay rate, let us consider the energy of an alpha particle at various distances from the center of the nucleus. While it is within the nucleus, it is subject to very strong nuclear forces due to the mutual attraction of all nucleons. At our level of sophistication, we cannot account for these nuclear forces; it seems that the repulsion of the like charges on the protons would disrupt the nucleus. Nevertheless, we know as a practical fact that, in general, nuclei are stable. We know also that a mass defect is associated with any nucleus, and that this is an index of the energy necessary to disassemble the nucleus. Hence we must accept the fact that attractive forces stronger than the electrostatic repulsion of the protons are present in the nucleus. Once an alpha particle gets outside the nucleus, however, the electrostatic repulsion predominates. Thus the nuclear forces of mutual attraction must be very short-range forces; they must decrease more rapidly with increasing distance than the inverse square law requires electrostatic forces to do.

Figure 37-9 indicates qualitatively the variation in the potential energy of an alpha particle in, or near, the nucleus of the atom. In this figure, the energy is plotted against the distance from the center of the nucleus. Distance and energy are both zero at the intersection of the two axes, the value of the potential energy arbitrarily being taken as zero when the distance is infinite.* Energies above the horizontal axis are positive and those below are negative. Distance from the center of the nucleus is represented on the horizontal axis, the radius of the nucleus being r_0, and the diameter of the nucleus being represented by the distance between the two points marked r_0.

Thus we see that the potential energy of the alpha particle is negative as long as the particle is well within the nucleus; it is in a "potential [energy] well." To be able to leave the nucleus, the particle apparently must have a quantity of energy corresponding to the distance from the bottom of the "well" to the top of the hump on either side of the "well." If it gets far enough from the center of the nucleus so that the repulsion between its charge and that of the rest of the nucleus exceeds the attraction of the nuclear force it will escape, its potential energy decreasing but reappearing as kinetic energy. The whole process appears much like the expulsion of a large boulder from a volcano. The throat of the volcano is the "potential well" in Fig. 37-9, and the rim of the volcano appears in cross section as the humps in the figure. To escape the volcano throat, a boulder must have enough energy to lift it to the rim; once there, it can roll down the exterior slope of the volcano, gaining kinetic energy as it goes.

---

* This is the same convention we used for the potential energy of an electron in developing the Bohr equations for the hydrogen atom (Sec. 34-5).

The higher the hump is above the zero energy level, the less chance any particular particle will have of acquiring sufficient energy to escape; hence the decay constant should be relatively low, and the half life comparatively long. But once it has escaped, the higher the hump was, the more energy the particle should have. Thus it seems that alpha emitters with relatively long half lives should emit alpha particles of higher energy than those produced by shorter-lived nuclides.

The emitted alpha particles, however, always have energies too low to correspond with this picture of the process, and the discrepancy is too large to assign to sources such as experimental error. Furthermore, alpha particles from long-lived nuclides have *less* energy, instead of more, than those emitted by shorter-lived nuclear species. Something definitely is amiss.

The thing that is amiss is that we have forgotten de Broglie waves and the uncertainty principle. Any alpha particle has a "patch"—a packet, or group—of de Broglie waves associated with it. We have seen that the amplitude of the waves at any point in the "patch" is an index of the probability that the particle is at that point (Sec. 35-7); there is *some* possibility that a particle may be at *any* location where the amplitude of its wave "patch" is not zero. Hence, even though in the classical sense an alpha particle which has an energy W is at a distance r from the center of the nucleus (Fig. 37-10), the amplitude of its waves may not be zero at the distance r' from the center of the nucleus. In such a case, it is possible though unlikely that the particle may *be* at r' rather than at r; hence it may "leak" through the potential barrier and escape. It is as if a boulder had found a tunnel through the shoulder of the volcano; it could escape through the tunnel even though its energy was too limited to allow it to reach the rim.

Quantization appears in this so-called tunnel effect, with the result that all alpha particles emitted from a given nuclide have a definite energy characteristic of that nuclide. This means that they emerge through the potential barrier at the same elevation on a diagram like Fig. 37-10. Obviously the less the distance between r_0 and r' is, the greater is the probability that an alpha particle can "leak" through the potential

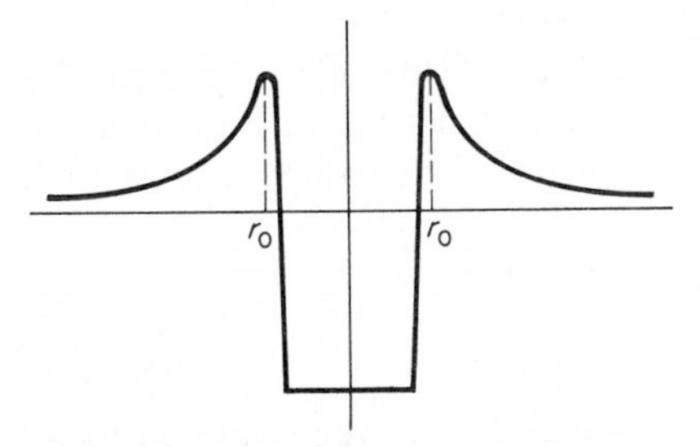

Fig. 37-9. Potential energy diagram for an alpha particle in or near a nucleus.

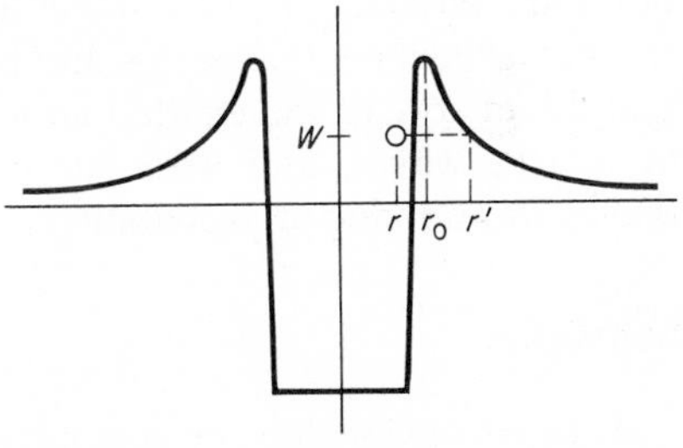

Fig. 37-10. "Leaking" of an alpha particle through the potential energy barrier.

barrier; and this is a way of saying that the decay constant should be greater, or the half life shorter. It is also obvious that the particle should emerge with more energy if the distance from r_0 to r' is smaller, for the particle would emerge higher up on the slope. Hence, if there is any validity in this seemingly strange concept, alpha particles emitted by relatively short-lived nuclides should have more energy than those from longer-lived nuclear species, and vice versa. In actual fact, such is the case. The energy of the alpha particles is an index of the half life, and an approximate value of the half life may be computed from the value of the energy, though the relationship is not exact. Thus the process of alpha emission offers dramatic support to the uncertainty principle and to the interpretation of wave amplitude as an index of probability.

Summary

During *radioactive decay* one class of nuclides emits *alpha particles;* another class emits *beta particles.* Either type of emission may, or may not, be accompanied by the production of gamma rays. Alpha particles are *helium nuclei,* and they have the *least penetrating ability* of the three kinds of rays. Beta particles are *electrons;* they have an *intermediate* ability to penetrate matter. *Gamma rays* are identical with X rays, and have the *greatest penetrating ability* of the three kinds of rays emitted from radioactive substances.

Many naturally occurring substances are radioactive, though radioactivity is far more common among nuclides of atomic number 83 and higher.

Three distinct *families* of *radioactive elements* occur in nature. Each has at its head a long-lived radioactive nuclide and one decay is followed by another through a series of about ten or a dozen, until the final decay yields a stable nuclide.

Radioactive decay is a *statistical process;* for reasonably large samples, the decay can be described quantitatively, but the accuracy of the equations becomes very low as the number of atoms in the sample is reduced. It is futile to try to state the life of a radioactive species, but the half life is definite. The *half life* is the time interval within which half of the atoms of a pure radioactive nuclide will undergo decay.

The experimental relationship between the half life of an alpha emitter and the energy of the emitted alpha particles is in accord with the concept of matter waves, and with our interpretation of the amplitude of such waves as an index of probability.

Self-Quiz

1. In what sense does the phenomenon of radioactivity correspond to the transmutation of elements sought by the alchemists? In what sense does it differ from what they sought?

2. Sort the following terms into three pairs so that there is a logical relationship between the members of a pair; compare and contrast the members of each pair: alpha particle, X ray, helium atom, electron, gamma ray, beta particle.

3. If the left portion of the curve in Fig. 36-3, which represents the binding energy per nucleon, is drawn with horizontal distances magnified, and if the curve is carefully drawn through the points, it has "peaks" corresponding to all values of A which are small integral multiples of 4. Because of this, it has been suggested that alpha particles may exist as such within nuclei. Does this suggestion seem to be in accord with Sec. 37-5? With Sec. 37-9? Explain, in each case.

4. State any changes in the values of Z and A which occur during alpha emission and explain the cause of such change(s). Repeat for beta emission.

5. Write the generalized equation for alpha emission, and that for beta emission, and show that they are in accord with your discussion of the preceding question.

6. Beta decay seems to be a paradox. Why? How is this apparent paradox explained?

7. What is the significance of the symbol Z? of the symbol A?

8. In terms of the values of Z and A define the terms "isotope," "isobar," and "nuclide."

9. Choose a nuclide fairly near the head of any series in Figs. 37-4–37-6, inclusive, and record its complete symbol in terms of Z, the element symbol, and A. Note the type of decay it undergoes, as shown on the figure, and write the equation for the decay in the form of Eq. (37-1) or Eq. (37-5). Continue through several successive decays, taking the type of the decay, but not the value of Z or A, from the figure. Compare the values of Z and A for the daughter product in the last equation with the values in the figure.

10. On a grid similar to those in Figs. 37-4–37-6, inclusive, record a nuclide of mass number 219 and atomic number 86. On the grid, plot two successive alpha decays, a beta decay, another alpha decay, and a final beta decay. Add to the chart the names of the elements to which the various nuclides belong. Compare your chart with the lower portion of Fig. 37-6.

11. What can be said about the time required for half the atoms in a sample of a radioactive nuclide to decay? What can be said about the time required for all of them to decay? Why are the answers to these two questions so different?

12. In a practical sense, what is the significance of the decay constant of a nuclide? Does a relatively large value of a decay constant correspond to a relatively long or to a relatively short half life? Why?

13. Discuss the "tunnel effect," including its logical basis, a concrete analogy of it, and the reason for the relatively low energies of alpha particles emitted from nuclides of comparatively long half life.

14. Survey instruments used for detecting radioactivity, or monitoring a radioactive area, usually are provided with a meter similar to an ordinary ammeter. If such an instrument is used where there is a very low level of radioactivity, the needle of the meter is "jittery," moving up-scale in jerks, and falling back; but where the level of radiation is fairly high the needle is relatively steady. Explain the difference.

Problems

1. If a sample contains $1.024 \cdot 10^{20}$ atoms of a radioactive nuclide, compute the number of atoms of the original nuclide left after eight half lives. Why would the same type of computation not be applicable to a sample of $1.024 \cdot 10^3$ atoms?

2. (a) Determine the fraction of the initial atoms of a pure nuclide which will remain after each of these intervals: 1 half life, 2 half lives, 3 half lives, 4 half lives, and 5 half lives. (b) Plot the data from part (a) on graph paper, using a scale that will make the graph reasonably large, and draw a *smooth curve* through the points. (c) From the graph, read the fraction of the original atoms remaining at these times: $\frac{1}{2}$, $\frac{3}{2}$, $\frac{5}{2}$, and $\frac{7}{2}$ half lives. (d) Compare the values from part (c) with corresponding values obtained by taking the average of appropriate pairs of values from part (a), and explain.

3. A pure radioactive nuclide is decaying to a stable daughter product. At one moment a meter used to measure the radioactivity reads 96.0, and 45.0 min later it reads 1.50. Calculate the half life.

4. A pure radioactive nuclide is decaying to a stable daughter product, and its activity decreases by a factor of 5.00 in 30.0 days. With the aid of your graph from Problem 2 estimate the half life.

The following problems require the use of logarithms.

5. Compute the half life in Problem 4.

6. The half life of radium is 1620 years. (a) What per cent of the atoms in the sample of radium separated from uranium by the Curies in 1898 will still exist (as radium) in 1998? (b) What per cent will remain in the year 2898? (c) What per cent will be extant in the year 10,000?

7. As a rough "rule of thumb," it is said that the activity of radium decreases about 1% every 25 years. Compute (a) the half life consistent with this rule, and (b) the per cent error of the rule.

8. The half life of $_{84}Po^{215}$ is $1.83 \cdot 10^{-3}$ sec. How long a time would be required for 99.9% of the atoms of this nuclide to decay?

9. The half life of $_{84}Po^{210}$ is 140 days. By what per cent does its activity decrease per week?

10. The number of atoms of $_{90}Th^{234}$ remaining after a year is $3.28 \cdot 10^{-5}$ of the number present at the start of the year. Compute (a) the half life and (b) the per cent undergoing decay per day.

38

DETECTION OF NUCLEAR RADIATIONS

38-1 Preview

Nuclear radiations were a part of the environment within which all forms of life developed. Within the last few decades man has developed a tremendous variety of new sources of radiation, ranging from X-ray tubes to thermonuclear weapons. Peaceful applications of these radiations run the gamut from the improvement of detergents to the use of forced mutation in the development of better varieties of plants. (A limited survey of such uses is given in Chapter 41.) These applications, and the continuing research in the various fields of nuclear radiations, require that means be available to detect the presence of such radiations, to measure their intensity, and to determine their nature. In this chapter, we shall take a brief look at some of the more common devices developed for these purposes.

38-2 The Basis for the Detection of Radiations

In a broad sense, we could say that a mass spectrograph and an experimental animal are radiation detectors. However, we shall confine our attention to instruments developed specifically for this purpose.

Such instruments do not detect the particles or photons of the nuclear radiations directly. Instead, they detect some effect produced by the particles or photons. One such effect very widely employed is ionization, and another is excitation. As the radiations pass through matter, they ionize or excite some of the atoms of the medium; and the measurement of the radiations is based on the evaluation of the ionization, or of the excitation, produced.

Some nuclear radiations, such as alpha particles, cause ionization directly; others, like neutrons, produce it only indirectly.

Detection based on ionization will be discussed in Sec. 38-3 – 38-12, inclusive, and detection based on excitation will be considered briefly in Sec. 38-13.

38-3 Ionization by Alpha and Beta Particles

We know that the nucleus of any atom is very small as compared with the whole atom, so nearly all of the volume preempted by any atom is empty space. Any particle of a dimension comparable with that of the nucleus or an electron can pass through an atom somewhat as a meteor can pass through the solar system. Since an alpha particle is a helium nucleus and a beta particle is an electron, either of these particles can pass through an atom. This situation is not new to us in the case of alpha particles, for it was on this basis that Rutherford established the fact that atoms possess extremely small cores or nuclei (Sec. 33-4).

Since alpha particles possess a positive electric charge there will be a force of electrostatic attraction between the particle and the electrons of any atom through which it passes, and this attraction may suffice to woo an electron away from the atom, thus changing the originally neutral atom into an ***ion pair*** consisting of the freed electron and the positive residue of the atom. In general, the velocity of the alpha particle is high enough to carry it away before the freed electron can catch up with it. Thus the particle continues on, ionizing many other particles before it eventually picks up one electron and then another, becoming a normal atom of helium.

Something very similar happens when a beta particle passes through an atom, although here the interaction of the charge of the particle with that of an electron in the atom is a repulsion rather than an attraction; a beta particle pushes electrons from atoms instead of pulling them out as an alpha particle does, but in either case the result is ionization.

38-4 Ionization by Gamma Rays

A gamma ray consists of photons, and since a photon does not carry an electric charge, it cannot produce ionization by the process outlined in the case of alpha and beta particles. A gamma ray photon may cause ionization by any one of three different mechanisms, and any of these may be followed by additional indirect ionization. The three mechanisms are photoelectric emission, Compton collisions, and pair production. We have met each of these previously.

We met the photoelectric effect in Sec. 35-2 – 35-4, inclusive. Though in most applications a solid medium, commonly a metal, is employed, photoelectric emission may occur from gases and liquids. A gamma photon passing through a gas may encounter an electron and free the electron from its parent atom by photoelectric emission. Its entire energy is used in removing the electron from the atom and giving the electron kinetic energy; so the photon ceases to exist, but leaves behind an ion pair as evidence of its having passed that way.

A Compton collision, which we studied in Sec. 35-6, resembles photoelectric emission in the respect that a single photon encounters an electron in an atom, and removes the electron from the atom. In a Compton collision, however, the photon does not surrender its entire store of energy to the electron; it retains most of its energy, and thus it continues to exist as a photon of reduced energy. A photon which takes part in photoelectric emission is like a honey bee, which forfeits its life when it stings. A photon which experiences a Compton collision resembles instead a wasp, which can sting repeatedly.

In Sec. 33-7 and again in Sec. 35-9, we met the phenomenon of pair production, in which a photon which possesses at least 1.02 Mev of energy is converted into an electron-positron pair. Here, as in photoelectric emission, the photon is annihilated in the process.

An ion pair is the end result of any one of these mechanisms. Either of the first two processes yields an electron plus an atom which lacks an electron, and the third produces an ordinary electron plus a positron. The electrons can cause further ionization as beta particles do; in fact, they are identical with beta particles. The positron will cause ionization in a similar manner, except that the electrostatic forces will be attractions instead of repulsions. The ionization produced by the gamma photons themselves is called ***primary ionization***, and that caused by the primary electrons is termed ***secondary ionization***. Some of the secondary electrons may themselves have sufficient energy to cause additional ionization. And of course the positron will eventually combine with an electron to produce the two 0.51 Mev photons of annihilation radiation (Sec. 35-9), each of which may participate in photoelectric emission or Compton collisions.

38-5 Ionization by Other Particles

Many of the other "fundamental" particles mentioned in Sec. 33-7 and Sec. 33-8 cause ionization by one of the processes mentioned in connection with alpha and beta particles and photons. The neutron is a common particle which cannot produce ionization by any of these methods. Its detection is based on a nuclear reaction in which the neutron enters the nucleus of an atom, usually an atom of boron, and ejects an alpha particle. The alpha particle thus generated acts like any other alpha particle, producing ionization.

38-6 The Relative Penetration of Various Rays

We have seen that the initial step toward the identification of the various rays resulting from radioactivity was the observation of a marked difference in their ability to penetrate matter (Sec. 37-2). For any one kind of ray—alpha, beta, or gamma—there is considerable variation of the energy, depending on the nuclide which produces the ray. However, the order of magnitude of the energy of an alpha particle is comparable with that of a beta particle or a gamma photon. Thus, unequal penetrations of the three kinds of rays does not result from marked differences in energy; rather, this inequality is due to the way in which the particles or photons interact with matter.

We have seen in Sec. 38-3 that both alpha and beta particles produce ionization as the result of electrostatic forces between the particle and electrons in atoms. The effectiveness of this mechanism obviously will depend on the magnitude of the force and on the length of the interval during which the force acts.

The force exerted by an alpha particle on an electron will be twice that exerted by a beta particle, other things being equal, because the alpha particle carries two electronic charges and the beta particle has but one—Eq. (20-2).

The alpha particle has a mass of about four amu (since it contains two protons and two electrons), whereas the beta particle (which is an electron) has a mass of $\frac{1}{1836}$ amu; hence the alpha particle has a mass roughly $7 \cdot 10^3$ times that of the beta particle.* The kinetic energy is given by the expression $mv^2/2$—Eq. (6-2). Hence, since an alpha particle and a beta particle have approximately equal energies, the fact that the mass of the former is greater by a factor of about $7 \cdot 10^3$ means that its speed must be less by a factor of about $\sqrt{7 \cdot 10^3}$, or very roughly 80. And if the speed of

* To simplify the discussion, it is based on non-relativistic concepts, and this may involve considerable error. However, we are concerned only with a rough comparison; and even if we were in error by a factor as large as 100 the conclusion would not be invalidated.

an alpha particle is something like $\frac{1}{50}$ to $\frac{1}{100}$ that of a beta particle, the interval during which the alpha particle exerts a force on an electron in an atom will be some 50 to 100 times as great as for a beta particle. Combined with the fact that the alpha particle exerts twice as great a force as the beta particle does, this means that alpha particles are far better ionizers than beta particles.

Depending on the nature of the gas used in the detector, the production of a single ion pair requires an energy roughly 20 to 35 ev; the ionizing particle loses this much energy every time it ionizes an atom. Obviously, then, the more effective an ionizer a particle is, the sooner it will run out of energy. This is the primary basis of the marked difference in the penetrating ability of alpha and beta rays; the beta particles go a greater distance before being absorbed for the same reason a motorcycle travels farther on a given quantity of gasoline than a truck does. A secondary factor, which reduces the disparity in the ranges of the two kinds of particles, is the very different sort of paths they follow. Since the alpha particle is so much more massive than the electrons with which it interacts, it is deflected hardly at all; its path is essentially a straight line unless it happens to encounter a nucleus. On the other hand, the masses of the beta particle and the electron are the same (neglecting possible relativistic effects), so the beta particle is deflected sharply each time it interacts with an electron. Hence its path is tortuous and is much longer than the distance from its point of origin to the point where it is absorbed.

Because of ever-present electrostatic forces, it is impossible for an alpha or a beta particle to pass through matter without interacting and losing energy. On the contrary, a gamma photon can pass through without any such drain on its energy. Only if it encounters an electron can it cause photoelectric emission or a Compton collision. Some photons make such an encounter almost immediately, but others travel relatively great distances before doing so; it is a matter of chance. Pair production also is a statistical matter. Hence there is no definite limit to the range of gamma rays, as there is for alphas and betas; the intensity of a beam of gamma rays decreases but (in theory) never becomes zero. In fact, the quantitative description of the intensity of gamma radiation which has penetrated any given thickness of a uniform medium is of exactly the same form as the equation which describes the quantity of a radioactive nuclide remaining at any specified time. Thus we may write

$$\log \frac{I}{I_0} = -\frac{0.301s}{S_{1/2}} \tag{38-1}$$

in which I_0 is the original intensity of a beam of gamma rays and I is its intensity after passing through a thickness s of a uniform medium, $S_{1/2}$ being the ***half-value thickness*** of the medium; that is, the thickness required to reduce the intensity by 50.0%. Compare this equation with Eq.

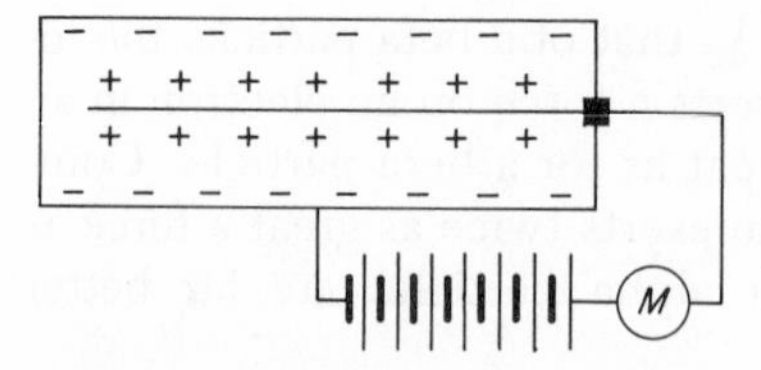

Fig. 38-1. The basic principle of a radiation detector.

(37-11). Other forms of Eq. (38-1) may be written, analogous to Eq. (37-9) and Eq. (37-10).

38-7 The Basic Principle of Detection of Ionization

Even the simplest radiation detector based on the principle to be discussed is far more complex than that shown schematically in Fig. 38-1; but the essence of the principle can be gotten from this diagram, and the refinements belong in books devoted to such detectors.

The detector consists essentially of a metal wire mounted at the axis of a hollow cylinder of conducting material, a source of voltage to make the wire positive with respect to the cylinder, and some sort of a meter or other indicating device. Commonly the cylinder is enclosed and contains some gas other than air, and the pressure in the cylinder may differ from the external pressure. A simple meter is never used as shown; there is an amplifying circuit of some sort ahead of the meter, and the meter itself may be replaced by an oscillograph or by an electrical or mechanical register.

38-8 Response of the Detector at Low Voltages

The manner in which such a device functions depends very strongly on the magnitude of the voltage applied between the wire and the cylinder, as shown in Fig. 38-2. In this figure "Size of pulse" refers to the magnitude of the response the detector makes to the entry of a single ionizing particle into the sensitive volume within the cylinder. The figure is schematic only; the vertical range is too great to permit quantitative accuracy in the graph.

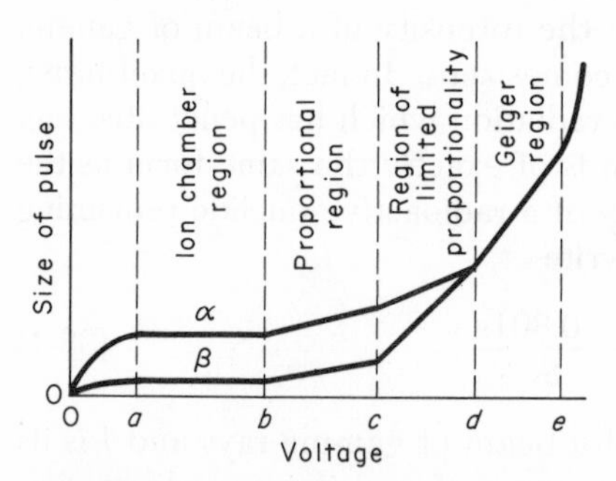

Fig. 38-2. Schematic voltage representation of the variation of pulse size with voltage.

Suppose that a strongly ionizing particle, such as an alpha particle, has entered the cylinder; it may produce something like 10^4 ion pairs. These tend to recombine because of the attraction of unlike charges, and if no voltage is applied they will do so, with no external evidence of ionization having occurred. If a low voltage is applied, electrons will be carried toward the positively charged wire and the positive ions will move sluggishly (because of their much greater mass) toward the cylinder. Both processes will result in a slight flow of electrons through the meter, causing a pulse. If the voltage is low, however, many ions will recombine, rather than reach the opposite electrodes.

38-9 Response of the Detector: the Ion Chamber Region

Gradual increase of the voltage will cause more rapid motion of the ions, allowing them less opportunity to recombine; hence a larger proportion of them will reach the electrodes and a stronger pulse will result. However, when the point a on the graph (Fig. 38-2) has been reached, a relatively large additional increment of the voltage has essentially no effect on the pulse size. This is due to the fact that a voltage corresponding to point a is sufficient to sweep essentially all the ions formed to the electrodes, allowing virtually no recombination. Thus the size of the pulse is the same at any voltage between a and b on the figure. This range is called the ***ion chamber region.***

Though the pulse size in this region is independent of the voltage, it does depend very strongly on the nature of the ionizing particle, for only such ions as are produced by the passage of the particle through the gas can be swept to the electrodes to produce a pulse. Thus a beta particle might cause a fraction of one per cent of the number of ions an alpha particle would, and the resulting pulse would be relatively small, as indicated in the figure. This beta particle could be an original beta particle, or it could be a secondary particle produced by a Compton collision or some similar process.

Remember that Fig. 38-2 is only schematic. There is a considerable range of energies of alpha particles and the same is true of beta particles; and though the lines α and β indicate quite definitely that the pulse due to an alpha particle is much greater than that caused by a beta particle, they are not intended to be an accurate index of the relative pulse sizes.

38-10 Response of the Detector: Proportional Region and Region of Limited Proportionality

Though the pulse size is unaffected as the voltage is increased through the ion chamber region (between a and b, in Fig. 38-2), the greater electric field intensity results in higher velocities of the ions, just as the more intense gravitational field on Jupiter would cause a fall through a given distance to yield a higher velocity than would be the case on the earth. When the voltage has been increased to point b, some electrons produced by primary ionization have almost enough energy to cause ionization by collision, so increase of the voltage beyond this point causes secondary ionization due to such collisions. In effect, an electron produced by the original particle becomes a beta particle. Further increase of the voltage augments the fraction of the primary electrons which have enough energy to ionize by collision, and at still higher voltages, a given electron may take part in several ionizing collisions before it reaches the wire. Thus, each primary electron may be the direct or indirect cause of many others, and the pulse size is greatly increased. This process is called ***gas amplification,*** and may increase the pulse size by a factor as great as 10^7.

For a considerable range of voltages, the gas amplification factor is constant; the pulses due to alpha and beta particles will both increase markedly, but their sizes will stand in the same ratio as they would in the ion chamber region. The range of voltages over which this definite proportionality exists is termed the ***proportional region.*** In Fig. 38-2 it extends from b to c.

Continued increase in the applied voltage causes the response of the detector to depart from this definite proportionality; the amplification factor continues to increase, but it increases less for good ionizers like alpha particles than for relatively poor ionizers, such as beta particles. Thus the difference in the sizes of the pulses they cause is reduced, and at a voltage indicated on the figure by d the distinction disappears. The voltage range from c to d is the ***region of limited proportionality.***

38-11 Response of the Detector: the Geiger Region

The discussion in the latter part of the preceding section and the graph in Fig. 38-2 show that at a voltage above point d the size of the pulse bears no relation to the number of ions originally produced by the entry of some ionizing particle into the sensitive volume within the cylinder. The gas amplification has been increased to a degree such that the appearance of a single primary electron, from a gamma photon or any ionizing event, causes complete ionization of the gas in the cylinder and an "avalanche" results.

Since the positive ions move so much more slowly than the electrons, momentarily they form a sheath of positive ions around the wire and this reduces the electric field intensity near the wire. The effect is to tend to snuff out the avalanche. This must be augmented by some other provision for "quenching" the discharge. Commonly this is done by adding to the gas in the cylinder a small percentage of an organic vapor, such as alcohol, or of a halogen gas, such as chlorine; but it may be accomplished by an auxiliary electronic circuit which causes a sharp drop in the potential across the tube when an avalanche occurs. However, above a certain voltage indicated by the point e, the provision for quenching becomes inadequate and a continuous discharge occurs. This can have no useful effect and tends to destroy the detecting device. The voltage range between points d and e in Fig. 38-2 is known as the ***Geiger region.***

38-12 Comparison of Ion Chambers, Proportional Counters, and Geiger Counters

Of the various voltage ranges indicated in Fig. 38-2 and discussed in Sec. 38-8 – 38-11, inclusive, three are used extensively: the ion chamber, proportional counter, and Geiger regions.

Since no gas amplification occurs in the ion chamber region, an ***ion chamber*** is the least sensitive of the instruments based on these three voltage ranges. On the other hand, an ion chamber is useful for the measurement of relatively high levels of radiation. Its response depends on the energies of the individual particles or photons, as well as on their number.

The ***proportional counter*** is used where an ion chamber is not sufficiently sensitive and where it is desired to distinguish between particles of different energies. In practical applications, this type of instrument is associated with a very stable amplifier; because of this, it is primarily a laboratory type of instrument, not readily adaptable to portable form for survey purposes.

The ***Geiger counter*** is the most sensitive of the three types; hence it is most useful in the measurement of relatively low intensities. However, it is unable to distinguish between kinds of particles, as the others can, since the size of its pulse is independent of the energy of the particle.

The sensitive volume of a detector may be within a sealed cylinder, or in some cases, it may be a chamber into which a radioactive sample may be put. In the latter case, alpha particles as well as betas and gammas may be detected. On the other hand, if the sensitive volume is sealed, alpha rays from an external sample will be absorbed unless the wall of the chamber is extremely light. For this reason, few portable instruments will detect alpha radiation. Almost all Geiger tubes have walls which block out all alpha particles.

Many instruments of the portable type are provided with a movable metal shield sufficiently thick to absorb all beta radiations; with the shield in the "open" position, such an instrument will detect both betas and gammas, but it will respond to gammas only when the shield is "closed."

Typically, a Geiger counter has another characteristic not shared by the others: it will "paralyze" or "block" in a field of high intensity. A radiologist hunting a misplaced radium needle with the aid of a Geiger counter knows that he is getting warm when the response on the counter increases up to a certain point, and he knows that he is very close to the needle when the response falls off.

This effect apparently is associated with the "quenching" which is necessary to prevent continuous discharge (Sec. 38-11). Whether the "quench" is accomplished chemically or electronically, it renders the detector insensitive for a small fraction of a second. The sensitivity does not return suddenly; it builds up gradually. Hence if a second ionizing event occurs in the detector when it is just starting to recover from the first, the pulse will be abnormally small. In a fairly intense radiation field, ionizing events in the detector follow each other so rapidly that the detector never has time to recover its sensitivity; hence its response may drop essentially to zero.

It obviously is important that this quirk of Geiger counters be realized. If you get a very low response from a Geiger counter, you know that *one* of *two* situations exists: either there is almost no radiation *or* you are in a fairly intense radiation field. *But your Geiger counter won't tell you which is the true situation!* It must be "backed up" by an ion chamber.

38-13 Scintillation Counters

Thus far we have considered only detectors which make use of the ionization caused by nuclear radiations. Scintillation counters employ instead the excitation such radiations cause in certain substances. Historically, zinc sulfide was the first substance used; Rutherford employed it in his alpha scattering experiments.

The impact of an alpha particle on zinc sulfide excites it—endows it with excess energy—and this energy of excitation is released as a single photon of light. This phenomenon is far more common than you may suppose; if you observe, in the dark, the markings of a watch with a luminous dial, you can see the firefly-like scintillations occurring spasmodically. The light is not steady and continuous, any more than the wetting of a pavement by raindrops is steady and continuous. Each minute flare of light is a single scintillation caused by an alpha particle, beta particle, or gamma photon.* Various other substances, liquids as well as solids, produce scintillations. In general, one such substance will have a greater sensitivity to one kind of radiation than to another, and its sensitivity commonly depends in some degree on the energy.

Though Rutherford and later scientists had to observe scintillations visually, today use is made of the photoelectric effect to observe them. A photosensitive surface is incorporated in a special tube which contains a series of metal plates. All these plates are positive to the photosensitive surface, but the potential difference increases considerably from plate to plate. A photoelectron falls on the first plate with sufficient energy to knock a number of other electrons out of the plate; these secondary elec-

---

* Consider these facts: Radium is extremely expensive. In 1620 years only half of any given quantity of radium will decay. In the decay to a stable product there will be 5 alphas and 4 betas produced, some accompanied by gammas; but many of these will escape without producing scintillations. At one time, radium was the only substance used for luminous watch dials. It was possible to buy a watch with a luminous dial for $1.50. Does this bring you any closer to a realization of the minuteness of atoms and of the number of atoms in even a very minute mass?

trons are accelerated toward the next plate, and on striking it each knocks out additional electrons, and so on. Thus the emission of a single photoelectron may initiate an avalanche of a million electrons. This pulse is delivered to appropriate associated circuitry, as with the detectors previously considered.

38-14 Dosimeters

The instruments thus far considered are commonly used for the purpose of determining the rate of radioactive decay or the intensity of a radiation field rather than measuring the total quantity of radiation over an extended period, though associated circuitry may convert them to the latter purpose. For purposes such as personnel protection, however, it is necessary to have simpler means to determine the total exposure to radiation. Any instrument designed for this purpose is a ***dosimeter.***

Two types of dosimeter are most common. One is a film badge dosimeter, which is based on the fact that any nuclear radiation will "expose" a piece of photographic film in a lightproof package just as light would "expose" the unprotected film. Special emulsions are used, and commonly part of the film area is protected by a metal plate which blocks out the beta particles so that the film will indicate the kind of radiations as well as the exposure. The other common type of dosimeter is essentially a specially designed electroscope which is charged before use and loses charge in proportion to the quantity of radiation to which it is subjected.

38-15 Cloud Chambers and Bubble Chambers

An extremely useful detector for research work is a ***cloud chamber,*** and a similar device more recently developed is a bubble chamber. Both of these make use of the fact that a change of state may not occur spontaneously under conditions appropriate to equilibrium and that such changes of state can be "triggered" by ions. Probably you have observed a fog appearing momentarily in the space above the liquid when you opened a bottle of carbonated beverage. The air in the bottle was saturated with moisture before the bottle was opened, and when you released the pressure by uncapping the bottle, the resulting expansion cooled the saturated air; thus it became supersaturated, and a fog formed. A fog should form in all similar situations if ions are present to act as centers on which the vapor can condense, but not if such condensation centers are absent.

A cloud chamber is a similar arrangement in more convenient (for research) and far more sophisticated form, and the condensation centers are provided in the form of ion pairs created by ionizing radiation. Provision is made for photographing the fog pattern, which consists of rows of minute droplets along the path taken by an ionizing particle, at the instant the particle passes through the chamber.

The ***bubble chamber*** makes use of a liquid almost at its boiling point. Release of pressure lowers its boiling point below the existing temperature of the liquid; and the first bubbles of vapor form where there are ions left by some sort of ionizing radiation, thus revealing the path of the ionizing particle to the camera.

For either type of chamber, cameras may be provided to photograph the patterns from two different angles, enabling the investigator to determine the path of the radiations in three dimensions.

Summary

The *detection* of *nuclear radiations* is based on their ability to produce, either directly or indirectly, *ionization* or *excitation*. *Alpha* and *beta particles* cause ionization because of the electrostatic force between the particle and an electron in an atom. Due to its greater charge and lower speed, an alpha particle is a much better ionizer than a beta particle is. This is the primary basis for the marked difference between the ranges of the two kinds of particle.

A *gamma photon* causes ionization by *photoelectric emission*, by *Compton collision*, or by *pair production*.

Measurements of radiation by an *ion chamber* are based on the ions produced directly by the radiation. In a *proportional counter*, *gas amplification* markedly increases the total number of ions produced. Any ionizing event in a *Geiger counter* ionizes the gas within the counter completely.

Ion chambers are used for relatively *high radiation levels*, and *Geiger counters* for comparatively *low* levels. A proportional counter usually is not suitable for use as a survey instrument.

Geiger counters have the unfortunate property of becoming *paralyzed* in the presence of a *fairly high level* of *radiation;* hence a *low reading* is unreliable unless *confirmed* by an *ion chamber*.

Dosimeters measure *total radiation* received over an extended time. They may make use of photographic film or of a specialized electroscope.

Cloud chambers and bubble chambers reveal the paths of ionizing radiations in terms of rows of minute fog droplets or vapor bubbles, respectively.

Self-Quiz

1. Proceeding as far as you can without reference to Fig. 38-2 or to the discussion, make a fully labeled diagram of the relation of pulse size to applied voltage. Check the diagram against Fig. 38-2.

2. On the basis of your diagram, discuss the operation of a counter in the ion chamber region, and the characteristics of an instrument operating in this region.

3. Repeat for the proportional region.

4. Repeat for the Geiger region.

5. If your discussion in the preceding questions did not include gas amplification, avalanches, and quenching, discuss these matters.

6. Outline the mechanism by which a charged particle causes ionization.

7. Which is the more efficient ionizer, an alpha particle or a beta particle? Explain fully.

8. Compare the ranges of alpha and beta particles; show that your discussion is consistent with that for the preceding question.

9. By what mechanisms do gamma photons cause ionization? Explain each in some detail.

10. Which has a higher speed, an alpha or a beta particle? How do you know this to be true?

11. What is a scintillation? How is it caused? What is a scintillation counter?

12. Discuss briefly the two principal types of dosimeters.

13. What is the principle of operation of a cloud chamber? Of a bubble chamber?

14. Assume that a cloud chamber photograph shows a short, thick line of droplets commencing at the chamber wall; a thin, tortuous line commencing in the interior of the chamber; and a similar trail commencing at the chamber wall. What type of nuclear radiation probably produced each trail? (There are two possibilities in one case.)

Problems

1. For gamma rays from Co^{60}, the half-value thickness of lead is about 1.2 cm. By what per cent will the intensity of a beam of these gamma rays be reduced by 3.6 cm of lead?

2. What thickness of lead is required to reduce the intensity of gamma radiation from Co^{60} to 6.25% of its initial value?

3. A sample of a radioactive nuclide which emits gammas of approximately the same energy as those from Co^{60} is placed in a lead shield with walls 6.0 cm thick, and a reading is taken with a survey meter outside the shield. Twenty-five hr later, the sample is removed from the shield and another reading taken, the distance between the sample and the meter being the same as before. The second reading is just four times the initial reading. What is the half life of the nuclide?

39

NUCLEAR REACTIONS

39-1 Preview

The discovery of the subatomic particles which comprise an atom destroyed the concept of the indivisibility of the atom, and in some degree, it suggested the possibility of transmutation. Natural radioactivity constitutes transmutation, but it is uncontrollable. In this chapter, we shall consider transmutations produced artificially and—for the most part—under controlled conditions. We also shall consider briefly one of the many types of machine developed for such purposes.

39-2 The Discovery of Nuclear Reactions

In 1919, Rutherford and Chadwick were working with a polonium isotope which is a member of the uranium series. They determined the range in various gases of the alpha particles given off. This they did by placing the source (the polonium isotope) in a vessel filled with the gas and observing how far it could be moved back from a zinc sulfide screen on the interior surface at the end of the vessel without terminating the scintillations observed on the screen. They found that when nitrogen was used the scintillations did not cease abruptly at a certain distance; their frequency dropped sharply, but some scintillations were observed at significantly larger distances. They attributed such scintillations to protons which had been knocked out of the nitrogen atoms by the alpha particles, and it is known now that their assumption was correct. This was the first observed nuclear reaction.*

Any nuclear reaction which does not involve pair production or annihilation may be represented by an equation which is balanced by making the total electric charge on one side equal to that on the other, and similarly making the total mass number the same on the two sides. Knowing that in this first observed reaction a nitrogen atom and an alpha particle are involved, and that one product is a proton (which is a hydrogen nucleus), we may write:

$$_7N^{14} + {_2\alpha^4} \rightarrow {_1H^1} + ?$$

The total charge on the left is 7 + 2 or 9, and only one charge is accounted for on the right; hence a nucleus with 8 charges must result. Since the number of charges on a nucleus is the atomic number, we may consult Table 36-1 (page 653) or Table AD-1 (page 759); either reference identifies the element of atomic number 8 as oxygen. The total mass number before the reaction is 18, so it must still be 18 after the reaction; thus the product must have a mass number of 17. Hence the complete equation† for the nuclear reaction is

$$_7N^{14} + {_2\alpha^4} \rightarrow {_1H^1} + {_8O^{17}}$$

* In a sense, any radioactive decay is a nuclear reaction. The term, however, is used commonly to refer to a process which may be initiated or terminated at will; in this book, the term is usually used in this sense.

† The equation is complete and balanced with respect to mass number and charge, but not with respect to energy. The actual mass of the two products exceeds that of the original particles, and about 1.2 Mev of energy is used up to produce this increase in mass. In advanced texts and references, such energy changes are included to balance the equation with respect to energy as well as charge and mass number; however, energy considerations will not be included explicitly in our equations, though we should bear in mind that they are there implicitly. Similarly, in general the presence (or absence) of a neutrino among the products will not be indicated.

This means that the nucleus of an atom of nitrogen and an alpha particle have been converted into a proton—that is, a hydrogen nucleus—and the nucleus of an isotope of oxygen.

The fact that the equation is balanced may mislead us if we overlook the fact that it is a *nuclear* equation. The nuclei represented may *not* be nuclei of electrically neutral atoms. In this instance, the nitrogen has 7 electrons and the alpha particle none; and the proton also has none. This leaves 7 electrons for the oxygen atom, which should have 8; hence it will be a singly ionized atom. In Problem 3, and in others at the end of this chapter, this sort of thing must be taken into consideration. In this case, the mass of the product is not the mass of the neutral ${}_8O^{17}$ atom; instead it is the difference between the mass of the atom and the mass of the missing electron.*

It was eleven years after this first nuclear reaction was observed that Cockroft and Walton brought about the first nuclear reaction by particles artificially produced and accelerated. They allowed protons to fall through a potential difference of 10^5 volts and used these to bombard lithium. They found that a proton and a lithium nucleus react to produce two alpha particles:

$$
{}_3Li^7 + {}_1H^1 \rightarrow {}_2\alpha^4 + {}_2\alpha^4
$$

Rutherford's and Chadwick's discovery, and later that of Cockroft and Walton, inspired research which has produced well over a thousand different nuclear reactions, nearly all of which resulted from the use of artificially accelerated particles. The last few decades have seen the development of powerful machines designed for the sole purpose of accelerating charged particles, then mammoth machines of this sort, and finally gargantuan ones. We shall consider but one of them, as an example of the general problem.

39-3 The Cyclotron

Energies of the order of a million electron volts are required for most nuclear reactions, and many reactions require much higher energies. Further research in this and related fields demands particle energies measured in billions of electron volts. One of the first machines designed to give a particle an energy measured in Bev (one Bev = one billion electron volts) was christened the bevatron.† It is quite obvious that an energy of 1 Bev, or even 1 Mev, cannot be given to a particle in one tremendous wallop. Instead, it is necessary for it to acquire successive increments of

* In principle, allowance should be made for the ionization energy of the atom, but this is utterly negligible in comparison with other quantities involved.

† This fact is cited as evidence that even front-rank nuclear physicists may be human beings with a sense of humor, rather than for the relatively unimportant purpose of conveying information about physics!

energy. One means of accomplishing this is to cause the charged particle to "fall" successively through a number of relatively small potential differences.

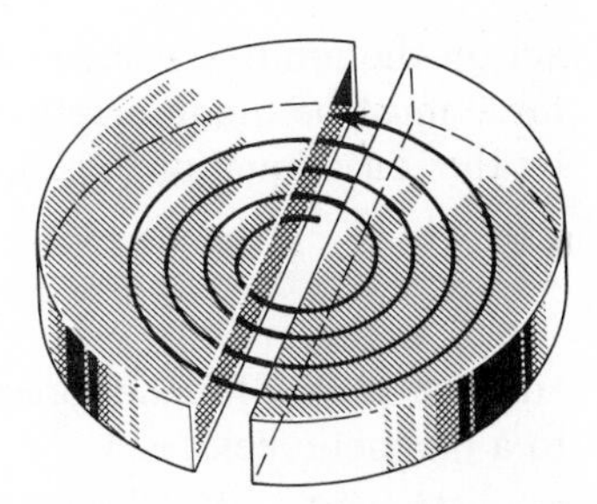

Fig. 39-1. The expanding spiral path of ions in the "dees" of a cyclotron.

The cyclotron, designed by Lawrence at the University of California, accomplishes this by causing a stream of charged particles to follow an expanding spiral path in a magnetic field and periodically subjecting the particles in the stream to a potential difference. The general arrangement is somewhat as in Fig. 39-1. The heart of the cyclotron is within an evacuated enclosure (this enclosure is not shown). It consists of two hollow metal "dees" which resemble a tremendous metal salve box cut open along a diameter. These dees lie in a horizontal position between the poles of a powerful magnet which maintains a strong vertical magnetic field within the dees. A high-frequency alternating voltage is applied to the dees by powerful oscillators, the phases of the potential applied to the two dees differing by 180°.

In auxiliary apparatus, protons may be produced by ionizing hydrogen, or alpha particles generated by ionizing helium doubly, etc. These ions are led into the chamber and injected at the center, at an instant when the phase of the potential between the dees is such that the electric field accelerates the ions toward one of the dees. Since the ion carries a positive charge, it moves toward the dee which is negative at the moment. Once inside the hollow dee, the particles drift, since the electric field always is zero within a hollow conductor.

Any charged particle moving in a magnetic field is subjected to a force, however, and this force is perpendicular to both the magnetic field and the velocity of the particle. Hence the ions follow a path which is a circular arc within the dee. This means that they must reach the open face and emerge into the space between the dees. If at this instant the phase of the voltage has reversed so that the dee from which the ions emerge is positive and the other negative, the ions will receive a second "kick"; their kinetic energy and hence their velocity will be augmented. If this sort of thing can be repeated enough times, a large quantity of energy can be stored up in an ion; but this requires that ions always pass from one dee to the other when the phase of the applied accelerating voltage is appropriate. This is equivalent to saying that the time the particle requires for half a circuit must be the time for a 180° phase change, or the time necessary for one complete circuit must be the period of the accelerating AC voltage.

In the case of the cyclotron, it is obvious that a centripetal force must act on the ion to constrain it to a curved path and that the source of this force must be the interaction of the magnetic field with the charge carried by the ion. Equation (8-23), for the centripetal force, is

$$F_c = \frac{mv^2}{r}$$

and Eq. (26-6), for the force on an electric charge moving at right angles to a magnetic field, is

$$F = \frac{Bqv}{c}$$

In these equations, m is the mass of the ion, in grams; v its speed, in cm/sec; q the charge it carries, in esu; r the radius of the curved path it follows, in cm; B the intensity of the magnetic field, in gauss; and c has a numerical value of $3 \cdot 10^{10}$. In this case, both equations represent the same force, so

$$\frac{mv^2}{r} = \frac{Bqv}{c}$$

Cancellation of one v on each side, and rearrangement, yields

$$v = \frac{Bqr}{mc}$$

The time required for an ion to make one complete circuit of the dees is the distance divided by the speed, or $2\pi r/v$; hence,

$$t = 2\pi r \div \frac{Bqr}{mc} = \frac{2\pi r \cdot mc}{Bqr} = \frac{2\pi mc}{Bq}$$

$$t = \frac{2\pi c}{B} \cdot \frac{m}{q} \qquad (39\text{-}1)$$

Since the values of B and c are constant, and the magnetic field is uniform over the path of the ions, this equation means that all ions which have the same ratio of mass to charge will make one circuit in the same time interval. But, more important, the radius has dropped out of the equation; and this means that the time interval will be the same for each of the many circuits an ion makes while completing its spiral and acquiring its maximum energy. Hence the alternating voltage may have a constant frequency, its period being given by Eq. (39-1).

With earlier cyclotrons, this analysis was valid, as far as it goes, though it is far from the whole story. However, it is inadequate for the more powerful cyclotrons, such as the one at the University of California.* During its first several turns an ion will maintain synchronization with the AC applied to the dees, but as its energy continues to increase, it falls a

* This machine has pole pieces 184 in. in diameter, and the magnetic field between them is of the order of 15,000 gauss.

bit behind; and this sets a limit on the maximum energy obtainable. The cause of this is the increase in the mass of the ion as its energy is augmented. According to Eq. (39-1), an increase in the mass will lengthen the time required to complete a turn of the spiral. To compensate for the relativistic increase in the mass, the oscillators of the University of California cyclotron were redesigned so that as the ions move outward on their spiral path the frequency of the AC decreased just enough to allow the ions to stay in synchronization with the applied voltage. This change had two very important results: it made a significant increase in the maximum energy the cyclotron could give to particles, and it furnished dramatic confirmation of the reality of the relativistic increase in mass.

When sufficient energy has been given to the ions, an auxiliary electric field deflects them against a target, and the ions interact with the nuclei of the atoms in the target.

Charged particles may be given high energies by any of several methods or by a combination of methods. Uncharged particles, however, cannot be accelerated in this manner. Neutrons, for example, must be produced indirectly, as the result of a nuclear reaction initiated by some charged particle.

39-4 General Types of Nuclear Reactions

Target materials for nuclear reactions include all the naturally occurring and artificially prepared nuclides there are. Possible bombarding particles include electrons, neutrons, protons, deuterons, tritons, and alpha particles, and sometimes more massive particles.* Of these, all are familiar except the deuteron and the triton. A ***deuteron*** is the nucleus of an atom of the ${}_1H^2$ isotope of hydrogen, which is called "deuterium." The ${}_1H^3$ isotope of hydrogen is called "tritium," and a ***triton*** is a nucleus of a tritium atom.

In the broad sense, nuclear reactions include scattering processes, such as we met in connection with Rutherford's alpha scattering experiment, processes in which the only change is an excitation which results in the emission of a gamma photon, and processes in which a particle enters the nucleus and a particle of the same kind is ejected. However, we shall confine our attention to reactions in which one nuclide is changed into another; there are far more variations of this kind of reaction than we can consider.

In general, a bombarding particle enters the target nucleus, forming a compound nucleus which may exist for a period of the order of 10^{-12} sec. What happens at the end of that time depends on the identities of the bombarding particle and the target nucleus and on the energy delivered to the nucleus by the particle. A gamma photon may be emitted, the

* Element number 103, lawrencium (Lw) was "discovered" early in 1961 by bombarding californium (atomic number 98) with nuclei of boron (atomic number 5).

bombarding particle remaining in the nucleus and no other particle being ejected. A single particle, usually a proton, a neutron, or an alpha particle, may be emitted; in relatively few but very important cases, much larger particles may be ejected. There may be two or more particles emitted, especially if the bombarding particle has a relatively high energy.

Some compound nuclei apparently can break down in only one way; only one combination of products results. On the other hand, other compound nuclei may give rise to any of a half dozen or so different combinations of products.

For identifying a particular type of nuclear reaction, a sort of shorthand symbolism has developed. According to this shorthand representation, if a reaction was initiated by a proton and one product was a neutron, this would be a (p, n) reaction; if the particle ejected from the compound nucleus had been an alpha particle, it would have been a (p, α) reaction. Similarly, in an (n, γ) reaction, a nucleus is bombarded by a neutron and emits only a gamma photon; and in a (p, d) reaction, the bombarding particle is a proton and a deuteron is emitted. In this symbolism a deuteron is represented by d and a triton by t, though in equations of the sort in Sec. 39-2 the corresponding symbols usually are D and T, respectively. This corresponds to the similar use of p and H for the proton in the two types of equation; on the other hand α is most common in both types of equation, though sometimes He is used instead of α in the type in Sec. 39-2. The expression for the energy of a photon, $h\nu$, may be used in a detailed equation to represent a gamma photon, but γ is nearly always employed in "shorthand" equations.

39-5 Proton-induced Reactions

The first reaction produced by artificial means was the proton-induced reaction given in the latter part of Sec. 39-2; this was a (p, 2α) reaction. Among other types of proton-induced reactions are (p, α), (p, d), and (p, γ) reactions. Examples of these, in that order, are:

$$_{11}Na^{23} + {}_1H^1 \rightarrow {}_{10}Ne^{20} + {}_2\alpha^4$$

$$_4Be^9 + {}_1H^1 \rightarrow {}_4Be^8 + {}_1H^2$$

$$_3Li^7 + {}_1H^1 \rightarrow {}_4Be^8 + \gamma$$

39-6 Deuteron-induced Reactions

Reaction types initiated by deuterons include (d, p) and (d, n) reactions. Examples are:

$$_3Li^7 + {}_1H^2 \rightarrow {}_3Li^8 + {}_1H^1$$

$$_{46}Pd^{105} + {}_1H^2 \rightarrow {}_{47}Ag^{106} + {}_0n^1$$

39-7 Photon-induced Reactions

Two of the types of reaction caused by photons are (γ, n) and (γ, 2p) reactions, such as:

$$_1H^2 + \gamma \rightarrow {}_1H^1 + {}_0n^1$$

$$_{13}Al^{27} + \gamma \rightarrow {}_{11}Na^{25} + {}_1H^1 + {}_1H^1$$

39-8 Alpha-induced Reactions

Included among the types of reactions due to alpha particles are (α, p), (α, n), and (α, 2n) reactions. Examples are:

$$_7N^{14} + {}_2\alpha^4 \rightarrow {}_8O^{17} + {}_1H^1$$

$$_{13}Al^{27} + {}_2\alpha^4 \rightarrow {}_{15}P^{30} + {}_0n^1$$

$$_{83}Bi^{209} + {}_2\alpha^4 \rightarrow {}_{85}At^{211} + {}_0n^1 + {}_0n^1$$

The first of these is the original nuclear reaction discovered by Rutherford and Chadwick, and the last is the reaction by which the element astatine, which does not occur naturally, was prepared. Another historically important nuclear reaction is the (α, n) reaction which led to the discovery of the neutron:

$$_4Be^9 + {}_2\alpha^4 \rightarrow {}_6C^{12} + {}_0n^1$$

39-9 Neutron-induced Reactions

Reactions due to neutrons fall into two distinct classes, one including reactions similar to those in the preceding sections and the other being a quite different type. We shall consider a few of the usual type in this section, and return to the other type in Sec. 39-13. Reactions of (n, α), (n, p), (n, γ), and (n, 2n) types are observed. Examples are:

$$_{11}Na^{23} + {}_0n^1 \rightarrow {}_9F^{20} + {}_2\alpha^4$$

$$_{16}S^{32} + {}_0n^1 \rightarrow {}_{15}P^{32} + {}_1H^1$$

$$_{79}Au^{197} + {}_0n^1 \rightarrow {}_{79}Au^{198} + \gamma$$

$$_{51}Sb^{121} + {}_0n^1 \rightarrow {}_{51}Sb^{120} + {}_0n^1 + {}_0n^1$$

39-10 Variety in Nuclear Reactions

Neither the listing of types nor their illustration by examples, in the preceding sections, should be considered exhaustive. A complete compilation of types or examples would be out of place in an introductory physics text even if space were available.

Variety may exist also, as previously mentioned, in the modes of disintegration of a compound nucleus. For example, a compound nucleus $_{30}Zn^{65}$ formed by the bombardment of Cu^{63} nuclei by deuterons has been found experimentally to give any of at least five sets of products. These reactions, and their types, are:

$$_{29}Cu^{63} + {}_1D^2 \rightarrow {}_{30}Zn^{64} + {}_0n^1 \qquad \text{(d, n)}$$

$$_{29}Cu^{63} + {}_1D^2 \rightarrow {}_{30}Zn^{63} + {}_0n^1 + {}_0n^1 \qquad \text{(d, 2n)}$$

$$_{29}Cu^{63} + {}_1D^2 \rightarrow {}_{29}Cu^{64} + {}_1H^1 \qquad \text{(d, p)}$$

$$_{29}Cu^{63} + {}_1D^2 \rightarrow {}_{29}Cu^{62} + {}_1T^3 \qquad \text{(d, t)}$$

$$_{29}Cu^{63} + {}_1D^2 \rightarrow {}_{28}Ni^{61} + {}_2\alpha^4 \qquad (\text{d}, \alpha)$$

39-11 Induced Radioactivity

Nuclides which exist only as products of nuclear reactions, having no counterparts in nature, are typically radioactive whatever their atomic number, although (as noted in Sec. 37-2) there are rather few naturally occurring radionuclides of atomic number 82 or less. Many of these artificial radionuclides are negative beta emitters, like a considerable portion of natural radioactive nuclides. On the other hand, although natural alpha emitters are common, only about nine artificial nuclides exhibit alpha decay. Three of these have mass numbers of 8 or 9 and simply disintegrate into two alphas, or a proton and two alphas, the half lives varying from 0.5 sec down to about 10^{-19} sec. The other half dozen undergo more normal alpha decay; all are rare earth nuclides, their half lives ranging from 4 hr to over 10^7 yr.

Instead of alpha decay, most artificial radionuclides emit positrons—positive electrons or positive beta particles. However, there also is a less common type of decay, which will be considered in the second paragraph below.

The emission of a positron (positive beta particle) from a nucleus which contains only protons and neutrons raises the same sort of question that arose when we met ordinary beta emission (Sec. 37-6). The answer is similar; the over-all effect is the conversion of a proton to a positron and a neutron. There is evidence, however, that this conversion is indirect; apparently the excitation energy creates an electron-positron pair, the electron combining with a proton and converting it to a neutron, and the positron being emitted.

Some artificial radionuclides which might be expected to emit positive betas undergo an unusual type of reaction instead. For example, the following (d, p) reaction on copper may be carried out, and the nature of the products verified beyond doubt:

$$_{29}Cu^{63} + {}_1H^2 \rightarrow {}_{29}Cu^{64} + {}_1H^1$$

The Cu^{64} is radioactive, with a half life of 12.8 hr, part of it decaying by negative beta and part by positive beta emission. But there is also emission of gamma photons, and these include photons in the characteristic K series X-ray spectrum of *nickel!* What has happened to produce these photons is this: the nucleus has captured an electron from the K shell, leaving a "hole," and the electron which fills this "hole" emits a K X-ray photon in so doing (Sec. 34-10). Meantime, the captured K electron has converted a proton to a neutron, thereby reducing the atomic number by one. This may be represented by the equation:

$$_{29}Cu^{64} + {}_{-1}\beta^0 \rightarrow {}_{28}Ni^{64} + \gamma$$

This type of reaction is called ***K electron capture.***

39-12 Nuclear Stability

Why is it that some nuclides are stable, others tend to emit alpha particles, emit positrons, or capture K electrons, while still others tend to emit negative beta particles? The basis of this is the relationship between the number of protons and the number of neutrons in the nucleus. In Fig. 39-2 are two lines, a straight one and a curved one. For any point on the straight line, the number of protons in the nucleus is equal to the number of neutrons. Only one stable nuclide has a composition which would put it below this straight line (fewer neutrons than protons); this is $_2He^3$, which constitutes only 0.00013% of natural helium. Many nuclides of atomic number up through 20 fall on the straight line (equal numbers of protons and neutrons), though all but one of these has at least one stable isotope with more neutrons. Above atomic number 20, no stable nuclide falls on the straight line; all have more neutrons than protons, and as the atomic number goes up, the number of neutrons increases more rapidly than the number of protons does.

Thus, all the stable nuclides fall within a rather narrow band centered on the curved line in the chart. If a band were drawn in place of this curved line, its edges would have to be somewhat irregular or diffuse, so only the median line is shown.

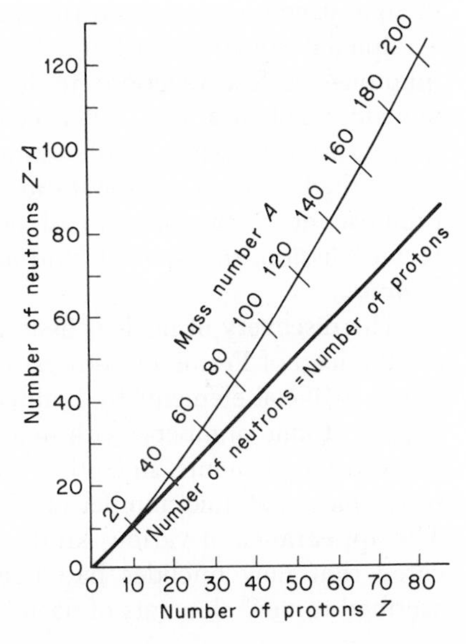

Fig. 39-2. Relation between number of neutrons and number of protons in stable nuclei.

For any nuclide which lies above and to the left of the band of stable nuclei, the ratio of the number of neutrons to the number of protons is abnormally large. If such a nuclide is to achieve stability, therefore, it must reduce the number of neutrons or increase the number of protons; and it can do both these things at once if a neutron changes to a proton plus an electron, the electron being ejected as a beta particle.

On the other hand, the neutron-proton ratio is abnormally low for any nuclide which lies below and to the right of the band of stable nuclides. Any change in the direction of greater stability must increase this ratio. Heavy natural radionuclides with a low neutron-proton ratio emit alpha particles; this reduces the number of neutrons by the same *number* as it does the number of protons, but since there are fewer protons it reduces their number by a larger *percentage.* The usual process for less massive artificial radionuclides with a low neutron-proton ratio is positive beta emission, which reduces the number of protons by one and increases the number of neutrons by one. The neutron-proton ratio may also be raised by K electron capture, since this process changes a proton to a neutron.

39-13 The Fission Process

Thus far, nearly every nuclear reaction we have met,* whether natural or artificial, and whatever its type, has involved a change of two or less in the atomic number. Except in the case of relatively few reactions involving nuclides of low mass number, one product of the reaction has been comparatively massive and the other particle has had a mass, in amu, of 4 (alpha particle), 3 (triton), 2 (deuteron), 1 (proton or neutron), or 0 (photon). A few reactions in which a neutron impinges on a massive nuclide result in a very different type of reaction, however; the nucleus splits into two portions of comparable mass, with a few neutrons as by-products. Since this separation of a nucleus into two major portions is reminiscent of the division of certain single-cell organisms, a process termed fission, this special kind of nuclear reaction is known as ***nuclear fission.***

The discovery of nuclear fission was another historic accident. Following the lead of Fermi and others, Hahn and Strassman were attempting to create artificial elements by bombarding uranium—the natural element of highest atomic number—with neutrons. Such artificial elements are called ***transuranic*** elements, since their atomic numbers exceed that of uranium, which has an atomic number of 92. (See the lowest section of Table 36-1.) The appearance of various kinds and energies of nuclear radiations indicated that new nuclides had been formed, and these radiations were ascribed to new elements of atomic number greater than 92. In part, this

* The sole exception appeared in a footnote in Sec. 39-4.

conclusion was correct. However, by applying standard chemical procedures used to separate and identify a trace of one element in the presence of a relatively large quantity of other elements, Hahn and Strassman found evidence that an isotope of barium—atomic number 56—was present. Here was something startling; bombardment of an element of atomic number 92 with neutrons produced a trace of an element of atomic number 56! How did this happen, and what became of the other 36 protons in the original uranium nucleus?

The correct interpretation is usually ascribed to Frisch and Meitner, and to physicists today it seems quite obvious; but at the time it was offered it represented a sharp departure from the descriptions of previously observed nuclear reactions. The explanation is that the uranium nucleus splits, or undergoes fission, into two comparable parts, and that if one of them contains 56 of the original 92 protons the other must contain 92 − 56, or 36, protons. This must be a krypton nucleus, since the atomic number of krypton is 36. It developed that free neutrons also were produced. The reaction may be symbolized as follows:

$$_{92}\mathrm{U} + {_0}\mathrm{n} \rightarrow {_{56}}\mathrm{Ba} + {_{36}}\mathrm{Kr} + (x){_0}\mathrm{n}$$

Mass numbers are not specified because various different isotopes of the product nuclei result, and for the same reason, no definite number of free neutrons produced can be stated; hence the ambiguous x is used.

The variety of products of this fission reaction is vastly greater than the equation above implies, however, for it was found very soon that any of many other pairs of product nuclei might result; they might be $_{55}\mathrm{Cs} + {_{37}}\mathrm{Rb}$, or $_{19}\mathrm{K} + {_{73}}\mathrm{Ta}$, or any other combination such that the sum of the two atomic numbers—that is, the total number of protons—is 92.* If we use Pn to symbolize any product nucleus, Z for the atomic number of one product nucleus and (92 − Z) for that of the other, the generalized equation for the fission process is

$$_{92}\mathrm{U} + {_0}\mathrm{n} \rightarrow {_Z}\mathrm{Pn} + {_{(92-Z)}}\mathrm{Pn} + (x){_0}\mathrm{n} \qquad (39\text{-}2)$$

Though any pair of products which could be described by Eq. (39-2) is *possible*, all such pairs are not equally probable. The highest probability is that the two mass numbers should be about 95 and 139. The probability of the two fragments having essentially equal masses is about 0.1% of this maximum probability, and the probability of one fragment having a mass number of 70 is only about 10^{-6} as great as the chance that it will have a mass number of 95.

In Chapter 40, on nuclear energy, we shall return to the topic of fission

* Comparatively rarely, the nucleus splits into three or more fragments, (not counting free neutrons) which contain a total of 92 protons. Such multiple splitting is termed ***spallation*** rather than fission.

and to certain pertinent nuclear reactions. Before we turn to the next topic, however, recall that the discussion in Sec. 36-8 – 36-10, and Fig. 36-3, contain what is in effect a prediction of the possibility of obtaining energy from fission.

39-14 Fusion Processes

The discussion and diagram referred to in the preceding paragraph also carry an implied prediction of energy release as the result of combining nuclei of very light atoms to form a somewhat more massive nucleus. Such reactions are called ***fusion reactions,*** or since they occur spontaneously only at extreme temperatures, ***thermonuclear reactions.***

Since the very beginnings of astrophysics, the continued emission of tremendous quantities of energy by stars has been a mystery. The sun radiates energy at the amazing rate of 6.25 *kw from each square centimeter,** and evidently has been doing so for billions of years. Much of the mystery of the source of such fabulous quantities of energy has been dispelled by the discovery of chains of nuclear fusion reactions which have the end result of building helium nuclei from protons. Two such chains have been devised, and their steps verified and studied on a laboratory scale. It is believed that stellar energies have their origin in these series of nuclear reactions, though in general it has not been possible to determine which of the two chains of fusion reactions is primarily responsible for the energy of a given star.

The first series suggested is known as the ***carbon cycle*** or the ***carbon-nitrogen cycle*** because both carbon and nitrogen nuclei are involved but are not permanently changed.† Since the process is cyclic, one may commence with the equation for any one of the steps, but it is customary to record first the equation in which C^{12} is a reactant. After the other equations are listed, in order, the net or over-all equation is deduced by adding up the separate equations and canceling items which appear on both sides. The equations are:

$$\begin{aligned}
{}_6C^{12} + {}_1H^1 &\rightarrow {}_7N^{13} + \gamma \\
{}_7N^{13} &\rightarrow {}_6C^{13} + {}_{+1}\beta^0 \\
{}_6C^{13} + {}_1H^1 &\rightarrow {}_7N^{14} + \gamma \\
{}_7N^{14} + {}_1H^1 &\rightarrow {}_8O^{15} \\
{}_8O^{15} &\rightarrow {}_7N^{15} + {}_{+1}\beta^0 \\
{}_7N^{15} + {}_1H^1 &\rightarrow {}_6C^{12} + {}_2He^4 \\
\hline
4({}_1H^1) &\rightarrow {}_2He^4 + 2({}_{+1}\beta^0)
\end{aligned} \tag{39-3}$$

---

* This is 54 hp from each square inch!

† In the chemist's terminology, the carbon and nitrogen nuclei might be considered to be catalysts.

More recently, a series called the ***proton-proton chain*** has been worked out:

$$
\begin{aligned}
{}_1H^1 + {}_1H^1 &\rightarrow {}_1H^2 + {}_{+1}\beta^0 \\
{}_1H^2 + {}_1H^1 &\rightarrow {}_2He^3 + \gamma \qquad (39\text{-}4) \\
{}_2He^3 + {}_2He^3 &\rightarrow {}_2He^4 + {}_1H^1 + {}_1H^1
\end{aligned}
$$

Before this series of reactions is summed up, the first two equations must be doubled to provide the two ${}_2He^3$ nuclei needed for the third equation; and when this is done, the over-all reaction is found to be identical with that we found for the carbon-nitrogen cycle.

It is believed that the source of the sun's energy is primarily the second of these two series of fusion reactions, the series grouped together as Eq. (39-4).

If means can be developed for initiating and controlling fusion reactions on a commercial basis, they will open up virtually unlimited supplies of energy.

Summary

Artificial nuclear reactions can be carried out by using radiations from a radioactive substance or by employing particles accelerated in some machine designed for the purpose. One such machine is the cyclotron.

A nuclear reaction may take place between any nucleus and any of several kinds of bombarding particles including photons. Most commonly, a *new nucleus* results, the change in atomic number ranging from $+1$ to -2 (including zero) and the mass number changing by a correspondingly small number; and one, or a very few, particles, such as beta particles, protons, photons, etc., are by-products. In relatively few instances which involve massive nuclei, a neutron may cause the nucleus to undergo *fission*, splitting into two comparable fragments plus extra neutrons.

The *products* of *nuclear reactions* are *radioactive*. Those with a high proton-neutron ratio commonly decay by positron emission, though some capture a *K* electron; those with a high neutron-proton ratio are (negative) beta emitters.

Fusion reactions which take place in a number of successive steps are responsible for stellar energy, and may become highly important as a commercial source of energy.

Self-Quiz

1. Why do alpha particles, such as those used by Rutherford and Chadwick, have a definite range?

2. Derive Eq. (39-1). What is the significance of this equation?

3. Modify the derivation to show that the angular velocity ω of an ion ($= v/r$) is the same for the last turn of the spiral as for the first.

4. According to Eq. (8-23), how will an increase of mass affect the value of the radius, other things being equal? What is the practical result of this in the cyclotron? Why need an increase of mass be considered at all? What is done to compensate for the effect of the mass increase?

5. Assume that different samples of $_{48}Cd^{110}$ undergo reactions of the following types. In each case write a balanced equation and identify the resulting nuclide. (α, p), (α, 2n), (d, p), (p, n), and (n, p).

6. The two stable isotopes of silver have mass numbers of 107 and 109. For each of the following isotopes indicate the type of decay to be expected, write a balanced equation for the process, and identify the daughter nuclide: $_{47}Ag^{103}$, $_{47}Ag^{112}$. For which of the two isotopes may an alternate type of decay be possible? State the type of decay, write the balanced equation, and identify the daughter nuclide.

7. In what marked respect does fission differ from other nuclear reactions? Write the generalized balanced equation for fission. Write equations for two specific examples other than those given in Sec. 39-13, and identify the products.

8. Write, in order, the balanced equations for the separate reactions of the carbon-nitrogen cycle and sum them up to obtain the equation for the over-all reaction.

9. Repeat Question 8 for the proton-proton series.

10. In a star within which the carbon-nitrogen cycle is predominant, what four elements are involved in the reactions? Of these, which, if any, is increasing in quantity? Which, if any, is decreasing? Which, if any, remains unchanged in quantity?

11. If the proton-proton series is predominant, what element or elements are involved? Which, if any, is increasing in quantity, which decreasing, and which unchanged?

12. Compare your answers to the last two questions, and explain.

Problems

1. In the 184 in. synchro-cyclotron at the Radiation Laboratory of the University of California, deuterons cover a spiral path of approximately 10^4 turns in about 10^{-3} sec. Compute the approximate value of the intensity of the magnetic field. (Take the mass of a deuteron as $3.34 \cdot 10^{-24}$ g.)

2. At the same laboratory, protons are accelerated to an energy of 6.2 Bev in the bevatron. The mass of a proton may be taken as $1.67 \cdot 10^{-24}$ g. Using the relativistic equation for kinetic energy, determine the fraction of the speed of light attained by the protons.

3. Calculate the minimum energy in Mev an alpha particle must have to cause an (α, p) reaction with $_7N^{14}$. The masses of an alpha particle, a $_7N^{14}$ atom, an

$_8O^{17}$ atom, a proton, and an electron are, respectively, 4.002775, 14.007528, 17.004537, 1.007593 and 0.000549 amu. (Make use of the fact that 1 amu = 931 Mev.)

4. Compute the minimum energy required for an alpha particle to produce an (α, p) reaction with $_{16}S^{32}$, and identify the product nuclide. The mass of $_{16}S^{32}$ is 31.982239 and that of the product atom is 34.979972. Other masses are given in the preceding problem.

5. Identify the product nuclide resulting from a (γ, 2p) reaction with $_{13}Al^{27}$. Compute the minimum energy the gamma photon must have, in Mev, and calculate the wavelength of the photon. (The mass of the $_{13}Al^{27}$ atom is 26.99011 amu and that of the product atom is 24.99715 amu.)

6. Taking the mass of an alpha particle as 4.002775 amu, calculate the energy in ergs and in Mev produced by one cycle of the carbon-nitrogen cycle.

7. Using the energy value computed in the preceding problem, calculate (a) the number of protons which would be required to produce 1 kilowatt hour (kwhr) of energy and (b) the mass of hydrogen represented by this number of protons.

8. Mercury can be transmuted into gold by a (n, d) reaction on $_{80}Hg^{198}$. The masses of the mercury atom, neutron, gold atom, and deuteron are 198.0303, 1.008986, 197.0298, and 2.01474, respectively. There are $8.67 \cdot 10^{22}$ atoms in 1 oz of gold. Compute (a) the energy in ergs required to produce one atom of gold by this method, (b) the energy needed to produce 1 oz of gold, and (c) the cost of this energy at 2.00 cents per kwhr.

9. By making use of Avogadro's number and other pertinent data, confirm that 1 amu = 931 Mev.

40
NUCLEAR ENERGY

40-1 Preview

In Sec. 36-8 – 36-10, inclusive, we learned of mass defects and met the concept of binding energy, with its implications that either the splitting of a massive nucleus into two comparable fragments or the fusion of very light nuclei into a somewhat more massive nucleus should release energy. We considered the first of these processes in Sec. 39-13 and the second in Sec. 39-14. Energy produced by a reaction of either type, fission or fusion, respectively, is termed ***nuclear energy*** *since its origin is the nucleus of the atom.* In this chapter, we shall make a brief survey of the production and application of nuclear energy.*

40-2 Perspective

When the possibility of obtaining energy from nuclear reactions was first suggested, this idea seemed startlingly new and different from anything in the past experience of the human race. Even today, many people view nuclear energy in this same light. Some actually have been afraid of using electricity which was produced from nuclear energy.

The fact is that nuclear energy is by no means new; it is one of the oldest attributes of the universe. Edison's original electric power system produced electric energy from nuclear energy, and the same is true of every electric power system since. Whether electric generators are turned by steam turbines or by water power, the energy used to turn them came ultimately from the sun. It was the sun's energy which made possible the existence and growth of the plants and other organisms which, over the ages, became the coal, oil, or gas used to fire boilers; it was the sun's energy which evaporated water to form the clouds which delivered rain to the hydroelectric reservoirs. And as we found in Sec. 39-14, nuclear reactions constitute the source of the energy given off by the sun or by any other star. Thus the ultimate source of energy of a conventional generating plant is the same as that of a nuclear power plant, though the conventional plant makes the conversion from nuclear to electric energy much less directly; and the most common kind of energy in the universe is nuclear energy.

40-3 The Importance of Nuclear Energy

Until the middle of the twentieth century, the world's industrial economy was based on water power and the energy derived by burning the so-called fossil fuels: coal, petroleum, and natural gas. There is an obvious limit to the energy available from hydroelectric sources, and there is a somewhat more elastic limit to the world's supply of fossil fuels. Discovery of new oil fields has nullified the predictions made by some people early in this century that our stock of fossil fuels would be exhausted even before the present time. The development of practical processes for the recovery of petroleum from oil shale will greatly augment the store of energy available to the world from fossil fuels. Nevertheless, the ever-increasing demands of our industrial civilization for energy unavoidably will exhaust the fossil fuels of the earth at some time in the future; a recent estimate set the time at about 2100 A.D.

---

* Outside of scientific journals, the term "atomic energy" rather than nuclear energy was applied, perhaps because the concept of the atom was more familiar to non-scientists than the concept of the nucleus. Fortunately, the better term, "nuclear energy," is appearing more commonly in the popular press.

Nuclear energy offers an additional source of energy. The fission of all the atoms in 1 pound of U^{235} would produce as much energy as the complete combustion of 2.4 million pounds—1200 tons—of the best coal! Though this potential source of energy is sufficient to supply our needs for a very long time, fission unavoidably results in the production of very highly radioactive fission products; and the problem of the safe storage or disposal of these may preclude the continued use of energy from fission on a scale comparable with the present rate of energy consumption.

There remains the possibility of learning how to produce a controlled fusion reaction on a commercial basis. The ${}_1H^2$ isotope of hydrogen, called "deuterium," is present in natural hydrogen to the extent of 0.015%; and though this is a rather small percentage, the oceans contain a tremendous quantity of deuterium. This can be separated from the ${}_1H^1$ isotope without great difficulty and—in theory, and perhaps eventually in commercial practice—used in the last two reactions of the set of equations identified as Eq. (39-4), or in some equivalent process. If such a process can be developed, the energy available from the deuterium in 1 gallon of sea water will be equivalent to that obtainable from over 500 gallons of gasoline! Furthermore, such a reaction would produce "clean"—nonradioactive—products instead of the highly radioactive products of a fission reaction, although neutrons produced in the reaction would tend to render the environment of the reactor strongly radioactive. However, the production of energy by a fusion process will not be achieved commercially in the immediate future. A release by the United States Atomic Energy Commission in 1960 made the following statements: it was not certain that controlled fusion had been achieved even on a laboratory scale; a self-sustaining fusion reaction on a laboratory scale might be achieved in considerably less than a decade; the development of a machine or reactor which will have a sustained net power output "may well be fifteen to twenty years away"; and commercial power generation from fusion, at a cost comparable with other sources, was not expected for "several additional decades."

40-4 Fission: the Chain Reaction

The generalized equation for the fission process of uranium is given by Eq. (39-2):

$$ {}_{92}U + {}_0n \rightarrow {}_ZPn + {}_{(92-Z)}Pn + (x){}_0n $$

Three isotopes of uranium, with mass numbers of 233, 235, and 238, occur naturally. The last constitutes 99.27% of natural uranium, but it does not undergo fission unless the neutrons have exceptionally high energies. The lightest isotope constitutes only about 0.01% of natural uranium. Hence the isotope most convenient for fission is the 0.72% of uranium 235 occurring in natural uranium or the ${}_{92}U^{233}$ prepared from thorium^{232} in a breeder reactor (Sec. 40-11). One of the many possible fission reactions of U^{235} might be

$$_{92}U^{235} + {_0n^1} \rightarrow {_{42}Mo^?} + {_{50}Sn^?} + (?){_0n^1}$$

If you consult a suitable reference, you will find that the most massive stable isotopes of molybdenum (Mo) and tin (Sn) have mass numbers of 100 and 124, respectively; and the sum of these is 224. On the left side of the equation the total mass number is 235 + 1 or 236; thus it appears that there should be 12 free neutrons produced. Since 1 neutron was used in the reaction, apparently there should be a net gain of 11 free neutrons. For pairs of products other than molybdenum and tin, the situation is similar, though the actual number of free neutrons predicted would vary somewhat. All this is implied in Fig. 39-2, if we imagine the stability curve to be extended to mass number 235.

However, the number of free neutrons produced in a fission reaction turns out to be much smaller than such considerations predict; the statistical average of the number of free neutrons produced in the fission of one U^{235} nucleus by a "thermal" (relatively low-energy) neutron is roughly 2.5. This means that in general the ***fission fragments***—the nuclei resulting from the splitting of the original nucleus—will contain too many neutrons for stability. We shall return to this matter in Sec. 40-9 and again in Chapter 42.

Taken together, the facts that 1 neutron is used in each fission process, and that on the average about 2.5 neutrons are produced, indicate that a fission process in U^{235} may be self-sustaining. If at least one of the neutrons resulting from an initial fission causes fission of a second U^{235} nucleus, and if at least one of the neutrons from this second fission induces a third fission, etc., the reaction will continue at the same level. If on the average more than one neutron produced by a fission process induces a subsequent fission, the reaction will not only continue, it will proceed at an increasing rate. In either case, the process is self-sustaining. These self-propagating processes are called ***chain reactions.*** If on the other hand, on the average less than one neutron per fission induces a subsequent fission, the reaction will die down like a fire in wet fuel.

40-5 Fission: the Critical Mass

Whether or not a chain reaction will occur in U^{235} depends, as we have just seen, on the average number of the free neutrons produced by any one fission which induce fission reactions in other nuclei. The two major factors which operate to reduce this number and thus prevent a chain reaction are the escape of the free neutrons from the mass of U^{235} and their absorption by nuclei other than those of U^{235}.

The escape, or "leakage," of neutrons depends on the size and the geometrical shape of the mass of U^{235} used. The rate of production of neutrons by the fissioning nuclei will be determined by the number of atoms present, so it will be directly proportional to the volume of the uranium. Hence, if the uranium is in a solid spherical shape, the rate of production of free neutrons will be directly proportional to the cube of the radius of the sphere. On the other hand, neutrons can escape only through the surface, and the surface of the sphere is directly proportional to the square of the radius. Therefore the fraction of newly produced neutrons which escape will be proportional to r^2/r^3, or $1/r$; that is, it will be inversely proportional to the radius. Thus a chain reaction cannot occur in a very small body of U^{235} but it can take place in a sufficiently large body. Since a spherical shape minimizes the surface area, this is the best shape if a chain reaction is desired.

The minimum mass of U^{235}, or of any other fissionable material, which can support a chain reaction is called the ***critical mass*** of the material. Evidently the value of the critical mass depends on the shape; the critical mass for a cube of U^{235} would be considerably greater than for a sphere, and the critical mass of a thin sheet of U^{235} would be infinite, since nearly all the neutrons would escape.

The concept of critical mass becomes more nebulous if we take other factors than shape into account. Leakage of neutrons may be reduced if the fissionable material is surrounded by some substance which does not absorb neutrons, since some escaping neutrons will strike nuclei in this material and be reflected back toward the fissionable material. Obviously, the use of such a neutron reflector will reduce the critical mass. Also, neutrons may be supplied, other than those resulting from fission. For example, beryllium undergoes an (α, n) reaction (Sec. 39-8), and a combination of radium (to supply the α particles) and beryllium is commonly used as a laboratory source of neutrons. If such a neutron source is buried inside the mass of fissionable material, it will compensate for neutron leakage and thus reduce the critical mass. Use of both a neutron source and a neutron reflector evidently should reduce the critical mass considerably.

40-6 The Separation of U^{235} from U^{238}

We have noted previously that U^{238}, which constitutes about 99.3% of natural uranium, undergoes fission only if bombarded with neutrons of very high energies. With neutrons of less energy, it undergoes an (n, γ) reaction. This means that it absorbs neutrons but produces none, so its presence tends to snuff out the chain reaction of U^{235} fission. Trying to produce a chain reaction in natural uranium is like trying to make a fire in a pile of wooden sticks when 7 out of every 1000 sticks are dry and all the others are saturated with water. Hence the U^{235} must be separated from the U^{238}, or at least some of the U^{238} must be removed so that the percentage of U^{235} is very greatly augmented.

But how does one separate U^{235} from U^{238}? Various chemical methods are available for separating one element from another, but here we must separate two isotopes of the *same* element. Since they are isotopes, their chemical properties do not differ, and separation by chemical methods is impossible.*

There have been two principal approaches to this problem, both based on the mass difference of the two isotopes.

One is the gaseous diffusion process. According to the kinetic theory of gases, on the average the kinetic energy of any molecule of a gas is the same as that of any other molecule, whether the molecules are alike or not. Since the kinetic energy is equal to $mv^2/2$, where m is the mass of the molecule and v its velocity, Eq. (6-2), the effective average velocity of a molecule is inversely proportional to the square root of its mass; hence, less massive molecules will diffuse from place to place, or through a porous barrier, more rapidly than will more massive molecules.

The only feasible gaseous compound of uranium is uranium hexafluoride, UF_6. For U^{235} the weight of the hexafluoride molecule is about 349 amu, and about 352 for the hexafluoride of U^{238}. These values stand approximately in the ratio of 1.0000 to 1.0085; and, since the rate of diffusion depends on the square root of the mass, the ratio of diffusion rates is about 1.0000 to 1.0043. Thus the diffusion rate of the U^{235} compound will exceed that of the U^{238} compound by less than 0.5%; under the most ideal conceivable circumstances, the passage of the hexafluorides of natural uranium through a porous barrier would augment the proportion of U^{235} by less than 0.5%, increasing it from 0.72% to $1.005 \cdot 0.72\%$ or about 0.7236%. In practice, the enrichment of the U^{235} in the gas which has passed a barrier is perhaps a half or a third as great as this. Obviously, a tremendous number of cycles of passage through successive barriers is necessary; nevertheless, this is one of the two principal methods of separation.

The other of the major methods of separating U^{235} from U^{238} is an electromagnetic method. A device which is essentially a mass spectrograph (Sec. 36-5) causes U^{235} ions to collect at a different place than U^{238} ions, ions of the two kinds traversing slightly different paths because of their unequal masses.

40-7 The Production of Plutonium

Though U^{238} will undergo fission if bombarded with neutrons of very high energy, neutrons of less velocity do not induce fission of this nuclide.

* The difference between the masses of two isotopes may affect the *rate* of a chemical reaction slightly, and this fact may be used as the basis for partial separation of isotopes of light elements; but this approach becomes less useful as the atomic weight of the element increases.

Instead, they cause an (n, γ) reaction:

$$_{92}U^{238} + {}_0n^1 \rightarrow {}_{92}U^{239} + \gamma$$

The U^{239} is radioactive, being a beta emitter with a half life of 23.5 min:

$$_{92}U^{239} \rightarrow {}_{93}Np^{239} + {}_{-1}\beta^0$$

The daughter is neptunium, an element which does not exist in nature. It also is a beta emitter, having a half life of 2.3 days:

$$_{93}Np^{239} \rightarrow {}_{94}Pu^{239} + {}_{-1}\beta^0$$

The daughter product is plutonium. Like neptunium, it is an artificial element. It also is radioactive, but it is an alpha emitter with the very long half life of about 24,300 yr.

Pu^{239}, like U^{235}, is fissionable, and neutrons of ordinary energies are able to induce fission in it. Thus this series of reactions converts U^{238}, which is fissionable with such difficulty, into easily fissionable Pu^{239}.

40-8 Reactors

A ***nuclear reactor*** is any arrangement in which a self-sustaining nuclear chain reaction takes place. The fissionable material, commonly called the "fuel,"* is only part of such a reactor. An important component is a ***moderator,*** which may be any substance containing atoms of low atomic weight but lacking in nuclei which readily undergo any neutron-initiated reaction. Commonly employed moderators are graphite (carbon) and "heavy water," which is water in which the oxygen is combined with the H^2 isotope (deuterium) rather than with the far more common H^1 isotope. Provided that no nuclear reaction occurs, both kinetic energy and momentum are conserved when a neutron strikes a nucleus; and an analysis of this situation shows that the neutron will lose a greater part of its energy if it collides with a light nucleus than it would in a collision with a more massive nucleus. A neutron has a fairly high energy (though not enough to make fission of U^{238} possible as a chain reaction) when it is produced in a fission process; but after successive collisions with various nuclei in the moderator its energy is reduced to a value appropriate to cause fission of a U^{235} nucleus, which is much less likely to occur with a high-energy neutron than with one of relatively low energy.

---

* To exorcise some of the mystery uninitiated persons find in nuclear energy, terms appropriate to combustion are employed by many writers and lecturers. Thus, fissionable material is "fuel," the products of a fission process are "ashes," etc. Unfortunately, such terminology is misleading. Ordinary burning, or combustion, is a chemical process which involves the outer electrons of atoms and affects their nuclei not at all. Chemical properties and reactions have no pertinence to the production of nuclear energy, however; only the nuclei are involved. Thus terms like "fuel" and "ashes" are very misleading when applied to the production of nuclear energy.

A third component of a nuclear reactor, and an essential one, is some device for controlling the chain reaction. The reactor must be critical—that is, the neutron or neutrons resulting from the fission of one nucleus must, on the average, produce at least one subsequent fission; otherwise there would be no chain reaction. But if more than one new fission results from each prior fission, the reaction will "build up" and the nuclear reactor may become a nuclear bomb instead. Hence, means must be available for removing some neutrons if the reaction tends to become dangerously rapid. The usual way of accomplishing this is to provide rods of cadmium which may be inserted more or less deeply into the reactor. The Cd^{113} isotope undergoes an (n, γ) reaction very readily, producing Cd^{114}; and this reaction removes neutrons which otherwise would be available to cause fission.

The fissionable material commonly is in the form of rods or strips, though in some reactors it is in the form of a soluble compound. The moderator may be in liquid or solid form, depending on its nature. The cadmium control rods are controlled automatically to maintain the reaction at the desired reaction level, the automatic control being supplemented with manual control. Most commonly, the control rods are suspended above the reactor, being lowered to reduce the rate of the reaction and partially withdrawn to increase it. The arrangements are such that any type of failure of the automatic controls will allow the rods to drop down, greatly increasing their absorption of neutrons and thus rendering the reactor subcritical.

In general, a reactor is interlaced with pipes through which some coolant may be circulated to remove the heat of the reaction from the reactor.

40-9 The Production of Radioisotopes

We have seen in the preceding chapter that a tremendous variety of nuclear reactions may be produced by bombarding matter with radiations of various kinds, and that some of these yield artificially radioactive products. In the following chapter, we shall meet a sampling of the great number of useful applications of these radioisotopes.

Since there is a copious flux of beta rays, gamma rays, and neutrons within a nuclear reactor, radioisotopes may be prepared by inserting appropriate material into openings provided for the purpose. This is the primary source of all artificial radionuclides produced.

40-10 Fission Products

In Sec. 40-4, we found that the mass number of a U^{235} nucleus exceeds the sum of the mass numbers of the most stable isotopes of the product nuclei by about ten, although there is no similar discrepancy in the atomic numbers. Though this means that we might expect some ten free neutrons to appear, on the average only about a fourth of this number actually are emitted. This means that at least one of the product nuclei contains more neutrons than are found in any stable isotope of that element; generally this is true of both product nuclei. We found in Sec. 39-12 that any nuclide for which the neutron-proton ratio is too high for stability is a beta emitter; hence we should expect that the nuclei resulting from a nuclear fission should be beta emitters, and this proves to be the case. The emission of a beta particle from some nuclides is accompanied by gamma radiation, but other nuclides are pure beta emitters. Furthermore, since not one but several extra neutrons are associated with the two product nuclei, a series of beta decays must be expected before both of the unstable product nuclei finally yield stable daughter nuclei. Various half lives will be involved though for the most part they will be reasonably short. Fairly typically, the level of radioactivity will be reduced by a factor of 10 in the first seven hours. However, the nuclides produced in a nuclear reactor, and their various daughter products, are so extremely varied that we cannot apply the concept of half life to this complex mixture in the manner appropriate for a single radioactive species. We shall return to this matter in Sec. 42-10.

The result of all this is that although the fissionable material put into a nuclear reactor is only very mildly radioactive* the products of the fission are very highly radioactive. This situation immediately demands some safe means of storing or disposing of the fission products; and how to do this is not a simple problem.

The matter is complicated by the fact that some fission products can enter into some sort of neutron-induced reaction; thus they absorb neutrons and tend to snuff out or "poison" the chain reaction after a time. Hence the mixture of fissionable material and fission products must be removed from the reactor after a time, the fission products removed by chemical means, the unused fissionable material recovered and put in the proper form for reuse in the reactor. Because of the high levels of radioactivity, all of the chemical and mechanical processes involved must be carried out by remote control.

40-11 Types of Fission Reactors

Reactors may be classified on a number of different bases. A very common basis of classification specifies the nature (chemical, physical, etc.)

* U^{235}, U^{238}, and Pu^{239} are all alpha emitters but their half lives are $7.1 \cdot 10^8$, $4.5 \cdot 10^9$, and $2.4 \cdot 10^4$ years, respectively. Though each has a long line of daughter products, the level of activity due to these is limited by the extreme slowness at which the first daughters are produced by the original nuclides.

of the fissionable material, the nature of the moderator, the means of cooling, the level of energy production, etc. Although highly important, this sort of classification is more appropriate to a text in nuclear engineering than to a general physics text. For our purposes, a more pertinent classification specifies the function for which the reactor is designed.

On this basis, a reactor may be classified as a research reactor, a power reactor, or a breeder reactor, though these functions are not necessarily mutually exclusive.

A research reactor is intended, as the term implies, primarily for investigation of nature. The spectrum of research may be very broad. It may have to do with the physics, chemistry, engineering, or economics of the reactor or any of its parts or components; it may be concerned with nuclear reactions induced in various materials subjected to the intense flux of neutrons and other radiations present in the reactor, or with the effects of these radiations on the materials of the reactor itself; it may be directed toward any of various aspects of the design or operation of a large reactor of which the research reactor is a prototype.

As is obvious, the purpose of a power reactor is producing power. To date, practical production of power has made use of a system closely similar to that employed in electric generating plants other than hydroelectric plants. In these, coal, oil, or gas is burned to heat a boiler, and the superheated steam (or other working substance) is led through turbines which drive generators. In a nuclear power plant, the source of heat is a nuclear reactor. A fluid circulates through the reactor somewhat as through a boiler. Commonly, this heated fluid is not used directly in the turbines but passes through a heat interchanger where its heat is absorbed by fluid in a second system, and this indirectly heated fluid drives the turbines.

A breeder reactor is so designed and controlled that, while some neutrons are used to produce fission and sustain the chain reaction, other neutrons are allowed to react with a non-fissionable nuclide to produce fissionable material. Thus a reactor using a mixture of U^{235} and U^{238} may serve any of the usual purposes of a reactor and at the same time convert U^{238} to Pu^{239} as discussed in Sec. 40-7. By the same series of reactions, a breeder reactor may convert non-fissionable ${}_{90}Th^{232}$ to fissionable U^{233}, the half life of the intermediate nuclides being respectively 23.5 min and 27.4 days in this case. The U^{233} is an alpha emitter with a half life of $1.6 \cdot 10^5$ yr.

Since U^{235} is the only readily fissionable nuclide occurring in nature, and because it constitutes only about 0.72% of natural uranium, the supply of fissionable materials would be severely limited, like the supply of fossil fuels, if we were restricted to naturally fissionable materials. However, almost 99.3% of natural uranium is U^{238}, which can be converted into fissionable Pu^{239}, and all of natural thorium is Th^{232}, which is convertible to fissionable U^{233}. Hence, breeding extends our potential supply of fissionable materials tremendously.

40-12 The Source of the Energy Released in a Fission Process

For many purposes, it is convenient to consider nuclear phenomena in terms of the so-called liquid drop model of a nucleus. The fact that the particles which comprise a nucleus remain together tells us that some force of mutual attraction is involved. These forces of mutual attraction would give rise to a phenomenon similar to the surface tension observed in a drop of liquid (Sec. 10-18). Though the cause of the effect is similar in the two cases, the effect is very many orders of magnitude stronger in the case of the nucleus, for it is sufficient to overcome the very strong mutual forces of repulsion of the protons within the nucleus.

On the basis of this liquid drop concept, consider Fig. 40-1. In part (a), the surface tension is sufficient to hold the parts of the nucleus to the right and left of the dotted line together against the mutual repulsions of the protons. Since surface tension is evaluated in terms of force per unit length, the force holding the nucleus together is the product of the surface tension and the equatorial circumference of the drop.

In part (b) of the figure, the neutron which was approaching the nucleus in part (a) has struck the nucleus and been absorbed. Its impact has distorted the nucleus, which has developed a "waist"; and the "waistline" is smaller than the original equatorial circumference. But since the force due to surface tension is the product of the surface tension and the distance, the reduction of the "waistline" has reduced the force holding the right and left portions of the nucleus together. In a fissionable nucleus, this reduction makes the cohesive force smaller than the mutually repulsive force, so the latter predominates, reducing the "waist" to a "neck" as in part (c) of the figure and finally separating the nucleus into two distinct portions. Each portion carries a positive charge (since it contains protons) and the mutual repulsion of these like charges causes the two portions of the nucleus to move apart at a high relative velocity.

Thus we see that the energy released in fission really is due to electrostatic repulsion and that it appears initially as kinetic energy of the newly formed nuclei.

The same process may be viewed from a different standpoint; we may consider the forces of mutual attraction between particles on opposite sides of the plane indicated by the dotted line in Fig. 40-1(a), and the

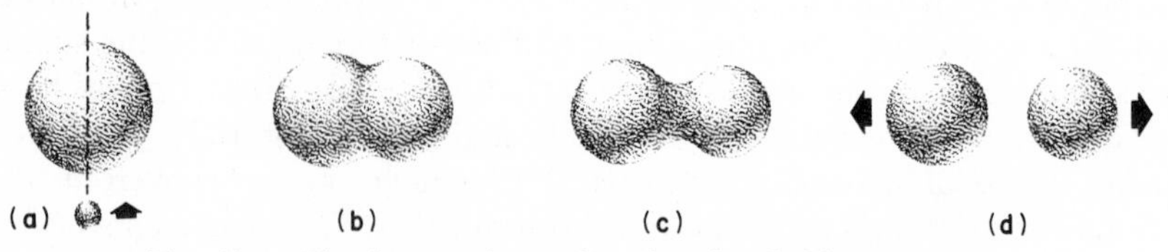

Fig. 40-1. The fission of a nucleus bombarded by a neutron.

mutual repulsions of the protons in these two parts of the nucleus. Ample evidence of various sorts tells us that the law governing the variation of the forces of mutual attraction with distance is not an inverse square law like so many of the force-distance relationships we have met; the magnitude of the force falls off much more rapidly than an inverse square law would require.

This means that although the appearance of a "waist" on the nucleus and the accompanying slight elongation of the nucleus will reduce the values of both the forces of attraction and those of repulsion, the former will be more strongly affected. Thus, though the forces of mutual attraction were able to predominate over the disruptive forces of repulsion while the nucleus was spherical, the appearance of the "waist" and the elongation of the nucleus allow the forces of electrostatic repulsion to become dominant. These forces then disrupt the nucleus and drive the two fragments apart.

40-13 Nuclear Weapons

Fission, fusion, and a combination of the two have been employed in nuclear weapons.

The first "atomic" bombs, which of course really were nuclear bombs, were straight fission bombs; the first and third such devices ever exploded used Pu^{239} and the second employed U^{235}. At least two different basic methods of detonating the bomb were employed.

One design is indicated schematically in Fig. 40-2(a); in effect it consists of two cannon barrels joined together at their mouths so that each fires toward the other. A charge of conventional explosive is placed behind a subcritical block of fissionable material. When the charges are fired, the two blocks of fissionable material are suddenly joined to form a single mass of supercritical size; and with no neutron absorbers present to control it, the chain reaction becomes violently explosive almost instantly. In principle and quite possibly in practice, three or more "cannon barrels" could be joined; as a rough approximation, if each block of fissionable material is just subcritical the total explosive energy available would be directly proportional to the number of individual masses, and hence directly proportional to the number of "cannon barrels" joined together.

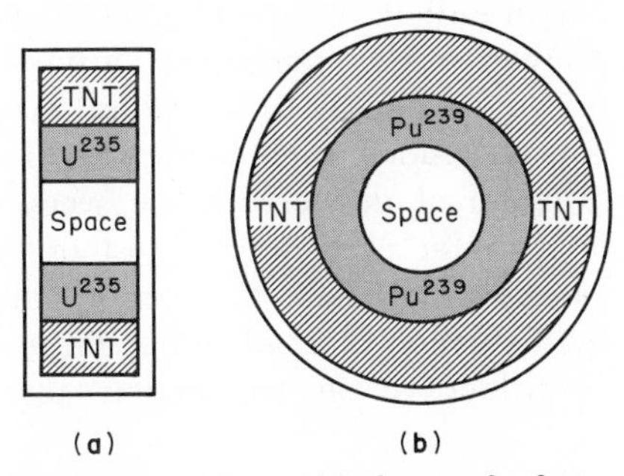

Fig. 40-2. Two possible forms of a fission weapon.

A different design is represented in part (b) of Fig. 40-2.

Here the fissionable material is in the form of a hollow sphere, the large exterior surface providing adequate "leakage" of neutrons to keep the mass subcritical. This sphere is surrounded with conventional explosive, which in turn is suitably encased. When the explosive charge is fired, the fissionable material is "imploded," forming a spherical mass at the center; and the reduction of its surface area renders it supercritical.

A fusion type weapon is variously referred to as a "hydrogen bomb," an "H-bomb," or a "thermonuclear weapon." It makes use of one or more of the fusion reactions previously discussed. We have seen that great difficulty has been encountered in the attempt to achieve a controlled fusion reaction in the laboratory, and this is due to the necessity of having an extremely high temperature and pressure to initiate the fusion reaction. In the weapon, these requirements are met by using a fission bomb as a fuse or detonator to initiate the fusion reaction. Early examples of this type of bomb made use of liquefied hydrogen,* which boils at about 20°K (−253°C); this was very inconvenient and difficult. Later models employed a solid compound of hydrogen, such as lithium hydride. In these, the lithium, as well as the hydrogen, enters into the fusion reaction.

In at least one instance, a fusion weapon encased in U^{238} was tested. The very high energy neutrons resulting from the fusion reaction caused the U^{238} to undergo fission; so this was a fission-fusion-fission weapon.

The energy yield of a nuclear weapon staggers the imagination. The first ones detonated yielded energy equivalent to that which would result from the explosion of ten to twenty thousand tons of trinitrotoluene (TNT) —10 to 20 kilotons. Later weapons, which employed fusion, multiplied this tremendous energy yield by a factor as high as a thousand; one such weapon may be equivalent to twenty million tons—20 megatons—of TNT.

What does 20 megatons of TNT mean? If you could pile that quantity of TNT on a football field, it would cover the field from sideline to sideline and from goal line to goal line—and it would be a little over 1.5 *miles* high!

A fusion type weapon, whether encased in U^{235} or not, is a virtually "open-ended" weapon. That is, no upper limit is placed by the laws of physics on the energy such a bomb could be designed to produce. The maximum energy such a bomb may be designed to yield is fixed only by considerations, such as the magnitude of the military effect desired, the problem of delivery of the weapon to the target, and the economics of manufacture; and the last of these probably is subject to the same factors which make the cost of waffle syrup, per ounce, less when bought by the gallon than when bought in a small bottle.

Added to the tremendous direct effect of the blast and heat of a

* As used here, "hydrogen" includes deuterium and/or tritium.

nuclear weapon are the indirect effect of a fire storm, the nuclear radiations generated during the explosion, the continuing radioactivity of the fission products, and perhaps additional nuclear radiations which have their origin in the induced radioactivity of other debris of the explosion. We shall consider these in Chapter 42.

Summary

Nuclear energy is as old as any other form of energy in the universe, and is the *most common* form. It appears that energy from nuclear reactors must replace that obtained from fossil fuels; within a century or so the supply of fossil fuels may approach exhaustion.

Nuclear energy may be produced by a *fission* or a *fusion* reaction. In either case, a *self-sustaining reaction* is a chain reaction. At present, all practical nuclear reactors employ fission. The ultimate source of the *energy* released in fission is electrostatic repulsion.

U^{235}, which constitutes less than 1% of natural uranium, is the only naturally occurring nuclide which will undergo fission when bombarded with low-energy neutrons. Its separation from U^{238} is very difficult and expensive. However, U^{238} will capture a low-energy neutron and, after two successive beta decays, it becomes Pu^{239}, which is fissionable. By an essentially identical process, non-fissionable Th^{232} may be converted into fissionable U^{233}. Either process may be carried out in a breeder reactor.

In a self-sustaining fission reaction, neutrons produced by fissions cause fission of other nuclei. A reaction, or a reactor, is critical if, on the average, neutrons from one fission produce at least one subsequent fission. A mass of fissionable material such that the reaction is barely critical is called the *critical mass.* The critical mass, however, depends not only on the mass of the fissionable material but also on its shape, the presence or absence of a reflector, and the presence or absence of a neutron source.

A *nuclear reactor* has a *moderator, control rods,* and usually provision for cooling, in addition to the *fissionable material. Fission products* are strongly radioactive, emitting beta radiation or beta and gamma rays.

A controlled and self-sustaining fusion reaction would make available an almost inexhaustible source of energy. It may or may not be possible to achieve such a reaction on a commercial scale; in any case, solution of all the problems in science and engineering is not expected for some decades.

A nuclear weapon may be based on fission or on fusion. If the latter, a small fission bomb is necessary as a starter for the fusion process. High-energy neutrons from the fusion process in the device may be used to cause fission of U^{238}. Whether fusion is supplemented with U^{238} fission or not, the energy available from a fusion type weapon is almost unlimited.

Self-Quiz

1. Discuss the applicability of the terms, "atomic energy" and "nuclear energy," to the energy produced from fission and fusion.

2. What advantages and/or disadvantages are there in the use of such expressions as "fuel" for fissionable material, "burn-up" to refer to the disintegration of the "fuel" by fission, "ashes" for fission products, etc.?

3. Why does the average person believe that nuclear energy is only a very few decades old?

4. Could a team of competent scientists, armed with all conceivable testing devices, come into your home and determine whether the electricity was produced by a nuclear reactor or a hydroelectric plant? Explain.

5. In a preceding chapter, we met an implied prediction of nuclear energy. Draw and label the diagram which accompanied the discussion, and explain clearly how the diagram reveals the possibility of energy from fusion and energy from fission. Refer to Chapter 36 *only* if, or to the minimum extent, necessary, except to check your completed diagram and confirm your explanation.

6. Write a generalized equation, and one specific example, for the fission of U^{235} and write similar pairs of equations for the fission of Pu^{239}, U^{233}, and U^{238}.

7. How do the equations for the preceding question predict the possibility of a chain reaction?

8. How do the equations predict the radioactivity of the fission products? What type of activity do they predict, and why?

9. Assume that the fission of a Pu^{239} nucleus yields three free neutrons and that the sum of the mass numbers of the most massive stable isotopes of the fission products is 225. What, if anything, can you say about the total number of beta decays which will result? about the number of gamma particles produced?

10. Outline the production of plutonium from U^{238}. The Pu^{239} will be mixed with unconverted U^{238}, and will have to be separated. Will this separation be more difficult, or less, than the separation of U^{235} from U^{238}? Explain clearly.

11. Give a full verbal discussion of the process described by the series of equations in Sec. 40-7. Write a similar set of equations for the conversion of Th^{232} to U^{233}.

12. Why is it necessary to separate U^{235} from U^{238}? Outline the problems associated with this separation, and two methods of accomplishing it.

13. How does the presence of cadmium rods in a reactor control the reaction? State the type of nuclear reaction involved and write a balanced equation for the reaction.

14. The fission reaction in a nuclear reactor cannot make complete use of all the fissionable material. Why not? What must be done to make the unfissioned material available for reuse? What problems are associated with the preparation of the material for reuse?

15. What is a breeder reactor? Of what special importance is it, if any?

16. Discuss the mechanism of the fission process, including a clear explanation of the actual source of the energy produced.

17. It is commonly said that nuclear energy results from the conversion of mass to energy according to the equation $E = mc^2$. In what sense is this statement valid, and in what sense is it inadequate?

41

APPLICATIONS OF RADIOISOTOPES

41-1 Preview

The main emphasis, in all that has gone before this chapter, has been on basic principles and their interrelationships. Many applications have been considered, but they have never been an end in themselves. Yet here we have a chapter which contains very little except *applications; and while there are some principles in the final chapter they comprise a minor portion of it. Unfortunately, the usual sources of public information fail to keep the public adequately informed on the matters considered in these two chapters, and too often what information they do print is of questionable scientific accuracy or is beclouded by extraneous factors, such as considerations of domestic political advantage. For these reasons, I feel that any author of an introductory text of this sort should offer his readers material such as you will find in these final chapters.*

Radioactive isotopes find amazingly numerous and diverse applications. In a few applications, the use of a radioisotope is a substitute for some other procedure, but most of the applications are possible only with radioactive substances. The widespread use of these substances is more surprising because most of them were not available in quantity or at reasonable cost until after World War II. Two well-informed writers estimated early in 1954 that the use of radioisotopes in industry had increased tenfold in less than five years. Early in 1959, one authority stated that the use of radioisotopes in industry was saving American consumers hundreds of millions of dollars a year, and he added that the potential benefits dwarf those realized at that date. A survey by a well-known research institute stated late in 1959 that the use of radioisotopes in agriculture will result in savings of at least $180,000,000 a year for the next two decades. Human life and health cannot be evaluated in these terms; but the use of radioactive isotopes in medical research, diagnosis, and therapy is extensive, and this field is growing rapidly. Even if space were available in a book of this sort, there would be no point in attempting to catalog all the diverse applications of radioisotopes. Only a few applications from each of various fields are cited, therefore; both the fields mentioned and the applications within those fields are illustrative rather than comprehensive.

Before considering any applications, however, it will be helpful to turn our attention briefly to some of the characteristics of radioactive nuclides that endow such substances with a unique usefulness.

41-2 Useful Attributes of Radioisotopes

The obvious factor here, of course, is the fact that radioactive isotopes emit alpha or beta particles, some producing gamma rays also. This makes it possible to locate an extremely small quantity of a radioisotope with the aid of a Geiger tube or some other detector. Suitable associated equipment makes it possible to determine the quantity of the radioisotope; in many cases this can be done with high accuracy. Procedures, such as the determination of half life, of the type of decay (alpha or beta, with or without gamma radiation), and of the energy of the particles and of the gamma photons (if any) emitted, may be used to establish the identity of the radionuclide used in an investigation and thereby minimize confusion due to any radionuclide initially present.

A radioactive isotope of an element has the less obvious, but equally important, property of acting the same as a stable isotope of that element in any chemical process; and although their masses differ, this disparity has very little effect on the action of the different isotopes in physical processes. Hence, for example, a chemical compound can be "tagged" by including a radioactive atom in its structure where there normally would be a stable atom of the same element, without altering significantly the properties of the compound.

Other extremely important factors are the very high sensitivity of apparatus for evaluating the radioactivity of even a very small quantity of a radioisotope, and the fact that radioactivity can be detected when its level is far below that necessary for a quantitative determination. Routine quantitative measurements may be possible after a radioactive isotope has been diluted by a factor of a hundred million or even a billion, and a measurable level of radiation may be produced by only 10^{-15} g (one-thousandth of a micromicrogram!) of some radioisotopes. We cannot really understand what such extreme sensitivity means, but we can get some idea of it from this fact: if the price of *one milli*gram of such an isotope were equal to the national debt, the activity of less than a *penny's* worth would be measurable!

41-3 General Types of Applications of Radioisotopes

The list of applications in this section should be regarded as suggestive rather than exhaustive. Also, the types recorded should not be considered to be mutually exclusive, since in some applications two or more types may be combined.

An important application involves ***penetration*** of matter by radiations from the radioisotope. This finds application in such diverse procedures as the control of the thickness of sheet metal in a rolling mill, and diagnosis for hyperthyroidism, in which radioiodine selectively absorbed by the thyroid gland is observed and measured by an external detector.

Reflection, or ***backscatter,*** of radiations is the basis of applications ranging from the measurement of soil moisture to the control of the thickness of tin plating on steel.

The ***ionization*** caused by nuclear radiations is very useful for many purposes other than radiation detection (Chapter 38). Examples are the control of difficulties caused by static electricity in industries such as printing and textiles, the production of luminescence on clock and instrument dials, and the chemical activation of substances. Associated with the last of these are various biological effects.

Tracing is an extremely important type of application. It may be a simple physical process in which a radioactive isotope is injected into a pipe suspected of having a leak; a leak in a pipe buried in concrete may be located by an abnormally high activity at the site of the leak, or by a significant decrease of activity along the pipe beyond the leak. On the other hand, tracing may be a matter of trying to unravel a very complicated process like photosynthesis or milk production by using "tagged" compounds. In any such application, the radioactive substance employed is known as a ***tracer.***

By adding a measured volume of a solution of a radioisotope, of known activity, to an unknown volume of fluid, allowing the added liquid to mix thoroughly with the fluid, and then measuring the activity of a sample of the mixture, the volume of the fluid may be determined accurately. This procedure is called ***isotope dilution.*** By this means, the blood volume of seriously wounded United Nations troops in Korea was measured to determine the advisability of blood transfusion.

Several varieties of applications depend on ***activation.*** This is the bombardment of a non-radioactive substance with some sort of nuclear radiations, often neutrons, which render the substance or some component of it radioactive. Thus, piston rings may be put into a nuclear reactor with the result that some of the atoms of iron are changed to a radioactive iron isotope; and a radiological study of the rate of wear may be made quickly and accurately. Or silver in an alloy may be identified, even if only a trace is present, by putting a sample of the alloy near a neutron source; two radioactive silver isotopes, with rather short half lives, are formed and may be identified from the half lives.

41-4 Medical Applications: Research

Numerous and varied studies of metabolism have been made with the aid of radioactive tracers such as tritium (H^3), radiocarbon (C^{14}), radioiron (Fe^{59}), radioiodine (I^{131}), and others. Many of these, and other types of studies also, have been directed toward finding significant differences between normal cells and cancer cells, which could be made the basis of a method of treating cancer. For example, C^{14} labeled amino acids have been used in the study of protein metabolism. Other studies have been made of the metabolism of calcium, iron, glucose, cholesterol, and insulin, among others. There is space for only a couple of examples. Studies with Ca^{47} showed that normally about 90% of the calcium intake of young animals goes to the bones, but only about 40% in old ones. It was also found that the availability of calcium is influenced by the diet. Studies of the life span of red blood cells in polycythemia vera solved a question concerning the source of iron deficiency in this disease by revealing that, in addition to red blood cells with a normal life of about four months, others with a much shorter life span are produced.

Studies of the action of substances such as anticancer agents, antibiotics, sulfa drugs, alkaloids, sugar substitutes, and hypnotics have been made with the aid of radioactive labeling of the substances. Similar investigations have been made of the action of injurious substances, including carcinogens, germs, viruses, allergenic substances, toxins, and poisons, with the aid of radioisotope techniques.

Research employing tracers has been made on such diverse problems as the healing of a bone fracture and the penetration of an inhalant intended to relieve colds.

41-5 Medical Applications: Diagnosis

The isotope dilution technique, mentioned in Sec. 41-3, is applicable to the determination of the volume of any fluid which is in a container of unknown shape and dimensions or which for some reason may not be removed from its container. Hence it is appropriate for the determination of the volume of a biological fluid in a living animal.

If a radioactive substance and an otherwise identical nonradioactive substance are separated by a biological membrane, the rate at which the radioactivity appears on the other side of the membrane provides a means of evaluating the rate of flow of the substance through the membrane. This technique is applicable, with suitable modifications, to the measurement of flow rate through an extensive membrane, like the wall of an intestine, or through a minute membrane such as a cell wall.

Some elements have an affinity for specific organs. Familiar examples of this include the concentration of calcium in the bones and of iodine in the thyroid gland. Such localization is the basis of a technique called ***autoradiography.*** For example, a diseased thyroid gland will take up radioiodine just as it does normal iodine. If the diseased gland is removed and sectioned, when a section is placed on a photographic plate the radiations from the radioiodine will "expose" the plate just as light rays would, and on development of the plate an image similar to an X-ray photograph will show the location of iodine in the gland and its relative concentration in the various locations.

The three techniques above are used in research also.

The penetrating properties of nuclear radiations enable a doctor to learn much about the interior of a patient's body without any surgical procedure. The presence of radioiodine in the thyroid gland, for example, may be detected and quantitatively determined by an external detector. In fact, a scintillation counter shielded so that it will accept radiations only from a certain direction may be moved automatically over the patient's throat while associated apparatus causes a marking pen to move in a similar pattern over a sheet of paper. There results a pattern of dots or short lines which is a "map" of the iodine in the thyroid, showing the size and shape of the gland and the approximate concentration of iodine in the various portions of it.

In cancer of the thyroid, fragments of tissue may separate from the gland and be carried to other parts of the body, tending to initiate new cancers where they lodge. Some—though unfortunately not all—such *metastases,* as they are called, retain the affinity for iodine characteristic of thyroid tissue; those which do can be located with the aid of radioiodine and an external detector.

Normally, brain tissue is protected by what is known as a blood-brain barrier, which interferes with the transfer of many substances from the blood to the brain tissue. This effect is impaired by a tumor, allowing substances which do not collect in normal brain tissue to collect in tumor cells and adjacent extracellular spaces. For this reason radioisotopes are useful in discovering and locating a brain tumor. Commonly radioiodine is used, in connection with special detecting equipment. Another very interesting modification of the technique employs Cu^{64} or As^{74}, radioactive isotopes of copper and arsenic, respectively, which are positron (positive beta) emitters. The positron will travel only a microscopic distance before it meets a negative electron; this meeting results in the annihilation of the positron and electron and the generation of the two gamma photons of annihilation radiation (Sec. 33-7 and 35-9). These two gamma photons shoot away in opposite directions. Two scintillation detectors are placed on opposite sides of the patient's head and connected to an electronic circuit so designed that it will respond only when *both* detectors are "triggered" simultaneously by gamma photons. Thus, when the circuit responds, the doctor knows that the site of the tumor is on a direct line between the two detectors. By moving the detectors he can determine the location and size of the tumor with much greater precision than by any other non-surgical method.

By injecting a radioisotope of sodium, Na^{24}, into the blood stream, one can study a circulatory disorder. For example, a blood vessel constriction will be revealed by a survey of the area with a Geiger or scintillation counter. This technique enables a doctor to observe the effectiveness of procedures taken to improve the circulation or determine whether an amputation is necessary and, if so, at what location it should be done.

Very shortly after X rays were discovered, they came into use for purposes ranging from examination of bone fractures to treatment of cancer. X-ray machines have been improved tremendously since the early models, but they are cumbersome and require a power supply. Where compactness or portability is important, radiations from radioisotopes may be used in place of X rays. Some radioisotopes have additional advantages over X rays for this purpose. For example, only a very expensive X-ray machine with a 2 million v power supply could produce rays as penetrating as those from Co^{60}; furthermore, the gamma radiation could be used more effectively in some cases because it contains photons of only two different energies, whereas a continuous spectrum of X rays would result. For such reasons, massive irradiating machines using Co^{60} are in use, in addition to portable ones.

41-6 Medical Applications: Therapy

The irradiation machines mentioned at the end of the preceding section may be used for cancer treatment as well as for diagnosis.

Radioisotopes find other modes of application to cancer treatment.

Small Co^{60} sources encased in stainless steel or some other inert substance may be placed in body cavities, just as has been done for over half a century with radium; or in the case of skin cancer, an appropriate source may be taped against the skin. Thin wires formed from radioisotopes may be cut into equal short lengths, alternated with short lengths of non-radioactive aluminum wire, and encased in thin plastic tubing; by using longer or shorter "spacers" of aluminum wire, the activity of the resulting suture-like radiation source may be adjusted as desired. This tubing may then be sewn into malignant tissues. Isotopes used in this manner include Co^{60}, Ir^{192} (iridium), and Ta^{182} (tantulum). Alternatively, short lengths of thin Co^{60} wire plated with stainless steel may be cut to any desired length, or Au^{198} (gold) in gold tubing may be used. In the latter case, the half life of gold is short enough so that it may be left permanently in the tissues. All other sources mentioned must be removed after the desired dosage of radiation has been achieved, because of the relatively long half life of the radioisotopes involved.

Colloidal suspensions of radioisotopes may be injected into malignant tissues or into spaces such as the chest and abdominal cavities. It is obvious that only nuclides with short half lives may be used for such purposes. Radioactive forms of gold, chromium, and yttrium have been employed.

The selective absorption of a particular element by some tissues offers an additional means of placing a radioactive source in such a tissue. The most common example is the treatment of hyperthyroidism with radioiodine (I^{131}).

41-7 Agricultural Applications: Plants

The metabolism of phosphorus, sulfur, calcium, copper, molybdenum, zinc, iron, and carbon by plants, and the translocation of these substances in the plants, have been studied with the aid of radioactive isotopes of these elements. The investigations have covered the point and rate of entry into the plant, the path and the mechanism of movement of the substance within the plant, and the mechanism of transfer to the interior of a plant cell.

A very large amount of money is spent each year on fertilizers, but it is reported that much of the fertilizer is wasted by customary practices. For these reasons, extensive research has been carried out in this field. Factors studied include the best chemical and physical form, pattern of placement, and depth of placement in the soil as related to absorption by the plant, also movement in the soil and leaching. Other matters investigated are the relation of method of fertilizing to the nature of the root system of the plant, the best time to apply fertilizer, the effect of irrigation, and so on.

Among other things, such research has shown that feeding the portions of the plant above the ground may be more effective than feeding the roots. One study showed that spraying fruit trees, even when dormant, and in subfreezing weather, with a dissolved fertilizer is effective. Other studies have shown in some cases a 95% uptake of fertilizer in soluble form sprayed on the leaves of a plant, as compared with 10% uptake of the same fertilizer when applied to the root system. Mineral deficiencies have been corrected by spraying the above-ground portions of the plant with appropriate substances. These include disorders in citrus trees due to lack of zinc and lack of iron, and magnesium deficiency in celery; and treatment of the celery by soil application of magnesium was quite ineffective.

Radioisotopes have greatly contributed to extensive study of photosynthesis. This is the extremely important and complex chemical process by which plants convert water and carbon dioxide to carbohydrates, and is the basic source of all foodstuffs, animal as well as vegetable.

Various control agents, such as a substance to thin blossoms on fruit trees, are becoming more common and are, at least potentially, quite valuable. One which causes defoliation of cotton before harvest is said to have made mechanical harvesting of cotton more effective, reduced harvesting costs by 50%, and improved the product. The action of such substances is studied with the aid of radioactive tracers. The same tracer technique is applied to the study of herbicides, fungicides, and insecticides. Most present agents of this sort have too general an effect; a weed killer kills desirable growth as well as weeds, and a similar situation obtains with insecticides. These researches may result in the development of specific killers which will destroy a particular kind of plant or insect without harming other kinds.

An extremely important type of research is directed toward the development of new and improved plants by forced mutations. Treatment of plants or seeds with intense radiations from a particular radioisotope or from fission products alters the genes and results in a mutation. In general, such mutations are undesirable or useless, but a small portion of them result in some useful change; and this technique of forced mutation tremendously accelerates the appearance of mutant varieties. Irradiation of wheat by fission products has resulted in a variety much more resistant to the disease called "wheat rust," and radiation by neutrons has produced another improved variety of wheat. A new and better peanut has been produced which suffers less damage in handling and shipping and yields 30% more per acre. A new variety of Elberta peach has been created which ripens two weeks later than the parent variety, has firmer flesh, and stands shipping better; and a mutant of another variety of peach ripens two weeks earlier than the parent variety. A large number of crop plants have been studied and improved with respect to factors such as food value, yield, adaptability to poor soil conditions, resistance to drought or to disease, suitability for mechanical harvesting, color, texture, and so on.

Plants of many varieties have been grown on "isotope farms" so that radioactive forms of substances they produce may be obtained directly from the plants; for example, radioactive digitoxin from foxglove plants. Two methods are employed. One is a small-scale open field method, the plants being subjected to controlled quantities of radiation from a source such as Co^{60}. The other method employs a greenhouse in which the atmosphere contains a controlled quantity of carbon dioxide in which the carbon is radioactive C^{14}.

Matters such as soil density and soil moisture may be determined quickly and accurately by special probes. In the former case there is a gamma ray source such as Co^{60} in the tip of the probe, and the gamma photons are scattered by the soil. The more dense the soil, the greater the backscatter, and the degree of backscattering is measured by a detector in the upper portion of the probe. A moisture probe employs a neutron source rather than a gamma source, and the degree of neutron scattering depends on the quantity of hydrogen in the soil, hydrogen being a constituent of the water molecule. Some of the scattered neutrons reach a special Geiger tube lined with silver, where they enter into an (n, γ) reaction with the silver, rendering it radioactive. The depth of the snow pack, on which the irrigation supplies in the subsequent months may depend, may be remotely monitored and reported by a Co^{60} source at ground level and a Geiger tube supported above the ground.

41-8 Agricultural Applications: Animal Husbandry

Radioisotopes have been used in studies of the utilization of fodder, and in investigations of the availability of calcium, phosphorous, sulphur, and other elements. Similar use has been made in research on the need for elements such as cesium, cobalt, copper, zinc, molybdenum, and tantulum in trace quantities. For example, such investigations showed that 4 to 7 parts of cobalt per 100 million parts of diet are required for sheep and cattle but that the cobalt requirement of other animals is lower; such investigations are well beyond the sensitivity of chemical procedures. Vitamin B_{12} deficiencies were shown to be caused (at least in some cases) by a lack of adequate cobalt in the diet.

Radioisotopes have also been used in studies of the biochemistry of body processes, the relation of cow feed to milk formation, the biochemical processes by which meat, milk, and eggs are formed, and so on. They have been useful also in investigating the availability of inorganic diet additives and the uptake of fission products from diet.

Though in principle radiation could be used in animal breeding to increase mutations as it has been in plant breeding, the large proportion of unfavorable mutations makes it a rather expensive process; however, some work has been done on forced mutations of poultry.

Animal pests and harmful insects have been subjected to research with radioisotopes. Large economic losses to cattle raisers are caused by the screw worm. In some areas which are relatively isolated geographically, the screw worm is said to have been eliminated. This was done by breeding larvae in a laboratory, and subjecting the larvae to radiation at a certain stage. This resulted in sterile but otherwise normal males, which were released to mix with the wild population. The female mates only once, and matings with sterile males yield only sterile eggs. Thus the screw worm population is reduced with each succeeding generation, and in each generation, the sterile males bred in the laboratory constitute a larger proportion of the total. After several generations, the species disappears.

Radioisotopes have been used in other research on insects, including studies of their flight range, migration, and hibernation, and on the absorption, metabolism, and elimination of insecticides by insects.

41-9 Industrial Applications

An enormous variety of industrial applications of radioisotopes is based in some manner on the penetrating ability of the radiations.

One such application is analogous to the medical use of a Co^{60} source in place of an X-ray machine. Flaw testing of castings, welds, etc., can be done with gamma rays just as with X rays, and often more conveniently. For example, a Co^{60} source can be placed inside a small hollow casting where it would be impossible to insert a relatively bulky X-ray tube. Instead of Co^{60}, Cs^{137} (cesium) or Ir^{192} (iridium) may be employed. Various types of thickness gages are in extensive use, most of them based on the penetration of beta particles. In a steel mill, for example, the thickness of sheet steel can be determined as it comes from the rollers by placing a pure beta source (no gamma radiation) above the sheet and a detector beneath. Any variation in thickness will affect the response of the detector. This type of gage has many unique advantages: nothing touches the sheet, so the measurement of its thickness can not mar it; the response of the detector may be fed to circuitry which automatically will cause the rolls to be adjusted, thereby correcting any deviation from the desired thickness; and the uniformity of the product is far better than could be obtained by any previous method. Similar gages are used for measurements of the thickness of almost any continuous sheet or layer—metal sheet, plastic sheet, paper, soda cracker dough, or glass, among others.

Other thickness gages are based on the backscatter of particles emitted by a source of pure betas. In this way, the thickness of tin plating of sheet steel can be measured and automatically controlled, and the same is true of a coating of rubber on steel, and of other coatings or platings.

Other devices which employ the penetration of betas determine, and may indirectly control, such things as the percentage of solids in tomato paste, the proportion of fat in meat products, the tobacco content of cigarettes, or the fill level of soup cans, beer bottles, cereal boxes, etc. Since hydrogen is a better absorber of beta radiation than carbon is, a device employing beta radiations enables a relatively unskilled operator to make some ten times as many determinations of the carbon-hydrogen ratio in petroleum products as a skilled chemist could make in the same time by conventional methods.

The use of radioisotopes as tracers is as diverse as the use of the penetrating power of their radiations. There are many techniques for their use in the single matter of leak detection. To distinguish between different products in a pipeline, a radioisotope is injected into a petroleum pipeline between one type of crude or refined product and another, so that at the delivery end of the line a detector signal will tell the operator that it is time to "cut" the delivery from one tank to another. Dirt, grease, and soil of various kinds may be tagged with a tracer and rubbed onto a fabric, which is then laundered. A Geiger or scintillation counter will reveal how effective the laundering was, thus providing a reliable means of testing the washing machine or the detergent, or even the dirt-shedding properties of the textile. Both automobile engines and lubricants have been improved by putting some part or parts of the engine, such as the piston rings, the valves, or the crankshaft, in a nuclear reactor. The neutron bombardment converts some of the iron to radioactive Fe^{59}. The treated component or components are then used in assembling the engine, lubricant is added, and the motor is started up and run. Significant wear studies used to require a week or more, and it was necessary to disassemble the motor and remeasure the parts accurately; and precise measurements of wear might require a month or more. But even if only one iron atom in a billion is present as radioiron, a sample of the lubricant withdrawn after only a few minutes of running will contain some radioactivity, and highly accurate measurements can be made in a matter of hours without any disassembly of the motor.

The ionization caused by nuclear radiation is employed in many ways. Static electricity may cause various troubles or inconveniences in a printing plant or a textile mill. The presence of a radioisotope may eliminate such difficulties by ionizing the air, thus enabling static charges to leak off into the air before they become large enough to become troublesome. Another application of ionization is in the luminous dials of watches, aircraft instruments, etc.; the atoms of the fluorescent material are excited by the radiations, and in returning to normal they emit photons.

The ionizing effect of radiations has been used also to kill bacteria, stop potatoes from sprouting, and in similar applications. Some antibiotics and other substances which would be damaged by heat are sterilized by subjecting them to nuclear radiations. Research has been directed toward sterilization of foods so that they could be stored without refrigeration; at present, it appears that this may be useful for some foods but the picture is not clear.

A very important field, and one which is expanding rapidly, is the use of nuclear radiations to activate chemical reactions or to supply the energy required to carry them out. For example, one process for producing polyethylene is a photochemical process; light is directed into ethylene gas and the energy of the light is used by the gas in polymerizing and forming solid polyethylene. One study found that radiations from fission products could produce this polymerization more cheaply than the usual method. Many other reactions have been, and are being, studied. There is some indication, for example, that we may soon be riding on automobile tires vulcanized by nuclear radiations rather than by a more conventional vulcanization process.

41-10 Applications in Science

In a sense, all the applications mentioned in the preceding sections are scientific in nature; and quite a few, such as the study of the mechanism of photosynthesis, have to do with fundamental research. But in addition to such investigations, a great quantity of basic research based on radioisotopes is being done by scientists in many areas, including not only obvious fields like chemistry, physics, physiology, medicine, and engineering, but also fields such as ornithology, botany, geology, and others. Such applications range from an investigation of the mechanism of a complex chemical reaction to the study of sedimentation at the mouth of a river.

Summary

Radioisotopes, and their radiations, find applications in widely diverse fields, including among others medicine, agriculture, industry, and pure research. Their usefulness in a given instance may be due to their chemical similarity to stable isotopes of the same element, to the *penetration* power of the radiations or their *backscattering*, to their *ability* to *cause ionization*, or in some cases, to their ability to *induce radioactivity*. Quantitative measurements based on radioactivity may have a sensitivity far beyond that of procedures of other kinds.

42

HEALTH PHYSICS

42-1 Preview

The many and diverse applications of radioisotopes mentioned in the preceding chapter—and those listed constitute a sampling rather than a complete catalog—make it obvious that radioisotopes, and the radiations they emit, are rapidly becoming a part of our normal experiences and environment. The presence of traces of uranium and other radioactive elements in the soil and rocks, cosmic radiation, diagnostic and therapeutic use of X rays and the fallout from nuclear weapons tests all add to our radiological environment. If the world is so unfortunate as to become the victim of a nuclear war, this radiological environment will be greatly amplified. All the aspects of radiological hazards to humans from any source, and all aspects of science which bear on the reduction of these hazards, are inclined in ***health physics.*** *In this final chapter, we shall survey briefly the various sources of nuclear radiations in man's environment and their biological effects. In our present world, any survey would be incomplete without some consideration of the effects of nuclear warfare and some of the things which can be done to increase chances of survival after a nuclear attack.*

42-2 Controversy and Confusion

It appears likely that the aspect of health physics which will continue to be given more space than any other in the public press will be centered around the biological hazards unavoidably resulting from the testing or use of nuclear weapons. It may seem amazing that there is so much disagreement and that science has not resolved the controversy. On closer inspection, however, one finds that it would be even more amazing if full agreement were reached at any time in the near future. Why is this?

Before proceeding further, I wish to make my philosophy of the duties of any person informed in these matters quite clear. First, as indicated below, the matter is highly complex—so complex that *no* person can possibly have sufficient competence in all the pertinent fields; he must seek the best information and advice he can get in fields other than his own. Then he must weigh and balance the multitude of often conflicting factors and make his judgment. Because we are individuals, two persons of equal competence in the same field, and with equal access to information and consultation from other fields, might reach quite different conclusions. Second, because anyone's attitude is necessarily a personal one based in large part on his evaluation of factors from fields in which he is not an expert, *no person whatever has any right to forcibly impose his views on others.* On the other hand, every individual who has more or better information *in his field* than his neighbors has the responsibility of informing them. He *also* has the equal responsibility of warning them that, *on the basis of his own knowledge,* he can give them only a very incomplete picture, and that they should seek much additional information elsewhere before attempting to reach any conclusion. It would be especially inappropriate to try to "sell" a particular conclusion in a physics text, though I do want to sell the idea of approaching the matter with an open mind and with some realization of its complexity. If in what follows I have been unsuccessful in trying to conceal my own conclusions, I apologize and ask that you give no weight to them. I hope that after you have studied the material presented you will go on to get other information in the fields treated, *and* in other fields which have no place in a physics text, and that you will study the entire matter with intelligence rather than with passion or prejudice.

Now, why all the controversy? No person could give a complete answer, and space isn't available for all the contributing factors; all we can do is to "hit the high spots." Probably the greatest single factor is the complexity of the matter; perhaps the other leading factor is human nature.

The problem is extremely complex. In addition to its scientific and military aspects there are moral, diplomatic, economic, political, and other implications. No one person can be an expert in all of these fields, and the proper course can be determined only by a dispassionate analysis of available information in all of them. No person who focuses our attention on one facet of the complex problem and attempts to force us to his view without regard to other aspects is doing the nation or mankind a service, and unfortunately prominent persons on both sides of the controversy have done just that.

Even within the purely scientific aspects of the problem there is a great deal of complexity. Added to this is the lack of definite knowledge. Though a tremendous amount of research has been done, far more is necessary before we understand thoroughly the mechanism of the biological action of radiations and their effect on humans. The difficulties are such that different teams of able research scientists working on the same problem find inconsistent results. For obvious reasons, extensive research on the effect of radiation damage to humans is impossible; such information must come almost entirely from studies of people unfortunate enough to have been subject to nuclear attack or nuclear accidents of some sort, and data on the radiation exposure of such individuals are inaccurate. Although studies of genetic effects have been made on many generations of some plants and animals, many decades must pass before data on such damage to humans are available; and even then the data will be subject to uncertainty concerning the quantity of radiation responsible for the damage.

This means that, even if all non-science aspects of the matter were to be ignored, only tentative conclusions could be drawn and that even these tentative conclusions must be based in some degree on judgment rather than on solid scientific fact. That is why we have seen sincere and able scientists take diametrically opposite stands. The resulting lack of unanimity among scientists has opened the door for impassioned or intemperate statements from a wide spectrum of individuals ranging from sincere and devoted persons to demagogues, including some politicians who appear to place political advantage above the good of the nation or of humanity. If we are to find the best solution of this fantastically complex matter, we must try to avoid prejudice, passion, and liking or dislike for personalities, and approach the solution on a calm and rational basis.

42-3 Background Radiation

Since the advent of the first living cells, the environment of living organisms has included nuclear radiations. These radiations have come from cosmic radiation and traces of radioactive substances in the earth, in the air, in the oceans, and even within the organism itself. The chemical composition of your body includes a fraction of 1 per cent of potassium, and 0.0119% of all natural potassium is a radioactive isotope, K^{40}, with a half life of $1.3 \cdot 10^9$ years. Despite the relatively minute proportion of K^{40}

in your makeup, and its long half life, while you were reading the first three sentences of this paragraph probably somewhere between 20,000 and 250,000 atoms of K^{40} disintegrated within your body, depending on your weight and how rapidly you were reading. Thus you have been subjected to internal irradiation by betas and gammas from disintegrating potassium since before you were born, and this has been true of all organisms since life began on the earth. In addition to the K^{40}, a small portion of the carbon in your body is radioactive C^{14}, a pure beta emitter with a half life of 5568 years.

The unit of radiation dosage is the ***roentgen*** (abbreviated r) which is based on the ionization produced in air by X rays; 1 r of X rays will produce $1.61 \cdot 10^{12}$ ion pairs in 1 g of air, and this is equivalent to the release of about 87 ergs of energy per gram of air. The absorption of nuclear radiations by human tissue also results in ionization, and the dosage is measured in units similar to the roentgen. Although there are two other units in use, neither differs seriously from the roentgen, so only the latter unit will be employed in our discussions.* Usually one-thousandth of a roentgen, or a milliroentgen (abbreviated mr) is more convenient than the larger unit.

Because of the radiocarbon and radiopotassium within the body, a person receives an annual dosage of about 20 mr, depending on body weight. From the natural radioactivity of the earth, he may receive from 20 to 110 mr per year, depending on his location; the minimum value applies to a mariner and the maximum to a person living where the rocks are granite. Dosage from cosmic radiation will add each year about 35 mr for a person at sea level, 50 mr for one living at an elevation of 5000 ft, or 100 mr for one who resides 10,000 ft above sea level, the values varying with geographical latitude as well as with elevation. Thus natural ***background radiation*** may be as low as 75 mr per annum for a mariner or as high as 230 mr a year for a mountaineer.

To this natural background radiation, which always has been part of man's environment, radiations must be added from other sources. So common an item as a wristwatch with a luminous dial may add 40 mr per year.

---

* The *roentgen equivalent, man* (abbreviated *rem*) is a unit based on the biological effectiveness of radiations of any kind, whereas the roentgen is based on the ionization of a gas by X rays. The *rad* is the quantity of ionizing radiation which produces 100 ergs of energy when absorbed by 1 g of any absorbing material. For air and for soft tissue, 1 rad is roughly equivalent to a roentgen. For X rays, gamma rays, and beta particles, 1 rad is approximately 1 rem; for neutrons, 1 rad is 4 to 10 rems; and for alpha particles 1 rad is 10 to 20 rems. Since all of these units are defined in terms of the effect produced *per gram* of absorbing material, the effect of whole body exposure is quite different from the effect resulting from the same exposure of a small part of the body; the biological damage due to the absorption of a given number of roentgens (or rems or rads) when a tooth is X-rayed may be negligible, whereas the absorption of the same number of units of radiation by the entire body might have serious consequences.

The "natural" background is augmented unnaturally when we live or work in stone or concrete buildings and walk on concrete sidewalks. Estimates place the average exposure of United States citizens at 40 to 100 mr per year, due to all of these sources.

Superimposed on this is the radiation dosage due to fallout. ***Fallout*** is a term which refers either to the radioactive debris which settles to earth after being produced by a nuclear explosion, or to the settling out of this material. There are various measures of fallout—Sr^{90} in the soil, in milk and other foods, in human bones, etc.; intensity of external radiation from fallout; Cs^{137} (cesium) in the soil, in foodstuffs, etc.; and others. On whatever basis it is evaluated, the value changes with time and differs with geographical location; thus no definite value can be given. However, the Joint Advisory Committee, composed of experts and charged with advising the United States Atomic Energy Commission, stated several months after the cessation of nuclear weapons tests at the end of 1958 that "the amount of total body external radiation resulting from fallout to date, together with future fallout in any part of the world from previous weapons tests, is (a) less than 5% as much as the average exposure to cosmic rays and other background radiation, (b) less than 5% of the estimated average radiation exposure of the American public to X rays for medical purposes."* This would seem to mean, in effect, that a person living in Denver could reduce his exposure to pre-1945 levels by moving to sea level, or that one residing in a stone house might be able to do so by moving into a wooden home. This is misleading, however, because the report refers to external sources of radiation, and much of the hazard is due to radiations which originate from fallout products which have entered the body.

The source of the major portion of the internal radiation from fission products is Sr^{90}. Since strontium is very similar chemically to calcium, nearly all the strontium localizes in the bones. The rapidly growing bones of babies and children take up a markedly higher proportion of the Sr^{90} which enters the body than do the bones of older people. Sr^{90} is a pure beta emitter which decays to Y^{90} (yttrium), also a pure beta emitter which yields stable Zr^{90} (zirconium). For a child born in 1958, the lifetime dosage resulting from the uptake of Sr^{90} by the bones is variously estimated at about 10% to 65% of the dosage from natural background and X rays, or about 9% to 39% of the total radiation exposure.† These values assumed that no nuclear debris would be added to the atmosphere after the cessation of nuclear weapons testing at the end of 1958, an assumption which is no longer valid. The wide spread of the values is attributable to different estimates of the exposure due to X-radiation and of the uptake of Sr^{90} during the child's lifetime.

---

* Statement by the General Advisory Committee to the U. S. Atomic Energy Commission, May 4, 1959, released by the Atomic Energy Commission May 7, 1959.

† Fowler, J. M., *Fallout* (New York: Basic Books, Inc., 1960), pp. 61–2.

42-4 Biological Half Life and Effective Half Life

When we consider the biological hazard of any radioactive substance which is within the body we find that the concept of the half life of a radionuclide, which we met in Sec. 37-8, is less significant than we might expect. For although the tissues of our bodies may remain essentially unchanged, there is a continual "turnover" of the atoms which comprise those tissues. For example, an atom of carbon or one of hydrogen which is a component of a molecule in one of your body tissues today may be replaced soon by a different atom of the same element, the replaced atom leaving the body. Thus the atoms which compose your body today will not all be present indefinitely; after a period of time, a considerable percentage of the atoms of any given element will have left, having been replaced by other atoms of the same element.

The rate of replacement of atoms varies widely among the different elements. For example, consider strontium and cesium, both of which are among the more hazardous components of fallout. Normal biological processes would require about 10 years to reduce the quantity of strontium in the body by 50%, but the quantity of cesium would be reduced 50% in only about 17 days by such processes.*

The length of time required for biological processes to reduce the number of atoms of a given element in the body by 50% is termed the ***biological half life*** of that element. The value of the biological half life is the same for all isotopes of a given element, regardless of whether any particular isotope is or is not radioactive; hence the concept of the biological half life of an element is quite independent of the half life of a radionuclide as defined in Sec. 37-8. To minimize confusion, we may use the term ***physical half life*** for the half life with respect to radioactive decay. Thus, although the biological half life of strontium is given above as 10 years, the physical half life of Sr^{90} is 28 years; and while the biological half life of cesium is only 17 days, the physical half life of Cs^{137} is 30 years. Since the process within a nucleus which results in radioactive decay is quite unrelated to the biochemical and biophysical processes involved in the biological replacement and removal of an atom, the lack of agreement between the biological and physical half lives of an element is by no means a paradox.

Thus the level of radioactivity due to any radioactive substance or substances within the body decreases as time passes because of two quite independent processes: radioactive decay continually reduces the number of radioactive atoms present; biological processes remove some of the atoms from the body before they decay. Hence neither the physical nor the biological half life, alone, is a reliable index of the

---

* These values do not take into consideration either any future uptake of the element or any reduction in quantity due to radioactive decay.

radiation exposure which will result from a given quantity of a radionuclide within the body. The pertinent index is the period within which the level of radioactivity will be reduced 50% by the *combined* effects of biological removal and radioactive decay; this period is called the ***effective half life.***

Thus far we have used the symbol $T_{1/2}$ for the (physical) half life, employing the subscript to differentiate between time periods which are half lives and time periods in general. At the moment, we are dealing exclusively with half lives, but we have three different varieties of half life. Let us drop the subscript 1/2 and write T_p, T_b, and T_e for the physical, the biological, and the effective half life, respectively. The effective half life is related to the other two by the equation

$$T_e = \frac{T_p \cdot T_b}{T_p + T_b} \tag{42-1}$$

By inverting Eq. (42-1) and simplifying it, you can alter it to the form

$$\frac{1}{T_e} = \frac{1}{T_p} + \frac{1}{T_b}$$

We have met this form of equation in connection with the effective resistance of two resistors connected in parallel, the effective capacitance of two capacitors connected in series, and the relationship of the focal length of a lens to the object distance and the image distance. In the last case, the equation was $1/f = 1/p + 1/q$—Eq. (29-1)—the symbols f, p, and q representing the focal length, object distance, and image distance, respectively. You may recall that when the object and image distances are equal, the focal length is half of either (for a positive lens); that as the object distance decreases the image moves toward the principal focal point so that the value of f approaches that of q as p approaches infinity; and that the value of f becomes approximately equal to that of p if the value of q is very large. Since Eq. (42-1) can be put into a form exactly similar to that of the lens equation, the relationship of T_e to T_b and T_p is identical with the relationship of f to p and q; you can easily verify this by analyzing Eq. (42-1) or by trying various combinations of values for T_b and T_p.

Thus we see that if the biological and physical half lives happened to be equal, the effective half life would be 50% of either. The biological and physical half lives would be equal only very rarely, if ever, and any inequality between them would reduce the effective half life to a value less than 50% of their average. The more disparate the values of the biological and physical half lives are, the more nearly the value of the effective half life will approach the *smaller* of the other two values. Obviously the form of Eq. (42-1) is a very favorable one, from the standpoint of the minimization of radiological hazards due to radioactive substances within the body. Thus, for Sr^{90}, $T_p = 28$ y, $T_b = 10$ y, and $T_e =$ approximately 7.4 y.

For Cs^{137}, T_e and T_b have almost identical values, because, whereas T_p is about 30 y, T_b is only approximately 17 days.*

42-5 Biological Effects of Radiation: General

The great quantity of research on the mechanism of biological damage by radiations has yielded much information but has not yet been able to supply a complete explanation. It appears that the primary processes are ionization and excitation. If some particle (alpha, beta, gamma photon, neutron, or other) strikes a molecule of an amino acid in protein, for example, it may break the amino acid molecule into two fragments, one positively charged and the other negatively charged. The disrupted molecule cannot carry on its normal function in the biochemistry of the cell. Furthermore, the resulting ions are highly reactive chemically. Apparently they tend to react primarily with oxygen if any is available, and some of the oxidation products may be deleterious to the normal functioning of the cell. If the molecule is excited rather than ionized, the effect seems to be similar though less marked. If the molecule struck by the particle is part of the composition of a gene, modification of the molecule modifies the gene; this appears to be the mechanism of the induction of mutations by radiation.

It is universally agreed that large doses of nuclear radiations or X rays are damaging, and it is generally conceded that smaller doses are harmful in some degree. There is considerable disagreement about the degree of damage, however. Also, although most authorities apparently think that any radiation is harmful, others believe that there may be a lower limit, radiation below this limiting level having no adverse effects.

This matter is complicated by many factors. One is the difficulty of distinguishing with certainty between minor effects due to low radiation levels and those due to non-radiation causes. Only a very extensive study of two groups studied under identical conditions, except for low levels of radiation applied to one group, could reveal the very minor effects radiation might produce. Both groups would have to be very large, since the size of the statistical sample required for significant results increases as the magnitude of the effect under investigation is reduced. Since some anticipated effects are not expected to appear within two decades or more, the study would have to continue for a generation or so; and only a study extended over several generations could reveal accurate information on genetic effects. Added to these difficulties are others. For example, it is known that a fairly large radiation dose received within a relatively short

* Of course Eq. (42-1), and the discussion above, apply to the quantity of a radionuclide within the body *at any given time*. If, as time passes, additional quantities of the radionuclide were taken into the body, the equation and the discussion would be invalidated.

time has a more marked effect than does the same total dosage received over a long period; hence reliable data could be obtained only by subjecting various groups to equal low dosages at unequal rates.

Those who feel there is no "threshold" below which no radiation damage will occur base this opinion on this fact: for larger doses of radiation (given in a comparable manner insofar as the rate of exposure is concerned), the damage is directly proportional to the dosage. Extrapolation of such data toward zero dosage implies some damage at any dosage. A few experiments at low levels (with experimental animals, not humans) seem to indicate that no appreciable damage occurs, or even that very low levels (above background) may be slightly beneficial. And, of course, man has evolved to his present state in an environment of low-level radiation.

As is so often the case, some controversy arises from ambiguity; damage due to radiation may be of two general types, and the situation is different with respect to the two. Damage which will affect the well-being of the individual himself is termed ***somatic*** damage. That which affects his ability to reproduce, or the well-being of his progeny, is ***genetic*** damage.

It is generally agreed that radiation levels considerably above background constitute a hazard, but there is much disagreement on both the tolerable level and the degree of hazard associated with higher levels. The situation is complicated by the fact that some relatively recent research using experimental animals indicates that at low radiation levels the genetic damage is only about one-fourth of that expected on the basis of the direct proportionality between dosage and damage previously found at higher levels, and that somatic damage falls even farther below the anticipated effects.

There is also much controversy over how we should view what hazards result. Some believe that we should consider the hazards themselves. Others feel that they should be viewed in the context of other hazards in contemporary life. The one group holds that if an actual or potential radiation hazard exists we should concentrate directly on controlling it. The other group prefers to consider whether the possible benefits of activities which produce some radiation may outweigh the hazards, and to compare the potential radiation hazard with other potential or actual hazards of life. They point out, for example, that the probability of lung cancer from smoking is as well established and as serious as the probability of leukemia from fallout radiation; that nicotine, like radiation, can cause mutations; and so forth. Also, one point of view stresses the number of individuals who may suffer, whereas another point of view stresses the percentage of such individuals in the total population.

42-6 Hazards of External Sources of Radiation

The nature and degree of the hazard due to an external source of radiation depend strongly on the nature of the radiations as well as on their intensity. In considering the hazards from radiation sources, it is essential that we distinguish clearly between the source of the radiations and the radiations themselves. This is much the same as the distinction between a loaded gun and the bullet it fires.

So long as it remains external, a pure alpha emitter (no gamma radiation) presents virtually no hazard. This is because of the high ionizing ability of alpha particles and the resulting shortness of their range (Sec. 37-2, 38-6); alpha particles are completely absorbed by the dead outer layers of your skin, never penetrating down to where you live.

A pure beta emitter outside the body is much more hazardous. Since the beta particles have much greater penetrating power—a much greater range—than alphas have, they penetrate the skin and continue a short distance into the tissues beneath the skin. The result is called a "beta burn," and resembles somewhat a sunburn except that it involves deeper tissues.

Gamma radiation is far more penetrating than alpha or beta particles, since its nature is identical with that of X rays; hence it may affect any part of the body rather than being restricted to the peripheral portions. An implication of this is that gamma radiation from an external source can reach the gonads—the ovaries or testes—hence such radiation may cause mutations. In fact, it appears that the evolution of man, and of all other living organisms, has been due in part to mutations induced by the natural background radiation.*

Irradiation by neutrons is seriously damaging. Since they carry no charge, their energy is not expended over a short range by electrostatically caused ionization, as is the case with alpha and beta particles, so they are able to penetrate deeply. The mechanical impact of a neutron on an electron or on the nucleus of an atom can cause ionization of the atom, and the neutron normally possesses enough energy to cause the ionization of many atoms.

42-7 Hazards of Internal Sources of Radiation

Radioactive substances from fallout or other sources can enter the body by ingestion in foods or drink, by inhalation, or through wounds. The resulting hazard depends on the nature of radiations emitted, on whether the radioactive substance tends to concentrate in any part of the body and if so where, on the effective half life (Sec. 42-4), and on the quantity in the body.

Radionuclides which tend to concentrate in the skeleton include those of calcium, strontium, yttrium, barium, lanthanum, uranium, and plutonium. Of these, the first three and their radioactive daughter products are pure

* This may seem contrary to the fact that in general mutations are unfavorable. Unfavorable mutations are recessive, however; over many generations they tend to be bred out, whereas the relatively uncommon favorable mutations persist.

beta emitters, barium and its daughter product are beta-gamma emitters, and the last two are alpha emitters of very long half life. Iodine concentrates strongly in the thyroid gland; and its radioactive daughters are beta-gamma or pure beta emitters. The liver tends to absorb manganese, cobalt, cerium, praseodymium, and neodymium; these and their radioactive products are mostly beta-gamma emitters, with relatively few pure beta emitters and one daughter which is an alpha emitter. Radioisotopes which spread fairly uniformly through the whole body rather than becoming largely localized include cesium and carbon, the former being a beta-gamma emitter and the latter a pure beta emitter.

As an example of the influence of the factors mentioned in the first paragraph of this section, consider Sr^{90} and Cs^{137}, both of which are among the major hazards of fallout. Sr^{90} is a pure beta emitter, as are its decay products; it localizes almost entirely in the bones, and its biological half life is 10 years. This means that the bone marrow, which is the site of the production of red blood cells, is subjected to continuous bombardment by beta particles; so an excessive quantity of Sr^{90} in the body may be expected to lead to anemia, leukemia, or bone cancer. Here, again, there is much disagreement due to lack of enough, or sufficiently reliable, data; for example, some authorities predict large numbers of leukemia cases due to fallout, whereas a few believe that present radiation levels could be increased without causing any leukemia. Whatever the somatic hazard of the Sr^{90} may be, however, it offers essentially no genetic hazard. This is because it is so largely localized in the skeletal structure; it and its radioactive decay products are pure beta emitters, and the range of beta particles in human tissue is less than the distance between any bones and the gonads of either sex.

On the other hand, Cs^{137} is a beta-gamma emitter and is distributed throughout the body. Since its effective half life is only 17 days, its somatic hazard is negligible compared to that of Sr^{90}, despite the gamma radiation Cs^{137} produces. Nevertheless, both the fairly uniform distribution of Cs^{137} in the body and its emission of gamma rays make it far more of a genetic hazard than Sr^{90}, notwithstanding the fact that the biological half life of strontium is some two hundred times that of cesium.

In general, pure alpha and pure beta emitters within the body can damage only those tissues in the immediate vicinity; this damage may occur only locally if the radioisotope is localized, or it may affect the body generally if the emitter is not localized. The effects of gamma radiation can produce damage much farther from the site of the origin of the radiations.

42-8 Hazards Due to Use of Radioisotopes

The various applications of radioactive isotopes may be expected to increase somewhat the total radiation exposure of the average person. The regulations which govern the use, applications, and disposal of such substances are designed to minimize this increment. Biologically hazardous radionuclides cannot be used in any manner which would constitute a danger to the public. In all probability, for the average person, the only change in his radiological environment will be a slight increase in the level of gamma activity; and this should be less than that due to fallout—or to wearing a watch with a luminous dial.

42-9 Peacetime Hazards from Nuclear Energy

Nothing designed and built by man will ever be absolutely foolproof, so the possibility of an accident in a nuclear reactor cannot be ignored. There have been several "excursions" of reactors, the reaction rate increasing sufficiently to cause damage of some sort to the reactor; but none has turned into a nuclear bomb, and the possibility that one ever will is extremely slight or non-existent. The manual and automatic controls, combined with the design of the reactors themselves, come very close to guaranteeing safety. To date, the most serious "excursion," at least from the standpoint of hazard to people, occurred in Great Britain and resulted in need to dump the milk produced in the area near the reactor into the sea, for some months.

Probably a greater hazard is inherent in the carrying of nuclear weapons by aircraft. The hazard appears to be limited to local contamination; the military assures us that a crash and fire could not result in a nuclear explosion. Though this seems overoptimistic, the probability apparently is very small, and such accidents have occurred with no nuclear explosion resulting. A fire may cause release and dispersal of some U^{233}, U^{235}, U^{238}, or Pu^{239}, as the case may be, and this would result in the contamination of the immediate and downwind areas with an alpha emitter. This would necessitate prompt and thorough decontamination of the area, but it should constitute negligible hazard except in a fairly small area.

42-10 Hazards from Fallout Due to Weapons Tests

In addition to the effects of fission products which find their way into the body, as discussed briefly in Sec. 42-7, there will be some gamma radiation from the general environment. This will be more significant, of course, in areas contiguous to the test sites. Any one fission product, like any other radionuclide, has a half life, and its activity follows the usual decay law described by Eqs. (37-6 – 37-11), inclusive. However, fission products contain very many different nuclides, each with its own characteristic half life and each constituting a different fraction of the total nuclear debris. Hence it is impractical to attempt to describe the decay in terms of individual half lives; instead, an empirical equation is used to relate the activity at any time with that at any previous time. This equation, which is only approximate, is

$$A = A_0 t^{-1.2} \tag{42-2}$$

where A_0 is the value of the initial activity 1 hr after the nuclear explosion and A is its value t hr after the detonation. Like all empirical equations, this one is valid only within certain limits. The actual activity several months after the explosion is lower than the equation would predict; recent findings imply that after six months it may be less than 15% of what Eq. (42-2) would require. Even in the early stages, the equation is not fully reliable, for experience shows that the value of the exponent of t may differ considerably from -1.2. Note that, according to Eq. (42-2), mixed fission products do not have a definite half life. The activity at 1 hr decreases by 50% in about 1.1 hr, but that at 10 hr requires roughly 8 hr to undergo a 50% reduction. This decrease in the rate of decay is to be expected because the relatively rapid decay of the shorter-lived isotopes is continually decreasing their percentage in the mixture and correspondingly augmenting the proportion of isotopes with longer half lives.

42-11 Hazards from Attack with Nuclear Weapons: Blast and Related Effects

The effects of nuclear weapons may be subdivided into those which differ only in degree from the effects of TNT and similar explosives, and effects peculiar to nuclear weapons.

The blast effect of any nuclear weapon is large as compared to that of an analogous conventional weapon, and in the case of weapons in the megaton range, the blast effect is so many orders of magnitude greater that it is hard to conceive. We may get some idea by setting the fact that the total tonnage of bombs dropped on Germany in World War II was roughly two million tons—in the parlance of nuclear weapons, only *two* megatons—alongside the fact that *single* nuclear bombs of over *fifty* megatons energy yield are available.

Some idea of the effect of blast from such weapons may be gotten from Fig. 42-1, which is adapted from a more extensive diagram in an official government publication.* Within Zone *A* all buildings except reinforced concrete and steel frame structures would be obliterated; buildings of the latter types would suffer severe damage and, near "ground zero," which is the point immediately beneath the explosion, they probably would be destroyed. Private homes and similar structures would be damaged beyond repair in Zone *B*, and the most rugged structures would suffer major damage. Interiors of the strongest structures would be damaged moderately in Zone *C*, and other buildings would not be habitable until after repair. Damage to ordinary buildings, and to interiors of more rugged ones, would

* Civil Defense *Technical Bulletin* TB-8-1, February, 1955.

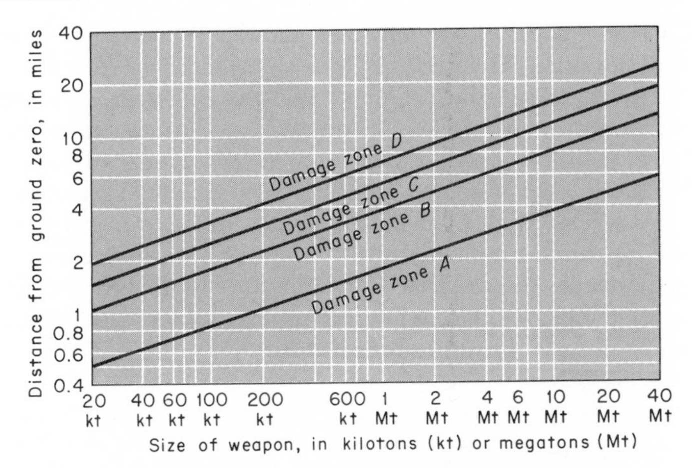

Fig. 42-1. Range of damage due to blast from nuclear weapons of various sizes. (See text for interpretation of the zones of damage.)

occur in Zone *C*. Ordinary buildings in Zone *D* would suffer partial damage, but would be habitable during repair. Highways and streets would be blocked (in built-up or forested areas) throughout Zones *A* and *B*, partially passable in Zone *C*, and would require some clearing in Zone *D*. Some vehicles would be usable in Zone *C* and most of those in Zone *D* could be used. Only in Zone *D* is there a strong probability that neither breakage of water lines nor destruction of elevated water tanks would interfere with water supplies for fire fighting. A similar situation would exist with respect to overhead power and telephone lines, and radio and TV towers, though underground power distribution systems would be less severely damaged.

The data presented in Fig. 42-1 are applicable to a fairly level area. If there are topographical features which afford shielding from blast, damage would be considerably lower in the sheltered areas. The effectiveness of topographical features, however, would depend on the height of the hill, its steepness of slope, its location with respect to ground zero, and the elevation at which the weapon was detonated. In the case of a metropolitan area on a flat plain, a single 10 megaton weapon could produce an area 22 or 23 miles in diameter, or roughly 400 square miles in area, within which the only immediately habitable structures remaining would be ruggedly constructed apartment houses well away from ground zero, and ingress into this area for fire fighting, rescue, or other purposes would be difficult or impossible.

On a clear day, the heat and light radiated from the exploding weapon could produce second-degree burns of unsheltered persons at distances up to about 25 miles, and third-degree burns up to 20 miles or so.

Unavoidably, some fires would start in ruined buildings. Almost certainly they would be sufficient in number so that their combined heat would cause some updraft over the area, and this would result in an inflow of air from the sides. The resulting breezes would fan the fires and tend to spread them toward the center of the area; this spread of the fires would increase the updraft and indirectly augment the strength of the winds blowing in toward the damaged area; the winds would speed the spreading of the fire; and so on. This vicious circle would generate what is called a ***fire storm,*** resulting in essentially complete burn-out of the area within the perimeter defined by the most remote initial fires. World War II experiences showed that a fire storm could deplete the oxygen in the air to such a degree that uninjured persons in blast-safe shelters were suffocated.

42-12 Hazards from Attack with Nuclear Weapons: Immediate Radiation

Aside from the heat and light radiations which are similar, except in degree, to those from the explosion of a conventional weapon, a nuclear explosion generates copious quantities of gamma rays and neutrons. Either of these may be lethal if an individual is subjected to a high dosage, but in a practical sense only the gamma radiation need be considered. The lethal range of neutrons is smaller than the radius of virtually certain death due to blast or heat.* The range of gamma rays is not similarly limited, but in a practical sense the dosage of the immediate radiation is limited by the short time during which they are produced. Although some damage from immediate gamma radiation may be expected, lethal dosages should not occur outside the area in which death is almost certain from blast or the ensuing fire.

42-13 Hazards from Attack with Nuclear Weapons: Delayed Radiation from Fallout

Equation (42-2) gives an approximate description of the rate of decay of the fission products. However, the inherent uncertainties of this empirical equation are augmented by physical and meteorological factors which govern the time of arrival of the nuclear debris at any particular location, its rate of fall, and the final concentration of fission products at that locality; and there are other complications.

If a nuclear explosion occurs at an elevation such that the fireball does not touch the ground, the radioactivity of the fallout will be at a minimum. A burst at a relatively low elevation allows the fireball to vaporize substances

* Some consideration has been given to a "neutron bomb" or "N-bomb," so designed that the major portion of the energy which normally would go into blast and heat effects would be given instead to a very copious flux of neutrons. If such a weapon were built and detonated over a populated area, essentially all of the immediate fatalities would be caused by neutrons.

from the earth's surface, and the intense neutron flux of the fireball induces radioactivity in such materials, greatly augmenting the total radioactivity resulting from the explosion.

As muddy water is clarified slowly by sedimentation, the larger particles settle first, followed by smaller particles, and a long time may be required for the smallest particles to settle. In the same way, the rate of fallout depends on particle size.

For this reason, fallout may be expected near the explosion earlier, and in greater quantity, if debris from the ground was taken up into the fireball; conversely, fallout locally would be less intense, and it would occur later, if the burst occurred high in the air.

The area affected by serious fallout would be determined by many factors, including the size and type of the weapon and meterological conditions. The test of a large fission-fusion-fission device on March 1, 1954, in the Marshall Islands resulted in dosages* during the 36 hr after the explosion of 5000 r (roentgens) at 10 miles downwind from ground zero, 2300 r at 100 miles, 2000 r at 110 miles, 1000 r at 125 miles, 500 r at 160 miles, and 300 r at 190 miles.† These data should be reviewed in terms of these facts: 600 or 700 r would be fatal to virtually 100% of the persons who receive that dosage; 50% fatalities should be expected from a dosage of the order of 450 r. The official report (cited in the footnote) on this test stated that it is unlikely that any deaths due to radiation would have occurred as the result of a 48 hr exposure, with no radiation shielding, beyond 220 miles downwind from the explosion. The contaminated area extended some 20 miles upwind from ground zero, and at some points, the width of the dangerously contaminated area was as great as 40 miles. The report states that about 7000 square miles of territory downwind from ground zero was contaminated to such a degree that survival might have depended on prompt evacuation or use of a radiation shelter. It offers no information on the size of the less heavily contaminated surrounding area within which there would have existed a serious threat to the health of the populace.

The meaning of this can best be realized by taking a map which includes your locality, assuming some location of the explosion, and marking on the map the distances, in the direction of the prevailing winds, and the corresponding dosages, as recorded in the preceding paragraph. However, this should *not* be interpreted as what *would* happen in case of a nuclear attack. Almost certainly, the wind patterns at the various pertinent elevations would differ from those existing during the test, and such differences could alter greatly both the area and the shape of the contaminated

* Obviously no persons were subjected to these dosages of radiation; the data were obtained with radiological instruments.

† *The Effects of High-Yield Nuclear Weapons: A Statement by Lewis L. Strauss and A Report by the United States Atomic Energy Commission* (February, 1955), pp. 14, 15.

region. The total radioactivity might be far less, because of a smaller bomb, a less "dirty" type of bomb, or greater elevation of the explosion. Also, the data assume no shelter whatever, and we shall see in Sec. 42-14 that shelter can greatly reduce exposure. On the other hand, the data given cover only the initial 36 hr, and radiation persists, though at greatly decreased levels, for months longer; so the data are realistic (for totally unsheltered persons) only if it is assumed that the entire populace could be evacuated into a "clean" area within a day and a half after the attack.

With the aid of the calculus and Eq. (42-2), an equation can be derived which gives the total exposure or dosage D from external sources of radiation in terms of the time t_1 of the arrival of fallout (or entry into a contaminated area), the time t_2 of departure from the contaminated area, and the intensity I_1 of the radiation at the time t_1:

$$D = 5I_1t_1 \cdot \left[1 - \left(\frac{t_1}{t_2}\right)^{0.2}\right] \tag{42-3}$$

If the value of t_2 is infinite—that is, if one remains throughout his life in an area with a low enough degree of radiological contamination to be habitable—Eq. (42-3) simplifies to

$$D = 5I_1t_1 \tag{42-4}$$

In either equation, the values of the time must be in hours and time must be measured from the time of the nuclear explosion. The radiation level or intensity I may be expressed in roentgens per hour or in milliroentgens per hour; if the former, the dosage will be in roentgens, or in the latter case it will be in milliroentgens.

Unfortunately Eq. (42-3) and Eq. (42-4) are subject to the same limitations and uncertainties which impair the usefulness of Eq. (42-2). In addition, the radiation level does not jump from background to its maximum value immediately, as the fallout arrives or as one enters a contaminated area, nor does it sharply decrease to a negligible value as one leaves the area; hence there is unavoidable uncertainty in the proper values to use for I_1, t_1, and t_2.

42-14 Shelter from Radiation

Because of their relatively low and limited ability to penetrate matter, shelter against alpha and beta radiation is quite easy—so long as the sources of such radiation are outside the body.* Any building or a closed automobile would provide fairly good shielding against them. Since gamma radiation is physically identical with X rays, shielding against it is quite

---

* Only unfissioned uranium or plutonium would produce alpha radiation, since fission products are beta emitters.

Table 42-1

GAMMA RADIATION SHIELDING BY SOME SUBSTANCES

(All thicknesses in inches)

Substance	Half-value thickness	Thickness for a shielding factor of			
		10	100	1,000	5,000
Steel	0.7	2.3	4.7	7.0	8.6
Concrete	2.2	7.3	15	22	27
Packed earth	3.3	11	22	33	41
Water	4.8	16	32	48	59

another matter. Complete shielding is quite impossible, but shielding which will reduce the gamma radiation to a tolerable level is possible. The essential factor here is the quantity of mass between you and the source of the radiation. The ***half-value thickness*** (see Eq. 38-1) of various substances, and the thickness of each required for certain shielding factors, are given in Table 42-1.

As a very rough rule of thumb, an ordinary house or closed car will provide about a 50% reduction as shielding, and a basement in a home will reduce the radiation intensity and dosage by a factor of about 10. As indicated by Table 42-1 real protection, except in areas with extremely heavy contamination, would be provided by a shelter which has 2 ft of concrete or 3 ft of packed earth on all sides *and* overhead. Such a shelter could be constructed of concrete in such a way that it would provide considerable protection from blast also, though obviously no shelter could provide safety from blast at, or close to, ground zero. The safety of any shelter would depend not only on its mechanical strength and radiation shielding but also on provision of food, bedding, elementary sanitary facilities, etc. Provision for filtering the air would be desirable, but would require occasional replacement of the filter unless the location of the filter is completely outside the shelter; in some tests, the accumulation of fallout in a filter within a shelter has elevated the radiation level in the shelter above that in the open.

42-15 Food and Water Supplies

Since internal sources of radiation are so much more damaging than external sources, it is imperative that care be taken to avoid eating seriously contaminated foods or drinking heavily contaminated water, though tolerable levels of contamination during the emergency period after an attack would necessarily be well above those desirable for long-continued consumption under ordinary circumstances.

Though nuclear radiations can induce radioactivity in previously inert matter, in general such reactions require higher energies of the beta particles or gamma photons than those typical of fallout material. Hence, at least under emergency conditions, any food which is in a dust-tight package can be used—*provided* that care is exercised to see that contamination on the outside of the package, in cooking utensils, or elsewhere, does not get into the food. Food in a refrigerator or freezer and all canned goods would be quite safe, subject to the same precautions. Water from a well should be quite safe unless its source is surface water from a fairly nearby source. Water in the mains is safe at first, but may become contaminated shortly if there are breaks in the mains or if the water comes from an open reservoir, lake, or river. A limited supply of safe water is available in a water heater. The gas or electricity at the water heater should be turned off and the inlet valve closed to prevent contaminated water from entering.

42-16 Decontamination

It is highly important for any person who has been out in the open when fallout is occurring to take all possible steps to remove radiological contamination from his person and clothing. This is important also for all others with whom he may come in contact, or who may be in locations he has unthinkingly contaminated by his presence. This does not mean that the person himself is made radioactive—science fiction stories to the contrary notwithstanding. It merely means that a person who has fallout on his clothing will spread it in the same way that a very dusty person coming into a spick-and-span house will leave minute bits of dust.

Personal decontamination involves two phases. One is very thorough bathing, with especially careful cleansing of dirt traps, such as the hair and creases or folds of the skin. The other phase is the discarding of at least the outer garments; if possible, inner garments should be changed also unless it is *known* that the original contamination was rather minor.

Obviously no decontamination of a home or its environment should be attempted while heavy fallout is occurring or while the radiation level is dangerously high. The exterior of a home may be at least partially decontaminated by sweeping or washing the roof, or both, and washing the walls; and the interior by the time-honored housekeeping procedures. In both cases, care must be taken to avoid transfer of the contamination to one's person, and to minimize its concentration in the soil adjacent to the walls, in the bag of a vacuum cleaner, or in a mop, and so on. Sidewalks and pavements may be swept. The contamination of unpaved areas may be considerably reduced by spading. Since this reduces the radiation level by putting the contamination below the surface and making use of the gamma absorption of the soil, the spading should be as deep as possible and mixing of the soil should be avoided insofar as possible.

42-17 Prospects

None of the material in this chapter makes very pleasant reading, and the three sections commencing with 42-11 present a most sobering picture. It is manifest that every effort should be made to minimize the possibility of a nuclear war at any time in the future—every effort, that is, which will not result in the loss of our freedom.

Until such efforts bear real fruit, it would seem that some possibility of a nuclear attack exists. Objective studies by independent organizations have shown that no measures we can take could prevent the deaths of many tens of millions of Americans in an all-out nuclear attack; but that the number of casualties could be reduced by a factor which might well make the difference between the extinction or survival of this country as a nation if radiation shelters adequate in both design and number were available. Many persons feel that an adequate shelter program is not possible, or that imprisonment in a shelter, perhaps for weeks, followed by a return to an essentially agricultural life while the nation's industrial and economic life is being resuscitated, is hardly to be preferred to death. At the time of writing, however, the most common attitude is essentially that of closing one's eyes to the problem, apparently in the hope that it will be exorcised by some good fairy. There are signs, though, of some awakening to the problem and to the possibility of its solution.

Summary

Some knowledge of health physics is needed because of the increasing importance of nuclear radiations in daily life and the possibility of a nuclear attack.

Biological damage caused by radiation appears to be due mainly to *ionization of molecules* in the tissues. It may be *somatic*, affecting the individual himself, or *genetic*. Sufficient data for an accurate assessment of the biological damage to humans caused by low levels of radiation are not available and will not be for many decades. This is the primary source of the controversy over the human damage which may result from *fallout*.

Living organisms have always been subjected to nuclear radiations.

Radiation due to fallout is much less than that from other sources and will remain so, barring extensive testing of nuclear weapons and nuclear war.

Because of elimination from the body, the *effective half life* of a radionuclide is somewhat less than its physical half life, and it may be very much less, depending on the nuclide.

Radioactive substances within the body constitute a far greater hazard than if they were outside the body. External sources of pure alpha radiation do no damage, and those of pure beta radiation cause relatively minor damage. Gamma radiation tends to be damaging whether its source is internal or external. Some radionuclides within the body localize in certain parts of the body; others do not.

The radioactivity of fallout decreases with time, but the decay equation is quite different from that for a single nuclide, and far less accurate.

Blast effects of any nuclear weapon are of a much higher order of magnitude than those due to conventional weapons, and those caused by range of blast and fire damage of a megaton range weapon is such that immediate nuclear radiation presents little additional hazard. Radiations from fallout, however, constitute a *major hazard* of *nuclear weapons*, the magnitude of the hazard depending on the *size* and *type* of the weapon, the *elevation* at which it is detonated, the *topography*, and *meteorological conditions*. Radiological shelter or prompt evacuation might be essential over an area of thousands of square miles, after the explosion of a single weapon.

The radiation hazard may be reduced to a tolerable level by adequate shelters, though no feasible shelter could stand the blast effect if it was near ground zero.

Foods will be safe after a nuclear attack if they have been protected in any manner that prevented fallout from getting into the food. A hot water heater contains a limited supply of safe water.

Personal radiological decontamination involves thorough bathing and the discarding of outer clothing.

Adequate radiation shelters could very greatly reduce the number of casualties which would result from a nuclear attack.

APPENDIX

Appendix A
SOME PHYSICAL CONSTANTS

Name	Symbol	Value
Avogadro's number		$6.02486 \cdot 10^{23}$ atoms per gram atomic weight or molecules per gram molecular weight
Charge on the electron	e	$4.80286 \cdot 10^{-10}$ statcoulomb $1.60206 \cdot 10^{-19}$ coulomb
Faraday constant		$9.65219 \cdot 10^{4}$ coulombs per gram molecular weight $9.65219 \cdot 10^{7}$ coulombs per kilogram molecular weight
Mass of the electron*		$9.1085 \cdot 10^{-28}$ g $5.48763 \cdot 10^{-4}$ amu 0.510976 Mev
Mass of the neutron*		$1.67470 \cdot 10^{-24}$ g 1.008982 amu 939.505 Mev
Mass of the proton*		$1.67239 \cdot 10^{-24}$ g 1.007593 amu 938.211 Mev
Planck's constant	h	$6.62517 \cdot 10^{-27}$ erg sec $6.62517 \cdot 10^{-34}$ joule sec
Speed of light in vacuum	c	$2.997930 \cdot 10^{10}$ cm/sec $2.997930 \cdot 10^{8}$ m/sec $1.86283 \cdot 10^{5}$ miles/sec
Temperature of absolute zero		$-273.15°$C
Universal gravitational constant	G	$6.670 \cdot 10^{-8}$ dyne cm^2/g^2 $6.670 \cdot 10^{-11}$ newton m^2/kg^2

* The mass given is the rest mass.

Table AD-1

THE ELEMENTS, IN THE ORDER OF THEIR ATOMIC NUMBERS*

1 Hydrogen	27 Cobalt	53 Iodine	79 Gold
2 Helium	28 Nickel	54 Xenon	80 Mercury
3 Lithium	29 Copper	55 Cesium	81 Thallium
4 Beryllium	30 Zinc	56 Barium	82 Lead
5 Boron	31 Gallium	57 Lanthanum	83 Bismuth
6 Carbon	32 Germanium	58 Cerium	84 Polonium
7 Nitrogen	33 Arsenic	59 Praseodymium	85 Astatine
8 Oxygen	34 Selenium	60 Neodymium	86 Radon
9 Fluorine	35 Bromine	61 Promethium	87 Francium
10 Neon	36 Krypton	62 Samarium	88 Radium
11 Sodium	37 Rubidium	63 Europium	89 Actinium
12 Magnesium	38 Strontium	64 Gadolinium	90 Thorium
13 Aluminum	39 Yttrium	65 Terbium	91 Protoactinium
14 Silicon	40 Zirconium	66 Dysprosium	92 Uranium
15 Phosphorus	41 Niobium	67 Holmium	93 Neptunium
16 Sulfur	42 Molybdenum	68 Erbium	94 Plutonium
17 Chlorine	43 Technetium	69 Thulium	95 Americium
18 Argon	44 Ruthenium	70 Ytterbium	96 Curium
19 Potassium	45 Rhodium	71 Lutecium	97 Berkelium
20 Calcium	46 Palladium	72 Hafnium	98 Californium
21 Scandium	47 Silver	73 Tantalum	99 Einsteinium
22 Titanium	48 Cadmium	74 Tungsten	100 Fermium
23 Vanadium	49 Indium	75 Rhenium	101 Mendelevium
24 Chromium	50 Tin	76 Osmium	102 Nobelium
25 Manganese	51 Antimony	77 Iridium	103 Lawrencium
26 Iron	52 Tellurium	78 Platinum	

* See also the Periodic Chart, Table 36-1 (page 653) and the more complete table of elements in alphabetic order (Table AD-2).

Table AD-2

NAMES, SYMBOLS, ATOMIC NUMBERS, AND ATOMIC WEIGHTS OF THE ELEMENTS

Element	Symbol	Atomic Number	Atomic Weight*	Element	Symbol	Atomic Number	Atomic Weight*
Actinium†	Ac	89	227	*Einsteinium*	E	99	(255)
Aluminum	Al	13	26.99	Erbium	Er	68	167.32
Americium	Am	95	(243)	Europium	Eu	63	152.0
Antimony	Sb	51	121.79	*Fermium*	Fm	100	(255)
Argon	A	18	39.955	Fluorine	F	9	19.01
Arsenic	As	33	74.93	*Francium*	Fr	87	223
Astatine	At	85	(210)	Gadolinium	Gd	64	157.30
Barium	Ba	56	137.40	Gallium	Ga	31	69.74
Berkelium	Bk	97	(249)	Germanium	Ge	32	72.62
Beryllium	Be	4	9.015	Gold	Au	79	197.1
Bismuth	Bi	83	209.06	Hafnium	Hf	72	178.55
Boron	B	5	10.82	Helium	He	2	4.0039
Bromine	Br	35	79.938	Holmium	Ho	67	164.98
Cadmium	Cd	48	112.44	Hydrogen	H	1	1.0083
Calcium	Ca	20	40.09	Indium‡	In	49	114.85
Californium	Cf	98	(249)	Iodine	I	53	126.94
Carbon	C	6	12.014	Iridium	Ir	77	192.2
Cerium	Ce	58	140.17	Iron	Fe	26	55.87
Cesium	Cs	55	132.95	Krypton	Kr	36	83.82
Chlorine	Cl	17	35.467	Lanthanum‡	La	57	138.96
Chromium	Cr	24	52.02	*Lawrencium*	Lw	103	(257)
Cobalt	Co	27	58.96	Lead	Pb	82	207.27
Copper	Cu	29	63.56	Lithium	Li	3	6.942
Curium	Cm	96	(245)	Lutecium‡	Lu	71	175.04
Dysprosium	Dy	66	162.55	Magnesium	Mg	12	24.33
				Manganese	Mn	25	54.95

* Atomic weights are given on the old physical scale (see last two paragraphs of Sec. 36-6), which is based on the O^{16} isotope as exactly 16; hence the values are slightly higher than those on the chemical scale, which are based on natural oxygen (which contains very small quantities of the O^{17} and O^{18} isotopes) as exactly 16.

† Elements in italics have no stable isotopes; all are radioactive. Elements which do not occur naturally have their atomic weights in parentheses. The term "atomic weight" in its usual sense does not apply to such elements; the values given are the mass numbers of the longest-lived isotope.

‡ These elements have at least one stable and one radioactive naturally occurring isotope.

Table AD-2 *(continued)*

Element	Symbol	Atomic Number	Atomic Weight*	Element	Symbol	Atomic Number	Atomic Weight*
Mendelevium	Mv	101	(256)	Ruthenium	Ru	44	101.7
Mercury	Hg	80	200.66	Samarium‡	Sm	62	150.39
Molybdenum	Mo	42	95.98	Scandium	Sc	21	44.97
Neodymium‡	Nd	60	144.31	Selenium	Se	34	78.98
Neon	Ne	10	20.188	Silicon	Si	14	28.10
Neptunium	Np	93	(237)	Silver	Ag	47	107.909
Nickel	Ni	28	58.73	Sodium	Na	11	22.997
Niobium	Nb	41	92.94	Strontium	Sr	38	87.65
Nitrogen	N	7	14.012	Sulfur	S	16	32.075
Nobelium	No	102	(253)	Tantalum	Ta	73	181.00
Osmium	Os	76	190.3	Technetium	Tc	43	(99)
Oxygen	O	8	16.0044	Tellurium	Te	52	127.64
Palladium	Pd	46	106.4	Terbium	Tb	65	158.97
Phosphorus	P	15	30.983	Thallium	Tl	81	204.45
Platinum‡	Pt	78	195.14	*Thorium*	Th	90	232.11
Plutonium	Pu	94	(242)	Thulium	Tm	69	168.99
Polonium	Po	84	210	Tin	Sn	50	118.73
Potassium‡	K	19	39.111	Titanium	Ti	22	47.91
Praseodymium	Pr	59	140.96	Tungsten	W	74	183.91
Promethium	Pm	61	(145)	*Uranium*	U	92	238.13
Protoactinium	Pa	91	231	Vanadium‡	V	23	50.96
Radium	Ra	88	226.11	Xenon	Xe	54	131.34
Radon	Rn	86	222	Ytterbium	Yb	70	173.09
Rhenium‡	Re	75	186.27	Yttrium	Y	39	88.94
Rhodium	Rh	45	102.94	Zinc	Zn	30	65.40
Rubidium‡	Rb	37	85.50	Zirconium	Zr	40	91.24

* Atomic weights are given on the old physical scale (see last two paragraphs of Sec. 36-6), which is based on the 0^{16} isotope as exactly 16; hence the values are slightly higher than those on the chemical scale, which are based on natural oxygen (which contains very small quantities of the 0^{17} and 0^{18} isotopes) as exactly 16.

† Elements in italics have no stable isotopes; all are radioactive. Elements which do not occur naturally have their atomic weights in parentheses. The term "atomic weight" in its usual sense does not apply to such elements; the values given are the mass numbers of the longest-lived isotope.

‡ These elements have at least one stable and one radioactive naturally occurring isotope.

APPENDIX E

THE SOLUTION OF EQUATIONS

To begin with, let us consider some typical equations and how they are solved, and then see whether we can find any generalized method of attack. To facilitate reference to a specific example, each one is numbered.

Suppose that we have an equation like this:

$$x + 9.73 = 22.85 \tag{1}$$

We are not interested in what x plus something is; we want the value of x itself. But our equation simply says that 22.85 is 9.73 more than x, so x must be 9.73 less than 22.85. Then

$$x = 22.85 - 9.73 = 13.12$$

We may have an equation such as

$$x - 0.22 = 5.91 \tag{2}$$

This means that 5.91 is 0.22 less than x, so x must be greater than 5.91 by 0.22:

$$x = 5.91 + 0.22 = 6.13$$

Again, if

$$4.55x = 22.75 \tag{3}$$

we know that 22.75 is 4.55 times as large as x, so x must be 1/4.55 of 22.75:

$$x = \frac{22.75}{4.55} = 5.00$$

We may have an equation like

$$\frac{x}{944} = 3.00 \tag{4}$$

This means that 3.00 is only $\frac{1}{944}$ of x, so x must be 944 times as large as 3.00:

$$x = 3.00 \times 944 = 2832$$

If we wish to find the length of one side of a square when we know the area, or in some similar situation, we might have an equation like

$$x^2 = 3.61 \tag{5}$$

Since the square of x is 3.61, x must be the square root of 3.61:

$$x = \sqrt{3.61} = 1.9$$

Finally, we might have a situation which is the reverse of the last one, such as

$$\sqrt[3]{x} = 4.00 \tag{6}$$

Now, if 4.00 is the cube root of x, this just means that 4.00 must be used as a factor three times to equal x:

$$x = 4.00 \cdot 4.00 \cdot 4.00 = 4.00^3 = 64.0$$

Now let us examine our six equations and their methods of solution.

In (1), where a term was *added to* x, we *subtracted* that term.

In (2), where a term was *subtracted from* x, we *added* that term.

In (3), where x was *multiplied by* a factor, we *divided by* that factor.

In (4), where x was *divided by* a quantity, we *multiplied by* that quantity.

In (5), where x was *squared,* we *took the square root.*

In (6), where we had a *root* of x, we *raised to the corresponding power.*

Thus, in every one of these six typical equations, we solved for the unknown by *performing* an *arithmetical operation* which was the *exact opposite* of the *operation* on x *which* the *equation stated.* Where something was added to x, we got x itself by subtracting; where x was raised to a power, we took the corresponding root; etc.

Of course, in every case we did the same thing to both sides of the equation, as we always must. If we subtracted a term on the left side of the equation to get x by itself, we also subtracted the same quantity from the right side; etc.

Appendix F
REVIEW OF MATHEMATICS

This section of the Appendix emphasizes specific procedures, for the most part. More general mathematical suggestions are given in Sec. 2-7 – 2-16, inclusive. Additional information will be found in Appendices E, G, and H.

The essential basis of any mathematical statement or procedure is the *equation.* An equation is a *statement of equality* between the quantities on the opposite sides of the equals sign. Although this is quite obvious, failure to realize it fully, and to make use of it habitually, leads many students into difficulties. If you put down an algebraic expression, such as $m_0/\sqrt{1-\beta^2}$, or a numerical expression like $4.71 \cdot 980/12.3$ without recording the *complete equation* of which the expression is a *part,* it seems to be very easy to lose track of the significance of the expression. If you *always* record *complete equations,* confusion and error from this source will be eliminated.

Nothing ever may be permitted to violate an equation. This means that if you do anything to one side of the equation, you must do the same thing to the other side so that the two sides of the equation will still be equal. This is the basis of transposition, "cross multiplying," and similar procedures. For example, given the equation

$$\frac{x}{3} + 12 = 5y$$

you can subtract 12 from *both* sides:

$$\begin{array}{rcl} \dfrac{x}{3} + 12 & = & 5y \\ -\ 12 & & -\ 12 \\ \hline \dfrac{x}{3} \qquad & = & 5y - 12 \end{array}$$

Thus, $+12$ has been transposed from the left side to the right, where it became -12; but this was legitimate *only* because it involved subtracting the *same* thing from *both* sides. Similarly, we can solve the new equation for x by cross multiplying, but this is simply a matter of multiplying *both* sides by 3 (or dividing both by $\frac{1}{3}$):

$$\frac{x}{3}\cdot 3 = (5y - 12)\cdot 3$$

$$x = 15y - 36$$

If an equation involves multiplication or division, and also addition or subtraction, in general all multiplication and division is to be done before any additions or subtractions are performed. Any quantities *enclosed within parentheses,* however, are to be added or subtracted *before* being multiplied or divided by any quantity *outside* the parentheses. For example, x does not have the same value in the two equations below:

$$2\cdot 3x + 8 = 26$$
$$2\cdot(3x + 8) = 26$$

The first of these becomes

$$6x + 8 = 26$$

from which
$$6x = 26 - 8 = 18$$

and
$$x = \frac{18}{6} = 3$$

But because of the parentheses in the second equation it becomes

$$6x + 16 = 26$$

and then
$$6x = 26 - 16 = 10$$

so in this case
$$x = \frac{10}{6} = \frac{5}{3}$$

which is vastly different from 3, the value obtained from an equation which differed only in that it lacked the parentheses.

A root may be expressed as a fractional exponent: $\sqrt[n]{a} = a^{1/n}$. For example, if $x^2 = y$, we may write the solution as $x = \pm\sqrt{y}$, or as $\pm y^{1/2}$. Note that the solution may have either a positive or a negative value.

A reciprocal of a quantity may be expressed by using a negative exponent. For example, $(1/x)^3$ or $1/x^3$ may be written as x^{-3}; $1/n = n^{-1}$; and so on.

A binomial, such as $a \pm b$, may always be raised to a power by multiplying it out, but often it is more convenient to use a general formula and fit it to the problem at hand. The generalized expansion is

$$(a + b)^n = a^n + n\cdot a^{n-1}b + \frac{n(n-1)}{2!}\cdot a^{n-2}b^2 + \frac{n(n-1)(n-2)}{3!}a^{n-3}b^3 + \cdots + b^n$$

An expression such as 3! is read as "three factorial," and represents $1\cdot 2\cdot 3$; thus 5! would equal $1\cdot 2\cdot 3\cdot 4\cdot 5$, and so forth.

As an example of this formula, consider $(x + y)^3$.

$$(x + y)^3 = x^3 + 3x^{3-1}y + \frac{3\cdot 2}{1\cdot 2}x^{3-2}y^2 + \frac{3\cdot 2\cdot 1}{1\cdot 2\cdot 3}x^{3-3}y^3$$
$$= x^3 + 3x^2y + 3xy^2 + y^3$$

The series ends with the term in which the exponent of the second term in the binomial becomes equal to the power to which the binomial is raised. Thus, in the general formula, in which $(a + b)$ is raised to the nth power, the series ends with b^n; and in the example of $(x + y)$ raised to the third power the series ends with y^3. In the example above, this final term does not include x, since the power of x is zero and anything to the zero power is equal to 1. This disappearance of the first member of the binomial from the final term of the expansion is general, if the power is integral. It does not disappear if the exponent is a fraction; also, in this case, there is no final term, the expansion yielding an infinite series.

As indicated, the formula for a binomial may be employed with fractional exponents as well as when the exponent is integral. An example of the usefulness of this appears in Sec. 32-6. The exponent need not be positive; in the example in Sec. 32-6, the exponent is negative as well as fractional.

Instead of having the form $(a + b)$ the binomial may be of the form $(a - b)$. In such a case, all terms containing odd powers of b will be negative and those with even powers of b will be positive. The result is that the first term will be positive, and positive and negative signs will alternate throughout the series of terms.

The inverse of expanding a binomial is finding the binomial corresponding to an equation in the expanded form. For example, expansion of $(a - b)^2$ yields $a^2 - 2ab + b^2$; so when we see an equation in the form of $a^2 - 2ab + b^2$ we know that it is the square of $(a - b)$. Thus if we have

$$9x^2 + 30x = -25$$

we may rearrange it to

$$9x^2 + 30x + 25 = 0$$

The first term is the square of $3x$, and the third term is the square of 5; also, the second term is equal to $2 \cdot 3x \cdot 5$. Thus the left side of the equation has the form $a^2 + 2ab + b^2$, and we know that this is the square of $(a + b)$. Hence

$$9x^2 + 30x + 25 = (3x + 5)^2 = 0$$

This equation can be true only if $3x + 5 = 0$, so

$$3x = -5$$

$$x = -\frac{5}{3}$$

Any equation which contains the square of a quantity (and no higher powers of that quantity) is a *quadratic* equation. Most quadratic equations are not perfect squares like the example above, so they cannot be solved in that manner.

Often a quadratic equation can be solved by factoring. It may be possible to do this by inspection, but the various tricks which aid in factoring by inspection are so numerous and require so much in the way of explanation and examples that space does not allow their inclusion here. Any algebra text should help.

It is always possible, though sometimes awkward, to solve a quadratic equation by a method called "completing the square." For example, consider the equation

$$9x^2 + 30x + 21 = 0$$

This differs from the example in the third paragraph above only in that the third term is 21 instead of 25; but this difference makes it impossible to proceed exactly as before. However, we can make the *left* side of the equation exactly the same as before by adding 4, and this is perfectly legal *if* we add 4 to the right side also. The result is

$$9x^2 + 30x + 25 = 4$$

Now each side is a perfect square, and on taking the square root of *each* side we obtain

$$3x + 5 = \pm 2$$

$$3x = \pm 2 - 5 = -3, \quad \text{or} \quad -7$$

$$x = -1, \quad \text{or} \quad -\frac{7}{3}$$

Note that there are *two* solutions of the equation. A quadratic equation always has two different solutions except in the case where one side of the equation is a perfect square and the other side is zero; in this case the two solutions are equal, so in effect there is but one.

The method of solving a quadratic equation by completing the square may be generalized and formalized as follows:

If
$$ax^2 + bx + c = 0$$

$$x = \frac{-b \pm \sqrt{b^2 - 4ac}}{2a}$$

Thus, in the equation $9x^2 + 30x + 21$, $a = 9$, $b = 30$, and $c = 21$; so

$$x = \frac{-30 \pm \sqrt{30^2 - 4 \cdot 9 \cdot 21}}{2 \cdot 9} = \frac{-30 \pm \sqrt{900 - 756}}{18} = \frac{-30 \pm \sqrt{144}}{18}$$

$$= \frac{-30 \pm 12}{18} = \frac{-18 \text{ or } -42}{18}$$

$$= -1 \quad \text{or} \quad -\frac{7}{3}$$

If two triangles are similar, corresponding sides stand in the same ratio. This means that if the sides of one are a, b, and c, and the corresponding sides of the other are a', b', and c',

$$\frac{a'}{a} = \frac{b'}{b} = \frac{c'}{c}$$

Two triangles are similar if two angles in one equal two angles in the other, or if their sides are mutually parallel, or if their sides are mutually perpendicular.

A line is said to be *perpendicular* to another if the angle between them (the lines being extended, if necessary, until they meet) is exactly 90°. A line which is constructed so that it is perpendicular to another line may be called a *normal* to the second line.

Appendix G

ELEMENTS OF TRIGONOMETRY

The "tri-" in trigonometry obviously implies "three," the "-gon-" comes from a Greek root meaning "corner," and "-metry" means "measurement"; thus

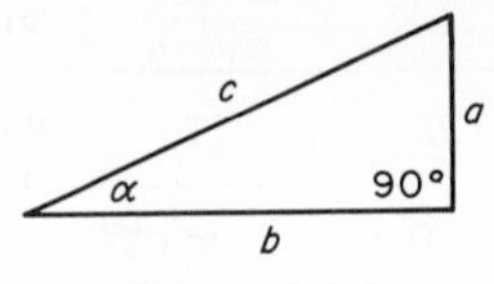

Figure AG-1

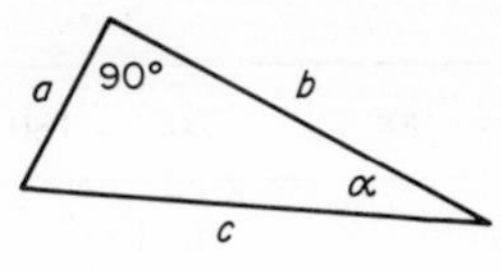

Figure AG-2

trigonometry has to do with the measurement of triangles. Trigonometry is very useful in physics because we have to deal so often with a triangle—in the addition or resolution of vector quantities, the computation of work when the directions of the force and the displacement are not exactly parallel, in the refraction of light, and in many other instances.

The most useful of the trigonometric functions are the ***sine,*** the ***cosine,*** and the ***tangent,*** which are abbreviated *sin, cos,* and *tan,* respectively. They are defined in terms of the sides of a right triangle, and the definitions are illustrated in Fig. AG-1. In this figure, the side a is termed the side ***opposite*** angle α, side b is called the side ***adjacent*** to angle α, and of course side c is the ***hypotenuse.***

The sine of an angle is the ratio of the opposite side to the hypotenuse:

$$\text{sine } \alpha = \frac{\text{side opposite}}{\text{hypotenuse}}, \quad \text{or} \quad \sin \alpha = \frac{a}{c}$$

The cosine of an angle is the ratio of the adjacent side to the hypotenuse:

$$\text{cosine } \alpha = \frac{\text{side adjacent}}{\text{hypotenuse}}, \quad \text{or} \quad \cos \alpha = \frac{b}{c}$$

The tangent of an angle is the ratio of the opposite side to the adjacent side:

$$\text{tangent } \alpha = \frac{\text{side opposite}}{\text{side adjacent}}, \quad \text{or} \quad \tan \alpha = \frac{a}{b}$$

These defining equations may be rearranged:

$$a = c \cdot \sin \alpha, \quad \text{and} \quad c = \frac{a}{\sin \alpha}$$

$$b = c \cdot \cos \alpha, \quad \text{and} \quad c = \frac{b}{\cos \alpha}$$

$$a = b \cdot \tan \alpha, \quad \text{and} \quad b = \frac{a}{\tan \alpha}$$

No importance should be attached to the orientation, or the shape, of the triangle in Fig. AG-1, except that one of its angles is 90°. Definitions based on Fig. AG-2, or any other similarly labeled right triangle, would be equally valid.

Values of the trigonometric functions must be obtained, in general, from tables. (See Appendix J.) Though the table is limited to angles from 0° to 90°, it may be used for any angle. Table AG-1 shows how this is done. Values of the functions for angles from 0° to 90°, taken directly from the table in Appendix J are represented in the left column. The next column of Table AG-1 shows that a function of an angle between 90° and 180° is obtained by subtracting the angle from 180° and looking up the function of the resulting angle; and as indicated, some of the values are negative rather

Table AG-1

$0° - 90°$	$90° - 180°$	$180° - 270°$	$270° - 360°$
$\sin \alpha$	$\sin (180° - \alpha)$	$-\sin (\alpha - 180°)$	$-\sin (360° - \alpha)$
$\cos \alpha$	$-\cos (180° - \alpha)$	$-\cos (\alpha - 180°)$	$\cos (360° - \alpha)$
$\tan \alpha$	$-\tan (180° - \alpha)$	$\tan (\alpha - 180°)$	$-\tan (360° - \alpha)$

than positive. For example, the sine of 20° is 0.3420. 160° lies between 90° and 180° so, according to the second column,

$$\sin 160° = \sin (180° - 160°) = \sin 20°$$

thus 0.3420 is also the sine of 160°. In accord with the third column,

$$\sin 200° = -\sin (200° - 180°) = -\sin 20°$$

So $\sin 200° = -0.3420$. Finally,

$$\sin 340° = -\sin (360° - 340°) = -\sin 20° = -0.3420$$

It is convenient to be able to use the trigonometric functions of a few common angles without having to look them up, and without rote memorization. From the definitions of the functions we know the values at 0° and 90°:

$$\sin 0° = 0, \quad \cos 0° = 1.0000, \quad \text{and} \quad \tan 0° = 0$$

$$\sin 90° = 1.0000, \quad \cos 90° = 0, \quad \text{and} \quad \tan 90° = \infty$$

The Pythagorean theorem enables us to deduce the values of the functions for 30°, 45°, and 60°. In any right triangle with a 30° angle, the hypotenuse is twice as long as the side opposite the 30° angle, as in Fig. AG-3; thus the side adjacent to the 30° angle is $\sqrt{3}$ times as long as the side opposite. Hence

$$\sin 30° = \frac{1}{2}, \quad \cos 30° = \frac{\sqrt{3}}{2}, \quad \text{and} \quad \tan 30° = \frac{1}{\sqrt{3}} = \frac{\sqrt{3}}{3}$$

The figure shows also that

$$\sin 60° = \frac{\sqrt{3}}{2}, \quad \cos 60° = 1/2, \quad \text{and} \quad \tan 60° = \sqrt{3}$$

In a right triangle with a 45° angle, as in Fig. AG-4, the side opposite and the side adjacent are equal, and the hypotenuse is $\sqrt{2}$ times as long as either. Hence

$$\sin 45° = \frac{1}{\sqrt{2}} = \frac{\sqrt{2}}{2}, \quad \cos 45° = \sin 45° = \frac{\sqrt{2}}{2}, \quad \text{and} \quad \tan 45° = 1$$

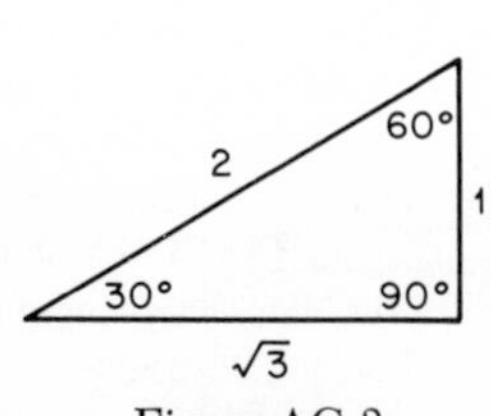

Figure AG-3

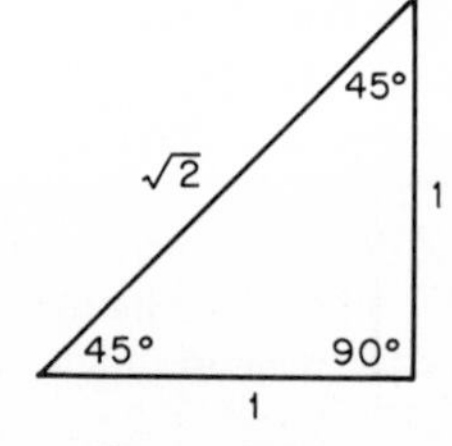

Figure AG-4

If the unlabeled acute angle in Fig. AG-1 or Fig. AG-2 is identified as angle β, review of the definitions of the functions will show that

$$\sin \alpha = \cos \beta,\ \cos \alpha = \sin \beta, \text{ and } \tan \alpha = 1/\tan \beta$$

Since the definitions are in terms of a right triangle and the sum of the angles in any triangle is 180°, the sum of α and β must be 90°; so

$$\alpha = 90° - \beta, \quad \text{and} \quad \beta = 90° - \alpha$$

Therefore, in general,

$$\sin \alpha = \cos (90° - \alpha)$$
$$\cos \alpha = \sin (90° - \alpha)$$
$$\tan \alpha = \frac{1}{\tan (90° - \alpha)}$$

Computations on triangles which are not right triangles may be made with the aid of one of two equations which are derived in trigonometry courses but are offered here without derivation. The first of these is the *law of sines*. If a triangle is labeled as in Fig. AG-5

$$\frac{a}{\sin \alpha} = \frac{b}{\sin \beta} = \frac{c}{\sin \gamma}$$

The second equation is the *law of cosines*. Referring again to the labeling in Fig. AG-5

$$b^2 = a^2 + c^2 - 2ac \cdot \cos \beta$$

Note that the law of cosines reduces to the Pythagorean theorem for a right triangle, for in that case

$$\beta = 90°, \quad \text{and} \quad \cos 90° = 0$$

Examples

1. If a force of 50.0 lb is exerted at 40.0° above the horizontal, find its horizontal component. If this is represented graphically, the horizontal component is the side of a right triangle adjacent to the 40.0° angle and the 50.0 lb force is the hypotenuse. Thus the horizontal component divided by the full force is the cosine of 40.0°, or the component is

$$(50.0 \cos 40.0°) \text{ lb}$$

From the table on page 782, cos 40.0° = 0.7660, so the horizontal component is

$$50.0 \cdot 0.7660 = 38.3 \text{ lb}$$

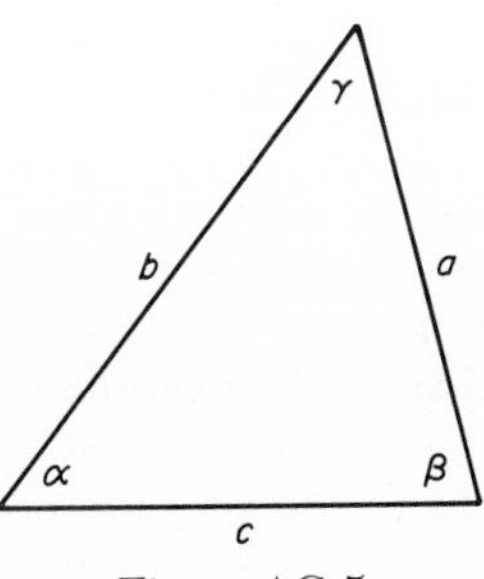

Figure AG-5

2. The angles of a triangle are 35.0°, 80.0°, and 65.0°. If the side joining the 35.0° and 80.0° angles is 20.0 cm long, how long are the others? If S_{80} and S_{35} represent the sides opposite the 80.0° and 35.0° angles, respectively, according to the law of sines

$$\frac{S_{80}}{\sin 80.0°} = \frac{20.0}{\sin 65.0°}$$

and

$$\frac{S_{35}}{\sin 35.0°} = \frac{20.0}{\sin 65.0°}$$

From the tables, sin 35.0° = 0.5736, sin 65.0° = 0.9063, and sin 80.0° = 0.9848. Inserting the appropriate values into the equations and rearranging them so that the unknowns are left alone, we have

$$S_{80} = \frac{20.0 \cdot 0.9848}{0.9063} = 21.7\bar{3} \text{ cm}$$

and

$$S_{35} = \frac{20.0 \cdot 0.5736}{0.9063} = 12.6\bar{6} \text{ cm}$$

3. Suppose that in this same triangle we knew only the size of the 80.0° angle and the lengths of the two sides adjacent to it—20.0 cm and 12.66 cm. To find the length of the third side we could use the law of cosines:

$$S^2 = 20.0^2 + 12.6\bar{6}^2 - 2 \cdot 20.0 \cdot 12.6\bar{6} \cdot \cos 80.0°$$

From the tables, the cosine of 80.0° is 0.1736, so

$$\begin{aligned} S^2 &= 400.\bar{0} + 160.\bar{3} - 2 \cdot 20.0 \cdot 12.6\bar{6} \cdot 0.1736 \\ &= 560.\bar{3} - 87.96 = 472.\bar{3} \\ S &= \sqrt{472.\bar{3}} = 21.7\bar{3} \text{ cm} \end{aligned}$$

which checks with the value derived by using the law of sines.

Appendix H
THE USE OF LOGARITHMS

1. Purpose

The study of physics, whether in the lecture part of the course or in the laboratory, involves a considerable amount of calculation. Where calculations involve the multiplication of many factors, the division of large numbers, or the finding of a power of a large number, much time and effort can be saved by performing the computations logarithmically. But it is in the finding of roots—which must be done sometimes—that the greatest saving of time, effort, and temper is effected.

Since many students have not had any opportunity to learn to use logarithms, and others have allowed their facility with logarithms to "get rusty," these instructions are provided for their use.

Don't let the word "logarithm" scare you. The use of these aids to computation is *not* difficult to learn.

2. What Is a Logarithm?

Logarithms of the kind we shall use are called common logarithms to distinguish them from another type which will not concern us. We shall speak simply of logarithms, dropping the adjective "common."

The ***logarithm*** of a number is the power to which 10 must be raised to give that number. Thus, to get 1000 you must take $10 \cdot 10 \cdot 10$, or 10^3. And since you must raise 10 to the third power to get 1000, the logarithm of 1000 is 3.

A logarithm need not be a whole number, however, and seldom is. The square root of 10 is 3.162. We may express this square root as $\sqrt{10}$, or we may write it as $10^{1/2}$ or $10^{0.5}$; so the logarithm of 3.162 is 0.5. But the logarithm need not even correspond to such a root; it may have any value. For example, the logarithm of 2000 is 3.3010, which is to say that $10^{3.3010}$ equals 2000. Don't worry about how these values are determined; all *we* need do is to look them up in a table.

3. The Parts of a Logarithm

Do you mind if I save a few pages by using the colloquialism "log" for logarithm? Thanks.

In Sec. 2 we found 3.3010 given as an example of a log, it being the log of 2000.

The part of this log—or any other—to the left of the decimal can always be determined by inspection. It is called the ***characteristic*** of the log.

The portion to the right of the decimal can be determined only by calculation or by reference to tables. We shall rely solely on tables! This portion is the ***mantissa*** of the logarithm.

4. Evaluating the Characteristic of the Log of a Number

Returning again to our example of log 2000 = 3.3010, I should like to convince you that you can tell by looking at the number 2000 that the characteristic of its log must be 3.

2000 is more than 1000 but less than 10,000. Any argument about that? Now, 1000 is 10^3, so its log is exactly 3. And the log of 10,000 is exactly 4, since $10{,}000 = 10^4$. Then, since 2000 is more than 1000, its log has to be larger than 3. But since it is smaller than 10,000 its log cannot be as large as 4. So the log of 2000 must be three-point-something.

What is the characteristic of the log of 4,729,000? The value of this number is greater than 1,000,000 and less than 10,000,000. 1,000,000 is 10^6 and 10,000,000 is 10^7. So the log of 4,729,000 cannot be less than 6 nor as much as 7; hence its characteristic must be 6.

By finding the characteristics of many such numbers, all larger than 1, we find that the value of the characteristic of any number larger than 1 is one less than the number of digits to the left of the decimal point.

In our two examples, 2000 had four digits to the left of the decimal and we found its characteristic to be 3; there are seven digits to the left of the decimal in 4,729,000, and we found its characteristic to be 6. And we would find our rule to check in any other example we might study as it does in these, so long as we deal with numbers greater than 1.

5. Characteristic of a Fraction

What of a number like 0.007, which has no digits other than zero to the left of the decimal?

To answer this question, let us take a number such as 5000, to find its characteristic; and then let us divide it repeatedly by 10, determining its characteristic after each division.

The characteristic of 5000 is 3, since there are four digits to the left of the decimal point.

Dividing by 10, we have 500, with a characteristic of 2.

Dividing again by 10, we have 50 and a characteristic of 1.

So far, each time we divide by 10 the characteristic has been reduced by one. (This is a necessary consequence of the nature of a log, isn't it?) So we may expect this to continue.

Thus, dividing 50 by 10, we get 5, with a characteristic of one less than 1, or 0.

Dividing 5 by 10, we have 0.5; and taking 1 from 0, we find the characteristic to be −1.

Continuing, we get 0.05; 0.005; 0.0005; etc., with characteristics respectively of −2; −3; −4; etc.

Thus, we arrive at the conclusion that if a number has no digits other than zero to the left of the decimal, its characteristic will be negative. The numerical value we may find by counting the number of zeros between the decimal and the first digit which is not zero, and adding one to this number.

We may combine our two rules into a single guide for finding the characteristic of any number, whether it is a fraction or not. This rule may be stated as follows:

> Starting *after* the first digit which is not zero, count the number of places over to the decimal point. This is the numerical value of the characteristic. If the number of which you are finding the logarithm is less than one (if the number is a fraction) the characteristic is negative.

Thus, the characteristic of 472,000 is 5; that of 0.00002 is −5; that of 77.32 is 1; that of 0.218 is −1; and that of 6.977 is 0.

For reasons that will appear later, a negative characteristic is written as the difference between some positive number and 10. Thus −2 is written as 8 − 10; −6 as 4 − 10; −1 as 9 − 10; etc.

6. The Characteristic of a Negative Number

Some students are confused when they have to find the log of a number which is negative, such as the log of −22.12. The minus sign is totally disregarded in finding the log of the number and in carrying out the calculations; −22.12 is treated exactly as if it were 22.12. Only when the numerical value of the final result has been determined is the minus sign considered. Then the sign of the final answer is determined exactly as if the calculation had been carried out without the aid of logs.

7. Evaluating the Mantissa. How to Use the Log Table

To find the value of the mantissa of the log of a number, we must use a log table. There are various forms of these, and they are "carried out" to different numbers of digits. For our purposes a "four-place" table will give sufficient accuracy, and such a table is much easier to use than a "five-place" or "seven-place" table.

A log table gives *only* the mantissa—the part of the log to the right of the decimal. The characteristic must be evaluated by inspection as outlined in the three sections preceding; and the student must remember to put a decimal point after the characteristic and before the mantissa.

The value of the mantissa found in the table for 2.2 (for example) will be precisely the same as that for 220 or 220,000,000 or 0.000000022. It is *only* the number sequence, 22, which is of any importance here. The position of the decimal point concerns us *only* in finding the characteristic.

Let's find the mantissa of the log of the number sequence 22.

In the table on page 778, at the extreme left is a column headed N. If you go down this column you will find 22 about a quarter of the way down. On the same horizontal line as 22, and in the column next to the right, you find the value 3424. This is the mantissa of the log of any number having the number sequence 22 with nothing, or only zeros, after the second 2.

Thus, if the number is 220, the characteristic is 2 and the mantissa is 3424, making the complete log 2.3424. If the number is 220,000, its log is 5.3424; if 0.022, 8.3424 − 10 (a characteristic of 8 − 10 and a mantissa of 3424, which really is 8.0000 − 10 + 0.3424 or 8.3424 − 10); etc.

Similarly, the mantissa of the number sequence 97 is 9868; that of 62 is 7924; that of 11 is 0414, etc.

Suppose that our number sequence is not 22, but 227. In this case we find the mantissa on the horizontal line with 22 but under the (wide) column headed 7 rather than in the 0 column. Here we find the value 3560 for the mantissa.

Similarly, the mantissa for the number sequence 971 is 9872; of 625, 7959; of 117, 0682; etc.

But what if our number sequence contains four numbers, such as 2273? Then we go along the same horizontal line where we found the mantissas of 22 and of 227, until we find the narrow column at the right which has 3, our last digit, at the top of the column. In this column and on this line we find the value 6. To get the mantissa of 2273 we must add 6 to the mantissa of 227, so we have 3560 + 6 or 3566.

For 9712, we find the mantissa to be 9872 + 1 or 9873; for 6259, 7959 + 6 or 7965; for 1177, 0682 + 26 or 0708; etc.

If the number has more than four digits, such as 22,736,629, then what? We shall have to "round it off" to four significant digits only. Thus, in the example given, we would find the mantissa of the number sequence 2274, and combine this with a characteristic of 7.

8. The Complete Logarithm

Following the methods of the four sections preceding we may look up the logarithms of several numbers. Work them out yourself, and check the values given.

Number	4218	0.002171	0.9190	2.037	0.5103	66720
Log	3.6251	7.3369−10	9.9633−10	0.3090	9.7079−10	4.8242

9. Antilogarithms

It may disappoint you to find that an antilogarithm does not protect from logs in the same way that an antifreeze protects from freezing. An ***antilogarithm*** (let's call it an antilog) is the number which corresponds to the logarithm. Thus, if the log of 4218 is 3.6251, 4218 is the antilog of 3.6251.

Antilogs may be "looked up" in a log table, but it is more convenient to use a special table of antilogs. (See the tables on pages 780, 781.)

10. Use of an Antilog Table

In using an antilog table, it is important to remember that *only* the mantissa is considered in looking up the antilog. Thus whether the log is 6.7170 or 0.7170 or 3.7170 − 10, you will look up the same value, .7170, in the table.

The technique of looking up an antilog in the antilog table is similar to that used in finding a log in the log table. Thus, if we wish the antilog of .7600, we look in the left-hand column to find .76. In the adjacent column, on the same horizontal line, we find 5754, so 5754 is the number sequence of the antilog of .7600.

If the mantissa is .7620 instead of .7600, the value in the column headed 2 will be taken; this is 5781. And if the mantissa is .7625, we look under the "5" column at the right, in the same horizontal line as .76, and find the value 7; so we add 7 to 5781, obtaining 5788.

11. "Spotting" the Decimal Point in the Antilog

Finding where the decimal point should go in the antilog, once we have found the antilog from the table, is just the reverse of finding the characteristic of the log of a number. In finding the characteristic, we observe the position of the decimal point and from this decide what the value of the characteristic is. In spotting the decimal point in an antilog, we observe the value of the characteristic of the log and this tells us where the decimal point must go.

You can develop the method by considering the meaning of the characteristic and proceeding somewhat as we did in Sec. 4 and 5. This would bring you to another simple rule.

> If the characteristic is positive, start after the first digit of the antilog and count to the right a number of places equal to the value of the characteristic; and put the decimal point there. If the characteristic is negative, count to the left instead.

Thus, if the antilog of 3.4151 is 2601, we start after the 2 and count 3 places to the right; so we have 2601. And if the antilog of 6.9139 − 10 has the number sequence 8202, we start after the 8 and count 4 places to the left, since the characteristic is 6 − 10 or −4; and so we get 0.0008202 for the antilog.

It will be excellent practice for you to look up the antilogs of the logs given in Sec. 8 and check your values against the numbers given. However, as pointed out in Sec. 18, you will not always get an *exact* check.

12. Multiplying with the Aid of Logs

If your algebra is not completely gone, you will remember that $a^m \cdot a^n$ is a^{m+n}. That is, to multiply you add exponents. Since logs are exponents of 10, we may multiply numbers by adding their logs.

Thus, if we have 6,783,000 · 0.002188, we proceed as follows:

$$\begin{aligned} \log 6{,}783{,}000 &= 6.8314 \\ \log 0.002188 &= \underline{7.3401 - 10} \\ \log \text{product} &= 14.1715 - 10 \text{ or } 4.1715 \\ \text{antilog } 4.1715 &= 14{,}850 \end{aligned}$$

Any number of factors may be multiplied together at once. For instance 2.937 · 480.3 · 0.09833 · 52.92 = ?

$$\begin{aligned} \log 2.937 &= 0.4679 \\ \log 480.3 &= 2.6815 \\ \log 0.09833 &= 8.9927 - 10 \\ \log 52.92 &= \underline{1.7237} \\ \log \text{product} &= 13.8658 - 10 \text{ or } 3.8658 \\ \text{antilog } 3.8658 &= 7342 \end{aligned}$$

13. Dividing Logarithmically

Again invoking your algebra, $a^m \div a^n = a^{m-n}$. Similarly, to divide with the aid of logs, we subtract the log of the *divisor from* that of the dividend.

If we wish to divide 4683 by 839.7, we have

$$\begin{aligned} \log 4683 &= 3.6705 \\ \log 839.7 &= \underline{2.9242} \\ \log \text{quotient} &= 0.7463 \\ \text{antilog } 0.7463 &= 5.576 \end{aligned}$$

Suppose that we wish to divide 839.7 by 4683, however. We run into difficulty:

$$\begin{aligned} \log 839.7 &= 2.9242 \\ \log 4683 &= \underline{3.6705} \\ \log \text{quotient} &= \;????\end{aligned}$$

We might subtract the other way around and give the value so obtained a negative sign, but that would give us the same number sequence in the log of the quotient as in the previous problem. If we look up the antilog of that, we would get the same answer as before, which cannot be right.

The way out of such a dilemma is to write the log 2.9242 as 12.9242 − 10. This does not change its value, but it does make it possible for us to subtract without difficulty:

$$\begin{aligned} \log 839.7 = 2.9242 &= 12.9242 - 10 \\ \log 4683 &= \underline{3.6705} \\ \log \text{quotient} &= 9.2537 - 10 \\ \text{antilog } 9.2537 - 10 &= 0.1794 \end{aligned}$$

14. Finding Some Power of a Number

Suppose that we wish to find the value of the fourth power of 73.01. We could treat this as an ordinary multiplication problem, since 73.01^4 is $73.01 \cdot 73.01 \cdot 73.01 \cdot 73.01$. Thus we could find the log of 73.01, which is 1.8634, write it down four times, and find the total. But we would get the same result with less work by just multiplying the log by 4:

$$\begin{aligned} \log 73.01 &= 1.8634 \\ &\ \ \underline{\times 4} \\ \log 73.01^4 &= 7.4536 \\ \text{antilog } 7.4536 &= 28{,}420{,}000 \end{aligned}$$

If the number being raised to a power is a fraction, we need modify our method only to the extent of simplifying the characteristic after multiplying:

$$\begin{aligned} \log 0.07301 &= 8.8634 - 10 \\ &\ \ \underline{\times 4} \\ \log 0.07301^4 &= 35.4536 - 40 \text{ or } 5.4536 - 10 \\ \text{antilog } 5.4536 - 10 &= 0.00002842 \end{aligned}$$

15. Taking a Root

Since we multiply the log of a number by the exponent of the number to raise the number to a power, we might expect that we could find the root of a number by dividing the log of the number by the index of the root. This is correct. If we wish to find the cube root of 91,060, we have

$$\begin{aligned} \log 91{,}060 &= 4.9593 \\ \log \sqrt[3]{91.060} &= 4.9593 \div 3 = 1.6531 \\ \text{antilog } 1.6531 &= 44.99 \end{aligned}$$

Again, we run into difficulty if we deal with fractions. If we wish the cube root of 0.009106 we have

$$\begin{aligned} \log 0.009106 &= 7.9593 - 10 \\ \log \sqrt[3]{0.009106} &= (7.9593 - 10) \div 3 = 2.6531 - 3.3333 \end{aligned}$$

How shall we interpret this? If we carry out the indicated subtraction, we end with a negative value for the log, and we would have the same trouble interpreting it as we had in Sec. 13. But again, we can get around the difficulty if we multiply the -10 of the characteristic by the index of the root before dividing. Then we must add enough to the positive part of the characteristic so that its net value is unchanged. In this case we would multiply the -10 by 3, since we are getting the cube root. $3 \cdot (-10)$ is -30. If we change -10 to -30 we have taken off 20, so we will have to compensate for it by adding 20; thus making the log $27.9593 - 30$.

Thus,

$$\begin{aligned} \log 0.009106 &= 7.9593 - 10 &&= 27.9593 - 30 \\ \log \sqrt[3]{0.009106} &= (27.9593 - 30) \div 3 &&= 9.3198 - 10 \\ \text{antilog } 9.3198 - 10 & &&= 0.2088 \end{aligned}$$

As another example, if we were taking the square root of the same fraction, we would have

$$\begin{aligned} \log 0.009106 &= 7.9593 - 10 &&= 17.9593 - 20 \\ \log \sqrt{0.009106} &= (17.9593 - 20) \div 2 &&= 8.9796 - 10 \\ \text{antilog } 8.9796 - 10 & &&= 0.09541 \end{aligned}$$

16. Suggestions for Practice

To practice finding logs and antilogs, look up all the values of either which appear in the examples in Sec. 12–15, inclusive, and check against the values given.

To practice multiplication, take the quotients found in Sec. 13 and multiply each by the appropriate figure which, in Sec. 13, was used as the divisor; and check the products against the original dividends in Sec. 13. In other words, work those division problems backwards.

To practice division, divide the product found in the first example in Sec. 12 by one of the factors of the original example, and check the quotient against the other factor of the original example. Repeat, dividing by the other factor.

You can also divide the product of the second example in Sec. 12 by any three of the factors in turn, checking your final quotient against the fourth factor. By varying the order of division with any one combination of three factors and taking different combinations of three factors, you can get enough different practice problems to keep you busy for a week.

You can also divide the product of the second example by any one or any two of the original factors, multiply the other factors, and check.

To practice finding a power, take the cube of the cube root found in Sec. 15, and the square of the square root found there, checking against the original values in each case.

To practice getting a root take the fourth root of each of the answers to the examples in Sec. 14. Then check by taking the square root twice, in each case, which should give the same result.

17. Pitfalls

Guard carefully against several common errors.

Be certain that you have the correct table. You won't get very good results if you use an antilog table to look up a log, or vice versa!

Always record the characteristic, whether in the original logarithm, or in some log found during the computation, or in the final log. Failure to record the characteristic, even though it may be zero, very often leads to error.

Remember that when you look up an antilog, you look up *only* the mantissa in the antilog table. For example, if the log is 2.6377 you look up .6377. You use the 2 only for spotting the decimal point. On the other hand, in looking up the *log* of a number, use the *entire* number sequence (to four significant figures), starting with the first digit which is not zero.

If the value of a mantissa you look up starts with a zero, don't drop it. Thus the mantissa of the log of 1022 is 0094, *not* just 94.

18. Accuracy

In using any log tables to work a problem, you will sometimes find discrepancies of one or two points in the last digit. For example, if in Sec. 11 you checked the values in Sec. 8, in two instances the antilog you found differed from the original number by one point in the last digit. However, this cannot introduce an error greater than 0.1%.

Appendix I

FOUR-PLACE LOGARITHMS

N	0	1	2	3	4	5	6	7	8	9	1	2	3	4	5	6	7	8	9
10	0000	0043	0086	0128	0170	0212	0253	0294	0334	0374	4	8	12	17	21	25	29	33	37
11	0414	0453	0492	0531	0569	0607	0645	0682	0719	0755	4	8	11	15	19	23	26	30	34
12	0792	0828	0864	0899	0934	0969	1004	1038	1072	1106	3	7	10	14	17	21	24	28	31
13	1139	1173	1206	1239	1271	1303	1335	1367	1399	1430	3	6	10	13	16	19	23	26	29
14	1461	1492	1523	1553	1584	1614	1644	1673	1703	1732	3	6	9	12	15	18	21	24	27
15	1761	1790	1818	1847	1875	1903	1931	1959	1987	2014	3	6	8	11	14	17	20	22	25
16	2041	2068	2095	2122	2148	2175	2201	2227	2253	2279	3	5	8	11	13	16	18	21	24
17	2304	2330	2355	2380	2405	2430	2455	2480	2504	2529	2	5	7	10	12	15	17	20	22
18	2553	2577	2601	2625	2648	2672	2695	2718	2742	2765	2	5	7	9	12	14	16	19	21
19	2788	2810	2833	2856	2878	2900	2923	2945	2967	2989	2	4	7	9	11	13	16	18	20
20	3010	3032	3054	3075	3096	3118	3139	3160	3181	3201	2	4	6	8	11	13	15	17	19
21	3222	3243	3263	3284	3304	3324	3345	3365	3385	3404	2	4	6	8	10	12	14	16	18
22	3424	3444	3464	3483	3502	3522	3541	3560	3579	3598	2	4	6	8	10	12	14	16	17
23	3617	3636	3655	3674	3692	3711	3729	3747	3766	3784	2	4	6	7	9	11	13	15	17
24	3802	3820	3838	3856	3874	3892	3909	3927	3945	3962	2	4	5	7	9	11	12	14	16
25	3979	3997	4014	4031	4048	4065	4082	4099	4116	4133	2	4	5	7	9	10	12	14	16
26	4150	4166	4183	4200	4216	4232	4249	4265	4281	4298	2	3	5	7	8	10	11	13	15
27	4314	4330	4346	4362	4378	4393	4409	4425	4440	4456	2	3	5	6	8	9	11	12	14
28	4472	4487	4502	4518	4533	4548	4564	4579	4594	4609	2	3	5	6	8	9	11	12	14
29	4624	4639	4654	4669	4683	4698	4713	4728	4742	4757	1	3	4	6	7	9	10	12	13
30	4771	4786	4800	4814	4829	4843	4857	4871	4886	4900	1	3	4	6	7	9	10	11	13
31	4914	4928	4942	4955	4969	4983	4997	5011	5024	5038	1	3	4	5	7	8	10	11	12
32	5051	5065	5079	5092	5105	5119	5132	5145	5159	5172	1	3	4	5	7	8	9	11	12
33	5185	5198	5211	5224	5237	5250	5263	5276	5289	5302	1	3	4	5	7	8	9	11	12
34	5315	5328	5340	5353	5366	5378	5391	5403	5416	5428	1	2	4	5	6	8	9	10	11
35	5441	5453	5465	5478	5490	5502	5514	5527	5539	5551	1	2	4	5	6	7	9	10	11
36	5563	5575	5587	5599	5611	5623	5635	5647	5658	5670	1	2	4	5	6	7	8	10	11
37	5682	5694	5705	5717	5729	5740	5752	5763	5775	5786	1	2	4	5	6	7	8	9	11
38	5798	5809	5821	5832	5843	5855	5866	5877	5888	5899	1	2	3	5	6	7	8	9	10
39	5911	5922	5933	5944	5955	5966	5977	5988	5999	6010	1	2	3	4	5	7	8	9	10
40	6021	6031	6042	6053	6064	6075	6085	6096	6107	6117	1	2	3	4	5	6	8	9	10
41	6128	6138	6149	6160	6170	6180	6191	6201	6212	6222	1	2	3	4	5	6	7	8	9
42	6232	6243	6253	6263	6274	6284	6294	6304	6314	6325	1	2	3	4	5	6	7	8	9
43	6335	6345	6355	6365	6375	6385	6395	6405	6415	6425	1	2	3	4	5	6	7	8	9
44	6435	6444	6454	6464	6474	6484	6493	6503	6513	6522	1	2	3	4	5	6	7	8	9
45	6532	6542	6551	6561	6571	6580	6590	6599	6609	6618	1	2	3	4	5	6	7	8	9
46	6628	6637	6646	6656	6665	6675	6684	6693	6702	6712	1	2	3	4	5	6	7	7	8
47	6721	6730	6739	6749	6758	6767	6776	6785	6794	6803	1	2	3	4	5	6	7	7	8
48	6812	6821	6830	6839	6848	6857	6866	6875	6884	6893	1	2	3	4	5	6	7	7	8
49	6902	6911	6920	6928	6937	6946	6955	6964	6972	6981	1	2	3	4	4	5	6	7	8
50	6990	6998	7007	7016	7024	7033	7042	7050	7059	7067	1	2	3	3	4	5	6	7	8
51	7076	7084	7093	7101	7110	7118	7126	7135	7143	7152	1	2	3	3	4	5	6	7	8
52	7160	7168	7177	7185	7193	7202	7210	7218	7226	7235	1	2	3	3	4	5	6	7	7
53	7243	7251	7259	7267	7275	7284	7292	7300	7308	7316	1	2	2	3	4	5	6	6	7
54	7324	7332	7340	7348	7356	7364	7372	7380	7388	7396	1	2	2	3	4	5	6	6	7
N	0	1	2	3	4	5	6	7	8	9	1	2	3	4	5	6	7	8	9

Appendix I

FOUR-PLACE LOGARITHMS (*Continued*)

N	0	1	2	3	4	5	6	7	8	9	1	2	3	4	5	6	7	8	9
55	7404	7412	7419	7427	7435	7443	7451	7459	7466	7474	1	2	2	3	4	5	5	6	7
56	7482	7490	7497	7505	7513	7520	7528	7536	7543	7551	1	2	2	3	4	5	5	6	7
57	7559	7566	7574	7582	7589	7597	7604	7612	7619	7627	1	1	2	3	4	5	5	6	7
58	7634	7642	7649	7657	7664	7672	7679	7686	7694	7701	1	1	2	3	4	4	5	6	7
59	7709	7716	7723	7731	7738	7745	7752	7760	7767	7774	1	1	2	3	4	4	5	6	7
60	7782	7789	7796	7803	7810	7818	7825	7832	7839	7846	1	1	2	3	4	4	5	6	6
61	7853	7860	7868	7875	7882	7889	7896	7903	7910	7917	1	1	2	3	3	4	5	6	6
62	7924	7931	7938	7945	7952	7959	7966	7973	7980	7987	1	1	2	3	3	4	5	5	6
63	7993	8000	8007	8014	8021	8028	8035	8041	8048	8055	1	1	2	3	3	4	5	5	6
64	8062	8069	8075	8082	8089	8096	8102	8109	8116	8122	1	1	2	3	3	4	5	5	6
65	8129	8136	8142	8149	8156	8162	8169	8176	8182	8189	1	1	2	3	3	4	5	5	6
66	8195	8202	8209	8215	8222	8228	8235	8241	8248	8254	1	1	2	3	3	4	5	5	6
67	8261	8267	8274	8280	8287	8293	8299	8306	8312	8319	1	1	2	3	3	4	5	5	6
68	8325	8331	8338	8344	8351	8357	8363	8370	8376	8382	1	1	2	3	3	4	4	5	6
69	8388	8395	8401	8407	8414	8420	8426	8432	8439	8445	1	1	2	3	3	4	4	5	6
70	8451	8457	8463	8470	8476	8482	8488	8494	8500	8506	1	1	2	3	3	4	4	5	6
71	8513	8519	8525	8531	8537	8543	8549	8555	8561	8567	1	1	2	3	3	4	4	5	6
72	8573	8579	8585	8591	8597	8603	8609	8615	8621	8627	1	1	2	3	3	4	4	5	6
73	8633	8639	8645	8651	8657	8663	8669	8675	8681	8686	1	1	2	2	3	4	4	5	5
74	8692	8698	8704	8710	8716	8722	8727	8733	8739	8745	1	1	2	2	3	4	4	5	5
75	8751	8756	8762	8768	8774	8779	8785	8791	8797	8802	1	1	2	2	3	3	4	5	5
76	8808	8814	8820	8825	8831	8837	8842	8848	8854	8859	1	1	2	2	3	3	4	4	5
77	8865	8871	8876	8882	8887	8893	8899	8904	8910	8915	1	1	2	2	3	3	4	4	5
78	8921	8927	8932	8938	8943	8949	8954	8960	8965	8971	1	1	2	2	3	3	4	4	5
79	8976	8982	8987	8993	8998	9004	9009	9015	9020	9025	1	1	2	2	3	3	4	4	5
80	9031	9036	9042	9047	9053	9058	9063	9069	9074	9079	1	1	2	2	3	3	4	4	5
81	9085	9090	9096	9101	9106	9112	9117	9122	9128	9133	1	1	2	2	3	3	4	4	5
82	9138	9143	9149	9154	9159	9165	9170	9175	9180	9186	1	1	2	2	3	3	4	4	5
83	9191	9196	9201	9206	9212	9217	9222	9227	9232	9238	1	1	2	2	3	3	4	4	5
84	9243	9248	9253	9258	9263	9269	9274	9279	9284	9289	1	1	2	2	3	3	4	4	5
85	9294	9299	9304	9309	9315	9320	9325	9330	9335	9340	1	1	2	2	3	3	4	4	5
86	9345	9350	9355	9360	9365	9370	9375	9380	9385	9390	1	1	2	2	3	3	4	4	5
87	9395	9400	9405	9410	9415	9420	9425	9430	9435	9440	1	1	2	2	3	3	4	4	5
88	9445	9450	9455	9460	9465	9469	9474	9479	9484	9489	0	1	1	2	2	3	3	4	4
89	9494	9499	9504	9509	9513	9518	9523	9528	9533	9538	0	1	1	2	2	3	3	4	4
90	9542	9547	9552	9557	9562	9566	9571	9576	9581	9586	0	1	1	2	2	3	3	4	4
91	9590	9595	9600	9605	9609	9614	9619	9624	9628	9633	0	1	1	2	2	3	3	4	4
92	9638	9643	9647	9652	9657	9661	9666	9671	9675	9680	0	1	1	2	2	3	3	4	4
93	9685	9689	9694	9699	9703	9708	9713	9717	9722	9727	0	1	1	2	2	3	3	4	4
94	9731	9736	9741	9745	9750	9754	9759	9763	9768	9773	0	1	1	2	2	3	3	4	4
95	9777	9782	9786	9791	9795	9800	9805	9809	9814	9818	0	1	1	2	2	3	3	4	4
96	9823	9827	9832	9836	9841	9845	9850	9854	9859	9863	0	1	1	2	2	3	3	4	4
97	9868	9872	9877	9881	9886	9890	9894	9899	9903	9908	0	1	1	2	2	3	3	4	4
98	9912	9917	9921	9926	9930	9934	9939	9943	9948	9952	0	1	1	2	2	3	3	3	4
99	9956	9961	9965	9969	9974	9978	9983	9987	9991	9996	0	1	1	2	2	3	3	3	4
N	0	1	2	3	4	5	6	7	8	9	1	2	3	4	5	6	7	8	9

Appendix I

ANTILOGARITHMS TO FOUR PLACES

	0	1	2	3	4	5	6	7	8	9	1	2	3	4	5	6	7	8	9
.00	1000	1002	1005	1007	1009	1012	1014	1016	1019	1021	0	0	1	1	1	1	2	2	2
.01	1023	1026	1028	1030	1033	1035	1038	1040	1042	1045	0	0	1	1	1	1	2	2	2
.02	1047	1050	1052	1054	1057	1059	1062	1064	1067	1069	0	0	1	1	1	1	2	2	2
.03	1072	1074	1076	1079	1081	1084	1086	1089	1091	1094	0	0	1	1	1	1	2	2	2
.04	1096	1099	1102	1104	1107	1109	1112	1114	1117	1119	0	1	1	1	1	2	2	2	2
.05	1122	1125	1127	1130	1132	1135	1138	1140	1143	1146	0	1	1	1	1	2	2	2	2
.06	1148	1151	1153	1156	1159	1161	1164	1167	1169	1172	0	1	1	1	1	2	2	2	2
.07	1175	1178	1180	1183	1186	1189	1191	1194	1197	1199	0	1	1	1	1	2	2	2	2
.08	1202	1205	1208	1211	1213	1216	1219	1222	1225	1227	0	1	1	1	1	2	2	2	3
.09	1230	1233	1236	1239	1242	1245	1247	1250	1253	1256	0	1	1	1	1	2	2	2	3
.10	1259	1262	1265	1268	1271	1274	1276	1279	1282	1285	0	1	1	1	1	2	2	2	3
.11	1288	1291	1294	1297	1300	1303	1306	1309	1312	1315	0	1	1	1	2	2	2	2	3
.12	1318	1321	1324	1327	1330	1334	1337	1340	1343	1346	0	1	1	1	2	2	2	2	3
.13	1349	1352	1355	1358	1361	1365	1368	1371	1374	1377	0	1	1	1	2	2	2	3	3
.14	1380	1384	1387	1390	1393	1396	1400	1403	1406	1409	0	1	1	1	2	2	2	3	3
.15	1413	1416	1419	1422	1426	1429	1432	1435	1439	1442	0	1	1	1	2	2	2	3	3
.16	1445	1449	1452	1455	1459	1462	1466	1469	1472	1476	0	1	1	1	2	2	2	3	3
.17	1479	1483	1486	1489	1493	1496	1500	1503	1507	1510	0	1	1	1	2	2	2	3	3
.18	1514	1517	1521	1524	1528	1531	1535	1538	1542	1545	0	1	1	1	2	2	2	3	3
.19	1549	1552	1556	1560	1563	1567	1570	1574	1578	1581	0	1	1	1	2	2	2	3	3
.20	1585	1589	1592	1596	1600	1603	1607	1611	1614	1618	0	1	1	1	2	2	3	3	3
.21	1622	1626	1629	1633	1637	1641	1644	1648	1652	1656	0	1	1	1	2	2	3	3	3
.22	1660	1663	1667	1671	1675	1679	1683	1687	1690	1694	0	1	1	2	2	2	3	3	3
.23	1698	1702	1706	1710	1714	1718	1722	1726	1730	1734	0	1	1	2	2	2	3	3	3
.24	1738	1742	1746	1750	1754	1758	1762	1766	1770	1774	0	1	1	2	2	2	3	3	4
.25	1778	1782	1786	1791	1795	1799	1803	1807	1811	1816	0	1	1	2	2	3	3	3	4
.26	1820	1824	1828	1832	1837	1841	1845	1849	1854	1858	0	1	1	2	2	3	3	3	4
.27	1862	1866	1871	1875	1879	1884	1888	1892	1897	1901	0	1	1	2	2	3	3	3	4
.28	1905	1910	1914	1919	1923	1928	1932	1936	1941	1945	0	1	1	2	2	3	3	4	4
.29	1950	1954	1959	1963	1968	1972	1977	1982	1986	1991	0	1	1	2	2	3	3	4	4
.30	1995	2000	2004	2009	2014	2018	2023	2028	2032	2037	0	1	1	2	2	3	3	4	4
.31	2042	2046	2051	2056	2061	2065	2070	2075	2080	2084	0	1	1	2	2	3	3	4	4
.32	2089	2094	2099	2104	2109	2113	2118	2123	2128	2133	0	1	1	2	2	3	3	4	4
.33	2138	2143	2148	2153	2158	2163	2168	2173	2178	2183	0	1	1	2	2	3	3	4	4
.34	2188	2193	2198	2203	2208	2213	2218	2223	2228	2234	1	1	2	2	3	3	4	4	5
.35	2239	2244	2249	2254	2259	2265	2270	2275	2280	2286	1	1	2	2	3	3	4	4	5
.36	2291	2296	2301	2307	2312	2317	2323	2328	2333	2339	1	1	2	2	3	3	4	4	5
.37	2344	2350	2355	2360	2366	2371	2377	2382	2388	2393	1	1	2	2	3	3	4	4	5
.38	2399	2404	2410	2415	2421	2427	2432	2438	2443	2449	1	1	2	2	3	3	4	5	5
.39	2455	2460	2466	2472	2477	2483	2489	2495	2500	2506	1	1	2	2	3	3	4	5	5
.40	2512	2518	2523	2529	2535	2541	2547	2553	2559	2564	1	1	2	2	3	4	4	5	5
.41	2570	2576	2582	2588	2594	2600	2606	2612	2618	2624	1	1	2	2	3	4	4	5	6
.42	2630	2636	2642	2649	2655	2661	2667	2673	2679	2685	1	1	2	2	3	4	4	5	6
.43	2692	2698	2704	2710	2716	2723	2729	2735	2742	2748	1	1	2	2	3	4	4	5	6
.44	2754	2761	2767	2773	2780	2786	2793	2799	2805	2812	1	1	2	3	3	4	4	5	6
.45	2818	2825	2831	2838	2844	2851	2858	2864	2871	2877	1	1	2	3	3	4	5	5	6
.46	2884	2891	2897	2904	2911	2917	2924	2931	2938	2944	1	1	2	3	3	4	5	5	6
.47	2951	2958	2965	2972	2979	2985	2992	2999	3006	3013	1	1	2	3	3	4	5	6	6
.48	3020	3027	3034	3041	3048	3055	3062	3069	3076	3083	1	1	2	3	3	4	5	6	6
.49	3090	3097	3105	3112	3119	3126	3133	3141	3148	3155	1	1	2	3	4	4	5	6	6
	0	1	2	3	4	5	6	7	8	9	1	2	3	4	5	6	7	8	9

Appendix I

ANTILOGARITHMS TO FOUR PLACES *(Continued)*

	0	1	2	3	4	5	6	7	8	9	1	2	3	4	5	6	7	8	9
.50	3162	3170	3177	3184	3192	3199	3206	3214	3221	3228	1	1	2	3	4	4	5	6	7
.51	3236	3243	3251	3258	3266	3273	3281	3289	3296	3304	1	1	2	3	4	4	5	6	7
.52	3311	3319	3327	3334	3342	3350	3357	3365	3373	3381	1	1	2	3	4	5	5	6	7
.53	3388	3396	3404	3412	3420	3428	3436	3443	3451	3459	1	2	2	3	4	5	6	6	7
.54	3467	3475	3483	3491	3499	3508	3516	3524	3532	3540	1	2	2	3	4	5	6	6	7
.55	3548	3556	3565	3573	3581	3589	3597	3606	3614	3622	1	2	2	3	4	5	6	7	7
.56	3631	3639	3648	3656	3664	3673	3681	3690	3698	3707	1	2	2	3	4	5	6	7	8
.57	3715	3724	3733	3741	3750	3758	3767	3776	3784	3793	1	2	3	3	4	5	6	7	8
.58	3802	3811	3819	3828	3837	3846	3855	3864	3873	3882	1	2	3	3	4	5	6	7	8
.59	3890	3899	3908	3917	3926	3936	3945	3954	3963	3972	1	2	3	4	5	5	6	7	8
.60	3981	3990	3999	4009	4018	4027	4036	4046	4055	4064	1	2	3	4	5	6	7	8	8
.61	4074	4083	4093	4102	4111	4121	4130	4140	4150	4159	1	2	3	4	5	6	7	8	9
.62	4169	4178	4188	4198	4207	4217	4227	4236	4246	4256	1	2	3	4	5	6	7	8	9
.63	4266	4276	4285	4295	4305	4315	4325	4335	4345	4355	1	2	3	4	5	6	7	8	9
.64	4365	4375	4385	4395	4406	4416	4426	4436	4446	4457	1	2	3	4	5	6	7	8	9
.65	4467	4477	4487	4498	4508	4519	4529	4539	4550	4560	1	2	3	4	5	6	7	8	9
.66	4571	4581	4592	4603	4613	4624	4634	4645	4656	4667	1	2	3	4	5	6	7	9	10
.67	4677	4688	4699	4710	4721	4732	4742	4753	4764	4775	1	2	3	4	5	7	8	9	10
.68	4786	4797	4808	4819	4831	4842	4853	4864	4875	4887	1	2	3	5	6	7	8	9	10
.69	4898	4909	4920	4932	4943	4955	4966	4977	4989	5000	1	2	3	5	6	7	8	9	10
.70	5012	5023	5035	5047	5058	5070	5082	5093	5105	5117	1	2	3	5	6	7	8	9	10
.71	5129	5140	5152	5164	5176	5188	5200	5212	5224	5236	1	2	4	5	6	7	8	10	11
.72	5248	5260	5272	5284	5297	5309	5321	5333	5346	5358	1	2	4	5	6	7	9	10	11
.73	5370	5383	5395	5408	5420	5433	5445	5458	5470	5483	1	3	4	5	6	7	9	10	11
.74	5495	5508	5521	5534	5546	5559	5572	5585	5598	5610	1	3	4	5	6	8	9	10	12
.75	5623	5636	5649	5662	5675	5689	5702	5715	5728	5741	1	3	4	5	7	8	9	11	12
.76	5754	5768	5781	5794	5808	5821	5834	5848	5861	5875	1	3	4	5	7	8	9	11	12
.77	5888	5902	5916	5929	5943	5957	5970	5984	5998	6012	1	3	4	5	7	8	10	11	12
.78	6026	6039	6053	6067	6081	6095	6109	6124	6138	6152	1	3	4	6	7	8	10	11	13
.79	6166	6180	6194	6209	6223	6237	6252	6266	6281	6295	1	3	4	6	7	9	10	11	13
.80	6310	6324	6339	6353	6368	6383	6397	6412	6427	6442	1	3	4	6	7	9	10	12	13
.81	6457	6471	6486	6501	6516	6531	6546	6561	6577	6592	2	3	5	6	8	9	11	12	14
.82	6607	6622	6637	6653	6668	6683	6699	6714	6730	6745	2	3	5	6	8	9	11	12	14
.83	6761	6776	6792	6808	6823	6839	6855	6871	6887	6902	2	3	5	6	8	9	11	13	14
.84	6918	6934	6950	6966	6982	6998	7015	7031	7047	7063	2	3	5	7	8	10	11	13	15
.85	7079	7096	7112	7129	7145	7161	7178	7194	7211	7228	2	3	5	7	8	10	12	13	15
.86	7244	7261	7278	7295	7311	7328	7345	7362	7379	7396	2	3	5	7	8	10	12	14	15
.87	7413	7430	7447	7464	7482	7499	7516	7534	7551	7568	2	4	5	7	9	10	12	14	16
.88	7586	7603	7621	7638	7656	7674	7691	7709	7727	7745	2	4	5	7	9	11	12	14	16
.89	7762	7780	7798	7816	7834	7852	7870	7889	7907	7925	2	4	6	7	9	11	13	15	16
.90	7943	7962	7980	7998	8017	8035	8054	8072	8091	8110	2	4	6	7	9	11	13	15	17
.91	8128	8147	8166	8185	8204	8222	8241	8260	8279	8299	2	4	6	8	9	11	13	15	17
.92	8318	8337	8356	8375	8395	8414	8433	8453	8472	8492	2	4	6	8	10	12	14	15	17
.93	8511	8531	8551	8570	8590	8610	8630	8650	8670	8690	2	4	6	8	10	12	14	16	18
.94	8710	8730	8750	8770	8790	8810	8831	8851	8872	8892	2	4	6	8	10	12	14	16	18
.95	8913	8933	8954	8974	8995	9016	9036	9057	9078	9099	2	4	6	8	10	12	15	17	19
.96	9120	9141	9162	9183	9204	9226	9247	9268	9290	9311	2	4	6	9	11	13	15	17	19
.97	9333	9354	9376	9397	9419	9441	9462	9484	9506	9528	2	4	6	9	11	13	15	17	19
.98	9550	9572	9594	9616	9638	9661	9683	9705	9727	9750	2	4	7	9	11	13	16	18	20
.99	9772	9795	9817	9840	9863	9886	9908	9931	9954	9977	2	5	7	9	11	14	16	18	21
	0	1	2	3	4	5	6	7	8	9	1	2	3	4	5	6	7	8	9

Appendix J

TRIGONOMETRIC FUNCTIONS

Angle in degrees	Sine	Cosine	Tangent	Angle in degrees	Sine	Cosine	Tangent
0	.0000	1.0000	.0000				
1	.0175	.9998	.0175	46	.7193	.6947	1.036
2	.0349	.9994	.0349	47	.7314	.6820	1.072
3	.0523	.9986	.0524	48	.7431	.6691	1.111
4	.0698	.9976	.0699	49	.7547	.6561	1.150
5	.0872	.9962	.0875	50	.7660	.6428	1.192
6	.1045	.9945	.1051	51	.7771	.6293	1.235
7	.1219	.9925	.1228	52	.7880	.6157	1.280
8	.1392	.9903	.1405	53	.7986	.6018	1.327
9	.1564	.9877	.1584	54	.8090	.5878	1.376
10	.1736	.9848	.1763	55	.8192	.5736	1.428
11	.1908	.9816	.1944	56	.8290	.5592	1.483
12	.2079	.9781	.2126	57	.8387	.5446	1.540
13	.2250	.9744	.2309	58	.8480	.5299	1.600
14	.2419	.9703	.2493	59	.8572	.5150	1.664
15	.2588	.9659	.2679	60	.8660	.5000	1.732
16	.2756	.9613	.2867	61	.8746	.4848	1.804
17	.2924	.9563	.3057	62	.8829	.4695	1.881
18	.3090	.9511	.3249	63	.8910	.4540	1.963
19	.3256	.9455	.3443	64	.8988	.4384	2.050
20	.3420	.9397	.3640	65	.9063	.4226	2.145
21	.3584	.9336	.3839	66	.9135	.4067	2.246
22	.3746	.9272	.4040	67	.9205	.3907	2.356
23	.3907	.9205	.4245	68	.9272	.3746	2.475
24	.4067	.9135	.4452	69	.9336	.3584	2.605
25	.4226	.9063	.4663	70	.9397	.3420	2.748
26	.4384	.8988	.4877	71	.9455	.3256	2.904
27	.4540	.8910	.5095	72	.9511	.3090	3.078
28	.4695	.8829	.5317	73	.9563	.2924	3.271
29	.4848	.8746	.5543	74	.9613	.2756	3.487
30	.5000	.8660	.5774	75	.9659	.2588	3.732
31	.5150	.8572	.6009	76	.9703	.2419	4.011
32	.5299	.8480	.6249	77	.9744	.2250	4.332
33	.5446	.8387	.6494	78	.9781	.2079	4.705
34	.5592	.8290	.6745	79	.9816	.1908	5.145
35	.5736	.8192	.7002	80	.9848	.1736	5.671
36	.5878	.8090	.7265	81	.9877	.1564	6.314
37	.6018	.7986	.7536	82	.9903	.1392	7.115
38	.6157	.7880	.7813	83	.9925	.1219	8.144
39	.6293	.7771	.8098	84	.9945	.1045	9.514
40	.6428	.7660	.8391	85	.9962	.0872	11.43
41	.6561	.7547	.8693	86	.9976	.0698	14.30
42	.6691	.7431	.9004	87	.9986	.0523	19.08
43	.6820	.7314	.9325	88	.9994	.0349	28.64
44	.6947	.7193	.9657	89	.9998	.0175	57.29
45	.7071	.7071	1.0000	90	1.0000	.0000	∞

Appendix K
ANSWERS TO PROBLEMS

Chap. 1, Sec. 1-15

1. (a) 7/6; 1/6; −1/6; 1/3; 4/3; 3/4. (b) 111/40; −81/40; 81/40; 9/10; 5/32; 32/5. (c) 0.143; −0.03$\overline{58}$; 0.03$\overline{58}$; 0.00477; 0.599; 1.67. **2.** 111; 4.92; 91.4. **3.** 6.25; 625; 0.0625; 1.$\overline{58}$; 5.0; 0.50. **4.** a is inversely proportional to the square root of b; b is inversely proportional to the square of a. **5.** 10,000; 1,000,000; 1.00; 5.00; 40.0. **6.** The frequency is directly proportional to the square root of the tension, inversely proportional to the length, and inversely proportional to the square root of the mass per unit length. **7.** $F = Gm_1m_2/d^2$. **8.** (a) 3. (b) −13. (c) 2/5. (d) 2/3. (e) +5. (f) 4.5. (g) 2/45. **9.** (a) −3. (b) 4 or −5. (c) 5/2 or −4/3. (d) 5. **10.** $v = \sqrt{u^2 + 2as}$; $u = \sqrt{v^2 - 2as}$; $a = (v^2 - u^2)/2s$; $s = (v^2 - u^2)/2a$. **11.** $f = 1/(2\pi \sqrt{LC})$. **12.** n.a. (no answer).

Chap. 2

1. $3.428 \cdot 10^5$ mg; $3.428 \cdot 10^{-1}$ kg. **2.** $2.91 \cdot 10^3$ cm^3; $2.91 \cdot 10^3$ ml. **3.** n.a. **4.** n.a. **5.** ml/t^2. **6.** $1/t$. **7.** $V = (4/3)\pi r^3$; $A = 4\pi r^2$. **8.** $2.44 \cdot 10^{-4}$; $7.913 \cdot 10^5$; $3.93 \cdot 10^{-1}$. **9.** 28,500,000; 0.000 000 000 077 1; 100.3. **10.** $7.65 \cdot 10^{-4}$; $6.23 \cdot 10^{-4}$; $4.72 \cdot 10^{-8}$; 9.48; $1.06 \cdot 10^{-1}$. **11.** $1.3\overline{0} \cdot 10^{11}$; $4.6\overline{7} \cdot 10^{16}$; $6.0 \cdot 10^2$. **12.** $7.29 \cdot 10^{-4}$; $1.97 \cdot 10^{-5}$; $3.0 \cdot 10^{-1}$. **13.** 8.70. **14.** 0.000223.

Chap. 3

1. 5 blocks; 36.9° S of E. **2.** 147 mph; 5.9° S of W. **3.** 0 (equilibrium). **4.** 0.73 g. **5.** 26.0 lbf. **6.** 667 lbf. **7.** 50.0 lbf. **8.** 200 lbf. **9.** (a) 150 ft/min. (b) 53.1°. **10.** 17.5 ft/sec.

Chap. 4

1. 3.33 ft. **2.** 7.71 ft. **3.** 7.33 ft from the 50 lb child. **4.** On the side of the 50 lb child; 120 lbf. **5.** 54 lbf. **6.** 320 lbf. **7.** 13.5 ft. **8.** (a) 0 lbf. (b) 31.8 lbf. (c) 63.6 lbf. **9.** L = 139 lbf; R = 171 lbf. **10.** $L = 23.3\ t$; $R = 16.7\ t$. **11.** 112 lbf. **12.** 53.1°; 67.2 lbf. **13.** $2.52 \cdot 10^3$ lbf; $3.92 \cdot 10^3$ lbf. **14.** $2.91 \cdot 10^3$ lbf; $1.41 \cdot 10^3$ lbf. **15.** 115 lbf. **16.** 115 lbf; 241 lbf 28.5° from vertical. **17.** 23.4 lbf perpendicular to ladder 36.9° above horizontal. **18.** 2.00 ft above fence (measured along ladder). **19.** n.a. **20.** n.a.

Chap. 5

1. 38.0 mph. **2.** 8.4 min late. **3.** 7.50 mph/sec. **4.** 17.6 sec. **5.** 774 ft. **6.** 774 ft. **7.** 774 ft. **8.** 48.0 ft/sec. **9.** 36.0 ft. **10.** 400 ft/sec. **11.** 22.5 ft. **12.** 3.75 sec. **13.** 4.00 ft. **14.** (a) 112 ft. (b) 112 ft. **15.** (a) 96.0 ft/sec upward. (b) 96.0 ft/sec downward. **16.** $1.20 \cdot 10^3$ dynes; 1.22 g. **17.** 0.750 lb. **18.** 24.0 lb. **19.** $5.49 \cdot 10^{17}$ cm/sec^2. **20.** $1.82 \cdot 10^{-19}$ sec. **21.** $1.91 \cdot 10^{-8}$ sec. **22.** $2.20 \cdot 10^3$ lb. **23.** 605 ft. **24.** 112 ft. **25.** 36.0 ft/sec. **26.** 10.0 ft/sec upward. **27.** 51.0 ft/sec 11.3° above horizontal.

Chap. 6

1. $5.12 \cdot 10^5$ ft-lb; $1.64 \cdot 10^7$ ft-pdl. **2.** $1.22 \cdot 10^7$ ft-lb. **3.** (a) $5.12 \cdot 10^5$ ft-lb. (b) $1.15 \cdot 10^6$ ft-lb. (c) $-5.12 \cdot 10^5$ ft-lb. **4.** $6.40 \cdot 10^5$ ft-lb. **5.** 0.172 hp. **6.** (a) $4.84 \cdot 10^5$ ft-lb. (b) $3.52 \cdot 10^5$ lb-ft/sec. **7.** $3.50 \cdot 10^{-7}$ g. **8.** (a) $\times$ 4. (b) $\times$ $\sqrt{2}/2$. **9.** 48.0 ft/sec. **10.** 36.0 ft. **11.** 400 ft/sec. **12.** 22.5 ft. **13.** $2.20 \cdot 10^3$ lb. **14.** 605 ft. **15.** 2.00 cm/sec E; KE not conserved. **16.** 23.8 m/sec; KE not conserved. **17.** 4.08 kg.

Chap. 7

1. (a) 0.37. (b) 2.7 **2.** (a) $0.12\bar{5}$. (b) 8.0. **3.** (a) 11.5. (b) $8.70 \cdot 10^{-2}$ **4.** (a) 12.5. (b) 1.09. **5.** Ma in Problem 4 larger by 8.7%. **6.** $2.16 \cdot 10^3$ lb. **7.** (a) $1.85 \cdot 10^3$ lb. (b) 105 lb. **8.** (a) 2.50. (b) 2.12. (c) 18.8 lb. **9.** 15.6 kg. **10.** 9.00 in. **11.** (a) 5.10. (b) 784 lb. **12.** 62.5 lb. **13.** 69.4%. **14.** (a) 75.0 lb. (b) 37.5 lb. **15.** 65.8 lb. **16.** 66.3 lb. **17.** 571 g. **18.** (a) 173 g. (b) 459 g. **19.** 193 cm/sec^2. **20.** 0.672. **21.** 180 ft. **22.** (a) 78.3 ft. (b) 143 ft.

Chap. 8

1. 57.3° **2.** 12.5 ft/sec; 8.52 mph. **3.** (a) 450 cm/sec^2. (b) 125 cm/sec^2. **4.** (a) $8.10 \cdot 10^3$ cm/sec^2. (b) $2.25 \cdot 10^3$ cm/sec^2. **5.** (a) $7.20 \cdot 10^3$ g cm^2; $3.00 \cdot 10^5$ g cm^2. (b) $3.07 \cdot 10^5$ g cm^2. **6.** 64.0 rad/sec^2. **7.** n.a. **8.** Sphere, 251 cm/sec; disk, 242 cm/sec; hollow cylinder, 210 cm/sec; block, 297 cm/sec. **9.** Sphere, 4.83 sec; hollow cylinder, 5.77 sec; block, 4.08 sec. **10.** 40.8 cm; 34.7 cm. **11.** $1.07 \cdot 10^3$ rad/sec. **12.** 5.88 sec. **13.** (a) 155 ft/sec^2. (b) 545 mph. **14.** n.a. **15.** (a) $1.21 \cdot 10^3$ lb. (b) 16.8°. **16.** (a) 3.02 kg. (b) 23.1 kg. **17.** 75.7 miles. **18.** 4.24 cm; 14.1 cm; 12.7 cm.

Chap. 9

1. 0.593 dyne. **2.** $3.70 \cdot 10^{-16}$ pdl. **3.** 25.8 cm. **4.** (a) 50/1. (b) 100/1. **5.** $1.102 \cdot 10^4$ cm/sec^2; 1125%. **6.** 9.80 m/sec^2. **7.** 363 cm/sec^2. **8.** (a) $6.96 \cdot 10^{10}$ ft-lb. (b) $7.45 \cdot 10^9$ ft-lb. (c) 10.7%. **9.** n.a. **10.** $3.6 \cdot 10^4$ miles.

Chap. 10

1. 67.9 lb/in.^{2}. **2.** 14.9 lb/in.^{2}. **3.** 37.5 in.^{2}. **4.** (a) 0.423 lb. (b) 0.635 lb. **5.** $4.83 \cdot 10^{-18}$ cm-g/sec. **6.** (a) $1.52 \cdot 10^6$ ergs. (b) $1.01\bar{3} \cdot 10^6$ dynes/cm^2. **7.** 75.0 ft^3. **8.** 0.680 ft^3. **9.** 21.5 lb/in.^{2}; 6.8 lb/in.^{2}. **10.** (a) 29.6 dynes/cm^2. (b) $3.56 \cdot 10^{-5}$ g/cm^3. **11.** (a) $2.61 \cdot 10^7$ dynes. (b) $4.02 \cdot 10^5$ dynes/cm^2. (c) $1.00\bar{5} \cdot 10^9$ dynes. (d) $9.79 \cdot 10^8$ dynes. **12.** (a) 56.2. (b) $2.87 \cdot 10^3$ lb. **13.** 73.4; $3.74 \cdot 10^3$ lb. **14.** (a) 2.70 g/cm^3. (b) $2.70 \cdot 10^3$ kg/m^3. (c) 2.70. **15.** 7.7. **16.** 0.802. **17.** (a) $1.81 \cdot 10^3$ kg. (b) $1.56 \cdot 10^3$ kg. **18.** (a) 3.47 lb/in.^{2}. (b) $3.32 \cdot 10^5$ ft-lb. (c) 10.1 hp. **19.** 582 dynes. **20.** 54.4 dynes/cm^2.

Chap. 11

1. $m/(lt^2)$. **2.** (a) 7.00 m/sec. (b) 6.30 m/sec. (c) 2.02 m. **3.** (a) 2.00 cm. (b) 300 g. **4.** 1.25 mm. **5.** 12.5 ft. **6.** 1.10 m. **7.** 15.4 cm. **8.** (a) 368 g-cm. (b) 120 g-cm. (c) 750 g-cm. **9.** 1.50 ft. **10.** 7.50 hr. **11.** n.a.

Chap. 12

1. (a) $3.33 \cdot 10^{-2}$ sec; $6.67 \cdot 10^{-5}$ sec. (b) 680 kc/sec. **2.** 62.8 ft/sec; 42.8 mph. **3.** (a) $3.03 \cdot 10^{-3}$ sec. (b) 330 v.p.s. (c) $1.29 \cdot 10^{6}$ cm/sec^2. **4.** 0.444 sec; 70.7 cm/sec. **5.** (a) $6.11 \cdot 10^{4}$ m/sec^2. (b) $1.53 \cdot 10^{4}$ m/sec^2. **6.** n.a. **7.** 1.72 mm or $6.79 \cdot 10^{-2}$ in. **8.** 99.3 cm; 3.24 ft. **9.** 982.0 cm/sec^2. **10.** 2.80 m/sec. **11.** 7.97 cm. **12.** $1.38 \cdot 10^{3}$ newtons/m. **13.** 36.0 cm. **14.** 6.25 cm.

Chap. 13

1. $5.10 \cdot 10^{3}$ m/sec. **2.** $7.03 \cdot 10^{11}$ dynes/cm^2. **3.** 2.22 kg. **4.** 37.7 ft; 0.904 in. **5.** 345 m/sec. **6.** 441 m; $1.44 \cdot 10^{3}$ ft. **7.** 0.463 joule. **8.** $4.79 \cdot 10^{-3}$ sec. **9.** (a) 880 v.p.s., 1320 v.p.s., or any other small integral multiple of 440 v.p.s. (b) 50 v.p.s. **10.** (a) $\times$ 8. (b) $\times\ 8\sqrt{2}$; $\times\ 4\sqrt{2}$.

Chap. 14

1. (a) 331 m/sec. (b) 343 m/sec. **2.** (a) 343.6 m/sec. (b) 344 m/sec. **3.** 61°F. **4.** n.a. **5.** (a) 1086 ft/sec. (b) 1174 ft/sec. (c) 1129 ft/sec. **6.** (a) 6.40 mm. (b) 3.00 mm. **7.** (a) 443 v.p.s.; 437 v.p.s. (b) 443 v.p.s. **8.** 265 v.p.s. **9.** (a) 480 v.p.s. (b) 864 v.p.s.

Chap. 15

1. 264 v.p.s. **2.** 660 v.p.s. **3.** Perfect fourth. **4.** Octave. **5.** 1.498. **6.** (a) 396 v.p.s. (b) 792 v.p.s.; 1188 v.p.s.; 1584 v.p.s. **7.** 330 v.p.s. **8.** $1.35 \cdot 10^{-2}$ g/cm. **9.** 550 v.p.s. **10.** 1320 v.p.s.; 1760 v.p.s. **11.** (a) 5.14 ft. (b) 10.3 ft. **12.** (a) 264 v.p.s. (b) 528 v.p.s.; 792 v.p.s.; 1056 v.p.s. **13.** (a) 99.0 v.p.s. (b) 297 v.p.s.; 495 v.p.s.; 693 v.p.s. **14.** (a) 660 v.p.s.; 824 v.p.s.; 1056 v.p.s.; and others. (b) 132 v.p.s.; 528 v.p.s.; 396 v.p.s.; 264 v.p.s.; and others. (c) 528 v.p.s.; 792 v.p.s.; 1056 v.p.s.; 1188 v.p.s.; and others. **15.** 5.33 cm. **16.** (a) M6. (b) P5. (c) m3. **17.** (a) 3rd, 4th; 7th, 9th; and others. (b) 4th, 7th; 9th, 15th; and others. (c) 14th, 15th; 29th, 31st; and others. **18.** 3.375; 3.333. **19.** (a) 8va. (b) P4. (c) m3. (d) M2. (e) m2. In all 5 cases, the open pipe has the higher pitch.

Chap. 16

1. -459.69°F. **2.** (a) -40.0°. (b) $F + 40 = (9/5)(C + 40)$; $C + 40 = (5/9)(F + 40)$. **3.** (a) 320°F. (b) 3.90°C. (c) -11.4°C. **4.** (a) 4.00 cal/C°. (b) $3.33 \cdot 10^{-2}$ cal/(g C°). **5.** (a) 248°F. (b) 392°F. (c) 144F°. (d) 144F°. **6.** 166°C. **7.** $9.17 \cdot 10^{-2}$ cal/(g C°). **8.** 295 g. **9.** 37.5 lb/in.^{2}. **10.** 5.65 lb/in.^{2}. **11.** 430°C. **12.** 622 Btu. **13.** $4.82 \cdot 10^{3}$ Btu. **14.** $9.86 \cdot 10^{-2}$C°. **15.** 1.84F°. **16.** 18.2%. **17.** 0.588 hp.

Chap. 17

1. 75.0 L. **2.** -33°C. **3.** 18.0 L. **4.** 6.25 atmospheres. **5.** 352°C. **6.** (a) 1.50282π cm. (b) 1.5 cm exactly; 1.50282 cm. (c) 1.50282 cm. **7.** 100 ft; 0.189 in. **8.** -0.0391%. **9.** 9.1%. **10.** n.a. **11.** Steel, $65.\overline{8}$ in.; brass, $35.\overline{8}$ in. **12.** 2.88 ml. **13.** 209°C. **14.** 68.5 tons. **15.** 3.95 kg.

Chap. 18

1. 67.5 g. **2.** 80.0 g. **3.** 8.81 g. **4.** (a) 9:06:45. (b) 9:27:00. **5.** 58.7°C. **6.** 835 g water, 15 g ice, temperature 0°C. **7.** Water at 17.0°C. **8.** 100.0°C; 967 g. **9.** 73.7 cal/g. **10.** 584.9 cal/g. **11.** 818 m/sec. **12.** 23.3%.

Chap. 19

1. n.a. **2.** $2.74 \cdot 10^3$ Btu. **3.** 7.07 cal/(cm sec C°). **4.** (a) 91C°. (b) 1.5C°/cm. **5.** $5.8 \cdot 10^2$ Btu. **6.** $1.7 \cdot 10^2$ sec. **7.** $1.3 \cdot 10^7$ lb. **8.** (a) $2.0\bar{6}$ C°/cm. (b) $18.\bar{2}$ C°/cm. **9.** 335C°. **10.** $2.76 \cdot 10^5$ cal/sec. **11.** (a) $4.0 \cdot 10^5$ ergs/sec. (b) 10 joules/sec. **12.** 0.65. **13.** 6%.

Chap. 20

1. 16.0 dynes. **2.** 96.4 esu. **3.** 5.00 dynes 53.1° S of E. **4.** (a) 0.500 dyne/esu southward. (b) 0.375 dyne/esu eastward. (c) 0.625 dyne/esu 53.1° S of E. (d) 0.625 dyne/esu 53.1° S of E. **5.** (a) $2.81 \cdot 10^5$ m/sec^2. (b) No. **6.** (a) $1.60 \cdot 10^{-9}$ dyne (b) $8.93 \cdot 10^{-25}$ dyne. (c) $1.79 \cdot 10^{15}$. **7.** $4.16 \cdot 10^{42}$ to 1. **8.** $5.58 \cdot 10^{-11}$ v/m. **9.** 10^7. **10.** (a) Point A is 5.00 v higher in potential than point B. (b) 1.25 v/cm.

Chap. 21

1. (a) $5.00 \cdot 10^{-2}$ A. (b) 540 coulombs. (c) $3.12 \cdot 10^{17}$. **2.** $1.60 \cdot 10^{-17}$ sec. 3. $2.30 \cdot 10^3$ ohms. **4.** 0.500 A. **5.** 220 v. **6.** (a) 8.13 ohms. (b) 2.48 ohms. **7.** (a) 3.11/1. (b) 1.76/1. **8.** $2.83 \cdot 10^{-6}$ ohm cm. **9.** $5 \cdot 10^{-3}$ cm **10.** $1.6 \cdot 10^{-15}$ erg. **11.** (a) 60.0 joules. (b) $1.92 \cdot 10^{-10}$ erg. (c) $3.12 \cdot 10^{18}$. **12.** (a) 0.500 A. (b) $3.12 \cdot 10^{18}$. **13.** 1 kwhr. $= 3.60 \cdot 10^6$ joules, or 1 joule $= 2.78 \cdot 10^{-7}$ kwhr. **14.** n.a. **15.** (a) 9.60 ohms. (b) 12.5 A. **16.** (a) 27.2 ma. (b) 73.5 v. **17.** (a) 170 v. (b) 120 v. **18.** 6.00 A. **19.** 339 v. **20.** Twice as great in the DC coil.

Chap. 22

1. 22.55 ohms. **2.** 2.86 ohms. **3.** 2.30 ohms. **4.** 5.48 ohms. **5.** (a) 15.00 ohms. (b) 0.400 A. (c) respectively 0.800 v, 2.00 v, and 3.20 v. **6.** (a) 4.00 ohms. (b) 0.750 A. (c) respectively, 0.500 A and 0.250 A. **7.** Respectively, 0.600 v, 1.80 v, 3.00 v, and 6.60 v. **8.** 1.25 ohms. **9.** 20.0 ohms; series. **10.** 30.0 ohms; parallel. **11.** (a) 5/3. (b) 2/3. (c) 15.0/1. **12.** (a) 14,975 ohms. (b) 29,975 ohms. **13.** (a) $1.2506 \cdot 10^{-2}$ ohm. (b) $2.50025 \cdot 10^{-3}$ ohm. **14.** (a) 12 in series. (b) 2 parallel branches, each with 6 cells in series. (c) 6 parallel branches, each with 2 cells in series. **15.** 1.4815 v. **16.** 0.10 ohm. **17.** 0.167 v. **18.** (a) 30.0 A. (b) 0.630 w. (c) 2.72C°/sec. **19.** 0.350 mho.

Chap. 23

1. (a) 0.622 v. (b) 0.472 v. (c) aluminum-silver; 2.47 v. **2.** $3.60 \cdot 10^5$ coulombs. **3.** (a) 0.329 mg/coulomb (b) 0.126 mg/coulomb (c) 0.339 mg/coulomb. **4.** 3, Al^{+++}; 1, Ag^+; 6, W^{+6}. **5.** $9.652 \cdot 10^4$ coulombs. **6.** 3.06 g. **7.** $1.044 \cdot 10^{-2}$ mg/coulomb; 13 hr 18 min. **8.** 32.4 L. **9.** $1.42 \cdot 10^{-2}$ mm. **10.** $7.81 \cdot 10^4$ cal.

Chap. 24

1. (a) $1.00 \cdot 10^3$ dynes 53.1° S of W. (b) $1.00 \cdot 10^3$ dynes 53.1° N of W. (c) $1.20 \cdot 10^3$ dynes W. (d) 6.00 dynes per unit pole W. **2.** 0.413 oersted N. **3.** 5.33 units. **4.** (a) $1.5 \cdot 10^3$ gauss. (b) $1.25 \cdot 10^3$. **5.** 0.400 oersted. **6.** (a) 0.283 oersted NW. (b) 0.400 oersted N. (c) 0.283 oersted NE. (d) 0. **7.** 37.0 ma toward right or 43.0 ma toward left. **8.** (a) 10.1 oersted. (b) $1.09 \cdot 10^3$. **9.** 3.06 A. **10.** 45.0 mv. **11.** 0.566 μv. **12.** 0.100 mv. **13.** 2.40 v AC.

Chap. 25

1. 1/40. **2.** (a) 2.00 A. (b) 1.96 A. **3.** 254 ma. **4.** (a) $2.19 \cdot 10^{10}$ maxwells/sec. (b) $9.12 \cdot 10^{7}$ maxwells. **5.** (a) 188 ohms. (b) 283 mv. (c) 565 mv. **6.** (a) 221 ohms. (b) 332 mv. (c) 166 mv. **7.** (a) 33 ohms. (b) 60 ohms. (c) 75.0 mv. (d) 90 mv. **8.** (a) 59.0 ohms. (b) 2.03 A. **9.** 9.19 megacycles/sec. **10.** (a) 9.90 $\mu\mu$f. (b) 4.40 $\mu\mu$f. **11.** (a) 48.0 ohms. (b) 0.250. (c) 75.0 w. **12.** 166 w. **13.** (a) 0.500. (b) 550 ohms. (c) 275 ohms. (d) 5.45 μf.

Chap. 26

1. 217 mv. **2.** (a) 2.41 v; 1.70 v. (b) 2.41 v; 1.70 v. **3.** (a) 0.597 v. (b) 0.299 v. (c) 0. (d) 0.422 v. **4.** (a) 0.169 A. (b) 1.02 cal. **5.** (a) $6.75 \cdot 10^{5}$ maxwells. (b) $1.68 \cdot 10^{4}$ gauss. **6.** 625 gauss. **7.** 0.256 dynes. **8.** $6.95 \cdot 10^{9}$ cm/sec. **9.** $1.98 \cdot 10^{17}$ cm/sec^2. **10.** 112 v/cm downward. **11.** (a) 2.22 ohms. (b) $5.00 \cdot 10^{-3}$ ohm. (c) $1.00 \cdot 10^{-4}$ ohm. **12.** (a) $3.98 \cdot 10^{3}$ ohms. (b) $2.00 \cdot 10^{4}$ ohms. (c) $3.00 \cdot 10^{6}$ ohms. **13.** 17.7 A. **14.** 2.39 m-newtons. **15.** 4.52 A. **16.** n.a. **17.** n.a.

Chap. 27

1. (a) $2.84 \cdot 10^{-12}$ erg. (b) $4.97 \cdot 10^{-12}$ erg. **2.** $8.29 \cdot 10^{-21}$ erg. **3.** $3.02 \cdot 10^{20}$/sec; $9.93 \cdot 10^{-3}$ Å. **4.** $1.03 \cdot 10^{19}$. **5.** $2.9971 \cdot 10^{8}$ m/sec. **6.** 1.43.

Chap. 28

1. (a) 1.20 ft c. (b) 0.300 lumens/m^2. **2.** 15.3 candles. **3.** 0.960 cp/w. **4.** 57.6 cp. **5.** 86.2 cp. **6.** 36.6 cm. **7.** 1.20 in. by 3.00 in. **8.** 37.5 cm. **9.** 11 ft 5 in. **10.** 58.9%. **11.** Father. **12.** (a) 37.0 in. (b) 34.5 in. **13.** 28.1°. **14.** 32.8°. **15.** 30.9°. **16.** 1.46. **17.** 21.1°. **18.** $4.60 \cdot 10^{3}$ A.

Chap. 29

1. 12.6 cm. **2.** 37.5 cm. **3.** −240 cm. **4.** −11.2 cm. **5.** −66.7 cm. **6.** (a) 4.50 m. (b) −3.60 m. **7.** 60.0 cm. **8.** $p = 2f$. **9.** 67.5 cm.; −1.35 m. **10.** 2.02 m. **11.** (a) 46.2 cm. (b) 2.31 m. **12.** (a) 2.61 m. (b) 0.383 diopters. **13.** −80.0 cm. **14.** 12.9 cm. **15.** 1.40.

Chap. 30

1. (a) 40.0 cm. (b) 33.3 cm. (c) −17%. **2.** 1.80 diopters; 55.6 cm. **3.** $5.00 \cdot 10^{3}$ Å. **4.** $8.33 \cdot 10^{-3}$ cm. **5.** (a) $1.22 \cdot 10^{-4}$ radian. (b) $2.44 \cdot 10^{3}$ Å. **6.** 1.46 Å. **7.** 1.23 Å.

Chap. 31

1. n.a. **2.** Negative; −1.25 diopters; myopia. **3.** Positive; +4.00 diopters; hypermetropia. **4.** 8.00 cm. **5.** 22.2 cm. **6.** −3.33 diopters. **7.** 6.0. **8.** 7.14 cm. **9.** +30.0 cm and +5.00 cm; 6.00. **10.** 5.67. **11.** −5.00 cm. **12.** 486.

Chap. 32

1. n.a. **2.** (a) 40.0 ft. (b) 20.0%. **3.** (a) $1.31 \cdot 10^{8}$ m/sec. (b) $2.60 \cdot 10^{8}$ m/sec. (c) $2.98 \cdot 10^{8}$ m/sec. **4.** (a, b, c) 100.0 ft. (d) 99.5 ft. (e) 86.6 ft. (f) 43.6 ft. **5.** $2.40 \cdot 10^{8}$ m/sec or $1.49 \cdot 10^{5}$ miles/sec. **6.** 74.4%. **7.** B; $1.66 \cdot 10^{8}$ m/sec or $1.03 \cdot 10^{5}$ miles/sec. **8.** 49.9 ft. **9.** $9.12 \cdot 10^{-27}$ g. **10.** (a) $7.38 \cdot 10^{-6}$ erg. (b) $4.06 \cdot 10^{-7}$ erg. **11.** $3.12 \cdot 10^{6}$ v. **12.** $3.24 \cdot 10^{6}$ m/sec. **13.** (a) $2.94 \cdot 10^{8}$ m/sec. (b) 3.90/1.

Chap. 33

1. (a) 7.28 Å. (b) $3.97 \cdot 10^{-3}$ Å. **2.** 3.31 Å.; 0.527Å. **3.** 7.78 Å. **4.** 607 v. **5.** n.a.

Chap. 34

1. (a) $2.47 \cdot 10^{15}$/sec; $3.29 \cdot 10^{15}$/sec. (b) $1.21 \cdot 10^{3}$ Å; 912 Å. **2.** $1.88 \cdot 10^{4}$ Å; $8.22 \cdot 10^{3}$ Å. **3.** (a) 15.4/1. (b) 9.00/1. **4.** (a) 2.78/1. (b) 1.33/1. **5.** $1.09\overline{3} \cdot 10^{5}$. **6.** 0.530 Å; 2.12 Å; 4.77 Å; 8.48 Å. **7.** (a) $2.19 \cdot 10^{8}$ cm/sec. (b) $6.57 \cdot 10^{15}$. **8.** (a) Respectively, $-4.35 \cdot 10^{-11}$ erg, $+2.17 \cdot 10^{-11}$ erg, and $-2.17 \cdot 10^{-11}$ erg. (b) Respectively, $-1.087 \cdot 10^{-11}$ erg, $+0.544 \cdot 10^{-11}$ erg, and $-0.544 \cdot 10^{-11}$ erg. **9.** (a) $1.63 \cdot 10^{-11}$ erg; 10.2 ev. (b) $2.46 \cdot 10^{15}$/sec. (c) $1.20 \cdot 10^{3}$ Å. **10.** $2.47 \cdot 10^{15}$/sec. **11.** 5.00 v. **12.** 10.2 v. **13.** (a) $1.94 \cdot 10^{18}$/sec; 1.55 Å. (b) $1.32 \cdot 10^{19}$/sec; 0.228 Å. **14.** (a) $8.02 \cdot 10^{3}$ ev. (b) $5.45 \cdot 10^{4}$ ev.

Chap. 35

1. (a) $5.45 \cdot 10^{3}$ Å. (b) $2.74 \cdot 10^{3}$ Å. **2.** (a) $4.3\overline{7} \cdot 10^{-13}$ erg; $3.10 \cdot 10^{5}$ m/sec. (b) no emission. **3.** $1.68 \cdot 10^{3}$ Å. **4.** $7.71 \cdot 10^{-12}$ erg; 4.83 ev. **5.** Platinum; 3%. **6.** $1.21 \cdot 10^{18}$/sec; 2.49 Å. **7.** 0.565 Å; $5.31 \cdot 10^{18}$/sec. **8.** 57.9 cm/sec. **9.** (a) 11.6 cm. (b) $6.29 \cdot 10^{-3}$ cm. **10.** $5.27 \cdot 10^{-27}$ cm. **11.** n.a.

Chap. 36

1. 24.31. **2.** 93.25% and 6.75%, respectively. **3.** 50.2% and 49.8%, respectively. **4.** (a) $1.66 \cdot 10^{-24}$ g. (b) 933 Mev. **5.** 0.511 Mev. **6.** (a) 298 Mev. (b) $2.28 \cdot 10^{8}$ kwhr. (c) 8.51 Mev. **7.** 59.949 amu.

Chap. 37

1. $4.00 \cdot 10^{17}$. **2.** (a) 1/2; 1/4; 1/8; 1/16; 1/32. (b) n.a. (c) approximately 0.708; 0.355; 0.176; 0.089. (d) 0.750; 0.375; 0.188; 0.094. **3.** 7 min 30 sec. **4.** 12.9 days. **5.** 12.9 days. **6.** (a) 95.8%. (b) 65.2%. (c) 3.13%. **7.** (a) $1.73 \cdot 10^{3}$ yr. (b) 7%. **8.** $1.82 \cdot 10^{-2}$ sec. **9.** 3.41% **10.** (a) 24.5 days. (b) 2.83%.

Chap. 38

1. $87.\overline{5}$%. **2.** 4.8 cm. **3.** 8.3 hr.

Chap. 39

1. $1.31 \cdot 10^{4}$ gauss. **2.** 99.1%. **3.** 0.679 Mev. **4.** 1.35 Mev. **5.** $_{11}Na^{25}$; 19.7 Mev; $6.35 \cdot 10^{-4}$ Å. **6.** $3.95 \cdot 10^{-5}$ erg; 24.7 Mev. **7.** (a) $3.64 \cdot 10^{18}$. (b) $6.10 \cdot 10^{-6}$ g. **8.** (a) $7.8 \cdot 10^{-6}$ erg. (b) $6.8 \cdot 10^{10}$ joules. (c) \$380. **9.** n.a.

INDEX

B

C

F

G

H

J

K

L

M

S

T

U

V